Merchant Marine Deck Examination Reference Material

Reprints from the 1983 TIDE TABLES and TIDAL CURRENT TABLES

This publication contains information to be used in examinations for Merchant Marine Licenses

NOT TO BE USED FOR NAVIGATION

COMDTPUB P16721.46

U.S. Department of Transportation

United States Coast Guard

Commandant
United States Coast Guard

2100 Second St. S.W.
Washington, DC 20593-0001
Staff Symbol: NMC
Phone: (703) 235-0018

COMDTPUB P16721.46

AUG 16 1996

COMMANDANT PUBLICATION P16721.46

Subj: MERCHANT MARINE DECK EXAMINATION REFERENCE MATERIAL, REPRINTS FROM THE TIDE TABLES AND TIDAL CURRENT TABLES

1. PURPOSE. This publication contains reference material for use during an examination for a merchant marine deck license. It contains excerpts from the Tide Tables and the Tidal Current Tables. This manual is current with the problems used in the examinations.

2. PROCEDURES. This publication is available to applicants taking a deck merchant marine examination. The covers available for sale from the Government Printing Office (GPO) are printed with red ink. The covers used in Regional Examination Centers are printed with green ink. Applicants who purchase copies of this publication from the GPO may not use their personal copies during examinations.

3. DISCUSSION. Applicants for merchant marine deck licenses are tested to ensure their professional qualification. Tide and current problems require the use of data contained in this publication.

4. ORDERING INFORMATION.

   a. Regional Examination Centers will be provided with an initial supply of this publication. Replacement and additional copies are available through standard distribution sources.

DISTRIBUTION - SDL No. 134

	a	b	c	d	e	f	g	h	i	j	k	l	m	n	o	p	q	r	s	t	u	v	w	x	y	z
A																										
B		1	1		1		1	1						1				1								
C					*								*													
D																										
E																										
F																										
G																										
H																										

NON-STANDARD DISTRIBUTION: (See page 2.)

b. The public and other Coast Guard units may order copies of this publication from the GPO at the following address:

Superintendent of Documents
U.S. Government Printing Office
Washington, DC 20402

This book may also be ordered by telephone and charged to a national credit card by calling (202) 783-3238.

NORMAN W. LEMLEY
Director, National Maritime Center

NON-STANDARD DISTRIBUTION:

C:e Toledo (350); Miami (225): New Orleans (150); Baltimore (100); Boston, San Francisco, Long Beach, Anchorage, Houston (75); Charleston; Portland, OR; Memphis, Puget Sound (30); Honolulu (20); St Louis (15); Norfolk, Guam, Juneau, San Juan, Ketchikan (10) (only)

C:m New York (250) (only)

INSTRUCTIONS

1. This reference contains extracts of the TIDE TABLES and TIDAL CURRENT TABLES. Some navigation problems require determining the tide or tidal current for a specific time of day. The data necessary for solving these problems is contained in this manual.

2. This manual is in two parts. Part one contains the information referring to tides. Part two contains the information referring to tidal currents.

3. Applicants who wish to comment on any material in this publication should complete a Comment/Protest form for the question involved and give it to the examiner.

4. Individuals not taking an examination who wish to make a comment about this publicaiton should send a written comment, citing this publication and the appropriate page and paragraph to:

Director, National Maritime Center (NMC-4B)
U.S. Coast Guard
REPRINTS from TIDE and TIDAL CURRENT TABLES
4200 Wilson Blvd., Suite 510
Arlington, VA 22203-1804

All comments are welcomed and will be acknowledged. Valid comments will be incorporated into this publication.

Merchant Marine Deck
Examination Reference Material

Reprints from the

TIDE TABLES and TIDAL CURRENT TABLES

PART ONE. 1983 TIDE TABLES

PART TWO. 1983 TIDAL CURRENT TABLES

MERCHANT MARINE DECK EXAMINATION
REFERENCE MATERIAL

PART ONE

1983
TIDE TABLES

High and low water predictions

EAST COAST of NORTH and SOUTH AMERICA

including GREENLAND

INDEX OF TIDE TABLE COVERAGE

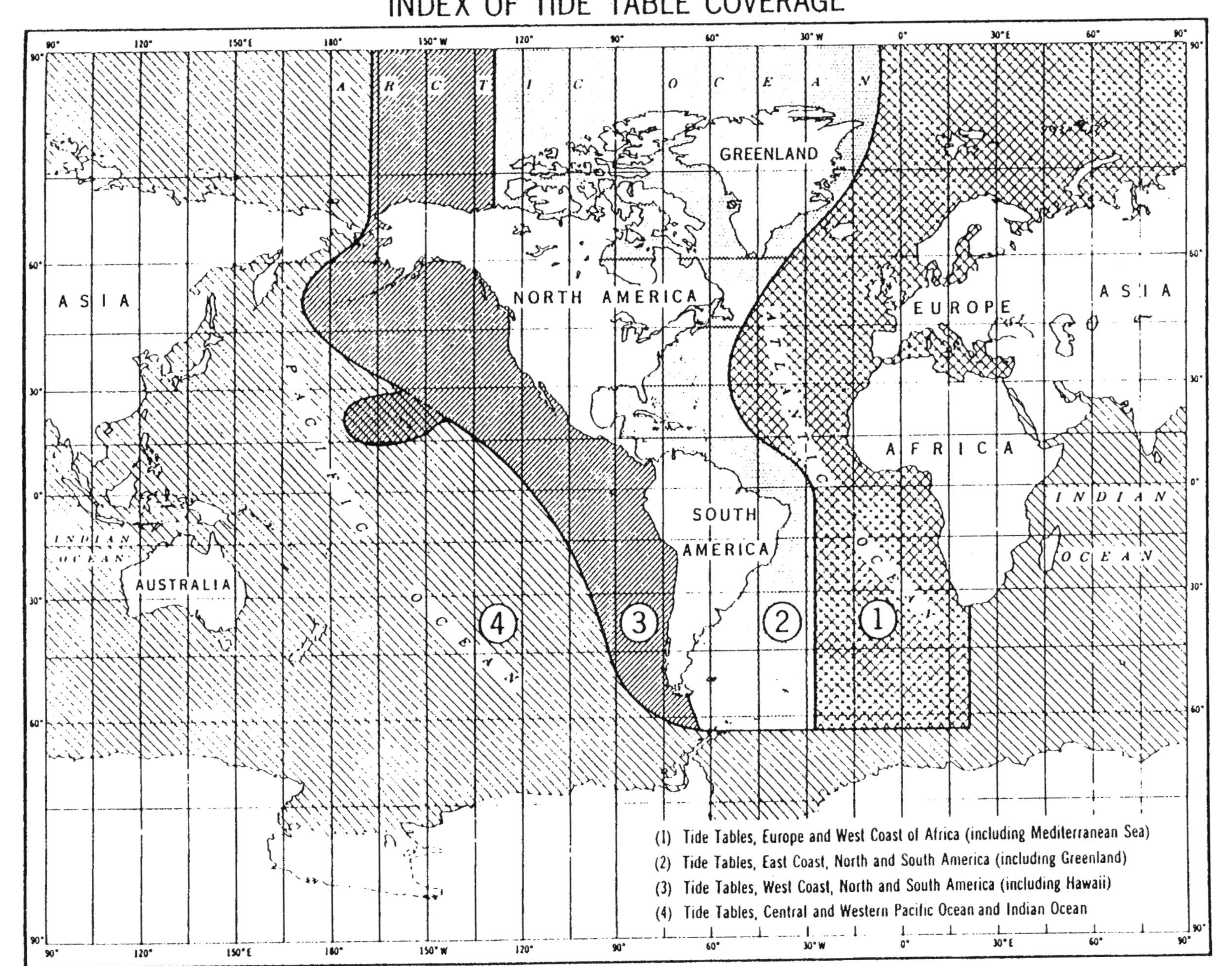

ASIA
NORTH AMERICA
GREENLAND
EUROPE
AFRICA
SOUTH AMERICA
AUSTRALIA
ARCTIC OCEAN
PACIFIC OCEAN
ATLANTIC OCEAN
INDIAN OCEAN
1
2
3
4
(1) Tide Tables, Europe and West Coast of Africa (including Mediterranean Sea)
(2) Tide Tables, East Coast, North and South America (including Greenland)
(3) Tide Tables, West Coast, North and South America (including Hawaii)
(4) Tide Tables, Central and Western Pacific Ocean and Indian Ocean

CONTENTS

IMPORTANT NOTICE

For the most part, tide predictions for U.S. reference stations are based upon analyses of tide observations for periods of at least one year. Since the extremes of meteorological conditions have been excluded from the analyses and predictions, the predicted tidal heights should be considered those expected under average weather conditions. The mariner must be cautioned that during times when weather conditions differ from what is considered average for the area, corresponding differences between predicted levels and those actually observed will be noted. Generally, prolonged onshore winds or a low barometric pressure can produce higher levels than predicted, while the opposite can result in lower levels than those predicted.

Exclusive of weather conditions, the astronomical tide is subject to range variations which should be noted. Decreased ranges may be expected near the times when the Moon is in apogee (apogean tides) or in quadrature (neap tides) and increased ranges when the Moon is in perigee (perigean tides) or in a new or full position (spring tides). A larger diurnal range may also result when the Moon is in its maximum declination (tropic tides). The actual range will depend upon the extent to which combinations of these positions reinforce or detract one from the other. The effect of these astronomical lineups is included in the predictions and may be apparent upon inspection.

The mariner may be kept aware of the times of these astronomical events by referring to the astronomical data listed in this book. He should realize, however, that there is generally a time lag from a few hours to several days from the time of the astronomical event to the time of the resultant tide. During times of storm surges or when extreme weather conditions are imminent, it would be prudent for the mariner to keep closely advised by local weather forecasts as they relate to the effects upon the tide levels.

TIDE TABLES

INTRODUCTION

Tide tables for the use of mariners have been published by the National Ocean Survey (formerly the Coast and Geodetic Survey) since 1853. For a number of years these tables appeared as appendixes to the annual reports of the Superintendent of the Survey, and consisted of more or less elaborated means for enabling the mariner to make his own prediction of tides as occasion arose.

The first tables to give predictions for each day were those for the year 1867. They gave the times and heights of high waters only and were published in two separate parts, one for the Atlantic coast and the other for the Pacific coast of the United States. Together they contained daily predictions for 19 stations and tidal differences for 124 stations. A few years later predictions for the low waters were also included, and for the year 1896 the tables were extended to include the entire maritime world, with full predictions for 70 ports and tidal differences for about 3,000 stations.

The tide tables are now issued in four volumes, as follows: *Europe and West Coast of Africa (including the Mediterranean Sea); East Coast of North and South America (including Greenland); West Coast of North and South America (including the Hawaiian Islands); Central and Western Pacific Ocean and Indian Ocean.* Together, they contain daily predictions for 198 reference ports and differences and other constants for about 6,000 stations.

This edition of the *Tide Tables, East Coast of North and South America* contains full daily predictions for 48 reference ports and differences and other constants for about 2,000 stations in North America, South America, and Greenland. It also contains a table for obtaining the approximate height of the tide at any time, a table of local mean time of sunrise and sunset for every 5th day of the year for different latitudes, a table for the reduction of local mean time to standard time, a table of moonrise and moonset for 8 places, a table of the Greenwich mean time of the Moon's phases, apogee, perigee, greatest north and south and zero declination, and the time of the solar equinoxes and solstices, and a glossary of terms.

Up to and including the tide tables for the year 1884, all the tide predictions were computed by means of auxiliary tables and curves constructed from the results of tide observations at the different ports. From 1885 to 1911, inclusive, the predictions were generally made by means of the Ferrel tide-predicting machine. From 1912 to 1965, inclusive, they were made by means of the Coast and Geodetic Survey tide predicting machine No. 2. Since 1966, predictions have been made by electronic computer.

In the preparation of these tables all available observations were used. In some cases, however, the observations were insufficient for obtaining final results, and as further information becomes available it will be included in subsequent editions. All persons using these tables are invited to send information or suggestions for increasing their usefulness to the Director, National Ocean Survey, Rockville, MD 20852, U.S.A.

In accordance with cooperative arrangements for the exchange of tide predictions, the authorities given below have furnished the predictions for the following stations in the present issue:

Canadian Hydrographic Service.—Harrington Harbour, Quebec, Halifax, St. John, Pictou, and Argentia.

Directoria de Hidrografia e Navegacao, Brazil.—Recife, Rio de Janeiro, and Santos.

Servicio Hidrografico, Argentina.—Buenos Aires, Puerto Belgrano, Comodoro Rivadavia, and Punta Loyola.

LIST OF REFERENCE STATIONS

Name of Station	Datum below mean sea level	Page	Name of Station	Datum below mean sea level	Page
	Feet			Feet	
Albany, N.Y.	*2.5	60	Pensacola, Fla.	0.6	128
Amuay, Venezuela	0.6	156	Philadelphia, Pa.	*3.2	76
Argentia, Newfoundland	4.3	4	Pictou, Nova Scotia	3.9	8
Baltimore, Md.	0.6	80	Portland, Maine	4.5	32
Boston, Mass.	4.9	36	Puerto Belgrano, Argentina	8.0	184
Breakwater Harbor, Del.	2.1	68	Punta Gorda, Venezuela	3.3	160
Bridgeport, Conn.	3.4	48	Punta Loyola, Argentina	20.3	192
Buenos Aires, Argentina	2.6	180	Quebec, Quebec	*8.5	16
Charleston, S.C.	2.7	96	Recife, Brazil	3.7	168
Comodoro Rivadavia, Argentina	10.3	188	Reedy Point, Del.	2.8	72
Cristobal, Panama	0.4	144	Rio de Janeiro, Brazil	2.2	172
Eastport, Maine	9.2	28	St. John, New Brunswick	14.5	24
Galveston, Tex.	0.8	136	St. Marks River Entrance, Fla.	1.8	124
Halifax, Nova Scotia	4.3	20	St. Petersburg, Fla.	1.2	120
Hampton Roads, Va.	1.2	88	Sandy Hook, N.J.	2.3	64
Harrington Harbour, Quebec	3.5	12	San Juan, Puerto Rico	0.6	148
Isla Zapara, Venezuela	2.7	152	Santos, Brazil	2.5	176
Key West, Fla.	0.9	116	Savannah, Ga.	*4.0	104
Mayport, Fla.	2.3	108	Savannah River Entrance, Ga.	3.6	100
Miami Harbor Entrance, Fla.	1.3	112	Suriname Rivier, Surinam	4.3	164
Mobile, Ala.	0.8	132	Tampico Harbor, Mexico	0.8	140
New London, Conn.	1.3	44	Washington, D.C.	*1.4	84
Newport, R.I.	1.6	40	Willets Point, N.Y.	3.6	52
New York, N.Y.	2.3	56	Wilmington, N.C.	*2.2	92

* Datum below mean river level.

Each datum figure above represents the difference in elevation between the local mean sea (or river) level and the reference level from which the predicted heights in table 1 were calculated.

Local mean sea level datum should not be confused with the National Geodetic Vertical Datum which is the datum of the geodetic level net of the United States. Relationships between geodetic and local tidal datums are published in connection with the tidal bench mark data of the National Ocean Survey.

TABLE 1.—DAILY TIDE PREDICTIONS

EXPLANATION OF TABLE

This table contains the predicted times and heights of the high and low waters for each day of the year at a number of places which are designated as *reference stations.* By using tidal differences from table 2, one can calculate the approximate times and heights of the tide at many other places which are called subordinate stations. Instructions on the use of the tidal differences are found in the explanation of table 2.

High water is the maximum height reached by each rising tide, and low water is the minimum height reached by each falling tide. High and low waters can be selected from the predictions by the comparison of consecutive heights. Because of diurnal inequality at certain places, however, there may be a difference of only a few tenths of a foot between one high water and low water of a day, but a marked difference in height between the other high water and low water. It is essential, therefore, in using the tide tables to note carefully the heights as well as the times of the tides.

Time.—The kind of time used for the predictions at each reference station is indicated by the time meridian at the bottom of each page. Daylight saving time is not used in this publication.

Datum.—The datum from which the predicted heights are reckoned is the same as that used for the charts of the locality. The datum for the Atlantic coast of the United States is mean low water. For foreign coasts a datum approximating to mean low water springs, Indian spring low water, or the lowest possible low water is generally used. The depression of the datum below mean sea level for each of the reference stations of this volume is given on the preceding page.

Depth of water.—The nautical charts published by the United States and other maritime nations show the depth of water as referred to a low water datum corresponding to that from which the predicted tidal heights are reckoned. To find the actual depth of water at any time the height of the tide should be added to the charted depth. If the height of the tide is negative—that is, if there is a minus sign (—) before the tabular height—it should be subtracted from the charted depth. For any time between high and low water, the height of the tide may be estimated from the heights of the preceding and following tides, or table 3 may be used. The reference stations in table 1 now contain the heights in meters as well as feet.

Variation in sea level.—Changes in winds and barometric conditions cause variations in sea level from day to day. In general, with onshore winds or a low barometer the heights of both the high and low waters will be higher than predicted while with offshore winds or a high barometer they will be lower. There are also seasonal variations in sea level, but these variations have been included in the predictions for each station. At ocean stations the seasonal variation in sea level is usually less than half a foot.

At stations on tidal rivers the average seasonal variation in river level due to freshets and droughts may be considerably more than a foot. The predictions for these stations include an allowance for this seasonal variation representing average freshet and drought conditions. Unusual freshets or droughts, however, will cause the tides to be higher or lower, respectively, than predicted.

Number of tides.—There are usually two high and two low waters in a day. Tides follow the Moon more closely than they do the Sun, and the lunar or tidal day is about 50 minutes longer than the solar day. This causes the tide to occur later each day, and a tide that has occurred near the end of one calendar day will be followed by a corresponding tide that may skip the next day and occur in the early morning of the third day. Thus on certain days of each month only a single high or a single low water occurs. At some stations, during portions of each month, the tide becomes diurnal—that is, only one high and one low water will occur during the period of a lunar day.

Relation of tide to current.—In using these tables of tide predictions it must be borne in mind that they give the times and heights of high and low waters and *not* the times of turning of the current or slack water. For stations on the outer coast there is usually but little difference between the time of high or low water and the beginning of ebb or flood current, but for places in narrow channels, landlocked harbors, or on tidal rivers, the time of slack water may differ by several hours from the time of high or low water stand. The relation of the times of high and low water to the turning of the current depends upon a number of factors, so that no simple or general rule can be given. For the predicted times of slack water reference should be made to the tidal current tables published by the National Ocean Survey in two separate volumes, one for the Atlantic coast of North America and the other for the Pacific coast of North America and Asia.

Typical tide curves.—The variations in the tide from day to day and from place to place are illustrated on the opposite page by the tide curves for representative ports along the Atlantic and Gulf coasts of the United States. It will be noted that the range of tide for stations along the Atlantic coast varies from place to place but that the type is uniformly semidiurnal with the principal variations following the changes in the Moon's distance and phase. In the Gulf of Mexico, however, the range of tide is uniformly small but the type of tide differs considerably. At certain ports such as Pensacola there is usually but one high and one low water a day while at other ports such as Galveston the inequality is such that the tide is semidiurnal around the times the Moon is on the Equator but becomes diurnal around the times of maximum north or south declination of the Moon. In the Gulf of Mexico, consequently, the principal variations in the tide are due to the changing declination of the Moon. Key West, at the entrance to the Gulf of Mexico, has a type of tide which is a mixture of semidaily and daily types. Here the tide is semidiurnal but there is considerable inequality in the heights of high and low waters. By reference to the curves it will be seen that where the inequality is large there are times when there is but a few tenths of a foot difference between high water and low water.

TYPICAL TIDE CURVES FOR UNITED STATES PORTS

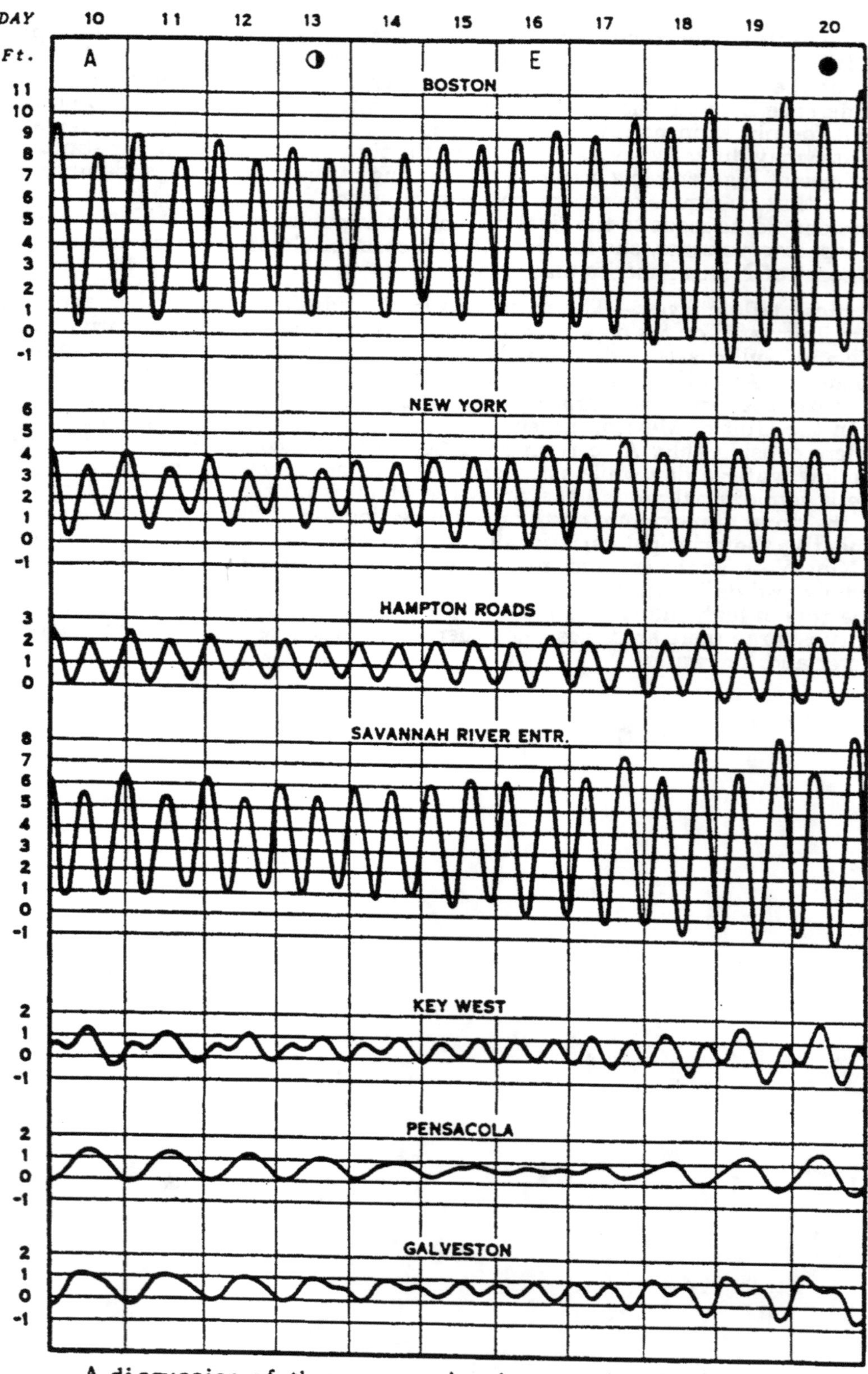

A discussion of these curves is given on the preceding page.

Lunar data: A - Moon in apogee
◑ - last quarter
E - Moon on Equator
● - new Moon

ARGENTIA, NEWFOUNDLAND, 1983

Times and Heights of High and Low Waters

JANUARY

Day	Time (h m)	Height (ft)	Height (m)
1 Sa	0240	1.2	0.4
	0930	8.7	2.7
	1525	1.5	0.5
	2210	7.0	2.1
2 Su	0330	1.3	0.4
	1030	8.5	2.6
	1610	1.7	0.5
	2300	6.9	2.1
3 M	0415	1.5	0.5
	1115	8.2	2.5
	1650	1.9	0.6
	2355	6.7	2.0
4 Tu	0510	1.8	0.5
	1220	7.7	2.3
	1730	2.3	0.7
5 W	0050	6.6	2.0
	0555	2.2	0.7
	1315	7.2	2.2
	1825	2.7	0.8
6 Th	0150	6.5	2.0
	0700	2.6	0.8
	1425	6.7	2.0
	1920	3.0	0.9
7 F	0255	6.5	2.0
	0900	2.9	0.9
	1515	6.3	1.9
	2145	3.1	0.9
8 Sa	0350	6.6	2.0
	1020	2.9	0.9
	1615	6.1	1.9
	2230	3.0	0.9
9 Su	0445	6.7	2.0
	1100	2.9	0.9
	1710	6.0	1.8
	2255	2.9	0.9
10 M	0540	6.9	2.1
	1150	2.8	0.9
	1800	6.1	1.9
	2340	2.8	0.9
11 Tu	0620	7.1	2.2
	1230	2.7	0.8
	1835	6.3	1.9
12 W	0010	2.6	0.8
	0710	7.4	2.3
	1310	2.6	0.8
	1910	6.4	2.0
13 Th	0050	2.5	0.8
	0745	7.6	2.3
	1345	2.4	0.7
	1955	6.6	2.0
14 F	0130	2.4	0.7
	0825	7.7	2.3
	1430	2.3	0.7
	2020	6.7	2.0
15 Sa	0220	2.3	0.7
	0855	7.8	2.4
	1510	2.2	0.7
	2100	6.7	2.0
16 Su	0255	2.2	0.7
	0935	7.8	2.4
	1530	2.2	0.7
	2135	6.7	2.0
17 M	0335	2.2	0.7
	1000	7.7	2.3
	1610	2.2	0.7
	2215	6.6	2.0
18 Tu	0410	2.2	0.7
	1050	7.4	2.3
	1635	2.3	0.7
	2255	6.6	2.0
19 W	0435	2.3	0.7
	1125	7.2	2.2
	1705	2.3	0.7
	2345	6.6	2.0
20 Th	0510	2.4	0.7
	1200	6.8	2.1
	1730	2.4	0.7
21 F	0015	6.7	2.0
	0555	2.6	0.8
	1240	6.5	2.0
	1815	2.4	0.7
22 Sa	0115	6.7	2.0
	0650	2.8	0.9
	1340	6.2	1.9
	1915	2.5	0.8
23 Su	0215	6.8	2.1
	0800	3.0	0.9
	1450	6.1	1.9
	2020	2.5	0.8
24 M	0335	7.0	2.1
	0925	3.0	0.9
	1625	6.2	1.9
	2145	2.4	0.7
25 Tu	0455	7.3	2.2
	1115	2.6	0.8
	1720	6.5	2.0
	2300	2.1	0.6
26 W	0545	7.7	2.3
	1225	2.2	0.7
	1815	6.8	2.1
27 Th	0000	1.8	0.5
	0655	8.1	2.5
	1320	1.9	0.6
	1920	7.1	2.2
28 F	0055	1.6	0.5
	0745	8.5	2.6
	1410	1.5	0.5
	2005	7.2	2.2
29 Sa	0200	1.4	0.4
	0830	8.7	2.7
	1450	1.4	0.4
	2100	7.3	2.2
30 Su	0240	1.2	0.4
	0925	8.6	2.6
	1515	1.3	0.4
	2155	7.3	2.2
31 M	0320	1.2	0.4
	1015	8.4	2.6
	1600	1.4	0.4
	2235	7.2	2.2

FEBRUARY

Day	Time (h m)	Height (ft)	Height (m)
1 Tu	0405	1.1	0.3
	1100	8.1	2.5
	1625	1.5	0.5
	2325	7.0	2.1
2 W	0455	1.3	0.4
	1150	7.5	2.3
	1710	1.8	0.5
3 Th	0025	6.8	2.1
	0525	1.8	0.5
	1235	6.9	2.1
	1750	2.2	0.7
4 F	0120	6.7	2.0
	0625	2.3	0.7
	1330	6.4	2.0
	1825	2.7	0.8
5 Sa	0215	6.5	2.0
	0720	2.8	0.9
	1435	5.9	1.8
	1915	3.0	0.9
6 Su	0310	6.4	2.0
	0905	3.2	1.0
	1530	5.6	1.7
	2055	3.2	1.0
7 M	0405	6.4	2.0
	1025	3.3	1.0
	1630	5.6	1.7
	2200	3.2	1.0
8 Tu	0505	6.5	2.0
	1125	3.2	1.0
	1735	5.7	1.7
	2310	3.1	0.9
9 W	0610	6.7	2.0
	1220	3.0	0.9
	1820	6.0	1.8
	2355	2.9	0.9
10 Th	0655	7.0	2.1
	1255	2.7	0.8
	1855	6.3	1.9
11 F	0050	2.6	0.8
	0725	7.3	2.2
	1335	2.4	0.7
	1930	6.6	2.0
12 Sa	0130	2.3	0.7
	0805	7.6	2.3
	1415	2.2	0.7
	2005	6.8	2.1
13 Su	0215	2.1	0.6
	0845	7.8	2.4
	1435	2.0	0.6
	2035	7.0	2.1
14 M	0245	1.9	0.6
	0900	7.8	2.4
	1500	1.8	0.5
	2110	7.1	2.2
15 Tu	0315	1.7	0.5
	0945	7.7	2.3
	1530	1.7	0.5
	2145	7.1	2.2
16 W	0355	1.6	0.5
	1015	7.4	2.3
	1610	1.7	0.5
	2225	7.1	2.2
17 Th	0420	1.7	0.5
	1050	7.1	2.2
	1640	1.6	0.5
	2300	7.1	2.2
18 F	0455	1.8	0.5
	1130	6.8	2.1
	1715	1.7	0.5
	2355	7.0	2.1
19 Sa	0540	2.0	0.6
	1215	6.4	2.0
	1745	1.8	0.5
20 Su	0055	6.9	2.1
	0620	2.3	0.7
	1310	6.1	1.9
	1840	2.0	0.6
21 M	0145	6.9	2.1
	0720	2.7	0.8
	1430	5.9	1.8
	1950	2.3	0.7
22 Tu	0305	6.9	2.1
	0855	2.9	0.9
	1545	5.9	1.8
	2105	2.4	0.7
23 W	0420	7.0	2.1
	1100	2.6	0.8
	1710	6.1	1.9
	2230	2.3	0.7
24 Th	0540	7.4	2.3
	1210	2.2	0.7
	1810	6.6	2.0
	2355	2.0	0.6
25 F	0635	7.8	2.4
	1310	1.7	0.5
	1905	7.0	2.1
26 Sa	0055	1.6	0.5
	0740	8.2	2.5
	1345	1.3	0.4
	1955	7.3	2.2
27 Su	0150	1.2	0.4
	0815	8.4	2.6
	1430	1.1	0.3
	2045	7.5	2.3
28 M	0230	0.9	0.3
	0900	8.4	2.6
	1455	1.0	0.3
	2125	7.5	2.3

MARCH

Day	Time (h m)	Height (ft)	Height (m)
1 Tu	0305	0.8	0.2
	0945	8.1	2.5
	1525	1.1	0.3
	2215	7.4	2.3
2 W	0355	0.8	0.2
	1030	7.7	2.3
	1605	1.3	0.4
	2305	7.2	2.2
3 Th	0420	1.1	0.3
	1120	7.1	2.2
	1640	1.6	0.5
	2355	7.0	2.1
4 F	0515	1.6	0.5
	1215	6.5	2.0
	1700	2.0	0.6
5 Sa	0040	6.7	2.0
	0555	2.1	0.6
	1310	6.0	1.8
	1745	2.4	0.7
6 Su	0140	6.4	2.0
	0630	2.8	0.9
	1355	5.6	1.7
	1835	3.0	0.9
7 M	0235	6.2	1.9
	0830	3.3	1.0
	1500	5.3	1.6
	1930	3.3	1.0
8 Tu	0335	6.0	1.8
	1030	3.4	1.0
	1610	5.3	1.6
	2205	3.4	1.0
9 W	0445	6.1	1.9
	1125	3.2	1.0
	1710	5.5	1.7
	2305	3.3	1.0
10 Th	0545	6.4	2.0
	1200	2.9	0.9
	1755	5.8	1.8
11 F	0000	2.9	0.9
	0630	6.7	2.0
	1245	2.6	0.8
	1830	6.2	1.9
12 Sa	0045	2.6	0.8
	0715	7.1	2.2
	1315	2.3	0.7
	1905	6.6	2.0
13 Su	0125	2.2	0.7
	0745	7.3	2.2
	1355	2.0	0.6
	1950	6.9	2.1
14 M	0155	1.8	0.5
	0815	7.5	2.3
	1415	1.7	0.5
	2020	7.2	2.2
15 Tu	0230	1.6	0.5
	0855	7.6	2.3
	1445	1.5	0.5
	2050	7.4	2.3
16 W	0300	1.4	0.4
	0925	7.4	2.3
	1500	1.3	0.4
	2125	7.4	2.3
17 Th	0325	1.3	0.4
	0955	7.2	2.2
	1545	1.3	0.4
	2215	7.4	2.3
18 F	0355	1.3	0.4
	1030	6.9	2.1
	1610	1.1	0.3
	2255	7.4	2.3
19 Sa	0430	1.4	0.4
	1105	6.6	2.0
	1645	1.3	0.4
	2335	7.2	2.2
20 Su	0515	1.6	0.5
	1155	6.2	1.9
	1725	1.4	0.4
21 M	0020	7.0	2.1
	0550	2.0	0.6
	1255	5.9	1.8
	1800	1.8	0.5
22 Tu	0125	6.8	2.1
	0645	2.5	0.8
	1405	5.7	1.7
	1900	2.3	0.7
23 W	0235	6.6	2.0
	0815	2.8	0.9
	1535	5.7	1.7
	2030	2.6	0.8
24 Th	0410	6.7	2.0
	1115	2.4	0.7
	1655	6.0	1.8
	2300	2.4	0.7
25 F	0525	7.0	2.1
	1200	1.9	0.6
	1805	6.5	2.0
26 Sa	0015	1.9	0.6
	0630	7.4	2.3
	1245	1.5	0.5
	1855	7.0	2.1
27 Su	0055	1.4	0.4
	0725	7.7	2.3
	1325	1.2	0.4
	1940	7.4	2.3
28 M	0140	1.0	0.3
	0800	7.9	2.4
	1400	1.0	0.3
	2020	7.6	2.3
29 Tu	0225	0.7	0.2
	0855	7.8	[illegible]
	1430	0.9	[illegible]
	2100	7.7	[illegible]
30 W	0255	0.7	[illegible]
	0935	7.5	[illegible]
	1505	[illegible]	[illegible]
	2155	[illegible]	[illegible]
31 Th	0335	[illegible]	[illegible]
	1015	[illegible]	[illegible]
	1540	[illegible]	[illegible]
	[illegible]	[illegible]	[illegible]

Time meridian 52° 30' W. 0000 is midnight. 1200 is noon.
Heights are referred to the Canadian chart datum of soundings. Subtract 1.7 feet (0.5 meter) to refer to the datum of N.O.S. charts.

ARGENTIA, NEWFOUNDLAND, 1983

Times and Heights of High and Low Waters

APRIL

Day	Time (h m)	Height (ft)	Height (m)
1 F	0415	1.0	0.3
	1045	6.6	2.0
	1600	1.3	0.4
	2315	7.0	2.1
2 Sa	0450	1.4	0.4
	1130	6.1	1.9
	1655	1.7	0.5
3 Su	0010	6.7	2.0
	0525	1.9	0.6
	1220	5.6	1.7
	1725	2.2	0.7
4 M	0100	6.3	1.9
	0615	2.6	0.8
	1335	5.3	1.6
	1805	2.8	0.9
5 Tu	0200	6.0	1.8
	0715	3.2	1.0
	1445	5.2	1.6
	1910	3.3	1.0
6 W	0305	5.9	1.8
	0945	3.2	1.0
	1545	5.2	1.6
	2150	3.4	1.0
7 Th	0410	5.9	1.8
	1055	3.1	0.9
	1635	5.4	1.6
	2250	3.2	1.0
8 F	0500	6.0	1.8
	1125	2.9	0.9
	1730	5.7	1.7
	2335	2.8	0.9
9 Sa	0600	6.3	1.9
	1200	2.5	0.8
	1800	6.2	1.9
10 Su	0015	2.4	0.7
	0645	6.6	2.0
	1245	2.2	0.7
	1855	6.6	2.0
11 M	0055	2.0	0.6
	0715	7.0	2.1
	1315	1.8	0.5
	1920	7.0	2.1
12 Tu	0130	1.5	0.5
	0755	7.1	2.2
	1355	1.4	0.4
	2000	7.3	2.2
13 W	0205	1.2	0.4
	0830	7.2	2.2
	1415	1.2	0.4
	2030	7.5	2.3
14 Th	0240	1.0	0.3
	0905	7.1	2.2
	1450	1.0	0.3
	2110	7.6	2.3
15 F	0305	1.0	0.3
	0935	6.9	2.1
	1515	0.8	0.2
	2150	7.6	2.3
16 Sa	0350	1.0	0.3
	1010	6.7	2.0
	1545	0.8	0.2
	2240	7.5	2.3
17 Su	0420	1.2	0.4
	1055	6.3	1.9
	1620	1.0	0.3
	2325	7.3	2.2
18 M	0455	1.4	0.4
	1150	5.9	1.8
	1710	1.3	0.4
19 Tu	0015	7.0	2.1
	0540	1.9	0.6
	1250	5.6	1.7
	1755	1.8	0.5
20 W	0115	6.7	2.0
	0630	2.4	0.7
	1420	5.5	1.7
	1900	2.4	0.7
21 Th	0230	6.5	2.0
	1000	2.5	0.8
	1540	5.7	1.7
	2130	2.5	0.8
22 F	0345	6.5	2.0
	1100	2.2	0.7
	1640	6.1	1.9
	2300	2.1	0.6
23 Sa	0500	6.6	2.0
	1145	1.8	0.5
	1745	6.5	2.0
	2345	1.7	0.5
24 Su	0615	6.8	2.1
	1220	1.5	0.5
	1840	7.0	2.1
25 M	0040	1.3	0.4
	0705	7.1	2.2
	1255	1.3	0.4
	1925	7.4	2.3
26 Tu	0120	0.9	0.3
	0750	7.2	2.2
	1330	1.1	0.3
	2000	7.6	2.3
27 W	0205	0.7	0.2
	0835	7.1	2.2
	1405	1.0	0.3
	2050	7.6	2.3
28 Th	0230	0.7	0.2
	0905	6.9	2.1
	1440	1.0	0.3
	2120	7.5	2.3
29 F	0305	0.8	0.2
	0945	6.6	2.0
	1515	1.1	0.3
	2210	7.3	2.2
30 Sa	0350	1.1	0.3
	1025	6.2	1.9
	1545	1.4	0.4
	2240	7.0	2.1

MAY

Day	Time (h m)	Height (ft)	Height (m)
1 Su	0425	1.4	0.4
	1110	5.9	1.8
	1620	1.7	0.5
	2325	6.7	2.0
2 M	0500	2.0	0.6
	1145	5.5	1.7
	1655	2.2	0.7
3 Tu	0025	6.4	2.0
	0545	2.5	0.8
	1250	5.2	1.6
	1730	2.7	0.8
4 W	0130	6.1	1.9
	0630	3.0	0.9
	1355	5.1	1.6
	1820	3.1	0.9
5 Th	0230	5.9	1.8
	0905	3.1	0.9
	1450	5.2	1.6
	2105	3.3	1.0
6 F	0315	5.8	1.8
	1000	2.9	0.9
	1600	5.4	1.6
	2210	3.1	0.9
7 Sa	0420	5.8	1.8
	1050	2.7	0.8
	1645	5.7	1.7
	2310	2.7	0.8
8 Su	0520	5.9	1.8
	1140	2.4	0.7
	1735	6.1	1.9
	2345	2.3	0.7
9 M	0600	6.2	1.9
	1205	2.0	0.6
	1820	6.6	2.0
10 Tu	0030	1.8	0.5
	0645	6.5	2.0
	1245	1.7	0.5
	1855	7.0	2.1
11 W	0115	1.4	0.4
	0730	6.7	2.0
	1315	1.3	0.4
	1930	7.4	2.3
12 Th	0155	1.1	0.3
	0810	6.9	2.1
	1350	1.0	0.3
	2015	7.7	2.3
13 F	0230	1.0	0.3
	0840	6.9	2.1
	1420	0.8	0.2
	2055	7.8	2.4
14 Sa	0250	0.9	0.3
	0920	6.8	2.1
	1450	0.7	0.2
	2135	7.8	2.4
15 Su	0325	0.9	0.3
	1000	6.5	2.0
	1530	0.7	0.2
	2215	7.6	2.3
16 M	0405	1.1	0.3
	1045	6.2	1.9
	1615	0.9	0.3
	2315	7.4	2.3
17 Tu	0445	1.4	0.4
	1140	5.9	1.8
	1650	1.2	0.4
18 W	0015	7.1	2.2
	0520	1.8	0.5
	1255	5.7	1.7
	1750	1.7	0.5
19 Th	0130	6.8	2.1
	0620	2.2	0.7
	1400	5.7	1.7
	1905	2.2	0.7
20 F	0220	6.5	2.0
	0945	2.2	0.7
	1510	5.8	1.8
	2140	2.2	0.7
21 Sa	0335	6.3	1.9
	1035	2.0	0.6
	1620	6.1	1.9
	2245	1.9	0.6
22 Su	0445	6.2	1.9
	1115	1.9	0.6
	1730	6.5	2.0
	2340	1.6	0.5
23 M	0545	6.4	2.0
	1150	1.6	0.5
	1815	6.9	2.1
24 Tu	0030	1.3	0.4
	0650	6.5	2.0
	1225	1.5	0.5
	1905	7.2	2.2
25 W	0105	1.1	0.3
	0725	6.5	2.0
	1300	1.4	0.4
	1940	7.4	2.3
26 Th	0145	1.0	0.3
	0810	6.5	2.0
	1340	1.3	0.4
	2025	7.4	2.3
27 F	0225	1.0	0.3
	0835	6.4	2.0
	1400	1.2	0.4
	2055	7.4	2.3
28 Sa	0250	1.1	0.3
	0910	6.2	1.9
	1450	1.3	0.4
	2140	7.2	2.2
29 Su	0325	1.3	0.4
	0955	6.1	1.9
	1525	1.5	0.5
	2220	7.0	2.1
30 M	0410	1.6	0.5
	1025	5.8	1.8
	1600	1.8	0.5
	2305	6.8	2.1
31 Tu	0445	1.9	0.6
	1120	5.6	1.7
	1635	2.1	0.6
	2345	6.5	2.0

JUNE

Day	Time (h m)	Height (ft)	Height (m)
1 W	0525	2.2	0.7
	1210	5.4	1.6
	1730	2.3	0.7
2 Th	0020	6.2	1.9
	0605	2.5	0.8
	1250	5.3	1.6
	1805	2.7	0.8
3 F	0115	5.9	1.8
	0700	2.8	0.9
	1350	5.3	1.6
	1910	2.9	0.9
4 Sa	0200	5.7	1.7
	0835	2.9	0.9
	1445	5.4	1.6
	2050	2.9	0.9
5 Su	0310	5.5	1.7
	0950	2.7	0.8
	1550	5.6	1.7
	2200	2.7	0.8
6 M	0430	5.6	1.7
	1035	2.4	0.7
	1645	6.0	1.8
	2300	2.3	0.7
7 Tu	0525	5.8	1.8
	1110	2.0	0.6
	1740	6.5	2.0
	2350	1.9	0.6
8 W	0610	6.1	1.9
	1155	1.6	0.5
	1825	7.0	2.1
9 Th	0030	1.6	0.5
	0700	6.4	2.0
	1225	1.2	0.4
	1910	7.4	2.3
10 F	0110	1.3	0.4
	0735	6.5	2.0
	1315	0.9	0.3
	1945	7.7	2.3
11 Sa	0150	1.1	0.3
	0810	6.6	2.0
	1355	0.7	0.2
	2030	7.9	2.4
12 Su	0240	0.9	0.3
	0900	6.6	2.0
	1435	0.6	0.2
	2120	7.9	2.4
13 M	0320	0.9	0.3
	0950	6.4	2.0
	1520	0.7	0.2
	2215	7.8	2.4
14 Tu	0400	1.0	0.3
	1035	6.2	1.9
	1605	0.8	0.2
	2300	7.6	2.3
15 W	0440	1.3	0.4
	1130	6.1	1.9
	1650	1.1	0.3
16 Th	0005	7.3	2.2
	0520	1.5	0.5
	1230	6.0	1.8
	1745	1.4	0.4
17 F	0100	6.8	2.1
	0620	1.9	0.6
	1340	5.9	1.8
	1845	1.8	0.5
18 Sa	0200	6.4	2.0
	0720	2.2	0.7
	1450	6.0	1.8
	2020	2.0	0.6
19 Su	0305	6.1	1.9
	0945	2.3	0.7
	1555	6.1	1.9
	2205	2.0	0.6
20 M	0425	5.9	1.8
	1035	2.2	0.7
	1655	6.3	1.9
	2300	1.9	0.6
21 Tu	0525	5.8	1.8
	1110	2.0	0.6
	1740	6.5	2.0
	2355	1.8	0.5
22 W	0605	5.8	1.8
	1145	1.9	0.6
	1830	6.7	2.0
23 Th	0025	1.7	0.5
	0650	5.9	1.8
	1215	1.8	0.5
	1915	6.9	2.1
24 F	0110	1.6	0.5
	0730	6.0	1.8
	1255	1.6	0.5
	1950	7.0	2.1
25 Sa	0150	1.6	0.5
	0815	6.0	1.8
	1335	1.6	0.5
	2035	7.1	2.2
26 Su	0225	1.6	0.5
	0840	6.0	1.8
	1425	1.5	0.5
	2110	7.1	2.2
27 M	0300	1.5	0.5
	0920	6.0	1.8
	1505	1.6	0.5
	2155	7.1	2.2
28 Tu	0350	1.6	0.5
	0955	5.9	1.8
	1545	1.7	0.5
	2225	7.0	2.1
29 W	0425	1.7	0.5
	1045	5.8	1.8
	1625	1.8	0.5
	2310	6.8	2.1
30 Th	0450	1.9	0.6
	1115	5.7	1.7
	1655	2.0	0.6
	2345	6.5	2.0

Time meridian 52° 30' W. 0000 is midnight. 1200 is noon.
Heights are referred to the Canadian chart datum of soundings. Subtract 1.7 feet (0.5 meter) to refer these levels to the datum of N.O.S. charts.

Times and Heights of High and Low Waters

JULY

Day	Time h m	Height ft	Height m	Day	Time h m	Height ft	Height m
1	0520	2.1	0.6	16	0030	6.9	2.1
F	1205	5.7	1.7	Sa	0550	1.7	0.5
	1730	2.2	0.7		1320	6.2	1.9
					1820	1.6	0.5
2	0025	6.2	1.9	17	0130	6.4	2.0
Sa	0600	2.3	0.7	Su	0645	2.1	0.6
	1245	5.7	1.7		1420	6.1	1.9
	1810	2.4	0.7		1930	2.1	0.6
3	0100	5.8	1.8	18	0240	5.9	1.8
Su	0645	2.5	0.8	M	0815	2.4	0.7
	1335	5.7	1.7		1515	6.1	1.9
	1905	2.6	0.8		2145	2.2	0.7
4	0205	5.6	1.7	19	0350	5.5	1.7
M	0730	2.5	0.8	Tu	0945	2.5	0.8
	1445	5.9	1.8		1620	6.1	1.9
	2015	2.6	0.8		2245	2.3	0.7
5	0310	5.4	1.6	20	0450	5.4	1.6
Tu	0905	2.4	0.7	W	1045	2.5	0.8
	1550	6.1	1.9		1710	6.2	1.9
	2200	2.5	0.8		2330	2.3	0.7
6	0425	5.5	1.7	21	0535	5.4	1.6
W	1005	2.1	0.6	Th	1115	2.4	0.7
	1655	6.5	2.0		1815	6.4	2.0
	2305	2.2	0.7				
7	0520	5.8	1.8	22	0020	2.3	0.7
Th	1105	1.7	0.5	F	0620	5.6	1.7
	1750	6.9	2.1		1205	2.3	0.7
					1850	6.6	2.0
8	0010	1.9	0.6	23	0100	2.2	0.7
F	0620	6.1	1.9	Sa	0710	5.8	1.8
	1145	1.3	0.4		1245	2.1	0.6
	1840	7.4	2.3		1930	6.9	2.1
9	0055	1.6	0.5	24	0145	2.1	0.6
Sa	0700	6.4	2.0	Su	0740	6.0	1.8
	1235	1.1	0.3		1330	2.0	0.6
	1940	7.7	2.3		2010	7.0	2.1
10	0145	1.3	0.4	25	0225	1.9	0.6
Su	0755	6.6	2.0	M	0815	6.1	1.9
	1335	0.9	0.3		1410	1.8	0.5
	2020	8.0	2.4		2055	7.2	2.2
11	0230	1.1	0.3	26	0250	1.8	0.5
M	0850	6.6	2.0	Tu	0845	6.2	1.9
	1415	0.7	0.2		1445	1.7	0.5
	2115	8.1	2.5		2120	7.2	2.2
12	0315	1.0	0.3	27	0320	1.7	0.5
Tu	0930	6.6	2.0	W	0925	6.2	1.9
	1510	0.7	0.2		1525	1.7	0.5
	2210	8.1	2.5		2200	7.1	2.2
13	0350	1.0	0.3	28	0355	1.7	0.5
W	1025	6.5	2.0	Th	1005	6.2	1.9
	1600	0.7	0.2		1600	1.7	0.5
	2250	7.8	2.4		2235	6.9	2.1
14	0425	1.1	0.3	29	0415	1.7	0.5
Th	1115	6.4	2.0	F	1040	6.2	1.9
	1640	0.9	0.3		1625	1.8	0.5
	2345	7.4	2.3		2315	6.7	2.0
15	0505	1.4	0.4	30	0445	1.9	0.6
F	1225	6.3	1.9	Sa	1120	6.1	1.9
	1720	1.2	0.4		1700	1.9	0.6
					2335	6.3	1.9
				31	0520	1.9	0.6
				Su	1200	6.1	1.9
					1730	2.0	0.6

AUGUST

Day	Time h m	Height ft	Height m	Day	Time h m	Height ft	Height m
1	0020	6.0	1.8	16	0210	5.7	1.7
M	0610	1.9	0.6	Tu	0710	2.4	0.7
	1255	6.2	1.9		1440	6.1	1.9
	1830	2.2	0.7		2020	2.6	0.8
2	0115	5.7	1.7	17	0310	5.4	1.6
Tu	0650	2.0	0.6	W	0810	2.7	0.8
	1350	6.2	1.9		1550	6.0	1.8
	1925	2.4	0.7		2230	2.9	0.9
3	0215	5.6	1.7	18	0410	5.2	1.6
W	0755	2.1	0.6	Th	0930	2.8	0.9
	1455	6.3	1.9		1645	6.1	1.9
	2045	2.6	0.8		2340	2.9	0.9
4	0325	5.5	1.7	19	0510	5.3	1.6
Th	0900	2.0	0.6	F	1055	2.7	0.8
	1600	6.6	2.0		1800	6.3	1.9
	2215	2.4	0.7				
5	0445	5.7	1.7	20	0010	2.7	0.8
F	1015	1.8	0.5	Sa	0605	5.6	1.7
	1715	6.9	2.1		1155	2.5	0.8
	2340	2.1	0.6		1835	6.6	2.0
6	0550	6.1	1.9	21	0050	2.5	0.8
Sa	1125	1.5	0.5	Su	0640	5.8	1.8
	1820	7.4	2.3		1240	2.3	0.7
					1915	6.9	2.1
7	0045	1.6	0.5	22	0120	2.2	0.7
Su	0645	6.5	2.0	M	0715	6.1	1.9
	1235	1.2	0.4		1310	2.0	0.6
	1925	7.9	2.4		1955	7.2	2.2
8	0135	1.2	0.4	23	0145	1.9	0.6
M	0740	6.8	2.1	Tu	0745	6.4	2.0
	1325	0.9	0.3		1350	1.8	0.5
	2005	8.2	2.5		2025	7.3	2.2
9	0215	0.9	0.3	24	0215	1.7	0.5
Tu	0830	6.9	2.1	W	0815	6.6	2.0
	1415	0.7	0.2		1430	1.6	0.5
	2100	8.2	2.5		2055	7.3	2.2
10	0250	0.8	0.2	25	0250	1.6	0.5
W	0920	7.0	2.1	Th	0855	6.7	2.0
	1500	0.5	0.2		1505	1.5	0.5
	2150	8.1	2.5		2130	7.2	2.2
11	0330	0.8	0.2	26	0315	1.5	0.5
Th	1005	6.9	2.1	F	0935	6.7	2.0
	1545	0.5	0.2		1540	1.4	0.4
	2240	7.8	2.4		2205	7.0	2.1
12	0415	0.9	0.3	27	0345	1.5	0.5
F	1105	6.8	2.1	Sa	1000	6.7	2.0
	1620	0.7	0.2		1610	1.4	0.4
	2325	7.4	2.3		2230	6.7	2.0
13	0450	1.2	0.4	28	0420	1.5	0.5
Sa	1155	6.6	2.0	Su	1045	6.7	2.0
	1700	1.0	0.3		1635	1.6	0.5
					2310	6.4	2.0
14	0025	6.8	2.1	29	0450	1.5	0.5
Su	0515	1.5	0.5	M	1140	6.7	2.0
	1255	6.5	2.0		1710	1.8	0.5
	1755	1.5	0.5		2350	6.1	1.9
15	0110	6.2	1.9	30	0525	1.7	0.5
M	0615	2.0	0.6	Tu	1230	6.6	2.0
	1345	6.3	1.9		1755	2.1	0.6
	1900	2.1	0.6				
				31	0040	5.8	1.8
				W	0605	1.8	0.5
					1320	6.5	2.0
					1855	2.4	0.7

SEPTEMBER

Day	Time h m	Height ft	Height m	Day	Time h m	Height ft	Height m
1	0140	5.6	1.7	16	0400	5.3	1.6
Th	0715	2.1	0.6	F	1015	3.2	1.0
	1415	6.5	2.0		1640	6.1	1.9
	2005	2.8	0.9		2315	3.1	0.9
2	0305	5.5	1.7	17	0500	5.4	1.6
F	0820	2.2	0.7	Sa	1105	3.0	0.9
	1545	6.6	2.0		1725	6.3	1.9
	2250	2.7	0.8		2350	2.9	0.9
3	0430	5.7	1.7	18	0535	5.8	1.8
Sa	1010	2.2	0.7	Su	1155	2.7	0.8
	1710	6.9	2.1		1810	6.6	2.0
	2355	2.2	0.7				
4	0540	6.2	1.9	19	0020	2.6	0.8
Su	1130	1.9	0.6	M	0620	6.1	1.9
	1805	7.4	2.3		1220	2.4	0.7
					1850	6.9	2.1
5	0040	1.7	0.5	20	0100	2.3	0.7
M	0635	6.7	2.0	Tu	0650	6.5	2.0
	1235	1.4	0.4		1305	2.1	0.6
	1910	7.9	2.4		1925	7.2	2.2
6	0115	1.2	0.4	21	0130	2.1	0.6
Tu	0725	7.0	2.1	W	0725	6.8	2.1
	1325	1.0	0.3		1335	1.8	0.5
	1955	8.2	2.5		2000	7.4	2.3
7	0200	0.9	0.3	22	0200	1.8	0.5
W	0815	7.3	2.2	Th	0800	7.0	2.1
	1415	0.7	0.2		1405	1.6	0.5
	2045	8.2	2.5		2035	7.4	2.3
8	0240	0.8	0.2	23	0225	1.6	0.5
Th	0910	7.4	2.3	F	0840	7.2	2.2
	1455	0.5	0.2		1445	1.5	0.5
	2130	8.0	2.4		2110	7.3	2.2
9	0300	0.8	0.2	24	0250	1.5	0.5
F	0955	7.4	2.3	Sa	0905	7.2	2.2
	1525	0.6	0.2		1505	1.4	0.4
	2220	7.7	2.3		2135	7.1	2.2
10	0345	1.0	0.3	25	0325	1.4	0.4
Sa	1035	7.2	2.2	Su	0955	7.3	2.2
	1600	0.8	0.2		1540	1.5	0.5
	2310	7.2	2.2		2205	6.8	2.1
11	0420	1.3	0.4	26	0345	1.4	0.4
Su	1130	7.0	2.1	M	1025	7.2	2.2
	1655	1.2	0.4		1605	1.6	0.5
	2355	6.6	2.0		2255	6.5	2.0
12	0455	1.6	0.5	27	0425	1.4	0.4
M	1225	6.7	2.0	Tu	1110	7.1	2.2
	1725	1.8	0.5		1645	1.9	0.6
					2330	6.2	1.9
13	0040	6.0	1.8	28	0500	1.5	0.5
Tu	0530	2.1	0.6	W	1205	7.0	2.1
	1320	6.4	2.0		1730	2.2	0.7
	1815	2.5	0.8				
14	0140	5.6	1.7	29	0025	5.9	1.8
W	0615	2.6	0.8	Th	0550	1.8	0.5
	1425	6.2	1.9		1300	6.8	2.1
	1920	3.1	0.9		1815	2.6	0.8
15	0250	5.3	1.6	30	0120	5.7	1.7
Th	0725	3.1	0.9	F	0635	2.2	0.7
	1530	6.0	1.8		1405	6.7	2.0
	2230	3.2	1.0		1925	2.9	0.9

Time meridian 52° 30' W. 0000 is midnight. 1200 is noon.
Heights are referred to the Canadian chart datum of soundings. Subtract 1.7 feet (0.5 meter) to refer these levels to the datum of N.O.S. charts.

Times and Heights of High and Low Waters

OCTOBER

Day	Time h m	Height ft	Height m
1	0315	5.7	1.7
Sa	0825	2.6	0.8
	1530	6.7	2.0
	2245	2.7	0.8
2	0415	6.0	1.8
Su	1020	2.4	0.7
	1655	7.0	2.1
	2340	2.2	0.7
3	0525	6.5	2.0
M	1115	2.0	0.6
	1750	7.4	2.3
4	0015	1.7	0.5
Tu	0620	7.0	2.1
	1225	1.5	0.5
	1850	7.7	2.3
5	0050	1.3	0.4
W	0720	7.4	2.3
	1300	1.0	0.3
	1945	8.0	2.4
6	0135	1.0	0.3
Th	0805	7.7	2.3
	1345	0.7	0.2
	2030	8.0	2.4
7	0200	0.9	0.3
F	0850	7.8	2.4
	1435	0.6	0.2
	2110	7.8	2.4
8	0240	1.0	0.3
Sa	0925	7.8	2.4
	1505	0.7	0.2
	2145	7.4	2.3
9	0315	1.1	0.3
Su	1010	7.6	2.3
	1555	1.0	0.3
	2235	6.9	2.1
10	0350	1.4	0.4
M	1100	7.2	2.2
	1620	1.5	0.5
	2320	6.4	2.0
11	0425	1.8	0.5
Tu	1150	6.9	2.1
	1710	2.1	0.6
12	0015	5.9	1.8
W	0515	2.3	0.7
	1250	6.6	2.0
	1800	2.8	0.9
13	0130	5.5	1.7
Th	0545	2.8	0.9
	1355	6.4	2.0
	1920	3.4	1.0
14	0235	5.4	1.6
F	0710	3.3	1.0
	1455	6.3	1.9
	2145	3.4	1.0
15	0330	5.4	1.6
Sa	0945	3.4	1.0
	1555	6.3	1.9
	2240	3.3	1.0

Day	Time h m	Height ft	Height m
16	0420	5.6	1.7
Su	1035	3.2	1.0
	1650	6.4	2.0
	2320	3.0	0.9
17	0505	5.9	1.8
M	1115	2.9	0.9
	1745	6.6	2.0
	2350	2.7	0.8
18	0550	6.3	1.9
Tu	1200	2.6	0.8
	1825	6.8	2.1
19	0020	2.4	0.7
W	0635	6.7	2.0
	1235	2.2	0.7
	1910	7.1	2.2
20	0055	2.1	0.6
Th	0715	7.1	2.2
	1315	1.9	0.6
	1935	7.2	2.2
21	0125	1.8	0.5
F	0740	7.4	2.3
	1345	1.6	0.5
	2005	7.3	2.2
22	0155	1.6	0.5
Sa	0815	7.6	2.3
	1415	1.5	0.5
	2045	7.2	2.2
23	0225	1.4	0.4
Su	0850	7.7	2.3
	1450	1.5	0.5
	2115	7.0	2.1
24	0255	1.3	0.4
M	0935	7.7	2.3
	1520	1.5	0.5
	2145	6.8	2.1
25	0325	1.3	0.4
Tu	1005	7.7	2.3
	1600	1.7	0.5
	2225	6.5	2.0
26	0405	1.4	0.4
W	1055	7.5	2.3
	1640	2.0	0.6
	2310	6.2	1.9
27	0450	1.7	0.5
Th	1155	7.3	2.2
	1710	2.3	0.7
28	0015	5.9	1.8
F	0525	2.1	0.6
	1250	7.0	2.1
	1810	2.7	0.8
29	0140	5.8	1.8
Sa	0615	2.5	0.8
	1405	6.9	2.1
	1900	3.1	0.9
30	0255	6.0	1.8
Su	0820	2.8	0.9
	1525	6.9	2.1
	2230	2.6	0.8
31	0410	6.4	2.0
M	1020	2.5	0.8
	1630	7.0	2.1
	2315	2.2	0.7

NOVEMBER

Day	Time h m	Height ft	Height m
1	0505	6.8	2.1
Tu	1125	2.0	0.6
	1730	7.3	2.2
	2350	1.8	0.5
2	0600	7.3	2.2
W	1210	1.6	0.5
	1840	7.5	2.3
3	0035	1.5	0.5
Th	0655	7.7	2.3
	1255	1.3	0.4
	1920	7.6	2.3
4	0110	1.3	0.4
F	0740	8.0	2.4
	1330	1.0	0.3
	2010	7.6	2.3
5	0135	1.2	0.4
Sa	0815	8.1	2.5
	1415	1.0	0.3
	2045	7.4	2.3
6	0210	1.3	0.4
Su	0910	8.1	2.5
	1450	1.1	0.3
	2115	7.1	2.2
7	0300	1.4	0.4
M	0945	7.8	2.4
	1525	1.5	0.5
	2205	6.7	2.0
8	0320	1.7	0.5
Tu	1025	7.5	2.3
	1615	1.9	0.6
	2245	6.2	1.9
9	0405	2.0	0.6
W	1115	7.2	2.2
	1645	2.4	0.7
	2345	5.9	1.8
10	0440	2.5	0.8
Th	1235	6.9	2.1
	1720	2.9	0.9
11	0100	5.7	1.7
F	0525	3.0	0.9
	1320	6.6	2.0
	1825	3.4	1.0
12	0145	5.7	1.7
Sa	0615	3.4	1.0
	1425	6.5	2.0
	2105	3.5	1.1
13	0255	5.7	1.7
Su	0850	3.6	1.1
	1500	6.4	2.0
	2155	3.3	1.0
14	0340	5.8	1.8
M	0955	3.4	1.0
	1610	6.4	2.0
	2240	3.1	0.9
15	0425	6.1	1.9
Tu	1055	3.1	0.9
	1700	6.5	2.0
	2320	2.9	0.9

Day	Time h m	Height ft	Height m
16	0515	6.5	2.0
W	1130	2.8	0.9
	1755	6.7	2.0
	2350	2.5	0.8
17	0600	6.9	2.1
Th	1215	2.4	0.7
	1835	6.9	2.1
18	0020	2.2	0.7
F	0635	7.4	2.3
	1250	2.1	0.6
	1900	7.1	2.2
19	0050	1.9	0.6
Sa	0720	7.7	2.3
	1335	1.9	0.6
	1945	7.2	2.2
20	0120	1.6	0.5
Su	0755	8.0	2.4
	1410	1.7	0.5
	2020	7.2	2.2
21	0155	1.5	0.5
M	0840	8.2	2.5
	1440	1.7	0.5
	2050	7.1	2.2
22	0230	1.4	0.4
Tu	0910	8.2	2.5
	1500	1.7	0.5
	2130	6.9	2.1
23	0310	1.3	0.4
W	1000	8.1	2.5
	1545	1.9	0.6
	2210	6.6	2.0
24	0350	1.5	0.5
Th	1050	7.9	2.4
	1620	2.1	0.6
	2305	6.4	2.0
25	0425	1.8	0.5
F	1140	7.7	2.3
	1705	2.3	0.7
26	0015	6.2	1.9
Sa	0515	2.2	0.7
	1250	7.4	2.3
	1800	2.7	0.8
27	0130	6.2	1.9
Su	0620	2.6	0.8
	1345	7.2	2.2
	1925	2.9	0.9
28	0240	6.4	2.0
M	0840	2.7	0.8
	1455	7.0	2.1
	2145	2.6	0.8
29	0345	6.7	2.0
Tu	1005	2.5	0.8
	1610	6.9	2.1
	2250	2.3	0.7
30	0450	7.0	2.1
W	1105	2.1	0.6
	1715	6.9	2.1
	2330	2.1	0.6

DECEMBER

Day	Time h m	Height ft	Height m
1	0540	7.4	2.3
Th	1140	1.9	0.6
	1805	7.0	2.1
	2350	1.9	0.6
2	0630	7.7	2.3
F	1220	1.7	0.5
	1850	7.0	2.1
3	0015	1.8	0.5
Sa	0715	7.9	2.4
	1315	1.6	0.5
	1940	7.0	2.1
4	0100	1.7	0.5
Su	0750	8.0	2.4
	1350	1.6	0.5
	2010	6.9	2.1
5	0135	1.7	0.5
M	0840	8.0	2.4
	1420	1.7	0.5
	2055	6.7	2.0
6	0220	1.8	0.5
Tu	0920	7.8	2.4
	1515	1.9	0.6
	2125	6.5	2.0
7	0300	1.9	0.6
W	1005	7.7	2.3
	1550	2.2	0.7
	2210	6.3	1.9
8	0345	2.2	0.7
Th	1050	7.4	2.3
	1620	2.5	0.8
	2305	6.1	1.9
9	0420	2.5	0.8
F	1135	7.2	2.2
	1700	2.8	0.9
	2350	5.9	1.8
10	0515	2.9	0.9
Sa	1220	6.9	2.1
	1800	3.1	0.9
11	0050	5.8	1.8
Su	0600	3.2	1.0
	1310	6.6	2.0
	1850	3.4	1.0
12	0140	5.8	1.8
M	0700	3.5	1.1
	1355	6.3	1.9
	2020	3.5	1.1
13	0235	5.9	1.8
Tu	0840	3.6	1.1
	1455	6.1	1.9
	2140	3.3	1.0
14	0330	6.2	1.9
W	0945	3.4	1.0
	1600	6.1	1.9
	2215	3.1	0.9
15	0425	6.5	2.0
Th	1055	3.0	0.9
	1655	6.2	1.9
	2245	2.7	0.8

Day	Time h m	Height ft	Height m
16	0515	6.9	2.1
F	1140	2.7	0.8
	1750	6.4	2.0
	2330	2.4	0.7
17	0600	7.4	2.3
Sa	1210	2.4	0.7
	1825	6.7	2.0
18	0010	2.0	0.6
Su	0645	7.8	2.4
	1250	2.2	0.7
	1900	7.0	2.1
19	0045	1.7	0.5
M	0725	8.2	2.5
	1335	2.0	0.6
	1955	7.1	2.2
20	0120	1.5	0.5
Tu	0810	8.4	2.6
	1415	1.8	0.5
	2030	7.0	2.1
21	0215	1.4	0.4
W	0900	8.5	2.6
	1455	1.8	0.5
	2115	7.0	2.1
22	0250	1.3	0.4
Th	0955	8.4	2.6
	1530	1.8	0.5
	2215	6.8	2.1
23	0335	1.4	0.4
F	1030	8.3	2.5
	1620	1.9	0.6
	2305	6.7	2.0
24	0420	1.6	0.5
Sa	1130	8.0	2.4
	1705	2.0	0.6
25	0010	6.6	2.0
Su	0510	1.9	0.6
	1215	7.7	2.3
	1800	2.3	0.7
26	0100	6.5	2.0
M	0600	2.2	0.7
	1315	7.3	2.2
	1840	2.6	0.8
27	0210	6.6	2.0
Tu	0720	2.5	0.8
	1425	6.8	2.1
	2025	2.7	0.8
28	0325	6.7	2.0
W	0930	2.7	0.8
	1530	6.5	2.0
	2150	2.7	0.8
29	0420	6.9	2.1
Th	1035	2.5	0.8
	1645	6.4	2.0
	2230	2.5	0.8
30	0510	7.2	2.2
F	1125	2.4	0.7
	1740	6.4	2.0
	2315	2.4	0.7
31	0610	7.5	2.3
Sa	1215	2.3	0.7
	1830	6.4	2.0
	2355	2.3	0.7

Time meridian 52° 30' W. 0000 is midnight. 1200 is noon.
Heights are referred to the Canadian chart datum of soundings. Subtract 1.7 feet (0.5 meter) to refer these levels to the datum of N.O.S. charts.

EASTPORT, MAINE, 1983

Times and Heights of High and Low Waters

JANUARY

Day	Time (h m)	Height (ft)	Height (m)
1 Sa	0553	-1.5	-0.5
	1157	21.3	6.5
	1827	-3.1	-0.9
2 Su	0030	19.7	6.0
	0647	-1.5	-0.5
	1251	21.0	6.4
	1920	-2.8	-0.9
3 M	0125	19.5	5.9
	0741	-1.2	-0.4
	1345	20.3	6.2
	2013	-2.2	-0.7
4 Tu	0219	19.1	5.8
	0837	-0.8	-0.2
	1441	19.4	5.9
	2107	-1.4	-0.4
5 W	0315	18.7	5.7
	0935	-0.2	-0.1
	1540	18.5	5.6
	2203	-0.6	-0.2
6 Th	0414	18.2	5.5
	1034	0.3	0.1
	1641	17.6	5.4
	2300	0.2	0.1
7 F	0513	17.9	5.5
	1135	0.6	0.2
	1742	16.9	5.2
	2359	0.8	0.2
8 Sa	0610	17.6	5.4
	1235	0.8	0.2
	1842	16.5	5.0
9 Su	0056	1.2	0.4
	0708	17.6	5.4
	1333	0.7	0.2
	1940	16.4	5.0
10 M	0152	1.4	0.4
	0801	17.6	5.4
	1426	0.6	0.2
	2033	16.4	5.0
11 Tu	0242	1.5	0.5
	0849	17.7	5.4
	1515	0.4	0.1
	2120	16.5	5.0
12 W	0331	1.4	0.4
	0933	17.9	5.5
	1601	0.2	0.1
	2203	16.6	5.1
13 Th	0414	1.3	0.4
	1015	18.0	5.5
	1643	0.0	0.0
	2243	16.7	5.1
14 F	0456	1.2	0.4
	1055	18.1	5.5
	1722	0.0	0.0
	2322	16.9	5.2
15 Sa	0535	1.2	0.4
	1133	18.1	5.5
	1801	0.0	0.0
	2359	17.0	5.2

Day	Time (h m)	Height (ft)	Height (m)
16 Su	0614	1.2	0.4
	1212	18.1	5.5
	1839	0.1	0.0
17 M	0038	17.0	5.2
	0652	1.2	0.4
	1249	18.0	5.5
	1917	0.2	0.1
18 Tu	0115	17.1	5.2
	0731	1.3	0.4
	1329	17.8	5.4
	1955	0.5	0.2
19 W	0155	17.1	5.2
	0813	1.4	0.4
	1411	17.5	5.3
	2035	0.7	0.2
20 Th	0237	17.1	5.2
	0858	1.5	0.5
	1457	17.1	5.2
	2120	1.0	0.3
21 F	0325	17.1	5.2
	0945	1.6	0.5
	1545	16.8	5.1
	2207	1.3	0.4
22 Sa	0413	17.2	5.2
	1039	1.5	0.5
	1640	16.5	5.0
	2300	1.5	0.5
23 Su	0508	17.4	5.3
	1136	1.2	0.4
	1739	16.5	5.0
	2358	1.5	0.5
24 M	0607	17.8	5.4
	1235	0.7	0.2
	1840	16.7	5.1
25 Tu	0057	1.3	0.4
	0706	18.4	5.6
	1336	0.0	0.0
	1943	17.2	5.2
26 W	0158	0.7	0.2
	0805	19.2	5.9
	1436	-0.9	-0.3
	2041	18.0	5.5
27 Th	0255	-0.1	0.0
	0903	20.1	6.1
	1534	-1.9	-0.6
	2137	18.8	5.7
28 F	0353	-0.9	-0.3
	0958	20.9	6.4
	1627	-2.7	-0.8
	2232	19.5	5.9
29 Sa	0446	-1.6	-0.5
	1052	21.4	6.5
	1720	-3.2	-1.0
	2324	20.1	6.1
30 Su	0539	-2.1	-0.6
	1144	21.5	6.6
	1811	-3.4	-1.0
31 M	0015	20.3	6.2
	0630	-2.2	-0.7
	1235	21.3	6.5
	1900	-3.1	-0.9

FEBRUARY

Day	Time (h m)	Height (ft)	Height (m)
1 Tu	0105	20.2	6.2
	0723	-2.0	-0.6
	1326	20.6	6.3
	1950	-2.4	-0.7
2 W	0155	19.8	6.0
	0814	-1.4	-0.4
	1419	19.6	6.0
	2040	-1.5	-0.5
3 Th	0248	19.1	5.8
	0907	-0.7	-0.2
	1512	18.4	5.6
	2133	-0.4	-0.1
4 F	0340	18.4	5.6
	1002	0.2	0.1
	1607	17.3	5.3
	2226	0.7	0.2
5 Sa	0435	17.6	5.4
	1100	0.9	0.3
	1708	16.3	5.0
	2322	1.6	0.5
6 Su	0534	17.0	5.2
	1159	1.4	0.4
	1808	15.7	4.8
7 M	0022	2.2	0.7
	0635	16.7	5.1
	1259	1.6	0.5
	1908	15.5	4.7
8 Tu	0119	2.4	0.7
	0730	16.7	5.1
	1357	1.4	0.4
	2004	15.6	4.8
9 W	0215	2.3	0.7
	0822	16.9	5.2
	1449	1.1	0.3
	2054	15.9	4.8
10 Th	0304	1.9	0.6
	0910	17.3	5.3
	1536	0.7	0.2
	2139	16.3	5.0
11 F	0350	1.5	0.5
	0953	17.7	5.4
	1618	0.3	0.1
	2220	16.8	5.1
12 Sa	0432	1.1	0.3
	1032	18.1	5.5
	1658	0.0	0.0
	2257	17.2	5.2
13 Su	0512	0.8	0.2
	1111	18.4	5.6
	1736	-0.2	-0.1
	2334	17.5	5.3
14 M	0548	0.5	0.2
	1147	18.5	5.6
	1812	-0.3	-0.1
15 Tu	0009	17.8	5.4
	0625	0.4	0.1
	1224	18.5	5.6
	1847	-0.2	-0.1

Day	Time (h m)	Height (ft)	Height (m)
16 W	0046	18.0	5.5
	0704	0.4	0.1
	1302	18.3	5.6
	1923	0.0	0.0
17 Th	0123	18.0	5.5
	0742	0.4	0.1
	1342	18.0	5.5
	2003	0.3	0.1
18 F	0204	18.0	5.5
	0824	0.6	0.2
	1424	17.6	5.4
	2045	0.7	0.2
19 Sa	0248	17.9	5.5
	0912	0.8	0.2
	1514	17.1	5.2
	2133	1.2	0.4
20 Su	0338	17.7	5.4
	1005	1.0	0.3
	1609	16.7	5.1
	2227	1.6	0.5
21 M	0434	17.6	5.4
	1105	1.0	0.3
	1710	16.4	5.0
	2328	1.8	0.5
22 Tu	0537	17.7	5.4
	1210	0.8	0.2
	1816	16.4	5.0
23 W	0033	1.6	0.5
	0642	18.1	5.5
	1315	0.2	0.1
	1922	17.0	5.2
24 Th	0138	1.0	0.3
	0748	18.9	5.8
	1418	-0.7	-0.2
	2025	17.8	5.4
25 F	0241	0.0	0.0
	0847	19.8	6.0
	1516	-1.7	-0.5
	2122	18.8	5.7
26 Sa	0339	-1.0	-0.3
	0945	20.6	6.3
	1611	-2.6	-0.8
	2216	19.8	6.0
27 Su	0432	-1.9	-0.6
	1037	21.2	6.5
	1702	-3.1	-0.9
	2307	20.4	6.2
28 M	0523	-2.5	-0.8
	1128	21.3	6.5
	1751	-3.2	-1.0
	2355	20.7	6.3

MARCH

Day	Time (h m)	Height (ft)	Height (m)
1 Tu	0613	-2.6	-0.8
	1217	21.0	6.4
	1837	-2.9	-0.9
2 W	0041	20.5	6.2
	0700	-2.4	-0.7
	1305	20.3	6.2
	1924	-2.1	-0.6
3 Th	0128	20.0	6.1
	0750	-1.7	-0.5
	1352	19.3	5.9
	2011	-1.0	-0.3
4 F	0216	19.2	5.9
	0837	-0.8	-0.2
	1442	18.0	5.5
	2101	0.2	0.1
5 Sa	0305	18.2	5.5
	0929	0.3	0.1
	1533	16.8	5.1
	2152	1.4	0.4
6 Su	0359	17.2	5.2
	1024	1.2	0.4
	1629	15.8	4.8
	2247	2.3	0.7
7 M	0455	16.4	5.0
	1124	1.9	0.6
	1729	15.1	4.6
	2346	2.9	0.9
8 Tu	0555	16.0	4.9
	1224	2.2	0.7
	1832	14.9	4.5
9 W	0046	3.0	0.9
	0655	16.1	4.9
	1324	2.0	0.6
	1931	15.2	4.6
10 Th	0143	2.7	0.8
	0751	16.4	5.0
	1417	1.6	0.5
	2023	15.7	4.8
11 F	0234	2.1	0.6
	0841	17.0	5.2
	1505	1.0	0.3
	2109	16.4	5.0
12 Sa	0321	1.4	0.4
	0924	17.6	5.4
	1547	0.4	0.1
	2150	17.0	5.2
13 Su	0404	0.8	0.2
	1006	18.1	5.5
	1627	0.0	0.0
	2227	17.7	5.4
14 M	0443	0.3	0.1
	1043	18.5	5.6
	1705	-0.4	-0.1
	2304	18.2	5.5
15 Tu	0521	-0.1	0.0
	1121	18.7	5.7
	1740	-0.5	-0.2
	2340	18.6	5.7

Day	Time (h m)	Height (ft)	Height (m)
16 W	0559	-0.4	-0.1
	1158	18.8	5.7
	1817	-0.5	-0.2
17 Th	0016	18.8	5.7
	0636	-0.5	-0.2
	1235	18.7	5.7
	1854	-0.3	-0.1
18 F	0053	18.9	5.8
	0716	-0.5	-0.2
	1316	18.4	5.6
	1933	0.1	0.0
19 Sa	0135	18.8	5.7
	0758	-0.3	-0.1
	1358	17.9	5.5
	2016	0.6	0.2
20 Su	0221	18.5	5.6
	0847	0.1	0.0
	1450	17.3	5.3
	2107	1.1	0.3
21 M	0312	18.1	5.5
	0941	0.5	0.2
	1546	16.7	5.1
	2205	1.6	0.5
22 Tu	0412	17.7	5.4
	1044	0.8	0.2
	1650	16.4	5.0
	2309	1.9	0.6
23 W	0517	17.6	5.4
	1150	0.7	0.2
	1759	16.5	5.0
24 Th	0017	1.6	0.5
	0626	17.9	5.5
	1258	0.2	0.1
	1908	17.1	5.2
25 F	0124	0.9	0.3
	0732	18.6	5.7
	1401	-0.6	-0.2
	2009	18.0	5.5
26 Sa	0225	-0.1	0.0
	0833	19.4	5.9
	1500	-1.5	-0.5
	2105	19.1	5.8
27 Su	0323	-1.2	-0.4
	0929	20.2	6.2
	1553	-2.2	-0.7
	2158	20.0	6.1
28 M	0415	-2.1	-0.6
	1021	20.6	6.3
	1641	-2.6	-0.8
	2246	20.5	6.2
29 Tu	0505	-2.6	-0.8
	1108	20.7	6.3
	1728	-2.5	-0.8
	2331	20.6	6.3
30 W	0552	-2.6	-0.8
	1154	20.3	6.2
	1812	-2.1	-0.6
31 Th	0016	20.4	6.2
	0636	-2.2	-0.7
	1240	19.6	6.0
	1857	-1.2	-0.4

Time meridian 75° W. 0000 is midnight. 1200 is noon.
Heights are referred to mean low water which is the chart datum of soundings.

EASTPORT, MAINE, 1983

Times and Heights of High and Low Waters

APRIL

Day	Time h m	Height ft	Height m	Day	Time h m	Height ft	Height m
1	0059	19.7	6.0	16	0027	19.6	6.0
F	0722	-1.5	-0.5	Sa	0652	-1.2	-0.4
	1326	18.6	5.7		1252	18.6	5.7
	1942	-0.2	-0.1		1910	0.0	0.0
2	0145	18.8	5.7	17	0110	19.4	5.9
Sa	0810	-0.5	-0.2	Su	0737	-0.9	-0.3
	1411	17.5	5.3		1339	18.1	5.5
	2029	0.9	0.3		1957	0.5	0.2
3	0230	17.8	5.4	18	0200	19.0	5.8
Su	0859	0.5	0.2	M	0830	-0.5	-0.2
	1501	16.4	5.0		1433	17.5	5.3
	2117	1.9	0.6		2051	1.0	0.3
4	0320	16.9	5.2	19	0253	18.4	5.6
M	0950	1.4	0.4	Tu	0927	0.0	0.0
	1554	15.5	4.7		1533	17.0	5.2
	2212	2.7	0.8		2149	1.5	0.5
5	0417	16.1	4.9	20	0357	18.0	5.5
Tu	1045	2.1	0.6	W	1029	0.3	0.1
	1653	15.0	4.6		1637	16.7	5.1
	2308	3.2	1.0		2255	1.6	0.5
6	0515	15.7	4.8	21	0504	17.7	5.4
W	1145	2.4	0.7	Th	1135	0.4	0.1
	1753	14.9	4.5		1746	16.9	5.2
7	0008	3.2	1.0	22	0003	1.3	0.4
Th	0616	15.8	4.8	F	0613	17.9	5.5
	1242	2.2	0.7		1240	0.0	0.0
	1850	15.2	4.6		1851	17.5	5.3
8	0106	2.8	0.9	23	0109	0.6	0.2
F	0711	16.2	4.9	Sa	0716	18.4	5.6
	1338	1.8	0.5		1343	-0.6	-0.2
	1943	15.8	4.8		1951	18.4	5.6
9	0159	2.1	0.6	24	0210	-0.4	-0.1
Sa	0804	16.8	5.1	Su	0817	19.0	5.8
	1426	1.2	0.4		1438	-1.1	-0.3
	2030	16.6	5.1		2046	19.2	5.9
10	0247	1.3	0.4	25	0305	-1.2	-0.4
Su	0849	17.4	5.3	M	0910	19.5	5.9
	1510	0.6	0.2		1531	-1.6	-0.5
	2113	17.4	5.3		2137	19.9	6.1
11	0331	0.5	0.2	26	0357	-1.9	-0.6
M	0931	18.0	5.5	Tu	1001	19.7	6.0
	1552	0.1	0.0		1619	-1.7	-0.5
	2153	18.2	5.5		2224	20.2	6.2
12	0411	-0.2	-0.1	27	0444	-2.2	-0.7
Tu	1011	18.5	5.6	W	1049	19.6	6.0
	1631	-0.3	-0.1		1704	-1.4	-0.4
	2230	18.8	5.7		2308	20.1	6.1
13	0451	-0.7	-0.2	28	0529	-2.1	-0.6
W	1051	18.8	5.7	Th	1133	19.2	5.9
	1708	-0.5	-0.2		1747	-0.9	-0.3
	2308	19.2	5.9		2350	19.8	6.0
14	0530	-1.1	-0.3	29	0615	-1.6	-0.5
Th	1130	18.9	5.8	F	1215	18.5	5.6
	1747	-0.5	-0.2		1831	-0.2	-0.1
	2347	19.5	5.9				
15	0610	-1.2	-0.4	30	0032	19.1	5.8
F	1210	18.8	5.7	Sa	0657	-1.0	-0.3
	1827	-0.4	-0.1		1300	17.8	5.4
					1915	0.6	0.2

MAY

Day	Time h m	Height ft	Height m	Day	Time h m	Height ft	Height m
1	0115	18.3	5.6	16	0052	19.9	6.1
Su	0742	-0.2	-0.1	M	0723	-1.5	-0.5
	1343	16.9	5.2		1326	18.3	5.6
	1958	1.5	0.5		1942	0.2	0.1
2	0158	17.5	5.3	17	0145	19.5	5.9
M	0829	0.7	0.2	Tu	0816	-1.1	-0.3
	1430	16.2	4.9		1422	17.9	5.5
	2047	2.2	0.7		2037	0.6	0.2
3	0247	16.8	5.1	18	0242	18.9	5.8
Tu	0917	1.4	0.4	W	0914	-0.7	-0.2
	1520	15.5	4.7		1520	17.5	5.3
	2138	2.8	0.9		2138	0.9	0.3
4	0338	16.2	4.9	19	0344	18.4	5.6
W	1010	1.9	0.6	Th	1015	-0.3	-0.1
	1615	15.2	4.6		1625	17.4	5.3
	2231	3.1	0.9		2242	1.0	0.3
5	0434	15.8	4.8	20	0449	18.0	5.5
Th	1105	2.2	0.7	F	1118	-0.1	0.0
	1711	15.2	4.6		1729	17.6	5.4
	2329	3.1	0.9		2348	0.7	0.2
6	0532	15.8	4.8	21	0555	17.9	5.5
F	1200	2.1	0.6	Sa	1221	-0.2	-0.1
	1806	15.5	4.7		1831	18.0	5.5
7	0025	2.7	0.8	22	0051	0.2	0.1
Sa	0629	16.1	4.9	Su	0659	18.1	5.5
	1253	1.8	0.5		1319	-0.4	-0.1
	1858	16.1	4.9		1930	18.6	5.7
8	0117	2.0	0.6	23	0151	-0.4	-0.1
Su	0721	16.6	5.1	M	0759	18.3	5.6
	1343	1.3	0.4		1415	-0.5	-0.2
	1948	16.9	5.2		2025	19.1	5.8
9	0207	1.2	0.4	24	0246	-1.0	-0.3
M	0809	17.2	5.2	Tu	0853	18.5	5.6
	1428	0.8	0.2		1508	-0.6	-0.2
	2031	17.8	5.4		2113	19.4	5.9
10	0254	0.4	0.1	25	0337	-1.3	-0.4
Tu	0854	17.7	5.4	W	0941	18.5	5.6
	1513	0.3	0.1		1555	-0.5	-0.2
	2114	18.5	5.6		2159	19.5	5.9
11	0337	-0.4	-0.1	26	0426	-1.4	-0.4
W	0938	18.2	5.5	Th	1027	18.3	5.6
	1555	-0.1	0.0		1641	-0.2	-0.1
	2156	19.2	5.9		2243	19.3	5.9
12	0419	-1.0	-0.3	27	0509	-1.3	-0.4
Th	1020	18.6	5.7	F	1112	18.0	5.5
	1636	-0.4	-0.1		1725	0.2	0.1
	2236	19.7	6.0		2325	19.0	5.8
13	0503	-1.5	-0.5	28	0552	-0.9	-0.3
F	1104	18.9	5.8	Sa	1155	17.6	5.4
	1720	-0.5	-0.2		1807	0.7	0.2
	2321	20.1	6.1				
14	0546	-1.8	-0.5	29	0007	18.5	5.6
Sa	1149	18.9	5.8	Su	0635	-0.4	-0.1
	1803	-0.4	-0.1		1236	17.1	5.2
					1849	1.3	0.4
15	0004	20.1	6.1	30	0048	18.0	5.5
Su	0633	-1.8	-0.5	M	0718	0.1	0.0
	1235	18.7	5.7		1318	16.6	5.1
	1851	-0.2	-0.1		1931	1.8	0.5
				31	0131	17.4	5.3
				Tu	0800	0.7	0.2
					1401	16.2	4.9
					2016	2.2	0.7

JUNE

Day	Time h m	Height ft	Height m	Day	Time h m	Height ft	Height m
1	0216	16.9	5.2	16	0230	19.5	5.9
W	0845	1.2	0.4	Th	0859	-1.4	-0.4
	1448	15.8	4.8		1507	18.4	5.6
	2104	2.6	0.8		2124	0.0	0.0
2	0304	16.5	5.0	17	0330	18.8	5.7
Th	0933	1.6	0.5	F	0956	-0.9	-0.3
	1538	15.7	4.8		1607	18.2	5.5
	2154	2.7	0.8		2226	0.2	0.1
3	0356	16.2	4.9	18	0431	18.2	5.5
F	1023	1.8	0.5	Sa	1055	-0.4	-0.1
	1629	15.7	4.8		1707	18.2	5.5
	2247	2.7	0.8		2328	0.3	0.1
4	0449	16.1	4.9	19	0535	17.8	5.4
Sa	1115	1.8	0.5	Su	1156	-0.1	0.0
	1722	16.0	4.9		1808	18.3	5.6
	2342	2.4	0.7				
5	0543	16.1	4.9	20	0030	0.1	0.0
Su	1205	1.7	0.5	M	0637	17.6	5.4
	1813	16.5	5.0		1255	0.2	0.1
					1906	18.4	5.6
6	0034	1.9	0.6	21	0129	-0.1	0.0
M	0635	16.4	5.0	Tu	0736	17.5	5.3
	1256	1.4	0.4		1351	0.3	0.1
	1903	17.2	5.2		2001	18.6	5.7
7	0124	1.2	0.4	22	0225	-0.3	-0.1
Tu	0727	16.9	5.2	W	0832	17.4	5.3
	1346	1.1	0.3		1443	0.4	0.1
	1951	18.0	5.5		2051	18.7	5.7
8	0215	0.4	0.1	23	0316	-0.5	-0.2
W	0817	17.4	5.3	Th	0923	17.4	5.3
	1433	0.6	0.2		1532	0.6	0.2
	2038	18.7	5.7		2139	18.7	5.7
9	0303	-0.5	-0.2	24	0404	-0.6	-0.2
Th	0906	17.9	5.5	F	1008	17.3	5.3
	1520	0.2	0.1		1619	0.8	0.2
	2124	19.5	5.9		2222	18.5	5.6
10	0350	-1.2	-0.4	25	0448	-0.5	-0.2
F	0953	18.4	5.6	Sa	1051	17.1	5.2
	1607	-0.2	-0.1		1702	1.0	0.3
	2210	20.1	6.1		2302	18.4	5.6
11	0438	-1.8	-0.5	26	0530	-0.3	-0.1
Sa	1040	18.8	5.7	Su	1130	17.0	5.2
	1654	-0.5	-0.2		1744	1.2	0.4
	2257	20.5	6.2		2343	18.2	5.5
12	0527	-2.2	-0.7	27	0611	-0.1	0.0
Su	1129	19.0	5.8	M	1211	16.8	5.1
	1744	-0.7	-0.2		1825	1.4	0.4
	2347	20.6	6.3				
13	0617	-2.3	-0.7	28	0024	17.9	5.5
M	1220	19.0	5.8	Tu	0652	0.2	0.1
	1835	-0.7	-0.2		1252	16.6	5.1
					1906	1.6	0.5
14	0038	20.5	6.2	29	0104	17.6	5.4
Tu	0709	-2.2	-0.7	W	0733	0.5	0.2
	1312	18.9	5.8		1333	16.5	5.0
	1929	-0.5	-0.2		1947	1.8	0.5
15	0131	20.1	6.1	30	0145	17.3	5.3
W	0803	-1.9	-0.6	Th	0814	0.8	0.2
	1408	18.6	5.7		1415	16.4	5.0
	2024	-0.2	-0.1		2032	2.0	0.6

Time meridian 75° W. 0000 is midnight. 1200 is noon.
Heights are referred to mean low water which is the chart datum of soundings.

Times and Heights of High and Low Waters

JULY

Day	Time h m	Height ft	m	Day	Time h m	Height ft	m
1	0230	17.0	5.2	16	0309	19.1	5.8
F	0858	1.1	0.3	Sa	0933	-1.2	-0.4
	1459	16.3	5.0		1542	18.8	5.7
	2117	2.1	0.6		2203	-0.3	-0.1
2	0317	16.6	5.1	17	0410	18.2	5.5
Sa	0944	1.4	0.4	Su	1030	-0.4	-0.1
	1546	16.4	5.0		1641	18.4	5.6
	2205	2.2	0.7		2303	0.1	0.0
3	0405	16.4	5.0	18	0510	17.4	5.3
Su	1031	1.6	0.5	M	1127	0.4	0.1
	1636	16.6	5.1		1740	18.1	5.5
	2259	2.0	0.6				
4	0458	16.3	5.0	19	0004	0.4	0.1
M	1119	1.7	0.5	Tu	0612	16.9	5.2
	1726	16.9	5.2		1227	0.9	0.3
	2351	1.7	0.5		1839	17.9	5.5
5	0554	16.3	5.0	20	0104	0.5	0.2
Tu	1213	1.6	0.5	W	0714	16.6	5.1
	1818	17.4	5.3		1324	1.3	0.4
					1936	17.8	5.4
6	0045	1.2	0.4	21	0201	0.4	0.1
W	0647	16.6	5.1	Th	0809	16.5	5.0
	1303	1.4	0.4		1420	1.4	0.4
	1911	18.0	5.5		2028	17.8	5.4
7	0138	0.4	0.1	22	0255	0.3	0.1
Th	0743	17.0	5.2	F	0900	16.5	5.0
	1359	0.9	0.3		1511	1.4	0.4
	2004	18.7	5.7		2117	17.9	5.5
8	0233	-0.4	-0.1	23	0342	0.2	0.1
F	0836	17.6	5.4	Sa	0947	16.6	5.1
	1451	0.4	0.1		1558	1.3	0.4
	2056	19.5	5.9		2200	18.0	5.5
9	0327	-1.2	-0.4	24	0428	0.0	0.0
Sa	0929	18.3	5.6	Su	1030	16.7	5.1
	1543	-0.2	-0.1		1640	1.2	0.4
	2147	20.3	6.2		2242	18.1	5.5
10	0418	-2.0	-0.6	25	0509	0.0	0.0
Su	1021	18.8	5.7	M	1109	16.9	5.2
	1636	-0.8	-0.2		1722	1.1	0.3
	2240	20.8	6.3		2321	18.1	5.5
11	0509	-2.5	-0.8	26	0548	0.0	0.0
M	1113	19.3	5.9	Tu	1146	17.0	5.2
	1728	-1.2	-0.4		1800	1.1	0.3
	2332	21.1	6.4		2359	18.1	5.5
12	0600	-2.8	-0.9	27	0626	0.1	0.0
Tu	1204	19.6	6.0	W	1225	17.0	5.2
	1820	-1.4	-0.4		1840	1.1	0.3
13	0024	21.0	6.4	28	0038	18.0	5.5
W	0652	-2.8	-0.9	Th	0703	0.2	0.1
	1257	19.7	6.0		1302	17.1	5.2
	1913	-1.4	-0.4		1918	1.2	0.4
14	0118	20.7	6.3	29	0115	17.7	5.4
Th	0745	-2.5	-0.8	F	0742	0.5	0.2
	1350	19.5	5.9		1342	17.1	5.2
	2008	-1.2	-0.4		1958	1.3	0.4
15	0213	20.0	6.1	30	0157	17.4	5.3
F	0838	-1.9	-0.6	Sa	0821	0.8	0.2
	1445	19.2	5.9		1422	17.1	5.2
	2104	-0.8	-0.2		2042	1.5	0.5
				31	0240	17.1	5.2
				Su	0903	1.1	0.3
					1505	17.0	5.2
					2125	1.6	0.5

AUGUST

Day	Time h m	Height ft	m	Day	Time h m	Height ft	m
1	0325	16.7	5.1	16	0442	16.8	5.1
M	0948	1.5	0.5	Tu	1057	1.2	0.4
	1552	17.0	5.2		1709	17.5	5.3
	2217	1.6	0.5		2335	0.9	0.3
2	0419	16.4	5.0	17	0544	16.1	4.9
Tu	1038	1.7	0.5	W	1158	1.8	0.5
	1644	17.1	5.2		1810	17.1	5.2
	2310	1.5	0.5				
3	0513	16.2	4.9	18	0037	1.2	0.4
W	1133	1.8	0.5	Th	0647	15.8	4.8
	1740	17.4	5.3		1258	2.1	0.6
					1909	16.9	5.2
4	0008	1.2	0.4	19	0135	1.2	0.4
Th	0613	16.3	5.0	F	0746	15.8	4.8
	1229	1.7	0.5		1356	2.1	0.6
	1839	17.9	5.5		2003	17.1	5.2
5	0108	0.6	0.2	20	0230	1.0	0.3
F	0714	16.8	5.1	Sa	0838	16.0	4.9
	1330	1.2	0.4		1449	1.8	0.5
	1938	18.6	5.7		2054	17.4	5.3
6	0207	-0.3	-0.1	21	0319	0.6	0.2
Sa	0812	17.4	5.3	Su	0923	16.4	5.0
	1428	0.5	0.2		1534	1.4	0.4
	2034	19.5	5.9		2139	17.7	5.4
7	0305	-1.2	-0.4	22	0403	0.3	0.1
Su	0908	18.3	5.6	M	1006	16.8	5.1
	1524	-0.4	-0.1		1616	1.0	0.3
	2130	20.4	6.2		2219	18.1	5.5
8	0358	-2.1	-0.6	23	0443	0.0	0.0
M	1003	19.2	5.9	Tu	1042	17.2	5.2
	1619	-1.3	-0.4		1656	0.7	0.2
	2224	21.1	6.4		2256	18.3	5.6
9	0451	-2.9	-0.9	24	0520	-0.2	-0.1
Tu	1055	19.9	6.1	W	1119	17.5	5.3
	1711	-1.9	-0.6		1734	0.5	0.2
	2316	21.5	6.6		2333	18.4	5.6
10	0542	-3.2	-1.0	25	0556	-0.2	-0.1
W	1147	20.3	6.2	Th	1154	17.7	5.4
	1803	-2.3	-0.7		1812	0.4	0.1
11	0007	21.4	6.5	26	0009	18.3	5.6
Th	0633	-3.2	-1.0	F	0632	0.0	0.0
	1237	20.5	6.2		1230	17.8	5.4
	1856	-2.3	-0.7		1849	0.4	0.1
12	0059	21.0	6.4	27	0046	18.1	5.5
F	0723	-2.8	-0.9	Sa	0708	0.2	0.1
	1329	20.3	6.2		1306	17.9	5.5
	1947	-2.0	-0.6		1927	0.6	0.2
13	0152	20.1	6.1	28	0123	17.8	5.4
Sa	0814	-2.0	-0.6	Su	0745	0.6	0.2
	1420	19.7	6.0		1345	17.8	5.4
	2040	-1.3	-0.4		2008	0.8	0.2
14	0245	19.0	5.8	29	0206	17.4	5.3
Su	0906	-0.9	-0.3	M	0826	1.0	0.3
	1514	19.0	5.8		1427	17.6	5.4
	2136	-0.5	-0.2		2051	1.0	0.3
15	0343	17.9	5.5	30	0251	16.9	5.2
M	1001	0.2	0.1	Tu	0909	1.5	0.5
	1610	18.2	5.5		1515	17.4	5.3
	2234	0.3	0.1		2141	1.2	0.4
				31	0345	16.4	5.0
				W	1002	1.9	0.6
					1609	17.3	5.3
					2237	1.3	0.4

SEPTEMBER

Day	Time h m	Height ft	m	Day	Time h m	Height ft	m
1	0442	16.1	4.9	16	0005	1.8	0.5
Th	1100	2.1	0.6	F	0616	15.2	4.6
	1708	17.3	5.3		1228	2.7	0.8
	2341	1.2	0.4		1837	16.3	5.0
2	0546	16.2	4.9	17	0105	1.7	0.5
F	1204	1.9	0.6	Sa	0716	15.4	4.7
	1813	17.7	5.4		1327	2.5	0.8
					1935	16.6	5.1
3	0045	0.6	0.2	18	0201	1.4	0.4
Sa	0651	16.6	5.1	Su	0809	15.9	4.8
	1308	1.3	0.4		1419	1.9	0.6
	1916	18.4	5.6		2025	17.1	5.2
4	0148	-0.2	-0.1	19	0249	0.9	0.3
Su	0753	17.5	5.3	M	0854	16.5	5.0
	1409	0.4	0.1		1505	1.3	0.4
	2017	19.4	5.9		2110	17.6	5.4
5	0246	-1.3	-0.4	20	0332	0.4	0.1
M	0852	18.6	5.7	Tu	0934	17.2	5.2
	1508	-0.8	-0.2		1547	0.7	0.2
	2114	20.4	6.2		2150	18.1	5.5
6	0341	-2.3	-0.7	21	0411	0.0	0.0
Tu	0945	19.7	6.0	W	1011	17.7	5.4
	1603	-1.8	-0.5		1627	0.2	0.1
	2208	21.1	6.4		2227	18.4	5.6
7	0433	-3.0	-0.9	22	0448	-0.2	-0.1
W	1037	20.5	6.2	Th	1048	18.1	5.5
	1654	-2.6	-0.8		1706	-0.1	0.0
	2259	21.5	6.6		2304	18.5	5.6
8	0522	-3.3	-1.0	23	0525	-0.3	-0.1
Th	1126	20.9	6.4	F	1123	18.4	5.6
	1744	-2.9	-0.9		1742	-0.3	-0.1
	2349	21.3	6.5		2340	18.5	5.6
9	0611	-3.1	-0.9	24	0559	-0.2	-0.1
F	1214	21.0	6.4	Sa	1158	18.6	5.7
	1835	-2.8	-0.9		1820	-0.3	-0.1
10	0038	20.7	6.3	25	0017	18.3	5.6
Sa	0659	-2.5	-0.8	Su	0636	0.1	0.0
	1302	20.5	6.2		1234	18.6	5.7
	1923	-2.3	-0.7		1857	-0.2	-0.1
11	0128	19.8	6.0	26	0057	18.0	5.5
Su	0747	-1.5	-0.5	M	0713	0.5	0.2
	1352	19.7	6.0		1313	18.4	5.6
	2014	-1.4	-0.4		1938	0.1	0.0
12	0218	18.6	5.7	27	0138	17.6	5.4
M	0837	-0.3	-0.1	Tu	0754	1.0	0.3
	1443	18.7	5.7		1355	18.1	5.5
	2109	-0.3	-0.1		2022	0.4	0.1
13	0314	17.3	5.3	28	0224	17.0	5.2
Tu	0930	0.9	0.3	W	0843	1.5	0.5
	1536	17.7	5.4		1443	17.8	5.4
	2205	0.7	0.2		2115	0.8	0.2
14	0412	16.2	4.9	29	0317	16.5	5.0
W	1027	1.9	0.6	Th	0935	2.0	0.6
	1636	16.8	5.1		1541	17.4	5.3
	2304	1.4	0.4		2213	1.1	0.3
15	0514	15.5	4.7	30	0420	16.2	4.9
Th	1128	2.6	0.8	F	1039	2.2	0.7
	1737	16.3	5.0		1646	17.3	5.3
					2319	1.0	0.3

Time meridian 75° W. 0000 is midnight. 1200 is noon.
Heights are referred to mean low water which is the chart datum of soundings.

Times and Heights of High and Low Waters

OCTOBER

Day	Time h m	Height ft	m
1	0527	16.2	4.9
Sa	1145	1.9	0.6
	1754	17.6	5.4
2	0026	0.5	0.2
Su	0634	16.8	5.1
	1251	1.2	0.4
	1859	18.3	5.6
3	0128	-0.3	-0.1
M	0736	17.9	5.5
	1354	0.1	0.0
	2001	19.2	5.9
4	0226	-1.3	-0.4
Tu	0833	19.0	5.8
	1452	-1.1	-0.3
	2058	20.1	6.1
5	0321	-2.1	-0.6
W	0926	20.1	6.1
	1545	-2.2	-0.7
	2150	20.7	6.3
6	0411	-2.7	-0.8
Th	1016	20.8	6.3
	1636	-2.8	-0.9
	2240	20.9	6.4
7	0459	-2.8	-0.9
F	1104	21.1	6.4
	1725	-3.1	-0.9
	2329	20.7	6.3
8	0547	-2.4	-0.7
Sa	1150	20.9	6.4
	1813	-2.8	-0.9
9	0016	20.0	6.1
Su	0633	-1.7	-0.5
	1236	20.3	6.2
	1900	-2.1	-0.6
10	0104	19.0	5.8
M	0720	-0.6	-0.2
	1321	19.4	5.9
	1948	-1.1	-0.3
11	0152	17.9	5.5
Tu	0807	0.5	0.2
	1411	18.3	5.6
	2039	0.0	0.0
12	0243	16.8	5.1
W	0858	1.6	0.5
	1502	17.2	5.2
	2133	1.0	0.3
13	0338	15.8	4.8
Th	0953	2.5	0.8
	1600	16.4	5.0
	2229	1.8	0.5
14	0439	15.2	4.6
F	1054	3.0	0.9
	1700	15.9	4.8
	2330	2.1	0.6
15	0540	15.1	4.6
Sa	1154	3.0	0.9
	1802	15.9	4.8

Day	Time h m	Height ft	m
16	0029	2.0	0.6
Su	0639	15.4	4.7
	1253	2.7	0.8
	1858	16.2	4.9
17	0122	1.6	0.5
M	0730	16.0	4.9
	1345	2.0	0.6
	1949	16.7	5.1
18	0212	1.1	0.3
Tu	0817	16.7	5.1
	1431	1.2	0.4
	2036	17.3	5.3
19	0254	0.6	0.2
W	0857	17.5	5.3
	1516	0.5	0.2
	2116	17.9	5.5
20	0335	0.2	0.1
Th	0937	18.1	5.5
	1555	-0.1	0.0
	2155	18.2	5.5
21	0414	-0.1	0.0
F	1013	18.7	5.7
	1635	-0.5	-0.2
	2234	18.5	5.6
22	0451	-0.2	-0.1
Sa	1050	19.0	5.8
	1713	-0.8	-0.2
	2313	18.5	5.6
23	0528	-0.1	0.0
Su	1127	19.2	5.9
	1750	-0.9	-0.3
	2350	18.4	5.6
24	0606	0.1	0.0
M	1205	19.2	5.9
	1832	-0.8	-0.2
25	0032	18.1	5.5
Tu	0646	0.4	0.1
	1246	19.0	5.8
	1914	-0.5	-0.2
26	0115	17.7	5.4
W	0728	0.9	0.3
	1332	18.7	5.7
	2003	-0.2	-0.1
27	0205	17.2	5.2
Th	0821	1.3	0.4
	1424	18.2	5.5
	2056	0.2	0.1
28	0301	16.8	5.1
F	0919	1.7	0.5
	1524	17.8	5.4
	2157	0.5	0.2
29	0404	16.5	5.0
Sa	1023	1.8	0.5
	1629	17.5	5.3
	2301	0.6	0.2
30	0511	16.7	5.1
Su	1130	1.5	0.5
	1737	17.7	5.4
31	0005	0.2	0.1
M	0617	17.4	5.3
	1234	0.8	0.2
	1843	18.2	5.5

NOVEMBER

Day	Time h m	Height ft	m
1	0108	-0.4	-0.1
Tu	0719	18.3	5.6
	1338	-0.2	-0.1
	1944	18.9	5.8
2	0207	-1.1	-0.3
W	0815	19.3	5.9
	1434	-1.3	-0.4
	2041	19.5	5.9
3	0300	-1.6	-0.5
Th	0907	20.1	6.1
	1529	-2.1	-0.6
	2132	19.9	6.1
4	0350	-1.9	-0.6
F	0955	20.6	6.3
	1617	-2.6	-0.8
	2222	19.9	6.1
5	0437	-1.8	-0.5
Sa	1042	20.7	6.3
	1705	-2.6	-0.8
	2309	19.6	6.0
6	0523	-1.4	-0.4
Su	1126	20.4	6.2
	1751	-2.3	-0.7
	2355	19.0	5.8
7	0609	-0.7	-0.2
M	1209	19.7	6.0
	1837	-1.6	-0.5
8	0041	18.2	5.5
Tu	0654	0.2	0.1
	1256	18.9	5.8
	1923	-0.7	-0.2
9	0126	17.3	5.3
W	0742	1.1	0.3
	1342	18.0	5.5
	2011	0.2	0.1
10	0214	16.4	5.0
Th	0830	2.0	0.6
	1430	17.1	5.2
	2101	1.1	0.3
11	0305	15.7	4.8
F	0922	2.6	0.8
	1522	16.3	5.0
	2154	1.7	0.5
12	0400	15.3	4.7
Sa	1018	3.0	0.9
	1620	15.9	4.8
	2250	2.0	0.6
13	0456	15.2	4.6
Su	1114	3.0	0.9
	1719	15.8	4.8
	2344	2.1	0.6
14	0552	15.5	4.7
M	1210	2.7	0.8
	1814	16.0	4.9
15	0037	1.8	0.5
Tu	0645	16.1	4.9
	1303	2.1	0.6
	1906	16.4	5.0

Day	Time h m	Height ft	m
16	0127	1.4	0.4
W	0732	16.8	5.1
	1353	1.3	0.4
	1954	16.9	5.2
17	0212	1.0	0.3
Th	0817	17.6	5.4
	1438	0.6	0.2
	2039	17.4	5.3
18	0257	0.6	0.2
F	0857	18.3	5.6
	1521	-0.1	0.0
	2121	17.9	5.5
19	0339	0.2	0.1
Sa	0939	18.9	5.8
	1603	-0.7	-0.2
	2203	18.2	5.5
20	0418	0.0	0.0
Su	1019	19.4	5.9
	1644	-1.1	-0.3
	2246	18.4	5.6
21	0500	-0.1	0.0
M	1059	19.6	6.0
	1726	-1.3	-0.4
	2327	18.5	5.6
22	0542	0.0	0.0
Tu	1142	19.7	6.0
	1811	-1.4	-0.4
23	0011	18.4	5.6
W	0625	0.1	0.0
	1227	19.6	6.0
	1857	-1.2	-0.4
24	0059	18.1	5.5
Th	0713	0.4	0.1
	1316	19.3	5.9
	1947	-0.9	-0.3
25	0150	17.8	5.4
F	0807	0.7	0.2
	1411	18.9	5.8
	2042	-0.6	-0.2
26	0248	17.5	5.3
Sa	0904	1.0	0.3
	1509	18.4	5.6
	2141	-0.2	-0.1
27	0349	17.3	5.3
Su	1007	1.1	0.3
	1613	18.0	5.5
	2242	0.0	0.0
28	0452	17.5	5.3
M	1113	0.9	0.3
	1719	17.8	5.4
	2345	-0.1	0.0
29	0557	17.9	5.5
Tu	1217	0.4	0.1
	1824	18.0	5.5
30	0046	-0.2	-0.1
W	0657	18.6	5.7
	1319	-0.3	-0.1
	1926	18.2	5.5

DECEMBER

Day	Time h m	Height ft	m
1	0143	-0.5	-0.2
Th	0753	19.2	5.9
	1417	-1.0	-0.3
	2023	18.5	5.6
2	0238	-0.7	-0.2
F	0846	19.7	6.0
	1510	-1.5	-0.5
	2116	18.7	5.7
3	0329	-0.8	-0.2
Sa	0935	19.9	6.1
	1601	-1.8	-0.5
	2203	18.7	5.7
4	0417	-0.6	-0.2
Su	1021	19.9	6.1
	1648	-1.8	-0.5
	2251	18.4	5.6
5	0503	-0.3	-0.1
M	1105	19.6	6.0
	1733	-1.5	-0.5
	2335	18.0	5.5
6	0548	0.2	0.1
Tu	1148	19.1	5.8
	1817	-1.0	-0.3
7	0017	17.5	5.3
W	0631	0.8	0.2
	1231	18.5	5.6
	1900	-0.4	-0.1
8	0102	17.0	5.2
Th	0716	1.3	0.4
	1315	17.9	5.5
	1945	0.3	0.1
9	0145	16.5	5.0
F	0802	1.9	0.6
	1400	17.2	5.2
	2030	0.9	0.3
10	0231	16.1	4.9
Sa	0848	2.3	0.7
	1448	16.7	5.1
	2117	1.4	0.4
11	0320	15.8	4.8
Su	0938	2.6	0.8
	1538	16.2	4.9
	2205	1.7	0.5
12	0412	15.8	4.8
M	1030	2.7	0.8
	1631	16.0	4.9
	2257	1.9	0.6
13	0504	15.9	4.8
Tu	1123	2.5	0.8
	1726	15.9	4.8
	2348	1.9	0.6
14	0555	16.3	5.0
W	1218	2.1	0.6
	1819	16.1	4.9
15	0039	1.8	0.5
Th	0646	16.8	5.1
	1309	1.5	0.5
	1911	16.4	5.0

Day	Time h m	Height ft	m
16	0128	1.5	0.5
F	0733	17.5	5.3
	1359	0.8	0.2
	2001	16.8	5.1
17	0215	1.1	0.3
Sa	0820	18.2	5.5
	1446	0.1	0.0
	2047	17.3	5.3
18	0302	0.7	0.2
Su	0905	18.9	5.8
	1533	-0.6	-0.2
	2134	17.8	5.4
19	0349	0.3	0.1
M	0951	19.5	5.9
	1619	-1.2	-0.4
	2220	18.3	5.6
20	0435	-0.1	0.0
Tu	1037	20.0	6.1
	1706	-1.7	-0.5
	2307	18.6	5.7
21	0523	-0.4	-0.1
W	1123	20.3	6.2
	1753	-2.0	-0.6
	2356	18.8	5.7
22	0610	-0.5	-0.2
Th	1212	20.4	6.2
	1842	-2.1	-0.6
23	0044	18.8	5.7
F	0700	-0.5	-0.2
	1302	20.2	6.2
	1933	-1.9	-0.6
24	0137	18.7	5.7
Sa	0754	-0.3	-0.1
	1357	19.7	6.0
	2027	-1.5	-0.5
25	0232	18.6	5.7
Su	0851	-0.1	0.0
	1455	19.1	5.8
	2122	-1.0	-0.3
26	0330	18.4	5.6
M	0950	0.1	0.0
	1554	18.4	5.5
	2220	-0.5	-0.2
27	0431	18.3	5.6
Tu	1052	0.2	0.1
	1659	17.9	5.5
	2321	-0.1	0.0
28	0532	18.3	5.6
W	1155	0.2	0.1
	1802	17.5	5.3
29	0021	0.2	0.1
Th	0633	18.4	5.6
	1258	0.0	0.0
	1905	17.4	5.3
30	0119	0.4	0.1
F	0732	18.6	5.7
	1357	-0.3	-0.1
	2004	17.4	5.3
31	0218	0.4	0.1
Sa	0826	18.8	5.7
	1452	-0.6	-0.2
	2100	17.5	5.3

Time meridian 75° W. 0000 is midnight. 1200 is noon.
Heights are referred to mean low water which is the chart datum of soundings.

Times and Heights of High and Low Waters

JANUARY

Day	Time h m	Height ft	Height m	Day	Time h m	Height ft	Height m
1	0549	-0.7	-0.2	16	0022	8.2	2.5
Sa	1204	11.3	3.4	Su	0613	0.7	0.2
	1833	-2.1	-0.6		1224	9.3	2.8
					1847	-0.2	-0.1
2	0047	9.6	2.9	17	0055	8.2	2.5
Su	0643	-0.6	-0.2	M	0649	0.8	0.2
	1258	11.0	3.4		1259	9.1	2.8
	1927	-1.8	-0.5		1920	-0.1	0.0
3	0143	9.5	2.9	18	0129	8.2	2.5
M	0743	-0.4	-0.1	Tu	0727	0.8	0.2
	1356	10.5	3.2		1334	8.9	2.7
	2022	-1.4	-0.4		1956	0.1	0.0
4	0240	9.4	2.9	19	0206	8.3	2.5
Tu	0843	-0.1	0.0	W	0808	0.8	0.2
	1457	9.9	3.0		1415	8.7	2.7
	2118	-0.9	-0.3		2033	0.2	0.1
5	0339	9.3	2.8	20	0243	8.3	2.5
W	0947	0.1	0.0	Th	0853	0.7	0.2
	1559	9.3	2.8		1457	8.4	2.6
	2218	-0.4	-0.1		2115	0.3	0.1
6	0441	9.1	2.8	21	0329	8.5	2.6
Th	1053	0.3	0.1	F	0943	0.6	0.2
	1707	8.7	2.7		1547	8.2	2.5
	2318	0.0	0.0		2201	0.4	0.1
7	0544	9.1	2.8	22	0416	8.6	2.6
F	1200	0.3	0.1	Sa	1036	0.5	0.2
	1813	8.3	2.5		1643	8.0	2.4
					2252	0.5	0.2
8	0018	0.3	0.1	23	0510	8.8	2.7
Sa	0642	9.1	2.8	Su	1134	0.2	0.1
	1304	0.2	0.1		1743	7.9	2.4
	1917	8.1	2.5		2348	0.5	0.2
9	0117	0.5	0.2	24	0607	9.2	2.8
Su	0741	9.1	2.8	M	1237	-0.2	-0.1
	1400	0.0	0.0		1848	8.0	2.4
	2015	8.0	2.4				
10	0210	0.6	0.2	25	0048	0.4	0.1
M	0831	9.2	2.8	Tu	0707	9.6	2.9
	1455	-0.2	-0.1		1339	-0.6	-0.2
	2108	8.0	2.4		1951	8.2	2.5
11	0300	0.6	0.2	26	0148	0.1	0.0
Tu	0917	9.3	2.8	W	0807	10.1	3.1
	1541	-0.3	-0.1		1439	-1.1	-0.3
	2154	8.1	2.5		2052	8.6	2.6
12	0345	0.7	0.2	27	0248	-0.2	-0.1
W	0959	9.3	2.8	Th	0906	10.6	3.2
	1623	-0.4	-0.1		1537	-1.6	-0.5
	2236	8.1	2.5		2149	9.1	2.8
13	0423	0.7	0.2	28	0346	-0.5	-0.2
Th	1038	9.4	2.9	F	1004	11.1	3.4
	1702	-0.4	-0.1		1633	-1.9	-0.6
	2314	8.1	2.5		2245	9.5	2.9
14	0502	0.7	0.2	29	0442	-0.8	-0.2
F	1116	9.4	2.9	Sa	1058	11.3	3.4
	1737	-0.3	-0.1		1726	-2.1	-0.6
	2349	8.2	2.5		2338	9.8	3.0
15	0537	0.7	0.2	30	0537	-1.0	-0.3
Sa	1149	9.4	2.9	Su	1153	11.3	3.4
	1813	-0.3	-0.1		1818	-2.1	-0.6
				31	0030	9.9	3.0
				M	0632	-1.0	-0.3
					1246	11.0	3.4
					1908	-1.9	-0.6

FEBRUARY

Day	Time h m	Height ft	Height m	Day	Time h m	Height ft	Height m
1	0124	9.9	3.0	16	0056	8.7	2.7
Tu	0727	-0.9	-0.3	W	0700	0.1	0.0
	1339	10.4	3.2		1308	9.1	2.8
	2001	-1.5	-0.5		1922	-0.3	-0.1
2	0216	9.8	3.0	17	0132	8.8	2.7
W	0822	-0.6	-0.2	Th	0740	0.0	0.0
	1434	9.7	3.0		1345	8.8	2.7
	2051	-0.9	-0.3		1959	-0.2	-0.1
3	0310	9.5	2.9	18	0209	8.9	2.7
Th	0920	-0.3	-0.1	F	0822	0.0	0.0
	1533	9.0	2.7		1428	8.6	2.6
	2146	-0.3	-0.1		2041	0.0	0.0
4	0406	9.1	2.8	19	0254	9.0	2.7
F	1021	0.0	0.0	Sa	0910	-0.1	0.0
	1635	8.3	2.5		1518	8.3	2.5
	2243	0.2	0.1		2127	0.2	0.1
5	0506	8.8	2.7	20	0342	9.0	2.7
Sa	1126	0.3	0.1	Su	1005	0.0	0.0
	1739	7.8	2.4		1613	8.0	2.4
	2342	0.7	0.2		2217	0.5	0.2
6	0606	8.6	2.6	21	0436	9.1	2.8
Su	1230	0.4	0.1	M	1106	0.0	0.0
	1848	7.5	2.3		1715	7.9	2.4
					2319	0.6	0.2
7	0044	1.0	0.3	22	0539	9.3	2.8
M	0707	8.6	2.6	Tu	1213	-0.2	-0.1
	1331	0.4	0.1		1824	7.9	2.4
	1949	7.5	2.3				
8	0140	1.1	0.3	23	0024	0.6	0.2
Tu	0802	8.7	2.7	W	0646	9.6	2.9
	1427	0.3	0.1		1320	-0.4	-0.1
	2042	7.6	2.3		1933	8.2	2.5
9	0231	1.1	0.3	24	0131	0.4	0.1
W	0854	8.8	2.7	Th	0752	10.0	3.0
	1516	0.2	0.1		1423	-0.8	-0.2
	2131	7.8	2.4		2039	8.7	2.7
10	0321	1.0	0.3	25	0236	0.0	0.0
Th	0937	9.0	2.7	F	0855	10.5	3.2
	1559	0.0	0.0		1524	-1.3	-0.4
	2212	8.0	2.4		2137	9.2	2.8
11	0401	0.8	0.2	26	0335	-0.5	-0.2
F	1017	9.2	2.8	Sa	0953	10.9	3.3
	1638	-0.1	0.0		1619	-1.6	-0.5
	2249	8.2	2.5		2233	9.7	3.0
12	0439	0.7	0.2	27	0433	-0.9	-0.3
Sa	1054	9.3	2.8	Su	1049	11.1	3.4
	1713	-0.2	-0.1		1709	-1.9	-0.6
	2321	8.3	2.5		2322	10.1	3.1
13	0515	0.5	0.2	28	0526	-1.2	-0.4
Su	1127	9.4	2.9	M	1141	11.0	3.4
	1745	-0.2	-0.1		1758	-1.9	-0.6
	2353	8.5	2.6				
14	0550	0.4	0.1				
M	1159	9.3	2.8				
	1818	-0.3	-0.1				
15	0024	8.6	2.6				
Tu	0625	0.2	0.1				
	1233	9.2	2.8				
	1850	-0.3	-0.1				

MARCH

Day	Time h m	Height ft	Height m	Day	Time h m	Height ft	Height m
1	0011	10.3	3.1	16	0558	-0.3	-0.1
Tu	0618	-1.3	-0.4	W	1206	9.3	2.8
	1231	10.7	3.3		1816	-0.4	-0.1
	1846	-1.6	-0.5				
2	0100	10.2	3.1	17	0025	9.3	2.8
W	0708	-1.3	-0.4	Th	0635	-0.5	-0.2
	1321	10.1	3.1		1243	9.1	2.8
	1932	-1.2	-0.4		1852	-0.4	-0.1
3	0148	9.9	3.0	18	0101	9.4	2.9
Th	0800	-1.0	-0.3	F	0715	-0.7	-0.2
	1412	9.4	2.9		1323	9.0	2.7
	2020	-0.7	-0.2		1929	-0.2	-0.1
4	0236	9.5	2.9	19	0140	9.5	2.9
F	0851	-0.6	-0.2	Sa	0758	-0.7	-0.2
	1505	8.7	2.7		1408	8.7	2.7
	2109	0.0	0.0		2012	0.0	0.0
5	0328	9.1	2.8	20	0225	9.5	2.9
Sa	0949	-0.1	0.0	Su	0849	-0.5	-0.2
	1600	8.0	2.4		1457	8.4	2.6
	2203	0.6	0.2		2102	0.3	0.1
6	0423	8.6	2.6	21	0315	9.4	2.9
Su	1047	0.4	0.1	M	0944	-0.3	-0.1
	1703	7.5	2.3		1555	8.1	2.5
	2300	1.2	0.4		2158	0.6	0.2
7	0523	8.3	2.5	22	0415	9.3	2.8
M	1150	0.7	0.2	Tu	1047	-0.1	0.0
	1808	7.3	2.2		1700	8.0	2.4
					2302	0.9	0.3
8	0003	1.5	0.5	23	0521	9.4	2.9
Tu	0624	8.2	2.5	W	1155	-0.1	0.0
	1252	0.9	0.3		1812	8.1	2.5
	1910	7.3	2.2				
9	0104	1.6	0.5	24	0012	0.9	0.3
W	0727	8.3	2.5	Th	0631	9.5	2.9
	1352	0.8	0.2		1305	-0.2	-0.1
	2007	7.4	2.3		1922	8.5	2.6
10	0200	1.5	0.5	25	0122	0.6	0.2
Th	0819	8.5	2.6	F	0741	9.8	3.0
	1443	0.7	0.2		1410	-0.5	-0.2
	2057	7.7	2.3		2026	9.0	2.7
11	0250	1.3	0.4	26	0227	0.1	0.0
F	0906	8.8	2.7	Sa	0844	10.2	3.1
	1527	0.5	0.2		1508	-0.9	-0.3
	2138	8.0	2.4		2124	9.6	2.9
12	0332	1.0	0.3	27	0327	-0.5	-0.2
Sa	0947	9.1	2.8	Su	0943	10.5	3.2
	1606	0.3	0.1		1601	-1.2	-0.4
	2215	8.3	2.5		2215	10.0	3.0
13	0412	0.6	0.2	28	0422	-1.0	-0.3
Su	1025	9.2	2.8	M	1036	10.6	3.2
	1639	0.1	0.0		1651	-1.4	-0.4
	2248	8.6	2.6		2303	10.3	3.1
14	0448	0.3	0.1	29	0512	-1.3	-0.4
M	1058	9.3	2.8	Tu	1125	10.5	3.2
	1711	-0.1	0.0		1737	-1.4	-0.4
	2320	8.9	2.7		2349	10.4	3.2
15	0522	0.0	0.0	30	0601	-1.4	-0.4
Tu	1132	9.3	2.8	W	1214	10.1	3.1
	1743	-0.3	-0.1		1821	-1.1	-0.3
	2349	9.1	2.8				
				31	0034	10.3	3.1
				Th	0649	-1.3	-0.4
					1301	9.6	2.9
					1905	-0.7	-0.2

Time meridian 75° W. 0000 is midnight. 1200 is noon.
Heights are referred to mean low water which is the chart datum of soundings.

Times and Heights of High and Low Waters

APRIL

Day	Time h m	Height ft	Height m	Day	Time h m	Height ft	Height m
1	0116	9.9	3.0	16	0032	10.0	3.0
F	0735	-1.0	-0.3	Sa	0655	-1.2	-0.4
	1348	9.1	2.8		1304	9.0	2.7
	1949	-0.2	-0.1		1905	-0.2	-0.1
2	0202	9.5	2.9	17	0116	10.0	3.0
Sa	0824	-0.6	-0.2	Su	0742	-1.1	-0.3
	1435	8.5	2.6		1353	8.9	2.7
	2035	0.4	0.1		1952	0.1	0.0
3	0249	9.0	2.7	18	0204	10.0	3.0
Su	0912	0.0	0.0	M	0833	-0.8	-0.2
	1528	7.9	2.4		1446	8.6	2.6
	2126	1.0	0.3		2045	0.5	0.2
4	0340	8.6	2.6	19	0259	9.8	3.0
M	1007	0.5	0.2	Tu	0931	-0.5	-0.2
	1624	7.5	2.3		1544	8.4	2.6
	2221	1.5	0.5		2145	0.8	0.2
5	0439	8.2	2.5	20	0400	9.6	2.9
Tu	1108	0.9	0.3	W	1035	-0.2	-0.1
	1726	7.3	2.2		1652	8.4	2.6
	2320	1.8	0.5		2253	1.0	0.3
6	0540	8.1	2.5	21	0510	9.5	2.9
W	1208	1.2	0.4	Th	1142	-0.1	0.0
	1829	7.3	2.2		1803	8.5	2.6
7	0022	1.9	0.6	22	0006	0.9	0.3
Th	0640	8.1	2.5	F	0622	9.5	2.9
	1307	1.2	0.4		1250	-0.1	0.0
	1925	7.5	2.3		1912	8.9	2.7
8	0120	1.8	0.5	23	0115	0.6	0.2
F	0736	8.3	2.5	Sa	0731	9.6	2.9
	1359	1.1	0.3		1354	-0.3	-0.1
	2013	7.8	2.4		2013	9.4	2.9
9	0210	1.5	0.5	24	0219	0.1	0.0
Sa	0826	8.6	2.6	Su	0834	9.8	3.0
	1442	0.9	0.3		1450	-0.5	-0.2
	2055	8.2	2.5		2107	9.9	3.0
10	0256	1.0	0.3	25	0316	-0.5	-0.2
Su	0911	8.8	2.7	M	0930	9.9	3.0
	1521	0.6	0.2		1541	-0.7	-0.2
	2132	8.6	2.6		2156	10.2	3.1
11	0337	0.5	0.2	26	0409	-0.9	-0.3
M	0948	9.0	2.7	Tu	1022	9.9	3.0
	1557	0.3	0.1		1628	-0.8	-0.2
	2206	9.0	2.7		2242	10.4	3.2
12	0415	0.0	0.0	27	0459	-1.2	-0.4
Tu	1025	9.1	2.8	W	1110	9.8	3.0
	1633	0.0	0.0		1713	-0.7	-0.2
	2241	9.3	2.8		2327	10.3	3.1
13	0452	-0.4	-0.1	28	0542	-1.3	-0.4
W	1102	9.2	2.8	Th	1156	9.5	2.9
	1706	-0.2	-0.1		1756	-0.4	-0.1
	2315	9.6	2.9				
14	0532	-0.8	-0.2	29	0008	10.1	3.1
Th	1141	9.2	2.8	F	0628	-1.2	-0.4
	1744	-0.3	-0.1		1242	9.1	2.8
	2351	9.9	3.0		1837	-0.1	0.0
15	0610	-1.1	-0.3	30	0050	9.8	3.0
F	1219	9.2	2.8	Sa	0710	-0.8	-0.2
	1823	-0.3	-0.1		1324	8.7	2.7
					1919	0.4	0.1

MAY

Day	Time h m	Height ft	Height m	Day	Time h m	Height ft	Height m
1	0132	9.4	2.9	16	0058	10.5	3.2
Su	0756	-0.4	-0.1	M	0727	-1.3	-0.4
	1409	8.3	2.5		1340	9.1	2.8
	2004	0.9	0.3		1939	0.2	0.1
2	0217	9.0	2.7	17	0150	10.4	3.2
M	0841	0.1	0.0	Tu	0822	-1.1	-0.3
	1457	7.9	2.4		1437	8.9	2.7
	2051	1.3	0.4		2035	0.5	0.2
3	0305	8.7	2.7	18	0249	10.1	3.1
Tu	0931	0.6	0.2	W	0921	-0.7	-0.2
	1547	7.7	2.3		1538	8.8	2.7
	2142	1.7	0.5		2139	0.7	0.2
4	0355	8.4	2.6	19	0352	9.8	3.0
W	1024	1.0	0.3	Th	1024	-0.4	-0.1
	1641	7.5	2.3		1645	8.9	2.7
	2237	2.0	0.6		2246	0.8	0.2
5	0451	8.2	2.5	20	0501	9.5	2.9
Th	1119	1.2	0.4	F	1128	-0.2	-0.1
	1738	7.6	2.3		1751	9.0	2.7
	2334	2.0	0.6		2357	0.7	0.2
6	0549	8.1	2.5	21	0611	9.4	2.9
F	1211	1.3	0.4	Sa	1232	-0.1	0.0
	1832	7.8	2.4		1854	9.3	2.8
7	0032	1.8	0.5	22	0106	0.4	0.1
Sa	0644	8.2	2.5	Su	0719	9.3	2.8
	1301	1.2	0.4		1333	-0.1	0.0
	1920	8.1	2.5		1954	9.7	3.0
8	0123	1.5	0.5	23	0207	0.0	0.0
Su	0736	8.3	2.5	M	0821	9.3	2.8
	1349	1.0	0.3		1427	-0.2	-0.1
	2002	8.4	2.6		2047	10.0	3.0
9	0212	1.0	0.3	24	0303	-0.5	-0.2
M	0821	8.5	2.6	Tu	0916	9.3	2.8
	1431	0.7	0.2		1519	-0.2	-0.1
	2044	8.9	2.7		2135	10.1	3.1
10	0255	0.4	0.1	25	0353	-0.8	-0.2
Tu	0907	8.7	2.7	W	1007	9.2	2.8
	1511	0.4	0.1		1606	-0.1	0.0
	2121	9.3	2.8		2221	10.1	3.1
11	0339	-0.2	-0.1	26	0441	-1.0	-0.3
W	0948	8.9	2.7	Th	1054	9.0	2.7
	1551	0.1	0.0		1649	0.0	0.0
	2202	9.7	3.0		2303	10.1	3.1
12	0421	-0.7	-0.2	27	0526	-1.0	-0.3
Th	1030	9.0	2.7	F	1139	8.9	2.7
	1630	-0.1	0.0		1731	0.2	0.1
	2240	10.1	3.1		2345	9.9	3.0
13	0503	-1.2	-0.4	28	0608	-0.8	-0.2
F	1114	9.1	2.8	Sa	1222	8.6	2.6
	1713	-0.2	-0.1		1812	0.5	0.2
	2325	10.4	3.2				
14	0549	-1.4	-0.4	29	0026	9.6	2.9
Sa	1159	9.2	2.8	Su	0649	-0.5	-0.2
	1758	-0.2	-0.1		1303	8.4	2.6
					1854	0.8	0.2
15	0009	10.5	3.2	30	0105	9.4	2.9
Su	0636	-1.5	-0.5	M	0731	-0.2	-0.1
	1247	9.2	2.8		1345	8.2	2.5
	1846	-0.1	0.0		1935	1.1	0.3
				31	0145	9.1	2.8
				Tu	0812	0.2	0.1
					1427	8.0	2.4
					2020	1.4	0.4

JUNE

Day	Time h m	Height ft	Height m	Day	Time h m	Height ft	Height m
1	0230	8.9	2.7	16	0239	10.3	3.1
W	0857	0.6	0.2	Th	0907	-0.9	-0.3
	1513	7.9	2.4		1526	9.3	2.8
	2106	1.7	0.5		2128	0.4	0.1
2	0317	8.6	2.6	17	0342	9.9	3.0
Th	0942	0.9	0.3	F	1008	-0.6	-0.2
	1558	7.8	2.4		1630	9.3	2.8
	2155	1.8	0.5		2235	0.4	0.1
3	0405	8.4	2.6	18	0449	9.5	2.9
F	1030	1.1	0.3	Sa	1109	-0.3	-0.1
	1647	7.9	2.4		1733	9.4	2.9
	2248	1.8	0.5		2343	0.4	0.1
4	0457	8.2	2.5	19	0556	9.1	2.8
Sa	1118	1.1	0.3	Su	1210	-0.1	0.0
	1734	8.1	2.5		1835	9.5	2.9
	2342	1.6	0.5				
5	0551	8.1	2.5	20	0051	0.2	0.1
Su	1204	1.1	0.3	M	0701	8.8	2.7
	1823	8.3	2.5		1309	0.1	0.0
					1933	9.7	3.0
6	0037	1.2	0.4	21	0152	-0.1	0.0
M	0641	8.1	2.5	Tu	0803	8.7	2.7
	1252	1.0	0.3		1405	0.2	0.1
	1909	8.7	2.7		2024	9.8	3.0
7	0125	0.7	0.2	22	0247	-0.3	-0.1
Tu	0733	8.2	2.5	W	0900	8.6	2.6
	1338	0.7	0.2		1456	0.3	0.1
	1955	9.1	2.8		2114	9.8	3.0
8	0215	0.2	0.1	23	0337	-0.5	-0.2
W	0823	8.4	2.6	Th	0951	8.6	2.6
	1423	0.5	0.2		1543	0.4	0.1
	2039	9.6	2.9		2201	9.8	3.0
9	0303	-0.4	-0.1	24	0425	-0.6	-0.2
Th	0914	8.6	2.6	F	1038	8.5	2.6
	1511	0.2	0.1		1628	0.5	0.2
	2124	10.1	3.1		2243	9.7	3.0
10	0351	-1.0	-0.3	25	0508	-0.6	-0.2
F	1001	8.9	2.7	Sa	1122	8.4	2.6
	1557	0.0	0.0		1710	0.7	0.2
	2212	10.5	3.2		2324	9.7	3.0
11	0440	-1.4	-0.4	26	0548	-0.4	-0.1
Sa	1051	9.1	2.8	Su	1201	8.3	2.5
	1646	-0.2	-0.1		1751	0.8	0.2
	2301	10.8	3.3				
12	0529	-1.6	-0.5	27	0002	9.5	2.9
Su	1142	9.3	2.8	M	0628	-0.2	-0.1
	1737	-0.2	-0.1		1241	8.3	2.5
	2351	10.9	3.3		1828	1.0	0.3
13	0620	-1.7	-0.5	28	0042	9.4	2.9
M	1234	9.3	2.8	Tu	0706	0.0	0.0
	1830	-0.2	-0.1		1318	8.2	2.5
					1909	1.1	0.3
14	0044	10.9	3.3	29	0119	9.2	2.8
Tu	0715	-1.5	-0.5	W	0743	0.2	0.1
	1329	9.4	2.9		1356	8.1	2.5
	1926	0.0	0.0		1950	1.3	0.4
15	0140	10.7	3.3	30	0200	9.0	2.7
W	0809	-1.3	-0.4	Th	0822	0.4	0.1
	1425	9.3	2.8		1435	8.1	2.5
	2025	0.2	0.1		2032	1.4	0.4

Time meridian 75° W. 0000 is midnight. 1200 is noon.
Heights are referred to mean low water which is the chart datum of soundings.

Times and Heights of High and Low Waters

JULY

Day	Time (h m)	Height (ft)	Height (m)
1	0241	8.7	2.7
F	0902	0.6	0.2
	1515	8.1	2.5
	2118	1.4	0.4
2	0323	8.5	2.6
Sa	0944	0.7	0.2
	1558	8.2	2.5
	2205	1.3	0.4
3	0411	8.2	2.5
Su	1027	0.8	0.2
	1642	8.4	2.6
	2256	1.2	0.4
4	0502	8.1	2.5
M	1114	0.9	0.3
	1730	8.6	2.6
	2349	0.8	0.2
5	0555	8.0	2.4
Tu	1203	0.8	0.2
	1821	8.9	2.7
6	0044	0.4	0.1
W	0649	8.0	2.4
	1253	0.7	0.2
	1912	9.3	2.8
7	0138	-0.1	0.0
Th	0746	8.2	2.5
	1345	0.5	0.2
	2003	9.8	3.0
8	0231	-0.6	-0.2
F	0842	8.5	2.6
	1439	0.2	0.1
	2055	10.3	3.1
9	0327	-1.1	-0.3
Sa	0937	8.8	2.7
	1532	0.0	0.0
	2148	10.8	3.3
10	0418	-1.5	-0.5
Su	1031	9.2	2.8
	1626	-0.3	-0.1
	2241	11.1	3.4
11	0512	-1.7	-0.5
M	1123	9.4	2.9
	1720	-0.4	-0.1
	2336	11.2	3.4
12	0605	-1.8	-0.5
Tu	1219	9.7	3.0
	1816	-0.5	-0.2
13	0031	11.1	3.4
W	0659	-1.7	-0.5
	1313	9.8	3.0
	1913	-0.4	-0.1
14	0127	10.8	3.3
Th	0753	-1.5	-0.5
	1409	9.8	3.0
	2012	-0.3	-0.1
15	0225	10.4	3.2
F	0848	-1.1	-0.3
	1507	9.7	3.0
	2115	-0.1	0.0
16	0326	9.8	3.0
Sa	0947	-0.7	-0.2
	1608	9.6	2.9
	2219	0.0	0.0
17	0431	9.2	2.8
Su	1044	-0.2	-0.1
	1707	9.5	2.9
	2325	0.1	0.0
18	0536	8.7	2.7
M	1144	0.1	0.0
	1808	9.4	2.9
19	0029	0.1	0.0
Tu	0641	8.3	2.5
	1243	0.4	0.1
	1907	9.4	2.9
20	0130	0.0	0.0
W	0745	8.2	2.5
	1341	0.6	0.2
	2003	9.4	2.9
21	0227	-0.1	0.0
Th	0841	8.1	2.5
	1436	0.8	0.2
	2055	9.5	2.9
22	0318	-0.2	-0.1
F	0932	8.2	2.5
	1524	0.8	0.2
	2141	9.5	2.9
23	0404	-0.2	-0.1
Sa	1018	8.2	2.5
	1609	0.8	0.2
	2225	9.5	2.9
24	0446	-0.2	-0.1
Su	1100	8.3	2.5
	1649	0.9	0.3
	2304	9.5	2.9
25	0527	-0.1	0.0
M	1138	8.3	2.5
	1727	0.9	0.3
	2341	9.5	2.9
26	0603	-0.1	0.0
Tu	1213	8.3	2.5
	1804	0.9	0.3
27	0017	9.4	2.9
W	0638	0.0	0.0
	1247	8.4	2.6
	1842	0.9	0.3
28	0052	9.2	2.8
Th	0711	0.1	0.0
	1321	8.4	2.6
	1919	0.9	0.3
29	0128	9.0	2.7
F	0747	0.3	0.1
	1356	8.4	2.6
	2000	0.9	0.3
30	0206	8.8	2.7
Sa	0823	0.4	0.1
	1433	8.4	2.6
	2040	0.8	0.2
31	0246	8.5	2.6
Su	0901	0.5	0.2
	1514	8.5	2.6
	2126	0.8	0.2

AUGUST

Day	Time (h m)	Height (ft)	Height (m)
1	0332	8.2	2.5
M	0944	0.6	0.2
	1557	8.6	2.6
	2216	0.7	0.2
2	0421	8.0	2.4
Tu	1032	0.7	0.2
	1646	8.8	2.7
	2309	0.5	0.2
3	0515	7.9	2.4
W	1123	0.7	0.2
	1739	9.1	2.8
4	0007	0.2	0.1
Th	0615	8.0	2.4
	1219	0.7	0.2
	1837	9.5	2.9
5	0106	-0.2	-0.1
F	0717	8.2	2.5
	1317	0.5	0.2
	1934	9.9	3.0
6	0207	-0.6	-0.2
Sa	0818	8.5	2.6
	1415	0.2	0.1
	2034	10.4	3.2
7	0306	-1.0	-0.3
Su	0916	9.0	2.7
	1514	-0.1	0.0
	2132	10.9	3.3
8	0401	-1.4	-0.4
M	1012	9.4	2.9
	1610	-0.5	-0.2
	2228	11.2	3.4
9	0455	-1.7	-0.5
Tu	1107	9.8	3.0
	1707	-0.8	-0.2
	2323	11.3	3.4
10	0548	-1.8	-0.5
W	1200	10.1	3.1
	1802	-0.9	-0.3
11	0017	11.1	3.4
Th	0640	-1.7	-0.5
	1254	10.2	3.1
	1858	-0.9	-0.3
12	0111	10.7	3.3
F	0731	-1.5	-0.5
	1347	10.1	3.1
	1956	-0.8	-0.2
13	0208	10.1	3.1
Sa	0824	-1.0	-0.3
	1441	9.9	3.0
	2054	-0.6	-0.2
14	0305	9.5	2.9
Su	0918	-0.5	-0.2
	1538	9.6	2.9
	2155	-0.3	-0.1
15	0408	8.8	2.7
M	1015	0.1	0.0
	1637	9.3	2.8
	2257	0.0	0.0
16	0514	8.3	2.5
Tu	1115	0.6	0.2
	1738	9.1	2.8
17	0003	0.2	0.1
W	0619	7.9	2.4
	1215	0.9	0.3
	1839	9.0	2.7
18	0106	0.3	0.1
Th	0722	7.8	2.4
	1317	1.1	0.3
	1939	9.0	2.7
19	0205	0.3	0.1
F	0821	7.9	2.4
	1411	1.1	0.3
	2032	9.1	2.8
20	0255	0.2	0.1
Sa	0911	8.0	2.4
	1502	1.1	0.3
	2121	9.3	2.8
21	0341	0.2	0.1
Su	0953	8.2	2.5
	1546	1.0	0.3
	2202	9.4	2.9
22	0425	0.1	0.0
M	1034	8.4	2.6
	1625	0.8	0.2
	2241	9.5	2.9
23	0459	0.1	0.0
Tu	1108	8.5	2.6
	1702	0.7	0.2
	2316	9.5	2.9
24	0533	0.1	0.0
W	1142	8.6	2.6
	1738	0.6	0.2
	2349	9.4	2.9
25	0605	0.1	0.0
Th	1212	8.7	2.7
	1813	0.5	0.2
26	0023	9.2	2.8
F	0636	0.1	0.0
	1242	8.7	2.7
	1849	0.4	0.1
27	0056	9.0	2.7
Sa	0709	0.1	0.0
	1318	8.8	2.7
	1927	0.3	0.1
28	0135	8.7	2.7
Su	0744	0.3	0.1
	1353	8.8	2.7
	2008	0.2	0.1
29	0214	8.5	2.6
M	0822	0.4	0.1
	1433	8.9	2.7
	2053	0.2	0.1
30	0258	8.3	2.5
Tu	0907	0.6	0.2
	1518	8.9	2.7
	2144	0.2	0.1
31	0350	8.1	2.5
W	0956	0.8	0.2
	1612	9.1	2.8
	2240	0.2	0.1

SEPTEMBER

Day	Time (h m)	Height (ft)	Height (m)
1	0449	8.0	2.4
Th	1051	0.9	0.3
	1709	9.2	2.8
	2341	0.1	0.0
2	0551	8.0	2.4
F	1154	0.9	0.3
	1813	9.5	2.9
3	0045	-0.1	0.0
Sa	0659	8.3	2.5
	1259	0.7	0.2
	1917	10.0	3.0
4	0149	-0.5	-0.2
Su	0802	8.8	2.7
	1400	0.3	0.1
	2018	10.4	3.2
5	0248	-0.9	-0.3
M	0901	9.3	2.8
	1501	-0.2	-0.1
	2119	10.8	3.3
6	0344	-1.3	-0.4
Tu	0956	9.8	3.0
	1559	-0.7	-0.2
	2215	11.1	3.4
7	0436	-1.6	-0.5
W	1049	10.3	3.1
	1654	-1.1	-0.3
	2308	11.1	3.4
8	0527	-1.7	-0.5
Th	1140	10.5	3.2
	1748	-1.3	-0.4
9	0001	10.9	3.3
F	0616	-1.6	-0.5
	1230	10.5	3.2
	1842	-1.4	-0.4
10	0054	10.4	3.2
Sa	0705	-1.2	-0.4
	1319	10.3	3.1
	1934	-1.2	-0.4
11	0148	9.7	3.0
Su	0756	-0.7	-0.2
	1412	10.0	3.0
	2027	-0.8	-0.2
12	0243	9.0	2.7
M	0849	-0.1	0.0
	1504	9.5	2.9
	2126	-0.3	-0.1
13	0341	8.4	2.6
Tu	0944	0.5	0.2
	1603	9.1	2.8
	2227	0.1	0.0
14	0445	7.9	2.4
W	1043	1.1	0.3
	1704	8.7	2.7
	2332	0.5	0.2
15	0551	7.7	2.3
Th	1146	1.4	0.4
	1809	8.6	2.6
16	0036	0.7	0.2
F	0655	7.7	2.3
	1248	1.5	0.5
	1909	8.7	2.7
17	0135	0.7	0.2
Sa	0751	7.8	2.4
	1345	1.4	0.4
	2005	8.9	2.7
18	0226	0.6	0.2
Su	0839	8.1	2.5
	1436	1.2	0.4
	2051	9.1	2.8
19	0309	0.5	0.2
M	0923	8.4	2.6
	1519	1.0	0.3
	2133	9.2	2.8
20	0349	0.4	0.1
Tu	1000	8.6	2.6
	1557	0.7	0.2
	2212	9.3	2.8
21	0425	0.2	0.1
W	1033	8.8	2.7
	1633	0.4	0.1
	2246	9.3	2.8
22	0457	0.1	0.0
Th	1104	8.9	2.7
	1709	0.2	0.1
	2319	9.2	2.8
23	0528	0.1	0.0
F	1134	9.1	2.8
	1744	-0.1	0.0
	2351	9.1	2.8
24	0601	0.1	0.0
Sa	1205	9.2	2.8
	1819	-0.2	-0.1
25	0026	8.9	2.7
Su	0633	0.1	0.0
	1242	9.2	2.8
	1857	-0.3	-0.1
26	0103	8.7	2.7
M	0710	0.2	0.1
	1319	9.3	2.8
	1937	-0.3	-0.1
27	0147	8.5	2.6
Tu	0750	0.4	0.1
	1401	9.3	2.8
	2025	-0.2	-0.1
28	0233	8.3	2.5
W	0838	0.7	0.2
	1451	9.3	2.8
	2118	-0.1	0.0
29	0328	8.1	2.5
Th	0930	0.9	0.3
	1547	9.3	2.8
	2215	0.1	0.0
30	0429	8.1	2.5
F	1033	1.1	0.3
	1648	9.3	2.8
	2322	0.1	0.0

Time meridian 75° W. 0000 is midnight. 1200 is noon.
Heights are referred to mean low water which is the chart datum of soundings.

PORTLAND, MAINE, 1983

Times and Heights of High and Low Waters

OCTOBER

Day	Time h m	Height ft	Height m
1	0538	8.2	2.5
Sa	1138	1.0	0.3
	1757	9.5	2.9
2	0029	-0.1	0.0
Su	0646	8.6	2.6
	1246	0.7	0.2
	1903	9.9	3.0
3	0133	-0.4	-0.1
M	0749	9.1	2.8
	1352	0.2	0.1
	2009	10.2	3.1
4	0231	-0.8	-0.2
Tu	0847	9.7	3.0
	1452	-0.4	-0.1
	2108	10.6	3.2
5	0325	-1.1	-0.3
W	0940	10.2	3.1
	1548	-1.0	-0.3
	2202	10.7	3.3
6	0417	-1.3	-0.4
Th	1030	10.6	3.2
	1641	-1.4	-0.4
	2255	10.6	3.2
7	0504	-1.3	-0.4
F	1118	10.7	3.3
	1732	-1.6	-0.5
	2344	10.3	3.1
8	0551	-1.2	-0.4
Sa	1204	10.6	3.2
	1822	-1.5	-0.5
9	0034	9.8	3.0
Su	0638	-0.8	-0.2
	1252	10.3	3.1
	1911	-1.3	-0.4
10	0124	9.3	2.8
M	0727	-0.2	-0.1
	1340	9.9	3.0
	2001	-0.8	-0.2
11	0217	8.7	2.7
Tu	0815	0.4	0.1
	1429	9.3	2.8
	2057	-0.2	-0.1
12	0313	8.1	2.5
W	0910	1.0	0.3
	1525	8.9	2.7
	2152	0.3	0.1
13	0413	7.7	2.3
Th	1008	1.5	0.5
	1627	8.5	2.6
	2255	0.8	0.2
14	0516	7.6	2.3
F	1111	1.8	0.5
	1730	8.4	2.6
	2357	1.0	0.3
15	0619	7.6	2.3
Sa	1212	1.8	0.5
	1832	8.4	2.6
16	0053	1.0	0.3
Su	0715	7.9	2.4
	1312	1.7	0.5
	1927	8.6	2.6
17	0146	1.0	0.3
M	0802	8.2	2.5
	1402	1.3	0.4
	2016	8.7	2.7
18	0229	0.8	0.2
Tu	0844	8.5	2.6
	1444	0.9	0.3
	2058	8.9	2.7
19	0308	0.6	0.2
W	0921	8.8	2.7
	1525	0.5	0.2
	2137	9.0	2.7
20	0343	0.4	0.1
Th	0953	9.1	2.8
	1602	0.1	0.0
	2212	9.0	2.7
21	0417	0.2	0.1
F	1025	9.3	2.8
	1637	-0.3	-0.1
	2247	9.0	2.7
22	0449	0.1	0.0
Sa	1057	9.5	2.9
	1713	-0.6	-0.2
	2322	9.0	2.7
23	0523	0.0	0.0
Su	1131	9.6	2.9
	1751	-0.8	-0.2
	2359	8.9	2.7
24	0600	0.1	0.0
M	1209	9.8	3.0
	1831	-0.8	-0.2
25	0041	8.8	2.7
Tu	0640	0.2	0.1
	1250	9.8	3.0
	1915	-0.8	-0.2
26	0126	8.6	2.6
W	0726	0.4	0.1
	1337	9.7	3.0
	2003	-0.6	-0.2
27	0217	8.5	2.6
Th	0817	0.7	0.2
	1428	9.6	2.9
	2059	-0.3	-0.1
28	0313	8.3	2.5
F	0913	1.0	0.3
	1528	9.5	2.9
	2200	-0.1	0.0
29	0418	8.3	2.5
Sa	1019	1.1	0.3
	1635	9.4	2.9
	2307	0.0	0.0
30	0527	8.5	2.6
Su	1129	1.0	0.3
	1745	9.4	2.9
31	0014	-0.1	0.0
M	0635	8.9	2.7
	1239	0.6	0.2
	1855	9.6	2.9

NOVEMBER

Day	Time h m	Height ft	Height m
1	0117	-0.3	-0.1
Tu	0736	9.5	2.9
	1344	0.1	0.0
	1957	9.8	3.0
2	0214	-0.6	-0.2
W	0831	10.0	3.0
	1444	-0.6	-0.2
	2056	10.0	3.0
3	0307	-0.8	-0.2
Th	0922	10.4	3.2
	1537	-1.1	-0.3
	2150	10.0	3.0
4	0356	-0.9	-0.3
F	1011	10.6	3.2
	1628	-1.5	-0.5
	2241	9.9	3.0
5	0442	-0.9	-0.3
Sa	1057	10.7	3.3
	1716	-1.6	-0.5
	2330	9.6	2.9
6	0527	-0.6	-0.2
Su	1141	10.5	3.2
	1804	-1.5	-0.5
7	0016	9.3	2.8
M	0613	-0.2	-0.1
	1225	10.1	3.1
	1850	-1.1	-0.3
8	0103	8.8	2.7
Tu	0658	0.2	0.1
	1312	9.7	3.0
	1937	-0.7	-0.2
9	0153	8.4	2.6
W	0745	0.8	0.2
	1400	9.3	2.8
	2027	-0.1	0.0
10	0241	8.0	2.4
Th	0836	1.3	0.4
	1449	8.8	2.7
	2118	0.4	0.1
11	0337	7.7	2.3
F	0930	1.7	0.5
	1544	8.5	2.6
	2213	0.9	0.3
12	0434	7.6	2.3
Sa	1027	1.9	0.6
	1643	8.2	2.5
	2309	1.1	0.3
13	0533	7.6	2.3
Su	1127	1.9	0.6
	1742	8.1	2.5
14	0005	1.2	0.4
M	0625	7.8	2.4
	1227	1.7	0.5
	1837	8.2	2.5
15	0054	1.1	0.3
Tu	0714	8.1	2.5
	1318	1.4	0.4
	1930	8.3	2.5
16	0139	1.0	0.3
W	0754	8.5	2.6
	1405	0.9	0.3
	2015	8.4	2.6
17	0221	0.8	0.2
Th	0834	8.8	2.7
	1447	0.4	0.1
	2057	8.5	2.6
18	0258	0.5	0.2
F	0911	9.2	2.8
	1527	-0.1	0.0
	2136	8.6	2.6
19	0335	0.3	0.1
Sa	0945	9.5	2.9
	1606	-0.6	-0.2
	2215	8.7	2.7
20	0413	0.1	0.0
Su	1022	9.8	3.0
	1647	-1.0	-0.3
	2255	8.8	2.7
21	0452	0.0	0.0
M	1102	10.1	3.1
	1726	-1.2	-0.4
	2338	8.9	2.7
22	0533	0.0	0.0
Tu	1144	10.3	3.1
	1811	-1.3	-0.4
23	0021	8.9	2.7
W	0617	0.1	0.0
	1229	10.3	3.1
	1858	-1.2	-0.4
24	0111	8.8	2.7
Th	0708	0.3	0.1
	1320	10.2	3.1
	1950	-1.0	-0.3
25	0203	8.7	2.7
F	0801	0.5	0.2
	1414	10.0	3.0
	2046	-0.7	-0.2
26	0302	8.7	2.7
Sa	0902	0.7	0.2
	1515	9.7	3.0
	2147	-0.4	-0.1
27	0407	8.7	2.7
Su	1009	0.8	0.2
	1621	9.4	2.9
	2250	-0.2	-0.1
28	0513	8.9	2.7
M	1119	0.7	0.2
	1733	9.2	2.8
	2356	-0.2	-0.1
29	0617	9.2	2.8
Tu	1229	0.4	0.1
	1842	9.2	2.8
30	0057	-0.2	-0.1
W	0718	9.6	2.9
	1334	-0.1	0.0
	1946	9.2	2.8

DECEMBER

Day	Time h m	Height ft	Height m
1	0154	-0.3	-0.1
Th	0815	10.0	3.0
	1434	-0.7	-0.2
	2045	9.2	2.8
2	0247	-0.4	-0.1
F	0906	10.3	3.1
	1525	-1.1	-0.3
	2138	9.2	2.8
3	0338	-0.4	-0.1
Sa	0953	10.4	3.2
	1615	-1.3	-0.4
	2229	9.1	2.8
4	0425	-0.3	-0.1
Su	1039	10.3	3.1
	1702	-1.4	-0.4
	2315	9.0	2.7
5	0509	-0.1	0.0
M	1121	10.2	3.1
	1748	-1.2	-0.4
6	0000	8.8	2.7
Tu	0552	0.2	0.1
	1206	9.9	3.0
	1830	-0.9	-0.3
7	0043	8.5	2.6
W	0634	0.5	0.2
	1247	9.6	2.9
	1913	-0.5	-0.2
8	0127	8.3	2.5
Th	0719	0.9	0.3
	1329	9.3	2.8
	1958	-0.1	0.0
9	0211	8.0	2.4
F	0804	1.2	0.4
	1414	8.9	2.7
	2041	0.3	0.1
10	0257	7.8	2.4
Sa	0853	1.5	0.5
	1502	8.5	2.6
	2128	0.7	0.2
11	0347	7.7	2.3
Su	0942	1.7	0.5
	1554	8.2	2.5
	2218	1.0	0.3
12	0435	7.7	2.3
M	1037	1.7	0.5
	1646	8.0	2.4
	2306	1.1	0.3
13	0526	7.8	2.4
Tu	1132	1.6	0.5
	1741	7.8	2.4
	2354	1.1	0.3
14	0614	8.1	2.5
W	1227	1.3	0.4
	1834	7.8	2.4
15	0041	1.0	0.3
Th	0659	8.4	2.6
	1318	0.8	0.2
	1923	7.8	2.4
16	0128	0.9	0.3
F	0742	8.8	2.7
	1405	0.3	0.1
	2013	8.0	2.4
17	0213	0.6	0.2
Sa	0827	9.2	2.8
	1450	-0.2	-0.1
	2059	8.2	2.5
18	0255	0.4	0.1
Su	0908	9.7	3.0
	1536	-0.8	-0.2
	2145	8.5	2.6
19	0341	0.1	0.0
M	0953	10.1	3.1
	1620	-1.2	-0.4
	2230	8.8	2.7
20	0424	-0.1	0.0
Tu	1038	10.5	3.2
	1706	-1.5	-0.5
	2318	9.0	2.7
21	0513	-0.2	-0.1
W	1124	10.7	3.3
	1755	-1.6	-0.5
22	0005	9.1	2.8
Th	0601	-0.2	-0.1
	1214	10.7	3.3
	1844	-1.6	-0.5
23	0056	9.2	2.8
F	0655	-0.2	-0.1
	1308	10.6	3.2
	1937	-1.4	-0.4
24	0150	9.2	2.8
Sa	0750	0.0	0.0
	1404	10.3	3.1
	2030	-1.1	-0.3
25	0248	9.2	2.8
Su	0851	0.2	0.1
	1504	9.8	3.0
	2130	-0.8	-0.2
26	0350	9.2	2.8
M	0957	0.3	0.1
	1608	9.3	2.8
	2229	-0.4	-0.1
27	0452	9.2	2.8
Tu	1105	0.3	0.1
	1718	8.9	2.7
	2333	-0.2	-0.1
28	0557	9.3	2.8
W	1214	0.1	0.0
	1827	8.6	2.6
29	0035	0.0	0.0
Th	0659	9.5	2.9
	1320	-0.2	-0.1
	1933	8.5	2.6
30	0133	0.1	0.0
F	0757	9.7	3.0
	1421	-0.6	-0.2
	2033	8.5	2.6
31	0230	0.1	0.0
Sa	0850	9.9	3.0
	1514	-0.8	-0.2
	2128	8.5	2.6

Time meridian 75° W. 0000 is midnight. 1200 is noon.
Heights are referred to mean low water which is the chart datum of soundings.

Times and Heights of High and Low Waters

JANUARY

Day	Time (h m)	Height (ft)	Height (m)
1 Sa	0009	10.0	3.0
	0608	-0.9	-0.3
	1223	11.7	3.6
	1847	-2.2	-0.7
2 Su	0102	10.1	3.1
	0701	-0.9	-0.3
	1318	11.5	3.5
	1940	-2.0	-0.6
3 M	0156	10.0	3.0
	0756	-0.7	-0.2
	1413	11.0	3.4
	2033	-1.6	-0.5
4 Tu	0252	9.9	3.0
	0854	-0.4	-0.1
	1510	10.4	3.2
	2129	-1.1	-0.3
5 W	0349	9.7	3.0
	0955	-0.1	0.0
	1608	9.8	3.0
	2224	-0.5	-0.2
6 Th	0446	9.6	2.9
	1056	0.2	0.1
	1710	9.2	2.8
	2322	0.0	0.0
7 F	0543	9.5	2.9
	1201	0.3	0.1
	1811	8.7	2.7
8 Sa	0019	0.4	0.1
	0641	9.5	2.9
	1301	0.3	0.1
	1913	8.4	2.6
9 Su	0115	0.6	0.2
	0734	9.5	2.9
	1357	0.2	0.1
	2010	8.2	2.5
10 M	0206	0.8	0.2
	0827	9.5	2.9
	1451	0.1	0.0
	2103	8.2	2.5
11 Tu	0255	0.8	0.2
	0914	9.6	2.9
	1538	0.0	0.0
	2148	8.3	2.5
12 W	0340	0.8	0.2
	0957	9.7	3.0
	1620	-0.2	-0.1
	2233	8.3	2.5
13 Th	0423	0.7	0.2
	1039	9.7	3.0
	1700	-0.3	-0.1
	2311	8.4	2.6
14 F	0504	0.7	0.2
	1119	9.8	3.0
	1737	-0.4	-0.1
	2351	8.5	2.6
15 Sa	0544	0.6	0.2
	1158	9.8	3.0
	1816	-0.4	-0.1
16 Su	0028	8.6	2.6
	0624	0.6	0.2
	1237	9.7	3.0
	1855	-0.4	-0.1
17 M	0106	8.6	2.6
	0703	0.6	0.2
	1315	9.6	2.9
	1935	-0.3	-0.1
18 Tu	0145	8.7	2.7
	0745	0.7	0.2
	1356	9.4	2.9
	2014	-0.1	0.0
19 W	0227	8.7	2.7
	0830	0.7	0.2
	1438	9.2	2.8
	2056	0.1	0.0
20 Th	0310	8.8	2.7
	0917	0.7	0.2
	1526	8.9	2.7
	2140	0.3	0.1
21 F	0355	8.9	2.7
	1007	0.7	0.2
	1616	8.7	2.7
	2229	0.4	0.1
22 Sa	0444	9.1	2.8
	1103	0.6	0.2
	1709	8.5	2.6
	2321	0.6	0.2
23 Su	0536	9.3	2.8
	1200	0.3	0.1
	1808	8.4	2.6
24 M	0017	0.6	0.2
	0632	9.7	3.0
	1259	-0.1	0.0
	1908	8.5	2.6
25 Tu	0115	0.4	0.1
	0731	10.1	3.1
	1400	-0.6	-0.2
	2008	8.8	2.7
26 W	0213	0.1	0.0
	0827	10.6	3.2
	1458	-1.1	-0.3
	2106	9.1	2.8
27 Th	0311	-0.3	-0.1
	0924	11.1	3.4
	1554	-1.6	-0.5
	2204	9.5	2.9
28 F	0405	-0.7	-0.2
	1020	11.5	3.5
	1646	-2.0	-0.6
	2259	9.9	3.0
29 Sa	0500	-1.0	-0.3
	1115	11.7	3.6
	1738	-2.3	-0.7
	2352	10.2	3.1
30 Su	0553	-1.2	-0.4
	1209	11.7	3.6
	1829	-2.2	-0.7
31 M	0044	10.4	3.2
	0645	-1.3	-0.4
	1302	11.4	3.5
	1919	-2.0	-0.6

FEBRUARY

Day	Time (h m)	Height (ft)	Height (m)
1 Tu	0135	10.4	3.2
	0738	-1.1	-0.3
	1354	10.9	3.3
	2009	-1.6	-0.5
2 W	0227	10.3	3.1
	0833	-0.8	-0.2
	1449	10.3	3.1
	2059	-1.0	-0.3
3 Th	0318	10.0	3.0
	0929	-0.4	-0.1
	1542	9.6	2.9
	2152	-0.3	-0.1
4 F	0413	9.7	3.0
	1027	0.0	0.0
	1639	8.9	2.7
	2245	0.3	0.1
5 Sa	0507	9.4	2.9
	1126	0.4	0.1
	1739	8.3	2.5
	2341	0.8	0.2
6 Su	0603	9.2	2.8
	1227	0.6	0.2
	1838	7.9	2.4
7 M	0038	1.1	0.3
	0700	9.0	2.7
	1326	0.6	0.2
	1939	7.8	2.4
8 Tu	0136	1.3	0.4
	0755	9.0	2.7
	1421	0.5	0.2
	2035	7.8	2.4
9 W	0228	1.2	0.4
	0846	9.1	2.8
	1509	0.4	0.1
	2124	8.0	2.4
10 Th	0316	1.0	0.3
	0932	9.3	2.8
	1554	0.1	0.0
	2207	8.2	2.5
11 F	0359	0.8	0.2
	1015	9.5	2.9
	1634	-0.1	0.0
	2246	8.4	2.6
12 Sa	0441	0.6	0.2
	1054	9.7	3.0
	1713	-0.3	-0.1
	2324	8.7	2.7
13 Su	0521	0.4	0.1
	1134	9.8	3.0
	1750	-0.4	-0.1
14 M	0002	8.9	2.7
	0600	0.2	0.1
	1211	9.8	3.0
	1828	-0.5	-0.2
15 Tu	0038	9.0	2.7
	0639	0.1	0.0
	1250	9.8	3.0
	1905	-0.4	-0.1
16 W	0116	9.2	2.8
	0719	0.1	0.0
	1329	9.6	2.9
	1943	-0.3	-0.1
17 Th	0153	9.3	2.8
	0801	0.1	0.0
	1411	9.4	2.9
	2024	-0.1	0.0
18 F	0235	9.4	2.9
	0847	0.1	0.0
	1456	9.1	2.8
	2105	0.2	0.1
19 Sa	0321	9.4	2.9
	0938	0.1	0.0
	1547	8.8	2.7
	2156	0.4	0.1
20 Su	0410	9.5	2.9
	1032	0.2	0.1
	1643	8.5	2.6
	2249	0.6	0.2
21 M	0506	9.6	2.9
	1131	0.1	0.0
	1742	8.4	2.6
	2348	0.7	0.2
22 Tu	0606	9.7	3.0
	1235	-0.1	0.0
	1845	8.4	2.6
23 W	0051	0.6	0.2
	0707	10.0	3.0
	1339	-0.4	-0.1
	1949	8.7	2.7
24 Th	0154	0.3	0.1
	0810	10.4	3.2
	1439	-0.9	-0.3
	2050	9.1	2.8
25 F	0255	-0.2	-0.1
	0911	10.9	3.3
	1535	-1.4	-0.4
	2148	9.6	2.9
26 Sa	0351	-0.7	-0.2
	1007	11.2	3.4
	1628	-1.8	-0.5
	2242	10.1	3.1
27 Su	0445	-1.2	-0.4
	1102	11.5	3.5
	1719	-2.0	-0.6
	2333	10.5	3.2
28 M	0537	-1.5	-0.5
	1152	11.4	3.5
	1808	-2.0	-0.6

MARCH

Day	Time (h m)	Height (ft)	Height (m)
1 Tu	0023	10.7	3.3
	0627	-1.5	-0.5
	1243	11.2	3.4
	1855	-1.7	-0.5
2 W	0110	10.7	3.3
	0718	-1.4	-0.4
	1332	10.7	3.3
	1942	-1.2	-0.4
3 Th	0157	10.5	3.2
	0807	-1.0	-0.3
	1423	10.0	3.0
	2029	-0.6	-0.2
4 F	0246	10.2	3.1
	0859	-0.5	-0.2
	1515	9.3	2.8
	2118	0.1	0.0
5 Sa	0334	9.7	3.0
	0952	0.0	0.0
	1606	8.6	2.6
	2208	0.7	0.2
6 Su	0429	9.3	2.8
	1048	0.5	0.2
	1702	8.1	2.5
	2304	1.3	0.4
7 M	0523	8.9	2.7
	1148	0.8	0.2
	1802	7.7	2.3
8 Tu	0002	1.6	0.5
	0621	8.7	2.7
	1249	1.0	0.3
	1901	7.6	2.3
9 W	0101	1.6	0.5
	0720	8.7	2.7
	1344	0.9	0.3
	2000	7.7	2.3
10 Th	0157	1.5	0.5
	0812	8.8	2.7
	1435	0.7	0.2
	2050	8.0	2.4
11 F	0247	1.2	0.4
	0903	9.1	2.8
	1521	0.4	0.1
	2135	8.3	2.5
12 Sa	0332	0.8	0.2
	0946	9.3	2.8
	1604	0.1	0.0
	2215	8.6	2.6
13 Su	0415	0.5	0.2
	1028	9.6	2.9
	1642	-0.2	-0.1
	2254	9.0	2.7
14 M	0454	0.1	0.0
	1107	9.8	3.0
	1719	-0.3	-0.1
	2330	9.3	2.8
15 Tu	0534	-0.2	-0.1
	1145	9.9	3.0
	1757	-0.4	-0.1
16 W	0005	9.6	2.9
	0614	-0.4	-0.1
	1224	9.9	3.0
	1834	-0.4	-0.1
17 Th	0045	9.8	3.0
	0654	-0.5	-0.2
	1303	9.7	3.0
	1913	-0.3	-0.1
18 F	0122	9.9	3.0
	0737	-0.5	-0.2
	1347	9.5	2.9
	1954	-0.1	0.0
19 Sa	0204	10.0	3.0
	0823	-0.5	-0.2
	1433	9.2	2.8
	2039	0.2	0.1
20 Su	0252	9.9	3.0
	0913	-0.3	-0.1
	1525	8.9	2.7
	2128	0.5	0.2
21 M	0345	9.8	3.0
	1010	-0.1	0.0
	1622	8.6	2.6
	2227	0.8	0.2
22 Tu	0442	9.7	3.0
	1111	0.0	0.0
	1723	8.4	2.6
	2328	0.9	0.3
23 W	0545	9.7	3.0
	1216	-0.1	0.0
	1828	8.5	2.6
24 Th	0035	0.7	0.2
	0651	9.9	3.0
	1320	-0.3	-0.1
	1933	8.8	2.7
25 F	0139	0.4	0.1
	0755	10.2	3.1
	1421	-0.7	-0.2
	2034	9.4	2.9
26 Sa	0240	-0.2	-0.1
	0855	10.6	3.2
	1517	-1.1	-0.3
	2132	9.9	3.0
27 Su	0338	-0.7	-0.2
	0952	10.9	3.3
	1609	-1.4	-0.4
	2223	10.4	3.2
28 M	0431	-1.2	-0.4
	1046	11.0	3.4
	1657	-1.5	-0.5
	2312	10.8	3.3
29 Tu	0520	-1.5	-0.5
	1135	10.9	3.3
	1744	-1.4	-0.4
	2358	10.9	3.3
30 W	0608	-1.5	-0.5
	1223	10.6	3.2
	1827	-1.1	-0.3
31 Th	0041	10.9	3.3
	0655	-1.3	-0.4
	1309	10.2	3.1
	1912	-0.6	-0.2

Time meridian 75° W. 0000 is midnight. 1200 is noon.
Heights are referred to mean low water which is the chart datum of soundings.

Times and Heights of High and Low Waters

APRIL

Day	Time (h m)	Height (ft)	Height (m)
1	0127	10.6	3.2
F	0741	-1.0	-0.3
	1355	9.6	2.9
	1958	0.0	0.0
2	0212	10.2	3.1
Sa	0827	-0.5	-0.2
	1444	9.0	2.7
	2044	0.6	0.2
3	0300	9.7	3.0
Su	0918	0.1	0.0
	1534	8.5	2.6
	2134	1.1	0.3
4	0350	9.2	2.8
M	1011	0.6	0.2
	1627	8.0	2.4
	2227	1.6	0.5
5	0443	8.8	2.7
Tu	1107	0.9	0.3
	1723	7.7	2.3
	2323	1.8	0.5
6	0541	8.5	2.6
W	1205	1.1	0.3
	1822	7.7	2.3
7	0022	1.8	0.5
Th	0637	8.5	2.6
	1302	1.1	0.3
	1917	7.8	2.4
8	0119	1.6	0.5
F	0733	8.6	2.6
	1355	0.9	0.3
	2009	8.1	2.5
9	0213	1.3	0.4
Sa	0825	8.9	2.7
	1442	0.6	0.2
	2055	8.5	2.6
10	0258	0.8	0.2
Su	0911	9.2	2.8
	1525	0.3	0.1
	2136	9.0	2.7
11	0343	0.3	0.1
M	0954	9.5	2.9
	1606	0.0	0.0
	2215	9.5	2.9
12	0425	-0.1	0.0
Tu	1036	9.7	3.0
	1645	-0.2	-0.1
	2254	9.9	3.0
13	0506	-0.5	-0.2
W	1116	9.8	3.0
	1725	-0.3	-0.1
	2333	10.2	3.1
14	0548	-0.8	-0.2
Th	1158	9.8	3.0
	1804	-0.3	-0.1
15	0012	10.5	3.2
F	0630	-1.0	-0.3
	1241	9.8	3.0
	1845	-0.2	-0.1

Day	Time (h m)	Height (ft)	Height (m)
16	0054	10.6	3.2
Sa	0715	-1.0	-0.3
	1326	9.6	2.9
	1929	0.0	0.0
17	0140	10.5	3.2
Su	0804	-0.9	-0.3
	1415	9.3	2.8
	2017	0.3	0.1
18	0230	10.4	3.2
M	0857	-0.7	-0.2
	1509	9.0	2.7
	2111	0.6	0.2
19	0326	10.2	3.1
Tu	0953	-0.4	-0.1
	1608	8.8	2.7
	2211	0.8	0.2
20	0427	9.9	3.0
W	1055	-0.2	-0.1
	1711	8.7	2.7
	2315	0.9	0.3
21	0531	9.8	3.0
Th	1159	-0.2	-0.1
	1816	8.9	2.7
22	0021	0.7	0.2
F	0638	9.8	3.0
	1301	-0.3	-0.1
	1918	9.2	2.8
23	0127	0.3	0.1
Sa	0741	10.0	3.0
	1402	-0.5	-0.2
	2018	9.7	3.0
24	0227	-0.2	-0.1
Su	0840	10.2	3.1
	1456	-0.7	-0.2
	2111	10.2	3.1
25	0324	-0.7	-0.2
M	0937	10.3	3.1
	1546	-0.8	-0.2
	2202	10.6	3.2
26	0414	-1.1	-0.3
Tu	1028	10.3	3.1
	1633	-0.8	-0.2
	2248	10.8	3.3
27	0502	-1.3	-0.4
W	1116	10.2	3.1
	1718	-0.6	-0.2
	2332	10.9	3.3
28	0547	-1.3	-0.4
Th	1202	10.0	3.0
	1801	-0.3	-0.1
29	0015	10.7	3.3
F	0631	-1.1	-0.3
	1247	9.6	2.9
	1844	0.0	0.0
30	0058	10.5	3.2
Sa	0716	-0.8	-0.2
	1330	9.2	2.8
	1927	0.5	0.2

MAY

Day	Time (h m)	Height (ft)	Height (m)
1	0142	10.1	3.1
Su	0801	-0.3	-0.1
	1416	8.8	2.7
	2011	0.9	0.3
2	0225	9.6	2.9
M	0847	0.1	0.0
	1503	8.4	2.6
	2100	1.4	0.4
3	0315	9.2	2.8
Tu	0937	0.6	0.2
	1553	8.1	2.5
	2151	1.7	0.5
4	0406	8.8	2.7
W	1030	0.9	0.3
	1647	7.9	2.4
	2247	1.9	0.6
5	0459	8.6	2.6
Th	1123	1.1	0.3
	1740	7.9	2.4
	2344	1.9	0.6
6	0555	8.5	2.6
F	1219	1.1	0.3
	1834	8.1	2.5
7	0040	1.6	0.5
Sa	0650	8.6	2.6
	1309	0.9	0.3
	1923	8.4	2.6
8	0133	1.3	0.4
Su	0742	8.8	2.7
	1358	0.7	0.2
	2010	8.9	2.7
9	0222	0.8	0.2
M	0832	9.0	2.7
	1443	0.5	0.2
	2055	9.4	2.9
10	0309	0.2	0.1
Tu	0918	9.3	2.8
	1527	0.2	0.1
	2136	9.9	3.0
11	0355	-0.3	-0.1
W	1002	9.5	2.9
	1609	0.0	0.0
	2219	10.4	3.2
12	0438	-0.8	-0.2
Th	1047	9.7	3.0
	1651	-0.2	-0.1
	2301	10.7	3.3
13	0523	-1.2	-0.4
F	1133	9.8	3.0
	1736	-0.2	-0.1
	2343	11.0	3.4
14	0609	-1.4	-0.4
Sa	1219	9.8	3.0
	1820	-0.2	-0.1
15	0032	11.1	3.4
Su	0655	-1.4	-0.4
	1309	9.7	3.0
	1909	-0.1	0.0

Day	Time (h m)	Height (ft)	Height (m)
16	0122	11.0	3.4
M	0746	-1.3	-0.4
	1401	9.5	2.9
	2001	0.2	0.1
17	0215	10.8	3.3
Tu	0841	-1.0	-0.3
	1457	9.3	2.8
	2057	0.4	0.1
18	0313	10.5	3.2
W	0937	-0.7	-0.2
	1555	9.2	2.8
	2157	0.6	0.2
19	0414	10.1	3.1
Th	1039	-0.5	-0.2
	1658	9.2	2.8
	2303	0.7	0.2
20	0517	9.9	3.0
F	1140	-0.3	-0.1
	1800	9.4	2.9
21	0009	0.5	0.2
Sa	0623	9.7	3.0
	1242	-0.2	-0.1
	1900	9.7	3.0
22	0113	0.2	0.1
Su	0725	9.7	3.0
	1339	-0.2	-0.1
	1957	10.0	3.0
23	0213	-0.1	0.0
M	0824	9.6	2.9
	1432	-0.2	-0.1
	2051	10.3	3.1
24	0306	-0.5	-0.2
Tu	0919	9.6	2.9
	1522	-0.2	-0.1
	2138	10.6	3.2
25	0356	-0.8	-0.2
W	1009	9.6	2.9
	1609	-0.1	0.0
	2223	10.7	3.3
26	0442	-0.9	-0.3
Th	1056	9.5	2.9
	1651	0.1	0.0
	2307	10.6	3.2
27	0526	-0.9	-0.3
F	1141	9.3	2.8
	1735	0.3	0.1
	2349	10.5	3.2
28	0609	-0.7	-0.2
Sa	1223	9.1	2.8
	1817	0.6	0.2
29	0031	10.2	3.1
Su	0651	-0.5	-0.2
	1305	8.9	2.7
	1859	0.8	0.2
30	0114	9.9	3.0
M	0733	-0.2	-0.1
	1350	8.6	2.6
	1942	1.1	0.3
31	0156	9.6	2.9
Tu	0817	0.1	0.0
	1433	8.4	2.6
	2028	1.4	0.4

JUNE

Day	Time (h m)	Height (ft)	Height (m)
1	0241	9.3	2.8
W	0904	0.4	0.1
	1521	8.3	2.5
	2118	1.6	0.5
2	0331	9.0	2.7
Th	0952	0.7	0.2
	1608	8.2	2.5
	2210	1.7	0.5
3	0420	8.8	2.7
F	1042	0.8	0.2
	1659	8.3	2.5
	2303	1.7	0.5
4	0512	8.6	2.6
Sa	1133	0.9	0.3
	1748	8.5	2.6
	2358	1.5	0.5
5	0606	8.6	2.6
Su	1223	0.9	0.3
	1838	8.8	2.7
6	0053	1.1	0.3
M	0658	8.6	2.6
	1312	0.8	0.2
	1926	9.2	2.8
7	0144	0.7	0.2
Tu	0749	8.8	2.7
	1402	0.6	0.2
	2013	9.7	3.0
8	0234	0.1	0.0
W	0840	9.0	2.7
	1448	0.4	0.1
	2058	10.2	3.1
9	0322	-0.5	-0.2
Th	0930	9.3	2.8
	1535	0.1	0.0
	2145	10.7	3.3
10	0411	-1.0	-0.3
F	1019	9.5	2.9
	1621	-0.1	0.0
	2234	11.1	3.4
11	0459	-1.4	-0.4
Sa	1110	9.7	3.0
	1709	-0.3	-0.1
	2322	11.4	3.5
12	0548	-1.6	-0.5
Su	1200	9.8	3.0
	1759	-0.3	-0.1
13	0013	11.5	3.5
M	0639	-1.7	-0.5
	1253	9.8	3.0
	1851	-0.3	-0.1
14	0106	11.4	3.5
Tu	0730	-1.6	-0.5
	1346	9.8	3.0
	1945	-0.2	-0.1
15	0201	11.1	3.4
W	0825	-1.3	-0.4
	1441	9.8	3.0
	2043	0.0	0.0

Day	Time (h m)	Height (ft)	Height (m)
16	0259	10.7	3.3
Th	0921	-1.0	-0.3
	1541	9.7	3.0
	2144	0.2	0.1
17	0358	10.3	3.1
F	1019	-0.7	-0.2
	1640	9.7	3.0
	2247	0.3	0.1
18	0500	9.9	3.0
Sa	1118	-0.3	-0.1
	1739	9.8	3.0
	2351	0.3	0.1
19	0604	9.5	2.9
Su	1216	0.0	0.0
	1838	9.9	3.0
20	0053	0.2	0.1
M	0705	9.2	2.8
	1312	0.2	0.1
	1934	10.1	3.1
21	0154	0.0	0.0
Tu	0806	9.1	2.8
	1407	0.3	0.1
	2026	10.2	3.1
22	0248	-0.2	-0.1
W	0901	9.0	2.7
	1458	0.4	0.1
	2116	10.3	3.1
23	0337	-0.3	-0.1
Th	0951	8.9	2.7
	1544	0.5	0.2
	2202	10.3	3.1
24	0424	-0.4	-0.1
F	1038	8.9	2.7
	1628	0.6	0.2
	2244	10.3	3.1
25	0506	-0.4	-0.1
Sa	1120	8.8	2.7
	1711	0.7	0.2
	2326	10.2	3.1
26	0545	-0.3	-0.1
Su	1202	8.8	2.7
	1752	0.8	0.2
27	0007	10.0	3.0
M	0628	-0.2	-0.1
	1240	8.7	2.7
	1834	0.9	0.3
28	0049	9.9	3.0
Tu	0708	-0.1	0.0
	1322	8.6	2.6
	1916	1.1	0.3
29	0130	9.7	3.0
W	0749	0.1	0.0
	1404	8.6	2.6
	1959	1.2	0.4
30	0213	9.4	2.9
Th	0832	0.2	0.1
	1446	8.6	2.6
	2046	1.3	0.4

Time meridian 75° W. 0000 is midnight. 1200 is noon.
Heights are referred to mean low water which is the chart datum of soundings.

Times and Heights of High and Low Waters

JULY

Day	Time h m	Height ft	Height m	Day	Time h m	Height ft	Height m
1	0257	9.2	2.8	16	0339	10.3	3.1
F	0915	0.4	0.1	Sa	0955	-0.7	-0.2
	1531	8.6	2.6		1615	10.1	3.1
	2134	1.4	0.4		2226	0.0	0.0
2	0345	8.9	2.7	17	0440	9.7	3.0
Sa	1000	0.6	0.2	Su	1051	-0.1	0.0
	1618	8.6	2.6		1713	10.0	3.0
	2224	1.4	0.4		2328	0.2	0.1
3	0432	8.7	2.7	18	0540	9.2	2.8
Su	1050	0.8	0.2	M	1148	0.3	0.1
	1705	8.8	2.7		1810	9.9	3.0
	2318	1.2	0.4				
4	0523	8.6	2.6	19	0030	0.3	0.1
M	1138	0.9	0.3	Tu	0642	8.8	2.7
	1752	9.1	2.8		1246	0.7	0.2
					1908	9.9	3.0
5	0011	0.9	0.3	20	0130	0.3	0.1
Tu	0618	8.6	2.6	W	0742	8.6	2.6
	1229	0.9	0.3		1342	0.9	0.3
	1843	9.5	2.9		2001	9.8	3.0
6	0106	0.5	0.2	21	0226	0.2	0.1
W	0712	8.6	2.6	Th	0840	8.5	2.6
	1320	0.7	0.2		1433	1.0	0.3
	1933	9.9	3.0		2052	9.9	3.0
7	0200	0.0	0.0	22	0317	0.1	0.0
Th	0806	8.8	2.7	F	0932	8.5	2.6
	1414	0.5	0.2		1522	1.0	0.3
	2026	10.4	3.2		2140	9.9	3.0
8	0255	-0.5	-0.2	23	0401	0.0	0.0
F	0901	9.1	2.8	Sa	1015	8.5	2.6
	1506	0.2	0.1		1606	0.9	0.3
	2119	10.9	3.3		2224	9.9	3.0
9	0346	-1.1	-0.3	24	0445	-0.1	0.0
Sa	0956	9.4	2.9	Su	1057	8.6	2.6
	1556	-0.1	0.0		1649	0.9	0.3
	2210	11.3	3.4		2306	9.9	3.0
10	0437	-1.5	-0.5	25	0524	-0.1	0.0
Su	1049	9.7	3.0	M	1138	8.7	2.7
	1648	-0.4	-0.1		1729	0.8	0.2
	2303	11.6	3.5		2345	9.9	3.0
11	0529	-1.8	-0.5	26	0603	-0.1	0.0
M	1142	10.0	3.0	Tu	1215	8.8	2.7
	1741	-0.6	-0.2		1810	0.8	0.2
	2356	11.8	3.6				
12	0621	-1.9	-0.6	27	0023	9.9	3.0
Tu	1235	10.2	3.1	W	0642	-0.1	0.0
	1835	-0.7	-0.2		1253	8.8	2.7
					1850	0.8	0.2
13	0051	11.7	3.6	28	0103	9.8	3.0
W	0713	-1.8	-0.5	Th	0719	0.0	0.0
	1329	10.3	3.1		1332	8.9	2.7
	1930	-0.6	-0.2		1932	0.8	0.2
14	0146	11.4	3.5	29	0143	9.6	2.9
Th	0806	-1.6	-0.5	F	0759	0.1	0.0
	1423	10.3	3.1		1411	8.9	2.7
	2027	-0.5	-0.2		2015	0.9	0.3
15	0242	10.9	3.3	30	0225	9.4	2.9
F	0900	-1.2	-0.4	Sa	0840	0.3	0.1
	1518	10.2	3.1		1453	9.0	2.7
	2125	-0.2	-0.1		2100	0.9	0.3
				31	0308	9.1	2.8
				Su	0921	0.5	0.2
					1536	9.1	2.8
					2148	0.9	0.3

AUGUST

Day	Time h m	Height ft	Height m	Day	Time h m	Height ft	Height m
1	0357	8.8	2.7	16	0514	8.8	2.7
M	1008	0.8	0.2	Tu	1117	0.8	0.2
	1622	9.2	2.8		1739	9.7	3.0
	2240	0.9	0.3				
2	0448	8.6	2.6	17	0002	0.5	0.2
Tu	1058	0.9	0.3	W	0616	8.4	2.6
	1712	9.4	2.9		1217	1.2	0.4
	2335	0.7	0.2		1836	9.5	2.9
3	0542	8.5	2.6	18	0103	0.6	0.2
W	1150	1.0	0.3	Th	0717	8.2	2.5
	1807	9.6	2.9		1313	1.3	0.4
					1936	9.4	2.9
4	0032	0.4	0.1	19	0202	0.6	0.2
Th	0639	8.5	2.6	F	0816	8.2	2.5
	1248	0.9	0.3		1408	1.3	0.4
	1902	10.0	3.0		2029	9.4	2.9
5	0130	0.0	0.0	20	0253	0.5	0.2
F	0739	8.7	2.7	Sa	0907	8.3	2.5
	1344	0.6	0.2		1459	1.2	0.4
	2000	10.5	3.2		2116	9.5	2.9
6	0229	-0.5	-0.2	21	0338	0.3	0.1
Sa	0837	9.0	2.7	Su	0951	8.5	2.6
	1442	0.2	0.1		1543	1.0	0.3
	2056	10.9	3.3		2201	9.7	3.0
7	0324	-1.1	-0.3	22	0418	0.2	0.1
Su	0935	9.5	2.9	M	1031	8.7	2.7
	1537	-0.3	-0.1		1625	0.8	0.2
	2152	11.4	3.5		2241	9.8	3.0
8	0418	-1.5	-0.5	23	0457	0.0	0.0
M	1029	9.9	3.0	Tu	1110	8.9	2.7
	1631	-0.7	-0.2		1706	0.6	0.2
	2247	11.7	3.6		2319	9.9	3.0
9	0510	-1.9	-0.6	24	0535	-0.1	0.0
Tu	1123	10.3	3.1	W	1146	9.1	2.8
	1726	-1.0	-0.3		1746	0.4	0.1
	2341	11.8	3.6		2358	9.9	3.0
10	0602	-2.0	-0.6	25	0611	-0.1	0.0
W	1216	10.6	3.2	Th	1223	9.2	2.8
	1818	-1.2	-0.4		1824	0.4	0.1
11	0035	11.7	3.6	26	0035	9.8	3.0
Th	0652	-1.9	-0.6	F	0648	-0.1	0.0
	1307	10.8	3.3		1300	9.3	2.8
	1912	-1.1	-0.3		1904	0.3	0.1
12	0127	11.4	3.5	27	0114	9.7	3.0
F	0743	-1.5	-0.5	Sa	0724	0.1	0.0
	1358	10.8	3.3		1337	9.4	2.9
	2006	-0.9	-0.3		1943	0.3	0.1
13	0222	10.8	3.3	28	0155	9.4	2.9
Sa	0833	-1.0	-0.3	Su	0804	0.3	0.1
	1452	10.6	3.2		1415	9.4	2.9
	2102	-0.6	-0.2		2028	0.4	0.1
14	0316	10.1	3.1	29	0237	9.2	2.8
Su	0926	-0.4	-0.1	M	0846	0.5	0.2
	1545	10.3	3.1		1500	9.5	2.9
	2158	-0.2	-0.1		2115	0.4	0.1
15	0414	9.4	2.9	30	0325	8.9	2.7
M	1020	0.2	0.1	Tu	0932	0.8	0.2
	1640	10.0	3.0		1547	9.5	2.9
	2300	0.2	0.1		2206	0.5	0.2
				31	0418	8.6	2.6
				W	1023	1.0	0.3
					1639	9.5	2.9
					2305	0.5	0.2

SEPTEMBER

Day	Time h m	Height ft	Height m	Day	Time h m	Height ft	Height m
1	0514	8.4	2.6	16	0029	0.9	0.3
Th	1121	1.1	0.3	F	0647	8.0	2.4
	1737	9.7	3.0		1243	1.7	0.5
					1901	9.0	2.7
2	0005	0.3	0.1	17	0128	0.9	0.3
F	0615	8.5	2.6	Sa	0743	8.0	2.4
	1221	1.0	0.3		1341	1.6	0.5
	1837	10.0	3.0		1957	9.0	2.7
3	0107	0.0	0.0	18	0221	0.8	0.2
Sa	0717	8.7	2.7	Su	0837	8.3	2.5
	1324	0.7	0.2		1432	1.3	0.4
	1939	10.4	3.2		2047	9.2	2.8
4	0208	-0.5	-0.2	19	0306	0.5	0.2
Su	0819	9.2	2.8	M	0920	8.6	2.6
	1424	0.2	0.1		1519	1.0	0.3
	2039	10.8	3.3		2133	9.5	2.9
5	0306	-1.0	-0.3	20	0348	0.3	0.1
M	0916	9.7	3.0	Tu	1001	8.9	2.7
	1521	-0.4	-0.1		1601	0.6	0.2
	2136	11.3	3.4		2212	9.7	3.0
6	0359	-1.5	-0.5	21	0425	0.1	0.0
Tu	1010	10.3	3.1	W	1038	9.2	2.8
	1617	-1.0	-0.3		1640	0.3	0.1
	2231	11.6	3.5		2252	9.8	3.0
7	0449	-1.8	-0.5	22	0503	-0.1	0.0
W	1102	10.8	3.3	Th	1114	9.5	2.9
	1709	-1.4	-0.4		1718	0.1	0.0
	2324	11.7	3.6		2330	9.8	3.0
8	0540	-1.8	-0.5	23	0539	-0.1	0.0
Th	1153	11.1	3.4	F	1149	9.7	3.0
	1800	-1.6	-0.5		1757	-0.1	0.0
9	0016	11.5	3.5	24	0008	9.8	3.0
F	0628	-1.6	-0.5	Sa	0616	-0.1	0.0
	1242	11.2	3.4		1226	9.8	3.0
	1852	-1.5	-0.5		1836	-0.2	-0.1
10	0108	11.1	3.4	25	0046	9.7	3.0
Sa	0716	-1.2	-0.4	Su	0653	0.1	0.0
	1332	11.0	3.4		1302	9.9	3.0
	1943	-1.2	-0.4		1917	-0.2	-0.1
11	0159	10.5	3.2	26	0127	9.4	2.9
Su	0804	-0.6	-0.2	M	0732	0.3	0.1
	1421	10.7	3.3		1344	9.9	3.0
	2036	-0.8	-0.2		2001	-0.2	-0.1
12	0251	9.8	3.0	27	0212	9.2	2.8
M	0854	0.0	0.0	Tu	0816	0.6	0.2
	1513	10.3	3.1		1427	9.9	3.0
	2131	-0.2	-0.1		2049	0.0	0.0
13	0347	9.1	2.8	28	0300	8.9	2.7
Tu	0947	0.7	0.2	W	0903	0.9	0.3
	1606	9.8	3.0		1516	9.8	3.0
	2227	0.3	0.1		2142	0.1	0.0
14	0443	8.5	2.6	29	0354	8.6	2.6
W	1044	1.3	0.4	Th	0954	1.1	0.3
	1704	9.3	2.8		1613	9.7	3.0
	2328	0.7	0.2		2240	0.2	0.1
15	0544	8.1	2.5	30	0454	8.5	2.6
Th	1143	1.6	0.5	F	1059	1.2	0.4
	1804	9.0	2.7		1714	9.7	3.0
					2343	0.2	0.1

Time meridian 75° W. 0000 is midnight. 1200 is noon.
Heights are referred to mean low water which is the chart datum of soundings.

Times and Heights of High and Low Waters

OCTOBER

Day	Time h m	Height ft	Height m	Day	Time h m	Height ft	Height m
1	0557	8.6	2.6	16	0048	1.1	0.3
Sa	1203	1.0	0.3	Su	0704	8.0	2.4
	1817	9.9	3.0		1307	1.7	0.5
					1920	8.7	2.7
2	0049	-0.1	0.0	17	0141	0.9	0.3
Su	0701	8.9	2.7	M	0755	8.3	2.5
	1307	0.6	0.2		1358	1.3	0.4
	1923	10.2	3.1		2012	8.9	2.7
3	0149	-0.4	-0.1	18	0227	0.7	0.2
M	0802	9.4	2.9	Tu	0842	8.7	2.7
	1410	0.0	0.0		1447	0.9	0.3
	2024	10.6	3.2		2058	9.2	2.8
4	0245	-0.9	-0.3	19	0309	0.4	0.1
Tu	0859	10.0	3.0	W	0922	9.1	2.8
	1507	-0.6	-0.2		1530	0.5	0.2
	2122	10.9	3.3		2140	9.4	2.9
5	0338	-1.2	-0.4	20	0351	0.2	0.1
W	0951	10.6	3.2	Th	1001	9.5	2.9
	1601	-1.2	-0.4		1610	0.0	0.0
	2216	11.1	3.4		2220	9.5	2.9
6	0428	-1.4	-0.4	21	0428	0.0	0.0
Th	1041	11.1	3.4	F	1037	9.9	3.0
	1652	-1.6	-0.5		1650	-0.3	-0.1
	2306	11.1	3.4		2301	9.6	2.9
7	0516	-1.4	-0.4	22	0505	0.0	0.0
F	1129	11.3	3.4	Sa	1115	10.1	3.1
	1742	-1.7	-0.5		1729	-0.6	-0.2
	2357	10.9	3.3		2340	9.6	2.9
8	0603	-1.2	-0.4	23	0544	0.0	0.0
Sa	1217	11.3	3.4	Su	1153	10.3	3.1
	1830	-1.6	-0.5		1811	-0.8	-0.2
9	0045	10.5	3.2	24	0020	9.6	2.9
Su	0648	-0.7	-0.2	M	0623	0.1	0.0
	1303	11.1	3.4		1233	10.4	3.2
	1919	-1.3	-0.4		1853	-0.8	-0.2
10	0135	10.0	3.0	25	0105	9.4	2.9
M	0735	-0.2	-0.1	Tu	0705	0.3	0.1
	1351	10.6	3.2		1316	10.4	3.2
	2007	-0.8	-0.2		1938	-0.7	-0.2
11	0225	9.4	2.9	26	0151	9.2	2.8
Tu	0822	0.5	0.2	W	0751	0.5	0.2
	1440	10.1	3.1		1403	10.3	3.1
	2059	-0.2	-0.1		2028	-0.5	-0.2
12	0317	8.8	2.7	27	0242	8.9	2.7
W	0915	1.1	0.3	Th	0842	0.7	0.2
	1531	9.5	2.9		1456	10.1	3.1
	2154	0.4	0.1		2123	-0.3	-0.1
13	0411	8.3	2.5	28	0337	8.7	2.7
Th	1011	1.5	0.5	F	0939	1.0	0.3
	1627	9.0	2.7		1554	9.9	3.0
	2251	0.8	0.2		2222	-0.1	0.0
14	0509	8.0	2.4	29	0438	8.7	2.7
F	1108	1.8	0.5	Sa	1042	1.0	0.3
	1726	8.7	2.7		1657	9.7	3.0
	2350	1.1	0.3		2325	-0.1	0.0
15	0609	7.9	2.4	30	0542	8.8	2.7
Sa	1208	1.9	0.6	Su	1147	0.9	0.3
	1824	8.6	2.6		1802	9.7	3.0
				31	0028	-0.2	-0.1
				M	0645	9.2	2.8
					1254	0.5	0.2
					1907	9.9	3.0

NOVEMBER

Day	Time h m	Height ft	Height m	Day	Time h m	Height ft	Height m
1	0128	-0.4	-0.1	16	0144	0.8	0.2
Tu	0744	9.7	3.0	W	0757	8.8	2.7
	1357	-0.1	0.0		1410	0.8	0.2
	2008	10.1	3.1		2018	8.8	2.7
2	0224	-0.7	-0.2	17	0227	0.6	0.2
W	0840	10.3	3.1	Th	0840	9.3	2.8
	1453	-0.7	-0.2		1455	0.3	0.1
	2106	10.3	3.1		2103	9.0	2.7
3	0316	-0.9	-0.3	18	0309	0.4	0.1
Th	0932	10.8	3.3	F	0922	9.7	3.0
	1546	-1.2	-0.4		1538	-0.2	-0.1
	2159	10.4	3.2		2146	9.2	2.8
4	0406	-0.9	-0.3	19	0351	0.2	0.1
F	1020	11.1	3.4	Sa	1002	10.1	3.1
	1636	-1.5	-0.5		1621	-0.6	-0.2
	2249	10.4	3.2		2231	9.3	2.8
5	0452	-0.8	-0.2	20	0433	0.0	0.0
Sa	1106	11.2	3.4	Su	1041	10.5	3.2
	1724	-1.6	-0.5		1703	-1.0	-0.3
	2338	10.2	3.1		2312	9.4	2.9
6	0537	-0.6	-0.2	21	0514	0.0	0.0
Su	1152	11.1	3.4	M	1124	10.7	3.3
	1810	-1.5	-0.5		1747	-1.2	-0.4
					2359	9.5	2.9
7	0024	9.9	3.0	22	0558	0.0	0.0
M	0623	-0.2	-0.1	Tu	1208	10.8	3.3
	1236	10.8	3.3		1831	-1.3	-0.4
	1855	-1.1	-0.3				
8	0111	9.4	2.9	23	0045	9.4	2.9
Tu	0706	0.2	0.1	W	0643	0.0	0.0
	1322	10.4	3.2		1255	10.8	3.3
	1942	-0.7	-0.2		1920	-1.2	-0.4
9	0159	9.0	2.7	24	0132	9.3	2.8
W	0752	0.7	0.2	Th	0732	0.2	0.1
	1409	9.9	3.0		1345	10.6	3.2
	2029	-0.2	-0.1		2012	-1.0	-0.3
10	0246	8.5	2.6	25	0226	9.2	2.8
Th	0843	1.2	0.4	F	0827	0.4	0.1
	1457	9.4	2.9		1441	10.4	3.2
	2120	0.3	0.1		2105	-0.8	-0.2
11	0338	8.2	2.5	26	0323	9.1	2.8
F	0934	1.6	0.5	Sa	0923	0.6	0.2
	1550	8.9	2.7		1539	10.1	3.1
	2214	0.7	0.2		2204	-0.5	-0.2
12	0432	8.0	2.4	27	0422	9.1	2.8
Sa	1030	1.8	0.5	Su	1027	0.6	0.2
	1643	8.6	2.6		1642	9.8	3.0
	2306	1.0	0.3		2305	-0.4	-0.1
13	0525	8.0	2.4	28	0524	9.2	2.8
Su	1128	1.8	0.5	M	1133	0.5	0.2
	1741	8.5	2.6		1746	9.6	2.9
14	0002	1.0	0.3	29	0006	-0.3	-0.1
M	0620	8.1	2.5	Tu	0626	9.5	2.9
	1225	1.6	0.5		1238	0.2	0.1
	1837	8.4	2.6		1849	9.5	2.9
15	0054	0.9	0.3	30	0105	-0.3	-0.1
Tu	0711	8.4	2.6	W	0725	9.9	3.0
	1320	1.3	0.4		1341	-0.2	-0.1
	1929	8.6	2.6		1952	9.5	2.9

DECEMBER

Day	Time h m	Height ft	Height m	Day	Time h m	Height ft	Height m
1	0202	-0.3	-0.1	16	0144	0.7	0.2
Th	0821	10.3	3.1	F	0756	9.3	2.8
	1439	-0.7	-0.2		1418	0.3	0.1
	2050	9.6	2.9		2024	8.5	2.6
2	0255	-0.4	-0.1	17	0231	0.5	0.2
F	0911	10.6	3.2	Sa	0842	9.8	3.0
	1532	-1.0	-0.3		1506	-0.3	-0.1
	2143	9.6	2.9		2114	8.8	2.7
3	0344	-0.3	-0.1	18	0316	0.3	0.1
Sa	0959	10.8	3.3	Su	0928	10.2	3.1
	1620	-1.2	-0.4		1552	-0.8	-0.2
	2233	9.5	2.9		2201	9.0	2.7
4	0430	-0.2	-0.1	19	0401	0.1	0.0
Su	1045	10.8	3.3	M	1015	10.6	3.2
	1707	-1.3	-0.4		1639	-1.2	-0.4
	2321	9.4	2.9		2248	9.3	2.8
5	0513	0.0	0.0	20	0448	-0.2	-0.1
M	1129	10.7	3.3	Tu	1101	11.0	3.4
	1750	-1.1	-0.3		1726	-1.5	-0.5
					2338	9.4	2.9
6	0004	9.2	2.8	21	0536	-0.3	-0.1
Tu	0558	0.2	0.1	W	1148	11.2	3.4
	1213	10.5	3.2		1815	-1.7	-0.5
	1834	-0.9	-0.3				
7	0050	9.0	2.7	22	0026	9.6	2.9
W	0641	0.5	0.2	Th	0624	-0.4	-0.1
	1255	10.1	3.1		1239	11.2	3.4
	1916	-0.6	-0.2		1903	-1.7	-0.5
8	0132	8.7	2.7	23	0116	9.6	2.9
Th	0727	0.8	0.2	F	0716	-0.4	-0.1
	1340	9.8	3.0		1332	11.0	3.4
	2001	-0.2	-0.1		1955	-1.5	-0.5
9	0217	8.5	2.6	24	0211	9.6	2.9
F	0812	1.1	0.3	Sa	0812	-0.2	-0.1
	1426	9.4	2.9		1425	10.7	3.3
	2046	0.1	0.0		2048	-1.3	-0.4
10	0304	8.3	2.5	25	0307	9.6	2.9
Sa	0900	1.3	0.4	Su	0909	-0.1	0.0
	1513	9.0	2.7		1523	10.3	3.1
	2134	0.4	0.1		2145	-0.9	-0.3
11	0352	8.2	2.5	26	0403	9.6	2.9
Su	0953	1.5	0.5	M	1011	0.1	0.0
	1603	8.7	2.7		1625	9.8	3.0
	2224	0.7	0.2		2242	-0.6	-0.2
12	0442	8.2	2.5	27	0503	9.7	3.0
M	1046	1.6	0.5	Tu	1115	0.1	0.0
	1656	8.4	2.6		1727	9.4	2.9
	2315	0.8	0.2		2341	-0.3	-0.1
13	0532	8.3	2.5	28	0603	9.8	3.0
Tu	1141	1.5	0.5	W	1220	0.0	0.0
	1748	8.3	2.5		1832	9.1	2.8
14	0006	0.9	0.3	29	0041	0.0	0.0
W	0621	8.5	2.6	Th	0701	9.9	3.0
	1235	1.2	0.4		1323	-0.2	-0.1
	1843	8.3	2.5		1933	8.9	2.7
15	0056	0.9	0.3	30	0138	0.1	0.0
Th	0710	8.9	2.7	F	0757	10.1	3.1
	1328	0.8	0.2		1421	-0.4	-0.1
	1934	8.4	2.6		2034	8.8	2.7
				31	0233	0.2	0.1
				Sa	0851	10.2	3.1
					1514	-0.6	-0.2
					2128	8.8	2.7

Time meridian 75° W. 0000 is midnight. 1200 is noon.
Heights are referred to mean low water which is the chart datum of soundings.

Times and Heights of High and Low Waters

JANUARY

Day	Time (h m)	Height (ft)	Height (m)
1	0209	-1.0	-0.3
Sa	0857	4.6	1.4
	1500	-0.9	-0.3
	2125	3.8	1.2
2	0305	-0.9	-0.3
Su	0951	4.4	1.3
	1551	-0.7	-0.2
	2219	3.7	1.1
3	0400	-0.6	-0.2
M	1043	4.1	1.2
	1641	-0.5	-0.2
	2315	3.6	1.1
4	0459	-0.4	-0.1
Tu	1142	3.7	1.1
	1736	-0.3	-0.1
5	0011	3.5	1.1
W	0605	-0.1	0.0
	1238	3.4	1.0
	1833	-0.1	0.0
6	0111	3.4	1.0
Th	0720	0.1	0.0
	1337	3.1	0.9
	1933	0.1	0.0
7	0210	3.4	1.0
F	0843	0.3	0.1
	1435	2.9	0.9
	2038	0.1	0.0
8	0309	3.4	1.0
Sa	0957	0.3	0.1
	1531	2.8	0.9
	2138	0.2	0.1
9	0402	3.5	1.1
Su	1053	0.2	0.1
	1623	2.8	0.9
	2226	0.1	0.0
10	0452	3.5	1.1
M	1140	0.2	0.1
	1711	2.8	0.9
	2308	0.0	0.0
11	0537	3.6	1.1
Tu	1215	0.1	0.0
	1757	2.9	0.9
	2346	0.0	0.0
12	0620	3.7	1.1
W	1247	0.0	0.0
	1839	3.0	0.9
13	0020	-0.1	0.0
Th	0702	3.7	1.1
	1315	0.0	0.0
	1923	3.1	0.9
14	0054	-0.2	-0.1
F	0743	3.7	[illegible].1
	1341	-0.1	0.0
	2003	3.1	0.9
15	0129	-0.2	-0.1
Sa	0823	3.7	1.1
	1410	-0.1	0.0
	2044	3.1	0.9
16	0204	-0.2	-0.1
Su	0903	3.5	1.1
	1440	-0.1	0.0
	2124	3.0	0.9
17	0241	-0.1	0.0
M	0942	3.4	1.0
	1513	-0.1	0.0
	2206	3.0	0.9
18	0320	-0.1	0.0
Tu	1022	3.2	1.0
	1548	-0.1	0.0
	2249	2.9	0.9
19	0400	0.0	0.0
W	1105	3.0	0.9
	1625	-0.1	0.0
	2333	2.9	0.9
20	0446	0.1	0.0
Th	1152	2.8	0.9
	1710	0.0	0.0
21	0024	2.9	0.9
F	0539	0.2	0.1
	1244	2.7	0.8
	1758	0.0	0.0
22	0117	3.0	0.9
Sa	0639	0.2	0.1
	1341	2.7	0.8
	1855	-0.1	0.0
23	0217	3.2	1.0
Su	0745	0.2	0.1
	1445	2.7	0.8
	1958	-0.1	0.0
24	0318	3.5	1.1
M	0859	0.0	0.0
	1545	2.9	0.9
	2107	-0.3	-0.1
25	0417	3.8	1.2
Tu	1013	-0.2	-0.1
	1644	3.1	0.9
	2213	-0.5	-0.2
26	0514	4.1	1.2
W	1116	-0.5	-0.2
	1738	3.4	1.0
	2316	-0.8	-0.2
27	0607	4.4	1.3
Th	1214	-0.7	-0.2
	1833	3.7	1.1
28	0014	-1.0	-0.3
F	0659	4.6	1.4
	1305	-0.9	-0.3
	1924	3.9	1.2
29	0110	-1.1	-0.3
Sa	0750	4.6	1.4
	1354	-1.0	-0.3
	2015	4.0	1.2
30	0204	-1.1	-0.3
Su	0840	4.5	1.4
	1442	-1.0	-0.3
	2106	4.1	1.2
31	0256	-1.0	-0.3
M	0932	4.3	1.3
	1527	-0.9	-0.3
	2156	4.0	1.2

FEBRUARY

Day	Time (h m)	Height (ft)	Height (m)
1	0345	-0.8	-0.2
Tu	1022	4.0	1.2
	1612	-0.7	-0.2
	2248	3.8	1.2
2	0438	-0.5	-0.2
W	1113	3.6	1.1
	1659	-0.4	-0.1
	2340	3.6	1.1
3	0534	-0.2	-0.1
Th	1206	3.2	1.0
	1747	-0.1	0.0
4	0036	3.4	1.0
F	0635	0.2	0.1
	1301	2.9	0.9
	1836	0.1	0.0
5	0135	3.2	1.0
Sa	0752	0.4	0.1
	1359	2.6	0.8
	1936	0.3	0.1
6	0233	3.1	0.9
Su	0920	0.5	0.2
	1457	2.5	0.8
	2045	0.4	0.1
7	0331	3.1	0.9
M	1031	0.5	0.2
	1554	2.5	0.8
	2154	0.4	0.1
8	0423	3.2	1.0
Tu	1124	0.4	0.1
	1646	2.6	0.8
	2246	0.3	0.1
9	0512	3.3	1.0
W	1159	0.3	0.1
	1733	2.8	0.9
	2332	0.1	0.0
10	0557	3.4	1.0
Th	1227	0.1	0.0
	1817	3.0	0.9
11	0007	0.0	0.0
F	0641	3.5	1.1
	1252	0.0	0.0
	1859	3.1	0.9
12	0041	-0.2	-0.1
Sa	0721	3.6	1.1
	1318	-0.1	0.0
	1940	3.2	1.0
13	0115	-0.3	-0.1
Su	0759	3.6	1.1
	1344	-0.2	-0.1
	2019	3.3	1.0
14	0149	-0.3	-0.1
M	0838	3.6	1.1
	1414	-0.3	-0.1
	2058	3.3	1.0
15	0224	-0.4	-0.1
Tu	0916	3.5	1.1
	1446	-0.3	-0.1
	2135	3.3	1.0
16	0300	-0.3	-0.1
W	0956	3.3	1.0
	1519	-0.3	-0.1
	2214	3.3	1.0
17	0340	-0.3	-0.1
Th	1035	3.1	0.9
	1556	-0.3	-0.1
	2257	3.2	1.0
18	0424	-0.2	-0.1
F	1120	2.9	0.9
	1638	-0.2	-0.1
	2347	3.2	1.0
19	0514	-0.1	0.0
Sa	1211	2.7	0.8
	1726	-0.2	-0.1
20	0043	3.2	1.0
Su	0611	0.1	0.0
	1311	2.6	0.8
	1824	-0.1	0.0
21	0148	3.3	1.0
M	0719	0.1	0.0
	1417	2.6	0.8
	1929	-0.1	0.0
22	0253	3.4	1.0
Tu	0839	0.1	0.0
	1525	2.8	0.9
	2045	-0.2	-0.1
23	0357	3.7	1.1
W	0957	-0.1	0.0
	1626	3.1	0.9
	2200	-0.4	-0.1
24	0455	4.0	1.2
Th	1103	-0.4	-0.1
	1722	3.5	1.1
	2308	-0.7	-0.2
25	0551	4.2	1.3
F	1159	-0.7	-0.2
	1815	3.8	1.2
26	0009	-0.9	-0.3
Sa	0643	4.4	1.3
	1249	-0.9	-0.3
	1906	4.1	1.2
27	0103	-1.1	-0.3
Su	0732	4.4	1.3
	1335	-1.0	-0.3
	1955	4.3	1.3
28	0152	-1.1	-0.3
M	0821	4.4	1.3
	1418	-1.0	-0.3
	2043	4.3	1.3

MARCH

Day	Time (h m)	Height (ft)	Height (m)
1	0242	-1.0	-0.3
Tu	0908	4.1	1.2
	1500	-0.9	-0.3
	2129	4.2	1.3
2	0327	-0.8	-0.2
W	0956	3.8	1.2
	1540	-0.6	-0.2
	2219	4.0	1.2
3	0412	-0.5	-0.2
Th	1043	3.4	1.0
	1619	-0.4	-0.1
	2307	3.7	1.1
4	0457	-0.1	0.0
F	1133	3.1	0.9
	1659	-0.1	0.0
5	0000	3.4	1.0
Sa	0547	0.2	0.1
	1224	2.7	0.8
	1742	0.2	0.1
6	0056	3.1	0.9
Su	0643	0.5	0.2
	1322	2.5	0.8
	1832	0.4	0.1
7	0156	2.9	0.9
M	0807	0.7	0.2
	1424	2.4	0.7
	1937	0.6	0.2
8	0256	2.9	0.9
Tu	0954	0.7	0.2
	1522	2.4	0.7
	2107	0.6	0.2
9	0352	2.9	0.9
W	1049	0.6	0.2
	1616	2.6	0.8
	2221	0.5	0.2
10	0444	3.1	0.9
Th	1124	0.4	0.1
	1706	2.8	0.9
	2311	0.3	0.1
11	0529	3.2	1.0
F	1151	0.2	0.1
	1751	3.1	0.9
	2345	0.0	0.0
12	0613	3.4	1.0
Sa	1217	0.0	0.0
	1833	3.3	1.0
13	0020	-0.2	-0.1
Su	0654	3.5	1.1
	1243	-0.2	-0.1
	1911	3.5	1.1
14	0054	-0.3	-0.1
M	0732	3.6	1.1
	1312	-0.3	-0.1
	1950	3.6	1.1
15	0128	-0.5	-0.2
Tu	0810	3.6	1.1
	1344	-0.4	-0.1
	2028	3.7	1.1
16	0203	-0.5	-0.2
W	0849	3.5	1.1
	1417	-0.5	-0.2
	2108	3.7	1.1
17	0242	-0.5	-0.2
Th	0927	3.4	1.0
	1452	-0.5	-0.2
	2147	3.7	1.1
18	0321	-0.5	-0.2
F	1009	3.2	1.0
	1531	-0.4	-0.1
	2232	3.6	1.1
19	0407	-0.3	-0.1
Sa	1057	3.0	0.9
	1612	-0.3	-0.1
	2321	3.5	1.1
20	0457	-0.2	-0.1
Su	1150	2.8	0.9
	1704	-0.2	-0.1
21	0019	3.4	1.0
M	0555	0.0	0.0
	1254	2.7	0.8
	1803	-0.1	0.0
22	0125	3.4	1.0
Tu	0704	0.1	0.0
	1400	2.7	0.8
	1913	0.0	0.0
23	0233	3.4	1.0
W	0824	0.1	0.0
	1509	2.9	0.9
	2035	0.0	0.0
24	0338	3.6	1.1
Th	0942	-0.1	0.0
	1610	3.3	1.0
	2159	-0.3	-0.1
25	0437	3.8	1.2
F	1047	-0.3	-0.1
	1706	3.7	1.1
	2308	-0.6	-0.2
26	0533	4.0	1.2
Sa	1141	-0.6	-0.2
	1757	4.0	1.2
27	0004	-0.8	-0.2
Su	0625	4.2	1.3
	1228	-0.8	-0.2
	1846	4.3	1.3
28	0054	-1.0	-0.3
M	0712	4.2	1.3
	1310	-0.8	-0.2
	1932	4.4	1.3
29	0140	-1.0	-0.3
Tu	0759	4.1	1.2
	1350	-0.8	-0.2
	2018	4.4	1.3
30	0224	-0.9	-0.3
W	0844	3.9	1.2
	1427	-0.7	-0.2
	2103	4.3	1.3
31	0303	-0.7	-0.2
Th	0927	3.6	1.1
	1503	-0.5	-0.2
	2148	4.0	1.2

Time meridian 75° W. 0000 is midnight. 1200 is noon.
Heights are referred to mean low water which is the chart datum of soundings.

NEWPORT, R.I., 1983

Times and Heights of High and Low Waters

APRIL

Day	Time (h m)	Height (ft)	Height (m)
1 F	0345	-0.4	-0.1
	1013	3.3	1.0
	1540	-0.2	-0.1
	2235	3.7	1.1
2 Sa	0422	-0.1	0.0
	1100	3.0	0.9
	1617	0.0	0.0
	2323	3.4	1.0
3 Su	0503	0.3	0.1
	1152	2.7	0.8
	1657	0.3	0.1
4 M	0018	3.1	0.9
	0548	0.5	0.2
	1248	2.5	0.8
	1744	0.6	0.2
5 Tu	0116	2.9	0.9
	0644	0.7	0.2
	1349	2.4	0.7
	1845	0.7	0.2
6 W	0216	2.8	0.9
	0803	0.8	0.2
	1449	2.5	0.8
	2006	0.8	0.2
7 Th	0314	2.8	0.9
	0933	0.7	0.2
	1544	2.7	0.8
	2134	0.6	0.2
8 F	0407	2.9	0.9
	1021	0.5	0.2
	1634	2.9	0.9
	2231	0.4	0.1
9 Sa	0455	3.1	0.9
	1055	0.3	0.1
	1719	3.2	1.0
	2314	0.2	0.1
10 Su	0540	3.3	1.0
	1129	0.0	0.0
	1801	3.5	1.1
	2351	-0.1	0.0
11 M	0622	3.5	1.1
	1201	-0.2	-0.1
	1840	3.7	1.1
12 Tu	0029	-0.3	-0.1
	0702	3.6	1.1
	1233	-0.4	-0.1
	1920	3.9	1.2
13 W	0106	-0.5	-0.2
	0743	3.6	1.1
	1310	-0.5	-0.2
	1959	4.1	1.2
14 Th	0144	-0.6	-0.2
	0822	3.5	1.1
	1347	-0.5	-0.2
	2039	4.1	1.2
15 F	0224	-0.6	-0.2
	0906	3.4	1.0
	1426	-0.5	-0.2
	2124	4.1	1.2
16 Sa	0308	-0.6	-0.2
	0950	3.3	1.0
	1510	-0.5	-0.2
	2211	4.0	1.2
17 Su	0355	-0.4	-0.1
	1041	3.1	0.9
	1556	-0.3	-0.1
	2304	3.8	1.2
18 M	0446	-0.2	-0.1
	1139	3.0	0.9
	1649	-0.1	0.0
19 Tu	0003	3.6	1.1
	0546	0.0	0.0
	1240	2.9	0.9
	1755	0.1	0.0
20 W	0109	3.5	1.1
	0655	0.1	0.0
	1348	3.0	0.9
	1910	0.1	0.0
21 Th	0216	3.5	1.1
	0814	0.1	0.0
	1453	3.2	1.0
	2038	0.1	0.0
22 F	0320	3.6	1.1
	0928	-0.1	0.0
	1552	3.5	1.1
	2159	-0.1	0.0
23 Sa	0418	3.7	1.1
	1029	-0.2	-0.1
	1647	3.9	1.2
	2303	-0.4	-0.1
24 Su	0514	3.8	1.2
	1119	-0.4	-0.1
	1737	4.2	1.3
	2356	-0.6	-0.2
25 M	0602	3.9	1.2
	1201	-0.5	-0.2
	1823	4.4	1.3
26 Tu	0042	-0.7	-0.2
	0649	3.9	1.2
	1243	-0.6	-0.2
	1909	4.5	1.4
27 W	0124	-0.7	-0.2
	0734	3.8	1.2
	1319	-0.6	-0.2
	1953	4.5	1.4
28 Th	0205	-0.6	-0.2
	0818	3.6	1.1
	1356	-0.4	-0.1
	2037	4.3	1.3
29 F	0239	-0.4	-0.1
	0902	3.4	1.0
	1431	-0.3	-0.1
	2121	4.0	1.2
30 Sa	0316	-0.2	-0.1
	0945	3.2	1.0
	1506	-0.1	0.0
	2204	3.7	1.1

MAY

Day	Time (h m)	Height (ft)	Height (m)
1 Su	0351	0.1	0.0
	1030	3.0	0.9
	1542	0.2	0.1
	2251	3.4	1.0
2 M	0427	0.3	0.1
	1121	2.8	0.9
	1622	0.4	0.1
	2342	3.1	0.9
3 Tu	0507	0.5	0.2
	1216	2.6	0.8
	1707	0.6	0.2
4 W	0037	2.9	0.9
	0557	0.6	0.2
	1314	2.6	0.8
	1806	0.8	0.2
5 Th	0136	2.8	0.9
	0656	0.7	0.2
	1412	2.6	0.8
	1912	0.8	0.2
6 F	0233	2.8	0.9
	0759	0.7	0.2
	1507	2.8	0.9
	2031	0.8	0.2
7 Sa	0327	2.9	0.9
	0859	0.5	0.2
	1557	3.1	0.9
	2138	0.5	0.2
8 Su	0416	3.0	0.9
	0950	0.3	0.1
	1642	3.4	1.0
	2231	0.3	0.1
9 M	0503	3.2	1.0
	1034	0.1	0.0
	1725	3.7	1.1
	2316	0.0	0.0
10 Tu	0547	3.4	1.0
	1117	-0.1	0.0
	1807	4.0	1.2
	2359	-0.3	-0.1
11 W	0630	3.5	1.1
	1156	-0.3	-0.1
	1850	4.2	1.3
12 Th	0041	-0.5	-0.2
	0713	3.6	1.1
	1237	-0.5	-0.2
	1932	4.4	1.3
13 F	0123	-0.6	-0.2
	0759	3.6	1.1
	1322	-0.6	-0.2
	2018	4.4	1.3
14 Sa	0209	-0.7	-0.2
	0844	3.5	1.1
	1408	-0.5	-0.2
	2104	4.4	1.3
15 Su	0255	-0.6	-0.2
	0934	3.5	1.1
	1455	-0.4	-0.1
	2155	4.3	1.3
16 M	0345	-0.5	-0.2
	1028	3.4	1.0
	1548	-0.3	-0.1
	2249	4.1	1.2
17 Tu	0441	-0.3	-0.1
	1125	3.3	1.0
	1645	-0.1	0.0
	2350	3.9	1.2
18 W	0539	-0.1	0.0
	1227	3.3	1.0
	1752	0.1	0.0
19 Th	0053	3.7	1.1
	0645	0.0	0.0
	1332	3.4	1.0
	1912	0.2	0.1
20 F	0156	3.6	1.1
	0755	0.0	0.0
	1432	3.6	1.1
	2038	0.2	0.1
21 Sa	0259	3.5	1.1
	0904	0.0	0.0
	1530	3.8	1.2
	2152	0.0	0.0
22 Su	0357	3.5	1.1
	1002	-0.1	0.0
	1623	4.0	1.2
	2255	-0.2	-0.1
23 M	0450	3.6	1.1
	1050	-0.2	-0.1
	1714	4.2	1.3
	2345	-0.3	-0.1
24 Tu	0538	3.6	1.1
	1135	-0.2	-0.1
	1800	4.4	1.3
25 W	0028	-0.3	-0.1
	0626	3.6	1.1
	1214	-0.3	-0.1
	1846	4.4	1.3
26 Th	0108	-0.3	-0.1
	0709	3.5	1.1
	1250	-0.2	-0.1
	1928	4.4	1.3
27 F	0145	-0.2	-0.1
	0753	3.4	1.0
	1325	-0.2	-0.1
	2013	4.2	1.3
28 Sa	0218	-0.1	0.0
	0836	3.3	1.0
	1400	0.0	0.0
	2055	4.0	1.2
29 Su	0250	0.0	0.0
	0919	3.2	1.0
	1436	0.1	0.0
	2137	3.8	1.2
30 M	0323	0.2	0.1
	1005	3.0	0.9
	1514	0.3	0.1
	2222	3.5	1.1
31 Tu	0358	0.3	0.1
	1054	2.9	0.9
	1553	0.5	0.2
	2309	3.2	1.0

JUNE

Day	Time (h m)	Height (ft)	Height (m)
1 W	0436	0.4	0.1
	1142	2.8	0.9
	1638	0.7	0.2
	2358	3.0	0.9
2 Th	0518	0.5	0.2
	1237	2.8	0.9
	1731	0.8	0.2
3 F	0051	2.9	0.9
	0606	0.6	0.2
	1330	2.9	0.9
	1829	0.8	0.2
4 Sa	0146	2.8	0.9
	0701	0.5	0.2
	1423	3.0	0.9
	1935	0.8	0.2
5 Su	0241	2.9	0.9
	0756	0.5	0.2
	1514	3.2	1.0
	2043	0.6	0.2
6 M	0334	3.0	0.9
	0851	0.3	0.1
	1602	3.5	1.1
	2144	0.4	0.1
7 Tu	0423	3.1	0.9
	0944	0.1	0.0
	1648	3.9	1.2
	2239	0.1	0.0
8 W	0511	3.3	1.0
	1034	-0.1	0.0
	1735	4.2	1.3
	2329	-0.2	-0.1
9 Th	0559	3.4	1.0
	1124	-0.3	-0.1
	1822	4.5	1.4
10 F	0017	-0.4	-0.1
	0648	3.6	1.1
	1212	-0.5	-0.2
	1909	4.6	1.4
11 Sa	0106	-0.6	-0.2
	0736	3.7	1.1
	1302	-0.6	-0.2
	1957	4.7	1.4
12 Su	0155	-0.6	-0.2
	0826	3.7	1.1
	1352	-0.6	-0.2
	2047	4.7	1.4
13 M	0245	-0.6	-0.2
	0919	3.7	1.1
	1445	-0.5	-0.2
	2140	4.5	1.4
14 Tu	0337	-0.5	-0.2
	1012	3.7	1.1
	1540	-0.3	-0.1
	2235	4.3	1.3
15 W	0430	-0.4	-0.1
	1110	3.7	1.1
	1641	-0.1	0.0
	2333	4.1	1.2
16 Th	0526	-0.2	-0.1
	1208	3.7	1.1
	1750	0.1	0.0
17 F	0033	3.8	1.2
	0627	0.0	0.0
	1309	3.7	1.1
	1904	0.2	0.1
18 Sa	0133	3.6	1.1
	0730	0.1	0.0
	1409	3.8	1.2
	2025	0.3	0.1
19 Su	0235	3.4	1.0
	0832	0.1	0.0
	1507	3.9	1.2
	2139	0.2	0.1
20 M	0330	3.3	1.0
	0930	0.1	0.0
	1600	4.1	1.2
	2242	0.2	0.1
21 Tu	0424	3.3	1.0
	1021	0.1	0.0
	1650	4.2	1.3
	2332	0.1	0.0
22 W	0514	3.3	1.0
	1107	0.1	0.0
	1738	4.2	1.3
23 Th	0017	0.1	0.0
	0601	3.3	1.0
	1149	0.1	0.0
	1823	4.3	1.3
24 F	0053	0.0	0.0
	0646	3.3	1.0
	1225	0.1	0.0
	1907	4.2	1.3
25 Sa	0126	0.1	0.0
	0730	3.3	1.0
	1300	0.1	0.0
	1949	4.1	1.2
26 Su	0157	0.1	0.0
	0812	3.3	1.0
	1336	0.2	0.1
	2030	4.0	1.2
27 M	0226	0.1	0.0
	0856	3.3	1.0
	1413	0.2	0.1
	2113	3.8	1.2
28 Tu	0258	0.2	0.1
	0940	3.2	1.0
	1452	0.4	0.1
	2155	3.6	1.1
29 W	0332	0.3	0.1
	1024	3.1	0.9
	1532	0.5	0.2
	2238	3.4	1.0
30 Th	0404	0.3	0.1
	1110	3.1	0.9
	1612	0.6	0.2
	2322	3.2	1.0

Time meridian 75° W. 0000 is midnight. 1200 is noon.
Heights are referred to mean low water which is the chart datum of soundings.

Times and Heights of High and Low Waters

JULY

Day	Time (h m)	Height (ft)	Height (m)
1 F	0443	0.4	0.1
	1158	3.0	0.9
	1659	0.7	0.2
2 Sa	0011	3.0	0.9
	0526	0.4	0.1
	1248	3.1	0.9
	1752	0.7	0.2
3 Su	0101	2.9	0.9
	0613	0.4	0.1
	1339	3.2	1.0
	1850	0.7	0.2
4 M	0156	2.9	0.9
	0704	0.4	0.1
	1432	3.4	1.0
	1954	0.6	0.2
5 Tu	0251	2.9	0.9
	0803	0.3	0.1
	1523	3.7	1.1
	2059	0.5	0.2
6 W	0346	3.0	0.9
	0901	0.1	0.0
	1615	4.0	1.2
	2205	0.2	0.1
7 Th	0441	3.2	1.0
	0959	-0.1	0.0
	1707	4.3	1.3
	2303	0.0	0.0
8 F	0533	3.4	1.0
	1058	-0.3	-0.1
	1757	4.6	1.4
	2357	-0.3	-0.1
9 Sa	0625	3.7	1.1
	1152	-0.4	-0.1
	1849	4.8	1.5
10 Su	0051	-0.5	-0.2
	0717	3.9	1.2
	1248	-0.6	-0.2
	1940	4.9	1.5
11 M	0141	-0.6	-0.2
	0808	4.0	1.2
	1343	-0.6	-0.2
	2031	4.9	1.5
12 Tu	0232	-0.7	-0.2
	0900	4.1	1.2
	1438	-0.5	-0.2
	2124	4.7	1.4
13 W	0321	-0.6	-0.2
	0954	4.1	1.2
	1535	-0.4	-0.1
	2217	4.5	1.4
14 Th	0412	-0.5	-0.2
	1049	4.1	1.2
	1633	-0.2	-0.1
	2312	4.2	1.3
15 F	0504	-0.3	-0.1
	1144	4.1	1.2
	1736	0.1	0.0
16 Sa	0008	3.8	1.2
	0558	-0.1	0.0
	1242	4.0	1.2
	1845	0.3	0.1
17 Su	0105	3.5	1.1
	0655	0.1	0.0
	1340	3.9	1.2
	2003	0.4	0.1
18 M	0205	3.3	1.0
	0755	0.3	0.1
	1439	3.9	1.2
	2122	0.5	0.2
19 Tu	0302	3.1	0.9
	0856	0.4	0.1
	1533	3.9	1.2
	2229	0.5	0.2
20 W	0359	3.1	0.9
	0954	0.4	0.1
	1626	4.0	1.2
	2323	0.4	0.1
21 Th	0450	3.1	0.9
	1044	0.4	0.1
	1716	4.0	1.2
22 F	0004	0.4	0.1
	0538	3.2	1.0
	1128	0.3	0.1
	1801	4.1	1.2
23 Sa	0041	0.3	0.1
	0624	3.3	1.0
	1209	0.3	0.1
	1845	4.1	1.2
24 Su	0106	0.3	0.1
	0708	3.4	1.0
	1244	0.2	0.1
	1926	4.1	1.2
25 M	0135	0.2	0.1
	0750	3.4	1.0
	1319	0.2	0.1
	2007	4.0	1.2
26 Tu	0202	0.2	0.1
	0831	3.5	1.1
	1354	0.2	0.1
	2047	3.9	1.2
27 W	0231	0.2	0.1
	0911	3.5	1.1
	1431	0.3	0.1
	2127	3.7	1.1
28 Th	0302	0.2	0.1
	0953	3.4	1.0
	1508	0.4	0.1
	2206	3.5	1.1
29 F	0334	0.2	0.1
	1035	3.4	1.0
	1548	0.4	0.1
	2248	3.3	1.0
30 Sa	0408	0.2	0.1
	1118	3.3	1.0
	1630	0.5	0.2
	2331	3.1	0.9
31 Su	0449	0.3	0.1
	1206	3.3	1.0
	1718	0.6	0.2

AUGUST

Day	Time (h m)	Height (ft)	Height (m)
1 M	0021	3.0	0.9
	0533	0.3	0.1
	1257	3.4	1.0
	1813	0.6	0.2
2 Tu	0114	2.9	0.9
	0624	0.3	0.1
	1353	3.5	1.1
	1917	0.6	0.2
3 W	0214	2.9	0.9
	0724	0.3	0.1
	1449	3.7	1.1
	2027	0.5	0.2
4 Th	0316	3.0	0.9
	0829	0.2	0.1
	1549	4.0	1.2
	2136	0.3	0.1
5 F	0416	3.2	1.0
	0934	0.0	0.0
	1644	4.3	1.3
	2244	0.0	0.0
6 Sa	0512	3.5	1.1
	1039	-0.2	-0.1
	1738	4.6	1.4
	2341	-0.3	-0.1
7 Su	0607	3.8	1.2
	1140	-0.4	-0.1
	1831	4.8	1.5
8 M	0036	-0.5	-0.2
	0658	4.1	1.2
	1239	-0.6	-0.2
	1922	4.9	1.5
9 Tu	0125	-0.7	-0.2
	0750	4.3	1.3
	1334	-0.7	-0.2
	2013	4.9	1.5
10 W	0213	-0.7	-0.2
	0840	4.5	1.4
	1428	-0.7	-0.2
	2103	4.7	1.4
11 Th	0300	-0.7	-0.2
	0932	4.5	1.4
	1522	-0.5	-0.2
	2154	4.5	1.4
12 F	0348	-0.5	-0.2
	1024	4.4	1.3
	1616	-0.3	-0.1
	2246	4.1	1.2
13 Sa	0433	-0.3	-0.1
	1116	4.3	1.3
	1712	0.0	0.0
	2339	3.7	1.1
14 Su	0521	0.0	0.0
	1212	4.1	1.2
	1815	0.4	0.1
15 M	0035	3.4	1.0
	0611	0.3	0.1
	1311	3.9	1.2
	1930	0.6	0.2
16 Tu	0135	3.1	0.9
	0712	0.5	0.2
	1409	3.7	1.1
	2059	0.7	0.2
17 W	0235	2.9	0.9
	0817	0.6	0.2
	1507	3.7	1.1
	2213	0.7	0.2
18 Th	0333	2.9	0.9
	0930	0.7	0.2
	1602	3.7	1.1
	2308	0.6	0.2
19 F	0426	3.0	0.9
	1031	0.6	0.2
	1652	3.7	1.1
	2346	0.5	0.2
20 Sa	0516	3.1	0.9
	1116	0.5	0.2
	1738	3.8	1.2
21 Su	0018	0.4	0.1
	0601	3.3	1.0
	1153	0.4	0.1
	1822	3.9	1.2
22 M	0044	0.3	0.1
	0644	3.5	1.1
	1230	0.3	0.1
	1902	4.0	1.2
23 Tu	0108	0.2	0.1
	0724	3.6	1.1
	1302	0.2	0.1
	1941	4.0	1.2
24 W	0133	0.1	0.0
	0804	3.7	1.1
	1336	0.1	0.0
	2020	3.9	1.2
25 Th	0159	0.0	0.0
	0842	3.7	1.1
	1409	0.1	0.0
	2058	3.8	1.2
26 F	0228	0.0	0.0
	0919	3.7	1.1
	1445	0.2	0.1
	2137	3.6	1.1
27 Sa	0300	0.0	0.0
	1001	3.6	1.1
	1522	0.2	0.1
	2214	3.4	1.0
28 Su	0336	0.1	0.0
	1041	3.6	1.1
	1604	0.3	0.1
	2257	3.2	1.0
29 M	0414	0.1	0.0
	1127	3.5	1.1
	1651	0.4	0.1
	2344	3.0	0.9
30 Tu	0459	0.2	0.1
	1219	3.5	1.1
	1744	0.5	0.2
31 W	0043	2.8	0.9
	0552	0.3	0.1
	1319	3.6	1.1
	1848	0.6	0.2

SEPTEMBER

Day	Time (h m)	Height (ft)	Height (m)
1 Th	0147	2.8	0.9
	0653	0.3	0.1
	1423	3.7	1.1
	2000	0.5	0.2
2 F	0253	3.0	0.9
	0804	0.3	0.1
	1525	3.9	1.2
	2117	0.3	0.1
3 Sa	0357	3.3	1.0
	0920	0.1	0.0
	1626	4.2	1.3
	2229	0.0	0.0
4 Su	0453	3.6	1.1
	1031	-0.2	-0.1
	1720	4.5	1.4
	2325	-0.3	-0.1
5 M	0548	4.0	1.2
	1135	-0.5	-0.2
	1814	4.7	1.4
6 Tu	0017	-0.6	-0.2
	0639	4.4	1.3
	1230	-0.7	-0.2
	1903	4.8	1.5
7 W	0105	-0.7	-0.2
	0729	4.6	1.4
	1323	-0.8	-0.2
	1953	4.8	1.5
8 Th	0150	-0.8	-0.2
	0818	4.7	1.4
	1414	-0.7	-0.2
	2041	4.6	1.4
9 F	0234	-0.7	-0.2
	0906	4.7	1.4
	1503	-0.6	-0.2
	2129	4.3	1.3
10 Sa	0316	-0.5	-0.2
	0956	4.5	1.4
	1551	-0.3	-0.1
	2219	3.9	1.2
11 Su	0358	-0.3	-0.1
	1046	4.3	1.3
	1641	0.1	0.0
	2310	3.5	1.1
12 M	0441	0.1	0.0
	1140	4.0	1.2
	1737	0.4	0.1
13 Tu	0005	3.2	1.0
	0528	0.4	0.1
	1237	3.7	1.1
	1844	0.7	0.2
14 W	0103	2.9	0.9
	0619	0.6	0.2
	1336	3.5	1.1
	2020	0.9	0.3
15 Th	0205	2.8	0.9
	0728	0.8	0.2
	1437	3.4	1.0
	2146	0.9	0.3
16 F	0305	2.8	0.9
	0901	0.9	0.3
	1534	3.4	1.0
	2239	0.8	0.2
17 Sa	0400	2.9	0.9
	1015	0.8	0.2
	1624	3.5	1.1
	2322	0.6	0.2
18 Su	0450	3.1	0.9
	1100	0.6	0.2
	1711	3.6	1.1
	2347	0.5	0.2
19 M	0535	3.3	1.0
	1137	0.4	0.1
	1753	3.7	1.1
20 Tu	0007	0.3	0.1
	0617	3.6	1.1
	1209	0.2	0.1
	1833	3.8	1.2
21 W	0030	0.1	0.0
	0655	3.8	1.2
	1241	0.1	0.0
	1914	3.9	1.2
22 Th	0057	0.0	0.0
	0733	3.9	1.2
	1313	0.0	0.0
	1951	3.8	1.2
23 F	0124	-0.1	0.0
	0812	3.9	1.2
	1346	-0.1	0.0
	2030	3.7	1.1
24 Sa	0157	-0.2	-0.1
	0848	3.9	1.2
	1422	-0.1	0.0
	2107	3.6	1.1
25 Su	0229	-0.2	-0.1
	0927	3.9	1.2
	1502	0.0	0.0
	2148	3.4	1.0
26 M	0306	-0.1	0.0
	1009	3.8	1.2
	1543	0.1	0.0
	2230	3.1	0.9
27 Tu	0345	0.0	0.0
	1057	3.7	1.1
	1630	0.2	0.1
	2321	2.9	0.9
28 W	0433	0.1	0.0
	1153	3.6	1.1
	1725	0.4	0.1
29 Th	0021	2.8	0.9
	0528	0.2	0.1
	1255	3.6	1.1
	1829	0.5	0.2
30 F	0129	2.8	0.9
	0636	0.3	0.1
	1403	3.7	1.1
	1946	0.4	0.1

Time meridian 75° W. 0000 is midnight. 1200 is noon.
Heights are referred to mean low water which is the chart datum of soundings.

Times and Heights of High and Low Waters

OCTOBER

Day	Time h m	Height ft	Height m
1	0237	3.0	0.9
Sa	0754	0.3	0.1
	1508	3.8	1.2
	2104	0.2	0.1
2	0341	3.4	1.0
Su	0915	0.1	0.0
	1607	4.0	1.2
	2213	0.0	0.0
3	0437	3.8	1.2
M	1029	-0.2	-0.1
	1703	4.3	1.3
	2308	-0.3	-0.1
4	0529	4.2	1.3
Tu	1129	-0.5	-0.2
	1755	4.4	1.3
	2356	-0.6	-0.2
5	0620	4.5	1.4
W	1222	-0.7	-0.2
	1844	4.5	1.4
6	0041	-0.7	-0.2
Th	0707	4.8	1.5
	1312	-0.8	-0.2
	1931	4.4	1.3
7	0124	-0.8	-0.2
F	0754	4.8	1.5
	1358	-0.7	-0.2
	2017	4.3	1.3
8	0203	-0.7	-0.2
Sa	0840	4.7	1.4
	1442	-0.5	-0.2
	2103	4.0	1.2
9	0244	-0.5	-0.2
Su	0927	4.5	1.4
	1527	-0.3	-0.1
	2151	3.6	1.1
10	0321	-0.2	-0.1
M	1017	4.2	1.3
	1611	0.1	0.0
	2240	3.3	1.0
11	0403	0.1	0.0
Tu	1107	3.8	1.2
	1656	0.4	0.1
	2331	3.0	0.9
12	0444	0.4	0.1
W	1202	3.5	1.1
	1749	0.7	0.2
13	0031	2.7	0.8
Th	0534	0.7	0.2
	1259	3.2	1.0
	1903	0.9	0.3
14	0131	2.6	0.8
F	0639	0.9	0.3
	1359	3.1	0.9
	2050	0.9	0.3
15	0235	2.7	0.8
Sa	0808	0.9	0.3
	1459	3.1	0.9
	2154	0.8	0.2
16	0330	2.9	0.9
Su	0936	0.8	0.2
	1552	3.2	1.0
	2229	0.6	0.2
17	0418	3.1	0.9
M	1031	0.6	0.2
	1639	3.3	1.0
	2255	0.4	0.1
18	0503	3.4	1.0
Tu	1106	0.4	0.1
	1722	3.5	1.1
	2319	0.2	0.1
19	0545	3.6	1.1
W	1137	0.2	0.1
	1803	3.6	1.1
	2348	0.0	0.0
20	0625	3.8	1.2
Th	1212	0.0	0.0
	1842	3.7	1.1
21	0018	-0.2	-0.1
F	0702	4.0	1.2
	1247	-0.2	-0.1
	1921	3.7	1.1
22	0051	-0.3	-0.1
Sa	0742	4.1	1.2
	1323	-0.3	-0.1
	2000	3.6	1.1
23	0127	-0.4	-0.1
Su	0821	4.2	1.3
	1401	-0.3	-0.1
	2042	3.5	1.1
24	0202	-0.4	-0.1
M	0901	4.1	1.2
	1442	-0.2	-0.1
	2123	3.3	1.0
25	0242	-0.3	-0.1
Tu	0946	4.0	1.2
	1526	-0.1	0.0
	2211	3.1	0.9
26	0327	-0.2	-0.1
W	1037	3.9	1.2
	1616	0.0	0.0
	2305	3.0	0.9
27	0417	0.0	0.0
Th	1133	3.7	1.1
	1713	0.2	0.1
28	0008	2.9	0.9
F	0518	0.1	0.0
	1236	3.6	1.1
	1819	0.3	0.1
29	0115	3.0	0.9
Sa	0627	0.3	0.1
	1343	3.6	1.1
	1933	0.2	0.1
30	0220	3.2	1.0
Su	0751	0.2	0.1
	1449	3.7	1.1
	2049	0.1	0.0
31	0322	3.5	1.1
M	0914	0.1	0.0
	1549	3.8	1.2
	2152	-0.1	0.0

NOVEMBER

Day	Time h m	Height ft	Height m
1	0418	3.9	1.2
Tu	1023	-0.2	-0.1
	1644	3.9	1.2
	2247	-0.4	-0.1
2	0511	4.3	1.3
W	1122	-0.5	-0.2
	1735	4.0	1.2
	2332	-0.6	-0.2
3	0559	4.5	1.4
Th	1212	-0.6	-0.2
	1822	4.1	1.2
4	0017	-0.7	-0.2
F	0646	4.7	1.4
	1259	-0.7	-0.2
	1908	4.0	1.2
5	0056	-0.7	-0.2
Sa	0732	4.7	1.4
	1341	-0.6	-0.2
	1954	3.9	1.2
6	0137	-0.6	-0.2
Su	0817	4.6	1.4
	1421	-0.4	-0.1
	2038	3.7	1.1
7	0213	-0.4	-0.1
M	0901	4.3	1.3
	1501	-0.2	-0.1
	2124	3.4	1.0
8	0250	-0.2	-0.1
Tu	0947	4.0	1.2
	1542	0.1	0.0
	2212	3.1	0.9
9	0327	0.1	0.0
W	1036	3.7	1.1
	1619	0.3	0.1
	2301	2.9	0.9
10	0409	0.4	0.1
Th	1126	3.3	1.0
	1702	0.6	0.2
	2355	2.7	0.8
11	0454	0.6	0.2
F	1221	3.1	0.9
	1752	0.7	0.2
12	0056	2.6	0.8
Sa	0552	0.8	0.2
	1320	2.9	0.9
	1853	0.8	0.2
13	0155	2.6	0.8
Su	0701	0.9	0.3
	1416	2.9	0.9
	2002	0.7	0.2
14	0251	2.8	0.9
M	0821	0.8	0.2
	1511	2.9	0.9
	2101	0.6	0.2
15	0341	3.0	0.9
Tu	0930	0.7	0.2
	1600	3.0	0.9
	2144	0.4	0.1
16	0427	3.3	1.0
W	1021	0.4	0.1
	1645	3.2	1.0
	2223	0.2	0.1
17	0511	3.6	1.1
Th	1100	0.2	0.1
	1729	3.3	1.0
	2303	-0.1	0.0
18	0551	3.8	1.2
F	1140	-0.1	0.0
	1812	3.4	1.0
	2340	-0.3	-0.1
19	0633	4.1	1.2
Sa	1221	-0.3	-0.1
	1854	3.5	1.1
20	0020	-0.4	-0.1
Su	0713	4.2	1.3
	1303	-0.4	-0.1
	1935	3.5	1.1
21	0059	-0.5	-0.2
M	0756	4.3	1.3
	1344	-0.5	-0.2
	2018	3.4	1.0
22	0141	-0.6	-0.2
Tu	0841	4.3	1.3
	1430	-0.5	-0.2
	2106	3.4	1.0
23	0226	-0.5	-0.2
W	0929	4.2	1.3
	1516	-0.4	-0.1
	2156	3.3	1.0
24	0316	-0.4	-0.1
Th	1020	4.0	1.2
	1606	-0.3	-0.1
	2251	3.2	1.0
25	0409	-0.2	-0.1
F	1118	3.8	1.2
	1702	-0.1	0.0
	2352	3.1	0.9
26	0513	0.0	0.0
Sa	1219	3.7	1.1
	1806	0.0	0.0
27	0056	3.2	1.0
Su	0624	0.1	0.0
	1323	3.5	1.1
	1914	0.0	0.0
28	0200	3.4	1.0
M	0746	0.1	0.0
	1427	3.5	1.1
	2024	0.0	0.0
29	0301	3.6	1.1
Tu	0909	0.0	0.0
	1526	3.5	1.1
	2128	-0.2	-0.1
30	0357	3.9	1.2
W	1018	-0.2	-0.1
	1622	3.5	1.1
	2221	-0.3	-0.1

DECEMBER

Day	Time h m	Height ft	Height m
1	0450	4.1	1.2
Th	1114	-0.3	-0.1
	1714	3.6	1.1
	2311	-0.4	-0.1
2	0538	4.3	1.3
F	1203	-0.4	-0.1
	1801	3.6	1.1
	2353	-0.5	-0.2
3	0625	4.4	1.3
Sa	1245	-0.5	-0.2
	1847	3.6	1.1
4	0034	-0.5	-0.2
Su	0711	4.4	1.3
	1327	-0.4	-0.1
	1931	3.5	1.1
5	0112	-0.5	-0.2
M	0755	4.3	1.3
	1404	-0.3	-0.1
	2016	3.4	1.0
6	0149	-0.4	-0.1
Tu	0839	4.1	1.2
	1439	-0.2	-0.1
	2059	3.2	1.0
7	0226	-0.2	-0.1
W	0922	3.8	1.2
	1513	0.0	0.0
	2145	3.0	0.9
8	0303	0.0	0.0
Th	1006	3.6	1.1
	1548	0.2	0.1
	2232	2.9	0.9
9	0343	0.2	0.1
F	1054	3.3	1.0
	1625	0.3	0.1
	2321	2.7	0.8
10	0425	0.4	0.1
Sa	1142	3.0	0.9
	1705	0.4	0.1
11	0016	2.7	0.8
Su	0513	0.6	0.2
	1235	2.8	0.9
	1752	0.5	0.2
12	0110	2.7	0.8
M	0608	0.7	0.2
	1329	2.7	0.8
	1843	0.5	0.2
13	0206	2.7	0.8
Tu	0712	0.7	0.2
	1424	2.7	0.8
	1940	0.4	0.1
14	0259	2.9	0.9
W	0819	0.6	0.2
	1517	2.8	0.9
	2035	0.3	0.1
15	0347	3.2	1.0
Th	0924	0.4	0.1
	1607	2.9	0.9
	2128	0.1	0.0
16	0434	3.5	1.1
F	1018	0.2	0.1
	1655	3.0	0.9
	2216	-0.1	0.0
17	0519	3.8	1.2
Sa	1108	-0.1	0.0
	1740	3.2	1.0
	2303	-0.4	-0.1
18	0604	4.0	1.2
Su	1156	-0.3	-0.1
	1826	3.3	1.0
	2351	-0.6	-0.2
19	0649	4.3	1.3
M	1244	-0.5	-0.2
	1913	3.4	1.0
20	0039	-0.7	-0.2
Tu	0736	4.4	1.3
	1330	-0.7	-0.2
	2001	3.5	1.1
21	0128	-0.8	-0.2
W	0824	4.4	1.3
	1417	-0.7	-0.2
	2050	3.5	1.1
22	0218	-0.8	-0.2
Th	0913	4.3	1.3
	1506	-0.7	-0.2
	2143	3.5	1.1
23	0310	-0.7	-0.2
F	1006	4.2	1.3
	1556	-0.6	-0.2
	2236	3.5	1.1
24	0406	-0.5	-0.2
Sa	1102	3.9	1.2
	1649	-0.4	-0.1
	2334	3.5	1.1
25	0505	-0.3	-0.1
Su	1200	3.7	1.1
	1747	-0.3	-0.1
26	0033	3.5	1.1
M	0613	-0.1	0.0
	1259	3.4	1.0
	1847	-0.2	-0.1
27	0135	3.5	1.1
Tu	0733	0.0	0.0
	1401	3.3	1.0
	1954	-0.1	0.0
28	0235	3.6	1.1
W	0854	0.0	0.0
	1501	3.2	1.0
	2101	-0.1	0.0
29	0333	3.8	1.2
Th	1006	0.0	0.0
	1559	3.1	0.9
	2157	-0.2	-0.1
30	0429	3.9	1.2
F	1106	-0.1	0.0
	1652	3.1	0.9
	2250	-0.2	-0.1
31	0519	4.0	1.2
Sa	1156	-0.2	-0.1
	1740	3.2	1.0
	2337	-0.3	-0.1

Time meridian 75° W. 0000 is midnight. 1200 is noon.
Heights are referred to mean low water which is the chart datum of soundings.

NEW LONDON, CONN., 1983

Times and Heights of High and Low Waters

JANUARY

Day	Time h m	Height ft	Height m
1	0424	-0.4	-0.1
Sa	1024	3.3	1.0
	1712	-0.8	-0.2
	2306	2.4	0.7
2	0521	-0.4	-0.1
Su	1120	3.1	0.9
	1806	-0.7	-0.2
3	0002	2.4	0.7
M	0621	-0.3	-0.1
	1219	2.8	0.9
	1901	-0.6	-0.2
4	0101	2.4	0.7
Tu	0725	-0.2	-0.1
	1320	2.5	0.8
	1956	-0.4	-0.1
5	0206	2.4	0.7
W	0830	-0.1	0.0
	1425	2.2	0.7
	2053	-0.3	-0.1
6	0306	2.5	0.8
Th	0935	-0.1	0.0
	1533	2.0	0.6
	2150	-0.2	-0.1
7	0411	2.5	0.8
F	1037	-0.1	0.0
	1639	1.9	0.6
	2244	-0.1	0.0
8	0507	2.5	0.8
Sa	1135	-0.1	0.0
	1740	1.8	0.5
	2335	0.0	0.0
9	0558	2.6	0.8
Su	1230	-0.2	-0.1
	1830	1.7	0.5
10	0023	0.0	0.0
M	0644	2.6	0.8
	1317	-0.2	-0.1
	1916	1.7	0.5
11	0109	0.0	0.0
Tu	0726	2.6	0.8
	1400	-0.3	-0.1
	1958	1.8	0.5
12	0155	0.0	0.0
W	0803	2.6	0.8
	1440	-0.3	-0.1
	2035	1.8	0.5
13	0237	0.0	0.0
Th	0839	2.6	0.8
	1520	-0.3	-0.1
	2112	1.9	0.6
14	0319	0.0	0.0
F	0916	2.6	0.8
	1602	-0.3	-0.1
	2150	1.9	0.6
15	0401	0.0	0.0
Sa	0952	2.6	0.8
	1640	-0.3	-0.1
	2228	2.0	0.6
16	0445	0.1	0.0
Su	1029	2.5	0.8
	1722	-0.3	-0.1
	2308	2.0	0.6
17	0531	0.1	0.0
M	1108	2.4	0.7
	1803	-0.2	-0.1
	2347	2.0	0.6
18	0616	0.2	0.1
Tu	1149	2.3	0.7
	1845	-0.1	0.0
19	0029	2.1	0.6
W	0706	0.2	0.1
	1231	2.1	0.6
	1930	-0.1	0.0
20	0113	2.1	0.6
Th	0800	0.2	0.1
	1319	2.0	0.6
	2015	0.0	0.0
21	0203	2.2	0.7
F	0856	0.2	0.1
	1415	1.9	0.6
	2104	0.1	0.0
22	0255	2.3	0.7
Sa	0955	0.1	0.0
	1517	1.8	0.5
	2153	0.1	0.0
23	0350	2.5	0.8
Su	1052	-0.1	0.0
	1619	1.8	0.5
	2246	0.0	0.0
24	0447	2.7	0.8
M	1146	-0.3	-0.1
	1721	1.8	0.5
	2341	-0.1	0.0
25	0542	2.9	0.9
Tu	1239	-0.5	-0.2
	1820	1.9	0.6
26	0033	-0.2	-0.1
W	0638	3.0	0.9
	1331	-0.7	-0.2
	1915	2.1	0.6
27	0128	-0.4	-0.1
Th	0731	3.2	1.0
	1421	-0.8	-0.2
	2009	2.2	0.7
28	0221	-0.5	-0.2
F	0826	3.2	1.0
	1511	-0.9	-0.3
	2102	2.4	0.7
29	0315	-0.6	-0.2
Sa	0918	3.2	1.0
	1600	-0.9	-0.3
	2153	2.5	0.8
30	0411	-0.6	-0.2
Su	1011	3.1	0.9
	1650	-0.9	-0.3
	2246	2.6	0.8
31	0507	-0.6	-0.2
M	1106	2.9	0.9
	1741	-0.8	-0.2
	2339	2.6	0.8

FEBRUARY

Day	Time h m	Height ft	Height m
1	0604	-0.5	-0.2
Tu	1159	2.6	0.8
	1832	-0.6	-0.2
2	0035	2.6	0.8
W	0703	-0.4	-0.1
	1257	2.3	0.7
	1925	-0.4	-0.1
3	0131	2.5	0.8
Th	0804	-0.3	-0.1
	1355	2.1	0.6
	2019	-0.2	-0.1
4	0231	2.5	0.8
F	0908	-0.2	-0.1
	1459	1.8	0.5
	2115	-0.1	0.0
5	0333	2.4	0.7
Sa	1008	-0.1	0.0
	1605	1.7	0.5
	2211	0.0	0.0
6	0433	2.4	0.7
Su	1107	-0.1	0.0
	1709	1.6	0.5
	2305	0.1	0.0
7	0527	2.4	0.7
M	1201	-0.1	0.0
	1805	1.6	0.5
	2358	0.1	0.0
8	0620	2.4	0.7
Tu	1251	-0.1	0.0
	1852	1.7	0.5
9	0047	0.1	0.0
W	0702	2.4	0.7
	1333	-0.2	-0.1
	1933	1.7	0.5
10	0132	0.0	0.0
Th	0742	2.4	0.7
	1415	-0.2	-0.1
	2011	1.9	0.6
11	0216	0.0	0.0
F	0819	2.5	0.8
	1454	-0.3	-0.1
	2049	2.0	0.6
12	0258	-0.1	0.0
Sa	0855	2.5	0.8
	1532	-0.4	-0.1
	2125	2.1	0.6
13	0339	-0.1	0.0
Su	0930	2.5	0.8
	1611	-0.4	-0.1
	2159	2.1	0.6
14	0420	-0.1	0.0
M	1006	2.5	0.8
	1649	-0.3	-0.1
	2235	2.2	0.7
15	0503	-0.1	0.0
Tu	1044	2.4	0.7
	1728	-0.3	-0.1
	2311	2.3	0.7
16	0547	-0.1	0.0
W	1124	2.3	0.7
	1807	-0.2	-0.1
	2349	2.3	0.7
17	0634	0.0	0.0
Th	1203	2.2	0.7
	1848	-0.1	0.0
18	0032	2.4	0.7
F	0727	0.0	0.0
	1248	2.0	0.6
	1933	0.0	0.0
19	0120	2.4	0.7
Sa	0823	0.0	0.0
	1343	1.9	0.6
	2022	0.1	0.0
20	0215	2.5	0.8
Su	0922	0.0	0.0
	1446	1.8	0.5
	2118	0.1	0.0
21	0316	2.5	0.8
M	1025	-0.1	0.0
	1553	1.7	0.5
	2219	0.1	0.0
22	0420	2.6	0.8
Tu	1122	-0.2	-0.1
	1702	1.8	0.5
	2319	0.0	0.0
23	0524	2.8	0.9
W	1218	-0.4	-0.1
	1804	1.9	0.6
24	0018	-0.2	-0.1
Th	0623	2.9	0.9
	1312	-0.5	-0.2
	1900	2.2	0.7
25	0115	-0.4	-0.1
F	0720	3.0	0.9
	1401	-0.7	-0.2
	1955	2.4	0.7
26	0211	-0.5	-0.2
Sa	0814	3.0	0.9
	1450	-0.7	-0.2
	2046	2.6	0.8
27	0304	-0.7	-0.2
Su	0907	3.0	0.9
	1537	-0.8	-0.2
	2134	2.7	0.8
28	0357	-0.7	-0.2
M	0957	2.9	0.9
	1625	-0.7	-0.2
	2225	2.8	0.9

MARCH

Day	Time h m	Height ft	Height m
1	0451	-0.7	-0.2
Tu	1047	2.7	0.8
	1712	-0.6	-0.2
	2314	2.8	0.9
2	0543	-0.6	-0.2
W	1139	2.5	0.8
	1802	-0.4	-0.1
3	0003	2.8	0.9
Th	0639	-0.4	-0.1
	1229	2.3	0.7
	1851	-0.3	-0.1
4	0056	2.7	0.8
F	0735	-0.2	-0.1
	1325	2.0	0.6
	1944	-0.1	0.0
5	0151	2.5	0.8
Sa	0834	-0.1	0.0
	1425	1.8	0.5
	2040	0.1	0.0
6	0249	2.4	0.7
Su	0931	0.0	0.0
	1526	1.7	0.5
	2138	0.2	0.1
7	0353	2.3	0.7
M	1031	0.1	0.0
	1631	1.6	0.5
	2235	0.3	0.1
8	0452	2.2	0.7
Tu	1126	0.1	0.0
	1732	1.7	0.5
	2331	0.3	0.1
9	0545	2.3	0.7
W	1217	0.0	0.0
	1822	1.8	0.5
10	0022	0.2	0.1
Th	0633	2.3	0.7
	1302	0.0	0.0
	1907	1.9	0.6
11	0108	0.1	0.0
F	0712	2.4	0.7
	1344	-0.1	0.0
	1942	2.1	0.6
12	0152	0.0	0.0
Sa	0752	2.4	0.7
	1423	-0.2	-0.1
	2019	2.2	0.7
13	0235	-0.1	0.0
Su	0829	2.5	0.8
	1500	-0.3	-0.1
	2052	2.3	0.7
14	0315	-0.2	-0.1
M	0904	2.5	0.8
	1537	-0.3	-0.1
	2127	2.5	0.8
15	0356	-0.2	-0.1
Tu	0941	2.5	0.8
	1614	-0.2	-0.1
	2200	2.6	0.8
16	0437	-0.2	-0.1
W	1018	2.5	0.8
	1651	-0.2	-0.1
	2238	2.7	0.8
17	0523	-0.2	-0.1
Th	1059	2.4	0.7
	1730	-0.1	0.0
	2318	2.7	0.8
18	0609	-0.2	-0.1
F	1141	2.3	0.7
	1813	0.0	0.0
	2359	2.7	0.8
19	0701	-0.1	0.0
Sa	1229	2.1	0.6
	1858	0.1	0.0
20	0048	2.7	0.8
Su	0756	-0.1	0.0
	1324	2.0	0.6
	1953	0.2	0.1
21	0146	2.7	0.8
M	0857	0.0	0.0
	1428	1.9	0.6
	2055	0.3	0.1
22	0251	2.7	0.8
Tu	0959	-0.1	0.0
	1539	1.9	0.6
	2202	0.2	0.1
23	0400	2.7	0.8
W	1101	-0.1	0.0
	1647	2.0	0.6
	2308	0.1	0.0
24	0509	2.7	0.8
Th	1157	-0.2	-0.1
	1751	2.2	0.7
25	0009	-0.1	0.0
F	0612	2.8	0.9
	1250	-0.3	-0.1
	1847	2.4	0.7
26	0105	-0.3	-0.1
Sa	0710	2.8	0.9
	1339	-0.4	-0.1
	1939	2.7	0.8
27	0200	-0.5	-0.2
Su	0803	2.9	0.9
	1427	-0.5	-0.2
	2026	2.9	0.9
28	0251	-0.6	-0.2
M	0854	2.8	0.9
	1513	-0.5	-0.2
	2114	3.0	0.9
29	0342	-0.6	-0.2
Tu	0940	2.7	0.8
	1558	-0.4	-0.1
	2200	3.1	0.9
30	0432	-0.6	-0.2
W	1027	2.6	0.8
	1642	-0.3	-0.1
	2245	3.0	0.9
31	0521	-0.5	-0.2
Th	1114	2.4	0.7
	1730	-0.2	-0.1
	2331	2.9	0.9

Time meridian 75° W. 0000 is midnight. 1200 is noon.
Heights are referred to mean low water which is the chart datum of soundings.

Times and Heights of High and Low Waters

APRIL

Day	Time h m	Height ft	Height m
1 F	0613	-0.3	-0.1
	1200	2.2	0.7
	1818	0.0	0.0
2 Sa	0019	2.8	0.9
	0704	-0.1	0.0
	1253	2.0	0.6
	1911	0.2	0.1
3 Su	0110	2.6	0.8
	0801	0.1	0.0
	1349	1.9	0.6
	2007	0.4	0.1
4 M	0205	2.4	0.7
	0857	0.2	0.1
	1449	1.8	0.5
	2105	0.5	0.2
5 Tu	0305	2.3	0.7
	0952	0.2	0.1
	1554	1.8	0.5
	2206	0.5	0.2
6 W	0407	2.2	0.7
	1047	0.2	0.1
	1657	1.9	0.6
	2303	0.5	0.2
7 Th	0505	2.2	0.7
	1138	0.2	0.1
	1745	2.0	0.6
	2353	0.4	0.1
8 F	0554	2.3	0.7
	1225	0.1	0.0
	1828	2.2	0.7
9 Sa	0042	0.3	0.1
	0639	2.3	0.7
	1307	0.0	0.0
	1907	2.3	0.7
10 Su	0126	0.1	0.0
	0720	2.4	0.7
	1345	0.0	0.0
	1942	2.5	0.8
11 M	0207	0.0	0.0
	0757	2.5	0.8
	1424	-0.1	0.0
	2016	2.7	0.8
12 Tu	0249	-0.2	-0.1
	0836	2.6	0.8
	1502	-0.1	0.0
	2053	2.9	0.9
13 W	0330	-0.3	-0.1
	0916	2.6	0.8
	1539	-0.1	0.0
	2127	3.0	0.9
14 Th	0413	-0.3	-0.1
	0954	2.5	0.8
	1617	0.0	0.0
	2206	3.1	0.9
15 F	0458	-0.3	-0.1
	1039	2.5	0.8
	1657	0.0	0.0
	2248	3.1	0.9

Day	Time h m	Height ft	Height m
16 Sa	0546	-0.3	-0.1
	1123	2.4	0.7
	1741	0.1	0.0
	2334	3.1	0.9
17 Su	0639	-0.2	-0.1
	1213	2.2	0.7
	1834	0.2	0.1
18 M	0026	3.0	0.9
	0736	-0.1	0.0
	1314	2.1	0.6
	1935	0.3	0.1
19 Tu	0127	2.9	0.9
	0837	-0.1	0.0
	1420	2.1	0.6
	2044	0.4	0.1
20 W	0235	2.8	0.9
	0938	0.0	0.0
	1529	2.1	0.6
	2152	0.3	0.1
21 Th	0347	2.7	0.8
	1037	0.0	0.0
	1637	2.3	0.7
	2258	0.2	0.1
22 F	0457	2.7	0.8
	1135	-0.1	0.0
	1737	2.5	0.8
	2358	0.0	0.0
23 Sa	0602	2.7	0.8
	1227	-0.1	0.0
	1832	2.7	0.8
24 Su	0055	-0.2	-0.1
	0658	2.7	0.8
	1315	-0.2	-0.1
	1921	2.9	0.9
25 M	0147	-0.3	-0.1
	0750	2.7	0.8
	1402	-0.2	-0.1
	2007	3.1	0.9
26 Tu	0237	-0.4	-0.1
	0836	2.6	0.8
	1446	-0.2	-0.1
	2051	3.2	1.0
27 W	0325	-0.5	-0.2
	0921	2.5	0.8
	1530	-0.1	0.0
	2134	3.2	1.0
28 Th	0412	-0.4	-0.1
	1004	2.4	0.7
	1615	0.0	0.0
	2216	3.1	0.9
29 F	0458	-0.3	-0.1
	1049	2.3	0.7
	1701	0.1	0.0
	2258	3.0	0.9
30 Sa	0547	-0.1	0.0
	1134	2.2	0.7
	1747	0.3	0.1
	2344	2.9	0.9

MAY

Day	Time h m	Height ft	Height m
1 Su	0636	0.0	0.0
	1221	2.1	0.6
	1839	0.4	0.1
2 M	0032	2.7	0.8
	0725	0.2	0.1
	1317	2.0	0.6
	1935	0.6	0.2
3 Tu	0124	2.5	0.8
	0821	0.3	0.1
	1412	2.0	0.6
	2033	0.7	0.2
4 W	0221	2.3	0.7
	0914	0.3	0.1
	1515	2.0	0.6
	2132	0.7	0.2
5 Th	0320	2.2	0.7
	1007	0.3	0.1
	1612	2.1	0.6
	2229	0.6	0.2
6 F	0419	2.2	0.7
	1057	0.3	0.1
	1703	2.2	0.7
	2322	0.5	0.2
7 Sa	0510	2.2	0.7
	1142	0.2	0.1
	1745	2.4	0.7
8 Su	0010	0.4	0.1
	0600	2.3	0.7
	1225	0.2	0.1
	1825	2.6	0.8
9 M	0056	0.2	0.1
	0642	2.4	0.7
	1305	0.1	0.0
	1905	2.8	0.9
10 Tu	0139	0.0	0.0
	0724	2.5	0.8
	1346	0.1	0.0
	1939	3.0	0.9
11 W	0223	-0.2	-0.1
	0805	2.5	0.8
	1424	0.0	0.0
	2019	3.2	1.0
12 Th	0305	-0.3	-0.1
	0846	2.5	0.8
	1505	0.0	0.0
	2058	3.3	1.0
13 F	0348	-0.4	-0.1
	0930	2.5	0.8
	1546	0.0	0.0
	2141	3.4	1.0
14 Sa	0437	-0.4	-0.1
	1019	2.5	0.8
	1632	0.1	0.0
	2226	3.4	1.0
15 Su	0526	-0.4	-0.1
	1107	2.4	0.7
	1721	0.2	0.1
	2318	3.3	1.0

Day	Time h m	Height ft	Height m
16 M	0621	-0.3	-0.1
	1203	2.4	0.7
	1819	0.3	0.1
17 Tu	0011	3.2	1.0
	0717	-0.2	-0.1
	1304	2.3	0.7
	1925	0.3	0.1
18 W	0117	3.0	0.9
	0816	-0.1	0.0
	1410	2.3	0.7
	2031	0.3	0.1
19 Th	0223	2.8	0.9
	0916	0.0	0.0
	1516	2.4	0.7
	2140	0.3	0.1
20 F	0335	2.6	0.8
	1013	0.0	0.0
	1622	2.6	0.8
	2245	0.2	0.1
21 Sa	0444	2.5	0.8
	1110	0.0	0.0
	1721	2.8	0.9
	2345	0.0	0.0
22 Su	0547	2.5	0.8
	1201	0.0	0.0
	1814	2.9	0.9
23 M	0042	-0.1	0.0
	0643	2.5	0.8
	1251	0.0	0.0
	1902	3.1	0.9
24 Tu	0133	-0.2	-0.1
	0733	2.4	0.7
	1336	0.0	0.0
	1947	3.2	1.0
25 W	0222	-0.3	-0.1
	0819	2.4	0.7
	1419	0.0	0.0
	2029	3.2	1.0
26 Th	0306	-0.3	-0.1
	0901	2.3	0.7
	1504	0.1	0.0
	2110	3.2	1.0
27 F	0351	-0.2	-0.1
	0942	2.3	0.7
	1547	0.2	0.1
	2151	3.1	0.9
28 Sa	0437	-0.1	0.0
	1024	2.2	0.7
	1633	0.3	0.1
	2231	3.0	0.9
29 Su	0520	0.0	0.0
	1107	2.2	0.7
	1719	0.4	0.1
	2312	2.9	0.9
30 M	0605	0.1	0.0
	1155	2.2	0.7
	1809	0.5	0.2
	2355	2.7	0.8
31 Tu	0655	0.2	0.1
	1245	2.1	0.6
	1904	0.6	0.2

JUNE

Day	Time h m	Height ft	Height m
1 W	0044	2.5	0.8
	0743	0.2	0.1
	1337	2.1	0.6
	1959	0.7	0.2
2 Th	0137	2.4	0.7
	0834	0.3	0.1
	1433	2.2	0.7
	2057	0.7	0.2
3 F	0231	2.3	0.7
	0925	0.3	0.1
	1525	2.2	0.7
	2153	0.7	0.2
4 Sa	0330	2.2	0.7
	1013	0.3	0.1
	1614	2.4	0.7
	2247	0.6	0.2
5 Su	0422	2.2	0.7
	1059	0.3	0.1
	1659	2.5	0.8
	2337	0.4	0.1
6 M	0514	2.2	0.7
	1144	0.3	0.1
	1742	2.7	0.8
7 Tu	0023	0.2	0.1
	0603	2.3	0.7
	1226	0.2	0.1
	1822	3.0	0.9
8 W	0109	0.0	0.0
	0649	2.4	0.7
	1307	0.2	0.1
	1905	3.2	1.0
9 Th	0155	-0.2	-0.1
	0736	2.4	0.7
	1350	0.1	0.0
	1947	3.4	1.0
10 F	0240	-0.3	-0.1
	0821	2.5	0.8
	1435	0.0	0.0
	2032	3.5	1.1
11 Sa	0327	-0.4	-0.1
	0909	2.5	0.8
	1521	0.0	0.0
	2120	3.6	1.1
12 Su	0417	-0.5	-0.2
	1000	2.6	0.8
	1613	0.0	0.0
	2210	3.6	1.1
13 M	0507	-0.5	-0.2
	1054	2.6	0.8
	1708	0.1	0.0
	2304	3.4	1.0
14 Tu	0600	-0.4	-0.1
	1151	2.6	0.8
	1808	0.1	0.0
15 W	0003	3.2	1.0
	0656	-0.3	-0.1
	1250	2.6	0.8
	1911	0.2	0.1

Day	Time h m	Height ft	Height m
16 Th	0104	3.0	0.9
	0753	-0.2	-0.1
	1354	2.6	0.8
	2018	0.2	0.1
17 F	0211	2.7	0.8
	0850	-0.1	0.0
	1458	2.7	0.8
	2124	0.2	0.1
18 Sa	0320	2.5	0.8
	0947	0.0	0.0
	1600	2.8	0.9
	2228	0.1	0.0
19 Su	0426	2.4	0.7
	1042	0.1	0.0
	1659	2.9	0.9
	2329	0.1	0.0
20 M	0531	2.3	0.7
	1135	0.1	0.0
	1753	3.0	0.9
21 Tu	0025	0.0	0.0
	0627	2.2	0.7
	1226	0.2	0.1
	1843	3.1	0.9
22 W	0116	-0.1	0.0
	0716	2.2	0.7
	1312	0.2	0.1
	1927	3.1	0.9
23 Th	0203	-0.1	0.0
	0759	2.2	0.7
	1357	0.2	0.1
	2008	3.1	0.9
24 F	0247	-0.1	0.0
	0841	2.2	0.7
	1440	0.2	0.1
	2048	3.1	0.9
25 Sa	0329	-0.1	0.0
	0921	2.2	0.7
	1524	0.3	0.1
	2127	3.0	0.9
26 Su	0411	0.0	0.0
	1003	2.2	0.7
	1608	0.3	0.1
	2205	2.9	0.9
27 M	0454	0.0	0.0
	1042	2.2	0.7
	1654	0.4	0.1
	2245	2.8	0.9
28 Tu	0536	0.1	0.0
	1126	2.2	0.7
	1744	0.5	0.2
	2326	2.7	0.8
29 W	0621	0.1	0.0
	1211	2.2	0.7
	1832	0.6	0.2
30 Th	0011	2.6	0.8
	0707	0.2	0.1
	1258	2.3	0.7
	1925	0.6	0.2

Time meridian 75° W. 0000 is midnight. 1200 is noon.
Heights are referred to mean low water which is the chart datum of soundings.

Times and Heights of High and Low Waters

JULY

Day	Time h m	Height ft	Height m	Day	Time h m	Height ft	Height m
1	0056	2.4	0.7	16	0152	2.7	0.8
F	0754	0.3	0.1	Sa	0822	-0.1	0.0
	1346	2.3	0.7		1432	2.9	0.9
	2020	0.7	0.2		2103	0.1	0.0
2	0147	2.3	0.7	17	0259	2.4	0.7
Sa	0841	0.3	0.1	Su	0919	0.1	0.0
	1434	2.4	0.7		1534	2.9	0.9
	2114	0.6	0.2		2206	0.1	0.0
3	0239	2.2	0.7	18	0403	2.2	0.7
Su	0928	0.4	0.1	M	1015	0.2	0.1
	1523	2.5	0.8		1634	2.9	0.9
	2207	0.5	0.2		2306	0.1	0.0
4	0333	2.2	0.7	19	0506	2.1	0.6
M	1015	0.4	0.1	Tu	1108	0.2	0.1
	1613	2.6	0.8		1729	2.9	0.9
	2301	0.4	0.1				
5	0429	2.1	0.6	20	0005	0.1	0.0
Tu	1101	0.3	0.1	W	0606	2.1	0.6
	1700	2.8	0.9		1201	0.3	0.1
	2350	0.2	0.1		1822	3.0	0.9
6	0524	2.2	0.7	21	0054	0.1	0.0
W	1147	0.3	0.1	Th	0656	2.1	0.6
	1747	3.1	0.9		1248	0.3	0.1
					1906	3.0	0.9
7	0040	0.0	0.0	22	0143	0.1	0.0
Th	0617	2.2	0.7	F	0739	2.1	0.6
	1233	0.2	0.1		1334	0.3	0.1
	1833	3.3	1.0		1948	2.9	0.9
8	0129	-0.2	-0.1	23	0225	0.0	0.0
F	0708	2.3	0.7	Sa	0822	2.1	0.6
	1321	0.1	0.0		1420	0.3	0.1
	1923	3.5	1.1		2029	2.9	0.9
9	0216	-0.4	-0.1	24	0306	0.0	0.0
Sa	0759	2.5	0.8	Su	0859	2.2	0.7
	1411	0.0	0.0		1503	0.3	0.1
	2013	3.6	1.1		2105	2.9	0.9
10	0306	-0.5	-0.2	25	0345	0.0	0.0
Su	0851	2.6	0.8	M	0937	2.3	0.7
	1502	-0.1	0.0		1547	0.3	0.1
	2104	3.6	1.1		2143	2.8	0.9
11	0356	-0.5	-0.2	26	0425	0.0	0.0
M	0943	2.7	0.8	Tu	1016	2.3	0.7
	1557	-0.1	0.0		1631	0.4	0.1
	2156	3.6	1.1		2219	2.8	0.9
12	0446	-0.5	-0.2	27	0506	0.1	0.0
Tu	1036	2.7	0.8	W	1054	2.4	0.7
	1654	-0.1	0.0		1715	0.4	0.1
	2252	3.4	1.0		2258	2.7	0.8
13	0539	-0.5	-0.2	28	0547	0.1	0.0
W	1132	2.8	0.9	Th	1136	2.4	0.7
	1754	-0.1	0.0		1803	0.5	0.2
	2349	3.2	1.0		2339	2.6	0.8
14	0632	-0.3	-0.1	29	0629	0.2	0.1
Th	1231	2.8	0.9	F	1216	2.4	0.7
	1856	0.0	0.0		1850	0.5	0.2
15	0050	2.9	0.9	30	0021	2.5	0.8
F	0726	-0.2	-0.1	Sa	0713	0.3	0.1
	1330	2.8	0.9		1258	2.5	0.8
	1959	0.0	0.0		1943	0.5	0.2
				31	0106	2.3	0.7
				Su	0756	0.4	0.1
					1345	2.5	0.8
					2036	0.5	0.2

AUGUST

Day	Time h m	Height ft	Height m	Day	Time h m	Height ft	Height m
1	0155	2.2	0.7	16	0336	2.1	0.6
M	0844	0.4	0.1	Tu	0945	0.3	0.1
	1431	2.6	0.8		1604	2.8	0.9
	2131	0.5	0.2		2241	0.2	0.1
2	0251	2.1	0.6	17	0445	2.0	0.6
Tu	0931	0.5	0.2	W	1042	0.4	0.1
	1524	2.7	0.8		1704	2.8	0.9
	2226	0.4	0.1		2337	0.2	0.1
3	0351	2.1	0.6	18	0545	2.0	0.6
W	1022	0.4	0.1	Th	1138	0.4	0.1
	1621	2.9	0.9		1758	2.8	0.9
	2322	0.2	0.1				
4	0451	2.1	0.6	19	0030	0.2	0.1
Th	1114	0.4	0.1	F	0636	2.1	0.6
	1713	3.1	0.9		1227	0.4	0.1
					1846	2.8	0.9
5	0015	0.0	0.0	20	0116	0.2	0.1
F	0550	2.2	0.7	Sa	0718	2.1	0.6
	1209	0.2	0.1		1316	0.4	0.1
	1809	3.2	1.0		1928	2.8	0.9
6	0104	-0.2	-0.1	21	0158	0.2	0.1
Sa	0645	2.4	0.7	Su	0758	2.2	0.7
	1302	0.1	0.0		1400	0.3	0.1
	1904	3.4	1.0		2006	2.8	0.9
7	0155	-0.3	-0.1	22	0237	0.1	0.0
Su	0740	2.5	0.8	M	0833	2.3	0.7
	1355	-0.1	0.0		1443	0.3	0.1
	1957	3.5	1.1		2042	2.8	0.9
8	0244	-0.4	-0.1	23	0316	0.1	0.0
M	0833	2.7	0.8	Tu	0909	2.4	0.7
	1448	-0.2	-0.1		1525	0.3	0.1
	2050	3.5	1.1		2117	2.8	0.9
9	0333	-0.5	-0.2	24	0355	0.1	0.0
Tu	0925	2.9	0.9	W	0944	2.5	0.8
	1544	-0.3	-0.1		1606	0.3	0.1
	2144	3.5	1.1		2153	2.8	0.9
10	0422	-0.5	-0.2	25	0433	0.1	0.0
W	1017	3.0	0.9	Th	1019	2.6	0.8
	1639	-0.3	-0.1		1649	0.3	0.1
	2237	3.3	1.0		2231	2.7	0.8
11	0512	-0.4	-0.1	26	0510	0.1	0.0
Th	1110	3.1	0.9	F	1056	2.7	0.8
	1736	-0.3	-0.1		1733	0.3	0.1
	2332	3.1	0.9		2307	2.6	0.8
12	0603	-0.3	-0.1	27	0549	0.2	0.1
F	1203	3.1	0.9	Sa	1133	2.7	0.8
	1835	-0.2	-0.1		1819	0.3	0.1
					2347	2.5	0.8
13	0029	2.8	0.9	28	0631	0.3	0.1
Sa	0657	-0.1	0.0	Su	1214	2.7	0.8
	1301	3.0	0.9		1906	0.4	0.1
	1935	0.0	0.0				
14	0130	2.6	0.8	29	0031	2.4	0.7
Su	0752	0.0	0.0	M	0714	0.5	0.2
	1401	3.0	0.9		1257	2.7	0.8
	2038	0.1	0.0		2001	0.4	0.1
15	0231	2.3	0.7	30	0121	2.2	0.7
M	0848	0.2	0.1	Tu	0802	0.5	0.2
	1503	2.9	0.9		1346	2.8	0.9
	2141	0.2	0.1		2058	0.4	0.1
				31	0219	2.1	0.6
				W	0854	0.6	0.2
					1444	2.8	0.9
					2157	0.3	0.1

SEPTEMBER

Day	Time h m	Height ft	Height m	Day	Time h m	Height ft	Height m
1	0324	2.1	0.6	16	0516	2.1	0.6
Th	0952	0.5	0.2	F	1113	0.6	0.2
	1547	2.9	0.9		1729	2.6	0.8
	2254	0.2	0.1		2358	0.3	0.1
2	0429	2.1	0.6	17	0612	2.2	0.7
F	1052	0.4	0.1	Sa	1206	0.5	0.2
	1650	3.0	0.9		1820	2.6	0.8
	2350	0.1	0.0				
3	0532	2.3	0.7	18	0044	0.3	0.1
Sa	1152	0.3	0.1	Su	0653	2.3	0.7
	1753	3.2	1.0		1253	0.4	0.1
					1902	2.6	0.8
4	0043	-0.1	0.0	19	0126	0.2	0.1
Su	0630	2.5	0.8	M	0729	2.4	0.7
	1248	0.1	0.0		1339	0.3	0.1
	1849	3.3	1.0		1939	2.7	0.8
5	0133	-0.2	-0.1	20	0205	0.2	0.1
M	0723	2.7	0.8	Tu	0803	2.5	0.8
	1344	-0.1	0.0		1421	0.2	0.1
	1944	3.4	1.0		2016	2.7	0.8
6	0221	-0.3	-0.1	21	0242	0.1	0.0
Tu	0814	3.0	0.9	W	0839	2.7	0.8
	1437	-0.3	-0.1		1501	0.2	0.1
	2037	3.4	1.0		2051	2.8	0.9
7	0309	-0.4	-0.1	22	0319	0.1	0.0
W	0905	3.1	0.9	Th	0911	2.8	0.9
	1530	-0.4	-0.1		1540	0.1	0.0
	2129	3.3	1.0		2127	2.7	0.8
8	0356	-0.4	-0.1	23	0356	0.1	0.0
Th	0954	3.3	1.0	F	0945	2.9	0.9
	1623	-0.4	-0.1		1622	0.1	0.0
	2221	3.1	0.9		2203	2.7	0.8
9	0444	-0.3	-0.1	24	0433	0.2	0.1
F	1044	3.3	1.0	Sa	1018	2.9	0.9
	1717	-0.4	-0.1		1704	0.1	0.0
	2312	2.9	0.9		2241	2.6	0.8
10	0534	-0.2	-0.1	25	0510	0.3	0.1
Sa	1136	3.3	1.0	Su	1054	3.0	0.9
	1812	-0.2	-0.1		1749	0.1	0.0
					2321	2.5	0.8
11	0005	2.7	0.8	26	0549	0.4	0.1
Su	0624	0.0	0.0	M	1136	3.0	0.9
	1229	3.1	0.9		1837	0.2	0.1
	1911	0.0	0.0				
12	0101	2.4	0.7	27	0007	2.4	0.7
M	0720	0.2	0.1	Tu	0634	0.5	0.2
	1326	3.0	0.9		1221	3.0	0.9
	2010	0.1	0.0		1931	0.3	0.1
13	0202	2.2	0.7	28	0058	2.2	0.7
Tu	0815	0.4	0.1	W	0726	0.6	0.2
	1425	2.8	0.9		1314	2.9	0.9
	2109	0.3	0.1		2031	0.3	0.1
14	0308	2.1	0.6	29	0159	2.1	0.6
W	0916	0.5	0.2	Th	0826	0.6	0.2
	1530	2.7	0.8		1417	2.9	0.9
	2210	0.3	0.1		2132	0.3	0.1
15	0415	2.0	0.6	30	0308	2.1	0.6
Th	1016	0.6	0.2	F	0934	0.6	0.2
	1634	2.6	0.8		1524	2.9	0.9
	2307	0.4	0.1		2231	0.2	0.1

Time meridian 75° W. 0000 is midnight. 1200 is noon.
Heights are referred to mean low water which is the chart datum of soundings.

NEW LONDON, CONN., 1983

Times and Heights of High and Low Waters

OCTOBER

Day	Time (h m)	Height (ft)	Height (m)
1 Sa	0416	2.2	0.7
	1038	0.5	0.2
	1636	2.9	0.9
	2327	0.1	0.0
2 Su	0519	2.4	0.7
	1140	0.3	0.1
	1739	3.0	0.9
3 M	0020	0.0	0.0
	0615	2.7	0.8
	1238	0.0	0.0
	1838	3.1	0.9
4 Tu	0110	-0.2	-0.1
	0707	2.9	0.9
	1332	-0.2	-0.1
	1932	3.1	0.9
5 W	0158	-0.2	-0.1
	0756	3.2	1.0
	1424	-0.4	-0.1
	2024	3.1	0.9
6 Th	0244	-0.3	-0.1
	0844	3.4	1.0
	1515	-0.5	-0.2
	2113	3.0	0.9
7 F	0330	-0.2	-0.1
	0930	3.4	1.0
	1606	-0.5	-0.2
	2201	2.9	0.9
8 Sa	0417	-0.2	-0.1
	1019	3.4	1.0
	1656	-0.4	-0.1
	2249	2.7	0.8
9 Su	0504	0.0	0.0
	1106	3.3	1.0
	1749	-0.2	-0.1
	2340	2.5	0.8
10 M	0555	0.2	0.1
	1155	3.1	0.9
	1842	0.0	0.0
11 Tu	0034	2.3	0.7
	0648	0.4	0.1
	1250	2.9	0.9
	1938	0.2	0.1
12 W	0130	2.2	0.7
	0746	0.5	0.2
	1346	2.7	0.8
	2037	0.3	0.1
13 Th	0236	2.1	0.6
	0846	0.6	0.2
	1450	2.5	0.8
	2135	0.4	0.1
14 F	0341	2.1	0.6
	0948	0.7	0.2
	1554	2.4	0.7
	2231	0.4	0.1
15 Sa	0444	2.1	0.6
	1046	0.6	0.2
	1652	2.4	0.7
	2321	0.4	0.1
16 Su	0535	2.2	0.7
	1142	0.5	0.2
	1745	2.4	0.7
17 M	0007	0.3	0.1
	0617	2.4	0.7
	1228	0.4	0.1
	1827	2.5	0.8
18 Tu	0049	0.2	0.1
	0655	2.5	0.8
	1312	0.3	0.1
	1908	2.5	0.8
19 W	0128	0.2	0.1
	0728	2.7	0.8
	1354	0.2	0.1
	1947	2.6	0.8
20 Th	0206	0.1	0.0
	0803	2.9	0.9
	1433	0.0	0.0
	2022	2.6	0.8
21 F	0243	0.1	0.0
	0836	3.0	0.9
	1515	-0.1	0.0
	2058	2.6	0.8
22 Sa	0320	0.1	0.0
	0910	3.1	0.9
	1555	-0.1	0.0
	2136	2.6	0.8
23 Su	0357	0.2	0.1
	0947	3.2	1.0
	1638	-0.1	0.0
	2215	2.5	0.8
24 M	0435	0.2	0.1
	1024	3.2	1.0
	1724	-0.1	0.0
	2259	2.4	0.7
25 Tu	0516	0.3	0.1
	1107	3.2	1.0
	1813	0.0	0.0
	2347	2.3	0.7
26 W	0605	0.4	0.1
	1156	3.1	0.9
	1906	0.0	0.0
27 Th	0042	2.2	0.7
	0704	0.5	0.2
	1253	3.0	0.9
	2006	0.1	0.0
28 F	0146	2.2	0.7
	0811	0.6	0.2
	1358	2.8	0.9
	2107	0.1	0.0
29 Sa	0255	2.2	0.7
	0920	0.5	0.2
	1511	2.7	0.8
	2207	0.1	0.0
30 Su	0402	2.4	0.7
	1026	0.4	0.1
	1621	2.7	0.8
	2303	0.0	0.0
31 M	0505	2.6	0.8
	1129	0.1	0.0
	1727	2.7	0.8
	2356	0.0	0.0

NOVEMBER

Day	Time (h m)	Height (ft)	Height (m)
1 Tu	0559	2.8	0.9
	1227	-0.1	0.0
	1825	2.7	0.8
2 W	0046	-0.1	0.0
	0651	3.1	0.9
	1320	-0.3	-0.1
	1920	2.7	0.8
3 Th	0134	-0.2	-0.1
	0738	3.3	1.0
	1411	-0.4	-0.1
	2009	2.7	0.8
4 F	0219	-0.2	-0.1
	0824	3.4	1.0
	1501	-0.5	-0.2
	2055	2.6	0.8
5 Sa	0304	-0.1	0.0
	0909	3.4	1.0
	1548	-0.5	-0.2
	2142	2.6	0.8
6 Su	0349	-0.1	0.0
	0952	3.3	1.0
	1636	-0.4	-0.1
	2227	2.4	0.7
7 M	0437	0.1	0.0
	1038	3.2	1.0
	1725	-0.2	-0.1
	2315	2.3	0.7
8 Tu	0525	0.2	0.1
	1125	3.0	0.9
	1815	-0.1	0.0
9 W	0005	2.2	0.7
	0619	0.4	0.1
	1215	2.8	0.9
	1906	0.1	0.0
10 Th	0101	2.1	0.6
	0714	0.5	0.2
	1306	2.6	0.8
	2001	0.2	0.1
11 F	0158	2.0	0.6
	0815	0.6	0.2
	1406	2.4	0.7
	2057	0.3	0.1
12 Sa	0302	2.0	0.6
	0915	0.7	0.2
	1507	2.2	0.7
	2149	0.3	0.1
13 Su	0401	2.1	0.6
	1015	0.6	0.2
	1607	2.2	0.7
	2239	0.3	0.1
14 M	0453	2.2	0.7
	1108	0.5	0.2
	1658	2.2	0.7
	2326	0.2	0.1
15 Tu	0535	2.4	0.7
	1158	0.4	0.1
	1748	2.2	0.7
16 W	0009	0.2	0.1
	0614	2.6	0.8
	1243	0.2	0.1
	1830	2.3	0.7
17 Th	0051	0.1	0.0
	0651	2.7	0.8
	1325	0.0	0.0
	1911	2.3	0.7
18 F	0130	0.1	0.0
	0726	2.9	0.9
	1406	-0.1	0.0
	1950	2.4	0.7
19 Sa	0208	0.1	0.0
	0800	3.1	0.9
	1448	-0.3	-0.1
	2029	2.4	0.7
20 Su	0245	0.0	0.0
	0838	3.2	1.0
	1531	-0.4	-0.1
	2110	2.4	0.7
21 M	0324	0.0	0.0
	0918	3.3	1.0
	1615	-0.4	-0.1
	2154	2.4	0.7
22 Tu	0408	0.1	0.0
	1001	3.3	1.0
	1702	-0.4	-0.1
	2241	2.3	0.7
23 W	0454	0.1	0.0
	1046	3.2	1.0
	1751	-0.3	-0.1
	2333	2.3	0.7
24 Th	0547	0.2	0.1
	1139	3.1	0.9
	1847	-0.3	-0.1
25 F	0029	2.2	0.7
	0650	0.3	0.1
	1237	2.9	0.9
	1943	-0.2	-0.1
26 Sa	0133	2.3	0.7
	0757	0.3	0.1
	1345	2.7	0.8
	2042	-0.1	0.0
27 Su	0239	2.3	0.7
	0907	0.3	0.1
	1455	2.5	0.8
	2142	-0.1	0.0
28 M	0345	2.5	0.8
	1014	0.1	0.0
	1606	2.4	0.7
	2237	-0.1	0.0
29 Tu	0447	2.7	0.8
	1116	0.0	0.0
	1713	2.4	0.7
	2332	-0.1	0.0
30 W	0542	2.8	0.9
	1214	-0.2	-0.1
	1812	2.3	0.7

DECEMBER

Day	Time (h m)	Height (ft)	Height (m)
1 Th	0022	-0.1	0.0
	0635	3.0	0.9
	1307	-0.4	-0.1
	1905	2.3	0.7
2 F	0110	-0.1	0.0
	0721	3.1	0.9
	1357	-0.4	-0.1
	1955	2.3	0.7
3 Sa	0156	-0.1	0.0
	0806	3.2	1.0
	1445	-0.5	-0.2
	2039	2.2	0.7
4 Su	0241	-0.1	0.0
	0849	3.2	1.0
	1530	-0.4	-0.1
	2123	2.2	0.7
5 M	0327	-0.1	0.0
	0932	3.1	0.9
	1616	-0.4	-0.1
	2205	2.1	0.6
6 Tu	0413	0.0	0.0
	1014	3.0	0.9
	1702	-0.3	-0.1
	2251	2.1	0.6
7 W	0459	0.2	0.1
	1056	2.8	0.9
	1747	-0.2	-0.1
	2336	2.0	0.6
8 Th	0551	0.3	0.1
	1141	2.6	0.8
	1834	-0.1	0.0
9 F	0026	2.0	0.6
	0645	0.4	0.1
	1230	2.4	0.7
	1923	0.0	0.0
10 Sa	0119	2.0	0.6
	0741	0.5	0.2
	1319	2.2	0.7
	2014	0.1	0.0
11 Su	0215	2.0	0.6
	0838	0.5	0.2
	1415	2.1	0.6
	2105	0.2	0.1
12 M	0309	2.1	0.6
	0937	0.5	0.2
	1512	2.0	0.6
	2156	0.2	0.1
13 Tu	0401	2.2	0.7
	1030	0.4	0.1
	1609	1.9	0.6
	2242	0.2	0.1
14 W	0447	2.3	0.7
	1121	0.3	0.1
	1701	1.9	0.6
	2327	0.1	0.0
15 Th	0530	2.5	0.8
	1209	0.1	0.0
	1748	2.0	0.6
16 F	0010	0.1	0.0
	0609	2.7	0.8
	1254	-0.1	0.0
	1834	2.0	0.6
17 Sa	0052	0.0	0.0
	0649	2.9	0.9
	1339	-0.3	-0.1
	1920	2.1	0.6
18 Su	0133	0.0	0.0
	0731	3.0	0.9
	1422	-0.5	-0.2
	2003	2.2	0.7
19 M	0215	-0.1	0.0
	0813	3.2	1.0
	1507	-0.6	-0.2
	2048	2.2	0.7
20 Tu	0258	-0.2	-0.1
	0857	3.3	1.0
	1553	-0.7	-0.2
	2135	2.3	0.7
21 W	0347	-0.2	-0.1
	0944	3.3	1.0
	1640	-0.7	-0.2
	2225	2.3	0.7
22 Th	0439	-0.2	-0.1
	1035	3.2	1.0
	1731	-0.6	-0.2
	2317	2.3	0.7
23 F	0536	-0.1	0.0
	1129	3.0	0.9
	1824	-0.5	-0.2
24 Sa	0013	2.3	0.7
	0637	-0.1	0.0
	1228	2.8	0.9
	1919	-0.4	-0.1
25 Su	0115	2.4	0.7
	0742	0.0	0.0
	1332	2.5	0.8
	2017	-0.3	-0.1
26 M	0218	2.4	0.7
	0849	-0.1	0.0
	1440	2.3	0.7
	2114	-0.2	-0.1
27 Tu	0324	2.5	0.8
	0956	-0.1	0.0
	1549	2.1	0.6
	2211	-0.2	-0.1
28 W	0425	2.6	0.8
	1058	-0.2	-0.1
	1655	2.0	0.6
	2305	-0.1	0.0
29 Th	0524	2.7	0.8
	1157	-0.3	-0.1
	1756	2.0	0.6
	2358	-0.1	0.0
30 F	0617	2.8	0.9
	1251	-0.4	-0.1
	1852	1.9	0.6
31 Sa	0048	-0.1	0.0
	0705	2.9	0.9
	1342	-0.4	-0.1
	1939	1.9	0.6

Time meridian 75° W. 0000 is midnight. 1200 is noon.
Heights are referred to mean low water which is the chart datum of soundings.

Times and Heights of High and Low Waters

JANUARY

Day	Time (h m)	Height (ft)	Height (m)
1 Sa	0004	6.8	2.1
	0612	-0.8	-0.2
	1222	7.7	2.3
	1849	-1.4	-0.4
2 Su	0059	6.8	2.1
	0707	-0.7	-0.2
	1318	7.5	2.3
	1944	-1.2	-0.4
3 M	0155	6.8	2.1
	0806	-0.6	-0.2
	1415	7.1	2.2
	2040	-0.9	-0.3
4 Tu	0251	6.7	2.0
	0906	-0.4	-0.1
	1514	6.7	2.0
	2135	-0.6	-0.2
5 W	0350	6.6	2.0
	1009	-0.3	-0.1
	1615	6.3	1.9
	2234	-0.4	-0.1
6 Th	0449	6.5	2.0
	1111	-0.2	-0.1
	1718	6.0	1.8
	2333	-0.1	0.0
7 F	0549	6.5	2.0
	1214	-0.2	-0.1
	1820	5.8	1.8
8 Sa	0032	0.0	0.0
	0648	6.6	2.0
	1315	-0.2	-0.1
	1919	5.7	1.7
9 Su	0126	0.0	0.0
	0740	6.6	2.0
	1408	-0.3	-0.1
	2014	5.7	1.7
10 M	0217	0.1	0.0
	0831	6.7	2.0
	1459	-0.4	-0.1
	2102	5.8	1.8
11 Tu	0305	0.1	0.0
	0917	6.8	2.1
	1544	-0.4	-0.1
	2145	5.9	1.8
12 W	0348	0.0	0.0
	0958	6.9	2.1
	1624	-0.5	-0.2
	2226	6.0	1.8
13 Th	0429	0.1	0.0
	1038	6.9	2.1
	1701	-0.4	-0.1
	2303	6.1	1.9
14 F	0508	0.1	0.0
	1114	6.9	2.1
	1737	-0.4	-0.1
	2340	6.2	1.9
15 Sa	0544	0.1	0.0
	1150	6.9	2.1
	1813	-0.3	-0.1
16 Su	0016	6.2	1.9
	0621	0.1	0.0
	1227	6.8	2.1
	1848	-0.3	-0.1
17 M	0051	6.3	1.9
	0659	0.2	0.1
	1302	6.7	2.0
	1923	-0.2	-0.1
18 Tu	0128	6.3	1.9
	0736	0.2	0.1
	1341	6.5	2.0
	2000	-0.1	0.0
19 W	0208	6.3	1.9
	0819	0.3	0.1
	1422	6.3	1.9
	2040	0.0	0.0
20 Th	0249	6.3	1.9
	0904	0.3	0.1
	1509	6.1	1.9
	2122	0.1	0.0
21 F	0337	6.4	2.0
	0954	0.3	0.1
	1559	5.9	1.8
	2213	0.2	0.1
22 Sa	0428	6.4	2.0
	1055	0.3	0.1
	1656	5.7	1.7
	2309	0.3	0.1
23 Su	0527	6.5	2.0
	1156	0.1	0.0
	1759	5.6	1.7
24 M	0009	0.2	0.1
	0627	6.6	2.0
	1300	-0.1	0.0
	1904	5.7	1.7
25 Tu	0111	0.1	0.0
	0729	6.9	2.1
	1401	-0.5	-0.2
	2006	5.9	1.8
26 W	0214	-0.2	-0.1
	0828	7.2	2.2
	1500	-0.8	-0.2
	2105	6.2	1.9
27 Th	0313	-0.5	-0.2
	0927	7.4	2.3
	1556	-1.2	-0.4
	2203	6.5	2.0
28 F	0410	-0.8	-0.2
	1022	7.6	2.3
	1650	-1.4	-0.4
	2256	6.8	2.1
29 Sa	0505	-1.0	-0.3
	1116	7.7	2.3
	1741	-1.5	-0.5
	2349	7.0	2.1
30 Su	0558	-1.2	-0.4
	1209	7.6	2.3
	1832	-1.5	-0.5
31 M	0041	7.1	2.2
	0653	-1.2	-0.4
	1302	7.4	2.3
	1923	-1.4	-0.4

FEBRUARY

Day	Time (h m)	Height (ft)	Height (m)
1 Tu	0131	7.0	2.1
	0747	-1.1	-0.3
	1355	7.0	2.1
	2014	-1.1	-0.3
2 W	0224	6.9	2.1
	0842	-0.8	-0.2
	1450	6.6	2.0
	2106	-0.7	-0.2
3 Th	0317	6.7	2.0
	0941	-0.6	-0.2
	1546	6.1	1.9
	2200	-0.3	-0.1
4 F	0414	6.5	2.0
	1039	-0.3	-0.1
	1645	5.7	1.7
	2258	0.0	0.0
5 Sa	0513	6.3	1.9
	1141	-0.1	0.0
	1746	5.5	1.7
	2356	0.2	0.1
6 Su	0610	6.2	1.9
	1240	0.0	0.0
	1847	5.4	1.6
7 M	0052	0.4	0.1
	0708	6.3	1.9
	1337	0.1	0.0
	1943	5.5	1.7
8 Tu	0148	0.4	0.1
	0801	6.4	2.0
	1428	0.0	0.0
	2033	5.6	1.7
9 W	0238	0.3	0.1
	0851	6.5	2.0
	1515	-0.1	0.0
	2118	5.8	1.8
10 Th	0323	0.2	0.1
	0932	6.7	2.0
	1556	-0.2	-0.1
	2200	6.0	1.8
11 F	0406	0.1	0.0
	1012	6.8	2.1
	1634	-0.3	-0.1
	2237	6.2	1.9
12 Sa	0443	0.0	0.0
	1051	6.8	2.1
	1710	-0.4	-0.1
	2313	6.4	2.0
13 Su	0520	-0.1	0.0
	1126	6.9	2.1
	1745	-0.4	-0.1
	2347	6.5	2.0
14 M	0557	-0.2	-0.1
	1202	6.8	2.1
	1818	-0.4	-0.1
15 Tu	0022	6.6	2.0
	0633	-0.2	-0.1
	1237	6.7	2.0
	1853	-0.4	-0.1
16 W	0057	6.6	2.0
	0710	-0.3	-0.1
	1313	6.6	2.0
	1928	-0.3	-0.1
17 Th	0134	6.6	2.0
	0750	-0.2	-0.1
	1352	6.4	2.0
	2006	-0.2	-0.1
18 F	0216	6.6	2.0
	0834	-0.1	0.0
	1439	6.1	1.9
	2048	0.0	0.0
19 Sa	0303	6.6	2.0
	0925	0.0	0.0
	1530	5.9	1.8
	2139	0.2	0.1
20 Su	0357	6.5	2.0
	1025	0.1	0.0
	1630	5.6	1.7
	2238	0.4	0.1
21 M	0454	6.5	2.0
	1130	0.1	0.0
	1736	5.6	1.7
	2345	0.4	0.1
22 Tu	0603	6.5	2.0
	1239	0.0	0.0
	1844	5.7	1.7
23 W	0055	0.3	0.1
	0711	6.7	2.0
	1344	-0.3	-0.1
	1951	5.9	1.8
24 Th	0201	0.0	0.0
	0814	7.0	2.1
	1444	-0.6	-0.2
	2051	6.3	1.9
25 F	0302	-0.4	-0.1
	0915	7.3	2.2
	1540	-1.0	-0.3
	2147	6.7	2.0
26 Sa	0358	-0.9	-0.3
	1011	7.5	2.3
	1633	-1.3	-0.4
	2239	7.1	2.2
27 Su	0453	-1.2	-0.4
	1103	7.6	2.3
	1722	-1.4	-0.4
	2329	7.3	2.2
28 M	0544	-1.4	-0.4
	1153	7.5	2.3
	1809	-1.4	-0.4

MARCH

Day	Time (h m)	Height (ft)	Height (m)
1 Tu	0017	7.3	2.2
	0634	-1.4	-0.4
	1243	7.2	2.2
	1857	-1.2	-0.4
2 W	0105	7.3	2.2
	0725	-1.3	-0.4
	1332	6.9	2.1
	1944	-0.9	-0.3
3 Th	0153	7.0	2.1
	0815	-1.0	-0.3
	1421	6.4	2.0
	2034	-0.5	-0.2
4 F	0243	6.8	2.1
	0908	-0.6	-0.2
	1512	6.0	1.8
	2125	-0.1	0.0
5 Sa	0335	6.5	2.0
	1003	-0.2	-0.1
	1608	5.7	1.7
	2220	0.3	0.1
6 Su	0431	6.2	1.9
	1101	0.2	0.1
	1708	5.5	1.7
	2317	0.6	0.2
7 M	0531	6.1	1.9
	1159	0.4	0.1
	1807	5.4	1.6
8 Tu	0017	0.8	0.2
	0630	6.1	1.9
	1259	0.5	0.2
	1904	5.5	1.7
9 W	0114	0.8	0.2
	0725	6.2	1.9
	1352	0.4	0.1
	1957	5.7	1.7
10 Th	0207	0.7	0.2
	0817	6.4	2.0
	1438	0.3	0.1
	2044	6.0	1.8
11 F	0254	0.5	0.2
	0902	6.5	2.0
	1521	0.1	0.0
	2126	6.3	1.9
12 Sa	0336	0.2	0.1
	0944	6.7	2.0
	1600	-0.1	0.0
	2204	6.5	2.0
13 Su	0416	0.0	0.0
	1021	6.8	2.1
	1637	-0.2	-0.1
	2241	6.7	2.0
14 M	0453	-0.3	-0.1
	1058	6.9	2.1
	1712	-0.3	-0.1
	2316	6.9	2.1
15 Tu	0530	-0.4	-0.1
	1133	6.9	2.1
	1746	-0.4	-0.1
	2351	7.0	2.1
16 W	0606	-0.6	-0.2
	1209	6.8	2.1
	1821	-0.4	-0.1
17 Th	0027	7.0	2.1
	0644	-0.6	-0.2
	1249	6.6	2.0
	1857	-0.3	-0.1
18 F	0105	7.0	2.1
	0725	-0.5	-0.2
	1332	6.4	2.0
	1937	-0.1	0.0
19 Sa	0150	7.0	2.1
	0811	-0.4	-0.1
	1418	6.2	1.9
	2023	0.1	0.0
20 Su	0237	6.8	2.1
	0904	-0.1	0.0
	1512	5.9	1.8
	2117	0.4	0.1
21 M	0333	6.7	2.0
	1005	0.1	0.0
	1614	5.8	1.8
	2221	0.6	0.2
22 Tu	0439	6.5	2.0
	1114	0.2	0.1
	1722	5.7	1.7
	2334	0.6	0.2
23 W	0549	6.5	2.0
	1223	0.1	0.0
	1831	5.9	1.8
24 Th	0045	0.5	0.2
	0658	6.6	2.0
	1329	-0.1	0.0
	1938	6.2	1.9
25 F	0152	0.1	0.0
	0804	6.9	2.1
	1428	-0.4	-0.1
	2038	6.7	2.0
26 Sa	0252	-0.4	-0.1
	0903	7.1	2.2
	1523	-0.7	-0.2
	2131	7.1	2.2
27 Su	0347	-0.9	-0.3
	0956	7.3	2.2
	1612	-1.0	-0.3
	2219	7.4	2.3
28 M	0438	-1.3	-0.4
	1047	7.3	2.2
	1701	-1.1	-0.3
	2308	7.5	2.3
29 Tu	0527	-1.4	-0.4
	1136	7.2	2.2
	1745	-1.0	-0.3
	2353	7.5	2.3
30 W	0614	-1.4	-0.4
	1222	7.0	2.1
	1831	-0.8	-0.2
31 Th	0038	7.4	2.3
	0700	-1.2	-0.4
	1307	6.7	2.0
	1915	-0.5	-0.2

Time meridian 75° W. 0000 is midnight. 1200 is noon.
Heights are referred to mean low water which is the chart datum of soundings.

BRIDGEPORT, CONN., 1983

Times and Heights of High and Low Waters

APRIL

Day	Time h m	Height ft	Height m	Day	Time h m	Height ft	Height m
1 F	0123	7.1	2.2	16 Sa	0041	7.4	2.3
	0747	-0.8	-0.2		0707	-0.7	-0.2
	1352	6.4	2.0		1313	6.5	2.0
	2000	-0.1	0.0		1917	0.1	0.0
2 Sa	0210	6.8	2.1	17 Su	0128	7.3	2.2
	0835	-0.4	-0.1		0757	-0.5	-0.2
	1442	6.0	1.8		1404	6.3	1.9
	2050	0.3	0.1		2008	0.3	0.1
3 Su	0259	6.5	2.0	18 M	0221	7.1	2.2
	0927	0.1	0.0		0852	-0.2	-0.1
	1533	5.8	1.8		1501	6.2	1.9
	2141	0.7	0.2		2108	0.6	0.2
4 M	0351	6.3	1.9	19 Tu	0320	6.8	2.1
	1020	0.5	0.2		0954	0.1	0.0
	1628	5.6	1.7		1605	6.1	1.9
	2238	1.0	0.3		2216	0.7	0.2
5 Tu	0447	6.1	1.9	20 W	0428	6.6	2.0
	1115	0.7	0.2		1100	0.2	0.1
	1724	5.6	1.7		1713	6.1	1.9
	2338	1.2	0.4		2328	0.7	0.2
6 W	0546	6.0	1.8	21 Th	0538	6.6	2.0
	1214	0.8	0.2		1208	0.2	0.1
	1823	5.8	1.8		1821	6.3	1.9
7 Th	0036	1.1	0.3	22 F	0037	0.4	0.1
	0642	6.1	1.9		0647	6.6	2.0
	1306	0.8	0.2		1311	0.0	0.0
	1915	6.0	1.8		1922	6.7	2.0
8 F	0129	0.9	0.3	23 Sa	0141	0.0	0.0
	0735	6.3	1.9		0751	6.8	2.1
	1356	0.6	0.2		1409	-0.2	-0.1
	2001	6.3	1.9		2020	7.0	2.1
9 Sa	0217	0.7	0.2	24 Su	0241	-0.5	-0.2
	0823	6.5	2.0		0849	6.9	2.1
	1441	0.4	0.1		1503	-0.4	-0.1
	2046	6.6	2.0		2111	7.4	2.3
10 Su	0302	0.3	0.1	25 M	0334	-0.9	-0.3
	0907	6.6	2.0		0940	7.0	2.1
	1521	0.2	0.1		1552	-0.6	-0.2
	2126	6.8	2.1		2159	7.6	2.3
11 M	0344	0.0	0.0	26 Tu	0422	-1.1	-0.3
	0947	6.8	2.1		1029	7.0	2.1
	1559	0.0	0.0		1636	-0.6	-0.2
	2203	7.1	2.2		2245	7.6	2.3
12 Tu	0422	-0.4	-0.1	27 W	0508	-1.2	-0.4
	1027	6.8	2.1		1115	6.9	2.1
	1636	-0.2	-0.1		1721	-0.6	-0.2
	2242	7.2	2.2		2329	7.6	2.3
13 W	0501	-0.6	-0.2	28 Th	0553	-1.1	-0.3
	1107	6.8	2.1		1158	6.7	2.0
	1714	-0.2	-0.1		1803	-0.4	-0.1
	2321	7.4	2.3				
14 Th	0540	-0.7	-0.2	29 F	0012	7.4	2.3
	1146	6.8	2.1		0636	-0.9	-0.3
	1753	-0.2	-0.1		1243	6.5	2.0
	2359	7.4	2.3		1847	-0.1	0.0
15 F	0622	-0.8	-0.2	30 Sa	0054	7.2	2.2
	1228	6.7	2.0		0720	-0.5	-0.2
	1832	-0.1	0.0		1326	6.3	1.9
					1930	0.3	0.1

MAY

Day	Time h m	Height ft	Height m	Day	Time h m	Height ft	Height m
1 Su	0138	6.9	2.1	16 M	0114	7.5	2.3
	0803	-0.1	0.0		0744	-0.6	-0.2
	1411	6.1	1.9		1355	6.6	2.0
	2016	0.7	0.2		1959	0.3	0.1
2 M	0224	6.7	2.0	17 Tu	0209	7.3	2.2
	0850	0.3	0.1		0843	-0.3	-0.1
	1458	6.0	1.8		1452	6.5	2.0
	2106	1.0	0.3		2101	0.5	0.2
3 Tu	0312	6.4	2.0	18 W	0312	7.0	2.1
	0940	0.6	0.2		0943	-0.1	0.0
	1549	5.9	1.8		1557	6.5	2.0
	2159	1.2	0.4		2210	0.6	0.2
4 W	0405	6.2	1.9	19 Th	0417	6.7	2.0
	1031	0.8	0.2		1046	0.1	0.0
	1641	6.0	1.8		1700	6.6	2.0
	2255	1.3	0.4		2319	0.5	0.2
5 Th	0500	6.1	1.9	20 F	0526	6.6	2.0
	1125	1.0	0.3		1150	0.1	0.0
	1734	6.1	1.9		1805	6.7	2.0
	2351	1.3	0.4				
6 F	0554	6.1	1.9	21 Sa	0025	0.3	0.1
	1216	0.9	0.3		0632	6.6	2.0
	1826	6.3	1.9		1252	0.1	0.0
					1905	7.0	2.1
7 Sa	0045	1.1	0.3	22 Su	0127	-0.1	0.0
	0648	6.2	1.9		0735	6.6	2.0
	1306	0.8	0.2		1348	-0.1	0.0
	1916	6.5	2.0		2001	7.3	2.2
8 Su	0137	0.8	0.2	23 M	0225	-0.4	-0.1
	0737	6.3	1.9		0833	6.7	2.0
	1353	0.6	0.2		1441	-0.2	-0.1
	2001	6.8	2.1		2051	7.4	2.3
9 M	0222	0.4	0.1	24 Tu	0317	-0.7	-0.2
	0825	6.5	2.0		0923	6.7	2.0
	1438	0.4	0.1		1529	-0.2	-0.1
	2044	7.1	2.2		2138	7.5	2.3
10 Tu	0307	0.0	0.0	25 W	0404	-0.9	-0.3
	0911	6.6	2.0		1011	6.6	2.0
	1519	0.2	0.1		1614	-0.2	-0.1
	2126	7.3	2.2		2224	7.6	2.3
11 W	0351	-0.4	-0.1	26 Th	0448	-0.9	-0.3
	0954	6.7	2.0		1055	6.6	2.0
	1600	0.0	0.0		1658	-0.1	0.0
	2208	7.5	2.3		2306	7.5	2.3
12 Th	0435	-0.7	-0.2	27 F	0531	-0.8	-0.2
	1037	6.8	2.1		1138	6.5	2.0
	1643	-0.1	0.0		1740	0.1	0.0
	2251	7.7	2.3		2347	7.3	2.2
13 F	0518	-0.8	-0.2	28 Sa	0613	-0.6	-0.2
	1124	6.8	2.1		1219	6.4	2.0
	1726	-0.1	0.0		1820	0.3	0.1
	2337	7.7	2.3				
14 Sa	0603	-0.9	-0.3	29 Su	0028	7.2	2.2
	1210	6.7	2.0		0654	-0.3	-0.1
	1812	0.0	0.0		1259	6.3	1.9
					1902	0.6	0.2
15 Su	0024	7.7	2.3	30 M	0109	7.0	2.1
	0653	-0.8	-0.2		0734	0.0	0.0
	1300	6.7	2.0		1342	6.3	1.9
	1902	0.1	0.0		1947	0.8	0.2
				31 Tu	0150	6.8	2.1
					0816	0.3	0.1
					1424	6.2	1.9
					2032	1.1	0.3

JUNE

Day	Time h m	Height ft	Height m	Day	Time h m	Height ft	Height m
1 W	0235	6.6	2.0	16 Th	0300	7.1	2.2
	0901	0.6	0.2		0927	-0.3	-0.1
	1509	6.2	1.9		1541	6.9	2.1
	2120	1.2	0.4		2157	0.2	0.1
2 Th	0322	6.4	2.0	17 F	0404	6.8	2.1
	0948	0.8	0.2		1027	-0.1	0.0
	1559	6.3	1.9		1642	6.9	2.1
	2212	1.3	0.4		2303	0.2	0.1
3 F	0412	6.3	1.9	18 Sa	0508	6.6	2.0
	1036	0.9	0.3		1128	0.0	0.0
	1647	6.4	2.0		1743	7.0	2.1
	2305	1.2	0.4				
4 Sa	0506	6.2	1.9	19 Su	0007	0.0	0.0
	1126	0.9	0.3		0613	6.4	2.0
	1737	6.5	2.0		1227	0.1	0.0
	2359	1.0	0.3		1842	7.1	2.2
5 Su	0559	6.2	1.9	20 M	0109	-0.2	-0.1
	1215	0.8	0.2		0717	6.3	1.9
	1827	6.7	2.0		1324	0.1	0.0
					1938	7.2	2.2
6 M	0051	0.7	0.2	21 Tu	0206	-0.3	-0.1
	0652	6.2	1.9		0812	6.3	1.9
	1303	0.7	0.2		1417	0.1	0.0
	1916	6.9	2.1		2030	7.3	2.2
7 Tu	0141	0.4	0.1	22 W	0259	-0.5	-0.2
	0744	6.3	1.9		0904	6.3	1.9
	1352	0.5	0.2		1507	0.1	0.0
	2004	7.2	2.2		2118	7.4	2.3
8 W	0232	0.0	0.0	23 Th	0345	-0.5	-0.2
	0835	6.4	2.0		0952	6.3	1.9
	1441	0.3	0.1		1553	0.1	0.0
	2051	7.5	2.3		2203	7.4	2.3
9 Th	0321	-0.4	-0.1	24 F	0430	-0.5	-0.2
	0923	6.5	2.0		1035	6.3	1.9
	1527	0.1	0.0		1636	0.2	0.1
	2139	7.7	2.3		2245	7.3	2.2
10 F	0408	-0.7	-0.2	25 Sa	0512	-0.4	-0.1
	1012	6.7	2.0		1117	6.4	2.0
	1615	0.0	0.0		1718	0.3	0.1
	2227	7.9	2.4		2325	7.3	2.2
11 Sa	0457	-0.9	-0.3	26 Su	0550	-0.3	-0.1
	1103	6.8	2.1		1155	6.4	2.0
	1705	-0.1	0.0		1757	0.5	0.2
	2317	7.9	2.4				
12 Su	0546	-1.0	-0.3	27 M	0003	7.1	2.2
	1154	6.8	2.1		0628	-0.1	0.0
	1757	-0.1	0.0		1233	6.4	2.0
					1838	0.6	0.2
13 M	0008	7.9	2.4	28 Tu	0041	7.0	2.1
	0638	-0.9	-0.3		0707	0.1	0.0
	1246	6.9	2.1		1313	6.4	2.0
	1851	0.0	0.0		1917	0.8	0.2
14 Tu	0102	7.7	2.3	29 W	0120	6.9	2.1
	0731	-0.8	-0.2		0744	0.2	0.1
	1342	6.9	2.1		1352	6.5	2.0
	1950	0.1	0.0		1958	0.9	0.3
15 W	0200	7.4	2.3	30 Th	0200	6.7	2.0
	0827	-0.5	-0.2		0824	0.4	0.1
	1440	6.9	2.1		1431	6.5	2.0
	2053	0.2	0.1		2042	1.0	0.3

Time meridian 75° W. 0000 is midnight. 1200 is noon.
Heights are referred to mean low water which is the chart datum of soundings.

Times and Heights of High and Low Waters

JULY

Day	Time (h m)	Height (ft)	Height (m)
1 F	0243	6.5	2.0
	0904	0.5	0.2
	1514	6.5	2.0
	2128	1.0	0.3
2 Sa	0328	6.4	2.0
	0949	0.7	0.2
	1602	6.6	2.0
	2220	1.0	0.3
3 Su	0420	6.2	1.9
	1034	0.7	0.2
	1651	6.7	2.0
	2314	0.9	0.3
4 M	0513	6.1	1.9
	1125	0.7	0.2
	1742	6.8	2.1
5 Tu	0007	0.7	0.2
	0607	6.0	1.8
	1219	0.7	0.2
	1834	7.0	2.1
6 W	0103	0.4	0.1
	0706	6.1	1.9
	1311	0.5	0.2
	1929	7.2	2.2
7 Th	0159	0.0	0.0
	0801	6.2	1.9
	1406	0.4	0.1
	2021	7.5	2.3
8 F	0252	-0.3	-0.1
	0857	6.4	2.0
	1501	0.2	0.1
	2115	7.7	2.3
9 Sa	0347	-0.6	-0.2
	0950	6.6	2.0
	1555	0.0	0.0
	2208	7.9	2.4
10 Su	0438	-0.9	-0.3
	1045	6.9	2.1
	1649	-0.2	-0.1
	2301	8.0	2.4
11 M	0529	-1.0	-0.3
	1138	7.1	2.2
	1743	-0.3	-0.1
	2354	8.0	2.4
12 Tu	0622	-1.1	-0.3
	1230	7.2	2.2
	1840	-0.4	-0.1
13 W	0049	7.8	2.4
	0715	-1.0	-0.3
	1325	7.2	2.2
	1936	-0.4	-0.1
14 Th	0145	7.5	2.3
	0808	-0.8	-0.2
	1421	7.2	2.2
	2037	-0.3	-0.1
15 F	0243	7.1	2.2
	0904	-0.5	-0.2
	1517	7.1	2.2
	2138	-0.2	-0.1
16 Sa	0343	6.7	2.0
	1001	-0.2	-0.1
	1617	7.1	2.2
	2241	-0.1	0.0
17 Su	0446	6.4	2.0
	1101	0.0	0.0
	1717	7.0	2.1
	2343	0.0	0.0
18 M	0550	6.2	1.9
	1200	0.2	0.1
	1816	7.0	2.1
19 Tu	0046	-0.1	0.0
	0652	6.1	1.9
	1258	0.3	0.1
	1914	7.0	2.1
20 W	0144	-0.1	0.0
	0751	6.0	1.8
	1353	0.4	0.1
	2007	7.1	2.2
21 Th	0238	-0.2	-0.1
	0842	6.1	1.9
	1444	0.4	0.1
	2057	7.2	2.2
22 F	0324	-0.2	-0.1
	0930	6.2	1.9
	1531	0.4	0.1
	2142	7.2	2.2
23 Sa	0407	-0.2	-0.1
	1012	6.3	1.9
	1614	0.4	0.1
	2224	7.2	2.2
24 Su	0448	-0.2	-0.1
	1052	6.4	2.0
	1656	0.4	0.1
	2301	7.2	2.2
25 M	0525	-0.1	0.0
	1130	6.5	2.0
	1734	0.4	0.1
	2339	7.1	2.2
26 Tu	0601	0.0	0.0
	1206	6.6	2.0
	1811	0.5	0.2
27 W	0015	7.1	2.2
	0635	0.0	0.0
	1241	6.7	2.0
	1849	0.5	0.2
28 Th	0051	6.9	2.1
	0710	0.1	0.0
	1317	6.7	2.0
	1926	0.6	0.2
29 F	0128	6.8	2.1
	0747	0.2	0.1
	1355	6.7	2.0
	2008	0.6	0.2
30 Sa	0208	6.6	2.0
	0824	0.4	0.1
	1435	6.8	2.1
	2050	0.6	0.2
31 Su	0253	6.4	2.0
	0904	0.5	0.2
	1516	6.8	2.1
	2138	0.7	0.2

AUGUST

Day	Time (h m)	Height (ft)	Height (m)
1 M	0338	6.2	1.9
	0950	0.6	0.2
	1607	6.8	2.1
	2231	0.7	0.2
2 Tu	0432	6.0	1.8
	1042	0.7	0.2
	1659	6.8	2.1
	2331	0.6	0.2
3 W	0531	5.9	1.8
	1138	0.8	0.2
	1757	7.0	2.1
4 Th	0031	0.4	0.1
	0634	6.0	1.8
	1240	0.7	0.2
	1859	7.2	2.2
5 F	0131	0.1	0.0
	0736	6.1	1.9
	1341	0.5	0.2
	1957	7.4	2.3
6 Sa	0230	-0.2	-0.1
	0836	6.4	2.0
	1441	0.2	0.1
	2055	7.7	2.3
7 Su	0326	-0.6	-0.2
	0932	6.8	2.1
	1539	-0.1	0.0
	2152	7.9	2.4
8 M	0419	-0.9	-0.3
	1027	7.1	2.2
	1636	-0.5	-0.2
	2246	8.0	2.4
9 Tu	0512	-1.1	-0.3
	1119	7.4	2.3
	1731	-0.7	-0.2
	2340	8.0	2.4
10 W	0602	-1.1	-0.3
	1211	7.5	2.3
	1825	-0.8	-0.2
11 Th	0033	7.8	2.4
	0654	-1.1	-0.3
	1303	7.6	2.3
	1919	-0.8	-0.2
12 F	0126	7.5	2.3
	0744	-0.8	-0.2
	1355	7.5	2.3
	2016	-0.6	-0.2
13 Sa	0221	7.0	2.1
	0837	-0.5	-0.2
	1450	7.3	2.2
	2113	-0.4	-0.1
14 Su	0320	6.6	2.0
	0932	-0.1	0.0
	1546	7.1	2.2
	2213	-0.2	-0.1
15 M	0420	6.2	1.9
	1031	0.2	0.1
	1646	6.9	2.1
	2316	0.1	0.0
16 Tu	0521	6.0	1.8
	1131	0.5	0.2
	1746	6.8	2.1
17 W	0018	0.2	0.1
	0623	5.9	1.8
	1232	0.7	0.2
	1846	6.8	2.1
18 Th	0116	0.3	0.1
	0723	5.9	1.8
	1328	0.7	0.2
	1942	6.8	2.1
19 F	0210	0.2	0.1
	0817	6.1	1.9
	1421	0.7	0.2
	2033	7.0	2.1
20 Sa	0259	0.2	0.1
	0905	6.3	1.9
	1509	0.6	0.2
	2118	7.1	2.2
21 Su	0342	0.1	0.0
	0946	6.5	2.0
	1551	0.5	0.2
	2200	7.1	2.2
22 M	0419	0.0	0.0
	1023	6.6	2.0
	1632	0.4	0.1
	2237	7.2	2.2
23 Tu	0456	0.0	0.0
	1100	6.8	2.1
	1708	0.3	0.1
	2313	7.2	2.2
24 W	0530	0.0	0.0
	1134	6.9	2.1
	1743	0.2	0.1
	2347	7.1	2.2
25 Th	0604	0.0	0.0
	1209	7.0	2.1
	1820	0.2	0.1
26 F	0024	7.0	2.1
	0638	0.1	0.0
	1243	7.0	2.1
	1856	0.2	0.1
27 Sa	0057	6.8	2.1
	0710	0.2	0.1
	1319	7.0	2.1
	1934	0.2	0.1
28 Su	0136	6.6	2.0
	0747	0.3	0.1
	1357	7.0	2.1
	2016	0.3	0.1
29 M	0219	6.4	2.0
	0826	0.5	0.2
	1440	7.0	2.1
	2105	0.4	0.1
30 Tu	0306	6.2	1.9
	0912	0.7	0.2
	1528	6.9	2.1
	2158	0.5	0.2
31 W	0402	6.0	1.8
	1007	0.8	0.2
	1626	6.9	2.1
	2301	0.6	0.2

SEPTEMBER

Day	Time (h m)	Height (ft)	Height (m)
1 Th	0506	5.9	1.8
	1110	0.9	0.3
	1731	6.9	2.1
2 F	0006	0.5	0.2
	0611	6.0	1.8
	1220	0.8	0.2
	1836	7.0	2.1
3 Sa	0111	0.3	0.1
	0717	6.2	1.9
	1327	0.6	0.2
	1940	7.3	2.2
4 Su	0211	-0.1	0.0
	0820	6.6	2.0
	1430	0.2	0.1
	2041	7.5	2.3
5 M	0307	-0.5	-0.2
	0915	7.1	2.2
	1527	-0.3	-0.1
	2138	7.8	2.4
6 Tu	0400	-0.8	-0.2
	1008	7.4	2.3
	1622	-0.7	-0.2
	2232	7.9	2.4
7 W	0451	-1.0	-0.3
	1100	7.7	2.3
	1715	-1.0	-0.3
	2323	7.8	2.4
8 Th	0541	-1.1	-0.3
	1149	7.8	2.4
	1806	-1.1	-0.3
9 F	0015	7.6	2.3
	0628	-1.0	-0.3
	1238	7.8	2.4
	1857	-1.1	-0.3
10 Sa	0105	7.3	2.2
	0718	-0.7	-0.2
	1329	7.6	2.3
	1951	-0.8	-0.2
11 Su	0158	6.9	2.1
	0808	-0.3	-0.1
	1419	7.3	2.2
	2045	-0.5	-0.2
12 M	0252	6.4	2.0
	0901	0.1	0.0
	1515	7.0	2.1
	2143	-0.1	0.0
13 Tu	0348	6.1	1.9
	0957	0.5	0.2
	1613	6.8	2.1
	2242	0.3	0.1
14 W	0450	5.9	1.8
	1058	0.9	0.3
	1711	6.6	2.0
	2344	0.5	0.2
15 Th	0552	5.8	1.8
	1201	1.0	0.3
	1812	6.5	2.0
16 F	0044	0.6	0.2
	0652	5.9	1.8
	1258	1.0	0.3
	1911	6.6	2.0
17 Sa	0135	0.6	0.2
	0745	6.2	1.9
	1353	0.9	0.3
	2001	6.8	2.1
18 Su	0225	0.5	0.2
	0830	6.4	2.0
	1440	0.7	0.2
	2049	6.9	2.1
19 M	0307	0.4	0.1
	0914	6.7	2.0
	1523	0.5	0.2
	2129	7.0	2.1
20 Tu	0347	0.2	0.1
	0951	6.9	2.1
	1603	0.3	0.1
	2207	7.1	2.2
21 W	0422	0.1	0.0
	1027	7.1	2.2
	1640	0.1	0.0
	2243	7.1	2.2
22 Th	0457	0.0	0.0
	1101	7.2	2.2
	1715	0.0	0.0
	2318	7.1	2.2
23 F	0529	0.0	0.0
	1136	7.3	2.2
	1752	-0.1	0.0
	2354	7.0	2.1
24 Sa	0604	0.0	0.0
	1209	7.3	2.2
	1828	-0.1	0.0
25 Su	0031	6.8	2.1
	0638	0.1	0.0
	1246	7.3	2.2
	1906	-0.1	0.0
26 M	0110	6.6	2.0
	0715	0.3	0.1
	1326	7.2	2.2
	1950	0.1	0.0
27 Tu	0154	6.4	2.0
	0755	0.5	0.2
	1411	7.1	2.2
	2037	0.2	0.1
28 W	0245	6.2	1.9
	0847	0.8	0.2
	1503	7.0	2.1
	2136	0.4	0.1
29 Th	0341	6.0	1.8
	0946	1.0	0.3
	1605	6.9	2.1
	2239	0.6	0.2
30 F	0447	6.0	1.8
	1057	1.1	0.3
	1713	6.8	2.1
	2347	0.5	0.2

Time meridian 75° W. 0000 is midnight. 1200 is noon.
Heights are referred to mean low water which is the chart datum of soundings.

Times and Heights of High and Low Waters

OCTOBER

Day	Time (h m)	Height (ft)	Height (m)
1 Sa	0556	6.1	1.9
	1209	0.9	0.3
	1823	6.9	2.1
2 Su	0052	0.3	0.1
	0702	6.5	2.0
	1316	0.5	0.2
	1928	7.1	2.2
3 M	0154	0.0	0.0
	0804	6.9	2.1
	1420	0.0	0.0
	2028	7.3	2.2
4 Tu	0249	-0.4	-0.1
	0859	7.3	2.2
	1515	-0.5	-0.2
	2123	7.5	2.3
5 W	0342	-0.7	-0.2
	0950	7.7	2.3
	1609	-0.9	-0.3
	2216	7.6	2.3
6 Th	0430	-0.9	-0.3
	1038	7.9	2.4
	1659	-1.2	-0.4
	2306	7.5	2.3
7 F	0517	-0.9	-0.3
	1127	7.9	2.4
	1748	-1.3	-0.4
	2355	7.3	2.2
8 Sa	0604	-0.8	-0.2
	1213	7.8	2.4
	1837	-1.1	-0.3
9 Su	0043	7.0	2.1
	0650	-0.5	-0.2
	1300	7.6	2.3
	1926	-0.8	-0.2
10 M	0131	6.6	2.0
	0739	-0.1	0.0
	1349	7.3	2.2
	2016	-0.4	-0.1
11 Tu	0223	6.3	1.9
	0829	0.4	0.1
	1440	6.9	2.1
	2109	0.1	0.0
12 W	0317	6.0	1.8
	0925	0.8	0.2
	1535	6.6	2.0
	2205	0.5	0.2
13 Th	0414	5.9	1.8
	1023	1.1	0.3
	1634	6.4	2.0
	2304	0.8	0.2
14 F	0514	5.9	1.8
	1123	1.3	0.4
	1733	6.3	1.9
15 Sa	0001	0.9	0.3
	0610	6.0	1.8
	1223	1.3	0.4
	1831	6.4	2.0
16 Su	0055	0.8	0.2
	0704	6.2	1.9
	1316	1.1	0.3
	1924	6.5	2.0
17 M	0143	0.7	0.2
	0751	6.5	2.0
	1405	0.8	0.2
	2009	6.6	2.0
18 Tu	0226	0.5	0.2
	0833	6.8	2.1
	1449	0.5	0.2
	2053	6.8	2.1
19 W	0307	0.3	0.1
	0912	7.0	2.1
	1529	0.2	0.1
	2134	6.9	2.1
20 Th	0344	0.2	0.1
	0950	7.2	2.2
	1608	-0.1	0.0
	2211	6.9	2.1
21 F	0421	0.0	0.0
	1026	7.4	2.3
	1645	-0.3	-0.1
	2248	6.9	2.1
22 Sa	0457	0.0	0.0
	1102	7.5	2.3
	1725	-0.4	-0.1
	2327	6.8	2.1
23 Su	0532	0.0	0.0
	1140	7.5	2.3
	1802	-0.5	-0.2
24 M	0006	6.7	2.0
	0611	0.1	0.0
	1220	7.5	2.3
	1843	-0.4	-0.1
25 Tu	0049	6.6	2.0
	0649	0.3	0.1
	1302	7.4	2.3
	1930	-0.2	-0.1
26 W	0136	6.4	2.0
	0738	0.5	0.2
	1350	7.2	2.2
	2021	0.0	0.0
27 Th	0229	6.2	1.9
	0832	0.8	0.2
	1448	7.0	2.1
	2120	0.2	0.1
28 F	0330	6.1	1.9
	0937	0.9	0.3
	1549	6.8	2.1
	2225	0.4	0.1
29 Sa	0435	6.1	1.9
	1048	0.9	0.3
	1659	6.7	2.0
	2331	0.4	0.1
30 Su	0544	6.3	1.9
	1200	0.7	0.2
	1808	6.7	2.0
31 M	0036	0.2	0.1
	0647	6.7	2.0
	1306	0.3	0.1
	1914	6.8	2.1

NOVEMBER

Day	Time (h m)	Height (ft)	Height (m)
1 Tu	0135	-0.1	0.0
	0746	7.1	2.2
	1408	-0.2	-0.1
	2014	7.0	2.1
2 W	0230	-0.4	-0.1
	0841	7.4	2.3
	1502	-0.7	-0.2
	2110	7.1	2.2
3 Th	0321	-0.6	-0.2
	0931	7.7	2.3
	1555	-1.0	-0.3
	2201	7.1	2.2
4 F	0409	-0.7	-0.2
	1019	7.8	2.4
	1643	-1.2	-0.4
	2248	7.0	2.1
5 Sa	0456	-0.7	-0.2
	1105	7.8	2.4
	1730	-1.2	-0.4
	2335	6.9	2.1
6 Su	0539	-0.5	-0.2
	1150	7.7	2.3
	1815	-1.0	-0.3
7 M	0021	6.6	2.0
	0625	-0.2	-0.1
	1235	7.5	2.3
	1902	-0.7	-0.2
8 Tu	0107	6.4	2.0
	0710	0.1	0.0
	1321	7.2	2.2
	1949	-0.3	-0.1
9 W	0155	6.2	1.9
	0758	0.5	0.2
	1407	6.8	2.1
	2035	0.1	0.0
10 Th	0243	6.0	1.8
	0849	0.9	0.3
	1458	6.6	2.0
	2126	0.5	0.2
11 F	0335	5.9	1.8
	0944	1.1	0.3
	1551	6.3	1.9
	2220	0.7	0.2
12 Sa	0430	5.9	1.8
	1041	1.3	0.4
	1647	6.2	1.9
	2312	0.9	0.3
13 Su	0524	6.0	1.8
	1138	1.3	0.4
	1743	6.1	1.9
14 M	0005	0.9	0.3
	0616	6.2	1.9
	1232	1.1	0.3
	1836	6.2	1.9
15 Tu	0055	0.8	0.2
	0705	6.5	2.0
	1324	0.8	0.2
	1924	6.3	1.9
16 W	0140	0.6	0.2
	0749	6.7	2.0
	1409	0.5	0.2
	2012	6.4	2.0
17 Th	0223	0.4	0.1
	0833	7.0	2.1
	1454	0.1	0.0
	2055	6.5	2.0
18 F	0305	0.2	0.1
	0913	7.2	2.2
	1536	-0.2	-0.1
	2137	6.5	2.0
19 Sa	0344	0.0	0.0
	0952	7.4	2.3
	1618	-0.5	-0.2
	2219	6.6	2.0
20 Su	0424	-0.1	0.0
	1033	7.5	2.3
	1657	-0.7	-0.2
	2301	6.6	2.0
21 M	0505	-0.1	0.0
	1114	7.6	2.3
	1742	-0.7	-0.2
	2346	6.6	2.0
22 Tu	0548	0.0	0.0
	1159	7.6	2.3
	1827	-0.7	-0.2
23 W	0033	6.5	2.0
	0634	0.1	0.0
	1246	7.5	2.3
	1915	-0.6	-0.2
24 Th	0123	6.4	2.0
	0726	0.3	0.1
	1338	7.3	2.2
	2008	-0.3	-0.1
25 F	0218	6.4	2.0
	0824	0.4	0.1
	1435	7.0	2.1
	2106	-0.1	0.0
26 Sa	0317	6.3	1.9
	0930	0.6	0.2
	1539	6.7	2.0
	2209	0.0	0.0
27 Su	0423	6.4	2.0
	1039	0.5	0.2
	1646	6.5	2.0
	2312	0.1	0.0
28 M	0527	6.5	2.0
	1147	0.3	0.1
	1754	6.4	2.0
29 Tu	0015	0.0	0.0
	0630	6.7	2.0
	1252	0.0	0.0
	1900	6.4	2.0
30 W	0114	-0.1	0.0
	0729	7.0	2.1
	1353	-0.4	-0.1
	1959	6.5	2.0

DECEMBER

Day	Time (h m)	Height (ft)	Height (m)
1 Th	0211	-0.3	-0.1
	0823	7.3	2.2
	1451	-0.8	-0.2
	2054	6.5	2.0
2 F	0302	-0.4	-0.1
	0913	7.5	2.3
	1540	-1.0	-0.3
	2145	6.5	2.0
3 Sa	0350	-0.5	-0.2
	1000	7.5	2.3
	1627	-1.1	-0.3
	2233	6.5	2.0
4 Su	0435	-0.5	-0.2
	1047	7.5	2.3
	1714	-1.1	-0.3
	2317	6.4	2.0
5 M	0519	-0.3	-0.1
	1129	7.4	2.3
	1756	-0.9	-0.3
6 Tu	0000	6.3	1.9
	0603	-0.1	0.0
	1212	7.2	2.2
	1839	-0.6	-0.2
7 W	0042	6.2	1.9
	0646	0.1	0.0
	1255	7.0	2.1
	1920	-0.3	-0.1
8 Th	0126	6.1	1.9
	0731	0.4	0.1
	1338	6.8	2.1
	2003	0.0	0.0
9 F	0210	6.1	1.9
	0816	-0.7	0.2
	1421	6.5	2.0
	2047	0.3	0.1
10 Sa	0256	6.0	1.8
	0904	0.9	0.3
	1509	6.3	1.9
	2133	0.5	0.2
11 Su	0343	6.0	1.8
	0956	1.0	0.3
	1558	6.1	1.9
	2221	0.6	0.2
12 M	0433	6.1	1.9
	1049	1.0	0.3
	1651	5.9	1.8
	2310	0.7	0.2
13 Tu	0523	6.2	1.9
	1143	0.9	0.3
	1744	5.9	1.8
14 W	0001	0.7	0.2
	0613	6.3	1.9
	1236	0.7	0.2
	1836	5.9	1.8
15 Th	0050	0.5	0.2
	0703	6.5	2.0
	1327	0.4	0.1
	1927	5.9	1.8
16 F	0137	0.4	0.1
	0749	6.8	2.1
	1417	0.0	0.0
	2017	6.0	1.8
17 Sa	0225	0.2	0.1
	0836	7.0	2.1
	1503	-0.3	-0.1
	2107	6.2	1.9
18 Su	0311	0.0	0.0
	0921	7.3	2.2
	1550	-0.6	-0.2
	2153	6.3	1.9
19 M	0355	-0.2	-0.1
	1007	7.5	2.3
	1635	-0.9	-0.3
	2240	6.4	2.0
20 Tu	0444	-0.3	-0.1
	1054	7.6	2.3
	1723	-1.0	-0.3
	2328	6.5	2.0
21 W	0531	-0.3	-0.1
	1142	7.6	2.3
	1812	-1.0	-0.3
22 Th	0017	6.6	2.0
	0622	-0.3	-0.1
	1233	7.5	2.3
	1902	-1.0	-0.3
23 F	0110	6.6	2.0
	0716	-0.3	-0.1
	1326	7.3	2.2
	1954	-0.8	-0.2
24 Sa	0203	6.6	2.0
	0816	-0.2	-0.1
	1424	7.0	2.1
	2050	-0.6	-0.2
25 Su	0301	6.6	2.0
	0917	-0.1	0.0
	1525	6.6	2.0
	2149	-0.4	-0.1
26 M	0404	6.5	2.0
	1023	0.0	0.0
	1630	6.3	1.9
	2250	-0.2	-0.1
27 Tu	0507	6.6	2.0
	1130	-0.1	0.0
	1735	6.1	1.9
	2352	-0.2	-0.1
28 W	0608	6.7	2.0
	1235	-0.3	-0.1
	1842	6.0	1.8
29 Th	0053	-0.2	-0.1
	0708	6.8	2.1
	1337	-0.5	-0.2
	1943	6.0	1.8
30 F	0149	-0.2	-0.1
	0804	7.0	2.1
	1433	-0.7	-0.2
	2039	6.0	1.8
31 Sa	0244	-0.3	-0.1
	0857	7.1	2.2
	1524	-0.9	-0.3
	2131	6.1	1.9

Time meridian 75° W. 0000 is midnight. 1200 is noon.
Heights are referred to mean low water which is the chart datum of soundings.

WILLETS POINT, N.Y., 1983

Times and Heights of High and Low Waters

JANUARY

Day	Time (h m)	Height (ft)	Height (m)
1 Sa	0016	7.2	2.2
	0644	-0.8	-0.2
	1224	8.1	2.5
	1935	-1.6	-0.5
2 Su	0113	7.2	2.2
	0746	-0.7	-0.2
	1322	7.8	2.4
	2031	-1.4	-0.4
3 M	0215	7.2	2.2
	0849	-0.6	-0.2
	1427	7.4	2.3
	2128	-1.1	-0.3
4 Tu	0318	7.1	2.2
	0955	-0.5	-0.2
	1541	7.0	2.1
	2227	-0.7	-0.2
5 W	0427	7.0	2.1
	1100	-0.4	-0.1
	1654	6.6	2.0
	2327	-0.5	-0.2
6 Th	0531	7.0	2.1
	1205	-0.4	-0.1
	1802	6.4	2.0
7 F	0027	-0.3	-0.1
	0633	7.0	2.1
	1305	-0.4	-0.1
	1905	6.3	1.9
8 Sa	0123	-0.1	0.0
	0731	7.1	2.2
	1403	-0.5	-0.2
	2001	6.3	1.9
9 Su	0216	-0.1	0.0
	0824	7.1	2.2
	1455	-0.6	-0.2
	2055	6.3	1.9
10 M	0307	-0.1	0.0
	0914	7.2	2.2
	1543	-0.7	-0.2
	2143	6.4	2.0
11 Tu	0352	0.0	0.0
	1000	7.2	2.2
	1629	-0.7	-0.2
	2228	6.4	2.0
12 W	0433	0.0	0.0
	1041	7.2	2.2
	1710	-0.7	-0.2
	2309	6.5	2.0
13 Th	0513	0.1	0.0
	1116	7.1	2.2
	1747	-0.6	-0.2
	2345	6.5	2.0
14 F	0545	0.2	0.1
	1141	7.0	2.1
	1822	-0.4	-0.1
15 Sa	0012	6.5	2.0
	0608	0.2	0.1
	1149	7.0	2.1
	1845	-0.3	-0.1
16 Su	0021	6.5	2.0
	0626	0.2	0.1
	1212	7.0	2.1
	1901	-0.2	-0.1
17 M	0042	6.6	2.0
	0656	0.2	0.1
	1247	7.1	2.2
	1921	-0.2	-0.1
18 Tu	0113	6.8	2.1
	0731	0.2	0.1
	1324	7.0	2.1
	1954	-0.1	0.0
19 W	0153	6.9	2.1
	0812	0.2	0.1
	1407	6.9	2.1
	2033	-0.1	0.0
20 Th	0235	7.0	2.1
	0857	0.2	0.1
	1456	6.7	2.0
	2116	0.0	0.0
21 F	0324	7.0	2.1
	0949	0.3	0.1
	1547	6.5	2.0
	2206	0.1	0.0
22 Sa	0416	7.1	2.2
	1047	0.3	0.1
	1644	6.2	1.9
	2259	0.2	0.1
23 Su	0512	7.1	2.2
	1153	0.2	0.1
	1747	6.1	1.9
24 M	0001	0.3	0.1
	0614	7.2	2.2
	1325	0.0	0.0
	1855	6.1	1.9
25 Tu	0107	0.2	0.1
	0717	7.3	2.2
	1450	-0.4	-0.1
	2005	6.3	1.9
26 W	0227	0.0	0.0
	0824	7.6	2.3
	1551	-0.9	-0.3
	2117	6.6	2.0
27 Th	0346	-0.3	-0.1
	0927	7.8	2.4
	1649	-1.3	-0.4
	2220	6.9	2.1
28 F	0449	-0.7	-0.2
	1030	8.0	2.4
	1740	-1.6	-0.5
	2316	7.3	2.2
29 Sa	0547	-1.0	-0.3
	1129	8.1	2.5
	1830	-1.8	-0.5
30 Su	0010	7.5	2.3
	0643	-1.2	-0.4
	1224	8.0	2.4
	1919	-1.7	-0.5
31 M	0102	7.6	2.3
	0738	-1.2	-0.4
	1320	7.8	2.4
	2007	-1.5	-0.5

FEBRUARY

Day	Time (h m)	Height (ft)	Height (m)
1 Tu	0156	7.5	2.3
	0831	-1.1	-0.3
	1415	7.4	2.3
	2100	-1.1	-0.3
2 W	0252	7.3	2.2
	0929	-0.8	-0.2
	1516	6.9	2.1
	2153	-0.7	-0.2
3 Th	0350	7.1	2.2
	1030	-0.5	-0.2
	1624	6.5	2.0
	2248	-0.3	-0.1
4 F	0453	6.9	2.1
	1131	-0.3	-0.1
	1728	6.2	1.9
	2349	0.1	0.0
5 Sa	0556	6.8	2.1
	1233	-0.1	0.0
	1831	6.0	1.8
6 Su	0048	0.3	0.1
	0659	6.7	2.0
	1331	-0.1	0.0
	1931	6.0	1.8
7 M	0144	0.4	0.1
	0756	6.8	2.1
	1427	-0.1	0.0
	2027	6.1	1.9
8 Tu	0237	0.4	0.1
	0847	6.9	2.1
	1517	-0.2	-0.1
	2117	6.2	1.9
9 W	0327	0.4	0.1
	0936	7.0	2.1
	1603	-0.3	-0.1
	2204	6.4	2.0
10 Th	0410	0.3	0.1
	1018	7.0	2.1
	1644	-0.3	-0.1
	2245	6.5	2.0
11 F	0450	0.2	0.1
	1055	7.1	2.2
	1722	-0.3	-0.1
	2320	6.6	2.0
12 Sa	0525	0.1	0.0
	1121	7.0	2.1
	1754	-0.3	-0.1
	2342	6.7	2.0
13 Su	0550	0.1	0.0
	1130	7.1	2.2
	1816	-0.3	-0.1
	2350	6.8	2.1
14 M	0610	0.0	0.0
	1150	7.1	2.2
	1832	-0.3	-0.1
15 Tu	0013	7.0	2.1
	0636	-0.1	0.0
	1222	7.2	2.2
	1854	-0.3	-0.1
16 W	0045	7.2	2.2
	0709	-0.2	-0.1
	1300	7.2	2.2
	1924	-0.3	-0.1
17 Th	0122	7.4	2.3
	0748	-0.2	-0.1
	1345	7.1	2.2
	2003	-0.3	-0.1
18 F	0206	7.4	2.3
	0831	-0.2	-0.1
	1431	6.9	2.1
	2046	-0.1	0.0
19 Sa	0254	7.4	2.3
	0922	0.0	0.0
	1523	6.6	2.0
	2134	0.1	0.0
20 Su	0345	7.3	2.2
	1018	0.2	0.1
	1619	6.3	1.9
	2230	0.3	0.1
21 M	0443	7.2	2.2
	1127	0.3	0.1
	1724	6.1	1.9
	2333	0.5	0.2
22 Tu	0548	7.1	2.2
	1323	0.2	0.1
	1838	6.0	1.8
23 W	0057	0.5	0.2
	0700	7.1	2.2
	1442	-0.2	-0.1
	2002	6.3	1.9
24 Th	0242	0.2	0.1
	0821	7.3	2.2
	1541	-0.7	-0.2
	2117	6.7	2.0
25 F	0351	-0.3	-0.1
	0932	7.6	2.3
	1635	-1.2	-0.4
	2217	7.2	2.2
26 Sa	0449	-0.9	-0.3
	1034	7.9	2.4
	1725	-1.5	-0.5
	2308	7.6	2.3
27 Su	0540	-1.2	-0.4
	1127	8.0	2.4
	1811	-1.6	-0.5
	2357	7.8	2.4
28 M	0631	-1.4	-0.4
	1218	8.0	2.4
	1858	-1.6	-0.5

MARCH

Day	Time (h m)	Height (ft)	Height (m)
1 Tu	0042	7.9	2.4
	0719	-1.4	-0.4
	1305	7.7	2.3
	1942	-1.3	-0.4
2 W	0130	7.8	2.4
	0810	-1.2	-0.4
	1356	7.3	2.2
	2027	-0.9	-0.3
3 Th	0217	7.5	2.3
	0900	-0.9	-0.3
	1449	6.9	2.1
	2113	-0.4	-0.1
4 F	0309	7.2	2.2
	0955	-0.4	-0.1
	1547	6.5	2.0
	2203	0.1	0.0
5 Sa	0409	6.8	2.1
	1054	0.0	0.0
	1651	6.1	1.9
	2301	0.5	0.2
6 Su	0515	6.6	2.0
	1156	0.3	0.1
	1756	5.9	1.8
7 M	0006	0.9	0.3
	0619	6.4	2.0
	1256	0.5	0.2
	1857	5.9	1.8
8 Tu	0106	1.0	0.3
	0723	6.5	2.0
	1352	0.5	0.2
	1956	6.1	1.9
9 W	0205	0.9	0.3
	0818	6.6	2.0
	1443	0.4	0.1
	2047	6.3	1.9
10 Th	0255	0.8	0.2
	0906	6.8	2.1
	1529	0.3	0.1
	2133	6.5	2.0
11 F	0340	0.6	0.2
	0951	6.9	2.1
	1610	0.1	0.0
	2212	6.7	2.0
12 Sa	0420	0.3	0.1
	1026	7.0	2.1
	1648	0.0	0.0
	2244	6.9	2.1
13 Su	0456	0.1	0.0
	1049	7.1	2.2
	1721	-0.1	0.0
	2302	7.0	2.1
14 M	0525	-0.1	0.0
	1102	7.2	2.2
	1740	-0.2	-0.1
	2313	7.2	2.2
15 Tu	0548	-0.3	-0.1
	1126	7.3	2.2
	1757	-0.3	-0.1
	2340	7.5	2.3
16 W	0616	-0.4	-0.1
	1201	7.3	2.2
	1824	-0.3	-0.1
17 Th	0015	7.7	2.3
	0648	-0.5	-0.2
	1239	7.3	2.2
	1857	-0.3	-0.1
18 F	0057	7.8	2.4
	0729	-0.5	-0.2
	1322	7.2	2.2
	1938	-0.2	-0.1
19 Sa	0140	7.8	2.4
	0811	-0.3	-0.1
	1409	6.9	2.1
	2022	0.0	0.0
20 Su	0227	7.7	2.3
	0902	-0.1	0.0
	1502	6.6	2.0
	2113	0.3	0.1
21 M	0322	7.4	2.3
	1003	0.2	0.1
	1601	6.3	1.9
	2211	0.7	0.2
22 Tu	0424	7.1	2.2
	1130	0.5	0.2
	1712	6.2	1.9
	2327	0.9	0.3
23 W	0533	7.0	2.1
	1320	0.3	0.1
	1840	6.2	1.9
24 Th	0131	0.7	0.2
	0702	7.0	2.1
	1429	-0.1	0.0
	2010	6.6	2.0
25 F	0247	0.2	0.1
	0832	7.2	2.2
	1527	-0.6	-0.2
	2111	7.1	2.2
26 Sa	0346	-0.5	-0.2
	0935	7.6	2.3
	1617	-1.0	-0.3
	2204	7.6	2.3
27 Su	0439	-1.0	-0.3
	1029	7.8	2.4
	1705	-1.2	-0.4
	2253	7.9	2.4
28 M	0527	-1.4	-0.4
	1118	7.9	2.4
	1750	-1.3	-0.4
	2338	8.1	2.5
29 Tu	0614	-1.5	-0.5
	1204	7.8	2.4
	1833	-1.2	-0.4
30 W	0021	8.0	2.4
	0701	-1.4	-0.4
	1249	7.5	2.3
	1912	-0.9	-0.3
31 Th	0103	7.9	2.4
	0745	-1.1	-0.3
	1332	7.2	2.2
	1954	-0.5	-0.2

Time meridian 75° W. 0000 is midnight. 1200 is noon.
Heights are referred to mean low water which is the chart datum of soundings.

Times and Heights of High and Low Waters

APRIL

Day	Time h m	Height ft	Height m
1	0143	7.6	2.3
F	0830	-0.7	-0.2
	1420	6.8	2.1
	2031	0.0	0.0
2	0223	7.2	2.2
Sa	0917	-0.2	-0.1
	1508	6.4	2.0
	2107	0.5	0.2
3	0310	6.8	2.1
Su	1013	0.3	0.1
	1608	6.1	1.9
	2153	0.9	0.3
4	0409	6.5	2.0
M	1110	0.7	0.2
	1712	6.0	1.8
	2307	1.3	0.4
5	0531	6.3	1.9
Tu	1212	0.9	0.3
	1818	6.0	1.8
6	0021	1.4	0.4
W	0640	6.3	1.9
	1309	1.0	0.3
	1917	6.2	1.9
7	0125	1.4	0.4
Th	0740	6.4	2.0
	1402	0.9	0.3
	2008	6.4	2.0
8	0218	1.1	0.3
F	0829	6.6	2.0
	1447	0.7	0.2
	2053	6.7	2.0
9	0304	0.8	0.2
Sa	0911	6.7	2.0
	1529	0.5	0.2
	2130	6.9	2.1
10	0346	0.4	0.1
Su	0943	6.9	2.1
	1605	0.3	0.1
	2154	7.1	2.2
11	0423	0.1	0.0
M	1005	7.0	2.1
	1633	0.1	0.0
	2209	7.4	2.3
12	0456	-0.2	-0.1
Tu	1025	7.2	2.2
	1657	-0.1	0.0
	2236	7.7	2.3
13	0524	-0.5	-0.2
W	1100	7.3	2.2
	1723	-0.2	-0.1
	2310	7.9	2.4
14	0555	-0.6	-0.2
Th	1136	7.3	2.2
	1755	-0.3	-0.1
	2350	8.1	2.5
15	0630	-0.7	-0.2
F	1219	7.3	2.2
	1834	-0.2	-0.1

Day	Time h m	Height ft	Height m
16	0033	8.2	2.5
Sa	0714	-0.6	-0.2
	1305	7.2	2.2
	1916	0.0	0.0
17	0119	8.0	2.4
Su	0801	-0.4	-0.1
	1354	7.0	2.1
	2004	0.2	0.1
18	0211	7.8	2.4
M	0855	-0.1	0.0
	1451	6.7	2.0
	2100	0.6	0.2
19	0308	7.4	2.3
Tu	1006	0.3	0.1
	1555	6.5	2.0
	2209	0.9	0.3
20	0413	7.1	2.2
W	1153	0.4	0.1
	1715	6.4	2.0
21	0010	0.9	0.3
Th	0537	6.8	2.1
	1308	0.2	0.1
	1854	6.7	2.0
22	0134	0.5	0.2
F	0720	6.9	2.1
	1410	-0.1	0.0
	2003	7.1	2.2
23	0237	-0.1	0.0
Sa	0829	7.2	2.2
	1506	-0.5	-0.2
	2058	7.5	2.3
24	0332	-0.6	-0.2
Su	0927	7.5	2.3
	1556	-0.7	-0.2
	2148	7.9	2.4
25	0423	-1.1	-0.3
M	1017	7.6	2.3
	1642	-0.9	-0.3
	2236	8.1	2.5
26	0511	-1.3	-0.4
Tu	1104	7.6	2.3
	1726	-0.8	-0.2
	2318	8.1	2.5
27	0557	-1.4	-0.4
W	1147	7.5	2.3
	1807	-0.7	-0.2
	2359	8.0	2.4
28	0641	-1.2	-0.4
Th	1229	7.2	2.2
	1845	-0.4	-0.1
29	0037	7.8	2.4
F	0722	-0.9	-0.3
	1311	7.0	2.1
	1919	0.0	0.0
30	0110	7.5	2.3
Sa	0804	-0.5	-0.2
	1351	6.7	2.0
	1946	0.4	0.1

MAY

Day	Time h m	Height ft	Height m
1	0142	7.2	2.2
Su	0843	0.0	0.0
	1431	6.5	2.0
	2015	0.8	0.2
2	0217	6.9	2.1
M	0924	0.5	0.2
	1515	6.3	1.9
	2054	1.1	0.3
3	0259	6.6	2.0
Tu	1014	0.8	0.2
	1609	6.1	1.9
	2145	1.4	0.4
4	0349	6.4	2.0
W	1109	1.1	0.3
	1719	6.1	1.9
	2253	1.6	0.5
5	0448	6.3	1.9
Th	1207	1.2	0.4
	1820	6.3	1.9
6	0022	1.5	0.5
F	0611	6.2	1.9
	1302	1.2	0.4
	1910	6.5	2.0
7	0125	1.3	0.4
Sa	0718	6.3	1.9
	1349	1.0	0.3
	1950	6.7	2.0
8	0218	0.9	0.3
Su	0802	6.5	2.0
	1430	0.8	0.2
	2018	7.0	2.1
9	0303	0.5	0.2
M	0835	6.7	2.0
	1506	0.5	0.2
	2048	7.3	2.2
10	0344	0.1	0.0
Tu	0911	6.9	2.1
	1540	0.3	0.1
	2121	7.7	2.3
11	0423	-0.3	-0.1
W	0950	7.1	2.2
	1612	0.0	0.0
	2159	8.0	2.4
12	0459	-0.6	-0.2
Th	1031	7.2	2.2
	1649	-0.1	0.0
	2241	8.2	2.5
13	0538	-0.8	-0.2
F	1116	7.3	2.2
	1730	-0.2	-0.1
	2327	8.3	2.5
14	0621	-0.8	-0.2
Sa	1203	7.3	2.2
	1815	-0.1	0.0
15	0013	8.3	2.5
Su	0709	-0.7	-0.2
	1253	7.2	2.2
	1905	0.1	0.0

Day	Time h m	Height ft	Height m
16	0104	8.1	2.5
M	0804	-0.5	-0.2
	1346	7.0	2.1
	2001	0.3	0.1
17	0159	7.8	2.4
Tu	0910	-0.2	-0.1
	1446	6.8	2.1
	2109	0.6	0.2
18	0300	7.4	2.3
W	1027	0.0	0.0
	1600	6.7	2.0
	2246	0.7	0.2
19	0416	7.0	2.1
Th	1143	0.1	0.0
	1730	6.8	2.1
20	0012	0.5	0.2
F	0556	6.9	2.1
	1248	0.0	0.0
	1846	7.1	2.2
21	0122	0.1	0.0
Sa	0715	6.9	2.1
	1348	-0.2	-0.1
	1947	7.4	2.3
22	0221	-0.3	-0.1
Su	0816	7.1	2.2
	1442	-0.3	-0.1
	2040	7.7	2.3
23	0314	-0.7	-0.2
M	0911	7.2	2.2
	1532	-0.5	-0.2
	2130	7.9	2.4
24	0405	-1.0	-0.3
Tu	0959	7.2	2.2
	1618	-0.5	-0.2
	2215	8.0	2.4
25	0453	-1.1	-0.3
W	1047	7.2	2.2
	1703	-0.4	-0.1
	2259	8.0	2.4
26	0538	-1.1	-0.3
Th	1131	7.1	2.2
	1744	-0.2	-0.1
	2339	7.8	2.4
27	0621	-0.9	-0.3
F	1213	6.9	2.1
	1821	0.0	0.0
28	0013	7.6	2.3
Sa	0700	-0.6	-0.2
	1252	6.8	2.1
	1853	0.3	0.1
29	0044	7.4	2.3
Su	0736	-0.2	-0.1
	1327	6.6	2.0
	1915	0.6	0.2
30	0108	7.2	2.2
M	0812	0.2	0.1
	1354	6.5	2.0
	1943	0.9	0.3
31	0139	7.0	2.1
Tu	0836	0.5	0.2
	1425	6.5	2.0
	2020	1.1	0.3

JUNE

Day	Time h m	Height ft	Height m
1	0217	6.8	2.1
W	0902	0.7	0.2
	1500	6.4	2.0
	2104	1.3	0.4
2	0300	6.7	2.0
Th	0942	0.9	0.3
	1545	6.5	2.0
	2155	1.4	0.4
3	0350	6.5	2.0
F	1027	1.0	0.3
	1632	6.5	2.0
	2255	1.4	0.4
4	0444	6.4	2.0
Sa	1118	1.0	0.3
	1723	6.7	2.0
5	0000	1.2	0.4
Su	0541	6.4	2.0
	1209	1.0	0.3
	1814	6.9	2.1
6	0105	0.9	0.3
M	0638	6.4	2.0
	1305	0.8	0.2
	1904	7.2	2.2
7	0206	0.5	0.2
Tu	0733	6.6	2.0
	1355	0.6	0.2
	1952	7.5	2.3
8	0303	0.1	0.0
W	0826	6.7	2.0
	1447	0.3	0.1
	2042	7.8	2.4
9	0351	-0.3	-0.1
Th	0919	6.9	2.1
	1535	0.1	0.0
	2130	8.1	2.5
10	0440	-0.6	-0.2
F	1007	7.1	2.2
	1623	-0.1	0.0
	2219	8.3	2.5
11	0529	-0.9	-0.3
Sa	1100	7.2	2.2
	1714	-0.2	-0.1
	2309	8.4	2.6
12	0620	-1.0	-0.3
Su	1151	7.3	2.2
	1808	-0.1	0.0
13	0001	8.4	2.6
M	0711	-0.9	-0.3
	1245	7.3	2.2
	1905	0.0	0.0
14	0054	8.1	2.5
Tu	0810	-0.8	-0.2
	1343	7.2	2.2
	2012	0.1	0.0
15	0154	7.8	2.4
W	0912	-0.6	-0.2
	1449	7.2	2.2
	2129	0.2	0.1

Day	Time h m	Height ft	Height m
16	0300	7.4	2.3
Th	1018	-0.4	-0.1
	1605	7.1	2.2
	2246	0.2	0.1
17	0424	7.1	2.2
F	1121	-0.2	-0.1
	1719	7.2	2.2
	2355	0.1	0.0
18	0548	6.9	2.1
Sa	1224	-0.1	0.0
	1824	7.4	2.3
19	0100	-0.1	0.0
Su	0656	6.9	2.1
	1322	-0.1	0.0
	1925	7.5	2.3
20	0159	-0.4	-0.1
M	0757	6.9	2.1
	1418	-0.1	0.0
	2019	7.7	2.3
21	0255	-0.6	-0.2
Tu	0851	6.9	2.1
	1509	-0.1	0.0
	2111	7.8	2.4
22	0346	-0.8	-0.2
W	0941	6.9	2.1
	1556	-0.1	0.0
	2157	7.8	2.4
23	0434	-0.8	-0.2
Th	1030	6.9	2.1
	1641	0.0	0.0
	2241	7.8	2.4
24	0518	-0.8	-0.2
F	1113	6.9	2.1
	1723	0.1	0.0
	2323	7.6	2.3
25	0600	-0.6	-0.2
Sa	1153	6.8	2.1
	1801	0.3	0.1
	2357	7.5	2.3
26	0638	-0.3	-0.1
Su	1231	6.7	2.0
	1831	0.5	0.2
27	0023	7.3	2.2
M	0711	-0.1	0.0
	1301	6.7	2.0
	1852	0.7	0.2
28	0041	7.2	2.2
Tu	0738	0.2	0.1
	1319	6.7	2.0
	1914	0.8	0.2
29	0106	7.1	2.2
W	0754	0.4	0.1
	1343	6.7	2.0
	1948	0.9	0.3
30	0143	7.0	2.1
Th	0820	0.5	0.2
	1417	6.8	2.1
	2031	0.9	0.3

Time meridian 75° W. 0000 is midnight. 1200 is noon.
Heights are referred to mean low water which is the chart datum of soundings.

Times and Heights of High and Low Waters

JULY

Day	Time h m	Height ft	Height m	Day	Time h m	Height ft	Height m
1	0225	6.9	2.1	16	0414	7.1	2.2
F	0857	0.6	0.2	Sa	1053	-0.3	-0.1
	1457	6.9	2.1		1653	7.4	2.3
	2116	1.0	0.3		2332	-0.2	-0.1
2	0311	6.8	2.1	17	0527	6.9	2.1
Sa	0937	0.7	0.2	Su	1154	0.0	0.0
	1542	7.0	2.1		1759	7.4	2.3
	2207	1.0	0.3				
3	0402	6.6	2.0	18	0036	-0.2	-0.1
Su	1025	0.7	0.2	M	0634	6.7	2.0
	1630	7.1	2.2		1254	0.1	0.0
	2302	0.9	0.3		1859	7.5	2.3
4	0454	6.5	2.0	19	0136	-0.3	-0.1
M	1114	0.7	0.2	Tu	0734	6.7	2.0
	1725	7.2	2.2		1350	0.2	0.1
					1957	7.5	2.3
5	0002	0.8	0.2	20	0232	-0.3	-0.1
Tu	0553	6.5	2.0	W	0830	6.7	2.0
	1209	0.7	0.2		1445	0.2	0.1
	1818	7.4	2.3		2050	7.6	2.3
6	0112	0.5	0.2	21	0323	-0.4	-0.1
W	0653	6.5	2.0	Th	0920	6.8	2.1
	1307	0.6	0.2		1533	0.3	0.1
	1913	7.6	2.3		2138	7.6	2.3
7	0222	0.2	0.1	22	0412	-0.4	-0.1
Th	0753	6.6	2.0	F	1009	6.8	2.1
	1405	0.4	0.1		1618	0.3	0.1
	2010	7.9	2.4		2226	7.6	2.3
8	0327	-0.2	-0.1	23	0455	-0.4	-0.1
F	0851	6.8	2.1	Sa	1051	6.9	2.1
	1507	0.2	0.1		1700	0.4	0.1
	2106	8.2	2.5		2304	7.6	2.3
9	0425	-0.6	-0.2	24	0537	-0.3	-0.1
Sa	0951	7.1	2.2	Su	1132	6.9	2.1
	1610	0.0	0.0		1737	0.4	0.1
	2202	8.3	2.5		2341	7.5	2.3
10	0519	-0.9	-0.3	25	0613	-0.1	0.0
Su	1047	7.3	2.2	M	1208	6.9	2.1
	1710	-0.2	-0.1		1809	0.5	0.2
	2257	8.4	2.6				
11	0613	-1.1	-0.3	26	0003	7.4	2.3
M	1142	7.5	2.3	Tu	0644	0.1	0.0
	1811	-0.3	-0.1		1230	6.9	2.1
	2353	8.4	2.6		1831	0.6	0.2
12	0706	-1.1	-0.3	27	0014	7.3	2.2
Tu	1239	7.6	2.3	W	0703	0.2	0.1
	1913	-0.4	-0.1		1242	7.0	2.1
					1852	0.6	0.2
13	0050	8.2	2.5	28	0039	7.3	2.2
W	0759	-1.0	-0.3	Th	0716	0.3	0.1
	1338	7.6	2.3		1305	7.1	2.2
	2015	-0.4	-0.1		1922	0.6	0.2
14	0151	7.9	2.4	29	0114	7.3	2.2
Th	0857	-0.8	-0.2	F	0742	0.3	0.1
	1439	7.6	2.3		1338	7.2	2.2
	2122	-0.3	-0.1		2000	0.6	0.2
15	0300	7.5	2.3	30	0154	7.2	2.2
F	0953	-0.6	-0.2	Sa	0818	0.4	0.1
	1545	7.5	2.3		1418	7.3	2.2
	2227	-0.2	-0.1		2041	0.6	0.2
				31	0237	7.0	2.1
				Su	0900	0.4	0.1
					1502	7.4	2.3
					2129	0.7	0.2

AUGUST

Day	Time h m	Height ft	Height m	Day	Time h m	Height ft	Height m
1	0327	6.9	2.1	16	0007	0.0	0.0
M	0944	0.5	0.2	Tu	0607	6.6	2.0
	1551	7.4	2.3		1221	0.5	0.2
	2223	0.7	0.2		1833	7.2	2.2
2	0419	6.7	2.0	17	0107	0.1	0.0
Tu	1034	0.7	0.2	W	0707	6.5	2.0
	1645	7.5	2.3		1323	0.7	0.2
	2320	0.7	0.2		1933	7.3	2.2
3	0519	6.5	2.0	18	0205	0.1	0.0
W	1130	0.7	0.2	Th	0805	6.6	2.0
	1742	7.5	2.3		1418	0.7	0.2
					2028	7.4	2.3
4	0030	0.6	0.2	19	0258	0.1	0.0
Th	0620	6.5	2.0	F	0858	6.8	2.1
	1233	0.7	0.2		1509	0.6	0.2
	1843	7.6	2.3		2116	7.5	2.3
5	0201	0.3	0.1	20	0346	0.0	0.0
F	0728	6.6	2.0	Sa	0944	6.9	2.1
	1342	0.6	0.2		1556	0.5	0.2
	1947	7.8	2.4		2203	7.5	2.3
6	0315	-0.1	0.0	21	0429	0.0	0.0
Sa	0834	6.9	2.1	Su	1028	7.1	2.2
	1459	0.3	0.1		1637	0.5	0.2
	2051	8.1	2.5		2244	7.6	2.3
7	0413	-0.5	-0.2	22	0507	0.0	0.0
Su	0940	7.2	2.2	M	1107	7.2	2.2
	1612	-0.1	0.0		1715	0.4	0.1
	2154	8.3	2.5		2316	7.5	2.3
8	0508	-0.9	-0.3	23	0542	0.1	0.0
M	1039	7.6	2.3	Tu	1138	7.2	2.2
	1713	-0.4	-0.1		1746	0.4	0.1
	2252	8.4	2.6		2337	7.4	2.3
9	0558	-1.1	-0.3	24	0610	0.1	0.0
Tu	1134	7.9	2.4	W	1153	7.2	2.2
	1809	-0.7	-0.2		1808	0.4	0.1
	2349	8.4	2.6		2349	7.4	2.3
10	0650	-1.2	-0.4	25	0626	0.2	0.1
W	1228	8.0	2.4	Th	1200	7.3	2.2
	1906	-0.8	-0.2		1827	0.3	0.1
11	0046	8.2	2.5	26	0012	7.4	2.3
Th	0738	-1.1	-0.3	F	0640	0.2	0.1
	1322	8.0	2.4		1230	7.5	2.3
	2003	-0.8	-0.2		1855	0.2	0.1
12	0143	7.9	2.4	27	0045	7.4	2.3
F	0831	-0.9	-0.3	Sa	0708	0.2	0.1
	1415	7.9	2.4		1303	7.6	2.3
	2100	-0.6	-0.2		1929	0.2	0.1
13	0244	7.5	2.3	28	0125	7.3	2.2
Sa	0924	-0.5	-0.2	Su	0744	0.3	0.1
	1515	7.7	2.3		1345	7.7	2.3
	2201	-0.4	-0.1		2012	0.3	0.1
14	0352	7.1	2.2	29	0209	7.2	2.2
Su	1020	-0.1	0.0	M	0825	0.4	0.1
	1622	7.5	2.3		1430	7.7	2.3
	2306	-0.1	0.0		2059	0.4	0.1
15	0501	6.7	2.0	30	0257	7.0	2.1
M	1122	0.3	0.1	Tu	0910	0.6	0.2
	1730	7.3	2.2		1518	7.7	2.3
					2150	0.6	0.2
				31	0353	6.7	2.0
				W	1001	0.8	0.2
					1614	7.6	2.3
					2251	0.7	0.2

SEPTEMBER

Day	Time h m	Height ft	Height m	Day	Time h m	Height ft	Height m
1	0451	6.5	2.0	16	0133	0.6	0.2
Th	1103	0.9	0.3	F	0736	6.6	2.0
	1715	7.5	2.3		1349	1.1	0.3
					2000	7.1	2.2
2	0009	0.8	0.2	17	0226	0.5	0.2
F	0558	6.5	2.0	Sa	0828	6.8	2.1
	1212	1.0	0.3		1442	0.9	0.3
	1822	7.5	2.3		2050	7.2	2.2
3	0157	0.5	0.2	18	0314	0.4	0.1
Sa	0713	6.7	2.0	Su	0917	7.1	2.2
	1341	0.8	0.2		1527	0.7	0.2
	1933	7.6	2.3		2136	7.4	2.3
4	0304	0.0	0.0	19	0356	0.3	0.1
Su	0829	7.1	2.2	M	0959	7.2	2.2
	1509	0.3	0.1		1608	0.5	0.2
	2047	7.9	2.4		2218	7.4	2.3
5	0400	-0.5	-0.2	20	0433	0.3	0.1
M	0935	7.5	2.3	Tu	1033	7.4	2.3
	1612	-0.3	-0.1		1646	0.3	0.1
	2151	8.2	2.5		2248	7.4	2.3
6	0452	-0.9	-0.3	21	0505	0.2	0.1
Tu	1029	7.9	2.4	W	1100	7.4	2.3
	1709	-0.8	-0.2		1718	0.2	0.1
	2250	8.3	2.5		2305	7.4	2.3
7	0540	-1.1	-0.3	22	0531	0.2	0.1
W	1121	8.2	2.5	Th	1108	7.5	2.3
	1801	-1.1	-0.3		1741	0.1	0.0
	2343	8.3	2.5		2316	7.4	2.3
8	0628	-1.2	-0.4	23	0544	0.2	0.1
Th	1209	8.3	2.5	F	1126	7.7	2.3
	1852	-1.2	-0.4		1801	0.0	0.0
					2343	7.4	2.3
9	0036	8.1	2.5	24	0605	0.1	0.0
F	0714	-1.0	-0.3	Sa	1156	7.9	2.4
	1258	8.3	2.5		1829	-0.1	0.0
	1943	-1.1	-0.3				
10	0127	7.8	2.4	25	0019	7.4	2.3
Sa	0759	-0.7	-0.2	Su	0637	0.1	0.0
	1348	8.1	2.5		1234	8.0	2.4
	2036	-0.8	-0.2		1906	-0.1	0.0
11	0222	7.4	2.3	26	0100	7.4	2.3
Su	0849	-0.2	-0.1	M	0714	0.2	0.1
	1441	7.7	2.3		1315	8.0	2.4
	2132	-0.4	-0.1		1947	0.0	0.0
12	0322	7.0	2.1	27	0144	7.2	2.2
M	0945	0.2	0.1	Tu	0756	0.4	0.1
	1545	7.4	2.3		1401	7.9	2.4
	2234	0.0	0.0		2033	0.2	0.1
13	0430	6.6	2.0	28	0234	7.0	2.1
Tu	1045	0.7	0.2	W	0844	0.7	0.2
	1654	7.1	2.2		1452	7.7	2.3
	2336	0.4	0.1		2128	0.5	0.2
14	0537	6.4	2.0	29	0330	6.7	2.0
W	1149	1.0	0.3	Th	0941	0.9	0.3
	1802	6.9	2.1		1550	7.5	2.3
					2235	0.7	0.2
15	0037	0.6	0.2	30	0433	6.5	2.0
Th	0640	6.4	2.0	F	1046	1.2	0.4
	1251	1.1	0.3		1656	7.3	2.2
	1904	7.0	2.1				

Time meridian 75° W. 0000 is midnight. 1200 is noon.
Heights are referred to mean low water which is the chart datum of soundings.

Times and Heights of High and Low Waters

OCTOBER

Day	Time (h m)	Height (ft)	Height (m)
1	0020	0.8	0.2
Sa	0548	6.5	2.0
	1218	1.1	0.3
	1811	7.2	2.2
2	0149	0.4	0.1
Su	0715	6.8	2.1
	1405	0.7	0.2
	1936	7.4	2.3
3	0250	0.0	0.0
M	0830	7.3	2.2
	1511	0.0	0.0
	2053	7.7	2.3
4	0344	-0.5	-0.2
Tu	0927	7.8	2.4
	1607	-0.6	-0.2
	2152	7.9	2.4
5	0433	-0.8	-0.2
W	1018	8.2	2.5
	1658	-1.1	-0.3
	2244	8.1	2.5
6	0519	-1.0	-0.3
Th	1105	8.4	2.6
	1747	-1.4	-0.4
	2333	8.0	2.4
7	0603	-1.0	-0.3
F	1148	8.4	2.6
	1837	-1.4	-0.4
8	0020	7.8	2.4
Sa	0647	-0.8	-0.2
	1234	8.3	2.5
	1922	-1.2	-0.4
9	0108	7.5	2.3
Su	0730	-0.4	-0.1
	1319	8.0	2.4
	2012	-0.8	-0.2
10	0159	7.1	2.2
M	0815	0.0	0.0
	1406	7.6	2.3
	2102	-0.3	-0.1
11	0252	6.8	2.1
Tu	0902	0.5	0.2
	1500	7.2	2.2
	2158	0.2	0.1
12	0353	6.5	2.0
W	1001	1.0	0.3
	1606	6.8	2.1
	2258	0.6	0.2
13	0502	6.3	1.9
Th	1107	1.3	0.4
	1721	6.6	2.0
	2358	0.9	0.3
14	0605	6.3	1.9
F	1212	1.4	0.4
	1827	6.6	2.0
15	0054	0.9	0.3
Sa	0703	6.5	2.0
	1312	1.3	0.4
	1926	6.7	2.0
16	0147	0.9	0.3
Su	0753	6.8	2.1
	1406	1.1	0.3
	2016	6.9	2.1
17	0234	0.8	0.2
M	0840	7.0	2.1
	1453	0.8	0.2
	2101	7.0	2.1
18	0317	0.6	0.2
Tu	0920	7.2	2.2
	1535	0.5	0.2
	2139	7.1	2.2
19	0351	0.4	0.1
W	0951	7.3	2.2
	1612	0.2	0.1
	2207	7.1	2.2
20	0423	0.3	0.1
Th	1008	7.5	2.3
	1646	0.0	0.0
	2225	7.2	2.2
21	0445	0.2	0.1
F	1023	7.7	2.3
	1713	-0.2	-0.1
	2245	7.2	2.2
22	0504	0.1	0.0
Sa	1051	7.9	2.4
	1737	-0.4	-0.1
	2318	7.3	2.2
23	0536	0.0	0.0
Su	1127	8.1	2.5
	1809	-0.4	-0.1
	2356	7.3	2.2
24	0610	0.0	0.0
M	1208	8.2	2.5
	1847	-0.4	-0.1
25	0040	7.2	2.2
Tu	0650	0.2	0.1
	1252	8.1	2.5
	1931	-0.2	-0.1
26	0126	7.1	2.2
W	0735	0.4	0.1
	1340	7.9	2.4
	2020	0.0	0.0
27	0217	6.9	2.1
Th	0828	0.7	0.2
	1433	7.6	2.3
	2118	0.3	0.1
28	0316	6.7	2.0
F	0929	1.0	0.3
	1534	7.3	2.2
	2239	0.6	0.2
29	0424	6.5	2.0
Sa	1051	1.1	0.3
	1645	7.0	2.1
30	0024	0.5	0.2
Su	0551	6.6	2.0
	1251	0.8	0.2
	1816	6.9	2.1
31	0133	0.2	0.1
M	0720	7.0	2.1
	1402	0.2	0.1
	1949	7.1	2.2

NOVEMBER

Day	Time (h m)	Height (ft)	Height (m)
1	0232	-0.2	-0.1
Tu	0822	7.5	2.3
	1501	-0.4	-0.1
	2051	7.3	2.2
2	0324	-0.5	-0.2
W	0915	7.9	2.4
	1554	-0.9	-0.3
	2146	7.5	2.3
3	0412	-0.8	-0.2
Th	1004	8.2	2.5
	1645	-1.3	-0.4
	2234	7.6	2.3
4	0459	-0.9	-0.3
F	1049	8.3	2.5
	1732	-1.5	-0.5
	2321	7.5	2.3
5	0541	-0.8	-0.2
Sa	1131	8.2	2.5
	1817	-1.4	-0.4
6	0006	7.4	2.3
Su	0623	-0.6	-0.2
	1213	8.0	2.4
	1903	-1.2	-0.4
7	0050	7.1	2.2
M	0705	-0.2	-0.1
	1254	7.7	2.3
	1946	-0.8	-0.2
8	0137	6.8	2.1
Tu	0740	0.2	0.1
	1332	7.4	2.3
	2033	-0.3	-0.1
9	0223	6.6	2.0
W	0820	0.6	0.2
	1412	7.0	2.1
	2121	0.2	0.1
10	0316	6.3	1.9
Th	0902	1.0	0.3
	1500	6.7	2.0
	2213	0.6	0.2
11	0416	6.2	1.9
F	1005	1.3	0.4
	1605	6.4	2.0
	2305	0.9	0.3
12	0519	6.2	1.9
Sa	1120	1.5	0.5
	1731	6.2	1.9
13	0001	1.0	0.3
Su	0615	6.3	1.9
	1223	1.4	0.4
	1835	6.2	1.9
14	0054	1.0	0.3
M	0707	6.5	2.0
	1320	1.2	0.4
	1928	6.3	1.9
15	0142	0.9	0.3
Tu	0752	6.7	2.0
	1410	0.9	0.3
	2014	6.4	2.0
16	0224	0.7	0.2
W	0829	6.9	2.1
	1455	0.5	0.2
	2048	6.5	2.0
17	0302	0.5	0.2
Th	0850	7.2	2.2
	1535	0.1	0.0
	2115	6.6	2.0
18	0330	0.3	0.1
F	0911	7.4	2.3
	1612	-0.2	-0.1
	2140	6.8	2.1
19	0357	0.1	0.0
Sa	0943	7.7	2.3
	1645	-0.5	-0.2
	2215	6.9	2.1
20	0431	0.0	0.0
Su	1021	8.0	2.4
	1721	-0.7	-0.2
	2254	7.1	2.2
21	0506	-0.1	0.0
M	1103	8.1	2.5
	1757	-0.8	-0.2
	2338	7.1	2.2
22	0549	-0.1	0.0
Tu	1148	8.2	2.5
	1838	-0.7	-0.2
23	0024	7.1	2.2
W	0634	0.0	0.0
	1234	8.1	2.5
	1926	-0.6	-0.2
24	0113	7.0	2.1
Th	0727	0.2	0.1
	1326	7.8	2.4
	2020	-0.3	-0.1
25	0208	6.8	2.1
F	0823	0.4	0.1
	1421	7.4	2.3
	2126	-0.1	0.0
26	0310	6.7	2.0
Sa	0937	0.6	0.2
	1526	7.0	2.1
	2253	0.1	0.0
27	0424	6.7	2.0
Su	1125	0.6	0.2
	1645	6.7	2.0
28	0008	0.1	0.0
M	0555	6.8	2.1
	1243	0.3	0.1
	1825	6.6	2.0
29	0112	-0.1	0.0
Tu	0709	7.1	2.2
	1349	-0.2	-0.1
	1941	6.7	2.0
30	0210	-0.3	-0.1
W	0808	7.4	2.3
	1447	-0.7	-0.2
	2040	6.9	2.1

DECEMBER

Day	Time (h m)	Height (ft)	Height (m)
1	0303	-0.5	-0.2
Th	0901	7.7	2.3
	1540	-1.2	-0.4
	2133	7.0	2.1
2	0356	-0.7	-0.2
F	0948	7.9	2.4
	1629	-1.4	-0.4
	2221	7.0	2.1
3	0440	-0.7	-0.2
Sa	1035	7.9	2.4
	1716	-1.5	-0.5
	2309	7.0	2.1
4	0524	-0.6	-0.2
Su	1119	7.9	2.4
	1802	-1.4	-0.4
	2352	6.9	2.1
5	0604	-0.4	-0.1
M	1158	7.7	2.3
	1844	-1.1	-0.3
6	0034	6.8	2.1
Tu	0642	-0.1	0.0
	1234	7.4	2.3
	1926	-0.7	-0.2
7	0114	6.6	2.0
W	0716	0.2	0.1
	1306	7.2	2.2
	2003	-0.3	-0.1
8	0153	6.5	2.0
Th	0746	0.5	0.2
	1338	6.9	2.1
	2039	0.1	0.0
9	0228	6.3	1.9
F	0815	0.8	0.2
	1411	6.6	2.0
	2108	0.4	0.1
10	0302	6.3	1.9
Sa	0857	1.0	0.3
	1452	6.4	2.0
	2139	0.6	0.2
11	0342	6.2	1.9
Su	0947	1.1	0.3
	1541	6.2	1.9
	2218	0.8	0.2
12	0427	6.2	1.9
M	1046	1.2	0.4
	1635	6.0	1.8
	2309	0.9	0.3
13	0517	6.3	1.9
Tu	1159	1.1	0.3
	1731	5.9	1.8
	2359	0.9	0.3
14	0606	6.5	2.0
W	1308	0.8	0.2
	1831	6.0	1.8
15	0051	0.7	0.2
Th	0654	6.7	2.0
	1404	0.5	0.2
	1923	6.1	1.9
16	0141	0.5	0.2
F	0739	7.0	2.1
	1453	0.1	0.0
	2015	6.2	1.9
17	0232	0.3	0.1
Sa	0824	7.3	2.2
	1541	-0.3	-0.1
	2103	6.4	2.0
18	0315	0.1	0.0
Su	0911	7.6	2.3
	1623	-0.6	-0.2
	2148	6.7	2.0
19	0402	-0.1	0.0
M	0956	7.9	2.4
	1706	-0.9	-0.3
	2236	6.9	2.1
20	0450	-0.3	-0.1
Tu	1045	8.1	2.5
	1751	-1.1	-0.3
	2324	7.0	2.1
21	0538	-0.4	-0.1
W	1132	8.1	2.5
	1837	-1.1	-0.3
22	0013	7.1	2.2
Th	0631	-0.3	-0.1
	1223	8.0	2.4
	1929	-1.0	-0.3
23	0106	7.1	2.2
F	0727	-0.2	-0.1
	1319	7.7	2.3
	2023	-0.8	-0.2
24	0203	7.0	2.1
Sa	0833	-0.1	0.0
	1417	7.3	2.2
	2126	-0.6	-0.2
25	0305	6.9	2.1
Su	0955	0.0	0.0
	1524	6.9	2.1
	2235	-0.4	-0.1
26	0421	6.9	2.1
M	1115	0.0	0.0
	1650	6.5	2.0
	2343	-0.3	-0.1
27	0540	6.9	2.1
Tu	1225	-0.2	-0.1
	1817	6.4	2.0
28	0048	-0.3	-0.1
W	0649	7.1	2.2
	1331	-0.5	-0.2
	1925	6.4	2.0
29	0147	-0.3	-0.1
Th	0749	7.3	2.2
	1428	-0.9	-0.3
	2024	6.5	2.0
30	0242	-0.4	-0.1
F	0845	7.4	2.3
	1522	-1.1	-0.3
	2119	6.6	2.0
31	0335	-0.5	-0.2
Sa	0936	7.5	2.3
	1613	-1.3	-0.4
	2208	6.6	2.0

Time meridian 75° W. 0000 is midnight. 1200 is noon.
Heights are referred to mean low water which is the chart datum of soundings.

NEW YORK (The Battery), N.Y., 1983

Times and Heights of High and Low Waters

JANUARY

Day	Time h m	Height ft	Height m
1 Sa	0321	-0.9	-0.3
	0940	5.5	1.7
	1607	-1.3	-0.4
	2219	4.4	1.3
2 Su	0414	-0.8	-0.2
	1037	5.3	1.6
	1656	-1.1	-0.3
	2317	4.4	1.3
3 M	0507	-0.6	-0.2
	1136	5.0	1.5
	1749	-0.9	-0.3
4 Tu	0015	4.4	1.3
	0607	-0.3	-0.1
	1231	4.7	1.4
	1847	-0.6	-0.2
5 W	0109	4.3	1.3
	0714	0.0	0.0
	1324	4.4	1.3
	1948	-0.4	-0.1
6 Th	0204	4.3	1.3
	0823	0.1	0.0
	1420	4.0	1.2
	2047	-0.3	-0.1
7 F	0258	4.3	1.3
	0925	0.1	0.0
	1518	3.8	1.2
	2143	-0.2	-0.1
8 Sa	0356	4.3	1.3
	1023	0.1	0.0
	1617	3.6	1.1
	2233	-0.2	-0.1
9 Su	0453	4.3	1.3
	1115	0.0	0.0
	1715	3.5	1.1
	2320	-0.2	-0.1
10 M	0543	4.5	1.4
	1202	-0.1	0.0
	1806	3.6	1.1
11 Tu	0006	-0.2	-0.1
	0631	4.6	1.4
	1248	-0.2	-0.1
	1853	3.6	1.1
12 W	0052	-0.2	-0.1
	0711	4.6	1.4
	1335	-0.3	-0.1
	1934	3.7	1.1
13 Th	0136	-0.2	-0.1
	0751	4.7	1.4
	1416	-0.4	-0.1
	2016	3.7	1.1
14 F	0218	-0.2	-0.1
	0829	4.6	1.4
	1457	-0.5	-0.2
	2057	3.7	1.1
15 Sa	0256	-0.1	0.0
	0906	4.6	1.4
	1534	-0.5	-0.2
	2136	3.6	1.1
16 Su	0332	-0.1	0.0
	0941	4.4	1.3
	1608	-0.4	-0.1
	2215	3.6	1.1
17 M	0403	0.1	0.0
	1016	4.3	1.3
	1640	-0.2	-0.1
	2253	3.6	1.1
18 Tu	0432	0.2	0.1
	1049	4.1	1.2
	1707	-0.1	0.0
	2328	3.6	1.1
19 W	0502	0.3	0.1
	1124	4.0	1.2
	1736	0.0	0.0
20 Th	0007	3.7	1.1
	0536	0.4	0.1
	1203	3.9	1.2
	1807	0.1	0.0
21 F	0044	3.8	1.2
	0631	0.5	0.2
	1249	3.7	1.1
	1855	0.2	0.1
22 Sa	0131	3.9	1.2
	0804	0.5	0.2
	1340	3.6	1.1
	2012	0.2	0.1
23 Su	0227	4.1	1.2
	0927	0.4	0.1
	1444	3.5	1.1
	2126	0.1	0.0
24 M	0336	4.3	1.3
	1031	0.1	0.0
	1603	3.5	1.1
	2231	-0.1	0.0
25 Tu	0446	4.6	1.4
	1128	-0.3	-0.1
	1718	3.7	1.1
	2331	-0.4	-0.1
26 W	0550	5.0	1.5
	1224	-0.6	-0.2
	1822	3.9	1.2
27 Th	0027	-0.6	-0.2
	0646	5.3	1.6
	1319	-0.9	-0.3
	1918	4.2	1.3
28 F	0125	-0.9	-0.3
	0740	5.5	1.7
	1411	-1.2	-0.4
	2010	4.5	1.4
29 Sa	0219	-1.1	-0.3
	0832	5.6	1.7
	1500	-1.4	-0.4
	2105	4.6	1.4
30 Su	0310	-1.1	-0.3
	0925	5.5	1.7
	1547	-1.4	-0.4
	2158	4.7	1.4
31 M	0400	-1.0	-0.3
	1019	5.3	1.6
	1634	-1.2	-0.4
	2253	4.7	1.4

FEBRUARY

Day	Time h m	Height ft	Height m
1 Tu	0450	-0.8	-0.2
	1112	5.0	1.5
	1720	-1.0	-0.3
	2346	4.6	1.4
2 W	0544	-0.5	-0.2
	1204	4.6	1.4
	1810	-0.6	-0.2
3 Th	0039	4.5	1.4
	0641	-0.1	0.0
	1255	4.2	1.3
	1906	-0.3	-0.1
4 F	0129	4.4	1.3
	0746	0.2	0.1
	1349	3.8	1.2
	2008	0.0	0.0
5 Sa	0222	4.2	1.3
	0851	0.3	0.1
	1441	3.5	1.1
	2108	0.2	0.1
6 Su	0318	4.1	1.2
	0951	0.3	0.1
	1541	3.3	1.0
	2202	0.2	0.1
7 M	0417	4.0	1.2
	1046	0.2	0.1
	1645	3.3	1.0
	2254	0.2	0.1
8 Tu	0513	4.1	1.2
	1137	0.1	0.0
	1742	3.4	1.0
	2342	0.1	0.0
9 W	0603	4.3	1.3
	1224	0.0	0.0
	1832	3.5	1.1
10 Th	0030	0.0	0.0
	0648	4.4	1.3
	1309	-0.2	-0.1
	1914	3.7	1.1
11 F	0115	-0.1	0.0
	0728	4.6	1.4
	1351	-0.4	-0.1
	1955	3.8	1.2
12 Sa	0158	-0.2	-0.1
	0808	4.6	1.4
	1432	-0.5	-0.2
	2032	3.9	1.2
13 Su	0237	-0.2	-0.1
	0844	4.6	1.4
	1508	-0.5	-0.2
	2107	4.0	1.2
14 M	0313	-0.2	-0.1
	0919	4.5	1.4
	1542	-0.5	-0.2
	2142	4.0	1.2
15 Tu	0347	-0.2	-0.1
	0947	4.4	1.3
	1611	-0.4	-0.1
	2216	4.0	1.2
16 W	0416	-0.1	0.0
	1024	4.2	1.3
	1635	-0.2	-0.1
	2248	4.0	1.2
17 Th	0445	0.0	0.0
	1056	4.1	1.2
	1701	-0.1	0.0
	2325	4.1	1.2
18 F	0520	0.1	0.0
	1133	3.9	1.2
	1728	0.0	0.0
19 Sa	0007	4.2	1.3
	0605	0.3	0.1
	1221	3.7	1.1
	1812	0.1	0.0
20 Su	0058	4.2	1.3
	0724	0.4	0.1
	1316	3.6	1.1
	1916	0.3	0.1
21 M	0157	4.3	1.3
	0858	0.4	0.1
	1424	3.5	1.1
	2057	0.3	0.1
22 Tu	0308	4.4	1.3
	1009	0.1	0.0
	1548	3.5	1.1
	2215	0.1	0.0
23 W	0427	4.6	1.4
	1111	-0.2	-0.1
	1707	3.7	1.1
	2318	-0.2	-0.1
24 Th	0534	4.9	1.5
	1208	-0.5	-0.2
	1811	4.1	1.2
25 F	0017	-0.5	-0.2
	0635	5.2	1.6
	1301	-0.9	-0.3
	1904	4.5	1.4
26 Sa	0112	-0.8	-0.2
	0726	5.4	1.6
	1351	-1.1	-0.3
	1955	4.8	1.5
27 Su	0206	-1.1	-0.3
	0817	5.5	1.7
	1438	-1.3	-0.4
	2045	5.0	1.5
28 M	0256	-1.2	-0.4
	0906	5.4	1.6
	1523	-1.3	-0.4
	2134	5.1	1.6

MARCH

Day	Time h m	Height ft	Height m
1 Tu	0343	-1.1	-0.3
	0957	5.1	1.6
	1606	-1.1	-0.3
	2224	5.0	1.5
2 W	0429	-0.9	-0.3
	1047	4.8	1.5
	1651	-0.8	-0.2
	2315	4.9	1.5
3 Th	0517	-0.5	-0.2
	1136	4.5	1.4
	1733	-0.4	-0.1
4 F	0005	4.7	1.4
	0607	-0.1	0.0
	1225	4.1	1.2
	1823	0.0	0.0
5 Sa	0053	4.4	1.3
	0706	0.3	0.1
	1316	3.7	1.1
	1920	0.4	0.1
6 Su	0143	4.2	1.3
	0814	0.5	0.2
	1407	3.4	1.0
	2028	0.6	0.2
7 M	0237	4.0	1.2
	0918	0.6	0.2
	1507	3.2	1.0
	2130	0.7	0.2
8 Tu	0335	3.9	1.2
	1015	0.5	0.2
	1612	3.2	1.0
	2225	0.6	0.2
9 W	0438	3.9	1.2
	1106	0.4	0.1
	1711	3.4	1.0
	2319	0.5	0.2
10 Th	0532	4.1	1.2
	1154	0.2	0.1
	1803	3.6	1.1
11 F	0006	0.3	0.1
	0623	4.3	1.3
	1239	0.0	0.0
	1848	3.9	1.2
12 Sa	0051	0.1	0.0
	0701	4.5	1.4
	1321	-0.2	-0.1
	1927	4.1	1.2
13 Su	0133	-0.1	0.0
	0741	4.6	1.4
	1400	-0.4	-0.1
	2003	4.3	1.3
14 M	0213	-0.3	-0.1
	0815	4.6	1.4
	1437	-0.4	-0.1
	2036	4.4	1.3
15 Tu	0251	-0.4	-0.1
	0850	4.6	1.4
	1510	-0.4	-0.1
	2108	4.5	1.4
16 W	0326	-0.4	-0.1
	0922	4.5	1.4
	1540	-0.3	-0.1
	2140	4.6	1.4
17 Th	0359	-0.3	-0.1
	0955	4.3	1.3
	1608	-0.2	-0.1
	2214	4.6	1.4
18 F	0432	-0.2	-0.1
	1036	4.2	1.3
	1635	-0.1	0.0
	2256	4.6	1.4
19 Sa	0509	-0.1	0.0
	1117	4.0	1.2
	1706	0.1	0.0
	2344	4.6	1.4
20 Su	0557	0.2	0.1
	1213	3.8	1.2
	1749	0.3	0.1
21 M	0039	4.5	1.4
	0713	0.4	0.1
	1314	3.6	1.1
	1859	0.5	0.2
22 Tu	0143	4.5	1.4
	0842	0.4	0.1
	1424	3.6	1.1
	2051	0.5	0.2
23 W	0256	4.5	1.4
	0953	0.2	0.1
	1543	3.7	1.1
	2205	0.3	0.1
24 Th	0412	4.6	1.4
	1052	-0.1	0.0
	1655	4.0	1.2
	2309	0.0	0.0
25 F	0521	4.8	1.5
	1147	-0.5	-0.2
	1755	4.5	1.4
26 Sa	0006	-0.4	-0.1
	0619	5.1	1.6
	1238	-0.7	-0.2
	1848	4.9	1.5
27 Su	0059	-0.7	-0.2
	0709	5.2	1.6
	1327	-0.9	-0.3
	1938	5.2	1.6
28 M	0150	-0.9	-0.3
	0758	5.3	1.6
	1413	-1.0	-0.3
	2023	5.4	1.6
29 Tu	0237	-1.0	-0.3
	0844	5.2	1.6
	1457	-1.0	-0.3
	2107	5.4	1.6
30 W	0323	-0.9	-0.3
	0932	4.9	1.5
	1538	-0.8	-0.2
	2155	5.2	1.6
31 Th	0408	-0.7	-0.2
	1019	4.6	1.4
	1618	-0.5	-0.2
	2241	5.0	1.5

Time meridian 75° W. 0000 is midnight. 1200 is noon.
Heights are referred to mean low water which is the chart datum of soundings.

Times and Heights of High and Low Waters

APRIL

Day	Time h m	Height ft	Height m	Day	Time h m	Height ft	Height m
1	0450	-0.4	-0.1	16	0421	-0.4	-0.1
F	1108	4.3	1.3	Sa	1022	4.2	1.3
	1658	-0.1	0.0		1615	0.0	0.0
	2327	4.7	1.4		2237	5.0	1.5
2	0536	0.0	0.0	17	0503	-0.2	-0.1
Sa	1157	3.9	1.2	Su	1117	4.0	1.2
	1738	0.3	0.1		1654	0.2	0.1
					2333	4.9	1.5
3	0015	4.5	1.4	18	0557	0.0	0.0
Su	0628	0.4	0.1	M	1218	3.9	1.2
	1246	3.7	1.1		1746	0.4	0.1
	1832	0.7	0.2				
4	0103	4.2	1.3	19	0034	4.8	1.5
M	0732	0.7	0.2	Tu	0711	0.2	0.1
	1337	3.4	1.0		1321	3.8	1.2
	1942	1.0	0.3		1913	0.7	0.2
5	0154	4.0	1.2	20	0139	4.6	1.4
Tu	0839	0.8	0.2	W	0830	0.2	0.1
	1434	3.3	1.0		1427	3.9	1.2
	2054	1.1	0.3		2046	0.6	0.2
6	0250	3.8	1.2	21	0248	4.6	1.4
W	0938	0.7	0.2	Th	0935	0.1	0.0
	1533	3.4	1.0		1535	4.1	1.2
	2156	1.0	0.3		2156	0.4	0.1
7	0353	3.8	1.2	22	0357	4.6	1.4
Th	1030	0.5	0.2	F	1033	-0.2	-0.1
	1635	3.5	1.1		1641	4.4	1.3
	2247	0.8	0.2		2257	0.0	0.0
8	0452	4.0	1.2	23	0503	4.7	1.4
F	1118	0.3	0.1	Sa	1124	-0.4	-0.1
	1729	3.8	1.2		1739	4.8	1.5
	2335	0.5	0.2		2351	-0.3	-0.1
9	0543	4.2	1.3	24	0600	4.9	1.5
Sa	1201	0.1	0.0	Su	1214	-0.6	-0.2
	1813	4.1	1.2		1828	5.2	1.6
10	0022	0.3	0.1	25	0043	-0.5	-0.2
Su	0628	4.4	1.3	M	0651	5.0	1.5
	1243	0.0	0.0		1301	-0.7	-0.2
	1853	4.4	1.3		1915	5.4	1.6
11	0104	0.0	0.0	26	0133	-0.7	-0.2
M	0707	4.5	1.4	Tu	0738	4.9	1.5
	1323	-0.2	-0.1		1346	-0.7	-0.2
	1927	4.7	1.4		1958	5.5	1.7
12	0146	-0.2	-0.1	27	0218	-0.7	-0.2
Tu	0744	4.6	1.4	W	0821	4.8	1.5
	1402	-0.3	-0.1		1430	-0.6	-0.2
	2002	4.9	1.5		2041	5.5	1.7
13	0225	-0.4	-0.1	28	0303	-0.7	-0.2
W	0821	4.6	1.4	Th	0906	4.6	1.4
	1437	-0.3	-0.1		1510	-0.4	-0.1
	2034	5.0	1.5		2124	5.3	1.6
14	0306	-0.5	-0.2	29	0345	-0.5	-0.2
Th	0857	4.5	1.4	F	0952	4.3	1.3
	1509	-0.3	-0.1		1548	-0.1	0.0
	2108	5.1	1.6		2207	5.1	1.6
15	0342	-0.5	-0.2	30	0427	-0.2	-0.1
F	0934	4.4	1.3	Sa	1039	4.1	1.2
	1541	-0.2	-0.1		1627	0.2	0.1
	2147	5.1	1.6		2253	4.8	1.5

MAY

Day	Time h m	Height ft	Height m	Day	Time h m	Height ft	Height m
1	0509	0.1	0.0	16	0501	-0.4	-0.1
Su	1130	3.8	1.2	M	1117	4.2	1.3
	1704	0.6	0.2		1653	0.2	0.1
	2338	4.5	1.4		2328	5.2	1.6
2	0554	0.4	0.1	17	0553	-0.2	-0.1
M	1221	3.6	1.1	Tu	1219	4.1	1.2
	1746	1.0	0.3		1754	0.5	0.2
3	0026	4.3	1.3	18	0031	5.0	1.5
Tu	0649	0.7	0.2	W	0700	0.0	0.0
	1309	3.5	1.1		1319	4.2	1.3
	1847	1.2	0.4		1916	0.6	0.2
4	0112	4.1	1.2	19	0132	4.8	1.5
W	0756	0.8	0.2	Th	0810	0.0	0.0
	1401	3.5	1.1		1419	4.3	1.3
	2012	1.3	0.4		2035	0.6	0.2
5	0204	3.9	1.2	20	0235	4.7	1.4
Th	0857	0.8	0.2	F	0912	-0.1	0.0
	1454	3.6	1.1		1519	4.5	1.4
	2116	1.2	0.4		2142	0.4	0.1
6	0301	3.9	1.2	21	0338	4.6	1.4
F	0949	0.6	0.2	Sa	1009	-0.2	-0.1
	1550	3.7	1.1		1620	4.8	1.5
	2211	1.0	0.3		2239	0.1	0.0
7	0401	3.9	1.2	22	0441	4.6	1.4
Sa	1036	0.5	0.2	Su	1100	-0.3	-0.1
	1644	4.0	1.2		1716	5.1	1.6
	2300	0.7	0.2		2333	-0.1	0.0
8	0457	4.0	1.2	23	0537	4.6	1.4
Su	1119	0.3	0.1	M	1147	-0.3	-0.1
	1731	4.3	1.3		1808	5.3	1.6
	2347	0.4	0.1				
9	0546	4.2	1.3	24	0024	-0.3	-0.1
M	1201	0.1	0.0	Tu	0628	4.6	1.4
	1812	4.7	1.4		1233	-0.4	-0.1
					1851	5.5	1.7
10	0032	0.1	0.0	25	0113	-0.4	-0.1
Tu	0628	4.4	1.3	W	0717	4.6	1.4
	1241	0.0	0.0		1319	-0.3	-0.1
	1851	5.0	1.5		1936	5.5	1.7
11	0117	-0.2	-0.1	26	0159	-0.4	-0.1
W	0710	4.5	1.4	Th	0800	4.5	1.4
	1323	-0.1	0.0		1402	-0.2	-0.1
	1927	5.3	1.6		2017	5.5	1.7
12	0200	-0.4	-0.1	27	0244	-0.4	-0.1
Th	0750	4.5	1.4	F	0845	4.3	1.3
	1401	-0.2	-0.1		1444	0.0	0.0
	2004	5.5	1.7		2058	5.3	1.6
13	0244	-0.5	-0.2	28	0326	-0.3	-0.1
F	0832	4.5	1.4	Sa	0928	4.1	1.2
	1441	-0.2	-0.1		1523	0.2	0.1
	2046	5.5	1.7		2139	5.1	1.6
14	0327	-0.6	-0.2	29	0405	-0.1	0.0
Sa	0919	4.4	1.3	Su	1016	3.9	1.2
	1522	-0.1	0.0		1600	0.5	0.2
	2133	5.5	1.7		2222	4.8	1.5
15	0411	-0.5	-0.2	30	0445	0.1	0.0
Su	1016	4.2	1.3	M	1104	3.8	1.2
	1605	0.0	0.0		1637	0.7	0.2
	2227	5.3	1.6		2305	4.6	1.4
				31	0525	0.3	0.1
				Tu	1152	3.7	1.1
					1714	1.0	0.3
					2351	4.4	1.3

JUNE

Day	Time h m	Height ft	Height m	Day	Time h m	Height ft	Height m
1	0610	0.5	0.2	16	0021	5.2	1.6
W	1241	3.7	1.1	Th	0641	-0.3	-0.1
	1757	1.2	0.4		1305	4.6	1.4
					1903	0.5	0.2
2	0034	4.2	1.3	17	0118	5.0	1.5
Th	0703	0.7	0.2	F	0744	-0.1	0.0
	1326	3.7	1.1		1401	4.7	1.4
	1914	1.4	0.4		2016	0.5	0.2
3	0116	4.1	1.2	18	0214	4.7	1.4
F	0806	0.7	0.2	Sa	0846	-0.1	0.0
	1411	3.8	1.2		1457	4.9	1.5
	2028	1.3	0.4		2122	0.4	0.1
4	0206	4.0	1.2	19	0314	4.5	1.4
Sa	0858	0.7	0.2	Su	0941	-0.1	0.0
	1457	3.9	1.2		1556	5.0	1.5
	2130	1.2	0.4		2220	0.3	0.1
5	0258	3.9	1.2	20	0415	4.3	1.3
Su	0948	0.6	0.2	M	1033	-0.1	0.0
	1548	4.2	1.3		1653	5.1	1.6
	2221	0.9	0.3		2313	0.1	0.0
6	0357	3.9	1.2	21	0515	4.3	1.3
M	1031	0.4	0.1	Tu	1121	-0.1	0.0
	1641	4.5	1.4		1743	5.3	1.6
	2310	0.6	0.2				
7	0454	4.0	1.2	22	0003	0.0	0.0
Tu	1116	0.3	0.1	W	0606	4.2	1.3
	1727	4.9	1.5		1208	0.0	0.0
	2358	0.2	0.1		1830	5.4	1.6
8	0548	4.2	1.3	23	0052	-0.1	0.0
W	1158	0.1	0.0	Th	0654	4.2	1.3
	1811	5.2	1.6		1254	0.1	0.0
					1912	5.4	1.6
9	0045	-0.1	0.0	24	0139	-0.1	0.0
Th	0636	4.3	1.3	F	0740	4.2	1.3
	1245	0.0	0.0		1339	0.2	0.1
	1857	5.5	1.7		1954	5.3	1.6
10	0136	-0.3	-0.1	25	0222	-0.1	0.0
F	0725	4.4	1.3	Sa	0824	4.1	1.2
	1330	-0.1	0.0		1421	0.3	0.1
	1941	5.7	1.7		2035	5.2	1.6
11	0224	-0.5	-0.2	26	0304	-0.1	0.0
Sa	0813	4.4	1.3	Su	0907	4.1	1.2
	1421	-0.2	-0.1		1503	0.4	0.1
	2029	5.8	1.8		2115	5.1	1.6
12	0312	-0.7	-0.2	27	0344	0.0	0.0
Su	0907	4.4	1.3	M	0952	4.0	1.2
	1508	-0.2	-0.1		1541	0.6	0.2
	2121	5.8	1.8		2155	4.9	1.5
13	0400	-0.7	-0.2	28	0422	0.1	0.0
M	1007	4.4	1.3	Tu	1039	3.9	1.2
	1558	-0.1	0.0		1617	0.7	0.2
	2221	5.6	1.7		2235	4.7	1.4
14	0448	-0.6	-0.2	29	0459	0.2	0.1
Tu	1107	4.5	1.4	W	1122	3.9	1.2
	1651	0.1	0.0		1651	0.9	0.3
	2320	5.4	1.6		2316	4.5	1.4
15	0541	-0.4	-0.1	30	0536	0.4	0.1
W	1207	4.6	1.4	Th	1205	3.9	1.2
	1752	0.3	0.1		1725	1.1	0.3
					2352	4.3	1.3

Time meridian 75° W. 0000 is midnight. 1200 is noon.
Heights are referred to mean low water which is the chart datum of soundings.

Times and Heights of High and Low Waters

JULY

Day	Time (h m)	Height (ft)	Height (m)
1 F	0610	0.6	0.2
	1244	3.9	1.2
	1805	1.2	0.4
2 Sa	0032	4.2	1.3
	0655	0.7	0.2
	1322	4.0	1.2
	1919	1.3	0.4
3 Su	0110	4.1	1.2
	0750	0.7	0.2
	1404	4.2	1.3
	2037	1.2	0.4
4 M	0159	4.0	1.2
	0847	0.7	0.2
	1450	4.4	1.3
	2140	1.0	0.3
5 Tu	0255	3.9	1.2
	0941	0.6	0.2
	1546	4.7	1.4
	2234	0.7	0.2
6 W	0401	3.9	1.2
	1030	0.4	0.1
	1644	5.0	1.5
	2329	0.4	0.1
7 Th	0509	4.0	1.2
	1123	0.3	0.1
	1742	5.3	1.6
8 F	0019	0.1	0.0
	0609	4.2	1.3
	1214	0.1	0.0
	1832	5.7	1.7
9 Sa	0115	-0.3	-0.1
	0705	4.4	1.3
	1309	-0.1	0.0
	1923	5.9	1.8
10 Su	0205	-0.5	-0.2
	0757	4.6	1.4
	1405	-0.2	-0.1
	2015	6.0	1.8
11 M	0254	-0.7	-0.2
	0854	4.7	1.4
	1457	-0.3	-0.1
	2110	5.9	1.8
12 Tu	0343	-0.8	-0.2
	0952	4.8	1.5
	1550	-0.3	-0.1
	2206	5.8	1.8
13 W	0431	-0.8	-0.2
	1050	4.9	1.5
	1643	-0.1	0.0
	2304	5.6	1.7
14 Th	0520	-0.6	-0.2
	1148	5.0	1.5
	1738	0.1	0.0
15 F	0002	5.3	1.6
	0615	-0.4	-0.1
	1242	5.1	1.6
	1842	0.3	0.1
16 Sa	0057	5.0	1.5
	0714	-0.1	0.0
	1336	5.1	1.6
	1951	0.5	0.2
17 Su	0151	4.7	1.4
	0813	0.1	0.0
	1428	5.0	1.5
	2057	0.5	0.2
18 M	0247	4.3	1.3
	0912	0.2	0.1
	1527	5.0	1.5
	2156	0.5	0.2
19 Tu	0347	4.1	1.2
	1005	0.3	0.1
	1623	5.0	1.5
	2252	0.4	0.1
20 W	0449	4.0	1.2
	1056	0.3	0.1
	1718	5.1	1.6
	2342	0.3	0.1
21 Th	0545	4.0	1.2
	1145	0.4	0.1
	1808	5.2	1.6
22 F	0032	0.2	0.1
	0635	4.1	1.2
	1232	0.4	0.1
	1853	5.2	1.6
23 Sa	0117	0.1	0.0
	0720	4.1	1.2
	1318	0.4	0.1
	1933	5.2	1.6
24 Su	0201	0.0	0.0
	0805	4.2	1.3
	1402	0.4	0.1
	2014	5.2	1.6
25 M	0242	0.0	0.0
	0844	4.2	1.3
	1443	0.5	0.2
	2052	5.1	1.6
26 Tu	0320	0.0	0.0
	0926	4.2	1.3
	1521	0.5	0.2
	2129	5.0	1.5
27 W	0356	0.0	0.0
	1008	4.2	1.3
	1555	0.6	0.2
	2206	4.8	1.5
28 Th	0429	0.2	0.1
	1047	4.2	1.3
	1629	0.7	0.2
	2240	4.6	1.4
29 F	0458	0.3	0.1
	1125	4.2	1.3
	1659	0.9	0.3
	2311	4.5	1.4
30 Sa	0525	0.5	0.2
	1157	4.3	1.3
	1730	1.0	0.3
	2346	4.3	1.3
31 Su	0549	0.6	0.2
	1234	4.4	1.3
	1812	1.1	0.3

AUGUST

Day	Time (h m)	Height (ft)	Height (m)
1 M	0029	4.2	1.3
	0626	0.7	0.2
	1311	4.5	1.4
	1931	1.2	0.4
2 Tu	0115	4.0	1.2
	0722	0.8	0.2
	1402	4.6	1.4
	2059	1.1	0.3
3 W	0211	3.9	1.2
	0841	0.8	0.2
	1458	4.8	1.5
	2205	0.8	0.2
4 Th	0321	3.9	1.2
	0953	0.6	0.2
	1609	5.0	1.5
	2303	0.5	0.2
5 F	0441	4.0	1.2
	1056	0.4	0.1
	1715	5.4	1.6
	2358	0.1	0.0
6 Sa	0550	4.2	1.3
	1155	0.2	0.1
	1816	5.7	1.7
7 Su	0053	-0.2	-0.1
	0649	4.6	1.4
	1254	-0.1	0.0
	1910	5.9	1.8
8 M	0145	-0.5	-0.2
	0743	4.9	1.5
	1351	-0.3	-0.1
	2002	6.1	1.9
9 Tu	0234	-0.8	-0.2
	0836	5.1	1.6
	1445	-0.5	-0.2
	2054	6.0	1.8
10 W	0322	-0.9	-0.3
	0931	5.3	1.6
	1536	-0.5	-0.2
	2150	5.9	1.8
11 Th	0408	-0.8	-0.2
	1026	5.4	1.6
	1626	-0.3	-0.1
	2245	5.6	1.7
12 F	0455	-0.6	-0.2
	1120	5.4	1.6
	1717	-0.1	0.0
	2338	5.3	1.6
13 Sa	0543	-0.3	-0.1
	1215	5.3	1.6
	1817	0.2	0.1
14 Su	0031	4.9	1.5
	0637	0.0	0.0
	1307	5.2	1.6
	1921	0.5	0.2
15 M	0126	4.5	1.4
	0738	0.4	0.1
	1358	5.0	1.5
	2028	0.7	0.2
16 Tu	0221	4.2	1.3
	0840	0.6	0.2
	1454	4.9	1.5
	2130	0.7	0.2
17 W	0320	3.9	1.2
	0939	0.7	0.2
	1553	4.8	1.5
	2226	0.7	0.2
18 Th	0422	3.8	1.2
	1031	0.7	0.2
	1652	4.8	1.5
	2318	0.6	0.2
19 F	0522	3.9	1.2
	1122	0.7	0.2
	1745	4.9	1.5
20 Sa	0006	0.4	0.1
	0614	4.0	1.2
	1211	0.6	0.2
	1830	5.0	1.5
21 Su	0053	0.3	0.1
	0659	4.2	1.3
	1257	0.5	0.2
	1912	5.1	1.6
22 M	0135	0.1	0.0
	0740	4.4	1.3
	1340	0.4	0.1
	1950	5.2	1.6
23 Tu	0215	0.0	0.0
	0818	4.5	1.4
	1422	0.4	0.1
	2027	5.1	1.6
24 W	0252	0.0	0.0
	0854	4.5	1.4
	1459	0.4	0.1
	2102	5.0	1.5
25 Th	0326	0.0	0.0
	0929	4.6	1.4
	1534	0.4	0.1
	2134	4.9	1.5
26 F	0357	0.1	0.0
	1005	4.6	1.4
	1606	0.5	0.2
	2204	4.7	1.4
27 Sa	0423	0.3	0.1
	1035	4.6	1.4
	1635	0.6	0.2
	2235	4.5	1.4
28 Su	0443	0.4	0.1
	1109	4.6	1.4
	1704	0.7	0.2
	2309	4.3	1.3
29 M	0509	0.5	0.2
	1146	4.7	1.4
	1744	0.9	0.3
	2352	4.1	1.2
30 Tu	0544	0.7	0.2
	1233	4.7	1.4
	1844	1.0	0.3
31 W	0044	4.0	1.2
	0633	0.8	0.2
	1327	4.8	1.5
	2027	1.1	0.3

SEPTEMBER

Day	Time (h m)	Height (ft)	Height (m)
1 Th	0147	3.9	1.2
	0757	0.9	0.3
	1432	4.9	1.5
	2142	0.8	0.2
2 F	0306	3.8	1.2
	0935	0.8	0.2
	1547	5.0	1.5
	2243	0.5	0.2
3 Sa	0430	4.0	1.2
	1044	0.5	0.2
	1700	5.3	1.6
	2338	0.1	0.0
4 Su	0539	4.4	1.3
	1145	0.2	0.1
	1801	5.6	1.7
5 M	0032	-0.3	-0.1
	0635	4.9	1.5
	1243	-0.2	-0.1
	1856	5.8	1.8
6 Tu	0123	-0.6	-0.2
	0727	5.2	1.6
	1338	-0.4	-0.1
	1947	6.0	1.8
7 W	0211	-0.8	-0.2
	0816	5.5	1.7
	1429	-0.6	-0.2
	2036	5.9	1.8
8 Th	0257	-0.9	-0.3
	0906	5.7	1.7
	1518	-0.6	-0.2
	2126	5.7	1.7
9 F	0342	-0.8	-0.2
	0958	5.7	1.7
	1606	-0.5	-0.2
	2219	5.4	1.6
10 Sa	0426	-0.6	-0.2
	1050	5.6	1.7
	1655	-0.2	-0.1
	2312	5.0	1.5
11 Su	0511	-0.2	-0.1
	1141	5.4	1.6
	1746	0.2	0.1
12 M	0005	4.6	1.4
	0559	0.2	0.1
	1233	5.1	1.6
	1847	0.6	0.2
13 Tu	0058	4.3	1.3
	0658	0.7	0.2
	1327	4.9	1.5
	1955	0.8	0.2
14 W	0152	4.0	1.2
	0804	1.0	0.3
	1420	4.7	1.4
	2100	0.9	0.3
15 Th	0252	3.8	1.2
	0910	1.1	0.3
	1519	4.5	1.4
	2157	0.8	0.2
16 F	0354	3.7	1.1
	1009	1.0	0.3
	1618	4.5	1.4
	2249	0.7	0.2
17 Sa	0455	3.8	1.2
	1100	0.9	0.3
	1715	4.6	1.4
	2337	0.5	0.2
18 Su	0547	4.1	1.2
	1147	0.7	0.2
	1802	4.8	1.5
19 M	0022	0.3	0.1
	0632	4.3	1.3
	1232	0.6	0.2
	1845	4.9	1.5
20 Tu	0104	0.1	0.0
	0711	4.6	1.4
	1315	0.4	0.1
	1923	5.0	1.5
21 W	0143	0.0	0.0
	0748	4.7	1.4
	1357	0.2	0.1
	1958	5.0	1.5
22 Th	0219	0.0	0.0
	0822	4.8	1.5
	1435	0.2	0.1
	2030	5.0	1.5
23 F	0254	0.0	0.0
	0853	4.9	1.5
	1510	0.1	0.0
	2102	4.8	1.5
24 Sa	0323	0.1	0.0
	0925	4.9	1.5
	1544	0.2	0.1
	2131	4.6	1.4
25 Su	0350	0.2	0.1
	0953	4.9	1.5
	1616	0.3	0.1
	2203	4.4	1.3
26 M	0411	0.3	0.1
	1027	4.9	1.5
	1648	0.5	0.2
	2245	4.2	1.3
27 Tu	0440	0.4	0.1
	1114	4.9	1.5
	1730	0.6	0.2
	2336	4.0	1.2
28 W	0516	0.6	0.2
	1207	4.8	1.5
	1833	0.8	0.2
29 Th	0036	3.9	1.2
	0609	0.8	0.2
	1308	4.8	1.5
	2008	0.9	0.3
30 F	0146	3.8	1.2
	0747	1.0	0.3
	1418	4.8	1.5
	2124	0.7	0.2

Time meridian 75° W. 0000 is midnight. 1200 is noon.
Heights are referred to mean low water which is the chart datum of soundings.

NEW YORK (The Battery), N.Y., 1983

Times and Heights of High and Low Waters

OCTOBER

Day	Time h m	Height ft	Height m
1	0303	3.9	1.2
Sa	0930	0.8	0.2
	1535	4.9	1.5
	2224	0.3	0.1
2	0420	4.2	1.3
Su	1036	0.5	0.2
	1645	5.1	1.6
	2318	0.0	0.0
3	0524	4.6	1.4
M	1134	0.1	0.0
	1745	5.3	1.6
4	0009	-0.4	-0.1
Tu	0619	5.1	1.6
	1230	-0.3	-0.1
	1839	5.5	1.7
5	0100	-0.7	-0.2
W	0709	5.5	1.7
	1321	-0.6	-0.2
	1928	5.6	1.7
6	0146	-0.8	-0.2
Th	0755	5.7	1.7
	1411	-0.7	-0.2
	2016	5.5	1.7
7	0231	-0.8	-0.2
F	0842	5.8	1.8
	1459	-0.7	-0.2
	2103	5.3	1.6
8	0314	-0.7	-0.2
Sa	0929	5.7	1.7
	1545	-0.6	-0.2
	2152	5.0	1.5
9	0356	-0.4	-0.1
Su	1019	5.5	1.7
	1631	-0.3	-0.1
	2245	4.6	1.4
10	0438	-0.1	0.0
M	1107	5.2	1.6
	1719	0.1	0.0
	2336	4.3	1.3
11	0522	0.4	0.1
Tu	1159	4.9	1.5
	1813	0.5	0.2
12	0031	4.0	1.2
W	0613	0.8	0.2
	1252	4.6	1.4
	1916	0.8	0.2
13	0124	3.7	1.1
Th	0722	1.1	0.3
	1344	4.4	1.3
	2023	0.9	0.3
14	0221	3.6	1.1
F	0835	1.3	0.4
	1438	4.2	1.3
	2125	0.8	0.2
15	0320	3.6	1.1
Sa	0938	1.2	0.4
	1539	4.2	1.3
	2217	0.7	0.2
16	0421	3.8	1.2
Su	1032	1.0	0.3
	1637	4.3	1.3
	2302	0.5	0.2
17	0514	4.0	1.2
M	1118	0.7	0.2
	1726	4.4	1.3
	2347	0.3	0.1
18	0600	4.3	1.3
Tu	1204	0.5	0.2
	1809	4.6	1.4
19	0027	0.1	0.0
W	0638	4.6	1.4
	1248	0.3	0.1
	1851	4.7	1.4
20	0107	0.0	0.0
Th	0715	4.8	1.5
	1328	0.1	0.0
	1928	4.7	1.4
21	0143	-0.1	0.0
F	0747	5.0	1.5
	1408	-0.1	0.0
	2001	4.7	1.4
22	0219	-0.1	0.0
Sa	0819	5.1	1.6
	1447	-0.2	-0.1
	2033	4.6	1.4
23	0251	-0.1	0.0
Su	0849	5.2	1.6
	1524	-0.1	0.0
	2105	4.4	1.3
24	0321	0.0	0.0
M	0923	5.1	1.6
	1601	-0.1	0.0
	2144	4.2	1.3
25	0351	0.1	0.0
Tu	1006	5.1	1.6
	1640	0.1	0.0
	2235	4.0	1.2
26	0424	0.3	0.1
W	1058	5.0	1.5
	1725	0.3	0.1
	2338	3.8	1.2
27	0507	0.5	0.2
Th	1157	4.8	1.5
	1829	0.4	0.1
28	0042	3.8	1.2
F	0610	0.7	0.2
	1303	4.7	1.4
	1953	0.5	0.2
29	0151	3.8	1.2
Sa	0759	0.8	0.2
	1410	4.7	1.4
	2103	0.3	0.1
30	0301	4.0	1.2
Su	0921	0.6	0.2
	1520	4.7	1.4
	2203	0.0	0.0
31	0407	4.3	1.3
M	1025	0.3	0.1
	1628	4.8	1.5
	2257	-0.3	-0.1

NOVEMBER

Day	Time h m	Height ft	Height m
1	0508	4.8	1.5
Tu	1121	-0.1	0.0
	1728	4.9	1.5
	2347	-0.5	-0.2
2	0600	5.2	1.6
W	1214	-0.4	-0.1
	1821	5.0	1.5
3	0033	-0.7	-0.2
Th	0649	5.5	1.7
	1305	-0.6	-0.2
	1909	5.1	1.6
4	0120	-0.8	-0.2
F	0734	5.7	1.7
	1354	-0.8	-0.2
	1956	5.0	1.5
5	0205	-0.7	-0.2
Sa	0818	5.7	1.7
	1440	-0.7	-0.2
	2042	4.8	1.5
6	0249	-0.6	-0.2
Su	0903	5.6	1.7
	1526	-0.6	-0.2
	2129	4.5	1.4
7	0329	-0.3	-0.1
M	0950	5.3	1.6
	1608	-0.4	-0.1
	2219	4.2	1.3
8	0410	0.0	0.0
Tu	1037	5.0	1.5
	1653	0.0	0.0
	2309	3.9	1.2
9	0451	0.4	0.1
W	1127	4.7	1.4
	1741	0.3	0.1
10	0002	3.7	1.1
Th	0536	0.7	0.2
	1215	4.4	1.3
	1834	0.5	0.2
11	0055	3.5	1.1
F	0634	1.1	0.3
	1306	4.2	1.3
	1939	0.7	0.2
12	0148	3.5	1.1
Sa	0751	1.2	0.4
	1356	4.0	1.2
	2042	0.7	0.2
13	0241	3.5	1.1
Su	0901	1.2	0.4
	1450	3.9	1.2
	2135	0.6	0.2
14	0336	3.6	1.1
M	0956	1.0	0.3
	1545	3.9	1.2
	2223	0.4	0.1
15	0430	3.9	1.2
Tu	1045	0.7	0.2
	1641	4.0	1.2
	2305	0.2	0.1
16	0518	4.2	1.3
W	1131	0.4	0.1
	1729	4.1	1.2
	2347	0.0	0.0
17	0600	4.5	1.4
Th	1216	0.2	0.1
	1812	4.2	1.3
18	0027	-0.1	0.0
F	0638	4.8	1.5
	1259	-0.1	0.0
	1854	4.3	1.3
19	0105	-0.2	-0.1
Sa	0713	5.0	1.5
	1342	-0.3	-0.1
	1931	4.3	1.3
20	0144	-0.3	-0.1
Su	0749	5.2	1.6
	1425	-0.4	-0.1
	2008	4.3	1.3
21	0223	-0.3	-0.1
M	0826	5.3	1.6
	1506	-0.5	-0.2
	2049	4.1	1.2
22	0259	-0.3	-0.1
Tu	0905	5.3	1.6
	1550	-0.5	-0.2
	2137	4.0	1.2
23	0337	-0.2	-0.1
W	0955	5.2	1.6
	1632	-0.4	-0.1
	2237	3.9	1.2
24	0422	0.0	0.0
Th	1053	5.0	1.5
	1722	-0.2	-0.1
	2341	3.8	1.2
25	0512	0.2	0.1
F	1157	4.8	1.5
	1822	-0.1	0.0
26	0042	3.9	1.2
Sa	0623	0.4	0.1
	1258	4.7	1.4
	1932	0.0	0.0
27	0143	4.0	1.2
Su	0751	0.5	0.2
	1359	4.5	1.4
	2040	-0.1	0.0
28	0245	4.2	1.3
M	0907	0.3	0.1
	1503	4.4	1.3
	2139	-0.3	-0.1
29	0345	4.4	1.3
Tu	1009	0.0	0.0
	1607	4.4	1.3
	2233	-0.5	-0.2
30	0446	4.7	1.4
W	1105	-0.2	-0.1
	1708	4.4	1.3
	2321	-0.6	-0.2

DECEMBER

Day	Time h m	Height ft	Height m
1	0539	5.0	1.5
Th	1158	-0.5	-0.2
	1801	4.4	1.3
2	0011	-0.7	-0.2
F	0630	5.3	1.6
	1248	-0.6	-0.2
	1851	4.4	1.3
3	0056	-0.7	-0.2
Sa	0714	5.4	1.6
	1336	-0.7	-0.2
	1936	4.4	1.3
4	0141	-0.6	-0.2
Su	0758	5.4	1.6
	1423	-0.7	-0.2
	2022	4.2	1.3
5	0226	-0.5	-0.2
M	0841	5.2	1.6
	1507	-0.6	-0.2
	2107	4.0	1.2
6	0307	-0.3	-0.1
Tu	0925	5.0	1.5
	1549	-0.5	-0.2
	2155	3.8	1.2
7	0347	-0.1	0.0
W	1008	4.7	1.4
	1631	-0.3	-0.1
	2245	3.6	1.1
8	0427	0.2	0.1
Th	1055	4.5	1.4
	1712	0.0	0.0
	2335	3.5	1.1
9	0504	0.5	0.2
F	1141	4.2	1.3
	1757	0.2	0.1
10	0023	3.4	1.0
Sa	0549	0.8	0.2
	1226	4.0	1.2
	1847	0.4	0.1
11	0109	3.4	1.0
Su	0652	1.0	0.3
	1311	3.8	1.2
	1946	0.5	0.2
12	0155	3.4	1.0
M	0807	1.0	0.3
	1355	3.7	1.1
	2045	0.4	0.1
13	0244	3.5	1.1
Tu	0911	0.9	0.3
	1446	3.6	1.1
	2135	0.4	0.1
14	0335	3.7	1.1
W	1004	0.7	0.2
	1542	3.6	1.1
	2220	0.2	0.1
15	0425	4.0	1.2
Th	1054	0.4	0.1
	1638	3.6	1.1
	2303	0.1	0.0
16	0515	4.3	1.3
F	1142	0.1	0.0
	1732	3.7	1.1
	2347	-0.1	0.0
17	0601	4.6	1.4
Sa	1230	-0.2	-0.1
	1820	3.8	1.2
18	0030	-0.3	-0.1
Su	0643	4.9	1.5
	1316	-0.4	-0.1
	1904	4.0	1.2
19	0115	-0.4	-0.1
M	0724	5.2	1.6
	1403	-0.7	-0.2
	1949	4.0	1.2
20	0201	-0.5	-0.2
Tu	0808	5.3	1.6
	1449	-0.8	-0.2
	2038	4.0	1.2
21	0247	-0.6	-0.2
W	0855	5.3	1.6
	1534	-0.9	-0.3
	2131	4.0	1.2
22	0332	-0.5	-0.2
Th	0947	5.2	1.6
	1622	-0.9	-0.3
	2231	4.1	1.2
23	0421	-0.4	-0.1
F	1048	5.1	1.6
	1711	-0.8	-0.2
	2330	4.1	1.2
24	0514	-0.3	-0.1
Sa	1146	4.9	1.5
	1805	-0.6	-0.2
25	0029	4.2	1.3
Su	0620	0.0	0.0
	1244	4.6	1.4
	1906	-0.5	-0.2
26	0127	4.3	1.3
M	0734	0.1	0.0
	1343	4.4	1.3
	2011	-0.4	-0.1
27	0222	4.3	1.3
Tu	0846	0.1	0.0
	1440	4.2	1.3
	2111	-0.4	-0.1
28	0322	4.5	1.4
W	0948	-0.1	0.0
	1543	4.0	1.2
	2207	-0.4	-0.1
29	0422	4.6	1.4
Th	1046	-0.2	-0.1
	1644	3.9	1.2
	2257	-0.5	-0.2
30	0519	4.8	1.5
F	1139	-0.4	-0.1
	1742	3.9	1.2
	2348	-0.5	-0.2
31	0611	4.9	1.5
Sa	1230	-0.5	-0.2
	1834	3.9	1.2

Time meridian 75° W. 0000 is midnight. 1200 is noon.
Heights are referred to mean low water which is the chart datum of soundings.

SANDY HOOK, N.J., 1983

Times and Heights of High and Low Waters

JANUARY

Day	Time h m	Height ft	Height m	Day	Time h m	Height ft	Height m
1	0249	-1.0	-0.3	16	0256	0.0	0.0
Sa	0900	5.7	1.7	Su	0901	4.6	1.4
	1537	-1.3	-0.4		1531	-0.4	-0.1
	2136	4.6	1.4		2122	3.7	1.1
2	0341	-0.9	-0.3	17	0331	0.1	0.0
Su	0955	5.5	1.7	M	0936	4.4	1.3
	1626	-1.2	-0.4		1605	-0.3	-0.1
	2233	4.5	1.4		2200	3.7	1.1
3	0435	-0.7	-0.2	18	0403	0.2	0.1
M	1050	5.1	1.6	Tu	1016	4.3	1.3
	1717	-1.0	-0.3		1639	-0.2	-0.1
	2330	4.4	1.3		2240	3.7	1.1
4	0532	-0.4	-0.1	19	0440	0.3	0.1
Tu	1146	4.8	1.5	W	1055	4.1	1.2
	1812	-0.7	-0.2		1711	-0.1	0.0
					2322	3.7	1.1
5	0026	4.4	1.3	20	0521	0.4	0.1
W	0633	-0.1	0.0	Th	1140	3.9	1.2
	1239	4.4	1.3		1754	0.0	0.0
	1910	-0.5	-0.2				
6	0121	4.3	1.3	21	0009	3.9	1.2
Th	0739	0.0	0.0	F	0618	0.4	0.1
	1336	4.1	1.2		1228	3.8	1.2
	2006	-0.3	-0.1		1846	0.0	0.0
7	0218	4.3	1.3	22	0102	4.0	1.2
F	0840	0.1	0.0	Sa	0732	0.4	0.1
	1433	3.8	1.2		1324	3.7	1.1
	2101	-0.2	-0.1		1949	0.0	0.0
8	0315	4.3	1.3	23	0202	4.2	1.3
Sa	0937	0.1	0.0	Su	0845	0.3	0.1
	1533	3.6	1.1		1430	3.6	1.1
	2152	-0.2	-0.1		2052	-0.1	0.0
9	0411	4.4	1.3	24	0308	4.4	1.3
Su	1030	0.0	0.0	M	0949	0.0	0.0
	1633	3.6	1.1		1540	3.7	1.1
	2241	-0.2	-0.1		2151	-0.3	-0.1
10	0502	4.5	1.4	25	0414	4.8	1.5
M	1120	-0.1	0.0	Tu	1049	-0.3	-0.1
	1724	3.6	1.1		1649	3.9	1.2
	2326	-0.2	-0.1		2250	-0.6	-0.2
11	0548	4.7	1.4	26	0518	5.1	1.6
Tu	1208	-0.2	-0.1	W	1147	-0.7	-0.2
	1808	3.7	1.1		1750	4.2	1.3
					2350	-0.8	-0.2
12	0011	-0.2	-0.1	27	0613	5.5	1.7
W	0629	4.8	1.5	Th	1245	-1.0	-0.3
	1254	-0.3	-0.1		1845	4.5	1.4
	1850	3.7	1.1				
13	0056	-0.2	-0.1	28	0048	-1.0	-0.3
Th	0709	4.8	1.5	F	0704	5.7	1.7
	1337	-0.4	-0.1		1338	-1.3	-0.4
	1930	3.8	1.2		1936	4.7	1.4
14	0139	-0.1	0.0	29	0143	-1.2	-0.4
F	0747	4.8	1.5	Sa	0755	5.8	1.8
	1418	-0.4	-0.1		1428	-1.4	-0.4
	2007	3.8	1.2		2026	4.9	1.5
15	0219	-0.1	0.0	30	0237	-1.2	-0.4
Sa	0824	4.7	1.4	Su	0845	5.7	1.7
	1456	-0.4	-0.1		1518	-1.4	-0.4
	2046	3.7	1.1		2118	4.9	1.5
				31	0328	-1.1	-0.3
				M	0936	5.4	1.6
					1603	-1.3	-0.4
					2210	4.8	1.5

FEBRUARY

Day	Time h m	Height ft	Height m	Day	Time h m	Height ft	Height m
1	0417	-0.9	-0.3	16	0347	-0.1	0.0
Tu	1026	5.1	1.6	W	0951	4.4	1.3
	1649	-1.1	-0.3		1608	-0.3	-0.1
	2303	4.7	1.4		2209	4.2	1.3
2	0508	-0.6	-0.2	17	0421	0.0	0.0
W	1117	4.7	1.4	Th	1029	4.2	1.3
	1738	-0.7	-0.2		1640	-0.2	-0.1
	2354	4.6	1.4		2251	4.2	1.3
3	0602	-0.3	-0.1	18	0501	0.1	0.0
Th	1207	4.3	1.3	F	1114	4.0	1.2
	1830	-0.4	-0.1		1716	-0.1	0.0
					2337	4.3	1.3
4	0045	4.4	1.3	19	0554	0.2	0.1
F	0702	0.0	0.0	Sa	1202	3.8	1.2
	1259	3.9	1.2		1804	0.0	0.0
	1925	-0.1	0.0				
5	0136	4.3	1.3	20	0028	4.3	1.3
Sa	0804	0.2	0.1	Su	0702	0.3	0.1
	1354	3.6	1.1		1257	3.7	1.1
	2022	0.1	0.0		1910	0.1	0.0
6	0231	4.1	1.2	21	0129	4.4	1.3
Su	0903	0.3	0.1	M	0819	0.3	0.1
	1452	3.3	1.0		1405	3.6	1.1
	2116	0.2	0.1		2024	0.1	0.0
7	0330	4.1	1.2	22	0239	4.5	1.4
M	0959	0.2	0.1	Tu	0929	0.1	0.0
	1555	3.3	1.0		1521	3.6	1.1
	2208	0.2	0.1		2133	-0.1	0.0
8	0427	4.2	1.3	23	0353	4.7	1.4
Tu	1051	0.1	0.0	W	1032	-0.3	-0.1
	1655	3.4	1.0		1634	3.9	1.2
	2259	0.1	0.0		2236	-0.3	-0.1
9	0520	4.4	1.3	24	0500	5.0	1.5
W	1140	0.0	0.0	Th	1131	-0.6	-0.2
	1745	3.5	1.1		1736	4.3	1.3
	2347	0.1	0.0		2337	-0.6	-0.2
10	0605	4.6	1.4	25	0557	5.4	1.6
Th	1227	-0.2	-0.1	F	1226	-0.9	-0.3
	1829	3.7	1.1		1829	4.7	1.4
11	0034	0.0	0.0	26	0035	-0.9	-0.3
F	0646	4.7	1.4	Sa	0651	5.6	1.7
	1312	-0.3	-0.1		1318	-1.2	-0.4
	1909	3.9	1.2		1920	5.0	1.5
12	0119	-0.1	0.0	27	0130	-1.1	-0.3
Sa	0725	4.8	1.5	Su	0740	5.7	1.7
	1352	-0.4	-0.1		1407	-1.3	-0.4
	1946	4.0	1.2		2007	5.2	1.6
13	0200	-0.2	-0.1	28	0221	-1.2	-0.4
Su	0802	4.8	1.5	M	0827	5.6	1.7
	1430	-0.5	-0.2		1453	-1.3	-0.4
	2023	4.1	1.2		2056	5.3	1.6
14	0237	-0.2	-0.1				
M	0839	4.7	1.4				
	1505	-0.4	-0.1				
	2056	4.1	1.2				
15	0312	-0.2	-0.1				
Tu	0914	4.6	1.4				
	1537	-0.4	-0.1				
	2133	4.1	1.2				

MARCH

Day	Time h m	Height ft	Height m	Day	Time h m	Height ft	Height m
1	0310	-1.1	-0.3	16	0252	-0.3	-0.1
Tu	0914	5.3	1.6	W	0849	4.7	1.4
	1536	-1.2	-0.4		1505	-0.4	-0.1
	2143	5.2	1.6		2104	4.7	1.4
2	0356	-0.9	-0.3	17	0328	-0.3	-0.1
W	1000	5.0	1.5	Th	0927	4.5	1.4
	1619	-0.9	-0.3		1539	-0.3	-0.1
	2229	5.0	1.5		2141	4.8	1.5
3	0442	-0.6	-0.2	18	0407	-0.2	-0.1
Th	1047	4.6	1.4	F	1007	4.3	1.3
	1701	-0.5	-0.2		1612	-0.2	-0.1
	2317	4.8	1.5		2224	4.8	1.5
4	0529	-0.2	-0.1	19	0448	-0.1	0.0
F	1135	4.2	1.3	Sa	1055	4.1	1.2
	1746	-0.1	0.0		1650	0.0	0.0
					2314	4.7	1.4
5	0006	4.5	1.4	20	0540	0.1	0.0
Sa	0623	0.1	0.0	Su	1146	3.9	1.2
	1223	3.8	1.2		1741	0.2	0.1
	1838	0.3	0.1				
6	0055	4.3	1.3	21	0007	4.6	1.4
Su	0722	0.4	0.1	M	0647	0.3	0.1
	1315	3.5	1.1		1246	3.7	1.1
	1937	0.5	0.2		1849	0.4	0.1
7	0148	4.1	1.2	22	0111	4.6	1.4
M	0824	0.5	0.2	Tu	0804	0.3	0.1
	1411	3.3	1.0		1354	3.7	1.1
	2038	0.6	0.2		2009	0.4	0.1
8	0247	4.0	1.2	23	0222	4.6	1.4
Tu	0923	0.5	0.2	W	0913	0.1	0.0
	1516	3.2	1.0		1509	3.8	1.2
	2139	0.6	0.2		2122	0.2	0.1
9	0348	4.0	1.2	24	0335	4.7	1.4
W	1016	0.4	0.1	Th	1014	-0.2	-0.1
	1622	3.4	1.0		1620	4.1	1.2
	2230	0.5	0.2		2227	-0.1	0.0
10	0446	4.2	1.3	25	0444	4.9	1.5
Th	1107	0.2	0.1	F	1112	-0.5	-0.2
	1716	3.6	1.1		1721	4.6	1.4
	2320	0.3	0.1		2326	-0.4	-0.1
11	0536	4.4	1.3	26	0543	5.2	1.6
F	1155	0.0	0.0	Sa	1205	-0.8	-0.2
	1803	3.9	1.2		1814	5.0	1.5
12	0008	0.1	0.0	27	0022	-0.7	-0.2
Sa	0621	4.6	1.4	Su	0633	5.4	1.6
	1238	-0.2	-0.1		1254	-0.9	-0.3
	1841	4.2	1.3		1902	5.4	1.6
13	0054	0.0	0.0	28	0114	-0.9	-0.3
Su	0659	4.8	1.5	M	0721	5.4	1.6
	1320	-0.3	-0.1		1341	-1.0	-0.3
	1919	4.4	1.3		1945	5.6	1.7
14	0135	-0.2	-0.1	29	0204	-1.0	-0.3
M	0738	4.8	1.5	Tu	0807	5.3	1.6
	1358	-0.4	-0.1		1426	-1.0	-0.3
	1954	4.6	1.4		2030	5.6	1.7
15	0214	-0.3	-0.1	30	0249	-1.0	-0.3
Tu	0813	4.8	1.5	W	0849	5.1	1.6
	1433	-0.4	-0.1		1508	-0.8	-0.2
	2027	4.7	1.4		2113	5.5	1.7
				31	0334	-0.8	-0.2
				Th	0933	4.8	1.5
					1547	-0.5	-0.2
					2157	5.2	1.6

Time meridian 75° W. 0000 is midnight. 1200 is noon.
Heights are referred to mean low water which is the chart datum of soundings.

SANDY HOOK, N.J., 1983

Times and Heights of High and Low Waters

APRIL

Day	Time (h m)	Height (ft)	Height (m)	Day	Time (h m)	Height (ft)	Height (m)
1 F	0416	-0.5	-0.2	16 Sa	0352	-0.4	-0.1
	1016	4.4	1.3		0951	4.4	1.3
	1626	-0.2	-0.1		1552	-0.1	0.0
	2240	4.9	1.5		2205	5.2	1.6
2 Sa	0458	-0.1	0.0	17 Su	0439	-0.2	-0.1
	1102	4.1	1.2		1043	4.2	1.3
	1707	0.2	0.1		1635	0.1	0.0
	2327	4.6	1.4		2258	5.1	1.6
3 Su	0546	0.2	0.1	18 M	0532	0.0	0.0
	1149	3.8	1.2		1141	4.0	1.2
	1753	0.6	0.2		1730	0.3	0.1
					2356	4.9	1.5
4 M	0012	4.4	1.3	19 Tu	0638	0.2	0.1
	0641	0.5	0.2		1243	3.9	1.2
	1239	3.5	1.1		1843	0.5	0.2
	1851	0.9	0.3				
5 Tu	0104	4.1	1.2	20 W	0100	4.8	1.5
	0742	0.7	0.2		0750	0.2	0.1
	1336	3.4	1.0		1349	4.0	1.2
	1958	1.0	0.3		2002	0.5	0.2
6 W	0201	4.0	1.2	21 Th	0209	4.7	1.4
	0844	0.7	0.2		0857	0.0	0.0
	1436	3.4	1.0		1458	4.2	1.3
	2103	1.0	0.3		2113	0.3	0.1
7 Th	0303	4.0	1.2	22 F	0320	4.7	1.4
	0940	0.5	0.2		0956	-0.2	-0.1
	1542	3.5	1.1		1606	4.5	1.4
	2158	0.8	0.2		2214	0.0	0.0
8 F	0404	4.1	1.2	23 Sa	0426	4.8	1.5
	1028	0.3	0.1		1049	-0.4	-0.1
	1641	3.8	1.2		1705	4.9	1.5
	2249	0.6	0.2		2312	-0.3	-0.1
9 Sa	0459	4.3	1.3	24 Su	0523	5.0	1.5
	1115	0.1	0.0		1140	-0.6	-0.2
	1729	4.2	1.3		1755	5.3	1.6
	2339	0.3	0.1				
10 Su	0548	4.6	1.4	25 M	0005	-0.5	-0.2
	1158	0.0	0.0		0614	5.1	1.6
	1811	4.5	1.4		1227	-0.7	-0.2
					1840	5.6	1.7
11 M	0024	0.0	0.0	26 Tu	0056	-0.7	-0.2
	0629	4.7	1.4		0700	5.1	1.6
	1240	-0.2	-0.1		1314	-0.7	-0.2
	1847	4.8	1.5		1922	5.7	1.7
12 Tu	0106	-0.2	-0.1	27 W	0143	-0.7	-0.2
	0706	4.8	1.5		0743	5.0	1.5
	1320	-0.3	-0.1		1357	-0.6	-0.2
	1924	5.1	1.6		2004	5.7	1.7
13 W	0149	-0.3	-0.1	28 Th	0229	-0.7	-0.2
	0747	4.8	1.5		0824	4.8	1.5
	1359	-0.3	-0.1		1439	-0.4	-0.1
	2001	5.2	1.6		2043	5.6	1.7
14 Th	0230	-0.4	-0.1	29 F	0311	-0.5	-0.2
	0824	4.8	1.5		0904	4.5	1.4
	1435	-0.3	-0.1		1515	-0.1	0.0
	2038	5.3	1.6		2125	5.3	1.6
15 F	0312	-0.4	-0.1	30 Sa	0351	-0.3	-0.1
	0906	4.6	1.4		0947	4.2	1.3
	1512	-0.3	-0.1		1555	0.2	0.1
	2118	5.3	1.6		2205	5.0	1.5

MAY

Day	Time (h m)	Height (ft)	Height (m)	Day	Time (h m)	Height (ft)	Height (m)
1 Su	0432	0.0	0.0	16 M	0431	-0.4	-0.1
	1032	4.0	1.2		1034	4.3	1.3
	1632	0.5	0.2		1629	0.1	0.0
	2248	4.7	1.4		2248	5.4	1.6
2 M	0515	0.3	0.1	17 Tu	0525	-0.2	-0.1
	1119	3.7	1.1		1135	4.3	1.3
	1714	0.8	0.2		1727	0.3	0.1
	2335	4.5	1.4		2348	5.1	1.6
3 Tu	0604	0.5	0.2	18 W	0626	-0.1	0.0
	1209	3.6	1.1		1236	4.3	1.3
	1807	1.1	0.3		1838	0.5	0.2
4 W	0025	4.2	1.3	19 Th	0049	4.9	1.5
	0700	0.7	0.2		0733	0.0	0.0
	1300	3.5	1.1		1339	4.4	1.3
	1915	1.2	0.4		1951	0.5	0.2
5 Th	0117	4.1	1.2	20 F	0154	4.7	1.4
	0801	0.7	0.2		0836	-0.1	0.0
	1357	3.6	1.1		1442	4.5	1.4
	2022	1.2	0.4		2059	0.4	0.1
6 F	0214	4.0	1.2	21 Sa	0258	4.6	1.4
	0856	0.6	0.2		0932	-0.2	-0.1
	1459	3.8	1.2		1545	4.8	1.5
	2121	1.0	0.3		2159	0.1	0.0
7 Sa	0316	4.1	1.2	22 Su	0404	4.6	1.4
	0945	0.4	0.1		1022	-0.3	-0.1
	1554	4.0	1.2		1641	5.1	1.6
	2214	0.7	0.2		2254	-0.1	0.0
8 Su	0414	4.2	1.3	23 M	0502	4.7	1.4
	1031	0.2	0.1		1112	-0.3	-0.1
	1646	4.4	1.3		1732	5.4	1.6
	2302	0.4	0.1		2345	-0.3	-0.1
9 M	0507	4.4	1.3	24 Tu	0552	4.7	1.4
	1115	0.0	0.0		1200	-0.3	-0.1
	1731	4.8	1.5		1817	5.6	1.7
	2350	0.1	0.0				
10 Tu	0552	4.6	1.4	25 W	0036	-0.4	-0.1
	1157	-0.1	0.0		0637	4.7	1.4
	1813	5.2	1.6		1245	-0.3	-0.1
					1858	5.7	1.7
11 W	0037	-0.1	0.0	26 Th	0122	-0.4	-0.1
	0637	4.7	1.4		0718	4.6	1.4
	1242	-0.2	-0.1		1327	-0.2	-0.1
	1853	5.5	1.7		1937	5.7	1.7
12 Th	0122	-0.4	-0.1	27 F	0208	-0.4	-0.1
	0718	4.8	1.5		0800	4.5	1.4
	1324	-0.3	-0.1		1409	0.0	0.0
	1933	5.7	1.7		2017	5.5	1.7
13 F	0208	-0.5	-0.2	28 Sa	0249	-0.3	-0.1
	0801	4.7	1.4		0840	4.3	1.3
	1408	-0.3	-0.1		1449	0.2	0.1
	2015	5.8	1.8		2055	5.3	1.6
14 Sa	0255	-0.6	-0.2	29 Su	0328	-0.1	0.0
	0847	4.6	1.4		0921	4.1	1.2
	1452	-0.2	-0.1		1527	0.4	0.1
	2101	5.7	1.7		2136	5.0	1.5
15 Su	0341	-0.5	-0.2	30 M	0408	0.1	0.0
	0938	4.5	1.4		1003	3.9	1.2
	1538	-0.1	0.0		1605	0.7	0.2
	2152	5.6	1.7		2218	4.8	1.5
				31 Tu	0448	0.3	0.1
					1050	3.8	1.2
					1644	0.9	0.3
					2301	4.6	1.4

JUNE

Day	Time (h m)	Height (ft)	Height (m)	Day	Time (h m)	Height (ft)	Height (m)
1 W	0530	0.5	0.2	16 Th	0609	-0.3	-0.1
	1137	3.7	1.1		1222	4.7	1.4
	1730	1.1	0.3		1825	0.3	0.1
	2349	4.4	1.3				
2 Th	0618	0.6	0.2	17 F	0034	5.0	1.5
	1226	3.7	1.1		0708	-0.2	-0.1
	1828	1.3	0.4		1320	4.8	1.5
					1934	0.4	0.1
3 F	0034	4.2	1.3	18 Sa	0133	4.8	1.5
	0712	0.6	0.2		0809	-0.1	0.0
	1317	3.8	1.2		1420	4.9	1.5
	1934	1.3	0.4		2039	0.4	0.1
4 Sa	0128	4.1	1.2	19 Su	0234	4.5	1.4
	0807	0.6	0.2		0903	-0.1	0.0
	1409	4.0	1.2		1518	5.0	1.5
	2039	1.1	0.3		2138	0.2	0.1
5 Su	0225	4.1	1.2	20 M	0334	4.4	1.3
	0857	0.5	0.2		0956	-0.1	0.0
	1506	4.3	1.3		1614	5.2	1.6
	2135	0.8	0.2		2233	0.1	0.0
6 M	0324	4.1	1.2	21 Tu	0435	4.3	1.3
	0945	0.3	0.1		1043	-0.1	0.0
	1601	4.6	1.4		1707	5.3	1.6
	2225	0.5	0.2		2323	0.0	0.0
7 Tu	0422	4.2	1.3	22 W	0528	4.3	1.3
	1030	0.1	0.0		1129	0.0	0.0
	1652	5.0	1.5		1753	5.5	1.7
	2315	0.2	0.1				
8 W	0515	4.4	1.3	23 Th	0013	0.0	0.0
	1118	-0.1	0.0		0615	4.3	1.3
	1739	5.4	1.6		1216	0.1	0.0
					1835	5.5	1.7
9 Th	0006	-0.1	0.0	24 F	0100	-0.1	0.0
	0606	4.6	1.4		0658	4.3	1.3
	1206	-0.2	-0.1		1302	0.2	0.1
	1825	5.7	1.7		1915	5.5	1.7
10 F	0057	-0.4	-0.1	25 Sa	0146	-0.1	0.0
	0653	4.7	1.4		0738	4.2	1.3
	1253	-0.3	-0.1		1347	0.3	0.1
	1911	6.0	1.8		1954	5.4	1.6
11 Sa	0149	-0.6	-0.2	26 Su	0228	-0.1	0.0
	0743	4.7	1.4		0818	4.2	1.3
	1344	-0.3	-0.1		1426	0.4	0.1
	1957	6.1	1.9		2033	5.3	1.6
12 Su	0238	-0.7	-0.2	27 M	0306	0.0	0.0
	0832	4.7	1.4		0858	4.1	1.2
	1436	-0.3	-0.1		1506	0.5	0.2
	2046	6.0	1.8		2110	5.1	1.6
13 M	0327	-0.7	-0.2	28 Tu	0344	0.1	0.0
	0925	4.7	1.4		0939	4.0	1.2
	1528	-0.2	-0.1		1543	0.7	0.2
	2139	5.8	1.8		2149	4.9	1.5
14 Tu	0419	-0.6	-0.2	29 W	0421	0.2	0.1
	1024	4.6	1.4		1022	3.9	1.2
	1621	0.0	0.0		1619	0.9	0.3
	2237	5.6	1.7		2231	4.7	1.4
15 W	0511	-0.5	-0.2	30 Th	0458	0.3	0.1
	1124	4.6	1.4		1104	3.9	1.2
	1719	0.2	0.1		1658	1.0	0.3
	2335	5.3	1.6		2313	4.5	1.4

Time meridian 75° W. 0000 is midnight. 1200 is noon.
Heights are referred to mean low water which is the chart datum of soundings.

Times and Heights of High and Low Waters

JULY

Day	Time h m	Height ft	Height m	Day	Time h m	Height ft	Height m
1	0537	0.5	0.2	16	0012	5.0	1.5
F	1149	4.0	1.2	Sa	0639	-0.2	-0.1
	1746	1.1	0.3		1255	5.1	1.6
	2356	4.3	1.3		1908	0.3	0.1
2	0620	0.5	0.2	17	0108	4.7	1.4
Sa	1234	4.1	1.2	Su	0735	0.0	0.0
	1846	1.2	0.4		1348	5.0	1.5
					2013	0.4	0.1
3	0044	4.2	1.3	18	0203	4.4	1.3
Su	0713	0.6	0.2	M	0832	0.1	0.0
	1322	4.3	1.3		1445	5.0	1.5
	1951	1.1	0.3		2113	0.4	0.1
4	0136	4.1	1.2	19	0305	4.1	1.2
M	0803	0.5	0.2	Tu	0925	0.2	0.1
	1415	4.5	1.4		1542	5.0	1.5
	2052	0.9	0.3		2208	0.4	0.1
5	0236	4.0	1.2	20	0405	4.0	1.2
Tu	0859	0.4	0.1	W	1017	0.3	0.1
	1513	4.7	1.4		1638	5.1	1.6
	2150	0.6	0.2		2300	0.3	0.1
6	0341	4.1	1.2	21	0502	4.0	1.2
W	0950	0.2	0.1	Th	1105	0.3	0.1
	1613	5.1	1.6		1728	5.2	1.6
	2243	0.3	0.1		2350	0.2	0.1
7	0443	4.2	1.3	22	0551	4.1	1.2
Th	1043	0.0	0.0	F	1151	0.4	0.1
	1709	5.5	1.7		1813	5.3	1.6
	2339	0.0	0.0				
8	0539	4.4	1.3	23	0038	0.2	0.1
F	1136	-0.1	0.0	Sa	0637	4.2	1.3
	1801	5.8	1.8		1237	0.4	0.1
					1853	5.4	1.6
9	0035	-0.3	-0.1	24	0122	0.1	0.0
Sa	0633	4.7	1.4	Su	0718	4.2	1.3
	1232	-0.3	-0.1		1323	0.4	0.1
	1851	6.1	1.9		1932	5.3	1.6
10	0129	-0.6	-0.2	25	0205	0.0	0.0
Su	0725	4.8	1.5	M	0756	4.3	1.3
	1327	-0.4	-0.1		1405	0.4	0.1
	1941	6.2	1.9		2010	5.3	1.6
11	0222	-0.8	-0.2	26	0242	0.0	0.0
M	0817	5.0	1.5	Tu	0835	4.3	1.3
	1423	-0.4	-0.1		1446	0.5	0.2
	2033	6.2	1.9		2046	5.1	1.6
12	0312	-0.9	-0.3	27	0319	0.1	0.0
Tu	0910	5.0	1.5	W	0914	4.2	1.3
	1517	-0.4	-0.1		1522	0.6	0.2
	2126	6.0	1.8		2123	4.9	1.5
13	0400	-0.8	-0.2	28	0352	0.1	0.0
W	1008	5.1	1.6	Th	0951	4.2	1.3
	1610	-0.3	-0.1		1557	0.7	0.2
	2221	5.7	1.7		2202	4.8	1.5
14	0450	-0.7	-0.2	29	0424	0.3	0.1
Th	1104	5.1	1.6	F	1029	4.3	1.3
	1704	-0.1	0.0		1632	0.8	0.2
	2317	5.4	1.6		2239	4.6	1.4
15	0543	-0.5	-0.2	30	0458	0.4	0.1
F	1159	5.1	1.6	Sa	1110	4.3	1.3
	1804	0.2	0.1		1711	0.9	0.3
					2321	4.4	1.3
				31	0533	0.5	0.2
				Su	1153	4.4	1.3
					1801	1.0	0.3

AUGUST

Day	Time h m	Height ft	Height m	Day	Time h m	Height ft	Height m
1	0006	4.2	1.3	16	0133	4.2	1.3
M	0615	0.6	0.2	Tu	0757	0.5	0.2
	1238	4.5	1.4		1411	4.9	1.5
	1906	1.0	0.3		2044	0.7	0.2
2	0057	4.1	1.2	17	0230	3.9	1.2
Tu	0713	0.6	0.2	W	0853	0.6	0.2
	1331	4.7	1.4		1507	4.8	1.5
	2016	0.9	0.3		2140	0.6	0.2
3	0157	4.0	1.2	18	0335	3.8	1.2
W	0815	0.5	0.2	Th	0948	0.7	0.2
	1434	4.9	1.5		1607	4.8	1.5
	2121	0.7	0.2		2235	0.6	0.2
4	0303	4.0	1.2	19	0435	3.8	1.2
Th	0917	0.4	0.1	F	1040	0.6	0.2
	1540	5.1	1.6		1702	5.0	1.5
	2221	0.4	0.1		2323	0.4	0.1
5	0417	4.1	1.2	20	0531	4.0	1.2
F	1017	0.2	0.1	Sa	1129	0.6	0.2
	1644	5.5	1.7		1748	5.1	1.6
	2318	0.0	0.0				
6	0521	4.4	1.3	21	0009	0.3	0.1
Sa	1116	-0.1	0.0	Su	0614	4.2	1.3
	1744	5.8	1.8		1216	0.5	0.2
					1830	5.2	1.6
7	0014	-0.3	-0.1	22	0054	0.1	0.0
Su	0616	4.8	1.5	M	0656	4.4	1.3
	1216	-0.3	-0.1		1301	0.4	0.1
	1837	6.1	1.9		1909	5.3	1.6
8	0109	-0.6	-0.2	23	0135	0.0	0.0
M	0709	5.1	1.6	Tu	0733	4.5	1.4
	1314	-0.5	-0.2		1345	0.4	0.1
	1927	6.3	1.9		1947	5.2	1.6
9	0202	-0.9	-0.3	24	0213	0.0	0.0
Tu	0800	5.3	1.6	W	0809	4.6	1.4
	1409	-0.6	-0.2		1423	0.4	0.1
	2017	6.2	1.9		2022	5.2	1.6
10	0250	-1.0	-0.3	25	0249	0.0	0.0
W	0851	5.5	1.7	Th	0845	4.6	1.4
	1502	-0.6	-0.2		1459	0.4	0.1
	2108	6.0	1.8		2056	5.0	1.5
11	0338	-0.9	-0.3	26	0322	0.1	0.0
Th	0944	5.5	1.7	F	0918	4.6	1.4
	1553	-0.5	-0.2		1534	0.5	0.2
	2200	5.7	1.7		2131	4.8	1.5
12	0425	-0.7	-0.2	27	0351	0.2	0.1
F	1037	5.5	1.7	Sa	0954	4.6	1.4
	1644	-0.3	-0.1		1608	0.6	0.2
	2253	5.3	1.6		2208	4.6	1.4
13	0513	-0.5	-0.2	28	0419	0.3	0.1
Sa	1130	5.4	1.6	Su	1032	4.7	1.4
	1739	0.0	0.0		1645	0.7	0.2
	2346	4.9	1.5		2250	4.4	1.3
14	0604	-0.1	0.0	29	0452	0.4	0.1
Su	1223	5.2	1.6	M	1114	4.7	1.4
	1839	0.4	0.1		1727	0.8	0.2
					2333	4.2	1.3
15	0039	4.5	1.4	30	0531	0.5	0.2
M	0658	0.2	0.1	Tu	1204	4.8	1.5
	1316	5.0	1.5		1832	0.9	0.3
	1941	0.6	0.2				
				31	0028	4.0	1.2
				W	0628	0.7	0.2
					1300	4.8	1.5
					1947	0.9	0.3

SEPTEMBER

Day	Time h m	Height ft	Height m	Day	Time h m	Height ft	Height m
1	0130	3.9	1.2	16	0301	3.7	1.1
Th	0743	0.7	0.2	F	0919	1.0	0.3
	1404	4.9	1.5		1529	4.5	1.4
	2057	0.7	0.2		2204	0.7	0.2
2	0242	3.9	1.2	17	0406	3.8	1.2
F	0858	0.6	0.2	Sa	1014	0.9	0.3
	1515	5.1	1.6		1627	4.7	1.4
	2201	0.4	0.1		2252	0.5	0.2
3	0358	4.1	1.2	18	0503	4.0	1.2
Sa	1004	0.3	0.1	Su	1103	0.7	0.2
	1625	5.4	1.6		1720	4.8	1.5
	2259	0.0	0.0		2338	0.3	0.1
4	0505	4.5	1.4	19	0547	4.3	1.3
Su	1105	0.0	0.0	M	1150	0.5	0.2
	1726	5.7	1.7		1804	5.0	1.5
	2355	-0.4	-0.1				
5	0601	5.0	1.5	20	0020	0.1	0.0
M	1203	-0.3	-0.1	Tu	0627	4.6	1.4
	1821	6.0	1.8		1235	0.4	0.1
					1843	5.1	1.6
6	0048	-0.7	-0.2	21	0101	0.0	0.0
Tu	0653	5.4	1.6	W	0705	4.8	1.5
	1301	-0.6	-0.2		1318	0.2	0.1
	1910	6.1	1.9		1920	5.2	1.6
7	0139	-0.9	-0.3	22	0139	-0.1	0.0
W	0743	5.7	1.7	Th	0739	4.9	1.5
	1354	-0.7	-0.2		1358	0.2	0.1
	1959	6.1	1.9		1954	5.1	1.6
8	0226	-1.0	-0.3	23	0216	-0.1	0.0
Th	0829	5.8	1.8	F	0813	5.0	1.5
	1444	-0.8	-0.2		1435	0.1	0.0
	2046	5.9	1.8		2030	5.0	1.5
9	0312	-0.9	-0.3	24	0248	0.0	0.0
F	0918	5.8	1.8	Sa	0846	5.0	1.5
	1533	-0.6	-0.2		1511	0.2	0.1
	2136	5.5	1.7		2104	4.8	1.5
10	0355	-0.7	-0.2	25	0320	0.1	0.0
Sa	1007	5.7	1.7	Su	0921	5.0	1.5
	1621	-0.4	-0.1		1548	0.3	0.1
	2225	5.1	1.6		2143	4.5	1.4
11	0440	-0.3	-0.1	26	0349	0.2	0.1
Su	1057	5.5	1.7	M	0959	5.0	1.5
	1711	0.0	0.0		1625	0.4	0.1
	2317	4.7	1.4		2225	4.3	1.3
12	0527	0.1	0.0	27	0421	0.3	0.1
M	1146	5.2	1.6	Tu	1045	5.0	1.5
	1805	0.4	0.1		1711	0.6	0.2
					2314	4.1	1.2
13	0007	4.3	1.3	28	0504	0.5	0.2
Tu	0618	0.5	0.2	W	1137	4.9	1.5
	1239	4.9	1.5		1812	0.7	0.2
	1905	0.7	0.2				
14	0100	3.9	1.2	29	0012	3.9	1.2
W	0718	0.8	0.2	Th	0604	0.7	0.2
	1333	4.7	1.4		1239	4.9	1.5
	2010	0.8	0.2		1929	0.7	0.2
15	0158	3.7	1.1	30	0119	3.8	1.2
Th	0821	1.0	0.3	F	0727	0.8	0.2
	1431	4.6	1.4		1345	4.8	1.5
	2109	0.8	0.2		2041	0.5	0.2

Time meridian 75° W. 0000 is midnight. 1200 is noon.
Heights are referred to mean low water which is the chart datum of soundings.

Times and Heights of High and Low Waters

OCTOBER

Day	Time h m	Height ft	Height m
1 Sa	0233	3.9	1.2
	0845	0.6	0.2
	1458	4.9	1.5
	2145	0.2	0.1
2 Su	0346	4.2	1.3
	0954	0.3	0.1
	1609	5.1	1.6
	2241	-0.1	0.0
3 M	0451	4.7	1.4
	1054	-0.1	0.0
	1710	5.4	1.6
	2334	-0.5	-0.2
4 Tu	0547	5.2	1.6
	1150	-0.4	-0.1
	1804	5.7	1.7
5 W	0024	-0.7	-0.2
	0635	5.6	1.7
	1245	-0.7	-0.2
	1853	5.8	1.8
6 Th	0112	-0.9	-0.3
	0721	5.9	1.8
	1337	-0.8	-0.2
	1939	5.7	1.7
7 F	0159	-0.9	-0.3
	0806	6.0	1.8
	1426	-0.8	-0.2
	2025	5.5	1.7
8 Sa	0243	-0.8	-0.2
	0849	5.9	1.8
	1512	-0.7	-0.2
	2109	5.1	1.6
9 Su	0326	-0.5	-0.2
	0936	5.7	1.7
	1557	-0.4	-0.1
	2155	4.7	1.4
10 M	0407	-0.2	-0.1
	1023	5.4	1.6
	1642	-0.1	0.0
	2244	4.3	1.3
11 Tu	0448	0.2	0.1
	1111	5.1	1.6
	1733	0.3	0.1
	2335	4.0	1.2
12 W	0538	0.6	0.2
	1202	4.7	1.4
	1828	0.6	0.2
13 Th	0028	3.7	1.1
	0635	1.0	0.3
	1254	4.5	1.4
	1931	0.8	0.2
14 F	0124	3.6	1.1
	0742	1.1	0.3
	1349	4.3	1.3
	2031	0.8	0.2
15 Sa	0226	3.5	1.1
	0848	1.1	0.3
	1448	4.2	1.3
	2127	0.6	0.2
16 Su	0327	3.7	1.1
	0945	1.0	0.3
	1548	4.3	1.3
	2215	0.4	0.1
17 M	0427	4.0	1.2
	1035	0.7	0.2
	1643	4.5	1.4
	2259	0.2	0.1
18 Tu	0513	4.3	1.3
	1120	0.5	0.2
	1728	4.7	1.4
	2342	0.0	0.0
19 W	0555	4.6	1.4
	1205	0.3	0.1
	1811	4.8	1.5
20 Th	0023	-0.1	0.0
	0632	4.9	1.5
	1248	0.1	0.0
	1850	4.9	1.5
21 F	0101	-0.2	-0.1
	0709	5.1	1.6
	1332	-0.1	0.0
	1926	4.9	1.5
22 Sa	0139	-0.2	-0.1
	0743	5.3	1.6
	1410	-0.2	-0.1
	2002	4.8	1.5
23 Su	0215	-0.2	-0.1
	0818	5.3	1.6
	1451	-0.2	-0.1
	2041	4.6	1.4
24 M	0251	-0.1	0.0
	0855	5.3	1.6
	1531	-0.1	0.0
	2123	4.4	1.3
25 Tu	0325	0.0	0.0
	0937	5.2	1.6
	1613	0.0	0.0
	2209	4.1	1.2
26 W	0405	0.2	0.1
	1026	5.1	1.6
	1701	0.2	0.1
	2305	3.9	1.2
27 Th	0453	0.4	0.1
	1122	4.9	1.5
	1804	0.3	0.1
28 F	0007	3.8	1.2
	0559	0.6	0.2
	1226	4.8	1.5
	1915	0.4	0.1
29 Sa	0115	3.9	1.2
	0719	0.7	0.2
	1332	4.7	1.4
	2024	0.2	0.1
30 Su	0222	4.0	1.2
	0838	0.5	0.2
	1443	4.7	1.4
	2126	0.0	0.0
31 M	0330	4.4	1.3
	0942	0.2	0.1
	1550	4.8	1.5
	2220	-0.3	-0.1

NOVEMBER

Day	Time h m	Height ft	Height m
1 Tu	0433	4.8	1.5
	1041	-0.2	-0.1
	1651	5.0	1.5
	2310	-0.6	-0.2
2 W	0526	5.3	1.6
	1136	-0.5	-0.2
	1747	5.1	1.6
3 Th	0000	-0.8	-0.2
	0614	5.6	1.7
	1229	-0.7	-0.2
	1833	5.2	1.6
4 F	0046	-0.8	-0.2
	0659	5.9	1.8
	1318	-0.8	-0.2
	1918	5.1	1.6
5 Sa	0133	-0.8	-0.2
	0741	5.9	1.8
	1405	-0.8	-0.2
	2001	4.9	1.5
6 Su	0216	-0.7	-0.2
	0823	5.8	1.8
	1451	-0.7	-0.2
	2044	4.6	1.4
7 M	0258	-0.4	-0.1
	0907	5.5	1.7
	1533	-0.4	-0.1
	2128	4.3	1.3
8 Tu	0338	-0.1	0.0
	0951	5.2	1.6
	1618	-0.2	-0.1
	2213	4.0	1.2
9 W	0419	0.3	0.1
	1037	4.9	1.5
	1701	0.1	0.0
	2301	3.7	1.1
10 Th	0501	0.6	0.2
	1124	4.5	1.4
	1751	0.4	0.1
	2356	3.5	1.1
11 F	0554	0.9	0.3
	1215	4.3	1.3
	1847	0.6	0.2
12 Sa	0047	3.4	1.0
	0658	1.1	0.3
	1305	4.1	1.2
	1947	0.6	0.2
13 Su	0144	3.5	1.1
	0805	1.1	0.3
	1401	4.0	1.2
	2043	0.5	0.2
14 M	0243	3.6	1.1
	0905	0.9	0.3
	1500	4.0	1.2
	2132	0.3	0.1
15 Tu	0339	3.8	1.2
	0958	0.7	0.2
	1557	4.1	1.2
	2217	0.1	0.0
16 W	0431	4.2	1.3
	1046	0.4	0.1
	1649	4.2	1.3
	2300	-0.1	0.0
17 Th	0518	4.5	1.4
	1132	0.1	0.0
	1736	4.4	1.3
	2342	-0.2	-0.1
18 F	0558	4.9	1.5
	1217	-0.1	0.0
	1818	4.5	1.4
19 Sa	0022	-0.3	-0.1
	0637	5.2	1.6
	1303	-0.3	-0.1
	1858	4.5	1.4
20 Su	0104	-0.4	-0.1
	0716	5.4	1.6
	1349	-0.5	-0.2
	1939	4.5	1.4
21 M	0146	-0.4	-0.1
	0754	5.5	1.7
	1432	-0.5	-0.2
	2021	4.4	1.3
22 Tu	0228	-0.4	-0.1
	0836	5.5	1.7
	1517	-0.5	-0.2
	2107	4.2	1.3
23 W	0311	-0.3	-0.1
	0923	5.4	1.6
	1603	-0.4	-0.1
	2200	4.1	1.2
24 Th	0357	-0.1	0.0
	1016	5.2	1.6
	1653	-0.3	-0.1
	2258	4.0	1.2
25 F	0450	0.1	0.0
	1114	5.0	1.5
	1751	-0.2	-0.1
26 Sa	0001	3.9	1.2
	0554	0.3	0.1
	1215	4.7	1.4
	1857	-0.1	0.0
27 Su	0103	4.0	1.2
	0711	0.3	0.1
	1319	4.6	1.4
	2003	-0.2	-0.1
28 M	0206	4.2	1.3
	0824	0.2	0.1
	1424	4.5	1.4
	2102	-0.3	-0.1
29 Tu	0311	4.5	1.4
	0927	0.0	0.0
	1530	4.4	1.3
	2156	-0.5	-0.2
30 W	0410	4.8	1.5
	1025	-0.3	-0.1
	1630	4.5	1.4
	2247	-0.6	-0.2

DECEMBER

Day	Time h m	Height ft	Height m
1 Th	0505	5.1	1.6
	1120	-0.5	-0.2
	1726	4.5	1.4
	2334	-0.7	-0.2
2 F	0555	5.4	1.6
	1211	-0.7	-0.2
	1813	4.5	1.4
3 Sa	0022	-0.7	-0.2
	0638	5.6	1.7
	1259	-0.7	-0.2
	1858	4.5	1.4
4 Su	0108	-0.7	-0.2
	0721	5.6	1.7
	1348	-0.7	-0.2
	1940	4.3	1.3
5 M	0151	-0.5	-0.2
	0802	5.4	1.6
	1430	-0.7	-0.2
	2022	4.2	1.3
6 Tu	0233	-0.3	-0.1
	0842	5.2	1.6
	1512	-0.5	-0.2
	2103	3.9	1.2
7 W	0312	-0.1	0.0
	0922	4.9	1.5
	1554	-0.3	-0.1
	2147	3.7	1.1
8 Th	0352	0.2	0.1
	1005	4.7	1.4
	1634	-0.1	0.0
	2234	3.6	1.1
9 F	0431	0.4	0.1
	1050	4.4	1.3
	1717	0.1	0.0
	2322	3.5	1.1
10 Sa	0517	0.7	0.2
	1135	4.1	1.2
	1802	0.2	0.1
11 Su	0009	3.4	1.0
	0610	0.8	0.2
	1223	4.0	1.2
	1855	0.3	0.1
12 M	0100	3.5	1.1
	0716	0.9	0.3
	1313	3.8	1.2
	1951	0.3	0.1
13 Tu	0151	3.6	1.1
	0819	0.8	0.2
	1406	3.7	1.1
	2043	0.2	0.1
14 W	0246	3.7	1.1
	0916	0.6	0.2
	1505	3.7	1.1
	2130	0.1	0.0
15 Th	0342	4.0	1.2
	1007	0.4	0.1
	1601	3.8	1.2
	2215	-0.1	0.0
16 F	0433	4.4	1.3
	1057	0.1	0.0
	1657	3.9	1.2
	2300	-0.3	-0.1
17 Sa	0524	4.8	1.5
	1147	-0.2	-0.1
	1747	4.1	1.2
	2347	-0.4	-0.1
18 Su	0608	5.1	1.6
	1237	-0.5	-0.2
	1833	4.2	1.3
19 M	0033	-0.6	-0.2
	0651	5.4	1.6
	1326	-0.7	-0.2
	1920	4.3	1.3
20 Tu	0122	-0.7	-0.2
	0736	5.5	1.7
	1415	-0.9	-0.3
	2006	4.3	1.3
21 W	0211	-0.7	-0.2
	0822	5.6	1.7
	1503	-0.9	-0.3
	2056	4.3	1.3
22 Th	0259	-0.7	-0.2
	0912	5.4	1.6
	1551	-0.9	-0.3
	2151	4.2	1.3
23 F	0351	-0.6	-0.2
	1006	5.3	1.6
	1640	-0.8	-0.2
	2248	4.2	1.3
24 Sa	0445	-0.4	-0.1
	1103	5.0	1.5
	1733	-0.7	-0.2
	2346	4.2	1.3
25 Su	0546	-0.2	-0.1
	1201	4.7	1.4
	1833	-0.5	-0.2
26 M	0045	4.3	1.3
	0654	0.0	0.0
	1300	4.4	1.3
	1934	-0.5	-0.2
27 Tu	0144	4.4	1.3
	0803	0.0	0.0
	1400	4.2	1.3
	2035	-0.4	-0.1
28 W	0244	4.5	1.4
	0908	-0.1	0.0
	1503	4.0	1.2
	2129	-0.5	-0.2
29 Th	0345	4.7	1.4
	1006	-0.3	-0.1
	1606	3.9	1.2
	2220	-0.5	-0.2
30 F	0443	4.8	1.5
	1059	-0.4	-0.1
	1705	3.9	1.2
	2310	-0.5	-0.2
31 Sa	0534	5.0	1.5
	1152	-0.5	-0.2
	1755	4.0	1.2
	2357	-0.5	-0.2

Time meridian 75° W. 0000 is midnight. 1200 is noon.
Heights are referred to mean low water which is the chart datum of soundings.

PHILADELPHIA, PA., 1983

Times and Heights of High and Low Waters

JANUARY

Day	Time (h m)	Height (ft)	Height (m)
1 Sa	0249	5.6	1.7
	0954	-0.6	-0.2
	1510	6.9	2.1
	2237	-0.8	-0.2
2 Su	0343	5.6	1.7
	1045	-0.6	-0.2
	1605	6.7	2.0
	2327	-0.8	-0.2
3 M	0440	5.6	1.7
	1137	-0.5	-0.2
	1700	6.5	2.0
4 Tu	0017	-0.7	-0.2
	0537	5.6	1.7
	1231	-0.4	-0.1
	1757	6.3	1.9
5 W	0106	-0.7	-0.2
	0636	5.6	1.7
	1324	-0.3	-0.1
	1855	6.0	1.8
6 Th	0156	-0.6	-0.2
	0735	5.7	1.7
	1420	-0.2	-0.1
	1954	5.7	1.7
7 F	0248	-0.5	-0.2
	0831	5.7	1.7
	1517	-0.1	0.0
	2050	5.5	1.7
8 Sa	0339	-0.4	-0.1
	0927	5.8	1.8
	1613	-0.1	0.0
	2145	5.4	1.6
9 Su	0430	-0.3	-0.1
	1018	5.9	1.8
	1708	-0.1	0.0
	2238	5.2	1.6
10 M	0520	-0.3	-0.1
	1108	5.9	1.8
	1800	-0.2	-0.1
	2329	5.2	1.6
11 Tu	0609	-0.2	-0.1
	1155	6.0	1.8
	1851	-0.2	-0.1
12 W	0016	5.1	1.6
	0656	-0.2	-0.1
	1240	6.0	1.8
	1939	-0.3	-0.1
13 Th	0103	5.1	1.6
	0741	-0.2	-0.1
	1321	6.0	1.8
	2024	-0.3	-0.1
14 F	0146	5.0	1.5
	0825	-0.2	-0.1
	1401	6.0	1.8
	2108	-0.3	-0.1
15 Sa	0227	4.9	1.5
	0908	-0.2	-0.1
	1439	5.9	1.8
	2150	-0.2	-0.1
16 Su	0306	4.9	1.5
	0949	-0.2	-0.1
	1515	5.9	1.8
	2230	-0.2	-0.1
17 M	0342	4.9	1.5
	1033	-0.2	-0.1
	1551	5.8	1.8
	2311	-0.2	-0.1
18 Tu	0418	4.9	1.5
	1117	-0.2	-0.1
	1623	5.7	1.7
	2352	-0.2	-0.1
19 W	0451	4.9	1.5
	1202	-0.1	0.0
	1701	5.5	1.7
20 Th	0034	-0.2	-0.1
	0532	5.0	1.5
	1252	-0.1	0.0
	1746	5.3	1.6
21 F	0117	-0.2	-0.1
	0621	5.1	1.6
	1347	0.0	0.0
	1841	5.1	1.6
22 Sa	0206	-0.2	-0.1
	0718	5.2	1.6
	1445	0.0	0.0
	1947	4.9	1.5
23 Su	0258	-0.2	-0.1
	0821	5.4	1.6
	1547	0.0	0.0
	2051	4.8	1.5
24 M	0356	-0.2	-0.1
	0923	5.6	1.7
	1649	0.0	0.0
	2152	4.9	1.5
25 Tu	0457	-0.3	-0.1
	1021	5.9	1.8
	1748	-0.2	-0.1
	2252	5.0	1.5
26 W	0556	-0.3	-0.1
	1119	6.3	1.9
	1848	-0.3	-0.1
	2350	5.2	1.6
27 Th	0653	-0.5	-0.2
	1214	6.6	2.0
	1942	-0.5	-0.2
28 F	0045	5.5	1.7
	0749	-0.6	-0.2
	1309	6.8	2.1
	2035	-0.6	-0.2
29 Sa	0138	5.7	1.7
	0842	-0.6	-0.2
	1401	6.9	2.1
	2127	-0.7	-0.2
30 Su	0232	5.9	1.8
	0935	-0.6	-0.2
	1452	6.9	2.1
	2214	-0.7	-0.2
31 M	0324	6.0	1.8
	1026	-0.6	-0.2
	1545	6.8	2.1
	2302	-0.7	-0.2

FEBRUARY

Day	Time (h m)	Height (ft)	Height (m)
1 Tu	0419	6.1	1.9
	1117	-0.5	-0.2
	1638	6.5	2.0
	2348	-0.6	-0.2
2 W	0512	6.0	1.8
	1207	-0.4	-0.1
	1732	6.2	1.9
3 Th	0034	-0.5	-0.2
	0607	5.9	1.8
	1259	-0.3	-0.1
	1827	5.8	1.8
4 F	0122	-0.4	-0.1
	0703	5.8	1.8
	1352	-0.2	-0.1
	1924	5.5	1.7
5 Sa	0211	-0.3	-0.1
	0757	5.7	1.7
	1446	-0.1	0.0
	2020	5.2	1.6
6 Su	0301	-0.3	-0.1
	0852	5.6	1.7
	1542	-0.1	0.0
	2117	5.0	1.5
7 M	0353	-0.2	-0.1
	0946	5.6	1.7
	1636	-0.1	0.0
	2211	4.9	1.5
8 Tu	0444	-0.2	-0.1
	1038	5.6	1.7
	1730	-0.1	0.0
	2303	4.9	1.5
9 W	0537	-0.2	-0.1
	1127	5.7	1.7
	1822	-0.2	-0.1
	2353	5.0	1.5
10 Th	0626	-0.2	-0.1
	1214	5.9	1.8
	1909	-0.2	-0.1
11 F	0040	5.1	1.6
	0714	-0.2	-0.1
	1257	6.0	1.8
	1957	-0.2	-0.1
12 Sa	0123	5.2	1.6
	0801	-0.2	-0.1
	1338	6.0	1.8
	2040	-0.2	-0.1
13 Su	0203	5.2	1.6
	0846	-0.2	-0.1
	1417	6.1	1.9
	2122	-0.1	0.0
14 M	0240	5.3	1.6
	0931	-0.2	-0.1
	1452	6.0	1.8
	2204	-0.1	0.0
15 Tu	0314	5.3	1.6
	1014	-0.2	-0.1
	1526	5.9	1.8
	2243	-0.1	0.0
16 W	0346	5.4	1.6
	1058	-0.1	0.0
	1559	5.8	1.8
	2322	-0.1	0.0
17 Th	0416	5.5	1.7
	1145	-0.1	0.0
	1635	5.6	1.7
18 F	0004	-0.1	0.0
	0456	5.5	1.7
	1233	-0.1	0.0
	1720	5.4	1.6
19 Sa	0047	-0.1	0.0
	0540	5.6	1.7
	1324	0.0	0.0
	1812	5.1	1.6
20 Su	0133	-0.1	0.0
	0642	5.6	1.7
	1422	0.1	0.0
	1916	4.9	1.5
21 M	0228	-0.1	0.0
	0748	5.6	1.7
	1524	0.1	0.0
	2024	4.8	1.5
22 Tu	0330	-0.1	0.0
	0854	5.8	1.8
	1627	0.1	0.0
	2131	4.9	1.5
23 W	0433	-0.1	0.0
	0959	6.0	1.8
	1727	0.0	0.0
	2233	5.2	1.6
24 Th	0535	-0.2	-0.1
	1059	6.3	1.9
	1824	-0.1	0.0
	2332	5.5	1.7
25 F	0634	-0.3	-0.1
	1156	6.7	2.0
	1920	-0.2	-0.1
26 Sa	0027	5.9	1.8
	0731	-0.3	-0.1
	1251	6.9	2.1
	2011	-0.3	-0.1
27 Su	0121	6.2	1.9
	0824	-0.4	-0.1
	1343	7.0	2.1
	2100	-0.4	-0.1
28 M	0212	6.5	2.0
	0915	-0.4	-0.1
	1433	7.0	2.1
	2148	-0.4	-0.1

MARCH

Day	Time (h m)	Height (ft)	Height (m)
1 Tu	0303	6.6	2.0
	1005	-0.3	-0.1
	1524	6.9	2.1
	2232	-0.3	-0.1
2 W	0353	6.6	2.0
	1054	-0.3	-0.1
	1613	6.6	2.0
	2317	-0.2	-0.1
3 Th	0442	6.4	2.0
	1141	-0.2	-0.1
	1704	6.2	1.9
4 F	0002	-0.2	-0.1
	0533	6.2	1.9
	1231	-0.1	0.0
	1757	5.7	1.7
5 Sa	0046	-0.1	0.0
	0626	5.9	1.8
	1321	0.0	0.0
	1852	5.4	1.6
6 Su	0132	0.0	0.0
	0719	5.7	1.7
	1412	0.1	0.0
	1948	5.1	1.6
7 M	0222	0.0	0.0
	0815	5.6	1.7
	1505	0.1	0.0
	2045	4.9	1.5
8 Tu	0313	0.1	0.0
	0910	5.5	1.7
	1600	0.1	0.0
	2141	4.9	1.5
9 W	0409	0.1	0.0
	1004	5.6	1.7
	1656	0.1	0.0
	2234	5.0	1.5
10 Th	0502	0.0	0.0
	1057	5.8	1.8
	1747	0.1	0.0
	2325	5.2	1.6
11 F	0556	0.0	0.0
	1145	5.9	1.8
	1838	0.1	0.0
12 Sa	0012	5.4	1.6
	0648	0.0	0.0
	1230	6.1	1.9
	1926	0.1	0.0
13 Su	0055	5.6	1.7
	0736	0.0	0.0
	1312	6.2	1.9
	2010	0.1	0.0
14 M	0134	5.7	1.7
	0824	0.0	0.0
	1350	6.2	1.9
	2053	0.1	0.0
15 Tu	0210	5.9	1.8
	0909	0.0	0.0
	1426	6.2	1.9
	2135	0.2	0.1
16 W	0245	6.0	1.8
	0955	0.0	0.0
	1502	6.1	1.9
	2215	0.2	0.1
17 Th	0315	6.1	1.9
	1040	0.0	0.0
	1537	5.9	1.8
	2257	0.2	0.1
18 F	0349	6.1	1.9
	1127	0.0	0.0
	1615	5.7	1.7
	2338	0.1	0.0
19 Sa	0429	6.1	1.9
	1215	0.0	0.0
	1701	5.4	1.6
20 Su	0022	0.1	0.0
	0517	6.1	1.9
	1308	0.1	0.0
	1757	5.2	1.6
21 M	0111	0.1	0.0
	0619	6.0	1.8
	1404	0.2	0.1
	1903	5.0	1.5
22 Tu	0209	0.2	0.1
	0727	5.9	1.8
	1504	0.2	0.1
	2010	5.0	1.5
23 W	0311	0.2	0.1
	0836	6.0	1.8
	1605	0.2	0.1
	2116	5.2	1.6
24 Th	0415	0.2	0.1
	0942	6.2	1.9
	1704	0.2	0.1
	2217	5.6	1.7
25 F	0516	0.2	0.1
	1042	6.5	2.0
	1803	0.1	0.0
	2316	6.0	1.8
26 Sa	0616	0.1	0.0
	1139	6.8	2.1
	1855	0.1	0.0
27 Su	0011	6.5	2.0
	0713	0.0	0.0
	1233	7.0	2.1
	1946	0.0	0.0
28 M	0102	6.8	2.1
	0806	0.0	0.0
	1324	7.1	2.2
	2033	0.0	0.0
29 Tu	0152	7.0	2.1
	0856	0.0	0.0
	1413	7.0	2.1
	2119	0.1	0.0
30 W	0239	7.1	2.2
	0944	0.0	0.0
	1500	6.8	2.1
	2202	0.2	0.1
31 Th	0325	7.0	2.1
	1030	0.0	0.0
	1547	6.5	2.0
	2244	0.2	0.1

Time meridian 75° W. 0000 is midnight. 1200 is noon.
Heights are referred to mean low water which is the chart datum of soundings.

Times and Heights of High and Low Waters

APRIL

Day	Time (h m)	Height (ft)	Height (m)
1	0411	6.8	2.1
F	1116	0.1	0.0
	1636	6.1	1.9
	2327	0.3	0.1
2	0457	6.4	2.0
Sa	1202	0.1	0.0
	1725	5.7	1.7
3	0010	0.3	0.1
Su	0546	6.1	1.9
	1248	0.2	0.1
	1819	5.3	1.6
4	0053	0.3	0.1
M	0639	5.8	1.8
	1338	0.2	0.1
	1914	5.1	1.6
5	0142	0.4	0.1
Tu	0734	5.7	1.7
	1430	0.3	0.1
	2011	5.0	1.5
6	0235	0.4	0.1
W	0831	5.6	1.7
	1523	0.3	0.1
	2108	5.1	1.6
7	0331	0.4	0.1
Th	0927	5.7	1.7
	1617	0.4	0.1
	2202	5.3	1.6
8	0428	0.4	0.1
F	1021	5.9	1.8
	1711	0.4	0.1
	2254	5.5	1.7
9	0525	0.3	0.1
Sa	1110	6.1	1.9
	1803	0.4	0.1
	2340	5.8	1.8
10	0619	0.3	0.1
Su	1158	6.2	1.9
	1851	0.4	0.1
11	0024	6.1	1.9
M	0710	0.2	0.1
	1240	6.3	1.9
	1937	0.4	0.1
12	0103	6.3	1.9
Tu	0800	0.2	0.1
	1320	6.3	1.9
	2022	0.4	0.1
13	0139	6.5	2.0
W	0847	0.1	0.0
	1359	6.2	1.9
	2105	0.4	0.1
14	0214	6.6	2.0
Th	0934	0.1	0.0
	1436	6.1	1.9
	2147	0.4	0.1
15	0249	6.7	2.0
F	1022	0.0	0.0
	1515	5.9	1.8
	2230	0.3	0.1
16	0327	6.7	2.0
Sa	1109	0.0	0.0
	1600	5.7	1.7
	2315	0.3	0.1
17	0412	6.6	2.0
Su	1200	0.1	0.0
	1649	5.5	1.7
18	0002	0.3	0.1
M	0503	6.5	2.0
	1252	0.1	0.0
	1746	5.3	1.6
19	0055	0.3	0.1
Tu	0605	6.3	1.9
	1347	0.2	0.1
	1851	5.3	1.6
20	0154	0.4	0.1
W	0711	6.3	1.9
	1444	0.3	0.1
	1958	5.4	1.6
21	0256	0.5	0.2
Th	0820	6.3	1.9
	1543	0.3	0.1
	2103	5.7	1.7
22	0358	0.5	0.2
F	0925	6.4	2.0
	1641	0.3	0.1
	2204	6.1	1.9
23	0500	0.4	0.1
Sa	1025	6.6	2.0
	1736	0.3	0.1
	2300	6.6	2.0
24	0558	0.4	0.1
Su	1121	6.8	2.1
	1829	0.3	0.1
	2353	7.0	2.1
25	0653	0.3	0.1
M	1214	6.9	2.1
	1918	0.3	0.1
26	0043	7.3	2.2
Tu	0746	0.3	0.1
	1304	6.9	2.1
	2005	0.4	0.1
27	0129	7.4	2.3
W	0834	0.2	0.1
	1350	6.7	2.0
	2050	0.4	0.1
28	0213	7.3	2.2
Th	0921	0.2	0.1
	1436	6.5	2.0
	2132	0.5	0.2
29	0257	7.2	2.2
F	1006	0.3	0.1
	1522	6.2	1.9
	2213	0.6	0.2
30	0339	6.9	2.1
Sa	1051	0.3	0.1
	1608	5.9	1.8
	2253	0.6	0.2

MAY

Day	Time (h m)	Height (ft)	Height (m)
1	0423	6.6	2.0
Su	1133	0.3	0.1
	1656	5.6	1.7
	2335	0.6	0.2
2	0507	6.3	1.9
M	1218	0.3	0.1
	1746	5.3	1.6
3	0018	0.6	0.2
Tu	0557	6.0	1.8
	1304	0.4	0.1
	1839	5.2	1.6
4	0106	0.6	0.2
W	0650	5.8	1.8
	1353	0.4	0.1
	1935	5.1	1.6
5	0159	0.6	0.2
Th	0748	5.7	1.7
	1445	0.5	0.2
	2031	5.2	1.6
6	0256	0.6	0.2
F	0846	5.8	1.8
	1538	0.5	0.2
	2126	5.5	1.7
7	0355	0.6	0.2
Sa	0941	5.9	1.8
	1633	0.5	0.2
	2217	5.8	1.8
8	0452	0.6	0.2
Su	1031	6.0	1.8
	1724	0.5	0.2
	2304	6.1	1.9
9	0550	0.5	0.2
M	1120	6.1	1.9
	1814	0.5	0.2
	2346	6.4	2.0
10	0643	0.4	0.1
Tu	1206	6.1	1.9
	1902	0.5	0.2
11	0028	6.7	2.0
W	0734	0.3	0.1
	1248	6.1	1.9
	1949	0.5	0.2
12	0106	6.9	2.1
Th	0825	0.1	0.0
	1330	6.1	1.9
	2035	0.4	0.1
13	0146	7.0	2.1
F	0915	0.1	0.0
	1411	6.0	1.8
	2121	0.4	0.1
14	0226	7.1	2.2
Sa	1003	0.0	0.0
	1457	5.9	1.8
	2208	0.3	0.1
15	0310	7.1	2.2
Su	1053	0.0	0.0
	1544	5.7	1.7
	2255	0.3	0.1
16	0358	7.0	2.1
M	1142	0.0	0.0
	1638	5.6	1.7
	2347	0.4	0.1
17	0453	6.8	2.1
Tu	1234	0.0	0.0
	1738	5.6	1.7
18	0042	0.4	0.1
W	0554	6.6	2.0
	1328	0.1	0.0
	1841	5.6	1.7
19	0138	0.5	0.2
Th	0700	6.5	2.0
	1423	0.2	0.1
	1946	5.8	1.8
20	0239	0.5	0.2
F	0805	6.4	2.0
	1519	0.2	0.1
	2048	6.1	1.9
21	0340	0.6	0.2
Sa	0907	6.4	2.0
	1615	0.2	0.1
	2148	6.5	2.0
22	0441	0.5	0.2
Su	1006	6.5	2.0
	1709	0.3	0.1
	2243	6.9	2.1
23	0539	0.5	0.2
M	1102	6.6	2.0
	1800	0.3	0.1
	2334	7.2	2.2
24	0632	0.4	0.1
Tu	1153	6.6	2.0
	1849	0.4	0.1
25	0021	7.3	2.2
W	0724	0.3	0.1
	1241	6.5	2.0
	1935	0.5	0.2
26	0106	7.3	2.2
Th	0812	0.3	0.1
	1329	6.3	1.9
	2019	0.6	0.2
27	0148	7.2	2.2
F	0858	0.3	0.1
	1413	6.1	1.9
	2101	0.6	0.2
28	0230	7.1	2.2
Sa	0940	0.3	0.1
	1457	5.9	1.8
	2142	0.7	0.2
29	0310	6.8	2.1
Su	1024	0.3	0.1
	1542	5.6	1.7
	2221	0.7	0.2
30	0351	6.6	2.0
M	1106	0.4	0.1
	1626	5.4	1.6
	2303	0.7	0.2
31	0433	6.3	1.9
Tu	1149	0.4	0.1
	1712	5.3	1.6
	2347	0.7	0.2

JUNE

Day	Time (h m)	Height (ft)	Height (m)
1	0517	6.1	1.9
W	1231	0.4	0.1
	1802	5.2	1.6
2	0034	0.7	0.2
Th	0607	5.9	1.8
	1319	0.4	0.1
	1856	5.2	1.6
3	0127	0.7	0.2
F	0701	5.8	1.8
	1407	0.4	0.1
	1950	5.3	1.6
4	0222	0.7	0.2
Sa	0800	5.7	1.7
	1459	0.5	0.2
	2043	5.5	1.7
5	0322	0.7	0.2
Su	0856	5.7	1.7
	1551	0.5	0.2
	2134	5.8	1.8
6	0421	0.7	0.2
M	0950	5.7	1.7
	1644	0.5	0.2
	2222	6.2	1.9
7	0520	0.5	0.2
Tu	1041	5.8	1.8
	1737	0.4	0.1
	2309	6.5	2.0
8	0616	0.4	0.1
W	1129	5.8	1.8
	1828	0.4	0.1
	2351	6.8	2.1
9	0709	0.2	0.1
Th	1216	5.8	1.8
	1917	0.4	0.1
10	0036	7.1	2.2
F	0802	0.1	0.0
	1303	5.9	1.8
	2006	0.3	0.1
11	0119	7.2	2.2
Sa	0852	0.0	0.0
	1349	5.9	1.8
	2056	0.2	0.1
12	0206	7.3	2.2
Su	0942	-0.1	0.0
	1439	5.9	1.8
	2147	0.2	0.1
13	0254	7.3	2.2
M	1033	-0.1	0.0
	1530	5.8	1.8
	2237	0.2	0.1
14	0345	7.2	2.2
Tu	1123	-0.1	0.0
	1626	5.8	1.8
	2330	0.3	0.1
15	0440	7.0	2.1
W	1215	-0.1	0.0
	1725	5.8	1.8
16	0025	0.3	0.1
Th	0541	6.8	2.1
	1306	-0.1	0.0
	1827	5.9	1.8
17	0122	0.4	0.1
F	0644	6.5	2.0
	1359	0.0	0.0
	1930	6.1	1.9
18	0220	0.5	0.2
Sa	0746	6.4	2.0
	1453	0.0	0.0
	2030	6.3	1.9
19	0319	0.5	0.2
Su	0847	6.3	1.9
	1546	0.1	0.0
	2128	6.6	2.0
20	0418	0.5	0.2
M	0945	6.2	1.9
	1639	0.2	0.1
	2221	6.8	2.1
21	0516	0.4	0.1
Tu	1040	6.1	1.9
	1731	0.2	0.1
	2311	7.0	2.1
22	0609	0.3	0.1
W	1131	6.1	1.9
	1819	0.3	0.1
	2358	7.1	2.2
23	0701	0.2	0.1
Th	1219	6.0	1.8
	1905	0.4	0.1
24	0042	7.1	2.2
F	0747	0.2	0.1
	1305	5.9	1.8
	1950	0.5	0.2
25	0125	7.0	2.1
Sa	0832	0.2	0.1
	1351	5.7	1.7
	2033	0.5	0.2
26	0205	6.9	2.1
Su	0915	0.3	0.1
	1433	5.6	1.7
	2113	0.6	0.2
27	0244	6.7	2.0
M	0957	0.3	0.1
	1515	5.5	1.7
	2155	0.6	0.2
28	0323	6.5	2.0
Tu	1039	0.3	0.1
	1557	5.4	1.6
	2237	0.6	0.2
29	0401	6.4	2.0
W	1120	0.4	0.1
	1639	5.3	1.6
	2320	0.6	0.2
30	0440	6.2	1.9
Th	1202	0.4	0.1
	1723	5.2	1.6

Time meridian 75° W. 0000 is midnight. 1200 is noon.
Heights are referred to mean low water which is the chart datum of soundings.

HAMPTON ROADS (Sewells Pt.), VA., 1983

Times and Heights of High and Low Waters

JANUARY

Day	Time h m	Height ft	m	Day	Time h m	Height ft	m
1	0406	-0.6	-0.2	16	0414	-0.4	-0.1
Sa	1031	3.0	0.9	Su	1033	2.1	0.6
	1656	-0.6	-0.2		1654	-0.5	-0.2
	2300	2.5	0.8		2256	1.7	0.5
2	0502	-0.5	-0.2	17	0452	-0.3	-0.1
Su	1124	2.9	0.9	M	1108	2.1	0.6
	1746	-0.5	-0.2		1728	-0.4	-0.1
	2354	2.5	0.8		2333	1.7	0.5
3	0559	-0.3	-0.1	18	0530	-0.2	-0.1
M	1218	2.8	0.9	Tu	1144	2.0	0.6
	1839	-0.3	-0.1		1801	-0.3	-0.1
4	0052	2.5	0.8	19	0010	1.8	0.5
Tu	0658	-0.1	0.0	W	0610	-0.2	-0.1
	1313	2.6	0.8		1223	1.9	0.6
	1933	-0.2	-0.1		1837	-0.3	-0.1
5	0150	2.5	0.8	20	0052	1.9	0.6
W	0801	0.0	0.0	Th	0657	-0.1	0.0
	1412	2.4	0.7		1302	1.8	0.5
	2029	-0.1	0.0		1916	-0.2	-0.1
6	0251	2.4	0.7	21	0137	2.0	0.6
Th	0907	0.1	0.0	F	0750	0.0	0.0
	1510	2.2	0.7		1351	1.8	0.5
	2125	0.0	0.0		2003	-0.2	-0.1
7	0352	2.4	0.7	22	0233	2.1	0.6
F	1012	0.2	0.1	Sa	0849	0.0	0.0
	1612	2.0	0.6		1445	1.7	0.5
	2221	0.0	0.0		2056	-0.2	-0.1
8	0449	2.4	0.7	23	0332	2.2	0.7
Sa	1115	0.1	0.0	Su	0956	0.0	0.0
	1709	1.8	0.5		1551	1.7	0.5
	2313	0.0	0.0		2157	-0.2	-0.1
9	0544	2.3	0.7	24	0434	2.3	0.7
Su	1214	0.0	0.0	M	1102	-0.1	0.0
	1804	1.7	0.5		1657	1.8	0.5
					2302	-0.3	-0.1
10	0003	-0.1	0.0	25	0539	2.5	0.8
M	0635	2.3	0.7	Tu	1208	-0.2	-0.1
	1304	-0.1	0.0		1803	1.9	0.6
	1855	1.7	0.5				
11	0053	-0.2	-0.1	26	0006	-0.4	-0.1
Tu	0718	2.3	0.7	W	0640	2.6	0.8
	1348	-0.3	-0.1		1307	-0.4	-0.1
	1941	1.6	0.5		1906	2.0	0.6
12	0136	-0.3	-0.1	27	0107	-0.6	-0.2
W	0800	2.3	0.7	Th	0738	2.8	0.9
	1430	-0.4	-0.1		1403	-0.5	-0.2
	2023	1.6	0.5		2003	2.2	0.7
13	0218	-0.4	-0.1	28	0207	-0.7	-0.2
Th	0841	2.3	0.7	F	0832	2.9	0.9
	1509	-0.5	-0.2		1456	-0.6	-0.2
	2104	1.6	0.5		2058	2.4	0.7
14	0257	-0.4	-0.1	29	0302	-0.7	-0.2
F	0919	2.2	0.7	Sa	0925	3.0	0.9
	1545	-0.5	-0.2		1547	-0.7	-0.2
	2142	1.6	0.5		2151	2.5	0.8
15	0336	-0.4	-0.1	30	0357	-0.7	-0.2
Sa	0956	2.2	0.7	Su	1016	3.0	0.9
	1619	-0.5	-0.2		1637	-0.7	-0.2
	2221	1.7	0.5		2243	2.6	0.8
				31	0450	-0.6	-0.2
				M	1106	2.9	0.9
					1724	-0.6	-0.2
					2335	2.6	0.8

FEBRUARY

Day	Time h m	Height ft	m	Day	Time h m	Height ft	m
1	0543	-0.4	-0.1	16	0506	-0.3	-0.1
Tu	1157	2.7	0.8	W	1114	2.1	0.6
	1813	-0.4	-0.1		1724	-0.3	-0.1
					2338	2.1	0.6
2	0028	2.6	0.8	17	0546	-0.2	-0.1
W	0638	-0.2	-0.1	Th	1151	2.0	0.6
	1247	2.5	0.8		1759	-0.3	-0.1
	1901	-0.3	-0.1				
3	0121	2.5	0.8	18	0017	2.2	0.7
Th	0735	0.0	0.0	F	0631	-0.1	0.0
	1340	2.3	0.7		1231	2.0	0.6
	1951	-0.1	0.0		1835	-0.2	-0.1
4	0217	2.4	0.7	19	0105	2.3	0.7
F	0834	0.1	0.0	Sa	0721	0.0	0.0
	1434	2.0	0.6		1321	1.9	0.6
	2043	0.0	0.0		1927	-0.1	0.0
5	0314	2.3	0.7	20	0158	2.3	0.7
Sa	0939	0.2	0.1	Su	0817	0.1	0.0
	1534	1.8	0.5		1417	1.9	0.6
	2139	0.1	0.0		2023	-0.1	0.0
6	0411	2.2	0.7	21	0302	2.4	0.7
Su	1044	0.2	0.1	M	0929	0.2	0.1
	1634	1.7	0.5		1522	1.8	0.5
	2237	0.1	0.0		2131	0.0	0.0
7	0511	2.2	0.7	22	0410	2.5	0.8
M	1143	0.1	0.0	Tu	1041	0.1	0.0
	1733	1.6	0.5		1636	1.9	0.6
	2330	0.0	0.0		2241	-0.1	0.0
8	0604	2.2	0.7	23	0519	2.6	0.8
Tu	1235	0.0	0.0	W	1150	0.0	0.0
	1829	1.6	0.5		1747	2.0	0.6
					2352	-0.2	-0.1
9	0025	-0.1	0.0	24	0624	2.7	0.8
W	0651	2.2	0.7	Th	1251	-0.2	-0.1
	1322	-0.2	-0.1		1853	2.2	0.7
	1917	1.6	0.5				
10	0112	-0.2	-0.1	25	0058	-0.4	-0.1
Th	0736	2.2	0.7	F	0724	2.9	0.9
	1403	-0.3	-0.1		1346	-0.4	-0.1
	1959	1.6	0.5		1951	2.5	0.8
11	0154	-0.3	-0.1	26	0157	-0.5	-0.2
F	0816	2.2	0.7	Sa	0818	3.0	0.9
	1440	-0.4	-0.1		1437	-0.5	-0.2
	2040	1.7	0.5		2044	2.7	0.8
12	0236	-0.4	-0.1	27	0252	-0.6	-0.2
Sa	0855	2.2	0.7	Su	0910	3.0	0.9
	1516	-0.5	-0.2		1526	-0.5	-0.2
	2116	1.8	0.5		2135	2.8	0.9
13	0315	-0.4	-0.1	28	0344	-0.6	-0.2
Su	0932	2.2	0.7	M	0959	3.0	0.9
	1550	-0.5	-0.2		1613	-0.5	-0.2
	2152	1.9	0.6		2224	2.9	0.9
14	0352	-0.4	-0.1				
M	1008	2.2	0.7				
	1622	-0.5	-0.2				
	2227	1.9	0.6				
15	0429	-0.4	-0.1				
Tu	1040	2.1	0.6				
	1652	-0.4	-0.1				
	2303	2.0	0.6				

MARCH

Day	Time h m	Height ft	m	Day	Time h m	Height ft	m
1	0435	-0.5	-0.2	16	0406	-0.3	-0.1
Tu	1046	2.8	0.9	W	1013	2.2	0.7
	1658	-0.4	-0.1		1619	-0.3	-0.1
	2313	2.9	0.9		2233	2.4	0.7
2	0525	-0.3	-0.1	17	0444	-0.3	-0.1
W	1132	2.7	0.8	Th	1048	2.2	0.7
	1741	-0.3	-0.1		1652	-0.2	-0.1
	2359	2.8	0.9		2311	2.5	0.8
3	0613	-0.1	0.0	18	0524	-0.1	0.0
Th	1218	2.5	0.8	F	1125	2.2	0.7
	1826	-0.1	0.0		1728	-0.1	0.0
					2353	2.6	0.8
4	0049	2.7	0.8	19	0610	0.0	0.0
F	0707	0.1	0.0	Sa	1210	2.2	0.7
	1308	2.2	0.7		1812	0.0	0.0
	1913	0.0	0.0				
5	0139	2.5	0.8	20	0041	2.6	0.8
Sa	0800	0.2	0.1	Su	0703	0.2	0.1
	1358	2.0	0.6		1258	2.1	0.6
	2003	0.2	0.1		1903	0.1	0.0
6	0232	2.4	0.7	21	0137	2.6	0.8
Su	0900	0.4	0.1	M	0804	0.3	0.1
	1453	1.8	0.5		1401	2.1	0.6
	2057	0.3	0.1		2006	0.2	0.1
7	0331	2.3	0.7	22	0241	2.6	0.8
M	1003	0.4	0.1	Tu	0913	0.4	0.1
	1555	1.7	0.5		1511	2.1	0.6
	2155	0.3	0.1		2117	0.2	0.1
8	0430	2.2	0.7	23	0353	2.6	0.8
Tu	1105	0.3	0.1	W	1025	0.3	0.1
	1659	1.7	0.5		1625	2.2	0.7
	2257	0.3	0.1		2233	0.2	0.1
9	0526	2.1	0.6	24	0505	2.7	0.8
W	1200	0.2	0.1	Th	1131	0.2	0.1
	1758	1.7	0.5		1736	2.4	0.7
	2353	0.1	0.0		2345	0.1	0.0
10	0619	2.2	0.7	25	0611	2.8	0.9
Th	1245	0.0	0.0	F	1232	0.0	0.0
	1845	1.7	0.5		1839	2.6	0.8
11	0045	0.0	0.0	26	0049	-0.1	0.0
F	0704	2.2	0.7	Sa	0709	2.9	0.9
	1328	-0.1	0.0		1326	-0.1	0.0
	1930	1.8	0.5		1936	2.8	0.9
12	0130	-0.2	-0.1	27	0146	-0.3	-0.1
Sa	0746	2.2	0.7	Su	0803	2.9	0.9
	1405	-0.3	-0.1		1415	-0.3	-0.1
	2009	2.0	0.6		2027	2.9	0.9
13	0210	-0.3	-0.1	28	0239	-0.3	-0.1
Su	0826	2.2	0.7	M	0852	2.9	0.9
	1440	-0.4	-0.1		1502	-0.3	-0.1
	2045	2.1	0.6		2116	3.0	0.9
14	0250	-0.4	-0.1	29	0329	-0.4	-0.1
M	0903	2.3	0.7	Tu	0939	2.9	0.9
	1515	-0.4	-0.1		1546	-0.3	-0.1
	2121	2.2	0.7		2201	3.1	0.9
15	0329	-0.4	-0.1	30	0416	-0.3	-0.1
Tu	0938	2.3	0.7	W	1024	2.8	0.9
	1547	-0.4	-0.1		1629	-0.2	-0.1
	2156	2.3	0.7		2246	3.0	0.9
				31	0503	-0.2	-0.1
				Th	1106	2.6	0.8
					1711	-0.1	0.0
					2329	2.9	0.9

Time meridian 75° W. 0000 is midnight. 1200 is noon.
Heights are referred to mean low water which is the chart datum of soundings.

Times and Heights of High and Low Waters

APRIL

Day	Time h m	Height ft	Height m	Day	Time h m	Height ft	Height m
1	0548	0.0	0.0	16	0509	-0.1	0.0
F	1150	2.4	0.7	Sa	1108	2.3	0.7
	1753	0.0	0.0		1706	-0.1	0.0
					2333	2.9	0.9
2	0015	2.8	0.9	17	0557	0.1	0.0
Sa	0636	0.2	0.1	Su	1157	2.3	0.7
	1234	2.2	0.7		1754	0.1	0.0
	1836	0.2	0.1				
3	0102	2.6	0.8	18	0025	2.9	0.9
Su	0727	0.3	0.1	M	0652	0.2	0.1
	1324	2.1	0.6		1250	2.3	0.7
	1924	0.4	0.1		1852	0.2	0.1
4	0150	2.4	0.7	19	0124	2.8	0.9
M	0821	0.4	0.1	Tu	0753	0.3	0.1
	1416	1.9	0.6		1355	2.3	0.7
	2015	0.5	0.2		1958	0.4	0.1
5	0246	2.3	0.7	20	0230	2.8	0.9
Tu	0920	0.5	0.2	W	0900	0.4	0.1
	1520	1.8	0.5		1505	2.3	0.7
	2116	0.5	0.2		2112	0.4	0.1
6	0344	2.2	0.7	21	0340	2.7	0.8
W	1017	0.4	0.1	Th	1009	0.4	0.1
	1621	1.8	0.5		1618	2.4	0.7
	2218	0.4	0.1		2228	0.4	0.1
7	0444	2.2	0.7	22	0449	2.8	0.9
Th	1113	0.3	0.1	F	1114	0.3	0.1
	1717	1.8	0.5		1725	2.6	0.8
	2318	0.3	0.1		2336	0.2	0.1
8	0536	2.2	0.7	23	0554	2.8	0.9
F	1201	0.2	0.1	Sa	1211	0.1	0.0
	1806	1.9	0.6		1824	2.8	0.9
9	0011	0.2	0.1	24	0038	-0.1	0.0
Sa	0625	2.2	0.7	Su	0651	2.8	0.9
	1243	0.0	0.0		1302	0.0	0.0
	1851	2.1	0.6		1917	2.9	0.9
10	0059	0.0	0.0	25	0134	-0.1	0.0
Su	0709	2.2	0.7	M	0741	2.8	0.9
	1322	-0.1	0.0		1351	-0.1	0.0
	1933	2.2	0.7		2007	3.1	0.9
11	0141	-0.2	-0.1	26	0224	-0.2	-0.1
M	0750	2.2	0.7	Tu	0831	2.7	0.8
	1359	-0.2	-0.1		1436	-0.2	-0.1
	2010	2.4	0.7		2054	3.1	0.9
12	0223	-0.3	-0.1	27	0312	-0.2	-0.1
Tu	0828	2.3	0.7	W	0916	2.7	0.8
	1434	-0.3	-0.1		1518	-0.2	-0.1
	2047	2.5	0.8		2137	3.1	0.9
13	0303	-0.3	-0.1	28	0358	-0.2	-0.1
W	0908	2.3	0.7	Th	0958	2.5	0.8
	1509	-0.3	-0.1		1558	-0.1	0.0
	2127	2.7	0.8		2218	3.0	0.9
14	0342	-0.3	-0.1	29	0442	-0.1	0.0
Th	0945	2.3	0.7	F	1040	2.4	0.7
	1545	-0.3	-0.1		1639	0.0	0.0
	2205	2.8	0.9		2300	2.9	0.9
15	0424	-0.2	-0.1	30	0525	0.0	0.0
F	1024	2.3	0.7	Sa	1122	2.3	0.7
	1624	-0.2	-0.1		1719	0.1	0.0
	2247	2.9	0.9		2343	2.7	0.8

MAY

Day	Time h m	Height ft	Height m	Day	Time h m	Height ft	Height m
1	0609	0.2	0.1	16	0546	0.0	0.0
Su	1207	2.1	0.6	M	1148	2.4	0.7
	1802	0.3	0.1		1746	0.1	0.0
2	0027	2.6	0.8	17	0015	3.0	0.9
M	0655	0.3	0.1	Tu	0642	0.1	0.0
	1255	2.0	0.6		1246	2.4	0.7
	1849	0.4	0.1		1847	0.2	0.1
3	0112	2.4	0.7	18	0113	2.9	0.9
Tu	0742	0.3	0.1	W	0742	0.2	0.1
	1345	1.9	0.6		1349	2.5	0.8
	1939	0.5	0.2		1953	0.3	0.1
4	0203	2.3	0.7	19	0219	2.8	0.9
W	0835	0.4	0.1	Th	0845	0.3	0.1
	1440	1.9	0.6		1458	2.5	0.8
	2036	0.5	0.2		2105	0.4	0.1
5	0257	2.2	0.7	20	0326	2.7	0.8
Th	0929	0.4	0.1	F	0948	0.3	0.1
	1539	1.9	0.6		1606	2.6	0.8
	2136	0.5	0.2		2218	0.4	0.1
6	0353	2.1	0.6	21	0430	2.7	0.8
F	1021	0.3	0.1	Sa	1049	0.2	0.1
	1633	1.9	0.6		1707	2.7	0.8
	2236	0.4	0.1		2324	0.3	0.1
7	0449	2.1	0.6	22	0532	2.6	0.8
Sa	1108	0.2	0.1	Su	1144	0.1	0.0
	1723	2.1	0.6		1806	2.8	0.9
	2331	0.2	0.1				
8	0539	2.1	0.6	23	0024	0.1	0.0
Su	1152	0.0	0.0	M	0629	2.6	0.8
	1808	2.2	0.7		1236	0.0	0.0
					1857	2.9	0.9
9	0021	0.0	0.0	24	0117	0.0	0.0
M	0625	2.1	0.6	Tu	0720	2.5	0.8
	1234	-0.1	0.0		1323	-0.1	0.0
	1853	2.4	0.7		1946	3.0	0.9
10	0107	-0.1	0.0	25	0207	-0.1	0.0
Tu	0711	2.1	0.6	W	0807	2.4	0.7
	1315	-0.2	-0.1		1407	-0.1	0.0
	1934	2.5	0.8		2030	3.0	0.9
11	0154	-0.2	-0.1	26	0254	-0.1	0.0
W	0753	2.2	0.7	Th	0852	2.3	0.7
	1353	-0.3	-0.1		1449	-0.1	0.0
	2016	2.7	0.8		2111	2.9	0.9
12	0236	-0.3	-0.1	27	0339	-0.1	0.0
Th	0837	2.3	0.7	F	0935	2.2	0.7
	1436	-0.3	-0.1		1530	-0.1	0.0
	2059	2.9	0.9		2155	2.8	0.9
13	0322	-0.3	-0.1	28	0421	-0.1	0.0
F	0920	2.3	0.7	Sa	1016	2.1	0.6
	1518	-0.3	-0.1		1612	0.0	0.0
	2143	3.0	0.9		2235	2.7	0.8
14	0407	-0.3	-0.1	29	0501	-0.1	0.0
Sa	1006	2.3	0.7	Su	1058	2.1	0.6
	1603	-0.2	-0.1		1652	0.1	0.0
	2229	3.0	0.9		2314	2.6	0.8
15	0457	-0.2	-0.1	30	0543	0.0	0.0
Su	1056	2.4	0.7	M	1140	2.0	0.6
	1653	-0.1	0.0		1734	0.2	0.1
	2320	3.0	0.9		2357	2.5	0.8
				31	0626	0.1	0.0
				Tu	1226	1.9	0.6
					1818	0.3	0.1

JUNE

Day	Time h m	Height ft	Height m	Day	Time h m	Height ft	Height m
1	0039	2.3	0.7	16	0102	2.9	0.9
W	0708	0.2	0.1	Th	0726	0.1	0.0
	1311	1.9	0.6		1339	2.6	0.8
	1905	0.4	0.1		1945	0.2	0.1
2	0123	2.2	0.7	17	0203	2.8	0.9
Th	0752	0.2	0.1	F	0825	0.2	0.1
	1401	1.9	0.6		1441	2.7	0.8
	1958	0.4	0.1		2054	0.3	0.1
3	0213	2.1	0.6	18	0305	2.6	0.8
F	0838	0.2	0.1	Sa	0923	0.2	0.1
	1453	1.9	0.6		1545	2.7	0.8
	2055	0.4	0.1		2201	0.3	0.1
4	0304	2.0	0.6	19	0407	2.5	0.8
Sa	0924	0.2	0.1	Su	1021	0.2	0.1
	1545	2.0	0.6		1647	2.8	0.9
	2153	0.3	0.1		2307	0.3	0.1
5	0357	2.0	0.6	20	0507	2.4	0.7
Su	1013	0.1	0.0	M	1115	0.1	0.0
	1634	2.1	0.6		1745	2.8	0.9
	2250	0.2	0.1				
6	0450	1.9	0.6	21	0008	0.2	0.1
M	1059	0.0	0.0	Tu	0603	2.3	0.7
	1723	2.3	0.7		1208	0.1	0.0
	2342	0.1	0.0		1835	2.8	0.9
7	0542	2.0	0.6	22	0101	0.1	0.0
Tu	1146	-0.1	0.0	W	0656	2.2	0.7
	1811	2.5	0.8		1256	0.0	0.0
					1923	2.8	0.9
8	0033	-0.1	0.0	23	0151	0.0	0.0
W	0632	2.0	0.6	Th	0744	2.1	0.6
	1233	-0.2	-0.1		1342	0.0	0.0
	1901	2.6	0.8		2008	2.8	0.9
9	0125	-0.2	-0.1	24	0236	-0.1	0.0
Th	0721	2.1	0.6	F	0830	2.1	0.6
	1318	-0.3	-0.1		1424	-0.1	0.0
	1947	2.8	0.9		2051	2.7	0.8
10	0214	-0.3	-0.1	25	0318	-0.1	0.0
F	0810	2.2	0.7	Sa	0914	2.0	0.6
	1407	-0.4	-0.1		1506	-0.1	0.0
	2037	3.0	0.9		2131	2.6	0.8
11	0301	-0.4	-0.1	26	0358	-0.2	-0.1
Sa	0900	2.3	0.7	Su	0955	2.0	0.6
	1457	-0.4	-0.1		1547	-0.1	0.0
	2126	3.1	0.9		2210	2.6	0.8
12	0352	-0.3	-0.1	27	0437	-0.1	0.0
Su	0951	2.4	0.7	M	1035	2.0	0.6
	1549	-0.3	-0.1		1627	0.0	0.0
	2217	3.1	0.9		2247	2.5	0.8
13	0442	-0.3	-0.1	28	0514	-0.1	0.0
M	1044	2.5	0.8	Tu	1114	1.9	0.6
	1643	-0.2	-0.1		1709	0.1	0.0
	2309	3.1	0.9		2325	2.4	0.7
14	0535	-0.2	-0.1	29	0551	-0.1	0.0
Tu	1140	2.5	0.8	W	1154	1.9	0.6
	1741	-0.1	0.0		1749	0.1	0.0
15	0005	3.0	0.9	30	0005	2.3	0.7
W	0630	-0.1	0.0	Th	0631	0.0	0.0
	1238	2.6	0.8		1236	1.9	0.6
	1842	0.1	0.0		1833	0.2	0.1

Time meridian 75° W. 0000 is midnight. 1200 is noon.
Heights are referred to mean low water which is the chart datum of soundings.

HAMPTON ROADS (Sewells Pt.), VA., 1983

Times and Heights of High and Low Waters

JULY

Day	Time h m	Height ft	m
1	0045	2.2	0.7
F	0708	0.1	0.0
	1320	2.0	0.6
	1920	0.3	0.1
2	0127	2.1	0.6
Sa	0748	0.1	0.0
	1406	2.0	0.6
	2011	0.3	0.1
3	0212	2.0	0.6
Su	0830	0.1	0.0
	1454	2.1	0.6
	2106	0.3	0.1
4	0306	1.9	0.6
M	0918	0.1	0.0
	1548	2.2	0.7
	2204	0.2	0.1
5	0402	1.9	0.6
Tu	1009	0.0	0.0
	1641	2.4	0.7
	2304	0.1	0.0
6	0457	1.9	0.6
W	1101	-0.1	0.0
	1736	2.5	0.8
7	0002	0.0	0.0
Th	0556	2.0	0.6
	1158	-0.2	-0.1
	1832	2.7	0.8
8	0058	-0.1	0.0
F	0653	2.1	0.6
	1253	-0.3	-0.1
	1925	2.9	0.9
9	0153	-0.3	-0.1
Sa	0749	2.2	0.7
	1349	-0.4	-0.1
	2018	3.1	0.9
10	0244	-0.3	-0.1
Su	0842	2.4	0.7
	1444	-0.4	-0.1
	2112	3.2	1.0
11	0335	-0.4	-0.1
M	0938	2.5	0.8
	1539	-0.4	-0.1
	2203	3.2	1.0
12	0426	-0.3	-0.1
Tu	1032	2.7	0.8
	1635	-0.3	-0.1
	2256	3.2	1.0
13	0518	-0.3	-0.1
W	1127	2.8	0.9
	1732	-0.1	0.0
	2349	3.1	0.9
14	0610	-0.1	0.0
Th	1223	2.8	0.9
	1830	0.0	0.0
15	0044	2.9	0.9
F	0702	0.0	0.0
	1319	2.8	0.9
	1930	0.2	0.1

Day	Time h m	Height ft	m
16	0142	2.8	0.9
Sa	0758	0.1	0.0
	1420	2.8	0.9
	2035	0.3	0.1
17	0241	2.6	0.8
Su	0853	0.2	0.1
	1520	2.8	0.9
	2140	0.4	0.1
18	0340	2.4	0.7
M	0949	0.3	0.1
	1619	2.8	0.9
	2245	0.4	0.1
19	0440	2.2	0.7
Tu	1046	0.3	0.1
	1717	2.7	0.8
	2347	0.4	0.1
20	0539	2.1	0.6
W	1140	0.2	0.1
	1812	2.7	0.8
21	0040	0.3	0.1
Th	0635	2.1	0.6
	1231	0.2	0.1
	1859	2.7	0.8
22	0130	0.1	0.0
F	0722	2.0	0.6
	1320	0.1	0.0
	1945	2.7	0.8
23	0213	0.0	0.0
Sa	0807	2.0	0.6
	1403	0.0	0.0
	2028	2.6	0.8
24	0254	-0.1	0.0
Su	0851	2.0	0.6
	1444	0.0	0.0
	2108	2.6	0.8
25	0331	-0.1	0.0
M	0931	2.0	0.6
	1526	-0.1	0.0
	2145	2.5	0.8
26	0408	-0.2	-0.1
Tu	1008	2.1	0.6
	1605	0.0	0.0
	2221	2.5	0.8
27	0443	-0.1	0.0
W	1047	2.1	0.6
	1642	0.0	0.0
	2257	2.4	0.7
28	0517	-0.1	0.0
Th	1122	2.1	0.6
	1721	0.1	0.0
	2332	2.3	0.7
29	0549	0.0	0.0
F	1159	2.2	0.7
	1801	0.2	0.1
30	0009	2.2	0.7
Sa	0623	0.1	0.0
	1238	2.2	0.7
	1844	0.3	0.1
31	0047	2.2	0.7
Su	0700	0.1	0.0
	1321	2.3	0.7
	1932	0.3	0.1

AUGUST

Day	Time h m	Height ft	m
1	0132	2.1	0.6
M	0742	0.2	0.1
	1409	2.4	0.7
	2027	0.4	0.1
2	0222	2.0	0.6
Tu	0831	0.2	0.1
	1505	2.5	0.8
	2126	0.4	0.1
3	0321	2.0	0.6
W	0927	0.2	0.1
	1604	2.6	0.8
	2231	0.3	0.1
4	0423	2.0	0.6
Th	1029	0.1	0.0
	1706	2.7	0.8
	2336	0.2	0.1
5	0529	2.1	0.6
F	1132	0.0	0.0
	1807	2.9	0.9
6	0037	0.1	0.0
Sa	0633	2.3	0.7
	1237	-0.1	0.0
	1906	3.1	0.9
7	0133	-0.1	0.0
Su	0733	2.5	0.8
	1333	-0.2	-0.1
	2002	3.2	1.0
8	0226	-0.2	-0.1
M	0828	2.7	0.8
	1432	-0.3	-0.1
	2056	3.3	1.0
9	0316	-0.3	-0.1
Tu	0921	2.9	0.9
	1527	-0.3	-0.1
	2149	3.3	1.0
10	0407	-0.3	-0.1
W	1015	3.0	0.9
	1623	-0.2	-0.1
	2239	3.3	1.0
11	0455	-0.2	-0.1
Th	1108	3.1	0.9
	1717	-0.1	0.0
	2330	3.2	1.0
12	0545	-0.1	0.0
F	1200	3.1	0.9
	1813	0.1	0.0
13	0023	3.0	0.9
Sa	0634	0.1	0.0
	1255	3.1	0.9
	1909	0.3	0.1
14	0115	2.8	0.9
Su	0727	0.3	0.1
	1350	3.0	0.9
	2009	0.5	0.2
15	0212	2.6	0.8
M	0819	0.4	0.1
	1447	2.9	0.9
	2113	0.6	0.2

Day	Time h m	Height ft	m
16	0310	2.4	0.7
Tu	0915	0.5	0.2
	1550	2.8	0.9
	2219	0.6	0.2
17	0414	2.2	0.7
W	1015	0.5	0.2
	1649	2.7	0.8
	2320	0.6	0.2
18	0513	2.1	0.6
Th	1113	0.5	0.2
	1744	2.7	0.8
19	0017	0.5	0.2
F	0611	2.1	0.6
	1206	0.4	0.1
	1834	2.7	0.8
20	0106	0.3	0.1
Sa	0701	2.1	0.6
	1257	0.3	0.1
	1920	2.6	0.8
21	0147	0.2	0.1
Su	0746	2.2	0.7
	1341	0.2	0.1
	2002	2.6	0.8
22	0224	0.1	0.0
M	0825	2.2	0.7
	1423	0.1	0.0
	2040	2.6	0.8
23	0301	0.0	0.0
Tu	0904	2.3	0.7
	1503	0.0	0.0
	2119	2.6	0.8
24	0334	-0.1	0.0
W	0939	2.3	0.7
	1540	0.0	0.0
	2152	2.6	0.8
25	0407	0.0	0.0
Th	1013	2.4	0.7
	1616	0.0	0.0
	2227	2.5	0.8
26	0439	0.0	0.0
F	1048	2.5	0.8
	1654	0.1	0.0
	2259	2.4	0.7
27	0509	0.1	0.0
Sa	1125	2.5	0.8
	1730	0.2	0.1
	2335	2.4	0.7
28	0542	0.2	0.1
Su	1202	2.6	0.8
	1813	0.3	0.1
29	0013	2.3	0.7
M	0618	0.3	0.1
	1243	2.6	0.8
	1858	0.5	0.2
30	0057	2.3	0.7
Tu	0700	0.3	0.1
	1332	2.7	0.8
	1953	0.6	0.2
31	0148	2.2	0.7
W	0753	0.4	0.1
	1430	2.7	0.8
	2058	0.6	0.2

SEPTEMBER

Day	Time h m	Height ft	m
1	0250	2.2	0.7
Th	0857	0.4	0.1
	1536	2.8	0.9
	2205	0.6	0.2
2	0401	2.3	0.7
F	1006	0.4	0.1
	1644	2.9	0.9
	2314	0.5	0.2
3	0513	2.4	0.7
Sa	1118	0.3	0.1
	1750	3.0	0.9
4	0016	0.3	0.1
Su	0617	2.6	0.8
	1224	0.1	0.0
	1851	3.2	1.0
5	0113	0.1	0.0
M	0717	2.9	0.9
	1325	0.0	0.0
	1946	3.3	1.0
6	0205	0.0	0.0
Tu	0813	3.1	0.9
	1421	-0.1	0.0
	2039	3.4	1.0
7	0255	-0.1	0.0
W	0905	3.3	1.0
	1516	-0.2	-0.1
	2131	3.4	1.0
8	0343	-0.1	0.0
Th	0955	3.4	1.0
	1608	-0.1	0.0
	2220	3.3	1.0
9	0429	-0.1	0.0
F	1043	3.4	1.0
	1658	0.0	0.0
	2307	3.2	1.0
10	0517	0.1	0.0
Sa	1135	3.4	1.0
	1751	0.2	0.1
	2357	3.0	0.9
11	0603	0.3	0.1
Su	1226	3.3	1.0
	1845	0.4	0.1
12	0047	2.8	0.9
M	0652	0.4	0.1
	1319	3.1	0.9
	1940	0.6	0.2
13	0140	2.6	0.8
Tu	0745	0.6	0.2
	1412	2.9	0.9
	2040	0.7	0.2
14	0238	2.4	0.7
W	0843	0.7	0.2
	1513	2.8	0.9
	2145	0.8	0.2
15	0343	2.3	0.7
Th	0945	0.8	0.2
	1613	2.7	0.8
	2249	0.7	0.2

Day	Time h m	Height ft	m
16	0445	2.2	0.7
F	1045	0.7	0.2
	1711	2.6	0.8
	2341	0.6	0.2
17	0542	2.2	0.7
Sa	1139	0.6	0.2
	1803	2.6	0.8
18	0029	0.5	0.2
Su	0632	2.3	0.7
	1232	0.5	0.2
	1848	2.6	0.8
19	0112	0.3	0.1
M	0714	2.3	0.7
	1317	0.3	0.1
	1930	2.6	0.8
20	0149	0.2	0.1
Tu	0754	2.4	0.7
	1359	0.2	0.1
	2010	2.6	0.8
21	0224	0.1	0.0
W	0831	2.5	0.8
	1436	0.1	0.0
	2047	2.6	0.8
22	0256	0.0	0.0
Th	0906	2.6	0.8
	1514	0.0	0.0
	2122	2.6	0.8
23	0329	0.0	0.0
F	0939	2.7	0.8
	1551	0.1	0.0
	2156	2.6	0.8
24	0359	0.1	0.0
Sa	1014	2.8	0.9
	1628	0.1	0.0
	2230	2.5	0.8
25	0432	0.2	0.1
Su	1051	2.8	0.9
	1705	0.2	0.1
	2304	2.5	0.8
26	0506	0.2	0.1
M	1128	2.9	0.9
	1749	0.4	0.1
	2346	2.4	0.7
27	0546	0.4	0.1
Tu	1214	2.9	0.9
	1836	0.5	0.2
28	0033	2.4	0.7
W	0634	0.5	0.2
	1307	2.9	0.9
	1933	0.6	0.2
29	0129	2.4	0.7
Th	0731	0.6	0.2
	1406	2.9	0.9
	2037	0.7	0.2
30	0235	2.4	0.7
F	0840	0.6	0.2
	1516	2.9	0.9
	2147	0.7	0.2

Time meridian 75° W. 0000 is midnight. 1200 is noon.
Heights are referred to mean low water which is the chart datum of soundings.

Times and Heights of High and Low Waters

OCTOBER

Day	Time h m	Height ft	Height m
1 Sa	0348	2.5	0.8
	0956	0.6	0.2
	1629	3.0	0.9
	2255	0.6	0.2
2 Su	0502	2.7	0.8
	1110	0.5	0.2
	1736	3.1	0.9
	2357	0.4	0.1
3 M	0604	2.9	0.9
	1216	0.3	0.1
	1835	3.2	1.0
4 Tu	0053	0.2	0.1
	0702	3.1	0.9
	1315	0.1	0.0
	1931	3.3	1.0
5 W	0142	0.1	0.0
	0755	3.3	1.0
	1410	0.0	0.0
	2023	3.3	1.0
6 Th	0231	0.0	0.0
	0846	3.5	1.1
	1501	-0.1	0.0
	2110	3.3	1.0
7 F	0318	0.0	0.0
	0933	3.5	1.1
	1551	0.0	0.0
	2157	3.2	1.0
8 Sa	0403	0.0	0.0
	1021	3.5	1.1
	1640	0.1	0.0
	2243	3.0	0.9
9 Su	0447	0.1	0.0
	1109	3.4	1.0
	1729	0.2	0.1
	2330	2.8	0.9
10 M	0532	0.3	0.1
	1155	3.2	1.0
	1818	0.4	0.1
11 Tu	0019	2.6	0.8
	0619	0.5	0.2
	1243	3.0	0.9
	1910	0.6	0.2
12 W	0109	2.4	0.7
	0708	0.7	0.2
	1337	2.9	0.9
	2008	0.7	0.2
13 Th	0206	2.3	0.7
	0805	0.8	0.2
	1433	2.7	0.8
	2106	0.7	0.2
14 F	0309	2.2	0.7
	0906	0.8	0.2
	1532	2.6	0.8
	2206	0.7	0.2
15 Sa	0411	2.2	0.7
	1008	0.8	0.2
	1629	2.5	0.8
	2300	0.6	0.2
16 Su	0507	2.2	0.7
	1108	0.6	0.2
	1723	2.5	0.8
	2347	0.4	0.1
17 M	0556	2.3	0.7
	1201	0.5	0.2
	1811	2.4	0.7
18 Tu	0029	0.3	0.1
	0639	2.4	0.7
	1245	0.3	0.1
	1854	2.5	0.8
19 W	0106	0.1	0.0
	0717	2.5	0.8
	1330	0.1	0.0
	1936	2.5	0.8
20 Th	0141	0.0	0.0
	0756	2.6	0.8
	1408	0.0	0.0
	2014	2.5	0.8
21 F	0217	0.0	0.0
	0831	2.7	0.8
	1447	-0.1	0.0
	2050	2.4	0.7
22 Sa	0252	0.0	0.0
	0908	2.8	0.9
	1526	-0.1	0.0
	2127	2.4	0.7
23 Su	0327	0.0	0.0
	0946	2.9	0.9
	1607	0.0	0.0
	2203	2.4	0.7
24 M	0402	0.0	0.0
	1024	3.0	0.9
	1645	0.1	0.0
	2245	2.4	0.7
25 Tu	0440	0.1	0.0
	1107	3.0	0.9
	1731	0.2	0.1
	2328	2.4	0.7
26 W	0526	0.3	0.1
	1154	3.0	0.9
	1823	0.4	0.1
27 Th	0019	2.4	0.7
	0618	0.4	0.1
	1249	3.0	0.9
	1919	0.5	0.2
28 F	0119	2.4	0.7
	0721	0.5	0.2
	1353	2.9	0.9
	2022	0.6	0.2
29 Sa	0227	2.5	0.8
	0833	0.6	0.2
	1502	2.9	0.9
	2129	0.6	0.2
30 Su	0340	2.6	0.8
	0949	0.6	0.2
	1612	2.9	0.9
	2235	0.5	0.2
31 M	0449	2.7	0.8
	1100	0.4	0.1
	1718	2.9	0.9
	2335	0.3	0.1

NOVEMBER

Day	Time h m	Height ft	Height m
1 Tu	0550	2.9	0.9
	1206	0.3	0.1
	1816	2.9	0.9
2 W	0029	0.2	0.1
	0647	3.1	0.9
	1304	0.1	0.0
	1912	2.9	0.9
3 Th	0120	0.0	0.0
	0738	3.3	1.0
	1357	0.0	0.0
	2002	2.9	0.9
4 F	0207	-0.1	0.0
	0827	3.3	1.0
	1447	-0.1	0.0
	2050	2.9	0.9
5 Sa	0252	-0.1	0.0
	0912	3.3	1.0
	1535	-0.1	0.0
	2136	2.8	0.9
6 Su	0337	0.0	0.0
	0958	3.3	1.0
	1621	0.0	0.0
	2220	2.6	0.8
7 M	0419	0.1	0.0
	1040	3.1	0.9
	1706	0.1	0.0
	2306	2.5	0.8
8 Tu	0502	0.2	0.1
	1127	3.0	0.9
	1754	0.2	0.1
	2354	2.3	0.7
9 W	0548	0.3	0.1
	1212	2.8	0.9
	1841	0.3	0.1
10 Th	0041	2.2	0.7
	0636	0.5	0.2
	1258	2.6	0.8
	1931	0.4	0.1
11 F	0135	2.1	0.6
	0727	0.6	0.2
	1350	2.4	0.7
	2022	0.5	0.2
12 Sa	0229	2.0	0.6
	0827	0.6	0.2
	1443	2.3	0.7
	2117	0.4	0.1
13 Su	0325	2.0	0.6
	0927	0.6	0.2
	1541	2.2	0.7
	2206	0.4	0.1
14 M	0421	2.1	0.6
	1028	0.5	0.2
	1634	2.1	0.6
	2254	0.3	0.1
15 Tu	0510	2.1	0.6
	1121	0.3	0.1
	1726	2.1	0.6
	2339	0.1	0.0
16 W	0556	2.3	0.7
	1211	0.1	0.0
	1811	2.1	0.6
17 Th	0019	0.0	0.0
	0638	2.4	0.7
	1256	0.0	0.0
	1857	2.1	0.6
18 F	0059	-0.1	0.0
	0719	2.5	0.8
	1339	-0.2	-0.1
	1938	2.1	0.6
19 Sa	0138	-0.2	-0.1
	0759	2.7	0.8
	1421	-0.2	-0.1
	2019	2.1	0.6
20 Su	0216	-0.3	-0.1
	0840	2.8	0.9
	1503	-0.3	-0.1
	2101	2.2	0.7
21 M	0256	-0.3	-0.1
	0921	2.9	0.9
	1547	-0.3	-0.1
	2143	2.2	0.7
22 Tu	0337	-0.2	-0.1
	1005	2.9	0.9
	1631	-0.2	-0.1
	2228	2.3	0.7
23 W	0424	-0.1	0.0
	1052	2.9	0.9
	1719	-0.1	0.0
	2317	2.3	0.7
24 Th	0514	0.0	0.0
	1143	2.9	0.9
	1810	0.1	0.0
25 F	0010	2.3	0.7
	0610	0.1	0.0
	1239	2.8	0.9
	1907	0.2	0.1
26 Sa	0111	2.4	0.7
	0713	0.3	0.1
	1340	2.7	0.8
	2006	0.2	0.1
27 Su	0218	2.4	0.7
	0825	0.4	0.1
	1445	2.7	0.8
	2109	0.3	0.1
28 M	0327	2.5	0.8
	0939	0.3	0.1
	1553	2.6	0.8
	2212	0.2	0.1
29 Tu	0433	2.7	0.8
	1049	0.3	0.1
	1659	2.5	0.8
	2310	0.1	0.0
30 W	0534	2.8	0.9
	1153	0.1	0.0
	1758	2.5	0.8

DECEMBER

Day	Time h m	Height ft	Height m
1 Th	0006	0.0	0.0
	0628	2.9	0.9
	1251	0.0	0.0
	1853	2.5	0.8
2 F	0056	-0.1	0.0
	0720	3.0	0.9
	1344	-0.1	0.0
	1943	2.4	0.7
3 Sa	0145	-0.2	-0.1
	0808	3.0	0.9
	1433	-0.2	-0.1
	2031	2.3	0.7
4 Su	0229	-0.2	-0.1
	0852	3.0	0.9
	1519	-0.3	-0.1
	2116	2.3	0.7
5 M	0314	-0.2	-0.1
	0936	2.9	0.9
	1602	-0.2	-0.1
	2200	2.2	0.7
6 Tu	0355	-0.2	-0.1
	1018	2.8	0.9
	1647	-0.2	-0.1
	2243	2.1	0.6
7 W	0437	-0.1	0.0
	1100	2.6	0.8
	1728	-0.1	0.0
	2325	2.0	0.6
8 Th	0520	0.0	0.0
	1141	2.5	0.8
	1809	0.0	0.0
9 F	0012	1.9	0.6
	0605	0.1	0.0
	1223	2.3	0.7
	1852	0.0	0.0
10 Sa	0058	1.9	0.6
	0652	0.2	0.1
	1308	2.1	0.6
	1935	0.1	0.0
11 Su	0147	1.8	0.5
	0743	0.3	0.1
	1354	2.0	0.6
	2022	0.1	0.0
12 M	0237	1.8	0.5
	0840	0.3	0.1
	1445	1.9	0.6
	2109	0.1	0.0
13 Tu	0329	1.9	0.6
	0936	0.2	0.1
	1538	1.8	0.5
	2156	0.0	0.0
14 W	0419	1.9	0.6
	1036	0.1	0.0
	1633	1.7	0.5
	2242	-0.1	0.0
15 Th	0509	2.1	0.6
	1129	0.0	0.0
	1723	1.7	0.5
	2331	-0.2	-0.1
16 F	0555	2.2	0.7
	1221	-0.2	-0.1
	1814	1.7	0.5
17 Sa	0015	-0.3	-0.1
	0645	2.3	0.7
	1309	-0.3	-0.1
	1903	1.8	0.5
18 Su	0101	-0.4	-0.1
	0730	2.5	0.8
	1354	-0.4	-0.1
	1949	1.9	0.6
19 M	0147	-0.5	-0.2
	0815	2.7	0.8
	1440	-0.5	-0.2
	2037	2.0	0.6
20 Tu	0236	-0.6	-0.2
	0903	2.8	0.9
	1527	-0.5	-0.2
	2127	2.1	0.6
21 W	0323	-0.5	-0.2
	0950	2.8	0.9
	1615	-0.5	-0.2
	2217	2.2	0.7
22 Th	0413	-0.5	-0.2
	1039	2.8	0.9
	1704	-0.4	-0.1
	2308	2.3	0.7
23 F	0509	-0.3	-0.1
	1132	2.8	0.9
	1756	-0.3	-0.1
24 Sa	0002	2.3	0.7
	0605	-0.2	-0.1
	1226	2.7	0.8
	1848	-0.2	-0.1
25 Su	0100	2.4	0.7
	0708	0.0	0.0
	1324	2.6	0.8
	1945	-0.1	0.0
26 M	0203	2.5	0.8
	0814	0.1	0.0
	1425	2.4	0.7
	2043	0.0	0.0
27 Tu	0307	2.5	0.8
	0924	0.1	0.0
	1531	2.3	0.7
	2144	0.0	0.0
28 W	0410	2.5	0.8
	1033	0.1	0.0
	1634	2.2	0.7
	2244	0.0	0.0
29 Th	0513	2.6	0.8
	1139	0.0	0.0
	1736	2.1	0.6
	2340	-0.1	0.0
30 F	0612	2.6	0.8
	1237	-0.1	0.0
	1835	2.0	0.6
31 Sa	0033	-0.2	-0.1
	0702	2.7	0.8
	1331	-0.2	-0.1
	1926	2.0	0.6

Time meridian 75° W. 0000 is midnight. 1200 is noon.
Heights are referred to mean low water which is the chart datum of soundings.

SAVANNAH RIVER ENTRANCE, GA., 1983

Times and Heights of High and Low Waters

JANUARY

Day	Time (h m)	Height (ft)	Height (m)
1	0312	-1.5	-0.5
Sa	0921	8.4	2.6
	1552	-1.1	-0.3
	2149	6.9	2.1
2	0405	-1.3	-0.4
Su	1016	8.1	2.5
	1643	-0.9	-0.3
	2248	6.8	2.1
3	0459	-1.0	-0.3
M	1111	7.7	2.3
	1736	-0.7	-0.2
	2348	6.7	2.0
4	0557	-0.7	-0.2
Tu	1207	7.3	2.2
	1829	-0.5	-0.2
5	0047	6.6	2.0
W	0657	-0.3	-0.1
	1303	6.8	2.1
	1927	-0.3	-0.1
6	0147	6.5	2.0
Th	0758	0.0	0.0
	1358	6.4	2.0
	2025	-0.2	-0.1
7	0248	6.5	2.0
F	0901	0.1	0.0
	1457	6.1	1.9
	2120	-0.1	0.0
8	0348	6.6	2.0
Sa	0957	0.2	0.1
	1554	5.9	1.8
	2212	-0.1	0.0
9	044[illegible]	6.7	2.0
Su	104[illegible]	0.1	0.0
	164[illegible]	5.8	1.8
	2256	-0.2	-0.1
10	0534	6.8	2.1
M	1140	0.1	0.0
	1740	5.8	1.8
	2346	-0.2	-0.1
11	0621	6.9	2.1
Tu	1226	0.0	0.0
	1824	5.9	1.8
12	0030	-0.3	-0.1
W	0701	7.0	2.1
	1312	0.0	0.0
	1903	5.9	1.8
13	0112	-0.3	-0.1
Th	0738	7.0	2.1
	1354	-0.1	0.0
	1940	6.0	1.8
14	0154	-0.3	-0.1
F	0812	7.0	2.1
	1435	-0.1	0.0
	2015	6.0	1.8
15	0234	-0.3	-0.1
Sa	0845	6.9	2.1
	1513	-0.1	0.0
	2050	6.0	1.8
16	0310	-0.2	-0.1
Su	0918	6.8	2.1
	1550	0.0	0.0
	2126	6.0	1.8
17	0347	-0.1	0.0
M	0951	6.7	2.0
	1627	0.0	0.0
	2203	6.0	1.8
18	0427	0.0	0.0
Tu	1027	6.5	2.0
	1701	0.1	0.0
	2245	6.0	1.8
19	0506	0.2	0.1
W	1108	6.3	1.9
	1741	0.1	0.0
	2331	6.1	1.9
20	0551	0.3	0.1
Th	1151	6.2	1.9
	1827	0.2	0.1
21	0021	6.2	1.9
F	0645	0.5	0.2
	1242	6.0	1.8
	1918	0.1	0.0
22	0115	6.4	2.0
Sa	0746	0.5	0.2
	1334	5.8	1.8
	2015	0.0	0.0
23	0214	6.6	2.0
Su	0852	0.4	0.1
	1433	5.8	1.8
	2116	-0.2	-0.1
24	0319	6.8	2.1
M	0957	0.2	0.1
	1543	5.8	1.8
	2215	-0.6	-0.2
25	0426	7.2	2.2
Tu	1100	-0.1	0.0
	1652	6.0	1.8
	2315	-0.9	-0.3
26	0531	7.6	2.3
W	1200	-0.5	-0.2
	1758	6.4	2.0
27	0011	-1.3	-0.4
Th	0631	8.0	2.4
	1256	-0.9	-0.3
	1856	6.7	2.0
28	0109	-1.6	-0.5
F	0725	8.3	2.5
	1352	-1.2	-0.4
	1951	7.0	2.1
29	0205	-1.8	-0.5
Sa	0817	8.4	2.6
	1443	-1.4	-0.4
	2043	7.2	2.2
30	0259	-1.8	-0.5
Su	0908	8.3	2.5
	1533	-1.4	-0.4
	2136	7.2	2.2
31	0350	-1.7	-0.5
M	0958	8.0	2.4
	1621	-1.3	-0.4
	2229	7.2	2.2

FEBRUARY

Day	Time (h m)	Height (ft)	Height (m)
1	0442	-1.4	-0.4
Tu	1049	7.6	2.3
	1709	-1.1	-0.3
	2323	7.0	2.1
2	0534	-0.9	-0.3
W	1141	7.0	2.1
	1759	-0.8	-0.2
3	0018	6.8	2.1
Th	0628	-0.5	-0.2
	1231	6.5	2.0
	1849	-0.4	-0.1
4	0110	6.6	2.0
F	0724	0.0	0.0
	1323	6.0	1.8
	1942	-0.1	0.0
5	0205	6.3	1.9
Sa	0824	0.3	0.1
	1414	5.7	1.7
	2041	0.1	0.0
6	0304	6.2	1.9
Su	0924	0.5	0.2
	1510	5.4	1.6
	2135	0.2	0.1
7	0406	6.2	1.9
M	1018	0.5	0.2
	1610	5.3	1.6
	2227	0.2	0.1
8	0503	6.2	1.9
Tu	1110	0.4	0.1
	1709	5.4	1.6
	2315	0.1	0.0
9	0555	6.4	2.0
W	1158	0.3	0.1
	1758	5.6	1.7
10	0003	-0.1	0.0
Th	0637	6.6	2.0
	1243	0.1	0.0
	1841	5.8	1.8
11	0048	-0.2	-0.1
F	0715	6.8	2.1
	1328	0.0	0.0
	1918	6.0	1.8
12	0131	-0.3	-0.1
Sa	0749	6.9	2.1
	1408	-0.2	-0.1
	1954	6.1	1.9
13	0212	-0.4	-0.1
Su	0823	6.9	2.1
	1445	-0.2	-0.1
	2028	6.3	1.9
14	0249	-0.4	-0.1
M	0854	6.8	2.1
	1521	-0.3	-0.1
	2102	6.4	2.0
15	0326	-0.4	-0.1
Tu	0926	6.7	2.0
	1557	-0.3	-0.1
	2139	6.5	2.0
16	0403	-0.3	-0.1
W	1000	6.6	2.0
	1631	-0.2	-0.1
	2218	6.6	2.0
17	0443	-0.1	0.0
Th	1039	6.4	2.0
	1706	-0.2	-0.1
	2302	6.7	2.0
18	0525	0.0	0.0
F	1121	6.2	1.9
	1749	-0.1	0.0
	2349	6.7	2.0
19	0616	0.3	0.1
Sa	1210	6.0	1.8
	1839	0.0	0.0
20	0043	6.7	2.0
Su	0716	0.5	0.2
	1306	5.8	1.8
	1941	0.0	0.0
21	0145	6.7	2.0
M	0825	0.5	0.2
	1409	5.7	1.7
	2049	-0.1	0.0
22	0254	6.8	2.1
Tu	0936	0.4	0.1
	1522	5.7	1.7
	2155	-0.4	-0.1
23	0407	7.0	2.1
W	1041	0.0	0.0
	1638	6.0	1.8
	2258	-0.8	-0.2
24	0518	7.4	2.3
Th	1142	-0.4	-0.1
	1747	6.4	2.0
25	0000	-1.2	-0.4
F	0619	7.8	2.4
	1240	-0.8	-0.2
	1847	7.0	2.1
26	0056	-1.5	-0.5
Sa	0712	8.1	2.5
	1333	-1.2	-0.4
	1941	7.4	2.3
27	0152	-1.7	-0.5
Su	0803	8.2	2.5
	1423	-1.4	-0.4
	2029	7.7	2.3
28	0245	-1.8	-0.5
M	0849	8.1	2.5
	1510	-1.5	-0.5
	2116	7.7	2.3

MARCH

Day	Time (h m)	Height (ft)	Height (m)
1	0333	-1.7	-0.5
Tu	0935	7.8	2.4
	1555	-1.3	-0.4
	2205	7.6	2.3
2	0421	-1.3	-0.4
W	1021	7.4	2.3
	1640	-1.1	-0.3
	2253	7.4	2.3
3	0509	-0.9	-0.3
Th	1107	6.9	2.1
	1724	-0.6	-0.2
	2340	7.0	2.1
4	0557	-0.3	-0.1
F	1153	6.4	2.0
	1810	-0.2	-0.1
5	0031	6.7	2.0
Sa	0649	0.2	0.1
	1240	5.9	1.8
	1900	0.3	0.1
6	0121	6.3	1.9
Su	0745	0.6	0.2
	1331	5.5	1.7
	1956	0.6	0.2
7	0216	6.1	1.9
M	0845	0.8	0.2
	1426	5.3	1.6
	2054	0.7	0.2
8	0317	5.9	1.8
Tu	0943	0.8	0.2
	1530	5.2	1.6
	2153	0.7	0.2
9	0422	6.0	1.8
W	1036	0.7	0.2
	1631	5.4	1.6
	2246	0.5	0.2
10	0518	6.2	1.9
Th	1126	0.5	0.2
	1726	5.6	1.7
	2335	0.3	0.1
11	0608	6.5	2.0
F	1211	0.3	0.1
	1812	6.0	1.8
12	0022	0.0	0.0
Sa	0648	6.7	2.0
	1256	0.1	0.0
	1853	6.3	1.9
13	0105	-0.2	-0.1
Su	0723	6.9	2.1
	1336	-0.1	0.0
	1928	6.6	2.0
14	0147	-0.3	-0.1
M	0755	6.9	2.1
	1414	-0.3	-0.1
	2002	6.9	2.1
15	0226	-0.4	-0.1
Tu	0827	6.9	2.1
	1451	-0.3	-0.1
	2037	7.1	2.2
16	0305	-0.4	-0.1
W	0900	6.9	2.1
	1524	-0.4	-0.1
	2113	7.2	2.2
17	0342	-0.4	-0.1
Th	0934	6.7	2.0
	1600	-0.3	-0.1
	2152	7.3	2.2
18	0423	-0.2	-0.1
F	1013	6.5	2.0
	1639	-0.3	-0.1
	2237	7.3	2.2
19	0506	0.0	0.0
Sa	1059	6.3	1.9
	1722	-0.1	0.0
	2327	7.2	2.2
20	0556	0.3	0.1
Su	1148	6.1	1.9
	1815	0.1	0.0
21	0023	7.1	2.2
M	0657	0.5	0.2
	1247	5.9	1.8
	1919	0.2	0.1
22	0127	6.9	2.1
Tu	0809	0.6	0.2
	1356	5.8	1.8
	2031	0.2	0.1
23	0237	6.9	2.1
W	0919	0.5	0.2
	1512	5.9	1.8
	2143	-0.1	0.0
24	0353	7.0	2.1
Th	1026	0.1	0.0
	1630	6.3	1.9
	2246	-0.5	-0.2
25	0505	7.3	2.2
F	1126	-0.3	-0.1
	1739	6.8	2.1
	2347	-0.9	-0.3
26	0604	7.7	2.3
Sa	1219	-0.7	-0.2
	1835	7.4	2.3
27	0044	-1.2	-0.4
Su	0657	7.9	2.4
	1310	-1.1	-0.3
	1925	7.9	2.4
28	0136	-1.4	-0.4
M	0744	8.0	2.4
	1358	-1.2	-0.4
	2010	8.1	2.5
29	0226	-1.5	-0.5
Tu	0828	7.9	2.4
	1443	-1.2	-0.4
	2054	8.2	2.5
30	0313	-1.3	-0.4
W	0910	7.6	2.3
	1526	-1.0	-0.3
	2138	8.0	2.4
31	0358	-1.0	-0.3
Th	0952	7.2	2.2
	1608	-0.7	-0.2
	2219	7.6	2.3

Time meridian 75° W. 0000 is midnight. 1200 is noon.
Heights are referred to mean low water which is the chart datum of soundings.

Times and Heights of High and Low Waters

APRIL

Day	Time h m	Height ft	m	Day	Time h m	Height ft	m
1	0442	-0.6	-0.2	16	0407	-0.3	-0.1
F	1033	6.7	2.0	Sa	0954	6.6	2.0
	1647	-0.3	-0.1		1616	-0.3	-0.1
	2304	7.2	2.2		2218	7.8	2.4
2	0525	-0.1	0.0	17	0453	0.0	0.0
Sa	1117	6.3	1.9	Su	1043	6.3	1.9
	1732	0.2	0.1		1704	-0.1	0.0
	2349	6.8	2.1		2312	7.6	2.3
3	0613	0.4	0.1	18	0546	0.2	0.1
Su	1201	5.9	1.8	M	1138	6.1	1.9
	1818	0.6	0.2		1802	0.2	0.1
4	0036	6.4	2.0	19	0010	7.3	2.2
M	0706	0.8	0.2	Tu	0647	0.5	0.2
	1251	5.6	1.7		1242	6.0	1.8
	1912	1.0	0.3		1908	0.3	0.1
5	0129	6.1	1.9	20	0116	7.1	2.2
Tu	0803	1.0	0.3	W	0757	0.5	0.2
	1346	5.4	1.6		1353	6.0	1.8
	2015	1.1	0.3		2020	0.3	0.1
6	0228	5.9	1.8	21	0226	7.0	2.1
W	0903	1.1	0.3	Th	0906	0.4	0.1
	1446	5.4	1.6		1509	6.2	1.9
	2115	1.1	0.3		2132	0.1	0.0
7	0331	5.9	1.8	22	0337	7.0	2.1
Th	0959	0.9	0.3	F	1009	0.0	0.0
	1548	5.5	1.7		1623	6.7	2.0
	2211	0.9	0.3		2234	-0.2	-0.1
8	0433	6.1	1.9	23	0446	7.2	2.2
F	1049	0.7	0.2	Sa	1105	-0.4	-0.1
	1646	5.9	1.8		1726	7.2	2.2
	2303	0.6	0.2		2331	-0.6	-0.2
9	0524	6.3	1.9	24	0545	7.4	2.3
Sa	1134	0.4	0.1	Su	1156	-0.7	-0.2
	1737	6.3	1.9		1819	7.8	2.4
	2350	0.3	0.1				
10	0608	6.6	2.0	25	0026	-0.9	-0.3
Su	1217	0.1	0.0	M	0636	7.5	2.3
	1819	6.7	2.0		1245	-0.9	-0.3
					1908	8.1	2.5
11	0035	0.0	0.0	26	0117	-1.0	-0.3
M	0645	6.8	2.1	Tu	0722	7.5	2.3
	1259	-0.1	0.0		1330	-0.9	-0.3
	1858	7.2	2.2		1950	8.3	2.5
12	0118	-0.2	-0.1	27	0205	-1.0	-0.3
Tu	0721	6.9	2.1	W	0803	7.4	2.3
	1338	-0.3	-0.1		1415	-0.9	-0.3
	1935	7.5	2.3		2031	8.3	2.5
13	0200	-0.4	-0.1	28	0250	-0.9	-0.3
W	0758	7.0	2.1	Th	0844	7.1	2.2
	1416	-0.4	-0.1		1456	-0.7	-0.2
	2012	7.8	2.4		2110	8.0	2.4
14	0241	-0.4	-0.1	29	0333	-0.6	-0.2
Th	0832	6.9	2.1	F	0922	6.8	2.1
	1453	-0.4	-0.1		1536	-0.4	-0.1
	2050	7.9	2.4		2149	7.7	2.3
15	0323	-0.4	-0.1	30	0415	-0.3	-0.1
F	0912	6.8	2.1	Sa	1002	6.4	2.0
	1535	-0.4	-0.1		1616	0.0	0.0
	2131	7.9	2.4		2229	7.3	2.2

MAY

Day	Time h m	Height ft	m	Day	Time h m	Height ft	m
1	0457	0.1	0.0	16	0443	-0.2	-0.1
Su	1043	6.1	1.9	M	1035	6.4	2.0
	1656	0.4	0.1		1654	-0.2	-0.1
	2312	6.8	2.1		2301	7.8	2.4
2	0540	0.5	0.2	17	0538	0.0	0.0
M	1126	5.8	1.8	Tu	1136	6.2	1.9
	1741	0.8	0.2		1753	0.0	0.0
	2357	6.5	2.0				
3	0629	0.8	0.2	18	0002	7.5	2.3
Tu	1215	5.6	1.7	W	0639	0.1	0.0
	1831	1.1	0.3		1242	6.2	1.9
					1858	0.2	0.1
4	0046	6.2	1.9	19	0106	7.2	2.2
W	0724	1.0	0.3	Th	0743	0.2	0.1
	1308	5.5	1.7		1351	6.3	1.9
	1930	1.3	0.4		2009	0.3	0.1
5	0139	6.0	1.8	20	0213	7.0	2.1
Th	0820	1.0	0.3	F	0848	0.0	0.0
	1404	5.6	1.7		1502	6.6	2.0
	2033	1.3	0.4		2117	0.1	0.0
6	0236	6.0	1.8	21	0319	6.9	2.1
F	0916	0.9	0.3	Sa	0946	-0.2	-0.1
	1503	5.8	1.8		1609	7.0	2.1
	2132	1.1	0.3		2218	-0.1	0.0
7	0333	6.0	1.8	22	0424	6.9	2.1
Sa	1005	0.6	0.2	Su	1041	-0.4	-0.1
	1601	6.1	1.9		1708	7.4	2.3
	2225	0.8	0.2		2315	-0.4	-0.1
8	0430	6.2	1.9	23	0523	6.9	2.1
Su	1052	0.3	0.1	M	1129	-0.6	-0.2
	1654	6.6	2.0		1800	7.8	2.4
	2315	0.5	0.2				
9	0521	6.4	2.0	24	0006	-0.5	-0.2
M	1134	0.0	0.0	Tu	0611	6.9	2.1
	1742	7.1	2.2		1216	-0.7	-0.2
					1845	8.0	2.4
10	0001	0.1	0.0	25	0056	-0.6	-0.2
Tu	0605	6.6	2.0	W	0657	6.9	2.1
	1219	-0.2	-0.1		1301	-0.7	-0.2
	1824	7.5	2.3		1928	8.1	2.5
11	0048	-0.1	0.0	26	0143	-0.6	-0.2
W	0647	6.7	2.0	Th	0738	6.8	2.1
	1300	-0.4	-0.1		1345	-0.6	-0.2
	1905	7.9	2.4		2006	8.0	2.4
12	0133	-0.3	-0.1	27	0227	-0.5	-0.2
Th	0728	6.8	2.1	F	0818	6.6	2.0
	1343	-0.6	-0.2		1427	-0.4	-0.1
	1947	8.2	2.5		2043	7.8	2.4
13	0219	-0.5	-0.2	28	0310	-0.3	-0.1
F	0808	6.8	2.1	Sa	0854	6.4	2.0
	1428	-0.6	-0.2		1509	-0.1	0.0
	2030	8.3	2.5		2120	7.5	2.3
14	0305	-0.5	-0.2	29	0350	-0.1	0.0
Sa	0851	6.7	2.0	Su	0933	6.1	1.9
	1514	-0.6	-0.2		1547	0.2	0.1
	2115	8.3	2.5		2157	7.2	2.2
15	0352	-0.4	-0.1	30	0432	0.2	0.1
Su	0939	6.6	2.0	M	1011	5.9	1.8
	1601	-0.5	-0.2		1627	0.5	0.2
	2206	8.1	2.5		2237	6.8	2.1
				31	0512	0.4	0.1
				Tu	1055	5.8	1.8
					1709	0.7	0.2
					2320	6.6	2.0

JUNE

Day	Time h m	Height ft	m	Day	Time h m	Height ft	m
1	0556	0.6	0.2	16	0623	-0.3	-0.1
W	1141	5.7	1.7	Th	1236	6.6	2.0
	1754	1.0	0.3		1846	0.0	0.0
2	0005	6.3	1.9	17	0052	7.2	2.2
Th	0644	0.8	0.2	F	0723	-0.3	-0.1
	1230	5.7	1.7		1340	6.7	2.0
	1850	1.2	0.4		1952	0.1	0.0
3	0055	6.2	1.9	18	0153	6.9	2.1
F	0737	0.8	0.2	Sa	0822	-0.3	-0.1
	1324	5.8	1.8		1444	6.9	2.1
	1947	1.2	0.4		2058	0.1	0.0
4	0144	6.0	1.8	19	0255	6.6	2.0
Sa	0830	0.7	0.2	Su	0920	-0.3	-0.1
	1416	6.0	1.8		1545	7.1	2.2
	2049	1.1	0.3		2159	0.0	0.0
5	0239	6.0	1.8	20	0356	6.5	2.0
Su	0919	0.5	0.2	M	1012	-0.4	-0.1
	1512	6.3	1.9		1644	7.3	2.2
	2144	0.9	0.3		2254	-0.1	0.0
6	0333	6.0	1.8	21	0454	6.4	2.0
M	1008	0.2	0.1	Tu	1102	-0.4	-0.1
	1607	6.7	2.0		1738	7.6	2.3
	2236	0.5	0.2		2345	-0.1	0.0
7	0430	6.1	1.9	22	0545	6.3	1.9
Tu	1054	-0.1	0.0	W	1150	-0.4	-0.1
	1700	7.2	2.2		1824	7.7	2.3
	2327	0.2	0.1				
8	0523	6.3	1.9	23	0034	-0.2	-0.1
W	1140	-0.4	-0.1	Th	0632	6.3	1.9
	1750	7.7	2.3		1235	-0.4	-0.1
					1907	7.7	2.3
9	0017	-0.1	0.0	24	0120	-0.2	-0.1
Th	0612	6.5	2.0	F	0713	6.3	1.9
	1226	-0.6	-0.2		1317	-0.3	-0.1
	1838	8.1	2.5		1946	7.7	2.3
10	0108	-0.3	-0.1	25	0204	-0.1	0.0
F	0701	6.6	2.0	Sa	0753	6.2	1.9
	1315	-0.8	-0.2		1402	-0.1	0.0
	1926	8.4	2.6		2023	7.5	2.3
11	0159	-0.5	-0.2	26	0246	-0.1	0.0
Sa	0749	6.7	2.0	Su	0830	6.1	1.9
	1405	-0.9	-0.3		1442	0.0	0.0
	2013	8.5	2.6		2057	7.3	2.2
12	0250	-0.6	-0.2	27	0327	0.0	0.0
Su	0838	6.7	2.0	M	0906	6.0	1.8
	1457	-0.9	-0.3		1522	0.2	0.1
	2103	8.4	2.6		2133	7.1	2.2
13	0341	-0.6	-0.2	28	0406	0.2	0.1
M	0931	6.6	2.0	Tu	0944	5.9	1.8
	1550	-0.8	-0.2		1602	0.4	0.1
	2157	8.2	2.5		2208	6.9	2.1
14	0432	-0.6	-0.2	29	0445	0.3	0.1
Tu	1029	6.6	2.0	W	1024	5.9	1.8
	1645	-0.6	-0.2		1640	0.6	0.2
	2253	7.9	2.4		2248	6.7	2.0
15	0527	-0.5	-0.2	30	0524	0.4	0.1
W	1133	6.5	2.0	Th	1109	5.9	1.8
	1744	-0.3	-0.1		1723	0.8	0.2
	2353	7.6	2.3		2328	6.5	2.0

Time meridian 75° W. 0000 is midnight. 1200 is noon.
Heights are referred to mean low water which is the chart datum of soundings.

Times and Heights of High and Low Waters

JANUARY

Day	Time (h m)	Height (ft)	Height (m)
1 Sa	0411	-1.5	-0.5
	1013	8.9	2.7
	1650	-0.9	-0.3
	2240	7.4	2.3
2 Su	0503	-1.3	-0.4
	1103	8.6	2.6
	1740	-0.8	-0.2
	2333	7.3	2.2
3 M	0554	-1.0	-0.3
	1154	8.2	2.5
	1829	-0.6	-0.2
4 Tu	0031	7.2	2.2
	0648	-0.7	-0.2
	1247	7.8	2.4
	1919	-0.4	-0.1
5 W	0127	7.1	2.2
	0743	-0.3	-0.1
	1340	7.4	2.3
	2012	-0.2	-0.1
6 Th	0222	7.1	2.2
	0840	0.0	0.0
	1431	7.0	2.1
	2106	-0.1	0.0
7 F	0317	7.1	2.2
	0938	0.1	0.0
	1524	6.7	2.0
	2159	-0.1	0.0
8 Sa	0413	7.1	2.2
	1034	0.2	0.1
	1618	6.5	2.0
	2251	-0.2	-0.1
9 Su	0509	7.2	2.2
	1127	0.1	0.0
	1713	6.4	2.0
	2341	-0.3	-0.1
10 M	0604	7.4	2.3
	1217	0.0	0.0
	1808	6.5	2.0
11 Tu	0029	-0.4	-0.1
	0654	7.5	2.3
	1306	-0.1	0.0
	1856	6.5	2.0
12 W	0116	-0.4	-0.1
	0738	7.6	2.3
	1351	-0.1	0.0
	1941	6.6	2.0
13 Th	0200	-0.4	-0.1
	0818	7.7	2.3
	1437	-0.1	0.0
	2018	6.7	2.0
14 F	0245	-0.4	-0.1
	0854	7.7	2.3
	1521	-0.1	0.0
	2052	6.7	2.0
15 Sa	0326	-0.3	-0.1
	0926	7.6	2.3
	1603	-0.1	0.0
	2126	6.7	2.0
16 Su	0405	-0.2	-0.1
	0956	7.5	2.3
	1640	0.0	0.0
	2158	6.8	2.1
17 M	0442	0.0	0.0
	1027	7.4	2.3
	1717	0.1	0.0
	2235	6.8	2.1
18 Tu	0517	0.1	0.0
	1100	7.3	2.2
	1754	0.1	0.0
	2314	6.9	2.1
19 W	0556	0.2	0.1
	1139	7.2	2.2
	1833	0.2	0.1
20 Th	0001	7.1	2.2
	0638	0.3	0.1
	1223	7.1	2.2
	1916	0.2	0.1
21 F	0052	7.2	2.2
	0733	0.5	0.2
	1315	6.9	2.1
	2010	0.2	0.1
22 Sa	0149	7.3	2.2
	0839	0.6	0.2
	1411	6.7	2.0
	2110	0.0	0.0
23 Su	0251	7.5	2.3
	0950	0.5	0.2
	1516	6.6	2.0
	2214	-0.2	-0.1
24 M	0357	7.6	2.3
	1057	0.2	0.1
	1627	6.5	2.0
	2315	-0.5	-0.2
25 Tu	0510	7.9	2.4
	1158	-0.1	0.0
	1742	6.7	2.0
26 W	0014	-0.9	-0.3
	0621	8.3	2.5
	1257	-0.5	-0.2
	1851	7.0	2.1
27 Th	0112	-1.3	-0.4
	0722	8.7	2.7
	1354	-0.8	-0.2
	1951	7.3	2.2
28 F	0208	-1.6	-0.5
	0817	8.9	2.7
	1448	-1.1	-0.3
	2044	7.6	2.3
29 Sa	0302	-1.8	-0.5
	0908	9.0	2.7
	1540	-1.2	-0.4
	2136	7.8	2.4
30 Su	0355	-1.8	-0.5
	0958	8.9	2.7
	1629	-1.3	-0.4
	2224	7.8	2.4
31 M	0445	-1.6	-0.5
	1045	8.5	2.6
	1716	-1.1	-0.3
	2314	7.7	2.3

FEBRUARY

Day	Time (h m)	Height (ft)	Height (m)
1 Tu	0535	-1.3	-0.4
	1133	8.1	2.5
	1801	-0.9	-0.3
2 W	0006	7.6	2.3
	0625	-0.9	-0.3
	1220	7.6	2.3
	1847	-0.6	-0.2
3 Th	0055	7.4	2.3
	0715	-0.4	-0.1
	1308	7.1	2.2
	1935	-0.3	-0.1
4 F	0147	7.2	2.2
	0809	0.0	0.0
	1356	6.7	2.0
	2028	0.0	0.0
5 Sa	0239	7.0	2.1
	0905	0.3	0.1
	1443	6.4	2.0
	2122	0.2	0.1
6 Su	0332	6.9	2.1
	1001	0.4	0.1
	1537	6.2	1.9
	2216	0.2	0.1
7 M	0430	6.9	2.1
	1055	0.4	0.1
	1633	6.1	1.9
	2310	0.1	0.0
8 Tu	0529	7.0	2.1
	1148	0.3	0.1
	1732	6.2	1.9
9 W	0000	0.0	0.0
	0621	7.1	2.2
	1237	0.2	0.1
	1827	6.4	2.0
10 Th	0049	-0.2	-0.1
	0712	7.3	2.2
	1323	0.0	0.0
	1914	6.6	2.0
11 F	0135	-0.3	-0.1
	0752	7.5	2.3
	1410	-0.1	0.0
	1955	6.8	2.1
12 Sa	0221	-0.3	-0.1
	0831	7.5	2.3
	1453	-0.1	0.0
	2031	6.9	2.1
13 Su	0303	-0.3	-0.1
	0903	7.5	2.3
	1534	-0.2	-0.1
	2104	7.0	2.1
14 M	0341	-0.2	-0.1
	0931	7.5	2.3
	1611	-0.1	0.0
	2136	7.2	2.2
15 Tu	0419	-0.1	0.0
	1000	7.4	2.3
	1648	-0.1	0.0
	2210	7.3	2.2
16 W	0455	0.0	0.0
	1033	7.3	2.2
	1722	0.0	0.0
	2248	7.5	2.3
17 Th	0533	0.1	0.0
	1109	7.2	2.2
	1759	0.0	0.0
	2333	7.6	2.3
18 F	0615	0.2	0.1
	1154	7.1	2.2
	1841	0.1	0.0
19 Sa	0023	7.6	2.3
	0708	0.4	0.1
	1244	6.9	2.1
	1932	0.1	0.0
20 Su	0121	7.7	2.3
	0812	0.6	0.2
	1345	6.6	2.0
	2038	0.1	0.0
21 M	0224	7.7	2.3
	0924	0.6	0.2
	1452	6.5	2.0
	2148	0.0	0.0
22 Tu	0336	7.7	2.3
	1036	0.3	0.1
	1608	6.5	2.0
	2254	-0.4	-0.1
23 W	0451	7.9	2.4
	1139	0.0	0.0
	1727	6.8	2.1
	2355	-0.8	-0.2
24 Th	0603	8.2	2.5
	1237	-0.5	-0.2
	1837	7.2	2.2
25 F	0055	-1.3	-0.4
	0706	8.6	2.6
	1333	-0.9	-0.3
	1936	7.7	2.3
26 Sa	0151	-1.6	-0.5
	0802	8.9	2.7
	1425	-1.2	-0.4
	2029	8.1	2.5
27 Su	0245	-1.8	-0.5
	0852	8.9	2.7
	1515	-1.3	-0.4
	2118	8.4	2.6
28 M	0336	-1.8	-0.5
	0936	8.7	2.7
	1603	-1.3	-0.4
	2204	8.4	2.6

MARCH

Day	Time (h m)	Height (ft)	Height (m)
1 Tu	0426	-1.6	-0.5
	1022	8.4	2.6
	1648	-1.1	-0.3
	2250	8.3	2.5
2 W	0513	-1.2	-0.4
	1104	7.9	2.4
	1732	-0.8	-0.2
	2335	8.0	2.4
3 Th	0559	-0.8	-0.2
	1149	7.4	2.3
	1813	-0.4	-0.1
4 F	0020	7.7	2.3
	0646	-0.3	-0.1
	1231	6.9	2.1
	1859	0.0	0.0
5 Sa	0108	7.4	2.3
	0737	0.2	0.1
	1313	6.6	2.0
	1949	0.3	0.1
6 Su	0155	7.1	2.2
	0830	0.6	0.2
	1403	6.3	1.9
	2041	0.6	0.2
7 M	0249	6.9	2.1
	0925	0.8	0.2
	1454	6.2	1.9
	2140	0.7	0.2
8 Tu	0345	6.8	2.1
	1021	0.8	0.2
	1553	6.1	1.9
	2236	0.6	0.2
9 W	0445	6.8	2.1
	1113	0.6	0.2
	1654	6.3	1.9
	2331	0.4	0.1
10 Th	0544	7.0	2.1
	1205	0.4	0.1
	1752	6.5	2.0
11 F	0021	0.2	0.1
	0637	7.2	2.2
	1253	0.2	0.1
	1843	6.8	2.1
12 Sa	0109	0.0	0.0
	0720	7.4	2.3
	1338	0.0	0.0
	1928	7.1	2.2
13 Su	0154	-0.1	0.0
	0759	7.5	2.3
	1421	-0.1	0.0
	2006	7.3	2.2
14 M	0237	-0.1	0.0
	0834	7.5	2.3
	1502	-0.1	0.0
	2039	7.6	2.3
15 Tu	0318	-0.1	0.0
	0906	7.5	2.3
	1540	-0.1	0.0
	2115	7.8	2.4
16 W	0358	-0.1	0.0
	0935	7.4	2.3
	1617	-0.1	0.0
	2149	7.9	2.4
17 Th	0435	0.0	0.0
	1008	7.3	2.2
	1653	0.0	0.0
	2227	8.1	2.5
18 F	0516	0.1	0.0
	1047	7.2	2.2
	1733	0.0	0.0
	2312	8.1	2.5
19 Sa	0602	0.3	0.1
	1133	7.0	2.1
	1815	0.2	0.1
20 Su	0002	8.1	2.5
	0652	0.5	0.2
	1225	6.8	2.1
	1911	0.3	0.1
21 M	0100	7.9	2.4
	0757	0.6	0.2
	1329	6.6	2.0
	2017	0.3	0.1
22 Tu	0206	7.8	2.4
	0907	0.6	0.2
	1441	6.6	2.0
	2130	0.2	0.1
23 W	0318	7.8	2.4
	1016	0.4	0.1
	1558	6.7	2.0
	2238	-0.1	0.0
24 Th	0433	7.9	2.4
	1118	0.0	0.0
	1715	7.1	2.2
	2339	-0.6	-0.2
25 F	0544	8.2	2.5
	1216	-0.4	-0.1
	1822	7.6	2.3
26 Sa	0037	-1.0	-0.3
	0646	8.5	2.6
	1309	-0.8	-0.2
	1920	8.2	2.5
27 Su	0133	-1.3	-0.4
	0741	8.7	2.7
	1359	-1.1	-0.3
	2011	8.6	2.6
28 M	0225	-1.5	-0.5
	0829	8.7	2.7
	1448	-1.2	-0.4
	2057	8.8	2.7
29 Tu	0316	-1.5	-0.5
	0914	8.4	2.6
	1534	-1.1	-0.3
	2141	8.8	2.7
30 W	0403	-1.3	-0.4
	0954	8.1	2.5
	1618	-0.9	-0.3
	2223	8.7	2.7
31 Th	0448	-0.9	-0.3
	1034	7.7	2.3
	1701	-0.5	-0.2
	2304	8.3	2.5

Time meridian 75° W. 0000 is midnight. 1200 is noon.
Heights are referred to mean low water which is the chart datum of soundings.

Times and Heights of High and Low Waters

APRIL

Day	Time h m	Height ft	Height m
1 F	0533	-0.5	-0.2
	1114	7.2	2.2
	1742	-0.1	0.0
	2343	8.0	2.4
2 Sa	0618	0.0	0.0
	1152	6.9	2.1
	1825	0.3	0.1
3 Su	0028	7.6	2.3
	0704	0.4	0.1
	1236	6.6	2.0
	1911	0.6	0.2
4 M	0113	7.3	2.2
	0753	0.7	0.2
	1324	6.4	2.0
	2004	0.9	0.3
5 Tu	0203	7.0	2.1
	0849	0.9	0.3
	1416	6.3	1.9
	2101	1.0	0.3
6 W	0257	6.9	2.1
	0944	0.9	0.3
	1511	6.3	1.9
	2201	1.0	0.3
7 Th	0356	6.9	2.1
	1039	0.8	0.2
	1612	6.5	2.0
	2256	0.8	0.2
8 F	0454	6.9	2.1
	1129	0.5	0.2
	1711	6.7	2.0
	2347	0.5	0.2
9 Sa	0550	7.1	2.2
	1218	0.3	0.1
	1806	7.1	2.2
10 Su	0037	0.3	0.1
	0639	7.3	2.2
	1303	0.1	0.0
	1854	7.5	2.3
11 M	0124	0.1	0.0
	0724	7.4	2.3
	1346	-0.1	0.0
	1936	7.8	2.4
12 Tu	0209	0.0	0.0
	0802	7.4	2.3
	1428	-0.1	0.0
	2013	8.1	2.5
13 W	0255	0.0	0.0
	0837	7.4	2.3
	1509	-0.2	-0.1
	2051	8.3	2.5
14 Th	0337	0.0	0.0
	0913	7.3	2.2
	1550	-0.1	0.0
	2129	8.5	2.6
15 F	0420	0.0	0.0
	0950	7.2	2.2
	1629	-0.1	0.0
	2211	8.5	2.6
16 Sa	0504	0.1	0.0
	1031	7.1	2.2
	1714	0.0	0.0
	2256	8.5	2.6
17 Su	0551	0.3	0.1
	1120	6.9	2.1
	1802	0.2	0.1
	2349	8.3	2.5
18 M	0645	0.4	0.1
	1217	6.7	2.0
	1858	0.3	0.1
19 Tu	0050	8.1	2.5
	0745	0.5	0.2
	1324	6.6	2.0
	2004	0.4	0.1
20 W	0156	7.9	2.4
	0852	0.5	0.2
	1438	6.7	2.0
	2114	0.3	0.1
21 Th	0306	7.8	2.4
	0956	0.3	0.1
	1551	7.0	2.1
	2220	0.0	0.0
22 F	0414	7.9	2.4
	1057	-0.1	0.0
	1659	7.4	2.3
	2321	-0.4	-0.1
23 Sa	0523	8.0	2.4
	1150	-0.5	-0.2
	1803	8.0	2.4
24 Su	0017	-0.7	-0.2
	0622	8.1	2.5
	1243	-0.8	-0.2
	1859	8.5	2.6
25 M	0112	-1.0	-0.3
	0715	8.2	2.5
	1331	-1.0	-0.3
	1950	8.8	2.7
26 Tu	0203	-1.1	-0.3
	0803	8.1	2.5
	1418	-1.0	-0.3
	2034	9.0	2.7
27 W	0252	-1.1	-0.3
	0846	7.9	2.4
	1504	-0.8	-0.2
	2115	8.9	2.7
28 Th	0340	-0.9	-0.3
	0927	7.6	2.3
	1549	-0.6	-0.2
	2155	8.7	2.7
29 F	0423	-0.6	-0.2
	1004	7.3	2.2
	1631	-0.3	-0.1
	2232	8.4	2.6
30 Sa	0508	-0.3	-0.1
	1040	7.0	2.1
	1712	0.1	0.0
	2311	8.0	2.4

MAY

Day	Time h m	Height ft	Height m
1 Su	0550	0.1	0.0
	1120	6.7	2.0
	1751	0.4	0.1
	2349	7.7	2.3
2 M	0634	0.4	0.1
	1201	6.6	2.0
	1836	0.7	0.2
3 Tu	0033	7.4	2.3
	0721	0.7	0.2
	1247	6.5	2.0
	1926	1.0	0.3
4 W	0119	7.2	2.2
	0812	0.8	0.2
	1337	6.4	2.0
	2020	1.1	0.3
5 Th	0211	7.0	2.1
	0905	0.8	0.2
	1433	6.5	2.0
	2120	1.1	0.3
6 F	0304	6.9	2.1
	0958	0.7	0.2
	1530	6.7	2.0
	2217	1.0	0.3
7 Sa	0402	6.9	2.1
	1049	0.4	0.1
	1628	7.0	2.1
	2313	0.7	0.2
8 Su	0457	7.0	2.1
	1139	0.2	0.1
	1723	7.3	2.2
9 M	0003	0.5	0.2
	0553	7.0	2.1
	1225	0.0	0.0
	1816	7.7	2.3
10 Tu	0053	0.2	0.1
	0643	7.1	2.2
	1311	-0.2	-0.1
	1904	8.1	2.5
11 W	0141	0.0	0.0
	0729	7.2	2.2
	1354	-0.3	-0.1
	1949	8.5	2.6
12 Th	0230	-0.1	0.0
	0811	7.2	2.2
	1439	-0.3	-0.1
	2031	8.7	2.7
13 F	0317	-0.1	0.0
	0853	7.1	2.2
	1525	-0.3	-0.1
	2115	8.8	2.7
14 Sa	0407	-0.1	0.0
	0936	7.0	2.1
	1613	-0.3	-0.1
	2200	8.8	2.7
15 Su	0453	-0.1	0.0
	1024	6.9	2.1
	1701	-0.2	-0.1
	2248	8.6	2.6
16 M	0544	0.0	0.0
	1117	6.8	2.1
	1754	-0.1	0.0
	2343	8.4	2.6
17 Tu	0636	0.1	0.0
	1218	6.7	2.0
	1850	0.1	0.0
18 W	0044	8.1	2.5
	0735	0.2	0.1
	1325	6.7	2.0
	1952	0.2	0.1
19 Th	0148	7.9	2.4
	0835	0.1	0.0
	1433	6.9	2.1
	2057	0.2	0.1
20 F	0249	7.7	2.3
	0934	-0.1	0.0
	1538	7.2	2.2
	2202	0.0	0.0
21 Sa	0353	7.6	2.3
	1030	-0.3	-0.1
	1641	7.6	2.3
	2300	-0.2	-0.1
22 Su	0455	7.5	2.3
	1124	-0.6	-0.2
	1741	8.0	2.4
	2356	-0.5	-0.2
23 M	0553	7.5	2.3
	1214	-0.8	-0.2
	1837	8.4	2.6
24 Tu	0048	-0.6	-0.2
	0648	7.5	2.3
	1302	-0.8	-0.2
	1925	8.7	2.7
25 W	0140	-0.7	-0.2
	0735	7.4	2.3
	1349	-0.8	-0.2
	2010	8.8	2.7
26 Th	0229	-0.7	-0.2
	0819	7.3	2.2
	1435	-0.6	-0.2
	2049	8.7	2.7
27 F	0315	-0.6	-0.2
	0858	7.1	2.2
	1520	-0.4	-0.1
	2129	8.5	2.6
28 Sa	0358	-0.4	-0.1
	0935	6.9	2.1
	1602	-0.2	-0.1
	2205	8.2	2.5
29 Su	0442	-0.2	-0.1
	1011	6.7	2.0
	1643	0.1	0.0
	2240	7.9	2.4
30 M	0524	0.1	0.0
	1048	6.6	2.0
	1724	0.4	0.1
	2317	7.6	2.3
31 Tu	0605	0.3	0.1
	1128	6.5	2.0
	1805	0.6	0.2
	2354	7.4	2.3

JUNE

Day	Time h m	Height ft	Height m
1 W	0647	0.4	0.1
	1213	6.5	2.0
	1847	0.9	0.3
2 Th	0038	7.2	2.2
	0734	0.5	0.2
	1259	6.5	2.0
	1939	1.0	0.3
3 F	0126	7.1	2.2
	0822	0.5	0.2
	1353	6.7	2.0
	2036	1.1	0.3
4 Sa	0214	7.0	2.1
	0915	0.4	0.1
	1447	6.9	2.1
	2136	1.0	0.3
5 Su	0306	6.9	2.1
	1006	0.3	0.1
	1541	7.2	2.2
	2233	0.8	0.2
6 M	0404	6.8	2.1
	1057	0.0	0.0
	1641	7.5	2.3
	2329	0.5	0.2
7 Tu	0502	6.8	2.1
	1147	-0.2	-0.1
	1736	7.9	2.4
8 W	0023	0.3	0.1
	0600	6.8	2.1
	1235	-0.4	-0.1
	1833	8.3	2.5
9 Th	0114	0.0	0.0
	0658	6.8	2.1
	1325	-0.5	-0.2
	1925	8.6	2.6
10 F	0207	-0.2	-0.1
	0751	6.9	2.1
	1414	-0.6	-0.2
	2014	8.9	2.7
11 Sa	0300	-0.3	-0.1
	0839	7.0	2.1
	1506	-0.7	-0.2
	2102	8.9	2.7
12 Su	0351	-0.4	-0.1
	0928	7.0	2.1
	1558	-0.7	-0.2
	2152	8.9	2.7
13 M	0442	-0.4	-0.1
	1020	6.9	2.1
	1650	-0.6	-0.2
	2243	8.7	2.7
14 Tu	0533	-0.4	-0.1
	1117	6.9	2.1
	1743	-0.5	-0.2
	2337	8.4	2.6
15 W	0623	-0.4	-0.1
	1217	6.9	2.1
	1839	-0.3	-0.1
16 Th	0034	8.1	2.5
	0716	-0.3	-0.1
	1318	7.0	2.1
	1937	-0.1	0.0
17 F	0132	7.8	2.4
	0812	-0.3	-0.1
	1418	7.2	2.2
	2038	0.1	0.0
18 Sa	0230	7.5	2.3
	0907	-0.3	-0.1
	1519	7.4	2.3
	2140	0.1	0.0
19 Su	0326	7.2	2.2
	1002	-0.4	-0.1
	1617	7.7	2.3
	2237	0.0	0.0
20 M	0423	7.0	2.1
	1055	-0.5	-0.2
	1715	7.9	2.4
	2332	-0.1	0.0
21 Tu	0521	6.9	2.1
	1145	-0.6	-0.2
	1810	8.1	2.5
22 W	0024	-0.3	-0.1
	0617	6.8	2.1
	1233	-0.6	-0.2
	1901	8.3	2.5
23 Th	0114	-0.3	-0.1
	0706	6.8	2.1
	1322	-0.6	-0.2
	1946	8.4	2.6
24 F	0202	-0.3	-0.1
	0751	6.8	2.1
	1407	-0.5	-0.2
	2027	8.3	2.5
25 Sa	0248	-0.3	-0.1
	0832	6.8	2.1
	1451	-0.3	-0.1
	2105	8.2	2.5
26 Su	0333	-0.2	-0.1
	0910	6.7	2.0
	1535	-0.1	0.0
	2139	8.0	2.4
27 M	0416	-0.1	0.0
	0945	6.7	2.0
	1616	0.1	0.0
	2213	7.8	2.4
28 Tu	0456	0.0	0.0
	1020	6.6	2.0
	1655	0.3	0.1
	2245	7.6	2.3
29 W	0535	0.1	0.0
	1056	6.6	2.0
	1735	0.5	0.2
	2320	7.5	2.3
30 Th	0615	0.2	0.1
	1138	6.7	2.0
	1815	0.7	0.2
	2357	7.3	2.2

Time meridian 75° W. 0000 is midnight. 1200 is noon.
Heights are referred to mean low water which is the chart datum of soundings.

Times and Heights of High and Low Waters

JULY

Day	Time h m	Height ft	Height m
1	0655	0.3	0.1
F	1223	6.8	2.1
	1858	0.8	0.2
2	0039	7.2	2.2
Sa	0739	0.3	0.1
	1312	7.0	2.1
	1952	1.0	0.3
3	0129	7.0	2.1
Su	0830	0.3	0.1
	1406	7.2	2.2
	2053	1.0	0.3
4	0220	6.9	2.1
M	0922	0.2	0.1
	1500	7.4	2.3
	2157	0.9	0.3
5	0316	6.7	2.0
Tu	1016	0.0	0.0
	1602	7.7	2.3
	2257	0.6	0.2
6	0420	6.6	2.0
W	1111	-0.2	-0.1
	1702	8.0	2.4
	2354	0.3	0.1
7	0527	6.6	2.0
Th	1206	-0.5	-0.2
	1807	8.4	2.6
8	0050	0.0	0.0
F	0632	6.7	2.0
	1259	-0.7	-0.2
	1906	8.7	2.7
9	0146	-0.3	-0.1
Sa	0733	6.9	2.1
	1354	-0.9	-0.3
	2000	9.0	2.7
10	0241	-0.5	-0.2
Su	0828	7.1	2.2
	1449	-1.0	-0.3
	2053	9.1	2.8
11	0335	-0.7	-0.2
M	0921	7.3	2.2
	1544	-1.1	-0.3
	2143	9.1	2.8
12	0425	-0.8	-0.2
Tu	1014	7.4	2.3
	1637	-1.0	-0.3
	2233	8.9	2.7
13	0514	-0.8	-0.2
W	1108	7.4	2.3
	1730	-0.8	-0.2
	2325	8.5	2.6
14	0603	-0.8	-0.2
Th	1205	7.4	2.3
	1822	-0.5	-0.2
15	0018	8.1	2.5
F	0652	-0.6	-0.2
	1300	7.5	2.3
	1916	-0.2	-0.1
16	0110	7.7	2.3
Sa	0744	-0.4	-0.1
	1358	7.5	2.3
	2014	0.1	0.0
17	0201	7.3	2.2
Su	0837	-0.3	-0.1
	1452	7.6	2.3
	2114	0.3	0.1
18	0257	6.9	2.1
M	0931	-0.2	-0.1
	1549	7.6	2.3
	2212	0.4	0.1
19	0351	6.6	2.0
Tu	1025	-0.2	-0.1
	1646	7.7	2.3
	2307	0.3	0.1
20	0449	6.5	2.0
W	1117	-0.2	-0.1
	1742	7.8	2.4
	2358	0.2	0.1
21	0545	6.5	2.0
Th	1206	-0.2	-0.1
	1835	8.0	2.4
22	0048	0.1	0.0
F	0639	6.6	2.0
	1254	-0.2	-0.1
	1922	8.1	2.5
23	0136	0.0	0.0
Sa	0726	6.7	2.0
	1341	-0.2	-0.1
	2003	8.1	2.5
24	0222	0.0	0.0
Su	0807	6.8	2.1
	1426	-0.1	0.0
	2040	8.1	2.5
25	0306	-0.1	0.0
M	0845	6.8	2.1
	1511	0.0	0.0
	2114	8.0	2.4
26	0348	-0.1	0.0
Tu	0920	6.9	2.1
	1550	0.2	0.1
	2145	7.9	2.4
27	0427	0.0	0.0
W	0952	6.9	2.1
	1629	0.3	0.1
	2214	7.8	2.4
28	0504	0.1	0.0
Th	1027	7.0	2.1
	1706	0.5	0.2
	2245	7.6	2.3
29	0541	0.2	0.1
F	1104	7.1	2.2
	1743	0.7	0.2
	2318	7.5	2.3
30	0618	0.2	0.1
Sa	1146	7.3	2.2
	1823	0.8	0.2
31	0000	7.3	2.2
Su	0655	0.3	0.1
	1236	7.4	2.3
	1913	1.0	0.3

AUGUST

Day	Time h m	Height ft	Height m
1	0047	7.2	2.2
M	0742	0.3	0.1
	1326	7.6	2.3
	2012	1.1	0.3
2	0141	7.0	2.1
Tu	0838	0.3	0.1
	1424	7.8	2.4
	2120	1.1	0.3
3	0241	6.8	2.1
W	0940	0.2	0.1
	1527	8.0	2.4
	2228	0.9	0.3
4	0346	6.6	2.0
Th	1042	0.0	0.0
	1634	8.2	2.5
	2329	0.5	0.2
5	0501	6.7	2.0
F	1142	-0.4	-0.1
	1744	8.5	2.6
6	0029	0.1	0.0
Sa	0614	6.9	2.1
	1240	-0.7	-0.2
	1848	8.9	2.7
7	0126	-0.3	-0.1
Su	0719	7.3	2.2
	1338	-1.0	-0.3
	1946	9.2	2.8
8	0221	-0.6	-0.2
M	0815	7.7	2.3
	1433	-1.2	-0.4
	2039	9.4	2.9
9	0314	-0.9	-0.3
Tu	0908	8.0	2.4
	1527	-1.2	-0.4
	2129	9.3	2.8
10	0403	-1.0	-0.3
W	0959	8.1	2.5
	1619	-1.1	-0.3
	2218	9.1	2.8
11	0451	-1.0	-0.3
Th	1050	8.2	2.5
	1711	-0.9	-0.3
	2304	8.6	2.6
12	0538	-0.8	-0.2
F	1142	8.1	2.5
	1802	-0.5	-0.2
	2354	8.1	2.5
13	0625	-0.6	-0.2
Sa	1236	8.0	2.4
	1854	-0.1	0.0
14	0042	7.6	2.3
Su	0713	-0.3	-0.1
	1327	7.9	2.4
	1947	0.4	0.1
15	0132	7.1	2.2
M	0804	0.1	0.0
	1422	7.8	2.4
	2045	0.7	0.2
16	0222	6.8	2.1
Tu	0859	0.3	0.1
	1515	7.6	2.3
	2143	0.9	0.3
17	0317	6.5	2.0
W	0953	0.4	0.1
	1614	7.6	2.3
	2238	0.8	0.2
18	0414	6.4	2.0
Th	1047	0.4	0.1
	1710	7.7	2.3
	2329	0.7	0.2
19	0513	6.5	2.0
F	1139	0.3	0.1
	1806	7.8	2.4
20	0020	0.6	0.2
Sa	0609	6.6	2.0
	1229	0.2	0.1
	1853	8.0	2.4
21	0106	0.4	0.1
Su	0659	6.9	2.1
	1315	0.2	0.1
	1938	8.1	2.5
22	0152	0.2	0.1
M	0742	7.1	2.2
	1401	0.2	0.1
	2015	8.2	2.5
23	0237	0.1	0.0
Tu	0821	7.3	2.2
	1443	0.2	0.1
	2048	8.1	2.5
24	0317	0.1	0.0
W	0853	7.4	2.3
	1525	0.3	0.1
	2117	8.1	2.5
25	0356	0.1	0.0
Th	0926	7.5	2.3
	1603	0.5	0.2
	2145	7.9	2.4
26	0432	0.2	0.1
F	0958	7.6	2.3
	1639	0.6	0.2
	2213	7.8	2.4
27	0507	0.3	0.1
Sa	1034	7.8	2.4
	1716	0.8	0.2
	2248	7.7	2.3
28	0541	0.4	0.1
Su	1114	7.9	2.4
	1753	1.0	0.3
	2327	7.5	2.3
29	0618	0.5	0.2
M	1202	8.0	2.4
	1844	1.1	0.3
30	0015	7.3	2.2
Tu	0703	0.5	0.2
	1255	8.1	2.5
	1942	1.3	0.4
31	0111	7.0	2.1
W	0802	0.6	0.2
	1356	8.1	2.5
	2053	1.3	0.4

SEPTEMBER

Day	Time h m	Height ft	Height m
1	0214	6.9	2.1
Th	0912	0.5	0.2
	1502	8.2	2.5
	2204	1.1	0.3
2	0325	6.8	2.1
F	1021	0.3	0.1
	1613	8.4	2.6
	2310	0.7	0.2
3	0444	7.0	2.1
Sa	1123	-0.1	0.0
	1726	8.7	2.7
4	0008	0.2	0.1
Su	0600	7.4	2.3
	1224	-0.6	-0.2
	1832	9.1	2.8
5	0104	-0.2	-0.1
M	0705	7.9	2.4
	1320	-0.9	-0.3
	1930	9.4	2.9
6	0157	-0.6	-0.2
Tu	0802	8.4	2.6
	1415	-1.1	-0.3
	2021	9.5	2.9
7	0249	-0.9	-0.3
W	0851	8.8	2.7
	1509	-1.2	-0.4
	2109	9.4	2.9
8	0338	-1.0	-0.3
Th	0940	8.9	2.7
	1600	-1.0	-0.3
	2155	9.1	2.8
9	0424	-0.9	-0.3
F	1029	8.9	2.7
	1650	-0.7	-0.2
	2240	8.6	2.6
10	0509	-0.7	-0.2
Sa	1116	8.7	2.7
	1739	-0.3	-0.1
	2324	8.1	2.5
11	0554	-0.3	-0.1
Su	1205	8.4	2.6
	1828	0.2	0.1
12	0010	7.5	2.3
M	0640	0.1	0.0
	1254	8.1	2.5
	1919	0.7	0.2
13	0057	7.1	2.2
Tu	0729	0.5	0.2
	1347	7.9	2.4
	2012	1.1	0.3
14	0148	6.8	2.1
W	0822	0.8	0.2
	1440	7.7	2.3
	2109	1.3	0.4
15	0240	6.6	2.0
Th	0921	1.0	0.3
	1536	7.6	2.3
	2204	1.3	0.4
16	0339	6.6	2.0
F	1017	0.9	0.3
	1633	7.6	2.3
	2259	1.1	0.3
17	0436	6.7	2.0
Sa	1111	0.8	0.2
	1729	7.7	2.3
	2349	0.9	0.3
18	0536	6.9	2.1
Su	1200	0.6	0.2
	1819	7.9	2.4
19	0035	0.6	0.2
M	0629	7.2	2.2
	1248	0.5	0.2
	1904	8.1	2.5
20	0121	0.4	0.1
Tu	0714	7.5	2.3
	1333	0.4	0.1
	1943	8.2	2.5
21	0203	0.3	0.1
W	0752	7.7	2.3
	1417	0.4	0.1
	2016	8.2	2.5
22	0245	0.2	0.1
Th	0826	8.0	2.4
	1459	0.5	0.2
	2047	8.1	2.5
23	0323	0.2	0.1
F	0900	8.1	2.5
	1538	0.6	0.2
	2116	8.0	2.4
24	0400	0.3	0.1
Sa	0932	8.3	2.5
	1615	0.8	0.2
	2146	7.8	2.4
25	0434	0.4	0.1
Su	1008	8.4	2.6
	1656	0.9	0.3
	2219	7.7	2.3
26	0510	0.5	0.2
M	1048	8.4	2.6
	1735	1.1	0.3
	2300	7.5	2.3
27	0549	0.6	0.2
Tu	1137	8.4	2.6
	1823	1.3	0.4
	2349	7.3	2.2
28	0639	0.7	0.2
W	1231	8.4	2.6
	1924	1.4	0.4
29	0049	7.0	2.1
Th	0742	0.8	0.2
	1335	8.3	2.5
	2033	1.4	0.4
30	0158	6.9	2.1
F	0851	0.7	0.2
	1443	8.4	2.6
	2145	1.2	0.4

Time meridian 75° W. 0000 is midnight. 1200 is noon.
Heights are referred to mean low water which is the chart datum of soundings.

Times and Heights of High and Low Waters

OCTOBER

Day	Time h m	Height ft	Height m	Day	Time h m	Height ft	Height m
1	0314	7.0	2.1	16	0357	6.8	2.1
Sa	1001	0.5	0.2	Su	1038	1.1	0.3
	1556	8.5	2.6		1641	7.5	2.3
	2249	0.7	0.2		2313	0.9	0.3
2	0433	7.3	2.2	17	0454	7.0	2.1
Su	1107	0.0	0.0	M	1129	0.9	0.3
	1707	8.7	2.7		1736	7.7	2.3
	2347	0.2	0.1				
3	0545	7.8	2.4	18	0001	0.6	0.2
M	1206	-0.4	-0.1	Tu	0550	7.4	2.3
	1812	9.0	2.7		1216	0.7	0.2
					1822	7.8	2.4
4	0041	-0.3	-0.1	19	0045	0.4	0.1
Tu	0648	8.4	2.6	W	0637	7.7	2.3
	1301	-0.8	-0.2		1304	0.6	0.2
	1909	9.3	2.8		1905	7.9	2.4
5	0133	-0.7	-0.2	20	0128	0.2	0.1
W	0743	9.0	2.7	Th	0721	8.0	2.4
	1356	-0.9	-0.3		1349	0.5	0.2
	1959	9.3	2.8		1944	7.9	2.4
6	0223	-0.9	-0.3	21	0210	0.2	0.1
Th	0832	9.3	2.8	F	0759	8.3	2.5
	1448	-1.0	-0.3		1432	0.5	0.2
	2047	9.2	2.8		2018	7.9	2.4
7	0310	-0.9	-0.3	22	0250	0.2	0.1
F	0919	9.4	2.9	Sa	0835	8.5	2.6
	1539	-0.8	-0.2		1514	0.6	0.2
	2131	8.8	2.7		2050	7.8	2.4
8	0356	-0.7	-0.2	23	0329	0.2	0.1
Sa	1003	9.3	2.8	Su	0909	8.6	2.6
	1627	-0.5	-0.2		1556	0.7	0.2
	2213	8.4	2.6		2122	7.6	2.3
9	0441	-0.4	-0.1	24	0408	0.3	0.1
Su	1048	9.0	2.7	M	0949	8.7	2.7
	1714	-0.1	0.0		1640	0.8	0.2
	2255	7.9	2.4		2202	7.5	2.3
10	0524	-0.1	0.0	25	0450	0.4	0.1
M	1133	8.6	2.6	Tu	1030	8.7	2.7
	1801	0.4	0.1		1724	1.0	0.3
	2337	7.4	2.3		2244	7.3	2.2
11	0609	0.4	0.1	26	0533	0.5	0.2
Tu	1220	8.2	2.5	W	1120	8.6	2.6
	1850	0.9	0.3		1813	1.1	0.3
					2335	7.1	2.2
12	0019	7.0	2.1	27	0626	0.6	0.2
W	0655	0.8	0.2	Th	1218	8.4	2.6
	1308	7.9	2.4		1912	1.2	0.4
	1940	1.2	0.4				
13	0110	6.8	2.1	28	0039	6.9	2.1
Th	0747	1.1	0.3	F	0727	0.7	0.2
	1400	7.6	2.3		1321	8.3	2.5
	2033	1.4	0.4		2017	1.2	0.4
14	0201	6.7	2.0	29	0152	6.9	2.1
F	0843	1.3	0.4	Sa	0837	0.7	0.2
	1452	7.5	2.3		1428	8.3	2.5
	2129	1.4	0.4		2125	0.9	0.3
15	0258	6.7	2.0	30	0307	7.1	2.2
Sa	0941	1.3	0.4	Su	0945	0.4	0.1
	1548	7.5	2.3		1538	8.3	2.5
	2224	1.2	0.4		2227	0.5	0.2
				31	0422	7.5	2.3
				M	1049	0.1	0.0
					1646	8.4	2.6
					2323	0.0	0.0

NOVEMBER

Day	Time h m	Height ft	Height m	Day	Time h m	Height ft	Height m
1	0530	8.0	2.4	16	0506	7.3	2.2
Tu	1147	-0.3	-0.1	W	1144	0.7	0.2
	1750	8.6	2.6		1736	7.3	2.2
2	0016	-0.5	-0.2	17	0008	0.2	0.1
W	0629	8.6	2.6	Th	0558	7.7	2.3
	1243	-0.6	-0.2		1233	0.6	0.2
	1845	8.7	2.7		1825	7.4	2.3
3	0106	-0.8	-0.2	18	0053	0.0	0.0
Th	0724	9.1	2.8	F	0645	8.0	2.4
	1336	-0.8	-0.2		1320	0.4	0.1
	1936	8.7	2.7		1910	7.4	2.3
4	0155	-0.9	-0.3	19	0138	-0.1	0.0
F	0813	9.3	2.8	Sa	0730	8.3	2.5
	1427	-0.8	-0.2		1407	0.3	0.1
	2022	8.5	2.6		1951	7.4	2.3
5	0242	-0.9	-0.3	20	0219	-0.1	0.0
Sa	0857	9.4	2.9	Su	0812	8.6	2.6
	1517	-0.6	-0.2		1453	0.3	0.1
	2106	8.2	2.5		2029	7.4	2.3
6	0328	-0.7	-0.2	21	0304	-0.2	-0.1
Su	0940	9.2	2.8	M	0852	8.7	2.7
	1604	-0.4	-0.1		1539	0.3	0.1
	2145	7.9	2.4		2108	7.3	2.2
7	0413	-0.4	-0.1	22	0347	-0.1	0.0
M	1021	8.8	2.7	Tu	0935	8.7	2.7
	1649	0.0	0.0		1626	0.4	0.1
	2226	7.5	2.3		2151	7.2	2.2
8	0456	0.0	0.0	23	0435	-0.1	0.0
Tu	1103	8.4	2.6	W	1020	8.6	2.6
	1734	0.4	0.1		1715	0.5	0.2
	2304	7.2	2.2		2237	7.0	2.1
9	0538	0.3	0.1	24	0524	0.0	0.0
W	1145	8.0	2.4	Th	1112	8.5	2.6
	1818	0.7	0.2		1805	0.6	0.2
	2346	6.9	2.1		2333	6.9	2.1
10	0622	0.7	0.2	25	0618	0.1	0.0
Th	1227	7.7	2.3	F	1210	8.3	2.5
	1905	1.0	0.3		1900	0.6	0.2
11	0031	6.7	2.0	26	0039	6.8	2.1
F	0710	1.0	0.3	Sa	0716	0.2	0.1
	1315	7.5	2.3		1311	8.1	2.5
	1956	1.2	0.4		2000	0.5	0.2
12	0122	6.6	2.0	27	0147	6.9	2.1
Sa	0804	1.2	0.4	Su	0821	0.3	0.1
	1404	7.3	2.2		1414	7.9	2.4
	2049	1.2	0.4		2102	0.4	0.1
13	0217	6.6	2.0	28	0257	7.2	2.2
Su	0901	1.2	0.4	M	0927	0.2	0.1
	1455	7.2	2.2		1518	7.8	2.4
	2143	1.0	0.3		2201	0.0	0.0
14	0312	6.8	2.1	29	0404	7.5	2.3
M	0959	1.2	0.4	Tu	1030	-0.1	0.0
	1549	7.2	2.2		1622	7.8	2.4
	2233	0.8	0.2		2257	-0.3	-0.1
15	0410	7.0	2.1	30	0508	7.9	2.4
Tu	1052	1.0	0.3	W	1127	-0.3	-0.1
	1644	7.3	2.2		1724	7.8	2.4
	2321	0.5	0.2		2350	-0.6	-0.2

DECEMBER

Day	Time h m	Height ft	Height m	Day	Time h m	Height ft	Height m
1	0608	8.4	2.6	16	0515	7.5	2.3
Th	1222	-0.5	-0.2	F	1200	0.5	0.2
	1821	7.8	2.4		1740	6.8	2.1
2	0040	-0.8	-0.2	17	0017	-0.2	-0.1
F	0702	8.7	2.7	Sa	0612	7.8	2.4
	1314	-0.7	-0.2		1251	0.2	0.1
	1914	7.8	2.4		1836	6.8	2.1
3	0129	-0.9	-0.3	18	0106	-0.4	-0.1
Sa	0751	8.9	2.7	Su	0704	8.2	2.5
	1405	-0.7	-0.2		1343	0.1	0.0
	2000	7.7	2.3		1926	6.9	2.1
4	0215	-0.9	-0.3	19	0154	-0.6	-0.2
Su	0836	8.9	2.7	M	0754	8.4	2.6
	1453	-0.6	-0.2		1433	-0.1	0.0
	2042	7.5	2.3		2013	7.0	2.1
5	0302	-0.7	-0.2	20	0245	-0.7	-0.2
M	0916	8.7	2.7	Tu	0840	8.6	2.6
	1541	-0.4	-0.1		1524	-0.1	0.0
	2122	7.3	2.2		2100	7.1	2.2
6	0347	-0.5	-0.2	21	0334	-0.8	-0.2
Tu	0957	8.4	2.6	W	0927	8.7	2.7
	1624	-0.2	-0.1		1613	-0.2	-0.1
	2157	7.1	2.2		2147	7.0	2.1
7	0429	-0.2	-0.1	22	0423	-0.8	-0.2
W	1034	8.1	2.5	Th	1015	8.6	2.6
	1706	0.1	0.0		1703	-0.2	-0.1
	2234	6.9	2.1		2237	7.0	2.1
8	0511	0.1	0.0	23	0514	-0.7	-0.2
Th	1112	7.8	2.4	F	1106	8.4	2.6
	1749	0.3	0.1		1752	-0.2	-0.1
	2314	6.7	2.0		2333	7.0	2.1
9	0552	0.3	0.1	24	0607	-0.5	-0.2
F	1149	7.5	2.3	Sa	1201	8.1	2.5
	1831	0.5	0.2		1844	-0.2	-0.1
	2354	6.6	2.0				
10	0634	0.6	0.2	25	0034	7.0	2.1
Sa	1231	7.3	2.2	Su	0703	-0.3	-0.1
	1916	0.7	0.2		1258	7.8	2.4
					1938	-0.1	0.0
11	0042	6.6	2.0	26	0136	7.1	2.2
Su	0723	0.8	0.2	M	0804	-0.2	-0.1
	1315	7.1	2.2		1354	7.5	2.3
	2005	0.7	0.2		2036	-0.2	-0.1
12	0132	6.6	2.0	27	0240	7.2	2.2
M	0815	1.0	0.3	Tu	0906	-0.1	0.0
	1401	7.0	2.1		1454	7.3	2.2
	2057	0.7	0.2		2134	-0.3	-0.1
13	0224	6.8	2.1	28	0343	7.4	2.3
Tu	0913	1.0	0.3	W	1008	-0.1	0.0
	1453	6.9	2.1		1553	7.1	2.2
	2149	0.5	0.2		2230	-0.4	-0.1
14	0319	6.9	2.1	29	0445	7.6	2.3
W	1012	0.9	0.3	Th	1106	-0.2	-0.1
	1545	6.8	2.1		1655	6.9	2.1
	2240	0.3	0.1		2323	-0.6	-0.2
15	0417	7.2	2.2	30	0545	7.9	2.4
Th	1108	0.7	0.2	F	1200	-0.4	-0.1
	1644	6.8	2.1		1755	6.9	2.1
	2331	0.0	0.0				
				31	0014	-0.7	-0.2
				Sa	0640	8.1	2.5
					1252	-0.5	-0.2
					1849	7.0	2.1

Time meridian 75° W. 0000 is midnight. 1200 is noon.
Heights are referred to mean low water which is the chart datum of soundings.

Times and Heights of High and Low Waters

JANUARY

Day	Time (h m)	Height (ft)	Height (m)
1 Sa	0315	-1.2	-0.4
	1006	5.3	1.6
	1609	-1.0	-0.3
	2227	4.3	1.3
2 Su	0413	-1.0	-0.3
	1059	5.1	1.6
	1703	-0.9	-0.3
	2324	4.3	1.3
3 M	0512	-0.7	-0.2
	1152	4.9	1.5
	1800	-0.7	-0.2
4 Tu	0020	4.3	1.3
	0615	-0.4	-0.1
	1246	4.6	1.4
	1855	-0.6	-0.2
5 W	0119	4.3	1.3
	0719	-0.2	-0.1
	1345	4.4	1.3
	1952	-0.4	-0.1
6 Th	0219	4.3	1.3
	0825	0.0	0.0
	1441	4.1	1.2
	2047	-0.3	-0.1
7 F	0317	4.3	1.3
	0928	0.1	0.0
	1538	3.9	1.2
	2141	-0.2	-0.1
8 Sa	0415	4.4	1.3
	1026	0.2	0.1
	1634	3.8	1.2
	2231	-0.2	-0.1
9 Su	0510	4.4	1.3
	1121	0.1	0.0
	1726	3.7	1.1
	2320	-0.2	-0.1
10 M	0558	4.5	1.4
	1209	0.0	0.0
	1815	3.6	1.1
11 Tu	0005	-0.3	-0.1
	0646	4.5	1.4
	1252	-0.1	0.0
	1902	3.6	1.1
12 W	0047	-0.3	-0.1
	0730	4.5	1.4
	1334	-0.1	0.0
	1943	3.6	1.1
13 Th	0125	-0.4	-0.1
	0810	4.5	1.4
	1413	-0.2	-0.1
	2024	3.6	1.1
14 F	0202	-0.4	-0.1
	0849	4.4	1.3
	1448	-0.2	-0.1
	2101	3.6	1.1
15 Sa	0236	-0.3	-0.1
	0926	4.4	1.3
	1523	-0.2	-0.1
	2138	3.6	1.1
16 Su	0310	-0.3	-0.1
	1002	4.3	1.3
	1555	-0.1	0.0
	2214	3.6	1.1
17 M	0347	-0.1	0.0
	1037	4.2	1.3
	1627	-0.1	0.0
	2249	3.7	1.1
18 Tu	0422	0.0	0.0
	1109	4.1	1.2
	1703	0.0	0.0
	2327	3.7	1.1
19 W	0507	0.1	0.0
	1145	4.0	1.2
	1741	0.0	0.0
20 Th	0004	3.8	1.2
	0554	0.3	0.1
	1222	3.9	1.2
	1826	0.0	0.0
21 F	0049	3.9	1.2
	0649	0.4	0.1
	1308	3.8	1.2
	1917	0.0	0.0
22 Sa	0143	4.0	1.2
	0751	0.4	0.1
	1403	3.6	1.1
	2013	-0.1	0.0
23 Su	0245	4.1	1.2
	0902	0.3	0.1
	1504	3.5	1.1
	2113	-0.3	-0.1
24 M	0352	4.3	1.3
	1010	0.1	0.0
	1618	3.5	1.1
	2215	-0.5	-0.2
25 Tu	0502	4.5	1.4
	1115	-0.3	-0.1
	1726	3.6	1.1
	2318	-0.8	-0.2
26 W	0609	4.7	1.4
	1215	-0.6	-0.2
	1832	3.7	1.1
27 Th	0015	-1.1	-0.3
	0709	4.9	1.5
	1312	-0.9	-0.3
	1928	3.9	1.2
28 F	0114	-1.4	-0.4
	0805	5.1	1.6
	1405	-1.2	-0.4
	2025	4.1	1.2
29 Sa	0209	-1.5	-0.5
	0857	5.1	1.6
	1457	-1.3	-0.4
	2118	4.3	1.3
30 Su	0305	-1.5	-0.5
	0949	5.1	1.6
	1547	-1.3	-0.4
	2209	4.3	1.3
31 M	0400	-1.3	-0.4
	1038	4.9	1.5
	1638	-1.2	-0.4
	2300	4.4	1.3

FEBRUARY

Day	Time (h m)	Height (ft)	Height (m)
1 Tu	0455	-1.1	-0.3
	1128	4.6	1.4
	1730	-1.1	-0.3
	2354	4.4	1.3
2 W	0554	-0.7	-0.2
	1218	4.3	1.3
	1821	-0.8	-0.2
3 Th	0046	4.3	1.3
	0653	-0.3	-0.1
	1309	4.0	1.2
	1914	-0.5	-0.2
4 F	0142	4.2	1.3
	0755	0.0	0.0
	1404	3.8	1.2
	2007	-0.3	-0.1
5 Sa	0239	4.1	1.2
	0856	0.2	0.1
	1500	3.5	1.1
	2103	-0.1	0.0
6 Su	0339	4.1	1.2
	0956	0.3	0.1
	1559	3.4	1.0
	2159	0.0	0.0
7 M	0437	4.1	1.2
	1049	0.3	0.1
	1655	3.4	1.0
	2249	0.0	0.0
8 Tu	0532	4.1	1.2
	1142	0.2	0.1
	1747	3.4	1.0
	2337	-0.1	0.0
9 W	0624	4.2	1.3
	1227	0.1	0.0
	1833	3.5	1.1
10 Th	0022	-0.2	-0.1
	0705	4.3	1.3
	1308	-0.1	0.0
	1919	3.6	1.1
11 F	0104	-0.3	-0.1
	0747	4.3	1.3
	1346	-0.2	-0.1
	1959	3.6	1.1
12 Sa	0142	-0.4	-0.1
	0826	4.3	1.3
	1421	-0.3	-0.1
	2037	3.7	1.1
13 Su	0217	-0.4	-0.1
	0903	4.3	1.3
	1453	-0.4	-0.1
	2114	3.8	1.2
14 M	0252	-0.4	-0.1
	0936	4.3	1.3
	1524	-0.4	-0.1
	2149	3.8	1.2
15 Tu	0326	-0.4	-0.1
	1011	4.2	1.3
	1556	-0.4	-0.1
	2222	3.9	1.2
16 W	0403	-0.3	-0.1
	1043	4.1	1.2
	1630	-0.3	-0.1
	2257	4.0	1.2
17 Th	0443	-0.2	-0.1
	1115	4.0	1.2
	1707	-0.3	-0.1
	2336	4.1	1.2
18 F	0531	0.0	0.0
	1154	3.8	1.2
	1752	-0.2	-0.1
19 Sa	0020	4.1	1.2
	0625	0.1	0.0
	1239	3.7	1.1
	1842	-0.2	-0.1
20 Su	0111	4.1	1.2
	0729	0.3	0.1
	1335	3.5	1.1
	1940	-0.1	0.0
21 M	0218	4.2	1.3
	0840	0.2	0.1
	1444	3.4	1.0
	2049	-0.2	-0.1
22 Tu	0334	4.2	1.3
	0953	0.1	0.0
	1557	3.4	1.0
	2157	-0.4	-0.1
23 W	0449	4.4	1.3
	1100	-0.2	-0.1
	1713	3.6	1.1
	2305	-0.7	-0.2
24 Th	0556	4.6	1.4
	1201	-0.6	-0.2
	1819	3.8	1.2
25 F	0006	-1.0	-0.3
	0656	4.8	1.5
	1254	-0.9	-0.3
	1915	4.1	1.2
26 Sa	0104	-1.3	-0.4
	0749	5.0	1.5
	1347	-1.2	-0.4
	2008	4.4	1.3
27 Su	0158	-1.4	-0.4
	0840	5.0	1.5
	1435	-1.3	-0.4
	2100	4.5	1.4
28 M	0251	-1.4	-0.4
	0929	4.9	1.5
	1523	-1.4	-0.4
	2147	4.6	1.4

MARCH

Day	Time (h m)	Height (ft)	Height (m)
1 Tu	0343	-1.3	-0.4
	1014	4.7	1.4
	1609	-1.2	-0.4
	2235	4.7	1.4
2 W	0434	-1.0	-0.3
	1101	4.5	1.4
	1654	-1.0	-0.3
	2323	4.6	1.4
3 Th	0528	-0.6	-0.2
	1146	4.2	1.3
	1741	-0.6	-0.2
4 F	0012	4.4	1.3
	0621	-0.2	-0.1
	1234	3.9	1.2
	1830	-0.3	-0.1
5 Sa	0104	4.3	1.3
	0719	0.1	0.0
	1326	3.7	1.1
	1925	0.0	0.0
6 Su	0158	4.1	1.2
	0817	0.4	0.1
	1420	3.5	1.1
	2021	0.3	0.1
7 M	0257	4.0	1.2
	0921	0.6	0.2
	1520	3.4	1.0
	2120	0.4	0.1
8 Tu	0358	4.0	1.2
	1017	0.6	0.2
	1617	3.4	1.0
	2217	0.4	0.1
9 W	0457	4.0	1.2
	1108	0.5	0.2
	1713	3.5	1.1
	2308	0.3	0.1
10 Th	0550	4.1	1.2
	1153	0.3	0.1
	1803	3.6	1.1
	2356	0.1	0.0
11 F	0635	4.2	1.3
	1235	0.1	0.0
	1848	3.8	1.2
12 Sa	0038	-0.1	0.0
	0717	4.3	1.3
	1312	-0.1	0.0
	1929	3.9	1.2
13 Su	0116	-0.2	-0.1
	0756	4.4	1.3
	1345	-0.2	-0.1
	2009	4.1	1.2
14 M	0153	-0.4	-0.1
	0834	4.4	1.3
	1418	-0.4	-0.1
	2046	4.2	1.3
15 Tu	0229	-0.4	-0.1
	0908	4.3	1.3
	1450	-0.4	-0.1
	2120	4.3	1.3
16 W	0306	-0.4	-0.1
	0941	4.2	1.3
	1523	-0.5	-0.2
	2155	4.4	1.3
17 Th	0345	-0.4	-0.1
	1018	4.1	1.2
	1559	-0.4	-0.1
	2232	4.4	1.3
18 F	0429	-0.2	-0.1
	1054	4.0	1.2
	1640	-0.4	-0.1
	2312	4.5	1.4
19 Sa	0515	-0.1	0.0
	1136	3.9	1.2
	1725	-0.2	-0.1
20 Su	0000	4.5	1.4
	0613	0.1	0.0
	1224	3.7	1.1
	1818	-0.1	0.0
21 M	0057	4.4	1.3
	0716	0.3	0.1
	1324	3.6	1.1
	1922	0.0	0.0
22 Tu	0206	4.3	1.3
	0828	0.3	0.1
	1437	3.6	1.1
	2034	0.0	0.0
23 W	0325	4.4	1.3
	0941	0.2	0.1
	1554	3.7	1.1
	2149	-0.1	0.0
24 Th	0439	4.5	1.4
	1047	-0.1	0.0
	1705	3.9	1.2
	2256	-0.4	-0.1
25 F	0542	4.7	1.4
	1142	-0.4	-0.1
	1806	4.2	1.3
	2358	-0.7	-0.2
26 Sa	0640	4.8	1.5
	1235	-0.8	-0.2
	1902	4.5	1.4
27 Su	0055	-1.0	-0.3
	0730	4.9	1.5
	1323	-1.0	-0.3
	1951	4.7	1.4
28 M	0146	-1.1	-0.3
	0819	4.9	1.5
	1409	-1.1	-0.3
	2037	4.9	1.5
29 Tu	0236	-1.1	-0.3
	0905	4.8	1.5
	1454	-1.1	-0.3
	2123	5.0	1.5
30 W	0323	-1.0	-0.3
	0949	4.6	1.4
	1537	-1.0	-0.3
	2208	4.9	1.5
31 Th	0412	-0.7	-0.2
	1031	4.3	1.3
	1618	-0.7	-0.2
	2251	4.8	1.5

Time meridian 75° W. 0000 is midnight. 1200 is noon.
Heights are referred to mean low water which is the chart datum of soundings.

Times and Heights of High and Low Waters

APRIL

Day	Time h m	Height ft	m	Day	Time h m	Height ft	m
1	0459	-0.4	-0.1	16	0416	-0.3	-0.1
F	1114	4.1	1.2	Sa	1039	4.1	1.2
	1703	-0.3	-0.1		1618	-0.4	-0.1
	2336	4.6	1.4		2259	4.8	1.5
2	0551	0.0	0.0	17	0506	-0.1	0.0
Sa	1200	3.9	1.2	Su	1126	3.9	1.2
	1746	0.0	0.0		1708	-0.2	-0.1
					2352	4.7	1.4
3	0023	4.4	1.3	18	0605	0.1	0.0
Su	0642	0.3	0.1	M	1221	3.8	1.2
	1247	3.7	1.1		1807	0.0	0.0
	1837	0.4	0.1				
4	0116	4.2	1.3	19	0053	4.6	1.4
M	0738	0.6	0.2	Tu	0712	0.2	0.1
	1340	3.6	1.1		1327	3.8	1.2
	1934	0.6	0.2		1915	0.2	0.1
5	0214	4.1	1.2	20	0203	4.5	1.4
Tu	0838	0.8	0.2	W	0822	0.2	0.1
	1438	3.5	1.1		1437	3.8	1.2
	2037	0.8	0.2		2031	0.2	0.1
6	0314	4.0	1.2	21	0317	4.5	1.4
W	0933	0.8	0.2	Th	0928	0.1	0.0
	1538	3.6	1.1		1548	4.0	1.2
	2137	0.8	0.2		2144	0.1	0.0
7	0415	4.0	1.2	22	0423	4.5	1.4
Th	1025	0.7	0.2	F	1028	-0.1	0.0
	1635	3.7	1.1		1652	4.3	1.3
	2231	0.6	0.2		2249	-0.2	-0.1
8	0508	4.1	1.2	23	0525	4.6	1.4
F	1111	0.6	0.2	Sa	1122	-0.4	-0.1
	1727	3.9	1.2		1751	4.6	1.4
	2321	0.4	0.1		2348	-0.4	-0.1
9	0556	4.2	1.3	24	0619	4.7	1.4
Sa	1153	0.3	0.1	Su	1211	-0.7	-0.2
	1814	4.1	1.2		1843	4.8	1.5
10	0006	0.2	0.1	25	0042	-0.6	-0.2
Su	0641	4.3	1.3	M	0709	4.6	1.4
	1230	0.1	0.0		1258	-0.8	-0.2
	1855	4.3	1.3		1931	5.0	1.5
11	0048	0.0	0.0	26	0131	-0.8	-0.2
M	0721	4.3	1.3	Tu	0755	4.6	1.4
	1304	-0.2	-0.1		1341	-0.9	-0.3
	1936	4.5	1.4		2017	5.1	1.6
12	0125	-0.2	-0.1	27	0219	-0.8	-0.2
Tu	0800	4.3	1.3	W	0839	4.4	1.3
	1339	-0.4	-0.1		1423	-0.8	-0.2
	2014	4.6	1.4		2059	5.1	1.6
13	0206	-0.4	-0.1	28	0303	-0.7	-0.2
W	0837	4.3	1.3	Th	0923	4.3	1.3
	1414	-0.5	-0.2		1505	-0.7	-0.2
	2053	4.7	1.4		2142	5.0	1.5
14	0246	-0.4	-0.1	29	0348	-0.5	-0.2
Th	0916	4.2	1.3	F	1005	4.1	1.2
	1452	-0.5	-0.2		1544	-0.4	-0.1
	2131	4.8	1.5		2224	4.8	1.5
15	0330	-0.4	-0.1	30	0432	-0.2	-0.1
F	0955	4.2	1.3	Sa	1046	3.9	1.2
	1534	-0.5	-0.2		1626	-0.1	0.0
	2211	4.9	1.5		2307	4.6	1.4

MAY

Day	Time h m	Height ft	m	Day	Time h m	Height ft	m
1	0517	0.1	0.0	16	0500	-0.3	-0.1
Su	1128	3.8	1.2	M	1120	4.0	1.2
	1707	0.2	0.1		1659	-0.3	-0.1
	2349	4.5	1.4		2349	4.9	1.5
2	0605	0.4	0.1	17	0600	-0.2	-0.1
M	1215	3.7	1.1	Tu	1221	3.9	1.2
	1753	0.5	0.2		1802	-0.1	0.0
3	0037	4.3	1.3	18	0050	4.7	1.4
Tu	0657	0.7	0.2	W	0705	-0.1	0.0
	1303	3.6	1.1		1324	4.0	1.2
	1845	0.8	0.2		1912	0.1	0.0
4	0130	4.1	1.2	19	0156	4.6	1.4
W	0749	0.8	0.2	Th	0808	-0.1	0.0
	1357	3.6	1.1		1430	4.1	1.2
	1945	0.9	0.3		2026	0.1	0.0
5	0225	4.0	1.2	20	0300	4.5	1.4
Th	0844	0.8	0.2	F	0910	-0.2	-0.1
	1454	3.7	1.1		1535	4.3	1.3
	2048	1.0	0.3		2135	0.1	0.0
6	0322	4.0	1.2	21	0404	4.4	1.3
F	0933	0.8	0.2	Sa	1007	-0.3	-0.1
	1549	3.8	1.2		1637	4.5	1.4
	2146	0.9	0.3		2239	-0.1	0.0
7	0418	4.0	1.2	22	0502	4.4	1.3
Sa	1018	0.6	0.2	Su	1058	-0.5	-0.2
	1641	4.0	1.2		1733	4.7	1.4
	2239	0.7	0.2		2334	-0.3	-0.1
8	0508	4.1	1.2	23	0555	4.3	1.3
Su	1100	0.3	0.1	M	1147	-0.6	-0.2
	1730	4.2	1.3		1822	4.9	1.5
	2328	0.4	0.1				
9	0555	4.1	1.2	24	0027	-0.4	-0.1
M	1142	0.0	0.0	Tu	0644	4.2	1.3
	1815	4.5	1.4		1232	-0.7	-0.2
					1910	5.0	1.5
10	0014	0.1	0.0	25	0115	-0.5	-0.2
Tu	0640	4.1	1.2	W	0731	4.2	1.3
	1219	-0.3	-0.1		1315	-0.7	-0.2
	1900	4.7	1.4		1955	5.0	1.5
11	0057	-0.2	-0.1	26	0201	-0.5	-0.2
W	0723	4.1	1.2	Th	0815	4.0	1.2
	1301	-0.5	-0.2		1356	-0.6	-0.2
	1943	4.9	1.5		2038	4.9	1.5
12	0141	-0.4	-0.1	27	0244	-0.5	-0.2
Th	0806	4.1	1.2	F	0856	3.9	1.2
	1343	-0.6	-0.2		1436	-0.5	-0.2
	2026	5.0	1.5		2117	4.8	1.5
13	0228	-0.5	-0.2	28	0326	-0.3	-0.1
F	0851	4.1	1.2	Sa	0937	3.8	1.2
	1427	-0.7	-0.2		1514	-0.3	-0.1
	2112	5.1	1.6		2200	4.7	1.4
14	0315	-0.6	-0.2	29	0408	-0.1	0.0
Sa	0937	4.1	1.2	Su	1019	3.7	1.1
	1514	-0.7	-0.2		1553	-0.1	0.0
	2201	5.1	1.6		2238	4.6	1.4
15	0405	-0.5	-0.2	30	0447	0.1	0.0
Su	1028	4.0	1.2	M	1059	3.7	1.1
	1604	-0.5	-0.2		1632	0.2	0.1
	2252	5.0	1.5		2320	4.4	1.3
				31	0531	0.3	0.1
				Tu	1141	3.6	1.1
					1715	0.5	0.2

JUNE

Day	Time h m	Height ft	m	Day	Time h m	Height ft	m
1	0002	4.3	1.3	16	0038	4.8	1.5
W	0613	0.5	0.2	Th	0648	-0.5	-0.2
	1226	3.6	1.1		1311	4.2	1.3
	1802	0.7	0.2		1905	-0.1	0.0
2	0049	4.1	1.2	17	0138	4.6	1.4
Th	0659	0.6	0.2	F	0748	-0.4	-0.1
	1316	3.6	1.1		1414	4.3	1.3
	1853	0.9	0.3		2014	0.0	0.0
3	0134	4.0	1.2	18	0238	4.4	1.3
F	0745	0.6	0.2	Sa	0845	-0.4	-0.1
	1407	3.7	1.1		1516	4.4	1.3
	1953	0.9	0.3		2120	0.0	0.0
4	0226	3.9	1.2	19	0338	4.2	1.3
Sa	0834	0.6	0.2	Su	0940	-0.4	-0.1
	1458	3.9	1.2		1615	4.6	1.4
	2054	0.9	0.3		2221	0.0	0.0
5	0317	3.9	1.2	20	0435	4.1	1.2
Su	0921	0.4	0.1	M	1031	-0.4	-0.1
	1551	4.0	1.2		1710	4.7	1.4
	2153	0.7	0.2		2318	-0.1	0.0
6	0412	3.8	1.2	21	0530	4.0	1.2
M	1007	0.2	0.1	Tu	1121	-0.5	-0.2
	1644	4.3	1.3		1803	4.8	1.5
	2248	0.4	0.1				
7	0503	3.8	1.2	22	0009	-0.2	-0.1
Tu	1055	-0.1	0.0	W	0619	3.9	1.2
	1735	4.5	1.4		1206	-0.5	-0.2
	2339	0.1	0.0		1849	4.8	1.5
8	0555	3.9	1.2	23	0056	-0.3	-0.1
W	1142	-0.4	-0.1	Th	0707	3.8	1.2
	1825	4.7	1.4		1249	-0.5	-0.2
					1934	4.8	1.5
9	0030	-0.2	-0.1	24	0141	-0.3	-0.1
Th	0646	3.9	1.2	F	0752	3.8	1.2
	1230	-0.7	-0.2		1331	-0.5	-0.2
	1914	4.9	1.5		2016	4.8	1.5
10	0119	-0.5	-0.2	25	0222	-0.3	-0.1
F	0739	3.9	1.2	Sa	0834	3.7	1.1
	1316	-0.9	-0.3		1411	-0.4	-0.1
	2005	5.1	1.6		2057	4.7	1.4
11	0210	-0.7	-0.2	26	0304	-0.2	-0.1
Sa	0829	4.0	1.2	Su	0913	3.7	1.1
	1405	-0.9	-0.3		1449	-0.3	-0.1
	2057	5.2	1.6		2136	4.6	1.4
12	0303	-0.8	-0.2	27	0342	-0.1	0.0
Su	0922	4.0	1.2	M	0953	3.7	1.1
	1459	-0.9	-0.3		1527	-0.1	0.0
	2149	5.2	1.6		2213	4.5	1.4
13	0355	-0.8	-0.2	28	0418	0.0	0.0
M	1015	4.0	1.2	Tu	1033	3.6	1.1
	1552	-0.8	-0.2		1603	0.1	0.0
	2245	5.1	1.6		2252	4.4	1.3
14	0451	-0.7	-0.2	29	0456	0.2	0.1
Tu	1112	4.1	1.2	W	1112	3.7	1.1
	1651	-0.6	-0.2		1641	0.3	0.1
	2339	5.0	1.5		2331	4.3	1.3
15	0549	-0.6	-0.2	30	0531	0.3	0.1
W	1210	4.1	1.2	Th	1152	3.7	1.1
	1757	-0.3	-0.1		1723	0.5	0.2

Time meridian 75° W. 0000 is midnight. 1200 is noon.
Heights are referred to mean low water which is the chart datum of soundings.

Times and Heights of High and Low Waters

JULY

Day	Time h m	Height ft	Height m	Day	Time h m	Height ft	Height m
1	0007	4.1	1.2	16	0113	4.6	1.4
F	0610	0.4	0.1	Sa	0719	-0.5	-0.2
	1234	3.8	1.2		1349	4.5	1.4
	1810	0.7	0.2		1954	0.0	0.0
2	0046	4.0	1.2	17	0211	4.3	1.3
Sa	0650	0.4	0.1	Su	0815	-0.4	-0.1
	1318	3.9	1.2		1447	4.6	1.4
	1905	0.8	0.2		2100	0.2	0.1
3	0132	3.9	1.2	18	0308	4.1	1.2
Su	0737	0.4	0.1	M	0910	-0.2	-0.1
	1407	4.0	1.2		1548	4.6	1.4
	2004	0.8	0.2		2200	0.2	0.1
4	0219	3.8	1.2	19	0406	3.9	1.2
M	0827	0.2	0.1	Tu	1004	-0.2	-0.1
	1500	4.1	1.2		1646	4.7	1.4
	2109	0.7	0.2		2257	0.2	0.1
5	0315	3.7	1.1	20	0501	3.8	1.2
Tu	0919	0.1	0.0	W	1056	-0.1	0.0
	1558	4.3	1.3		1738	4.7	1.4
	2210	0.4	0.1		2350	0.2	0.1
6	0414	3.7	1.1	21	0555	3.8	1.2
W	1014	-0.2	-0.1	Th	1142	-0.1	0.0
	1657	4.6	1.4		1827	4.7	1.4
	2308	0.1	0.0				
7	0516	3.7	1.1	22	0035	0.1	0.0
Th	1108	-0.5	-0.2	F	0643	3.8	1.2
	1756	4.8	1.5		1228	-0.2	-0.1
					1913	4.8	1.5
8	0005	-0.2	-0.1	23	0120	0.0	0.0
F	0617	3.8	1.2	Sa	0728	3.8	1.2
	1203	-0.7	-0.2		1310	-0.2	-0.1
	1852	5.0	1.5		1955	4.8	1.5
9	0101	-0.5	-0.2	24	0200	0.0	0.0
Sa	0715	3.9	1.2	Su	0810	3.8	1.2
	1256	-0.9	-0.3		1350	-0.2	-0.1
	1949	5.2	1.6		2034	4.7	1.4
10	0153	-0.7	-0.2	25	0238	0.0	0.0
Su	0811	4.0	1.2	M	0850	3.8	1.2
	1351	-1.1	-0.3		1426	-0.1	0.0
	2043	5.3	1.6		2113	4.7	1.4
11	0247	-0.9	-0.3	26	0314	0.0	0.0
M	0906	4.2	1.3	Tu	0928	3.9	1.2
	1447	-1.1	-0.3		1502	0.0	0.0
	2136	5.3	1.6		2149	4.6	1.4
12	0340	-1.0	-0.3	27	0345	0.0	0.0
Tu	1001	4.3	1.3	W	1006	3.9	1.2
	1542	-1.0	-0.3		1536	0.2	0.1
	2230	5.2	1.6		2224	4.5	1.4
13	0433	-0.9	-0.3	28	0417	0.1	0.0
W	1056	4.4	1.3	Th	1043	4.0	1.2
	1642	-0.8	-0.2		1613	0.3	0.1
	2323	5.1	1.6		2259	4.4	1.3
14	0528	-0.8	-0.2	29	0451	0.2	0.1
Th	1153	4.5	1.4	F	1117	4.0	1.2
	1744	-0.5	-0.2		1653	0.5	0.2
					2331	4.3	1.3
15	0018	4.8	1.5	30	0525	0.3	0.1
F	0623	-0.7	-0.2	Sa	1154	4.1	1.2
	1250	4.5	1.4		1736	0.7	0.2
	1847	-0.2	-0.1				
				31	0007	4.2	1.3
				Su	0604	0.3	0.1
					1235	4.2	1.3
					1826	0.8	0.2

AUGUST

Day	Time h m	Height ft	Height m	Day	Time h m	Height ft	Height m
1	0045	4.1	1.2	16	0236	4.1	1.2
M	0650	0.3	0.1	Tu	0839	0.3	0.1
	1321	4.3	1.3		1518	4.8	1.5
	1925	0.8	0.2		2135	0.7	0.2
2	0134	3.9	1.2	17	0336	4.0	1.2
Tu	0742	0.3	0.1	W	0936	0.4	0.1
	1417	4.4	1.3		1617	4.8	1.5
	2031	0.8	0.2		2232	0.7	0.2
3	0231	3.8	1.2	18	0434	3.9	1.2
W	0839	0.2	0.1	Th	1031	0.4	0.1
	1521	4.6	1.4		1713	4.8	1.5
	2140	0.7	0.2		2324	0.7	0.2
4	0338	3.8	1.2	19	0527	4.0	1.2
Th	0940	0.0	0.0	F	1121	0.4	0.1
	1628	4.7	1.4		1803	4.9	1.5
	2245	0.4	0.1				
5	0449	3.8	1.2	20	0009	0.6	0.2
F	1044	-0.2	-0.1	Sa	0617	4.0	1.2
	1736	5.0	1.5		1208	0.3	0.1
	2345	0.0	0.0		1851	4.9	1.5
6	0555	4.0	1.2	21	0054	0.4	0.1
Sa	1145	-0.5	-0.2	Su	0703	4.1	1.2
	1837	5.2	1.6		1250	0.2	0.1
					1931	5.0	1.5
7	0042	-0.3	-0.1	22	0132	0.3	0.1
Su	0657	4.2	1.3	M	0745	4.2	1.3
	1241	-0.8	-0.2		1329	0.2	0.1
	1933	5.4	1.6		2010	5.0	1.5
8	0136	-0.6	-0.2	23	0208	0.3	0.1
M	0755	4.4	1.3	Tu	0825	4.3	1.3
	1339	-1.0	-0.3		1405	0.2	0.1
	2028	5.5	1.7		2047	4.9	1.5
9	0227	-0.8	-0.2	24	0240	0.2	0.1
Tu	0849	4.6	1.4	W	0900	4.4	1.3
	1435	-1.0	-0.3		1439	0.2	0.1
	2119	5.5	1.7		2122	4.9	1.5
10	0318	-0.9	-0.3	25	0310	0.2	0.1
W	0943	4.8	1.5	Th	0937	4.5	1.4
	1530	-0.9	-0.3		1514	0.3	0.1
	2211	5.4	1.6		2154	4.8	1.5
11	0410	-0.9	-0.3	26	0342	0.3	0.1
Th	1035	4.9	1.5	F	1009	4.5	1.4
	1627	-0.7	-0.2		1547	0.5	0.2
	2301	5.2	1.6		2226	4.7	1.4
12	0459	-0.8	-0.2	27	0411	0.3	0.1
F	1128	5.0	1.5	Sa	1043	4.6	1.4
	1725	-0.4	-0.1		1625	0.6	0.2
	2352	4.9	1.5		2258	4.6	1.4
13	0552	-0.5	-0.2	28	0446	0.4	0.1
Sa	1223	4.9	1.5	Su	1119	4.7	1.4
	1826	0.0	0.0		1709	0.8	0.2
					2333	4.4	1.3
14	0045	4.6	1.4	29	0525	0.5	0.2
Su	0645	-0.2	-0.1	M	1200	4.7	1.4
	1319	4.9	1.5		1800	0.9	0.3
	1930	0.3	0.1				
15	0140	4.4	1.3	30	0012	4.3	1.3
M	0740	0.0	0.0	Tu	0613	0.6	0.2
	1418	4.8	1.5		1247	4.8	1.5
	2034	0.6	0.2		1858	1.1	0.3
				31	0101	4.2	1.3
				W	0709	0.6	0.2
					1348	4.8	1.5
					2007	1.1	0.3

SEPTEMBER

Day	Time h m	Height ft	Height m	Day	Time h m	Height ft	Height m
1	0206	4.1	1.2	16	0402	4.2	1.3
Th	0812	0.6	0.2	F	1002	1.1	0.3
	1457	4.9	1.5		1641	4.9	1.5
	2119	1.0	0.3		2253	1.2	0.4
2	0319	4.1	1.2	17	0457	4.3	1.3
F	0919	0.4	0.1	Sa	1057	1.0	0.3
	1612	5.0	1.5		1733	5.0	1.5
	2225	0.7	0.2		2342	1.0	0.3
3	0433	4.2	1.3	18	0547	4.4	1.3
Sa	1029	0.2	0.1	Su	1143	0.9	0.3
	1721	5.3	1.6		1819	5.1	1.6
	2327	0.3	0.1				
4	0543	4.4	1.3	19	0020	0.9	0.3
Su	1132	-0.1	0.0	M	0632	4.6	1.4
	1823	5.5	1.7		1225	0.7	0.2
					1900	5.2	1.6
5	0025	-0.1	0.0	20	0058	0.7	0.2
M	0643	4.7	1.4	Tu	0715	4.7	1.4
	1232	-0.4	-0.1		1304	0.6	0.2
	1918	5.6	1.7		1939	5.2	1.6
6	0115	-0.4	-0.1	21	0132	0.5	0.2
Tu	0738	5.0	1.5	W	0754	4.9	1.5
	1328	-0.6	-0.2		1340	0.5	0.2
	2010	5.7	1.7		2015	5.1	1.6
7	0205	-0.6	-0.2	22	0203	0.4	0.1
W	0830	5.3	1.6	Th	0831	5.0	1.5
	1421	-0.7	-0.2		1414	0.5	0.2
	2059	5.7	1.7		2050	5.1	1.6
8	0253	-0.7	-0.2	23	0233	0.4	0.1
Th	0921	5.4	1.6	F	0905	5.0	1.5
	1515	-0.6	-0.2		1449	0.5	0.2
	2147	5.5	1.7		2123	5.0	1.5
9	0341	-0.7	-0.2	24	0304	0.4	0.1
F	1011	5.5	1.7	Sa	0937	5.1	1.6
	1609	-0.4	-0.1		1526	0.6	0.2
	2236	5.3	1.6		2157	4.9	1.5
10	0429	-0.4	-0.1	25	0337	0.4	0.1
Sa	1101	5.5	1.7	Su	1013	5.1	1.6
	1704	0.0	0.0		1604	0.7	0.2
	2323	5.0	1.5		2230	4.7	1.4
11	0517	-0.1	0.0	26	0414	0.5	0.2
Su	1152	5.4	1.6	M	1050	5.2	1.6
	1800	0.4	0.1		1650	0.9	0.3
					2307	4.6	1.4
12	0013	4.7	1.4	27	0457	0.6	0.2
M	0608	0.2	0.1	Tu	1135	5.2	1.6
	1246	5.2	1.6		1740	1.1	0.3
	1901	0.7	0.2		2354	4.5	1.4
13	0106	4.5	1.4	28	0546	0.8	0.2
Tu	0705	0.6	0.2	W	1226	5.1	1.6
	1343	5.0	1.5		1842	1.2	0.4
	2002	1.0	0.3				
14	0203	4.3	1.3	29	0049	4.4	1.3
W	0804	0.9	0.3	Th	0645	0.9	0.3
	1443	4.9	1.5		1331	5.1	1.6
	2104	1.2	0.4		1951	1.3	0.4
15	0302	4.2	1.3	30	0156	4.3	1.3
Th	0904	1.0	0.3	F	0754	0.9	0.3
	1544	4.9	1.5		1446	5.1	1.6
	2202	1.2	0.4		2104	1.1	0.3

Time meridian 75° W. 0000 is midnight. 1200 is noon.
Heights are referred to mean low water which is the chart datum of soundings.

Times and Heights of High and Low Waters

OCTOBER

Day	Time h m	Height ft	m
1 Sa	0313	4.4	1.3
	0909	0.8	0.2
	1559	5.3	1.6
	2212	0.9	0.3
2 Su	0427	4.6	1.4
	1020	0.5	0.2
	1708	5.4	1.6
	2310	0.5	0.2
3 M	0532	4.9	1.5
	1124	0.2	0.1
	1806	5.6	1.7
4 Tu	0004	0.1	0.0
	0627	5.3	1.6
	1222	-0.1	0.0
	1859	5.7	1.7
5 W	0054	-0.2	-0.1
	0722	5.6	1.7
	1317	-0.3	-0.1
	1949	5.7	1.7
6 Th	0140	-0.4	-0.1
	0811	5.8	1.8
	1408	-0.4	-0.1
	2036	5.6	1.7
7 F	0226	-0.5	-0.2
	0859	5.9	1.8
	1458	-0.3	-0.1
	2122	5.4	1.6
8 Sa	0311	-0.4	-0.1
	0945	5.8	1.8
	1548	-0.1	0.0
	2208	5.2	1.6
9 Su	0357	-0.1	0.0
	1032	5.7	1.7
	1638	0.2	0.1
	2255	4.9	1.5
10 M	0441	0.2	0.1
	1120	5.5	1.7
	1731	0.6	0.2
	2341	4.7	1.4
11 Tu	0531	0.6	0.2
	1210	5.3	1.6
	1827	1.0	0.3
12 W	0032	4.5	1.4
	0624	1.0	0.3
	1304	5.1	1.6
	1926	1.3	0.4
13 Th	0127	4.4	1.3
	0722	1.3	0.4
	1403	5.0	1.5
	2027	1.5	0.5
14 F	0226	4.3	1.3
	0827	1.4	0.4
	1503	4.9	1.5
	2123	1.5	0.5
15 Sa	0325	4.3	1.3
	0927	1.4	0.4
	1600	4.9	1.5
	2215	1.4	0.4
16 Su	0421	4.5	1.4
	1023	1.4	0.4
	1653	5.0	1.5
	2300	1.2	0.4
17 M	0513	4.7	1.4
	1111	1.2	0.4
	1740	5.0	1.5
	2340	1.0	0.3
18 Tu	0558	4.8	1.5
	1155	1.0	0.3
	1822	5.1	1.6
19 W	0017	0.8	0.2
	0640	5.0	1.5
	1235	0.8	0.2
	1904	5.1	1.6
20 Th	0050	0.6	0.2
	0720	5.2	1.6
	1312	0.6	0.2
	1942	5.1	1.6
21 F	0124	0.4	0.1
	0758	5.3	1.6
	1349	0.5	0.2
	2018	5.0	1.5
22 Sa	0156	0.3	0.1
	0834	5.4	1.6
	1426	0.5	0.2
	2054	4.9	1.5
23 Su	0231	0.3	0.1
	0911	5.4	1.6
	1505	0.5	0.2
	2131	4.8	1.5
24 M	0310	0.3	0.1
	0950	5.4	1.6
	1550	0.6	0.2
	2210	4.7	1.4
25 Tu	0349	0.4	0.1
	1033	5.4	1.6
	1638	0.7	0.2
	2253	4.6	1.4
26 W	0438	0.5	0.2
	1122	5.4	1.6
	1731	0.9	0.3
	2345	4.5	1.4
27 Th	0531	0.7	0.2
	1220	5.3	1.6
	1834	1.0	0.3
28 F	0047	4.4	1.3
	0634	0.9	0.3
	1325	5.2	1.6
	1943	1.0	0.3
29 Sa	0157	4.4	1.3
	0748	0.9	0.3
	1437	5.2	1.6
	2052	0.9	0.3
30 Su	0309	4.6	1.4
	0904	0.8	0.2
	1546	5.2	1.6
	2154	0.7	0.2
31 M	0417	4.8	1.5
	1013	0.6	0.2
	1649	5.3	1.6
	2250	0.3	0.1

NOVEMBER

Day	Time h m	Height ft	m
1 Tu	0518	5.1	1.6
	1116	0.3	0.1
	1748	5.3	1.6
	2342	0.0	0.0
2 W	0614	5.4	1.6
	1211	0.0	0.0
	1838	5.3	1.6
3 Th	0030	-0.2	-0.1
	0703	5.7	1.7
	1304	-0.2	-0.1
	1928	5.3	1.6
4 F	0115	-0.4	-0.1
	0752	5.8	1.8
	1352	-0.2	-0.1
	2014	5.2	1.6
5 Sa	0200	-0.4	-0.1
	0837	5.8	1.8
	1441	-0.2	-0.1
	2059	5.0	1.5
6 Su	0243	-0.3	-0.1
	0923	5.7	1.7
	1528	0.0	0.0
	2143	4.8	1.5
7 M	0327	-0.1	0.0
	1007	5.6	1.7
	1614	0.2	0.1
	2227	4.6	1.4
8 Tu	0409	0.2	0.1
	1053	5.4	1.6
	1702	0.6	0.2
	2311	4.4	1.3
9 W	0454	0.6	0.2
	1139	5.1	1.6
	1752	0.9	0.3
10 Th	0000	4.3	1.3
	0543	0.9	0.3
	1229	4.9	1.5
	1845	1.1	0.3
11 F	0050	4.2	1.3
	0639	1.2	0.4
	1319	4.8	1.5
	1942	1.3	0.4
12 Sa	0144	4.2	1.3
	0738	1.4	0.4
	1415	4.7	1.4
	2035	1.3	0.4
13 Su	0240	4.2	1.3
	0840	1.5	0.5
	1510	4.6	1.4
	2124	1.3	0.4
14 M	0336	4.3	1.3
	0939	1.4	0.4
	1605	4.6	1.4
	2211	1.1	0.3
15 Tu	0428	4.5	1.4
	1031	1.2	0.4
	1655	4.6	1.4
	2250	0.9	0.3
16 W	0518	4.7	1.4
	1116	1.0	0.3
	1740	4.6	1.4
	2329	0.6	0.2
17 Th	0602	4.9	1.5
	1159	0.7	0.2
	1822	4.6	1.4
18 F	0006	0.4	0.1
	0645	5.1	1.6
	1240	0.5	0.2
	1904	4.6	1.4
19 Sa	0045	0.1	0.0
	0727	5.2	1.6
	1323	0.3	0.1
	1945	4.6	1.4
20 Su	0123	0.0	0.0
	0808	5.3	1.6
	1405	0.1	0.0
	2027	4.5	1.4
21 M	0204	-0.1	0.0
	0850	5.4	1.6
	1450	0.1	0.0
	2110	4.5	1.4
22 Tu	0248	-0.2	-0.1
	0936	5.4	1.6
	1537	0.1	0.0
	2155	4.4	1.3
23 W	0334	-0.1	0.0
	1023	5.4	1.6
	1630	0.2	0.1
	2246	4.3	1.3
24 Th	0425	0.1	0.0
	1115	5.3	1.6
	1723	0.3	0.1
	2341	4.3	1.3
25 F	0524	0.3	0.1
	1215	5.1	1.6
	1824	0.4	0.1
26 Sa	0044	4.3	1.3
	0630	0.5	0.2
	1319	5.0	1.5
	1930	0.4	0.1
27 Su	0150	4.4	1.3
	0743	0.6	0.2
	1423	4.9	1.5
	2033	0.3	0.1
28 M	0258	4.5	1.4
	0857	0.5	0.2
	1528	4.8	1.5
	2133	0.2	0.1
29 Tu	0402	4.8	1.5
	1004	0.4	0.1
	1628	4.8	1.5
	2228	0.0	0.0
30 W	0502	5.0	1.5
	1105	0.2	0.1
	1726	4.7	1.4
	2318	-0.2	-0.1

DECEMBER

Day	Time h m	Height ft	m
1 Th	0555	5.2	1.6
	1158	0.0	0.0
	1818	4.7	1.4
2 F	0007	-0.4	-0.1
	0646	5.4	1.6
	1251	-0.2	-0.1
	1907	4.6	1.4
3 Sa	0052	-0.5	-0.2
	0733	5.4	1.6
	1337	-0.3	-0.1
	1953	4.5	1.4
4 Su	0137	-0.5	-0.2
	0818	5.4	1.6
	1423	-0.3	-0.1
	2037	4.4	1.3
5 M	0218	-0.4	-0.1
	0900	5.3	1.6
	1508	-0.2	-0.1
	2120	4.2	1.3
6 Tu	0300	-0.2	-0.1
	0945	5.1	1.6
	1552	0.0	0.0
	2203	4.1	1.2
7 W	0341	0.0	0.0
	1027	4.9	1.5
	1635	0.2	0.1
	2245	4.0	1.2
8 Th	0422	0.3	0.1
	1109	4.8	1.5
	1717	0.5	0.2
	2327	3.9	1.2
9 F	0507	0.5	0.2
	1152	4.6	1.4
	1800	0.7	0.2
10 Sa	0013	3.9	1.2
	0552	0.8	0.2
	1237	4.4	1.3
	1849	0.8	0.2
11 Su	0101	3.9	1.2
	0645	1.0	0.3
	1324	4.3	1.3
	1935	0.9	0.3
12 M	0151	3.9	1.2
	0743	1.1	0.3
	1413	4.2	1.3
	2022	0.8	0.2
13 Tu	0245	4.0	1.2
	0841	1.1	0.3
	1506	4.1	1.2
	2108	0.7	0.2
14 W	0335	4.2	1.3
	0938	1.0	0.3
	1557	4.0	1.2
	2154	0.5	0.2
15 Th	0428	4.3	1.3
	1031	0.8	0.2
	1649	4.0	1.2
	2239	0.3	0.1
16 F	0520	4.5	1.4
	1121	0.5	0.2
	1738	4.0	1.2
	2324	0.0	0.0
17 Sa	0609	4.7	1.4
	1211	0.2	0.1
	1827	4.0	1.2
18 Su	0009	-0.3	-0.1
	0657	4.9	1.5
	1258	-0.1	0.0
	1917	4.0	1.2
19 M	0055	-0.5	-0.2
	0744	5.1	1.6
	1345	-0.3	-0.1
	2006	4.1	1.2
20 Tu	0143	-0.7	-0.2
	0834	5.2	1.6
	1434	-0.5	-0.2
	2054	4.1	1.2
21 W	0233	-0.8	-0.2
	0925	5.2	1.6
	1526	-0.5	-0.2
	2144	4.1	1.2
22 Th	0324	-0.7	-0.2
	1016	5.2	1.6
	1618	-0.5	-0.2
	2237	4.2	1.3
23 F	0418	-0.6	-0.2
	1109	5.1	1.6
	1712	-0.4	-0.1
	2333	4.2	1.3
24 Sa	0517	-0.4	-0.1
	1204	4.9	1.5
	1809	-0.4	-0.1
25 Su	0034	4.2	1.3
	0623	-0.1	0.0
	1301	4.7	1.4
	1909	-0.3	-0.1
26 M	0135	4.3	1.3
	0733	0.0	0.0
	1403	4.5	1.4
	2009	-0.3	-0.1
27 Tu	0239	4.4	1.3
	0843	0.1	0.0
	1505	4.3	1.3
	2106	-0.3	-0.1
28 W	0342	4.5	1.4
	0948	0.1	0.0
	1604	4.1	1.2
	2202	-0.4	-0.1
29 Th	0441	4.7	1.4
	1049	0.0	0.0
	1702	4.0	1.2
	2256	-0.4	-0.1
30 F	0537	4.8	1.5
	1145	-0.2	-0.1
	1757	4.0	1.2
	2345	-0.5	-0.2
31 Sa	0628	4.8	1.5
	1234	-0.3	-0.1
	1848	3.9	1.2

Time meridian 75° W. 0000 is midnight. 1200 is noon.
Heights are referred to mean low water which is the chart datum of soundings.

PUNTA GORDA, VENEZUELA, 1983

Times and Heights of High and Low Waters

JANUARY

Day	Time h m	Height ft	Height m
1	0045	-1.6	-0.5
Sa	0642	6.6	2.0
	1300	0.0	0.0
	1839	7.3	2.2
2	0132	-1.4	-0.4
Su	0730	6.5	2.0
	1350	0.0	0.0
	1928	7.1	2.2
3	0221	-1.2	-0.4
M	0818	6.3	1.9
	1444	0.2	0.1
	2020	6.6	2.0
4	0313	-0.7	-0.2
Tu	0908	6.1	1.9
	1539	0.3	0.1
	2113	6.1	1.9
5	0406	-0.3	-0.1
W	1003	5.9	1.8
	1639	0.5	0.2
	2213	5.6	1.7
6	0504	0.2	0.1
Th	1059	5.7	1.7
	1741	0.5	0.2
	2320	5.2	1.6
7	0604	0.5	0.2
F	1202	5.6	1.7
	1844	0.4	0.1
8	0034	4.9	1.5
Sa	0706	0.7	0.2
	1304	5.6	1.7
	1945	0.2	0.1
9	0145	4.9	1.5
Su	0805	0.8	0.2
	1403	5.6	1.7
	2042	0.0	0.0
10	0250	5.0	1.5
M	0858	0.8	0.2
	1455	5.8	1.8
	2131	-0.3	-0.1
11	0338	5.1	1.6
Tu	0946	0.7	0.2
	1541	5.9	1.8
	2218	-0.5	-0.2
12	0423	5.3	1.6
W	1031	0.6	0.2
	1620	6.1	1.9
	2300	-0.7	-0.2
13	0500	5.4	1.6
Th	1111	0.5	0.2
	1655	6.2	1.9
	2339	-0.8	-0.2
14	0532	5.5	1.7
F	1149	0.4	0.1
	1730	6.3	1.9
15	0016	-0.8	-0.2
Sa	0603	5.6	1.7
	1226	0.4	0.1
	1802	6.3	1.9

Day	Time h m	Height ft	Height m
16	0052	-0.7	-0.2
Su	0634	5.6	1.7
	1301	0.5	0.2
	1834	6.3	1.9
17	0127	-0.5	-0.2
M	0705	5.7	1.7
	1333	0.5	0.2
	1909	6.2	1.9
18	0202	-0.3	-0.1
Tu	0738	5.7	1.7
	1409	0.6	0.2
	1945	6.1	1.9
19	0236	-0.1	0.0
W	0815	5.7	1.7
	1447	0.7	0.2
	2025	5.8	1.8
20	0313	0.2	0.1
Th	0855	5.7	1.7
	1534	0.7	0.2
	2113	5.5	1.7
21	0401	0.6	0.2
F	0942	5.6	1.7
	1633	0.8	0.2
	2209	5.1	1.6
22	0457	0.9	0.3
Sa	1037	5.5	1.7
	1747	0.7	0.2
	2316	4.8	1.5
23	0609	1.1	0.3
Su	1138	5.5	1.7
	1859	0.4	0.1
24	0036	4.7	1.4
M	0720	1.1	0.3
	1248	5.5	1.7
	2008	0.0	0.0
25	0157	4.9	1.5
Tu	0826	0.9	0.3
	1401	5.8	1.8
	2109	-0.6	-0.2
26	0307	5.2	1.6
W	0927	0.5	0.2
	1506	6.2	1.9
	2204	-1.1	-0.3
27	0407	5.6	1.7
Th	1020	0.1	0.0
	1602	6.6	2.0
	2255	-1.6	-0.5
28	0458	6.0	1.8
F	1111	-0.3	-0.1
	1656	6.9	2.1
	2343	-1.9	-0.6
29	0545	6.3	1.9
Sa	1159	-0.6	-0.2
	1745	7.1	2.2
30	0029	-1.9	-0.6
Su	0629	6.5	2.0
	1246	-0.8	-0.2
	1831	7.1	2.2
31	0114	-1.8	-0.5
M	0714	6.5	2.0
	1333	-0.8	-0.2
	1917	6.9	2.1

FEBRUARY

Day	Time h m	Height ft	Height m
1	0159	-1.5	-0.5
Tu	0754	6.4	2.0
	1422	-0.7	-0.2
	2004	6.5	2.0
2	0247	-1.0	-0.3
W	0838	6.2	1.9
	1510	-0.5	-0.2
	2050	6.0	1.8
3	0334	-0.4	-0.1
Th	0924	5.9	1.8
	1606	-0.2	-0.1
	2142	5.4	1.6
4	0425	0.1	0.0
F	1011	5.5	1.7
	1702	0.1	0.0
	2238	4.9	1.5
5	0524	0.6	0.2
Sa	1106	5.2	1.6
	1804	0.2	0.1
	2345	4.5	1.4
6	0625	1.0	0.3
Su	1209	5.0	1.5
	1907	0.2	0.1
7	0102	4.3	1.3
M	0729	1.1	0.3
	1316	5.0	1.5
	2009	0.1	0.0
8	0216	4.4	1.3
Tu	0829	1.0	0.3
	1421	5.1	1.6
	2104	-0.1	0.0
9	0314	4.6	1.4
W	0922	0.8	0.2
	1515	5.3	1.6
	2154	-0.4	-0.1
10	0402	4.8	1.5
Th	1010	0.5	0.2
	1602	5.6	1.7
	2237	-0.6	-0.2
11	0439	5.1	1.6
F	1052	0.3	0.1
	1639	5.8	1.8
	2319	-0.8	-0.2
12	0513	5.3	1.6
Sa	1130	0.1	0.0
	1713	6.0	1.8
	2354	-0.9	-0.3
13	0542	5.5	1.7
Su	1206	0.0	0.0
	1747	6.1	1.9
14	0029	-0.9	-0.3
M	0610	5.7	1.7
	1239	-0.1	0.0
	1818	6.2	1.9
15	0102	-0.8	-0.2
Tu	0640	5.8	1.8
	1313	-0.1	0.0
	1850	6.2	1.9

Day	Time h m	Height ft	Height m
16	0133	-0.6	-0.2
W	0710	5.9	1.8
	1345	-0.1	0.0
	1926	6.1	1.9
17	0204	-0.3	-0.1
Th	0745	6.0	1.8
	1418	-0.1	0.0
	2004	5.9	1.8
18	0239	0.0	0.0
F	0821	6.0	1.8
	1500	0.0	0.0
	2049	5.5	1.7
19	0318	0.4	0.1
Sa	0905	5.8	1.8
	1555	0.2	0.1
	2140	5.1	1.6
20	0414	0.8	0.2
Su	0957	5.6	1.7
	1707	0.3	0.1
	2246	4.7	1.4
21	0531	1.2	0.4
M	1100	5.4	1.6
	1828	0.3	0.1
22	0009	4.5	1.4
Tu	0656	1.2	0.4
	1219	5.3	1.6
	1944	-0.1	0.0
23	0137	4.6	1.4
W	0808	0.9	0.3
	1341	5.5	1.7
	2050	-0.6	-0.2
24	0253	5.1	1.6
Th	0911	0.4	0.1
	1453	5.9	1.8
	2147	-1.1	-0.3
25	0354	5.6	1.7
F	1007	-0.2	-0.1
	1555	6.3	1.9
	2239	-1.5	-0.5
26	0444	6.1	1.9
Sa	1057	-0.7	-0.2
	1648	6.7	2.0
	2326	-1.8	-0.5
27	0528	6.5	2.0
Su	1143	-1.1	-0.3
	1734	6.9	2.1
28	0009	-1.9	-0.6
M	0609	6.7	2.0
	1229	-1.3	-0.4
	1818	7.0	2.1

MARCH

Day	Time h m	Height ft	Height m
1	0053	-1.7	-0.5
Tu	0648	6.7	2.0
	1314	-1.3	-0.4
	1901	6.8	2.1
2	0135	-1.3	-0.4
W	0725	6.6	2.0
	1356	-1.2	-0.4
	1943	6.4	2.0
3	0218	-0.8	-0.2
Th	0802	6.3	1.9
	1441	-0.9	-0.3
	2025	5.9	1.8
4	0300	-0.2	-0.1
F	0841	6.0	1.8
	1529	-0.5	-0.2
	2108	5.4	1.6
5	0348	0.4	0.1
Sa	0922	5.6	1.7
	1622	-0.1	0.0
	2158	4.9	1.5
6	0440	0.9	0.3
Su	1011	5.2	1.6
	1722	0.3	0.1
	2254	4.4	1.3
7	0545	1.3	0.4
M	1112	4.8	1.5
	1828	0.5	0.2
8	0009	4.2	1.3
Tu	0654	1.4	0.4
	1225	4.6	1.4
	1932	0.4	0.1
9	0131	4.2	1.3
W	0800	1.2	0.4
	1342	4.7	1.4
	2032	0.2	0.1
10	0242	4.4	1.3
Th	0856	0.9	0.3
	1446	5.0	1.5
	2125	-0.1	0.0
11	0330	4.8	1.5
F	0944	0.6	0.2
	1535	5.4	1.6
	2210	-0.4	-0.1
12	0410	5.1	1.6
Sa	1028	0.2	0.1
	1617	5.7	1.7
	2250	-0.6	-0.2
13	0444	5.5	1.7
Su	1106	-0.1	0.0
	1653	6.0	1.8
	2327	-0.7	-0.2
14	0513	5.7	1.7
M	1142	-0.4	-0.1
	1726	6.1	1.9
15	0002	-0.7	-0.2
Tu	0541	6.0	1.8
	1216	-0.5	-0.2
	1759	6.3	1.9

Day	Time h m	Height ft	Height m
16	0034	-0.6	-0.2
W	0610	6.2	1.9
	1249	-0.6	-0.2
	1832	6.3	1.9
17	0106	-0.4	-0.1
Th	0641	6.4	2.0
	1321	-0.6	-0.2
	1907	6.2	1.9
18	0138	-0.1	0.0
F	0714	6.4	2.0
	1356	-0.6	-0.2
	1946	6.0	1.8
19	0212	0.2	0.1
Sa	0753	6.3	1.9
	1438	-0.4	-0.1
	2029	5.7	1.7
20	0255	0.6	0.2
Su	0838	6.1	1.9
	1532	-0.1	0.0
	2124	5.3	1.6
21	0352	1.0	0.3
M	0929	5.7	1.7
	1643	0.1	0.0
	2230	4.9	1.5
22	0515	1.3	0.4
Tu	1036	5.4	1.6
	1807	0.2	0.1
	2354	4.7	1.4
23	0639	1.3	0.4
W	1200	5.2	1.6
	1923	0.0	0.0
24	0126	4.8	1.5
Th	0754	0.9	0.3
	1328	5.3	1.6
	2029	-0.4	-0.1
25	0240	5.3	1.6
F	0856	0.3	0.1
	1445	5.8	1.8
	2127	-0.8	-0.2
26	0338	5.9	1.8
Sa	0951	-0.3	-0.1
	1544	6.2	1.9
	2218	-1.2	-0.4
27	0423	6.4	2.0
Su	1041	-0.9	-0.3
	1636	6.6	2.0
	2305	-1.4	-0.4
28	0505	6.7	2.0
M	1125	-1.3	-0.4
	1721	6.8	2.1
	2347	-1.3	-0.4
29	0544	6.9	2.1
Tu	1207	-1.5	-0.5
	1802	6.8	2.1
30	0029	-1.1	-0.3
W	0620	6.9	2.1
	1249	-1.5	-0.5
	1842	6.6	2.0
31	0107	-0.7	-0.2
Th	0653	6.7	2.0
	1330	-1.3	-0.4
	1919	6.3	1.9

Time meridian 60° W. 0000 is midnight. 1200 is noon.
Heights are referred to the chart datum of soundings.

PUNTA GORDA, VENEZUELA, 1983

Times and Heights of High and Low Waters

APRIL

Day	Time (h m)	Height (ft)	Height (m)	Day	Time (h m)	Height (ft)	Height (m)
1	0147	-0.3	-0.1	16	0117	0.2	0.1
F	0727	6.5	2.0	Sa	0650	6.8	2.1
	1412	-1.0	-0.3		1341	-0.8	-0.2
	1957	5.9	1.8		1933	6.1	1.9
2	0228	0.3	0.1	17	0156	0.6	0.2
Sa	0802	6.1	1.9	Su	0732	6.6	2.0
	1455	-0.5	-0.2		1427	-0.6	-0.2
	2036	5.5	1.7		2018	5.8	1.8
3	0310	0.8	0.2	18	0246	0.9	0.3
Su	0839	5.7	1.7	M	0818	6.3	1.9
	1544	-0.1	0.0		1524	-0.3	-0.1
	2121	5.1	1.6		2116	5.5	1.7
4	0402	1.3	0.4	19	0348	1.2	0.4
M	0924	5.3	1.6	Tu	0915	5.9	1.8
	1642	0.4	0.1		1633	0.1	0.0
	2214	4.7	1.4		2225	5.2	1.6
5	0507	1.6	0.5	20	0506	1.4	0.4
Tu	1022	4.9	1.5	W	1025	5.5	1.7
	1745	0.7	0.2		1748	0.2	0.1
	2320	4.4	1.3		2345	5.1	1.6
6	0616	1.7	0.5	21	0627	1.3	0.4
W	1135	4.7	1.4	Th	1150	5.3	1.6
	1852	0.7	0.2		1902	0.1	0.0
7	0039	4.4	1.3	22	0108	5.3	1.6
Th	0723	1.5	0.5	F	0737	0.8	0.2
	1256	4.7	1.4		1317	5.4	1.6
	1955	0.6	0.2		2006	-0.1	0.0
8	0149	4.6	1.4	23	0216	5.7	1.7
F	0821	1.1	0.3	Sa	0837	0.2	0.1
	1408	4.9	1.5		1430	5.7	1.7
	2048	0.3	0.1		2104	-0.4	-0.1
9	0245	5.0	1.5	24	0311	6.2	1.9
Sa	0914	0.7	0.2	Su	0933	-0.4	-0.1
	1501	5.3	1.6		1530	6.1	1.9
	2135	0.1	0.0		2154	-0.6	-0.2
10	0327	5.4	1.6	25	0357	6.6	2.0
Su	0959	0.2	0.1	M	1020	-0.9	-0.3
	1546	5.6	1.7		1620	6.4	2.0
	2218	-0.1	0.0		2239	-0.7	-0.2
11	0404	5.8	1.8	26	0439	6.9	2.1
M	1037	-0.2	-0.1	Tu	1105	-1.3	-0.4
	1627	5.9	1.8		1705	6.6	2.0
	2256	-0.2	-0.1		2322	-0.6	-0.2
12	0436	6.1	1.9	27	0516	7.0	2.1
Tu	1116	-0.5	-0.2	W	1147	-1.4	-0.4
	1703	6.2	1.9		1744	6.6	2.0
	2332	-0.3	-0.1				
13	0509	6.4	2.0	28	0003	-0.4	-0.1
W	1150	-0.8	-0.2	Th	0550	6.9	2.1
	1737	6.3	1.9		1227	-1.4	-0.4
					1822	6.4	2.0
14	0005	-0.2	-0.1	29	0042	0.0	0.0
Th	0541	6.6	2.0	F	0623	6.8	2.1
	1227	-0.9	-0.3		1305	-1.2	-0.4
	1814	6.4	2.0		1857	6.2	1.9
15	0041	0.0	0.0	30	0119	0.3	0.1
F	0614	6.8	2.1	Sa	0655	6.6	2.0
	1302	-0.9	-0.3		1346	-0.8	-0.2
	1851	6.3	1.9		1932	5.9	1.8

MAY

Day	Time (h m)	Height (ft)	Height (m)	Day	Time (h m)	Height (ft)	Height (m)
1	0159	0.7	0.2	16	0148	0.7	0.2
Su	0730	6.3	1.9	M	0719	6.8	2.1
	1427	-0.4	-0.1		1420	-0.8	-0.2
	2010	5.6	1.7		2015	6.0	1.8
2	0241	1.1	0.3	17	0241	1.0	0.3
M	0806	5.9	1.8	Tu	0809	6.5	2.0
	1513	0.0	0.0		1516	-0.4	-0.1
	2050	5.3	1.6		2112	5.8	1.8
3	0329	1.5	0.5	18	0345	1.2	0.4
Tu	0849	5.6	1.7	W	0908	6.0	1.8
	1603	0.4	0.1		1621	-0.1	0.0
	2140	5.0	1.5		2217	5.6	1.7
4	0429	1.7	0.5	19	0456	1.2	0.4
W	0940	5.2	1.6	Th	1017	5.6	1.7
	1704	0.7	0.2		1729	0.1	0.0
	2238	4.8	1.5		2330	5.6	1.7
5	0536	1.8	0.5	20	0609	1.0	0.3
Th	1046	4.9	1.5	F	1138	5.4	1.6
	1807	0.9	0.3		1835	0.2	0.1
	2346	4.8	1.5				
6	0643	1.6	0.5	21	0042	5.8	1.8
F	1202	4.8	1.5	Sa	0715	0.6	0.2
	1908	0.8	0.2		1259	5.4	1.6
					1937	0.1	0.0
7	0052	4.9	1.5	22	0147	6.1	1.9
Sa	0743	1.3	0.4	Su	0814	0.1	0.0
	1315	4.9	1.5		1411	5.6	1.7
	2005	0.7	0.2		2034	0.1	0.0
8	0149	5.3	1.6	23	0240	6.4	2.0
Su	0837	0.8	0.2	M	0909	-0.4	-0.1
	1417	5.2	1.6		1511	5.9	1.8
	2053	0.5	0.2		2126	0.0	0.0
9	0237	5.6	1.7	24	0327	6.6	2.0
M	0922	0.3	0.1	Tu	0958	-0.8	-0.2
	1511	5.5	1.7		1602	6.1	1.9
	2139	0.4	0.1		2212	0.0	0.0
10	0319	6.0	1.8	25	0410	6.8	2.1
Tu	1007	-0.2	-0.1	W	1042	-1.1	-0.3
	1556	5.8	1.8		1645	6.2	1.9
	2220	0.3	0.1		2257	0.1	0.0
11	0357	6.4	2.0	26	0447	6.8	2.1
W	1047	-0.6	-0.2	Th	1124	-1.2	-0.4
	1636	6.1	1.9		1726	6.2	1.9
	2300	0.3	0.1		2338	0.3	0.1
12	0434	6.7	2.0	27	0521	6.8	2.1
Th	1126	-0.9	-0.3	F	1203	-1.1	-0.3
	1717	6.3	1.9		1802	6.1	1.9
	2339	0.3	0.1				
13	0511	6.9	2.1	28	0017	0.5	0.2
F	1204	-1.1	-0.3	Sa	0555	6.7	2.0
	1758	6.4	2.0		1244	-0.9	-0.3
					1835	6.0	1.8
14	0018	0.4	0.1	29	0056	0.8	0.2
Sa	0548	7.0	2.1	Su	0628	6.5	2.0
	1246	-1.1	-0.3		1322	-0.7	-0.2
	1839	6.3	1.9		1909	5.8	1.8
15	0101	0.5	0.2	30	0135	1.0	0.3
Su	0633	7.0	2.1	M	0703	6.3	1.9
	1330	-1.0	-0.3		1402	-0.4	-0.1
	1925	6.2	1.9		1946	5.7	1.7
				31	0215	1.3	0.4
				Tu	0739	6.1	1.9
					1444	0.0	0.0
					2025	5.5	1.7

JUNE

Day	Time (h m)	Height (ft)	Height (m)	Day	Time (h m)	Height (ft)	Height (m)
1	0300	1.5	0.5	16	0334	0.8	0.2
W	0820	5.8	1.8	Th	0902	6.2	1.9
	1529	0.3	0.1		1601	-0.3	-0.1
	2108	5.4	1.6		2201	6.1	1.9
2	0353	1.6	0.5	17	0438	0.8	0.2
Th	0908	5.5	1.7	F	1006	5.8	1.8
	1622	0.6	0.2		1703	0.0	0.0
	2158	5.3	1.6		2304	6.0	1.8
3	0454	1.7	0.5	18	0544	0.7	0.2
F	1006	5.2	1.6	Sa	1118	5.5	1.7
	1719	0.9	0.3		1806	0.3	0.1
	2254	5.2	1.6				
4	0557	1.6	0.5	19	0008	6.0	1.8
Sa	1110	5.0	1.5	Su	0649	0.4	0.1
	1819	1.0	0.3		1233	5.3	1.6
	2353	5.3	1.6		1907	0.5	0.2
5	0659	1.3	0.4	20	0110	6.1	1.9
Su	1219	5.0	1.5	M	0749	0.1	0.0
	1915	1.0	0.3		1347	5.3	1.6
					2005	0.6	0.2
6	0051	5.5	1.7	21	0205	6.3	1.9
M	0755	0.8	0.2	Tu	0843	-0.3	-0.1
	1329	5.1	1.6		1450	5.5	1.7
	2009	1.0	0.3		2059	0.7	0.2
7	0144	5.8	1.8	22	0256	6.4	2.0
Tu	0847	0.3	0.1	W	0933	-0.6	-0.2
	1429	5.3	1.6		1543	5.6	1.7
	2059	0.9	0.3		2149	0.7	0.2
8	0234	6.2	1.9	23	0341	6.5	2.0
W	0933	-0.2	-0.1	Th	1020	-0.8	-0.2
	1523	5.6	1.7		1628	5.8	1.8
	2146	0.8	0.2		2233	0.7	0.2
9	0319	6.5	2.0	24	0423	6.6	2.0
Th	1020	-0.6	-0.2	F	1103	-0.9	-0.3
	1612	5.9	1.8		1706	5.8	1.8
	2231	0.7	0.2		2315	0.8	0.2
10	0404	6.8	2.1	25	0458	6.6	2.0
F	1103	-1.0	-0.3	Sa	1143	-0.8	-0.2
	1700	6.2	1.9		1743	5.9	1.8
	2316	0.6	0.2		2356	0.8	0.2
11	0450	7.1	2.2	26	0534	6.5	2.0
Sa	1148	-1.2	-0.4	Su	1223	-0.7	-0.2
	1744	6.3	1.9		1816	5.9	1.8
12	0002	0.5	0.2	27	0036	0.9	0.3
Su	0535	7.2	2.2	M	0608	6.5	2.0
	1233	-1.3	-0.4		1301	-0.6	-0.2
	1830	6.4	2.0		1848	5.8	1.8
13	0048	0.6	0.2	28	0114	1.1	0.3
M	0621	7.1	2.2	Tu	0640	6.4	2.0
	1321	-1.2	-0.4		1338	-0.4	-0.1
	1919	6.4	2.0		1923	5.8	1.8
14	0140	0.6	0.2	29	0152	1.2	0.4
Tu	0711	7.0	2.1	W	0717	6.2	1.9
	1410	-1.0	-0.3		1418	-0.1	0.0
	2010	6.3	1.9		1959	5.8	1.8
15	0236	0.7	0.2	30	0231	1.3	0.4
W	0803	6.6	2.0	Th	0754	6.0	1.8
	1503	-0.7	-0.2		1457	0.2	0.1
	2103	6.2	1.9		2036	5.8	1.8

Time meridian 60° W. 0000 is midnight. 1200 is noon.
Heights are referred to the chart datum of soundings.

PUNTA GORDA, VENEZUELA, 1983

Times and Heights of High and Low Waters

JULY

Day	Time (h m)	Height (ft)	Height (m)
1	0316	1.4	0.4
F	0839	5.8	1.8
	1539	0.5	0.2
	2116	5.7	1.7
2	0409	1.4	0.4
Sa	0929	5.5	1.7
	1627	0.8	0.2
	2206	5.7	1.7
3	0507	1.4	0.4
Su	1025	5.2	1.6
	1723	1.1	0.3
	2258	5.7	1.7
4	0609	1.2	0.4
M	1130	5.1	1.6
	1822	1.3	0.4
	2355	5.8	1.8
5	0712	0.9	0.3
Tu	1241	5.0	1.5
	1923	1.4	0.4
6	0054	6.0	1.8
W	0811	0.4	0.1
	1352	5.2	1.6
	2021	1.3	0.4
7	0152	6.2	1.9
Th	0904	-0.1	0.0
	1456	5.5	1.7
	2117	1.1	0.3
8	0250	6.6	2.0
F	0956	-0.5	-0.2
	1554	5.8	1.8
	2210	0.9	0.3
9	0343	6.9	2.1
Sa	1045	-0.9	-0.3
	1645	6.2	1.9
	2300	0.7	0.2
10	0434	7.1	2.2
Su	1133	-1.2	-0.4
	1734	6.4	2.0
	2349	0.5	0.2
11	0524	7.3	2.2
M	1220	-1.4	-0.4
	1821	6.6	2.0
12	0037	0.3	0.1
Tu	0613	7.3	2.2
	1308	-1.3	-0.4
	1908	6.8	2.1
13	0127	0.3	0.1
W	0703	7.2	2.2
	1356	-1.1	-0.3
	1955	6.8	2.1
14	0220	0.3	0.1
Th	0754	6.9	2.1
	1446	-0.8	-0.2
	2044	6.7	2.0
15	0315	0.3	0.1
F	0847	6.4	2.0
	1537	-0.3	-0.1
	2134	6.5	2.0

Day	Time (h m)	Height (ft)	Height (m)
16	0414	0.4	0.1
Sa	0945	6.0	1.8
	1633	0.2	0.1
	2229	6.3	1.9
17	0515	0.4	0.1
Su	1051	5.5	1.7
	1731	0.7	0.2
	2328	6.2	1.9
18	0617	0.4	0.1
M	1203	5.2	1.6
	1833	1.0	0.3
19	0028	6.1	1.9
Tu	0718	0.3	0.1
	1315	5.1	1.6
	1935	1.2	0.4
20	0128	6.1	1.9
W	0816	0.1	0.0
	1426	5.2	1.6
	2031	1.2	0.4
21	0226	6.1	1.9
Th	0909	-0.2	-0.1
	1525	5.3	1.6
	2125	1.2	0.4
22	0317	6.3	1.9
F	0959	-0.3	-0.1
	1612	5.5	1.7
	2212	1.1	0.3
23	0400	6.4	2.0
Sa	1041	-0.5	-0.2
	1652	5.7	1.7
	2255	1.0	0.3
24	0439	6.5	2.0
Su	1124	-0.5	-0.2
	1725	5.8	1.8
	2336	1.0	0.3
25	0516	6.5	2.0
M	1202	-0.5	-0.2
	1757	6.0	1.8
26	0015	0.9	0.3
Tu	0549	6.6	2.0
	1239	-0.4	-0.1
	1826	6.1	1.9
27	0052	0.9	0.3
W	0623	6.6	2.0
	1314	-0.3	-0.1
	1858	6.2	1.9
28	0127	1.0	0.3
Th	0656	6.5	2.0
	1348	0.0	0.0
	1929	6.2	1.9
29	0202	1.0	0.3
F	0732	6.4	2.0
	1420	0.3	0.1
	2002	6.3	1.9
30	0241	1.1	0.3
Sa	0810	6.1	1.9
	1457	0.6	0.2
	2039	6.3	1.9
31	0324	1.1	0.3
Su	0855	5.9	1.8
	1537	1.0	0.3
	2121	6.2	1.9

AUGUST

Day	Time (h m)	Height (ft)	Height (m)
1	0417	1.2	0.4
M	0945	5.6	1.7
	1625	1.4	0.4
	2209	6.2	1.9
2	0520	1.2	0.4
Tu	1046	5.3	1.6
	1728	1.7	0.5
	2304	6.1	1.9
3	0630	1.0	0.3
W	1200	5.1	1.6
	1842	1.8	0.5
4	0011	6.1	1.9
Th	0739	0.7	0.2
	1321	5.2	1.6
	1952	1.7	0.5
5	0120	6.3	1.9
F	0840	0.2	0.1
	1434	5.5	1.7
	2056	1.4	0.4
6	0229	6.6	2.0
Sa	0936	-0.3	-0.1
	1538	5.9	1.8
	2152	1.1	0.3
7	0328	7.0	2.1
Su	1028	-0.8	-0.2
	1631	6.4	2.0
	2244	0.6	0.2
8	0424	7.3	2.2
M	1116	-1.1	-0.3
	1720	6.8	2.1
	2334	0.3	0.1
9	0516	7.5	2.3
Tu	1203	-1.3	-0.4
	1805	7.1	2.2
10	0022	0.0	0.0
W	0604	7.6	2.3
	1250	-1.3	-0.4
	1848	7.3	2.2
11	0110	-0.1	0.0
Th	0653	7.5	2.3
	1333	-1.0	-0.3
	1933	7.3	2.2
12	0159	-0.1	0.0
F	0740	7.2	2.2
	1420	-0.5	-0.2
	2015	7.2	2.2
13	0249	0.0	0.0
Sa	0828	6.7	2.0
	1508	0.0	0.0
	2100	6.9	2.1
14	0342	0.2	0.1
Su	0921	6.2	1.9
	1601	0.6	0.2
	2148	6.6	2.0
15	0440	0.5	0.2
M	1019	5.6	1.7
	1656	1.2	0.4
	2242	6.3	1.9

Day	Time (h m)	Height (ft)	Height (m)
16	0541	0.6	0.2
Tu	1125	5.2	1.6
	1800	1.6	0.5
	2343	6.0	1.8
17	0646	0.7	0.2
W	1242	5.0	1.5
	1904	1.8	0.5
18	0051	5.9	1.8
Th	0747	0.6	0.2
	1357	5.1	1.6
	2005	1.8	0.5
19	0157	6.0	1.8
F	0843	0.4	0.1
	1504	5.3	1.6
	2101	1.6	0.5
20	0253	6.1	1.9
Sa	0933	0.2	0.1
	1551	5.6	1.7
	2151	1.4	0.4
21	0341	6.4	2.0
Su	1020	0.0	0.0
	1628	5.9	1.8
	2234	1.2	0.4
22	0423	6.6	2.0
M	1100	-0.2	-0.1
	1700	6.1	1.9
	2315	1.0	0.3
23	0457	6.7	2.0
Tu	1137	-0.2	-0.1
	1732	6.3	1.9
	2352	0.8	0.2
24	0530	6.8	2.1
W	1213	-0.2	-0.1
	1800	6.5	2.0
25	0026	0.8	0.2
Th	0602	6.9	2.1
	1245	0.0	0.0
	1827	6.7	2.0
26	0100	0.7	0.2
F	0634	6.8	2.1
	1317	0.2	0.1
	1855	6.8	2.1
27	0133	0.8	0.2
Sa	0708	6.7	2.0
	1346	0.5	0.2
	1927	6.9	2.1
28	0207	0.8	0.2
Su	0743	6.5	2.0
	1418	0.9	0.3
	2002	6.9	2.1
29	0244	0.9	0.3
M	0825	6.2	1.9
	1452	1.3	0.4
	2043	6.8	2.1
30	0332	1.1	0.3
Tu	0913	5.9	1.8
	1534	1.7	0.5
	2129	6.6	2.0
31	0438	1.2	0.4
W	1014	5.5	1.7
	1648	2.1	0.6
	2227	6.4	2.0

SEPTEMBER

Day	Time (h m)	Height (ft)	Height (m)
1	0557	1.2	0.4
Th	1131	5.3	1.6
	1814	2.3	0.7
	2339	6.2	1.9
2	0713	0.9	0.3
F	1259	5.3	1.6
	1934	2.1	0.6
3	0100	6.3	1.9
Sa	0819	0.5	0.2
	1421	5.7	1.7
	2040	1.7	0.5
4	0213	6.6	2.0
Su	0919	-0.1	0.0
	1523	6.3	1.9
	2138	1.1	0.3
5	0319	7.1	2.2
M	1010	-0.5	-0.2
	1615	6.9	2.1
	2231	0.5	0.2
6	0415	7.5	2.3
Tu	1059	-0.9	-0.3
	1701	7.3	2.2
	2319	0.0	0.0
7	0505	7.8	2.4
W	1143	-1.0	-0.3
	1743	7.7	2.3
8	0005	-0.3	-0.1
Th	0552	7.8	2.4
	1226	-0.9	-0.3
	1825	7.8	2.4
9	0050	-0.4	-0.1
F	0637	7.7	2.3
	1309	-0.5	-0.2
	1903	7.8	2.4
10	0135	-0.4	-0.1
Sa	0719	7.4	2.3
	1354	0.0	0.0
	1943	7.6	2.3
11	0222	-0.1	0.0
Su	0804	6.9	2.1
	1436	0.6	0.2
	2023	7.3	2.2
12	0313	0.2	0.1
M	0852	6.3	1.9
	1526	1.2	0.4
	2105	6.8	2.1
13	0406	0.6	0.2
Tu	0940	5.8	1.8
	1619	1.8	0.5
	2153	6.4	2.0
14	0504	1.0	0.3
W	1043	5.3	1.6
	1722	2.2	0.7
	2254	6.0	1.8
15	0609	1.2	0.4
Th	1200	5.1	1.6
	1832	2.4	0.7

Day	Time (h m)	Height (ft)	Height (m)
16	0008	5.8	1.8
F	0714	1.1	0.3
	1323	5.1	1.6
	1937	2.3	0.7
17	0121	5.9	1.8
Sa	0814	1.0	0.3
	1432	5.4	1.6
	2037	2.0	0.6
18	0226	6.1	1.9
Su	0906	0.7	0.2
	1519	5.8	1.8
	2127	1.6	0.5
19	0317	6.4	2.0
M	0951	0.4	0.1
	1559	6.2	1.9
	2210	1.3	0.4
20	0359	6.7	2.0
Tu	1031	0.2	0.1
	1631	6.5	2.0
	2249	1.0	0.3
21	0436	6.9	2.1
W	1109	0.2	0.1
	1700	6.8	2.1
	2326	0.7	0.2
22	0508	7.0	2.1
Th	1142	0.2	0.1
	1726	7.0	2.1
23	0000	0.6	0.2
F	0540	7.1	2.2
	1216	0.4	0.1
	1756	7.2	2.2
24	0033	0.5	0.2
Sa	0612	7.1	2.2
	1247	0.6	0.2
	1822	7.4	2.3
25	0106	0.5	0.2
Su	0646	7.0	2.1
	1316	0.9	0.3
	1855	7.4	2.3
26	0138	0.6	0.2
M	0722	6.8	2.1
	1346	1.2	0.4
	1930	7.4	2.3
27	0215	0.7	0.2
Tu	0804	6.5	2.0
	1420	1.6	0.5
	2010	7.2	2.2
28	0305	1.0	0.3
W	0852	6.1	1.9
	1510	2.1	0.6
	2100	6.9	2.1
29	0411	1.2	0.4
Th	0953	5.7	1.7
	1628	2.4	0.7
	2201	6.6	2.0
30	0533	1.3	0.4
F	1114	5.5	1.7
	1801	2.5	0.8
	2319	6.3	1.9

Time meridian 60° W. 0000 is midnight. 1200 is noon.
Heights are referred to the chart datum of soundings.

PUNTA GORDA, VENEZUELA, 1983

Times and Heights of High and Low Waters

OCTOBER

Day	Time (h m)	Height (ft)	Height (m)	Day	Time (h m)	Height (ft)	Height (m)
1	0651	1.1	0.3	16	0039	5.8	1.8
Sa	1246	5.6	1.7	Su	0738	1.3	0.4
	1920	2.2	0.7		1344	5.5	1.7
					2005	2.1	0.6
2	0046	6.3	1.9	17	0149	6.0	1.8
Su	0800	0.7	0.2	M	0830	1.1	0.3
	1406	6.1	1.9		1437	5.9	1.8
	2026	1.6	0.5		2056	1.7	0.5
3	0205	6.7	2.0	18	0245	6.3	1.9
M	0858	0.2	0.1	Tu	0917	0.8	0.2
	1506	6.7	2.0		1517	6.3	1.9
	2122	0.9	0.3		2141	1.2	0.4
4	0311	7.1	2.2	19	0330	6.6	2.0
Tu	0949	-0.2	-0.1	W	0959	0.6	0.2
	1556	7.3	2.2		1551	6.7	2.0
	2213	0.3	0.1		2221	0.8	0.2
5	0404	7.5	2.3	20	0408	6.8	2.1
W	1037	-0.4	-0.1	Th	1036	0.6	0.2
	1639	7.8	2.4		1623	7.0	2.1
	2301	-0.2	-0.1		2258	0.5	0.2
6	0452	7.8	2.4	21	0444	7.0	2.1
Th	1120	-0.5	-0.2	F	1113	0.6	0.2
	1719	8.0	2.4		1652	7.3	2.2
	2345	-0.5	-0.2		2334	0.3	0.1
7	0537	7.8	2.4	22	0518	7.1	2.2
F	1202	-0.3	-0.1	Sa	1145	0.7	0.2
	1757	8.1	2.5		1721	7.5	2.3
8	0028	-0.6	-0.2	23	0009	0.2	0.1
Sa	0619	7.6	2.3	Su	0551	7.1	2.2
	1244	0.1	0.0		1218	0.9	0.3
	1833	8.0	2.4		1754	7.6	2.3
9	0111	-0.5	-0.2	24	0042	0.2	0.1
Su	0658	7.3	2.2	M	0626	7.0	2.1
	1324	0.5	0.2		1250	1.1	0.3
	1909	7.8	2.4		1828	7.7	2.3
10	0154	-0.2	-0.1	25	0119	0.3	0.1
M	0740	6.9	2.1	Tu	0706	6.8	2.1
	1406	1.1	0.3		1322	1.4	0.4
	1946	7.4	2.3		1906	7.6	2.3
11	0241	0.3	0.1	26	0202	0.4	0.1
Tu	0823	6.4	2.0	W	0750	6.5	2.0
	1452	1.7	0.5		1407	1.8	0.5
	2027	7.0	2.1		1951	7.3	2.2
12	0329	0.7	0.2	27	0252	0.7	0.2
W	0908	5.9	1.8	Th	0841	6.2	1.9
	1542	2.2	0.7		1503	2.1	0.6
	2110	6.5	2.0		2041	7.0	2.1
13	0429	1.2	0.4	28	0358	1.0	0.3
Th	1005	5.5	1.7	F	0945	5.9	1.8
	1646	2.5	0.8		1622	2.4	0.7
	2206	6.1	1.9		2145	6.5	2.0
14	0532	1.4	0.4	29	0515	1.1	0.3
F	1114	5.2	1.6	Sa	1104	5.7	1.7
	1757	2.7	0.8		1746	2.3	0.7
	2319	5.8	1.8		2304	6.2	1.9
15	0636	1.5	0.5	30	0628	1.0	0.3
Sa	1233	5.3	1.6	Su	1228	5.9	1.8
	1904	2.5	0.8		1902	1.9	0.6
				31	0033	6.2	1.9
				M	0736	0.7	0.2
					1344	6.4	2.0
					2006	1.3	0.4

NOVEMBER

Day	Time (h m)	Height (ft)	Height (m)	Day	Time (h m)	Height (ft)	Height (m)
1	0152	6.5	2.0	16	0200	5.8	1.8
Tu	0834	0.4	0.1	W	0837	1.1	0.3
	1442	6.9	2.1		1426	6.2	1.9
	2104	0.6	0.2		2106	1.1	0.3
2	0256	6.9	2.1	17	0253	6.1	1.9
W	0927	0.1	0.0	Th	0922	0.9	0.3
	1531	7.4	2.3		1506	6.5	2.0
	2154	0.0	0.0		2149	0.6	0.2
3	0351	7.2	2.2	18	0338	6.3	1.9
Th	1013	0.0	0.0	F	1004	0.8	0.2
	1613	7.7	2.3		1544	6.9	2.1
	2241	-0.4	-0.1		2231	0.2	0.1
4	0437	7.4	2.3	19	0418	6.5	2.0
F	1058	0.0	0.0	Sa	1042	0.8	0.2
	1655	7.9	2.4		1619	7.2	2.2
	2324	-0.7	-0.2		2308	-0.1	0.0
5	0521	7.4	2.3	20	0457	6.7	2.0
Sa	1140	0.2	0.1	Su	1119	0.8	0.2
	1731	7.9	2.4		1655	7.4	2.3
					2348	-0.2	-0.1
6	0007	-0.7	-0.2	21	0534	6.8	2.1
Su	0559	7.2	2.2	M	1157	0.9	0.3
	1220	0.5	0.2		1731	7.6	2.3
	1806	7.8	2.4				
7	0049	-0.6	-0.2	22	0026	-0.3	-0.1
M	0639	7.0	2.1	Tu	0615	6.7	2.0
	1259	0.9	0.3		1235	1.0	0.3
	1840	7.6	2.3		1810	7.6	2.3
8	0130	-0.3	-0.1	23	0106	-0.3	-0.1
Tu	0716	6.6	2.0	W	0656	6.6	2.0
	1340	1.3	0.4		1317	1.2	0.4
	1917	7.3	2.2		1852	7.5	2.3
9	0212	0.2	0.1	24	0153	-0.1	0.0
W	0754	6.3	1.9	Th	0743	6.4	2.0
	1423	1.7	0.5		1404	1.4	0.4
	1954	6.9	2.1		1940	7.2	2.2
10	0259	0.6	0.2	25	0246	0.1	0.0
Th	0836	5.9	1.8	F	0835	6.2	1.9
	1510	2.1	0.6		1503	1.6	0.5
	2036	6.5	2.0		2033	6.8	2.1
11	0350	1.0	0.3	26	0345	0.4	0.1
F	0926	5.6	1.7	Sa	0937	6.0	1.8
	1609	2.4	0.7		1614	1.8	0.5
	2124	6.1	1.9		2137	6.4	2.0
12	0451	1.3	0.4	27	0453	0.6	0.2
Sa	1025	5.4	1.6	Su	1046	5.9	1.8
	1714	2.5	0.8		1728	1.7	0.5
	2230	5.7	1.7		2251	6.0	1.8
13	0551	1.4	0.4	28	0601	0.7	0.2
Su	1132	5.3	1.6	M	1202	6.0	1.8
	1823	2.4	0.7		1839	1.3	0.4
	2342	5.6	1.7				
14	0651	1.4	0.4	29	0015	5.9	1.8
M	1241	5.5	1.7	Tu	0707	0.6	0.2
	1925	2.0	0.6		1312	6.3	1.9
					1944	0.8	0.2
15	0057	5.6	1.7	30	0134	6.0	1.8
Tu	0749	1.3	0.4	W	0806	0.5	0.2
	1339	5.8	1.8		1413	6.7	2.0
	2019	1.6	0.5		2042	0.2	0.1

DECEMBER

Day	Time (h m)	Height (ft)	Height (m)	Day	Time (h m)	Height (ft)	Height (m)
1	0240	6.2	1.9	16	0208	5.4	1.6
Th	0901	0.4	0.1	F	0842	1.1	0.3
	1506	7.0	2.1		1419	6.1	1.9
	2133	-0.3	-0.1		2119	0.4	0.1
2	0335	6.5	2.0	17	0304	5.6	1.7
F	0951	0.3	0.1	Sa	0931	0.9	0.3
	1549	7.2	2.2		1506	6.4	2.0
	2222	-0.7	-0.2		2202	-0.1	0.0
3	0423	6.6	2.0	18	0352	5.9	1.8
Sa	1036	0.3	0.1	Su	1015	0.8	0.2
	1631	7.4	2.3		1551	6.7	2.0
	2305	-0.9	-0.3		2247	-0.5	-0.2
4	0505	6.6	2.0	19	0436	6.1	1.9
Su	1119	0.4	0.1	M	1057	0.7	0.2
	1708	7.4	2.3		1634	7.0	2.1
	2348	-0.9	-0.3		2329	-0.8	-0.2
5	0544	6.5	2.0	20	0522	6.3	1.9
M	1200	0.6	0.2	Tu	1141	0.6	0.2
	1743	7.3	2.2		1716	7.2	2.2
6	0029	-0.7	-0.2	21	0013	-0.9	-0.3
Tu	0621	6.4	2.0	W	0604	6.4	2.0
	1239	0.8	0.2		1224	0.5	0.2
	1818	7.1	2.2		1759	7.3	2.2
7	0109	-0.5	-0.2	22	0057	-1.0	-0.3
W	0657	6.2	1.9	Th	0648	6.4	2.0
	1319	1.1	0.3		1309	0.5	0.2
	1853	6.9	2.1		1845	7.2	2.2
8	0148	-0.2	-0.1	23	0143	-0.9	-0.3
Th	0733	6.0	1.8	F	0737	6.3	1.9
	1359	1.3	0.4		1401	0.6	0.2
	1929	6.6	2.0		1933	7.0	2.1
9	0231	0.1	0.0	24	0233	-0.6	-0.2
F	0810	5.8	1.8	Sa	0826	6.2	1.9
	1441	1.6	0.5		1455	0.7	0.2
	2007	6.3	1.9		2028	6.6	2.0
10	0316	0.5	0.2	25	0329	-0.3	-0.1
Sa	0852	5.6	1.7	Su	0921	6.1	1.9
	1529	1.8	0.5		1558	0.8	0.2
	2052	6.0	1.8		2126	6.2	1.9
11	0406	0.8	0.2	26	0427	0.0	0.0
Su	0940	5.4	1.6	M	1022	5.9	1.8
	1627	1.9	0.6		1704	0.8	0.2
	2145	5.6	1.7		2235	5.7	1.7
12	0502	1.0	0.3	27	0532	0.3	0.1
M	1033	5.3	1.6	Tu	1128	5.9	1.8
	1731	1.9	0.6		1811	0.6	0.2
	2246	5.3	1.6		2349	5.4	1.6
13	0600	1.2	0.4	28	0635	0.5	0.2
Tu	1133	5.3	1.6	W	1235	5.9	1.8
	1836	1.7	0.5		1918	0.3	0.1
	2356	5.2	1.6				
14	0658	1.2	0.4	29	0109	5.3	1.6
W	1232	5.5	1.7	Th	0737	0.6	0.2
	1934	1.3	0.4		1339	6.1	1.9
					2016	-0.1	0.0
15	0104	5.2	1.6	30	0221	5.4	1.6
Th	0752	1.2	0.4	F	0837	0.6	0.2
	1328	5.7	1.7		1437	6.2	1.9
	2027	0.8	0.2		2112	-0.5	-0.2
				31	0319	5.6	1.7
				Sa	0928	0.5	0.2
					1527	6.4	2.0
					2202	-0.8	-0.2

Time meridian 60° W. 0000 is midnight. 1200 is noon.
Heights are referred to the chart datum of soundings.

SURINAME RIVIER ENTRANCE, SURINAM, 1983

Times and Heights of High and Low Waters

JANUARY

Day	Time h m	Height ft	m	Day	Time h m	Height ft	m
1	0548	7.8	2.4	16	0545	7.2	2.2
Sa	1151	0.8	0.2	Su	1146	1.3	0.4
	1802	8.3	2.5		1755	7.6	2.3
2	0023	0.3	0.1	17	0012	1.0	0.3
Su	0636	7.6	2.3	M	0620	7.2	2.2
	1239	1.0	0.3		1223	1.3	0.4
	1852	8.0	2.4		1834	7.6	2.3
3	0111	0.6	0.2	18	0049	1.1	0.3
M	0726	7.4	2.3	Tu	0700	7.2	2.2
	1332	1.3	0.4		1303	1.4	0.4
	1942	7.6	2.3		1913	7.4	2.3
4	0201	1.0	0.3	19	0129	1.2	0.4
Tu	0817	7.1	2.2	W	0739	7.1	2.2
	1425	1.6	0.5		1345	1.4	0.4
	2038	7.2	2.2		1958	7.3	2.2
5	0257	1.4	0.4	20	0214	1.4	0.4
W	0910	6.8	2.1	Th	0824	7.0	2.1
	1523	1.8	0.5		1433	1.6	0.5
	2134	6.8	2.1		2046	7.0	2.1
6	0352	1.8	0.5	21	0302	1.6	0.5
Th	1011	6.6	2.0	F	0915	6.9	2.1
	1625	2.0	0.6		1528	1.7	0.5
	2239	6.5	2.0		2144	6.8	2.1
7	0453	2.1	0.6	22	0357	1.8	0.5
F	1111	6.5	2.0	Sa	1013	6.8	2.1
	1729	2.1	0.6		1632	1.8	0.5
	2344	6.3	1.9		2248	6.6	2.0
8	0554	2.2	0.7	23	0501	2.0	0.6
Sa	1211	6.5	2.0	Su	1117	6.8	2.1
	1830	2.0	0.6		1741	1.7	0.5
9	0045	6.3	1.9	24	0000	6.6	2.0
Su	0653	2.2	0.7	M	0609	2.0	0.6
	1306	6.6	2.0		1227	6.9	2.1
	1928	1.9	0.6		1853	1.5	0.5
10	0141	6.4	2.0	25	0112	6.7	2.0
M	0746	2.1	0.6	Tu	0717	1.9	0.6
	1359	6.8	2.1		1333	7.2	2.2
	2020	1.7	0.5		1959	1.2	0.4
11	0231	6.6	2.0	26	0215	7.0	2.1
Tu	0831	2.0	0.6	W	0820	1.6	0.5
	1444	7.0	2.1		1434	7.6	2.3
	2103	1.5	0.5		2058	0.8	0.2
12	0314	6.7	2.0	27	0313	7.3	2.2
W	0916	1.8	0.5	Th	0919	1.2	0.4
	1524	7.2	2.2		1529	7.9	2.4
	2145	1.3	0.4		2151	0.4	0.1
13	0354	6.9	2.1	28	0406	7.7	2.3
Th	0956	1.6	0.5	F	1009	0.9	0.3
	1606	7.4	2.3		1621	8.2	2.5
	2222	1.1	0.3		2241	0.2	0.1
14	0432	7.0	2.1	29	0454	7.9	2.4
F	1033	1.5	0.5	Sa	1058	0.7	0.2
	1642	7.5	2.3		1709	8.4	2.6
	2259	1.0	0.3		2327	0.1	0.0
15	0508	7.1	2.2	30	0538	8.0	2.4
Sa	1110	1.4	0.4	Su	1143	0.5	0.2
	1720	7.6	2.3		1754	8.4	2.6
	2336	1.0	0.3				
				31	0011	0.2	0.1
				M	0622	8.0	2.4
					1228	0.6	0.2
					1839	8.2	2.5

FEBRUARY

Day	Time h m	Height ft	m	Day	Time h m	Height ft	m
1	0055	0.4	0.1	16	0028	0.7	0.2
Tu	0703	7.8	2.4	W	0634	7.7	2.3
	1311	0.7	0.2		1242	0.7	0.2
	1923	7.9	2.4		1854	7.9	2.4
2	0137	0.8	0.2	17	0103	0.8	0.2
W	0745	7.6	2.3	Th	0711	7.7	2.3
	1356	1.0	0.3		1321	0.8	0.2
	2008	7.5	2.3		1932	7.7	2.3
3	0219	1.2	0.4	18	0140	1.0	0.3
Th	0830	7.2	2.2	F	0750	7.5	2.3
	1441	1.4	0.4		1403	1.0	0.3
	2054	7.0	2.1		2017	7.4	2.3
4	0304	1.7	0.5	19	0225	1.4	0.4
F	0918	6.9	2.1	Sa	0835	7.3	2.2
	1531	1.8	0.5		1451	1.2	0.4
	2146	6.5	2.0		2107	7.0	2.1
5	0355	2.1	0.6	20	0315	1.8	0.5
Sa	1008	6.5	2.0	Su	0928	7.0	2.1
	1630	2.1	0.6		1549	1.6	0.5
	2246	6.2	1.9		2210	6.6	2.0
6	0453	2.5	0.8	21	0416	2.1	0.6
Su	1110	6.3	1.9	M	1034	6.7	2.0
	1736	2.3	0.7		1704	1.8	0.5
	2353	5.9	1.8		2326	6.3	1.9
7	0600	2.7	0.8	22	0536	2.4	0.7
M	1219	6.2	1.9	Tu	1155	6.6	2.0
	1845	2.3	0.7		1827	1.8	0.5
8	0106	5.9	1.8	23	0050	6.4	2.0
Tu	0709	2.6	0.8	W	0658	2.3	0.7
	1325	6.3	1.9		1315	6.8	2.1
	1951	2.2	0.7		1943	1.5	0.5
9	0207	6.1	1.9	24	0205	6.7	2.0
W	0810	2.4	0.7	Th	0813	1.9	0.6
	1423	6.5	2.0		1426	7.3	2.2
	2047	1.9	0.6		2050	1.1	0.3
10	0300	6.4	2.0	25	0305	7.2	2.2
Th	0903	2.1	0.6	F	0911	1.3	0.4
	1513	6.9	2.1		1524	7.7	2.3
	2132	1.6	0.5		2143	0.6	0.2
11	0343	6.7	2.0	26	0356	7.7	2.3
F	0945	1.8	0.5	Sa	1002	0.8	0.2
	1554	7.2	2.2		1612	8.2	2.5
	2210	1.3	0.4		2230	0.3	0.1
12	0420	7.0	2.1	27	0440	8.1	2.5
Sa	1022	1.5	0.5	Su	1047	0.4	0.1
	1633	7.5	2.3		1658	8.4	2.6
	2246	1.0	0.3		2311	0.1	0.0
13	0455	7.3	2.2	28	0520	8.3	2.5
Su	1059	1.2	0.4	M	1128	0.2	0.1
	1708	7.7	2.3		1739	8.5	2.6
	2321	0.8	0.2		2349	0.1	0.0
14	0528	7.5	2.3				
M	1132	1.0	0.3				
	1741	7.9	2.4				
	2354	0.7	0.2				
15	0602	7.7	2.3				
Tu	1207	0.8	0.2				
	1817	7.9	2.4				

MARCH

Day	Time h m	Height ft	m	Day	Time h m	Height ft	m
1	0559	8.3	2.5	16	0535	8.1	2.5
Tu	1207	0.2	0.1	W	1143	0.3	0.1
	1817	8.4	2.6		1755	8.2	2.5
2	0027	0.3	0.1	17	0001	0.5	0.2
W	0634	8.2	2.5	Th	0607	8.2	2.5
	1244	0.3	0.1		1218	0.3	0.1
	1857	8.1	2.5		1828	8.1	2.5
3	0103	0.7	0.2	18	0034	0.6	0.2
Th	0711	7.9	2.4	F	0642	8.1	2.5
	1324	0.6	0.2		1255	0.3	0.1
	1934	7.7	2.3		1907	7.9	2.4
4	0140	1.1	0.3	19	0113	0.9	0.3
F	0748	7.6	2.3	Sa	0721	7.9	2.4
	1401	1.0	0.3		1337	0.6	0.2
	2012	7.1	2.2		1950	7.5	2.3
5	0217	1.6	0.5	20	0155	1.3	0.4
Sa	0827	7.1	2.2	Su	0804	7.5	2.3
	1443	1.5	0.5		1425	1.0	0.3
	2057	6.6	2.0		2040	7.0	2.1
6	0302	2.2	0.7	21	0243	1.8	0.5
Su	0912	6.6	2.0	M	0853	7.1	2.2
	1534	2.1	0.6		1523	1.5	0.5
	2151	6.1	1.9		2144	6.4	2.0
7	0355	2.6	0.8	22	0349	2.3	0.7
M	1011	6.1	1.9	Tu	1005	6.6	2.0
	1640	2.5	0.8		1640	1.9	0.6
	2302	5.7	1.7		2307	6.1	1.9
8	0508	3.0	0.9	23	0516	2.6	0.8
Tu	1128	5.8	1.8	W	1135	6.4	2.0
	1803	2.7	0.8		1813	2.0	0.6
9	0029	5.6	1.7	24	0040	6.2	1.9
W	0637	3.0	0.9	Th	0650	2.4	0.7
	1253	5.9	1.8		1306	6.6	2.0
	1925	2.5	0.8		1935	1.7	0.5
10	0146	5.9	1.8	25	0157	6.7	2.0
Th	0754	2.7	0.8	F	0805	1.9	0.6
	1405	6.2	1.9		1416	7.1	2.2
	2026	2.1	0.6		2036	1.2	0.4
11	0242	6.3	1.9	26	0252	7.3	2.2
F	0847	2.2	0.7	Sa	0901	1.3	0.4
	1455	6.7	2.0		1511	7.7	2.3
	2113	1.7	0.5		2127	0.7	0.2
12	0324	6.8	2.1	27	0338	7.8	2.4
Sa	0929	1.7	0.5	Su	0948	0.7	0.2
	1537	7.2	2.2		1558	8.1	2.5
	2151	1.3	0.4		2209	0.4	0.1
13	0401	7.2	2.2	28	0418	8.2	2.5
Su	1006	1.3	0.4	M	1028	0.3	0.1
	1614	7.6	2.3		1638	8.3	2.5
	2225	0.9	0.3		2247	0.2	0.1
14	0433	7.6	2.3	29	0455	8.4	2.6
M	1039	0.9	0.3	Tu	1105	0.0	0.0
	1646	7.9	2.4		1715	8.4	2.6
	2257	0.7	0.2		2323	0.3	0.1
15	0505	7.9	2.4	30	0530	8.5	2.6
Tu	1111	0.5	0.2	W	1141	0.0	0.0
	1721	8.1	2.5		1751	8.3	2.5
	2329	0.5	0.2		2356	0.4	0.1
				31	0602	8.3	2.5
				Th	1215	0.2	0.1
					1826	8.0	2.4

Time meridian 52° 30' W. 0000 is midnight. 1200 is noon.
Heights are referred to the chart datum of soundings.
Seasonal variations in sea level have not been included in these predictions.

Times and Heights of High and Low Waters

APRIL

Day	Time h m	Height ft	Height m	Day	Time h m	Height ft	Height m
1	0028	0.7	0.2	16	0010	0.6	0.2
F	0636	8.1	2.5	Sa	0616	8.3	2.5
	1249	0.5	0.2		1234	0.2	0.1
	1900	7.6	2.3		1847	7.8	2.4
2	0103	1.1	0.3	17	0049	1.0	0.3
Sa	0709	7.7	2.3	Su	0657	8.0	2.4
	1326	0.9	0.3		1317	0.5	0.2
	1937	7.1	2.2		1932	7.4	2.3
3	0137	1.6	0.5	18	0133	1.4	0.4
Su	0745	7.2	2.2	M	0745	7.6	2.3
	1404	1.4	0.4		1409	1.0	0.3
	2017	6.6	2.0		2024	6.8	2.1
4	0217	2.2	0.7	19	0225	2.0	0.6
M	0829	6.7	2.0	Tu	0841	7.0	2.1
	1451	2.0	0.6		1510	1.6	0.5
	2107	6.0	1.8		2133	6.3	1.9
5	0310	2.7	0.8	20	0338	2.5	0.8
Tu	0923	6.1	1.9	W	0955	6.5	2.0
	1555	2.5	0.8		1631	2.0	0.6
	2219	5.6	1.7		2259	6.1	1.9
6	0427	3.1	0.9	21	0510	2.6	0.8
W	1044	5.8	1.8	Th	1126	6.3	1.9
	1721	2.7	0.8		1801	2.0	0.6
	2352	5.6	1.7				
7	0603	3.1	0.9	22	0029	6.3	1.9
Th	1219	5.8	1.8	F	0640	2.3	0.7
	1850	2.6	0.8		1253	6.6	2.0
					1917	1.7	0.5
8	0114	5.9	1.8	23	0138	6.8	2.1
F	0725	2.7	0.8	Sa	0747	1.8	0.5
	1335	6.1	1.9		1359	7.1	2.2
	1954	2.2	0.7		2015	1.3	0.4
9	0210	6.4	2.0	24	0228	7.3	2.2
Sa	0820	2.2	0.7	Su	0839	1.2	0.4
	1431	6.7	2.0		1450	7.5	2.3
	2042	1.7	0.5		2101	0.9	0.3
10	0252	6.9	2.1	25	0313	7.8	2.4
Su	0900	1.6	0.5	M	0924	0.7	0.2
	1509	7.2	2.2		1535	7.9	2.4
	2121	1.2	0.4		2140	0.7	0.2
11	0329	7.4	2.3	26	0350	8.1	2.5
M	0937	1.1	0.3	Tu	1002	0.3	0.1
	1545	7.6	2.3		1612	8.0	2.4
	2154	0.9	0.3		2217	0.6	0.2
12	0401	7.8	2.4	27	0425	8.3	2.5
Tu	1012	0.6	0.2	W	1038	0.2	0.1
	1621	8.0	2.4		1648	8.1	2.5
	2227	0.6	0.2		2252	0.6	0.2
13	0435	8.1	2.5	28	0459	8.3	2.5
W	1045	0.3	0.1	Th	1113	0.2	0.1
	1655	8.2	2.5		1722	8.0	2.4
	2300	0.5	0.2		2324	0.7	0.2
14	0507	8.4	2.6	29	0531	8.2	2.5
Th	1119	0.0	0.0	F	1146	0.3	0.1
	1730	8.2	2.5		1755	7.7	2.3
	2335	0.5	0.2		2357	1.0	0.3
15	0541	8.4	2.6	30	0604	8.0	2.4
F	1156	0.0	0.0	Sa	1220	0.6	0.2
	1807	8.1	2.5		1830	7.4	2.3

MAY

Day	Time h m	Height ft	Height m	Day	Time h m	Height ft	Height m
1	0030	1.3	0.4	16	0034	1.1	0.3
Su	0638	7.6	2.3	M	0644	8.0	2.4
	1255	1.0	0.3		1307	0.6	0.2
	1905	7.0	2.1		1921	7.2	2.2
2	0105	1.7	0.5	17	0124	1.5	0.5
M	0715	7.2	2.2	Tu	0734	7.5	2.3
	1337	1.4	0.4		1401	1.1	0.3
	1948	6.5	2.0		2019	6.8	2.1
3	0148	2.2	0.7	18	0222	2.0	0.6
Tu	0800	6.7	2.0	W	0835	7.0	2.1
	1424	1.9	0.6		1507	1.5	0.5
	2041	6.1	1.9		2128	6.5	2.0
4	0241	2.6	0.8	19	0334	2.3	0.7
W	0854	6.2	1.9	Th	0949	6.6	2.0
	1523	2.3	0.7		1621	1.8	0.5
	2147	5.8	1.8		2247	6.3	1.9
5	0355	2.9	0.9	20	0458	2.4	0.7
Th	1010	5.9	1.8	F	1112	6.5	2.0
	1642	2.6	0.8		1739	1.9	0.6
	2311	5.7	1.7				
6	0523	2.9	0.9	21	0003	6.5	2.0
F	1137	5.9	1.8	Sa	0616	2.1	0.6
	1803	2.5	0.8		1229	6.7	2.0
					1848	1.7	0.5
7	0027	6.0	1.8	22	0107	6.9	2.1
Sa	0639	2.6	0.8	Su	0720	1.7	0.5
	1248	6.2	1.9		1330	7.0	2.1
	1907	2.1	0.6		1943	1.5	0.5
8	0125	6.5	2.0	23	0157	7.3	2.2
Su	0735	2.1	0.6	M	0811	1.2	0.4
	1346	6.7	2.0		1423	7.2	2.2
	1957	1.7	0.5		2028	1.2	0.4
9	0210	7.0	2.1	24	0240	7.6	2.3
M	0821	1.5	0.5	Tu	0855	0.9	0.3
	1431	7.1	2.2		1505	7.5	2.3
	2039	1.3	0.4		2111	1.1	0.3
10	0250	7.5	2.3	25	0319	7.8	2.4
Tu	0901	1.0	0.3	W	0935	0.6	0.2
	1511	7.6	2.3		1545	7.6	2.3
	2119	0.9	0.3		2146	1.0	0.3
11	0327	7.9	2.4	26	0356	8.0	2.4
W	0940	0.5	0.2	Th	1010	0.5	0.2
	1550	7.9	2.4		1620	7.6	2.3
	2156	0.7	0.2		2221	1.0	0.3
12	0404	8.2	2.5	27	0428	8.0	2.4
Th	1017	0.2	0.1	F	1046	0.5	0.2
	1629	8.1	2.5		1656	7.5	2.3
	2233	0.6	0.2		2256	1.1	0.3
13	0440	8.4	2.6	28	0503	7.9	2.4
F	1057	0.0	0.0	Sa	1120	0.6	0.2
	1707	8.1	2.5		1731	7.4	2.3
	2310	0.6	0.2		2329	1.3	0.4
14	0519	8.5	2.6	29	0538	7.8	2.4
Sa	1136	0.0	0.0	Su	1156	0.8	0.2
	1747	7.9	2.4		1807	7.2	2.2
	2350	0.8	0.2				
15	0559	8.3	2.5	30	0005	1.5	0.5
Su	1220	0.2	0.1	M	0614	7.5	2.3
	1833	7.6	2.3		1234	1.1	0.3
					1844	6.9	2.1
				31	0044	1.8	0.5
				Tu	0655	7.2	2.2
					1316	1.4	0.4
					1927	6.6	2.0

JUNE

Day	Time h m	Height ft	Height m	Day	Time h m	Height ft	Height m
1	0129	2.1	0.6	16	0217	1.7	0.5
W	0740	6.8	2.1	Th	0830	7.2	2.2
	1404	1.8	0.5		1457	1.3	0.4
	2017	6.3	1.9		2115	6.8	2.1
2	0222	2.4	0.7	17	0323	1.9	0.6
Th	0833	6.5	2.0	F	0936	6.9	2.1
	1459	2.1	0.6		1600	1.6	0.5
	2118	6.1	1.9		2218	6.7	2.0
3	0323	2.6	0.8	18	0432	2.0	0.6
F	0936	6.3	1.9	Sa	1045	6.7	2.0
	1603	2.2	0.7		1704	1.8	0.5
	2224	6.1	1.9		2324	6.7	2.0
4	0434	2.6	0.8	19	0539	1.9	0.6
Sa	1048	6.2	1.9	Su	1153	6.7	2.0
	1710	2.2	0.7		1808	1.8	0.5
	2331	6.3	1.9				
5	0545	2.4	0.7	20	0024	6.8	2.1
Su	1155	6.4	2.0	M	0641	1.7	0.5
	1813	2.0	0.6		1253	6.7	2.0
					1904	1.8	0.5
6	0029	6.6	2.0	21	0117	7.0	2.1
M	0645	2.0	0.6	Tu	0735	1.5	0.5
	1256	6.7	2.0		1349	6.8	2.1
	1909	1.8	0.5		1954	1.7	0.5
7	0122	7.0	2.1	22	0205	7.2	2.2
Tu	0736	1.5	0.5	W	0823	1.3	0.4
	1347	7.0	2.1		1436	6.9	2.1
	1957	1.5	0.5		2036	1.6	0.5
8	0208	7.4	2.3	23	0247	7.4	2.3
W	0823	1.0	0.3	Th	0908	1.1	0.3
	1436	7.4	2.3		1516	7.0	2.1
	2042	1.2	0.4		2118	1.5	0.5
9	0252	7.8	2.4	24	0327	7.5	2.3
Th	0909	0.6	0.2	F	0946	1.0	0.3
	1521	7.6	2.3		1556	7.1	2.2
	2124	0.9	0.3		2157	1.5	0.5
10	0336	8.1	2.5	25	0406	7.6	2.3
F	0953	0.3	0.1	Sa	1025	1.0	0.3
	1606	7.8	2.4		1635	7.1	2.2
	2209	0.8	0.2		2234	1.5	0.5
11	0418	8.3	2.5	26	0443	7.6	2.3
Sa	1038	0.1	0.0	Su	1102	1.0	0.3
	1651	7.8	2.4		1712	7.1	2.2
	2251	0.8	0.2		2311	1.5	0.5
12	0503	8.3	2.5	27	0522	7.5	2.3
Su	1123	0.2	0.1	M	1140	1.0	0.3
	1736	7.8	2.4		1749	7.0	2.1
	2338	0.9	0.3		2349	1.5	0.5
13	0549	8.2	2.5	28	0559	7.4	2.3
M	1210	0.3	0.1	Tu	1218	1.2	0.4
	1826	7.6	2.3		1828	6.9	2.1
14	0026	1.1	0.3	29	0031	1.6	0.5
Tu	0639	8.0	2.4	W	0639	7.3	2.2
	1302	0.6	0.2		1300	1.3	0.4
	1916	7.3	2.2		1911	6.8	2.1
15	0119	1.4	0.4	30	0111	1.8	0.5
W	0732	7.6	2.3	Th	0724	7.1	2.2
	1356	1.0	0.3		1342	1.5	0.5
	2012	7.0	2.1		1955	6.7	2.0

Time meridian 52° 30' W. 0000 is midnight. 1200 is noon.
Heights are referred to the chart datum of soundings.
Seasonal variations in sea level have not been included in these predictions.

PUERTO BELGRANO, ARGENTINA, 1983

Times and Heights of High and Low Waters

JANUARY

Day	Time (h m)	Height (ft)	Height (m)
1	0054	5.2	1.6
Sa	0618	12.8	3.9
	1342	2.0	0.6
	1930	12.2	3.7
2	0148	4.8	1.5
Su	0712	12.9	3.9
	1430	1.6	0.5
	2018	12.4	3.8
3	0242	4.3	1.3
M	0806	13.0	4.0
	1518	1.3	0.4
	2106	12.7	3.9
4	0336	3.7	1.1
Tu	0900	13.0	4.0
	1606	1.1	0.4
	2200	13.0	4.0
5	0424	3.0	0.9
W	1000	13.0	4.0
	1654	1.1	0.3
	2254	13.3	4.1
6	0518	2.5	0.8
Th	1106	12.9	3.9
	1742	1.3	0.4
	2348	13.5	4.1
7	0612	2.0	0.6
F	1212	12.9	3.9
	1830	1.8	0.5
8	0042	13.6	4.2
Sa	0706	1.9	0.6
	1318	12.8	3.9
	1924	2.4	0.7
9	0136	13.5	4.1
Su	0806	1.9	0.6
	1418	12.7	3.9
	2024	3.1	1.0
10	0236	13.4	4.1
M	0912	2.0	0.6
	1530	12.6	3.8
	2130	3.7	1.1
11	0342	13.3	4.0
Tu	1018	2.1	0.6
	1636	12.7	3.9
	2236	4.1	1.3
12	0454	13.3	4.0
W	1118	2.0	0.6
	1736	12.8	3.9
	2336	4.3	1.3
13	0554	13.3	4.1
Th	1212	1.9	0.6
	1836	12.9	3.9
14	0030	4.4	1.4
F	0648	13.3	4.1
	1306	1.9	0.6
	1930	13.0	4.0
15	0118	4.5	1.4
Sa	0736	13.2	4.0
	1348	2.0	0.6
	2012	13.0	4.0

Day	Time (h m)	Height (ft)	Height (m)
16	0206	4.6	1.4
Su	0824	12.9	3.9
	1436	2.1	0.6
	2100	12.9	3.9
17	0248	4.5	1.4
M	0900	12.7	3.9
	1512	2.2	0.7
	2136	12.8	3.9
18	0324	4.3	1.3
Tu	0936	12.5	3.8
	1548	2.2	0.7
	2206	12.8	3.9
19	0400	3.9	1.2
W	1000	12.4	3.8
	1618	2.2	0.7
	2230	12.8	3.9
20	0436	3.3	1.0
Th	1024	12.4	3.8
	1654	2.2	0.7
	2248	13.0	4.0
21	0512	2.7	0.8
F	1100	12.5	3.8
	1724	2.2	0.7
	2318	13.1	4.0
22	0548	2.2	0.7
Sa	1142	12.6	3.8
	1806	2.5	0.8
	2354	13.2	4.0
23	0636	1.9	0.6
Su	1230	12.5	3.8
	1848	2.9	0.9
24	0036	13.2	4.0
M	0718	1.9	0.6
	1318	12.3	3.8
	1930	3.5	1.1
25	0118	13.1	4.0
Tu	0812	2.2	0.7
	1418	12.1	3.7
	2018	4.3	1.3
26	0212	12.9	3.9
W	0912	2.4	0.7
	1518	11.9	3.6
	2118	4.9	1.5
27	0306	12.8	3.9
Th	1018	2.6	0.8
	1624	11.8	3.6
	2224	5.4	1.7
28	0400	12.7	3.9
F	1118	2.6	0.8
	1724	11.9	3.6
	2324	5.6	1.7
29	0506	12.8	3.9
Sa	1218	2.5	0.8
	1818	12.2	3.7
30	0030	5.5	1.7
Su	0600	12.9	3.9
	1312	2.3	0.7
	1912	12.4	3.8
31	0130	5.1	1.6
M	0700	12.9	3.9
	1406	2.2	0.7
	2000	12.8	3.9

FEBRUARY

Day	Time (h m)	Height (ft)	Height (m)
1	0224	4.5	1.4
Tu	0754	12.9	3.9
	1500	2.0	0.6
	2054	13.1	4.0
2	0318	3.7	1.1
W	0854	12.9	3.9
	1548	1.9	0.6
	2142	13.4	4.1
3	0412	2.8	0.9
Th	1000	12.9	3.9
	1636	1.8	0.5
	2236	13.6	4.2
4	0506	2.0	0.6
F	1100	13.0	4.0
	1724	1.8	0.5
	2324	13.8	4.2
5	0554	1.4	0.4
Sa	1200	13.0	4.0
	1812	2.0	0.6
6	0018	13.9	4.2
Su	0648	1.1	0.4
	1300	12.9	3.9
	1900	2.4	0.7
7	0112	13.8	4.2
M	0742	1.1	0.4
	1354	12.8	3.9
	1954	2.9	0.9
8	0212	13.6	4.2
Tu	0842	1.3	0.4
	1500	12.7	3.9
	2054	3.5	1.1
9	0312	13.5	4.1
W	0942	1.6	0.5
	1600	12.7	3.9
	2154	4.0	1.2
10	0418	13.4	4.1
Th	1042	1.8	0.5
	1700	12.9	3.9
	2300	4.4	1.3
11	0518	13.4	4.1
F	1142	1.9	0.6
	1800	13.0	4.0
12	0000	4.6	1.4
Sa	0612	13.4	4.1
	1230	2.1	0.6
	1854	13.2	4.0
13	0048	4.8	1.5
Su	0706	13.3	4.0
	1324	2.3	0.7
	1942	13.2	4.0
14	0136	4.8	1.5
M	0748	13.0	4.0
	1406	2.6	0.8
	2030	13.1	4.0
15	0224	4.7	1.4
Tu	0830	12.7	3.9
	1442	2.8	0.9
	2106	13.0	4.0

Day	Time (h m)	Height (ft)	Height (m)
16	0306	4.4	1.3
W	0906	12.4	3.8
	1518	3.0	0.9
	2130	12.8	3.9
17	0336	3.9	1.2
Th	0924	12.2	3.7
	1554	3.0	0.9
	2142	12.7	3.9
18	0412	3.1	1.0
F	0948	12.2	3.7
	1624	2.9	0.9
	2200	12.8	3.9
19	0448	2.4	0.7
Sa	1024	12.3	3.7
	1700	2.8	0.8
	2230	13.0	4.0
20	0530	1.7	0.5
Su	1106	12.3	3.8
	1736	2.8	0.8
	2312	13.2	4.0
21	0612	1.4	0.4
M	1154	12.2	3.7
	1818	3.0	0.9
	2354	13.2	4.0
22	0654	1.3	0.4
Tu	1248	12.1	3.7
	1900	3.5	1.1
23	0042	13.2	4.0
W	0748	1.6	0.5
	1342	11.8	3.6
	1954	4.2	1.3
24	0136	13.0	4.0
Th	0842	2.0	0.6
	1448	11.6	3.5
	2048	4.9	1.5
25	0230	12.8	3.9
F	0948	2.4	0.7
	1600	11.6	3.6
	2154	5.5	1.7
26	0336	12.6	3.8
Sa	1054	2.7	0.8
	1706	11.9	3.6
	2306	5.7	1.7
27	0448	12.6	3.8
Su	1154	2.8	0.9
	1806	12.3	3.8
28	0012	5.5	1.7
M	0554	12.7	3.9
	1254	2.8	0.9
	1854	12.7	3.9

MARCH

Day	Time (h m)	Height (ft)	Height (m)
1	0112	5.0	1.5
Tu	0654	12.7	3.9
	1348	2.8	0.9
	1942	13.1	4.0
2	0212	4.2	1.3
W	0754	12.7	3.9
	1436	2.7	0.8
	2036	13.3	4.1
3	0306	3.3	1.0
Th	0854	12.7	3.9
	1530	2.6	0.8
	2124	13.5	4.1
4	0400	2.3	0.7
F	0954	12.8	3.9
	1612	2.3	0.7
	2212	13.7	4.2
5	0448	1.5	0.5
Sa	1054	12.9	3.9
	1700	2.1	0.7
	2306	13.8	4.2
6	0536	0.9	0.3
Su	1142	12.9	3.9
	1748	2.1	0.6
	2354	13.8	4.2
7	0624	0.6	0.2
M	1236	12.9	3.9
	1830	2.3	0.7
8	0048	13.8	4.2
Tu	0712	0.6	0.2
	1330	12.8	3.9
	1924	2.7	0.8
9	0142	13.6	4.2
W	0806	0.9	0.3
	1424	12.7	3.9
	2018	3.3	1.0
10	0242	13.5	4.1
Th	0906	1.3	0.4
	1524	12.8	3.9
	2118	3.9	1.2
11	0342	13.4	4.1
F	1006	1.7	0.5
	1624	12.9	3.9
	2218	4.4	1.4
12	0442	13.3	4.1
Sa	1100	2.1	0.6
	1718	13.2	4.0
	2324	4.7	1.4
13	0536	13.3	4.0
Su	1200	2.4	0.7
	1812	13.4	4.1
14	0018	4.8	1.5
M	0630	13.2	4.0
	1248	2.8	0.8
	1906	13.4	4.1
15	0112	4.7	1.4
Tu	0718	12.9	3.9
	1330	3.1	1.0
	1948	13.3	4.1

Day	Time (h m)	Height (ft)	Height (m)
16	0200	4.4	1.4
W	0800	12.6	3.9
	1412	3.4	1.0
	2024	13.0	4.0
17	0242	4.0	1.2
Th	0830	12.3	3.8
	1448	3.6	1.1
	2030	12.7	3.9
18	0318	3.4	1.0
F	0848	12.1	3.7
	1524	3.5	1.1
	2042	12.7	3.9
19	0348	2.6	0.8
Sa	0918	12.0	3.7
	1554	3.3	1.0
	2112	12.8	3.9
20	0430	1.8	0.6
Su	0954	12.0	3.7
	1630	3.1	1.0
	2148	13.0	4.0
21	0506	1.2	0.4
M	1042	12.0	3.7
	1712	3.0	0.9
	2230	13.2	4.0
22	0548	0.8	0.3
Tu	1130	11.9	3.6
	1748	3.1	0.9
	2318	13.3	4.0
23	0636	0.8	0.2
W	1224	11.8	3.6
	1836	3.5	1.1
24	0006	13.1	4.0
Th	0724	1.1	0.4
	1318	11.6	3.5
	1930	4.1	1.3
25	0106	12.9	3.9
F	0818	1.7	0.5
	1424	11.5	3.5
	2030	4.9	1.5
26	0212	12.5	3.8
Sa	0924	2.4	0.7
	1536	11.7	3.6
	2136	5.4	1.6
27	0324	12.3	3.7
Su	1030	3.0	0.9
	1648	12.0	3.7
	2248	5.5	1.7
28	0442	12.2	3.7
M	1130	3.3	1.0
	1748	12.5	3.8
29	0000	5.1	1.6
Tu	0554	12.3	3.8
	1230	3.4	1.0
	1842	13.0	4.0
30	0106	4.4	1.3
W	0700	12.5	3.8
	1330	3.4	1.1
	1930	13.3	4.0
31	0206	3.5	1.1
Th	0800	12.5	3.8
	1418	3.3	1.0
	2018	13.4	4.1

Time meridian 45° W. 0000 is midnight. 1200 is noon.
Heights are referred to the chart datum of soundings.

TABLE 2.—TIDAL DIFFERENCES AND OTHER CONSTANTS

EXPLANATION OF TABLE

The publication of full daily predictions is necessarily limited to a comparatively small number of stations. Tide predictions for many other places, however, can be obtained by applying certain differences to the predictions for the reference stations in table 1. The following pages list the places called "subordinate stations" for which such predictions can be made and the differences or ratios to be used. These differences or ratios are to be applied to the predictions for the proper reference station which is listed in table 2 in bold face type above the differences for the subordinate station. The stations in this table are arranged in geographical order. The index at the end of this volume will assist in locating a particular station.

Caution.—The time and height differences listed in table 2 are average differences derived from comparisons of simultaneous tide observations at the subordinate location and its reference station. Because these figures are constant, they cannot provide for the daily variances of the actual tide. Therefore, it must be realized that although the application of the time and height differences will generally provide reasonably accurate approximations, they cannot result in as accurate predictions as those for the reference stations which are based upon much longer periods of analyses and which do provide for daily variances. In addition, at subordinate stations where the tide is chiefly diurnal, the tide correctors are intended primarily to be used to approximate the times and heights of the higher high and the lower low waters. When the lower high water and higher low water at the reference station are nearly the same height, great reliance should not be placed on the calculated corresponding tides at the subordinate station.

Time difference.—To determine the time of high water or low water at any station listed in this table there is given in the columns headed "Differences, Time" the hours and minutes to be added to or subtracted from the time of high or low water at some reference station. A plus (+) sign indicates that the tide at the subordinate station is later than at the reference station and the difference should be added, a minus (—) sign that it is earlier and should be subtracted.

To obtain the tide at a subordinate station on any date apply the difference to the tide at the reference station for that same date. In some cases, however, to obtain an a. m. tide it may be necessary to use the preceding day's p. m. tide at the reference station, or to obtain a p. m. tide it may be necessary to use the following day's a. m. tide. For example, if a high water occurs at a reference station at 2200 on July 2, and the tide at the subordinate station occurs 3 hours later, then high water will occur at 0100 on July 3 at the subordinate station. For the second case, if a high water at a reference station occurs at 0200 on July 17, and the tide at the subordinate station occurs 5 hours earlier, the high water at the subordinate station will occur at 2100 on July 16. The necessary allowance for change in date when the international date line is crossed is included in the time differences. In such cases use the same date at the reference station as desired for the subordinate station as explained above.

The results obtained by the application of the time differences will be in the kind of time indicated by the time meridian shown above the name of the subordinate station. Summer or daylight saving time is not used in the tide tables.

Height differences.—The height of the tide, referred to the datum of charts, is obtained by means of the height differences or ratios. A plus (+) sign indicates that the difference should be added to the height at the reference station and a minus (—) sign that it should be subtracted. All height differences, ranges, and levels in table 2 are in feet but may be converted to meters by the use of table 7.

Ratio.—For some stations height differences would give unsatisfactory predictions. In such cases they have been omitted and one or two ratios are given. Where two ratios are given, one in the "height of high water" column and one in the "height of low water" column, the high waters and low waters at the reference station should be multiplied by these respective ratios. Where only one is given, the omitted ratio is either unreliable or unknown.

For some subordinate stations there is given in parentheses a ratio as well as a correction in feet. In those instances, each predicted high and low water at the reference station should first be multiplied by the ratio and then the correction in feet is to be added to or subtracted from each product as indicated.

As an example, at Port of Spain, Trinidad, the values in the time and height difference columns in Table 2 are given as —0 44, —1 12, and (*0.31+1.4) as referred to the reference station at Punta Gorda, Venezuela. If we assume that the time predictions in column (1) below are those of Punta Gorda on a particular day, application of the time and height corrections in columns (2) and (3) would result in the tide predictions for Port of Spain in column (4).

(1)		(2)	(3)	(4)		
Time h.m.	Height ft	Time Corrections h.m.	Height Corrections	Time h.m.	Height ft	Height meters
0326	0.6	—1 12	×0.31+1.4	0214	1.6	0.5
0900	5.1	—0 44	×0.31+1.4	0816	3.0	0.9
1608	—0.3	—1 12	×0.31+1.4	1456	1.3	0.4
2148	5.4	—0 44	×0.31+1.4	2104	3.1	0.9

Range.—The *mean range* is the difference in height between mean high water and mean low water. The *spring range* is the average semidiurnal range occurring semimonthly as the result of the Moon being new or full. It is larger than the mean range where the type of tide is either semidiurnal or mixed, and is of no practical significance where the type of tide is diurnal. Where the tide is chiefly of the diurnal type the table gives the *diurnal range*, which is the difference in height between mean higher high water and mean lower low water.

Datum.—The datum of the predictions obtained through the height differences or ratios is also the datum of the largest scale chart for the locality. To obtain the depth at the time of high or low water, the predicted height should be added to the depth on the chart unless such height is negative (—), when it should be subtracted. To find the height at times between high and low water see table 3. On some charts the depths are given in meters and in such cases the heights of the tide can be reduced to meters by the use of table 7. The chart datum for the Atlantic Coast of the United States and for a part of the West Indies is *mean low water*. For the rest of the area covered by these tables the datums generally used are approximately *mean low water, mean low water springs, Gulf Coast Low Water Datum, mean lower low water, Indian spring low water, or the lowest possible low water.*

Mean Tide Level (Half Tide Level).—The mean tide level is a plane midway between mean low water and mean high water. Tabular values are reckoned from chart datum.

NOTE.—Dashes are entered in the place of data which are unknown, unreliable, or not applicable.

Mean Lower Low Water

Effective November 28, 1980, the term Mean Lower Low Water (MLLW) began to replace the term Gulf Coast Low Water Datum (GCLWD) as chart datum on nautical charts, bathymetric maps, and in the Tide Tables and Coast Pilots of the National Ocean Survey covering the Gulf Coast of the United States.

The area affected by this action extends from the International Border between the United States and Mexico, then easterly along the Gulf Coast of the United States to the southeast corner of Florida, including the Florida Keys.

More specifically, the boundary between the datum of Mean Low Water of the Atlantic Coast and the datum of Mean Lower Low Water of the Gulf Coast is defined as extending:

a. from the intersection of the most westerly segment of the southern boundary of the Biscayne National Monument and the land (just south of Mangrove Point);

b. along the southwest segments of the southern boundary of the Monument to Old Rhodes Point on the southeast corner of Old Rhodes Key;

c. then from Old Rhodes Point to the northwest corner of the John Pennekamp Coral Reef State Park;

d. along the land of the northwestern boundary of the Park (with the exception of the coastal indentations of Largo Sound) to the southwest corner (just southwest of Rock Harbor); and

e. then from the southwest corner of the John Pennekamp Coral Reef State Park along its southwestern boundary and continuing straight out to sea just south of and beyond Molasses Reef.

Appropriate content changes have been made in this tide table to conform to the newly defined chart datum.

NO.	PLACE	POSITION Lat.	Long.	DIFFERENCES Time High Water	Time Low Water	Height High Water	Height Low Water	RANGES Mean	Spring	Mean Tide Level
		° ' N	° ' W	h. m.	h. m.	ft	ft	ft	ft	ft
	LABRADOR Time meridian, 52°30'W			on HALIFAX, p.20						
171	Cartwright Harbour	53 42	57 02	-0 03	-0 34	-1.3	-0.6	3.7	4.9	3.4
173	Curlew Harbour	53 45	56 33	-0 07	-0 38	-1.6	-0.9	3.7	4.9	3.1
175	Comfort Bight	53 09	55 46	-0 32	-1 03	-1.9	-1.0	3.5	4.6	2.9
177	Square Island Harbour	52 44	55 49	-0 34	-1 05	-2.0	-1.1	3.5	4.7	2.8
179	Port Marnham	52 23	55 44	-0 43	-1 14	-2.7	-1.0	2.7	3.6	2.5
180	Battle Harbour	52 16	55 36	-1 03	-1 30	-2.1	-0.3	2.6	3.8	3.1
	Strait of Bell Isle			on HARRINGTON HARBOUR, p.12						
181	Chateau Bay	52 00	55 50	-3 08	-3 19	*0.69	*0.81	2.4	3.1	2.5
183	Red Bay	51 43	56 25	-2 00	-1 55	*0.56	*0.56	2.1	2.6	2.0
185	Forteau Bay	51 27	56 53	-0 26	-0 17	*0.78	*0.81	2.9	3.7	2.8
	NEWFOUNDLAND, East Coast			on HALIFAX, p.20						
201	Pistolet Bay	51 30	55 44	-0 14	-0 28	*0.46	*0.29	2.4	3.1	1.8
203	Ariege Bay	51 10	56 00	-0 34	-0 34	-2.6	-1.5	3.3	4.3	2.3
205	Wild Cove	50 42	56 10	-0 49	-1 01	-2.0	-1.1	3.5	4.7	2.8
207	Sops Island, White Bay	49 50	56 46	-0 49	-1 24	*0.46	*0.29	2.4	3.4	1.8
209	Exploits Lower Harbour	49 32	55 04	-0 34	-1 09	-3.1	-1.3	2.6	3.5	2.1
211	Fogo Harbour	49 43	54 16	-0 34	-0 42	-2.6	-1.3	3.1	4.2	2.4
213	Valleyfield	49 10	53 37	-0 46	-1 13	*0.45	*0.33	2.2	2.9	1.8
215	Port Union	48 30	53 05	-0 53	-1 15	*0.49	*0.48	2.2	3.0	2.1
217	Random Head Harbour, Trinity Bay	48 06	53 34	-0 53	-1 05	*0.48	*0.33	2.4	3.2	1.9
219	Harbour Grace, Conception Bay	47 41	53 12	-0 28	-0 46	*0.51	*0.33	2.6	3.5	2.0
221	St. John's	47 34	52 42	-0 34	-0 46	*0.52	*0.38	2.6	3.5	2.1
	NEWFOUNDLAND, South Coast			on ARGENTIA, p.4						
223	Trepassey Harbour	46 43	53 23	-0 19	-0 11	-1.2	-0.5	4.2	5.6	3.5
225	St. Mary Harbour, St. Mary Bay	46 55	53 35	-0 14	-0 06	-1.2	-0.5	4.2	5.6	3.5
	Placentia Bay									
227	ARGENTIA	47 18	53 59	Daily predictions				4.9	6.3	4.4
229	Woody Island	47 47	54 10	+0 09	+0 09	-0.5	-0.3	4.7	6.0	4.0
231	Mortier Bay	47 10	55 09	+0 15	+0 26	-1.0	-0.8	4.7	6.0	3.5
233	Great St. Lawrence Harbour	46 55	55 22	+0 28	+0 55	-0.7	+0.3	3.9	5.0	4.2
	Time meridian, 60°W									
235	St. Pierre Hbr., St. Pierre Island	46 47	56 10	-0 09	+0 13	-0.8	+0.2	3.9	5.0	4.1
	Time meridian, 52°30'W									
	Fortune Bay									
237	Grande le Pierre Harbour	47 40	54 47	+1 09	+1 09	-1.0	+0.2	3.7	4.8	4.0
239	Belleoram	47 32	55 25	+0 57	+0 57	(*0.67+0.8)		3.3	4.3	3.8
241	Ship Cove, Bay d'Espoir	47 52	55 50	+0 45	+0 53	-0.4	0.0	4.5	5.5	4.2
243	Great Jervis Harbour, Bay d'Espoir	47 39	56 11	+0 38	+1 05	-1.1	+0.1	3.7	4.8	3.9
245	Hare Bay	47 37	56 32	+0 41	+1 08	(*0.67+0.6)		3.3	4.3	3.6
247	Grey River	47 34	57 07	+0 45	+1 12	(*0.63+0.7)		3.1	4.0	3.5
249	Connoire Bay	47 40	57 54	+0 50	+0 50	(*0.59+0.7)		2.9	3.8	3.3
251	La Poile Bay	47 40	58 24	+1 15	+1 15	(*0.63+0.6)		3.1	4.0	3.4
				on HARRINGTON HARBOUR, p.12						
253	Port Aux Basques	47 35	59 09	-1 24	-1 28	*0.80	*0.75	3.1	4.0	2.8
255	Codroy Road	47 53	59 24	-1 22	-1 27	*0.74	*0.75	2.8	3.7	2.6
	NEWFOUNDLAND, West Coast									
257	St. Georges Harbour	48 27	58 30	-0 28	-0 38	*0.78	*0.88	2.8	3.5	2.8
259	Port-au-Port	48 33	58 45	+0 05	+0 10	-1.3	-1.0	3.5	4.5	2.4
261	Frenchman's Cove, Bay of Islands	49 04	58 10	+0 10	+0 10	-0.5	0.0	3.3	4.2	3.3
263	Norris Cove, Bonne Bay	49 31	57 52	+0 10	+0 10	-0.7	-0.4	3.5	4.4	3.0
265	Portland Cove	50 11	57 36	+0 19	+0 19	-0.6	-0.4	3.6	4.6	3.0
267	Port Saunders	50 39	57 18	+0 07	+0 03	-0.3	-0.3	3.8	4.9	3.2
269	Castors Harbour, St. John Bay	50 55	56 59	+0 10	+0 10	*0.78	*0.75	3.0	4.1	2.7
271	St. Barbe Bay	51 12	56 46	0 00	0 00	*0.78	*0.56	3.3	4.4	2.6
	QUEBEC, Gulf of St. Lawrence Time meridian, 60°W									
273	Bradore Bay	51 28	57 15	-0 35	-0 30	-0.6	-0.1	3.3	4.4	3.1
275	Mistanoque Harbour	51 16	58 12	-0 15	-0 15	-0.4	-0.1	3.5	4.6	3.3
277	HARRINGTON HARBOUR	50 30	59 28	Daily predictions				3.8	4.9	3.5
279	Wapitagun Harbour	50 12	60 01	+0 15	+0 15	-0.3	+0.1	3.4	4.4	3.4
281	Kegaska	50 12	61 14	+0 40	+0 40	-0.9	-0.2	3.1	4.0	3.0
283	Natashquan	50 12	61 50	+1 00	+1 10	-0.8	-0.1	3.1	4.0	3.1
285	Betchewun Harbour	50 14	63 11	+2 09	+2 13	-0.7	-0.4	3.5	4.6	3.0

Endnotes can be found at the end of table 2.

NO.	PLACE	POSITION Lat.	POSITION Long.	DIFFERENCES Time High Water	DIFFERENCES Time Low Water	DIFFERENCES Height High Water	DIFFERENCES Height Low Water	RANGES Mean	RANGES Spring	Mean Tide Level
		° ' N	° ' W	h. m.	h. m.	ft	ft	ft	ft	ft
	NOVA SCOTIA, Bay of Fundy Time meridian, 60°W			on ST. JOHN, N. B., p.24						
565	Ile Haute	45 15	65 00	-0 02	-0 02	+7.4	+0.7	27.5	31.5	18.5
567	Spencer Island	45 20	64 42	+0 17	+0 21	*1.47	*1.50	30.5	35.0	21.2
	Minas Basin									
569	Parrsboro (Partridge Island) <2>	45 22	64 20	+0 51	+0 49	+14.7	- -	34.4	39.0	22.3
571	Horton Bluff, Avon River	45 06	64 13	+0 58	+1 02	*1.76	*1.38	38.1	43.6	24.6
573	Windsor <2>	45 00	64 08	+1 03	- - -	+19.5	- -	- -	- -	- -
575	Burntcoat Head	45 18	63 49	+1 06	+1 12	*1.90	*2.18	38.4	43.5	27.9
577	Truro <2>	45 22	63 20	+1 43	- - -	+26.1	- -	- -	- -	- -
579	Spicer Cove, Chignecto Bay	45 26	64 54	+0 12	+0 16	+7.0	+0.8	27.0	30.0	18.3
581	Joggins <2>	45 41	64 28	+0 14	+0 26	+14.2	+1.8	33.2	37.0	22.4
583	Amherst Point, Cumberland Basin	45 50	64 17	+0 33	+0 45	*1.69	*1.55	35.6	40.5	24.0
	NEW BRUNSWICK, Bay of Fundy									
	Petitcodiac River <3>									
585	Grindstone Island	45 43	64 37	+0 21	+0 28	*1.49	*1.45	31.1	35.6	21.4
587	Hopewell Cape	45 52	64 35	+0 14	+0 39	*1.64	*1.85	33.2	38.0	24.0
589	Moncton <2> <3>	46 05	64 46	+0 46	- - -	+17.2	- -	- -	- -	- -
591	Salisbury	46 01	65 03	+1 31	- - -	+18.2	- -	- -	- -	- -
601	Herring Cove	45 35	64 58	+0 22	+0 20	+8.4	+0.9	28.3	32.4	19.1
603	Quaco Bay	45 20	65 32	+0 11	+0 12	+2.0	-0.3	23.1	26.3	15.3
605	ST. JOHN <4>	45 15	66 04	Daily predictions				20.8	23.7	14.4
607	Indiantown, St. John River	45 16	66 05	+1 30	+2 25	- -	- -	1.2	1.4	2.4
609	Lepreau Harbour	45 07	66 29	-0 01	+0 03	-2.3	-0.5	19.0	21.7	13.0
611	L'Etang Harbour	45 02	66 49	+0 01	+0 05	-3.2	-0.8	18.4	21.0	12.4
613	North Head, Grand Manan Island	44 46	66 45	-0 05	-0 05	-4.5	-0.9	17.2	19.3	11.7
615	Seal Cove, Grand Manan Island	44 37	66 51	-0 15	-0 17	*0.68	*0.65	14.3	16.3	9.8
617	Outer Wood Island <5>	44 36	66 48	-0 25	-0 27	-7.8	-0.8	13.8	16.2	10.1
619	Machias Seal Island <5>	44 30	67 06	-0 01	- - -	-9.6	-1.7	12.9	14.5	8.8
620	Welshpool, Campobello Island <5>	44 53	66 57	-0 01	+0 06	-3.5	-1.0	18.3	21.2	12.1
621	Wilsons Beach, Campobello Island <5>	44 56	66 56	0 00	+0 01	-3.7	+0.1	17.0	19.4	12.6
622	Back Bay, Letite Harbour <5>	45 03	66 52	0 00	-0 03	-3.5	0.0	17.3	20.1	12.6
623	Midjik Bluff, Passamaquoddy Bay <5>	45 07	66 54	+0 12	+0 17	-2.0	-0.5	19.3	22.0	13.1
624	St. Andrews, Passamaquoddy Bay <5>	45 04	67 03	+0 14	+0 20	-2.3	0.0	18.5	21.2	13.2
625	The Ledge, St. Croix River <5>	45 10	67 12	+0 17	+0 30	-0.8	0.0	20.0	22.8	14.0
	MAINE Time meridian, 75°W			on EASTPORT, p.28						
627	EASTPORT	44 54	66 59	Daily predictions				18.2	20.7	9.1
629	Gleason Cove, Western Passage	44 58	67 03	+0 08	+0 07	+0.2	0.0	18.4	20.9	9.2
	St. Croix River									
631	Robbinston	45 05	67 06	+0 09	+0 09	+1.0	0.0	19.2	21.8	9.6
633	St. Croix Island	45 08	67 08	+0 10	+0 12	+1.4	0.0	19.6	22.3	9.8
637	Calais	45 11	67 17	+0 31	+0 34	+1.8	0.0	20.0	22.8	10.0
	Cobscook Bay									
639	Deep Cove, Moose Island	44 54	67 01	+0 08	+0 09	+0.5	0.0	18.7	21.3	9.3
641	East Bay	44 56	67 07	+0 14	+0 16	+0.9	0.0	19.1	21.8	9.5
643	Coffins Point	44 52	67 07	+0 33	+0 38	+0.1	0.0	18.3	20.8	9.1
645	Birch Islands	44 52	67 09	+1 05	+1 17	-0.6	0.0	17.6	20.0	8.8
647	Horan Head, South Bay	44 52	67 04	+0 18	+0 21	+1.0	0.0	19.2	21.9	9.6
649	Lubec	44 52	66 59	-0 03	-0 01	-0.7	0.0	17.5	20.0	8.7
651	West Quoddy Head	44 49	66 59	-0 09	-0 15	-2.5	0.0	15.7	17.9	7.8
653	Moose Cove	44 44	67 06	-0 10	-0 16	-3.4	0.0	14.8	16.9	7.4
655	Cutler, Little River	44 39	67 13	-0 12	-0 17	-4.6	0.0	13.6	15.5	6.8
657	Stone Island, Machias Bay	44 36	67 22	-0 12	-0 29	-5.8	0.0	12.4	14.1	6.2
659	Machiasport, Machias River	44 42	67 24	0 00	-0 10	-5.6	0.0	12.6	14.4	6.3
661	Shoppee Point, Englishman Bay	44 37	67 30	-0 06	-0 14	-6.1	0.0	12.1	13.8	6.1
663	Roque Island Harbor, Englishman Bay	44 34	67 31	-0 11	-0 14	-5.9	0.0	12.3	14.0	6.1
				on PORTLAND, p.32						
665	Steele Harbor Island	44 30	67 33	-0 28	-0 20	+2.5	0.0	11.6	13.3	5.8
667	Jonesport, Moosabec Reach	44 32	67 36	-0 23	-0 17	+2.4	0.0	11.5	13.2	5.8
669	Gibbs Island, Pleasant River	44 33	67 46	-0 20	-0 11	+2.2	0.0	11.3	13.0	5.6
671	Addison, Pleasant River	44 37	67 45	0 00	+0 04	+2.7	0.0	11.8	13.6	5.9
673	Trafton Island, Narraguagus Bay	44 29	67 50	-0 23	-0 20	+2.0	0.0	11.1	12.8	5.5
675	Milbridge, Narraguagus River	44 32	67 53	-0 20	-0 05	+2.2	0.0	11.3	13.0	5.6
677	Pigeon Hill Bay	44 27	67 52	-0 21	-0 18	+2.0	0.0	11.1	12.8	5.6
678	Green Island, Petit Manan Bar	44 22	67 52	-0 28	-0 24	+1.5	0.0	10.6	12.2	5.3
679	Pinkham Bay, Dyer Bay	44 28	67 55	-0 23	-0 18	+1.8	0.0	10.9	12.5	5.4
681	Garden Point, Gouldsboro Bay	44 28	67 59	-0 23	-0 18	+1.7	0.0	10.8	12.4	5.4
683	Corea Harbor	44 24	67 58	-0 25	-0 20	+1.4	0.0	10.5	12.1	5.2
685	Prospect Harbor	44 24	68 01	-0 24	-0 15	+1.4	0.0	10.5	12.1	5.2
	Frenchman Bay									
701	Winter Harbor	44 23	68 05	-0 23	-0 09	+1.0	0.0	10.1	11.6	5.0
703	Eastern Point Harbor	44 28	68 10	-0 20	-0 14	+1.4	0.0	10.5	12.1	5.2
705	Sullivan	44 31	68 12	-0 10	-0 05	+1.4	0.0	10.5	12.1	5.2
707	Mount Desert Narrows	44 26	68 22	-0 08	-0 08	+1.4	0.0	10.5	12.1	5.3

Endnotes can be found at the end of table 2.

NO.	PLACE	POSITION Lat.	POSITION Long.	DIFFERENCES Time High Water	DIFFERENCES Time Low Water	DIFFERENCES Height High Water	DIFFERENCES Height Low Water	RANGES Mean	RANGES Spring	Mean Tide Level
		° ' N	° ' W	h. m.	h. m.	ft	ft	ft	ft	ft
	MAINE Time meridian, 75°W			on PORTLAND, p.32						
	Mount Desert Island									
709	Salsbury Cove	44 26	68 17	-0 15	-0 12	+1.5	0.0	10.6	12.2	5.3
711	Bar Harbor	44 23	68 12	-0 22	-0 19	+1.4	0.0	10.5	12.1	5.2
713	Southwest Harbor	44 16	68 19	-0 22	-0 12	+1.1	0.0	10.2	11.7	5.1
715	Mount Desert	44 22	68 20	-0 16	-0 08	+1.5	0.0	10.6	12.2	5.3
717	Bass Harbor	44 14	68 21	-0 18	-0 11	+0.8	0.0	9.9	11.3	5.0
719	Pretty Marsh Harbor	44 20	68 25	-0 13	-0 13	+1.1	0.0	10.2	11.7	5.1
	Blue Hill Bay									
721	Union River	44 30	68 26	-0 09	-0 08	+1.3	0.0	10.4	11.9	5.2
723	Blue Hill Harbor	44 24	68 34	-0 13	-0 08	+1.0	0.0	10.1	11.6	5.0
725	Allen Cove	44 18	68 33	-0 12	-0 12	+1.2	0.0	10.3	11.8	5.1
727	Mackerel Cove	44 10	68 26	-0 20	-0 13	+0.9	0.0	10.0	11.5	5.0
729	Burnt Coat Harbor, Swans Island	44 09	68 27	-0 23	-0 13	+0.4	0.0	9.5	10.8	4.7
	MAINE, Penobscot Bay									
	Eggemoggin Reach									
731	Naskeag Harbor	44 14	68 33	-0 16	-0 14	+1.1	0.0	10.2	11.6	5.1
733	Center Harbor	44 16	68 35	-0 13	-0 07	+1.0	0.0	10.1	11.5	5.0
735	Sedgwick	44 18	68 38	-0 11	-0 06	+1.1	0.0	10.2	11.7	5.1
736	Isle Au Haut	44 04	68 38	-0 23	-0 19	+0.2	0.0	9.3	10.7	4.7
737	Head Harbor, Isle Au Haut	44 01	68 37	-0 20	-0 20	0.0	0.0	9.1	10.4	4.6
739	Kimball Island	44 04	68 39	-0 20	-0 22	+0.5	0.0	9.6	10.9	4.8
741	Oceanville, Deer Isle	44 12	68 38	-0 18	-0 17	+1.0	0.0	10.1	11.5	5.0
743	Stonington, Deer Isle	44 09	68 40	-0 18	-0 17	+0.6	0.0	9.7	11.0	4.8
745	Northwest Harbor, Deer Isle	44 14	68 41	-0 12	-0 12	+1.0	0.0	10.1	11.5	5.0
747	Matinicus Harbor	43 52	68 53	-0 17	-0 12	-0.1	0.0	9.0	10.4	4.5
749	Vinalhaven, Vinalhaven Island	44 03	68 50	-0 13	-0 06	+0.2	0.0	9.3	10.7	4.6
751	Iron Point, North Haven Island	44 08	68 52	-0 13	-0 13	+0.4	0.0	9.5	10.8	4.8
753	Pulpit Harbor, North Haven Island	44 09	68 53	-0 13	-0 15	+0.7	0.0	9.8	11.1	4.9
755	Castine	44 23	68 48	-0 04	-0 01	+0.6	0.0	9.7	11.1	4.8
757	Pumpkin Island, South Bay	44 25	68 44	+0 11	+0 29	+1.2	0.0	10.3	11.7	5.1
	Penobscot River									
759	Fort Point	44 28	68 49	-0 06	-0 05	+1.2	0.0	10.3	11.8	5.1
761	Bucksport	44 34	68 48	-0 02	-0 01	+1.9	0.0	11.0	12.5	5.5
763	South Orrington	44 42	68 49	+0 01	+0 04	+3.2	0.0	12.3	14.0	6.1
765	Hampden	44 45	68 50	+0 02	+0 06	+3.7	0.0	12.8	14.6	6.4
767	Bangor	44 48	68 46	+0 04	+0 13	+4.0	0.0	13.1	14.9	6.5
769	Belfast	44 26	69 00	-0 08	-0 01	+0.9	0.0	10.0	11.5	5.0
771	Camden	44 12	69 03	-0 12	-0 06	+0.5	0.0	9.6	10.9	4.8
773	Rockland	44 06	69 06	-0 16	-0 13	+0.6	0.0	9.7	11.2	4.8
775	Owls Head	44 06	69 03	-0 16	-0 13	+0.3	0.0	9.4	10.7	4.7
777	Dyer Point, Weskeag River	44 02	69 07	-0 10	-0 10	+0.5	0.0	9.6	10.9	4.8
	MAINE, Outer Coast									
779	Tenants Harbor	43 58	69 12	-0 11	-0 11	+0.2	0.0	9.3	10.6	4.6
781	Monhegan Island	43 46	69 19	-0 13	-0 09	-0.3	0.0	8.8	10.1	4.4
783	Burnt Island, Georges Islands	43 52	69 18	-0 13	-0 12	-0.2	0.0	8.9	10.2	4.4
	St. George River									
785	Port Clyde	43 56	69 16	-0 11	-0 07	-0.2	0.0	8.9	10.2	4.4
787	Otis Cove	43 59	69 14	-0 15	-0 14	0.0	0.0	9.1	10.5	4.5
789	Thomaston	44 04	69 11	-0 04	-0 03	+0.3	0.0	9.4	10.8	4.7
791	New Harbor, Muscongus Bay	43 52	69 29	-0 10	-0 05	-0.3	0.0	8.8	10.1	4.4
793	Muscongus Harbor, Muscongus Sound	43 58	69 27	-0 09	-0 03	-0.1	0.0	9.0	10.4	4.5
795	Friendship Harbor	43 58	69 20	-0 18	-0 11	-0.1	0.0	9.0	10.4	4.5
	Medomak River									
797	Jones Neck	44 01	69 23	-0 10	-0 05	0.0	0.0	9.1	10.5	4.5
799	Waldoboro	44 06	69 23	-0 16	-0 04	+0.4	0.0	9.5	10.9	4.8
801	Pemaquid Harbor, Johns Bay	43 53	69 32	-0 05	-0 01	-0.3	0.0	8.8	10.1	4.4
	Damariscotta River									
803	East Boothbay	43 52	69 35	-0 02	+0 04	-0.2	0.0	8.9	10.2	4.4
805	Newcastle	44 02	69 32	+0 16	+0 28	+0.2	0.0	9.3	10.7	4.6
807	Damariscove Harbor, Damariscove Island	43 46	69 37	-0 09	-0 10	-0.3	0.0	8.8	10.1	4.4
809	Boothbay Harbor	43 51	69 38	-0 06	-0 05	-0.3	0.0	8.8	10.1	4.4
811	Southport, Townsend Gut	43 51	69 40	+0 01	+0 01	-0.2	0.0	8.9	10.2	4.4
	Sheepscot River									
813	Isle of Springs	43 52	69 41	-0 02	-0 04	-0.2	0.0	8.9	10.3	4.4
815	Cross River entrance	43 56	69 40	+0 07	+0 04	0.0	0.0	9.1	10.5	4.5
817	Wiscasset	44 00	69 40	+0 16	+0 04	+0.3	0.0	9.4	10.8	4.7
819	Sheepscot (below rapids)	44 03	69 37	+0 20	+0 20	+0.5	0.0	9.6	11.0	4.8
821	Back River	43 57	69 41	+0 34	+0 31	0.0	0.0	9.1	10.5	4.5
823	Robinhood, Sasanoa River	43 51	69 44	+0 14	+0 14	-0.3	0.0	8.8	10.1	4.4
825	Mill Point, Sasanoa River	43 53	69 46	+0 35	+0 43	-0.3	0.0	8.8	10.1	4.4
827	Upper Hell Gate, Sasanoa River	43 54	69 47	+1 11	+1 31	-2.1	0.0	7.0	8.0	3.5
	MAINE, Kennebec River									
829	Fort Popham	43 45	69 47	+0 09	+0 04	-0.7	0.0	8.4	9.7	4.2
831	Phippsburg	43 49	69 49	+0 26	+0 28	-1.1	0.0	8.0	9.2	4.0

Endnotes can be found at the end of table 2.

NO.	PLACE	POSITION Lat.	POSITION Long.	DIFFERENCES Time High Water	DIFFERENCES Time Low Water	DIFFERENCES Height High Water	DIFFERENCES Height Low Water	RANGES Mean	RANGES Spring	Mean Tide Level
		° ' N	° ' W	h. m.	h. m.	ft	ft	ft	ft	ft
	Maine, Kennebac River Time meridian, 75°W			on PORTLAND, p.32						
833	Bath	43 55	69 49	+1 01	+1 17	-2.7	0.0	6.4	7.4	3.2
835	Sturgeon Island, Merrymeeting Bay	43 59	69 50	+2 00	+2 04	*0.58	*0.58	5.3	6.1	2.6
837	Androscoggin River entrance	43 57	69 53	+2 24	+3 26	*0.52	*0.52	4.7	5.4	2.3
839	Brunswick, Androscoggin River	43 55	69 58	+2 35	+4 36	*0.42	*0.42	3.8	4.4	1.9
841	Bowdoinham, Cathance River	44 00	69 54	+2 34	+2 42	*0.63	*0.63	5.7	6.6	2.8
843	Richmond	44 05	69 48	+2 48	+3 03	*0.58	*0.58	5.3	6.0	2.6
845	Nehumkeag Island	44 10	69 45	+3 21	+3 46	*0.58	*0.58	5.3	6.0	2.6
847	Gardiner	44 14	69 46	+3 43	+4 25	*0.55	*0.55	5.0	5.7	2.5
849	Hallowell	44 17	69 47	+3 54	+5 03	*0.47	*0.47	4.3	4.9	2.1
851	Augusta	44 19	69 46	+4 03	+5 33	*0.45	*0.45	4.1	4.6	2.0
	MAINE, Casco Bay									
853	Small Point Harbor	43 44	69 51	-0 12	-0 09	-0.3	0.0	8.8	10.1	4.4
855	Cundy Harbor, New Meadows River	43 47	69 54	-0 01	-0 02	-0.2	0.0	8.9	10.2	4.4
857	Howard Point, New Meadows River	43 53	69 53	-0 05	+0 01	-0.1	0.0	9.0	10.3	4.5
859	Lowell Cove, Orrs Island	43 45	69 59	-0 07	-0 06	-0.3	0.0	8.8	10.1	4.4
861	Harpswell Harbor	43 46	70 00	-0 05	-0 05	-0.1	0.0	9.0	10.4	4.5
863	South Harpswell, Potts Harbor	43 44	70 01	+0 02	+0 01	-0.2	0.0	8.9	10.2	4.4
865	Wilson Cove, Middle Bay	43 49	69 59	+0 02	+0 02	0.0	0.0	9.1	10.5	4.5
867	Little Flying Point, Maquoit Bay	43 50	70 03	-0 01	-0 01	-0.1	0.0	9.0	10.3	4.5
869	South Freeport	43 49	70 06	+0 12	+0 10	-0.1	0.0	9.0	10.3	4.5
871	Chebeague Point, Great Chebeague Island	43 46	70 06	-0 04	-0 06	-0.1	0.0	9.0	10.4	4.5
873	Prince Point	43 46	70 10	-0 02	-0 04	-0.1	0.0	9.0	10.4	4.5
875	Peaks Island	43 39	70 12	-0 04	-0 08	-0.1	0.0	9.0	10.4	4.5
877	PORTLAND	43 40	70 15	Daily predictions				9.1	10.4	4.6
	MAINE, Outer Coast-Continued									
879	Richmond Island	43 33	70 14	-0 03	0 00	-0.2	0.0	8.9	10.1	4.4
881	Old Orchard Beach	43 31	70 22	0 00	-0 03	-0.3	0.0	8.8	10.1	4.4
883	Wood Island Harbor	43 27	70 21	+0 02	-0 04	-0.4	0.0	8.7	9.9	4.3
885	Cape Porpoise	43 22	70 26	+0 12	+0 17	-0.4	0.0	8.7	9.9	4.3
887	Kennebunkport	43 21	70 28	+0 16	+0 16	-0.5	0.0	8.6	9.9	4.3
889	York Harbor	43 08	70 38	+0 03	+0 13	-0.5	0.0	8.6	9.9	4.3
	MAINE and NEW HAMPSHIRE									
	Portsmouth Harbor									
891	Jaffrey Point	43 03	70 43	-0 03	-0 05	-0.4	0.0	8.7	10.0	4.4
893	Gerrish Island	43 04	70 42	-0 02	-0 03	-0.4	0.0	8.7	10.0	4.4
895	Fort Point	43 04	70 43	+0 03	+0 07	-0.5	0.0	8.6	9.9	4.3
897	Kittery Point	43 05	70 42	-0 07	+0 01	-0.4	0.0	8.7	10.0	4.4
899	Seavey Island	43 05	70 45	+0 23	+0 13	-1.0	0.0	8.1	9.3	4.0
901	Portsmouth	43 05	70 45	+0 22	+0 17	-1.3	0.0	7.8	9.0	3.9
	Piscataqua River									
903	Atlantic Heights	43 05	70 46	+0 37	+0 28	-1.6	0.0	7.5	8.6	3.7
905	Dover Point	43 07	70 50	+1 33	+1 27	-2.7	0.0	6.4	7.4	3.2
907	Salmon Falls River entrance	43 11	70 50	+1 35	+1 52	-2.3	0.0	6.8	7.8	3.4
909	Squamscott River RR Bridge	43 03	70 55	+2 19	+2 41	-2.3	0.0	6.8	7.8	3.4
911	Gosport Harbor, Isles of Shoals	42 59	70 37	+0 02	-0 02	-0.6	0.0	8.5	9.8	4.2
913	Hampton Harbor	42 54	70 49	+0 14	+0 32	-0.8	0.0	8.3	9.5	4.1
	MASSACHUSETTS, Outer Coast									
915	Merrimack River entrance	42 49	70 49	+0 20	+0 24	-0.8	0.0	8.3	9.5	4.1
917	Newburyport, Merrimack River	42 49	70 52	+0 31	+1 11	-1.3	0.0	7.8	9.0	3.9
919	Plum Island Sound (south end)	42 43	70 47	+0 12	+0 37	-0.5	0.0	8.6	9.9	4.3
921	Annisquam	42 39	70 41	0 00	-0 07	-0.4	0.0	8.7	10.1	4.4
923	Rockport	42 40	70 37	+0 04	+0 02	-0.5	0.0	8.6	10.0	4.3
				on BOSTON, p.36						
925	Gloucester	42 36	70 40	-0 03	-0 06	-0.8	0.0	8.7	10.1	4.3
927	Manchester Harbor	42 34	70 47	-0 02	-0 06	-0.7	0.0	8.8	10.2	4.4
929	Beverly	42 32	70 53	0 00	-0 05	-0.5	0.0	9.0	10.4	4.5
931	Salem	42 31	70 53	+0 02	+0 01	-0.7	0.0	8.8	10.2	4.4
933	Marblehead	42 30	70 51	-0 02	-0 06	-0.4	0.0	9.1	10.6	4.5
	Broad Sound									
935	Nahant	42 25	70 55	-0 01	-0 02	-0.5	0.0	9.0	10.4	4.5
937	Lynn Harbor	42 27	70 58	+0 08	+0 04	-0.3	0.0	9.2	10.7	4.6
	Boston Harbor									
939	Boston Light	42 20	70 53	0 00	+0 01	-0.5	0.0	9.0	10.4	4.5
941	Lovell Island, The Narrows	42 20	70 56	+0 02	+0 01	-0.4	0.0	9.1	10.6	4.5
943	Deer Island (south end)	42 21	70 58	-0 01	-0 02	-0.2	0.0	9.3	10.8	4.6
945	Belle Isle Inlet entrance	42 23	71 00	+0 18	+0 15	0.0	0.0	9.5	11.0	4.7
947	Castle Island	42 20	71 01	-0 02	0 00	-0.1	0.0	9.4	10.9	4.7

Endnotes can be found at the end of table 2.

NO.	PLACE	POSITION Lat.	POSITION Long.	DIFFERENCES Time High Water	DIFFERENCES Time Low Water	DIFFERENCES Height High Water	DIFFERENCES Height Low Water	RANGES Mean	RANGES Spring	Mean Tide Level
		° ′ N	° ′ W	h. m.	h. m.	ft	ft	ft	ft	ft
	Boston Harbor Time meridian, 75°W			on BOSTON, p.36						
949	BOSTON	42 21	71 03	Daily predictions				9.5	11.0	4.7
951	Dover St. Bridge, Fort Point Channel	42 21	71 04	+0 04	+0 06	+0.1	0.0	9.6	11.0	4.8
	Charles River									
953	Charlestown Bridge	42 22	71 04	+0 02	+0 02	0.0	0.0	9.5	11.0	4.7
955	Charles River Dam	42 22	71 04	+0 05	+0 04	0.0	0.0	9.5	11.0	4.7
957	Charlestown	42 22	71 03	-0 02	-0 01	0.0	0.0	9.5	11.0	4.7
959	Chelsea St. Bridge, Chelsea River	42 23	71 01	-0 01	+0 04	+0.1	0.0	9.6	11.1	4.8
965	Neponset, Neponset River	42 17	71 02	-0 04	+0 01	0.0	0.0	9.5	11.0	4.7
967	Moon Head	42 19	70 59	-0 01	+0 02	-0.1	0.0	9.4	10.9	4.7
969	Rainsford Island, Nantasket Roads	42 19	70 57	-0 02	0 00	-0.4	0.0	9.1	10.6	4.5
	Hingham Bay									
971	Nut Island	42 17	70 57	+0 07	+0 03	-0.3	0.0	9.2	10.7	4.6
973	Sheep Island	42 17	70 55	+0 07	+0 03	0.0	0.0	9.5	11.0	4.7
975	Weymouth Fore River Bridge	42 15	70 58	+0 07	+0 04	0.0	0.0	9.5	11.0	4.7
977	Weymouth Back River Bridge	42 15	70 56	+0 06	+0 05	0.0	0.0	9.5	11.0	4.7
979	Crow Point, Hingham Harbor entrance	42 16	70 54	0 00	+0 03	-0.1	0.0	9.4	10.9	4.7
981	Hingham	42 15	70 53	+0 07	+0 06	0.0	0.0	9.5	11.0	4.7
983	Nantasket Beach, Weir River	42 16	70 52	+0 04	+0 05	-0.1	0.0	9.4	10.9	4.7
985	Strawberry Hill	42 17	70 53	+0 05	+0 05	0.0	0.0	9.5	11.0	4.7
987	Hull	42 18	70 55	+0 03	+0 05	-0.2	0.0	9.3	10.8	4.7
	Cohasset Harbor to Davis Bank									
989	Cohasset Harbor (White Head)	42 15	70 47	+0 02	-0 04	-0.7	0.0	8.8	10.2	4.4
991	Scituate	42 12	70 43	-0 05	0 00	-0.7	0.0	8.8	10.2	4.4
992	Damons Point, North River	42 10	70 44	+0 18	+0 34	-1.0	0.0	8.5	9.9	4.2
	Cape Cod Bay									
993	Gurnet Point	42 00	70 36	+0 02	+0 07	-0.3	0.0	9.2	10.7	4.6
995	Plymouth	41 58	70 40	+0 05	+0 20	0.0	0.0	9.5	11.0	4.7
997	Cape Cod Canal, east entrance	41 46	70 30	-0 01	-0 02	-0.8	0.0	8.7	10.1	4.3
999	Barnstable Harbor, Beach Point	41 43	70 17	+0 09	+0 28	0.0	0.0	9.5	11.0	4.7
1001	Wellfleet	41 55	70 02	+0 12	+0 28	+0.5	0.0	10.0	11.6	5.0
1003	Provincetown	42 03	70 11	+0 14	+0 16	-0.4	0.0	9.1	10.6	4.5
1005	Race Point	42 04	70 15	-0 03	-0 04	-0.5	0.0	9.0	10.4	4.5
	Cape Cod									
1007	Cape Cod Lighthouse, SE of	42 00	70 01	+0 10	+0 09	-1.9	0.0	7.6	8.8	3.8
1009	Nauset Harbor	41 48	69 56	+0 30	+0 56	*0.63	*0.63	6.0	7.0	3.0
1011	Chatham (outer coast)	41 40	69 56	+0 30	+0 24	-2.8	0.0	6.7	7.8	3.3
1013	Chatham (inside)	41 41	69 57	+1 54	+2 24	*0.38	*0.38	3.6	4.2	1.8
1015	Pleasant Bay	41 44	69 59	+2 26	+3 25	*0.34	*0.34	3.2	3.7	1.6
1017	Monomoy Point	41 33	70 00	+0 40	+0 32	*0.39	*0.39	3.7	4.3	1.8
1019	Georges Shoal	41 42	67 46	-0 49	-0 45	*0.44	*0.44	4.2	4.8	2.1
1021	Davis Bank, Nantucket Shoals	41 08	69 39	+0 04	-0 27	*0.14	*0.14	1.3	1.5	0.6
	Nantucket Sound, North Side									
1023	Stage Harbor	41 40	69 58	+0 55	+0 46	*0.41	*0.41	3.9	4.7	1.9
1025	Wychmere Harbor	41 40	70 04	+0 50	+0 23	*0.39	*0.39	3.7	4.3	1.8
1027	Dennis Port	41 39	70 07	+1 01	+0 36	*0.36	*0.36	3.4	4.1	1.7
1029	South Yarmouth, Bass River	41 40	70 11	+1 46	+1 44	*0.29	*0.29	2.8	3.4	1.4
1031	Hyannis Port	41 38	70 18	+1 01	+0 29	*0.33	*0.33	3.1	3.7	1.5
1033	Cotuit Highlands	41 36	70 26	+1 15	+0 45	*0.26	*0.26	2.5	3.0	1.2
1035	Poponesset Island, Poponesset Bay	41 35	70 28	+2 01	+1 50	*0.24	*0.24	2.3	2.8	1.1
1037	Succonnesset Point	41 33	70 29	+0 52	+0 37	*0.20	*0.20	1.9	2.3	0.9
1039	Falmouth Heights	41 33	70 36	-0 18	-0 11	*0.14	*0.14	1.3	1.6	0.6
	Nantucket Island									
1041	Tom Nevers Head	41 14	70 01	-0 57	-1 22	*0.13	*0.13	1.2	1.4	0.6
1043	Siasconset	41 16	69 58	+0 15	+0 19	*0.13	*0.13	1.2	1.4	0.6
1045	Wauwinet (outer shore)	41 20	70 00	+1 06	+0 57	*0.35	*0.35	3.3	4.0	1.6
1047	Great Point	41 23	70 03	+0 41	+0 26	*0.33	*0.33	3.1	3.7	1.5
1049	Nantucket	41 17	70 06	+1 05	+0 50	*0.32	*0.32	3.0	3.6	1.5
1051	Eel Point	41 17	70 12	+0 37	+0 05	*0.24	*0.24	2.3	2.7	1.1
1053	Tuckernuck Island, East Pond	41 18	70 15	+0 46	+0 27	*0.27	*0.27	2.6	3.1	1.3
1055	Muskeget Island, north side	41 20	70 18	+0 23	+0 13	*0.21	*0.21	2.0	2.4	1.0
1057	Smith Point, north side	41 17	70 14	+0 46	-0 32	*0.16	*0.16	1.5	1.9	0.8
				on NEWPORT, p.40						
1059	Miacomet Rip	41 14	70 06	+0 18	+0 55	*0.49	*0.49	1.7	2.0	0.8
	Martha's Vineyard									
1061	Wasque Point, Chappaquiddick Island	41 22	70 27	+2 05	+3 25	*0.31	*0.31	1.1	1.4	0.6
1063	Off Jobs Neck Pond	41 21	70 35	+0 04	+0 27	-0.8	0.0	2.7	3.2	1.3
1065	Off Chilmark Pond	41 20	70 43	-0 13	+0 09	-0.6	0.0	2.9	3.5	1.4

Endnotes can be found at the end of table 2.

NO.	PLACE	POSITION Lat.	POSITION Long.	DIFFERENCES Time High Water	DIFFERENCES Time Low Water	DIFFERENCES Height High Water	DIFFERENCES Height Low Water	RANGES Mean	RANGES Spring	Mean Tide Level
		° ' N	° ' W	h. m.	h. m.	ft	ft	ft	ft	ft
	Martha's Vineyard Time meridian, 75°W			on NEWPORT, p.40						
1066	Squibnocket Point	41 19	70 46	-0 42	+0 03	-0.6	0.0	2.9	3.7	1.5
1067	Nomans Land	41 16	70 49	-0 16	+0 23	-0.5	0.0	3.0	3.6	1.5
1069	Gay Head	41 21	70 50	-0 03	+0 50	-0.6	0.0	2.9	3.5	1.4
1071	Menemsha Bight	41 21	70 46	+0 05	+0 42	-0.8	0.0	2.7	3.4	1.3
1073	Cedar Tree Neck	41 26	70 42	+0 13	+1 37	-1.3	0.0	2.2	2.8	1.1
1075	Off Lake Tashmoo	41 28	70 38	+1 11	+2 16	*0.60	*0.60	2.1	2.5	1.0
				on BOSTON, p.36						
1077	West Chop	41 29	70 36	+0 16	-0 31	*0.15	*0.15	1.4	1.7	0.7
1079	Vineyard Haven	41 27	70 36	+0 25	-0 01	*0.18	*0.18	1.7	2.0	0.8
1081	East Chop	41 28	70 34	+0 27	-0 14	*0.18	*0.18	1.7	2.0	0.8
1083	Oak Bluffs	41 27	70 33	+0 30	-0 14	*0.18	*0.18	1.7	2.0	0.8
1085	Edgartown	41 23	70 31	+0 55	+0 16	*0.20	*0.20	1.9	2.3	0.9
1087	Cape Poge, Chappaquiddick Island	41 25	70 27	+0 44	+0 02	*0.23	*0.23	2.2	2.6	1.1
	Vineyard Sound			on NEWPORT, p.40						
1089	Nobska Point	41 31	70 39	+0 44	+2 10	*0.43	*0.43	1.5	1.9	0.7
	Woods Hole									
1091	Little Harbor	41 31	70 40	+0 35	+2 26	*0.40	*0.40	1.4	1.8	0.7
1093	Oceanographic Institution	41 31	70 40	+0 27	+2 04	*0.51	*0.51	1.8	2.2	0.9
1095	Uncatena Island (south side)	41 31	70 42	+0 15	+0 27	+0.1	0.0	3.6	4.5	1.8
1097	Tarpaulin Cove	41 28	70 46	+0 14	+1 28	*0.54	*0.54	1.9	2.4	0.9
	Quicks Hole									
1099	South side	41 26	70 51	-0 07	+0 14	-1.0	0.0	2.5	3.1	1.2
1101	Middle	41 27	70 51	+0 03	+0 15	-0.5	0.0	3.0	3.7	1.5
1103	North side	41 27	70 51	-0 05	-0 03	0.0	0.0	3.5	4.4	1.7
	Buzzards Bay									
1105	Cuttyhunk Pond entrance	41 25	70 55	+0 04	+0 06	-0.1	0.0	3.4	4.2	1.7
1107	Penikese Island	41 27	70 55	-0 14	-0 11	-0.1	0.0	3.4	4.2	1.7
1109	Kettle Cove	41 29	70 47	+0 12	+0 07	+0.3	0.0	3.8	4.7	1.9
1111	West Falmouth Harbor	41 36	70 39	+0 24	+0 23	+0.5	0.0	4.0	5.0	2.0
1113	Barlows Landing, Pocasset Harbor	41 41	70 38	+0 27	+0 23	+0.5	0.0	4.0	5.0	2.0
1115	Abiels Ledge	41 42	70 40	+0 14	+0 21	+0.4	0.0	3.9	4.9	2.0
1117	Monument Beach	41 43	70 37	+0 26	+0 23	+0.5	0.0	4.0	5.0	2.0
1119	Cape Cod Canal, RR. bridge <6>	41 44	70 37	+1 18	- - -	0.0	0.0	3.5	4.1	1.8
1121	Great Hill	41 43	70 43	+0 20	+0 20	+0.6	0.0	4.1	5.1	2.0
1123	Wareham, Wareham River	41 45	70 43	+0 25	+0 21	+0.6	0.0	4.1	5.1	2.0
1125	Bird Island	41 40	70 43	+0 08	+0 03	+0.7	0.0	4.2	5.2	2.1
1127	Marion	41 42	70 46	+0 12	+0 15	+0.5	0.0	4.0	5.0	2.0
1129	Mattapoisett	41 39	70 49	+0 13	+0 10	+0.4	0.0	3.9	4.9	2.0
1131	West Island (west side)	41 36	70 50	+0 12	+0 13	+0.2	0.0	3.7	4.6	1.8
1133	Clarks Point	41 36	70 54	+0 06	+0 08	+0.2	0.0	3.7	4.6	1.8
1135	New Bedford	41 38	70 55	+0 10	+0 12	+0.2	0.0	3.7	4.6	1.8
1137	Belleville, Acushnet River	41 40	70 55	+0 10	+0 14	+0.3	0.0	3.8	4.7	1.9
1139	South Dartmouth, Apponagansett Bay	41 35	70 57	+0 28	+0 38	+0.2	0.0	3.7	4.6	1.8
1141	Dumpling Rocks	41 32	70 55	+0 04	+0 03	+0.2	0.0	3.7	4.6	1.8
	Westport River									
1143	Westport Harbor	41 30	71 06	+0 12	+0 38	-0.5	0.0	3.0	3.7	1.5
1145	Hix Bridge, East Branch	41 34	71 04	+1 43	+2 35	-0.8	0.0	2.7	3.4	1.3
	RHODE ISLAND, Narragansett Bay									
1147	Sakonnet	41 28	71 12	-0 10	+0 04	-0.4	0.0	3.1	3.9	1.6
1149	Tiverton (between bridges)	41 38	71 13	+0 21	+0 21	+0.3	0.0	3.8	4.7	1.9
1151	Beavertail Point	41 27	71 24	-0 02	-0 05	0.0	0.0	3.5	4.4	1.8
1153	NEWPORT	41 30	71 20	Daily predictions				3.5	4.4	1.8
1155	Prudence Island, Sandy Point	41 36	71 18	+0 10	+0 09	+0.4	0.0	3.9	4.9	2.0
1157	Bristol Point	41 39	71 16	+0 21	+0 12	+0.5	0.0	4.0	5.0	2.0
	RHODE ISLAND and MASSACHUSETTS Narragansett Bay-Continued									
1159	Fall River, Massachusetts	41 44	71 08	+0 31	+0 34	+0.9	0.0	4.4	5.5	2.2
1161	Taunton, Taunton River, Mass	41 53	71 06	+1 09	+2 26	-0.7	0.0	2.8	3.5	1.4
1163	Bristol	41 40	71 16	+0 10	0 00	+0.6	0.0	4.1	5.1	2.0
1165	Warren	41 44	71 17	+0 21	+0 04	+1.1	0.0	4.6	5.7	2.3
1167	Nayatt Point	41 43	71 20	+0 12	+0 03	+1.1	0.0	4.6	5.7	2.3
1169	Providence	41 48	71 24	+0 14	+0 05	+1.1	0.0	4.6	5.7	2.3
1171	Pawtucket, Seekonk River	41 52	71 23	+0 21	+0 14	+1.1	0.0	4.6	5.8	2.3
1173	East Greenwich	41 40	71 27	+0 16	+0 08	+0.5	0.0	4.0	5.0	2.0
1175	Wickford	41 34	71 27	+0 12	+0 07	+0.3	0.0	3.8	4.7	1.9
1177	Narragansett Pier	41 25	71 27	-0 08	+0 16	-0.3	0.0	3.2	4.0	1.6

Endnotes can be found at the end of table 2.

CAUTION

Cape Cod Canal, Railroad Bridge, No. 1119

Predictions of the times of low water must be used with caution because of the peculiarities in the behavior of the tide. Since the tide may be practically at a stand for as much as two hours before or after the predicted times of low water, the levels at other than high and low water times cannot be obtained in the usual way as in Table 3 (Height of Tide at Any Time). The peculiar behavior of the tide near low water, which is prevalent at this place, is illustrated by the first three curves; however there are brief periods each month when the behavior is as depicted by the fourth curve.

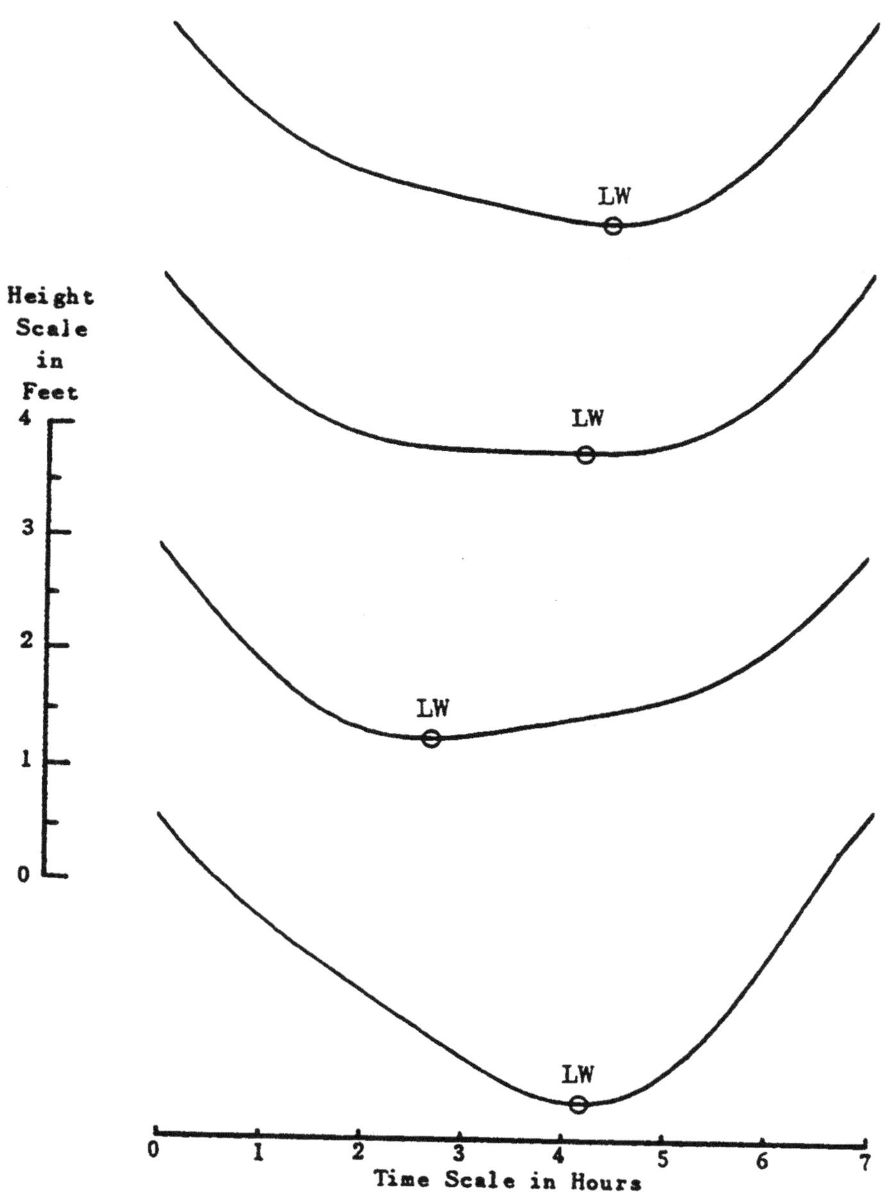

NO.	PLACE	POSITION Lat.	POSITION Long.	DIFFERENCES Time High Water	DIFFERENCES Time Low Water	DIFFERENCES Height High Water	DIFFERENCES Height Low Water	RANGES Mean	RANGES Spring	Mean Tide Level
		° ' N	° ' W	h. m.	h. m.	ft	ft	ft	ft	ft
	RHODE ISLAND, Outer Coast Time meridian, 75°W			on NEWPORT, p.40						
1179	Point Judith Harbor of Refuge...........	41 22	71 29	-0 07	+0 22	-0.4	0.0	3.1	3.9	1.5
1181	Block Island (Great Salt Pond)..........	41 11	71 35	+0 05	+0 12	-0.9	0.0	2.6	3.2	1.3
1183	Block Island (Old Harbor)...............	41 10	71 33	-0 14	+0 17	-0.6	0.0	2.9	3.6	1.4
1185	Watch Hill Point........................	41 18	71 52	+0 44	+1 21	-0.9	0.0	2.6	3.2	1.3
				on NEW LONDON, p.44						
1186	Westerly, Pawcatuck River...............	41 23	71 50	-0 27	+0 02	+0.1	0.0	2.7	3.2	1.3
	CONNECTICUT, Long Island Sound									
1187	Stonington, Fishers Island Sound........	41 20	71 54	-0 33	-0 41	+0.1	0.0	2.7	3.2	1.3
1189	Noank, Mystic River entrance............	41 19	71 59	-0 23	-0 08	-0.3	0.0	2.3	2.7	1.2
1191	West Harbor, Fishers Island, N. Y.......	41 16	72 00	-0 01	-0 06	-0.1	0.0	2.5	3.0	1.2
1192	Silver Eel Pond, Fishers Island, N. Y...	41 15	72 02	-0 17	-0 04	-0.3	0.0	2.3	2.7	1.1
	Thames River									
1193	NEW LONDON, State Pier..............	41 22	72 06	Daily predictions				2.6	3.1	1.3
1195	Smith Cove entrance.................	41 24	72 06	-0 01	+0 10	-0.1	0.0	2.5	3.0	1.2
1197	Norwich.............................	41 31	72 05	+0 12	+0 25	+0.4	0.0	3.0	3.6	1.5
1199	Millstone Point.........................	41 18	72 10	+0 08	+0 01	+0.1	0.0	2.7	3.2	1.3
	Connecticut River									
1200	Saybrook Jetty......................	41 16	72 21	+1 10	+0 45	+0.9	0.0	3.5	4.2	1.7
1201	Saybrook Point......................	41 17	72 21	+1 10	+0 53	+0.6	0.0	3.2	3.8	1.6
1202	Lyme, highway bridge................	41 19	72 21	+1 24	+1 10	+0.5	0.0	3.1	3.7	1.5
1203	Essex...............................	41 21	72 23	+1 38	+1 38	+0.4	0.0	3.0	3.6	1.5
	Connecticut River									
1204	Hadlyme <7>.........................	41 25	72 26	+2 18	+2 23	+0.1	0.0	2.7	3.2	1.3
1205	East Haddam.........................	41 27	72 28	+2 41	+2 53	+0.3	0.0	2.9	3.5	1.4
1206	Haddam <7>..........................	41 29	72 30	+2 47	+3 08	-0.1	0.0	2.5	3.0	1.2
1207	Higganum Creek......................	41 30	72 33	+2 54	+3 25	0.0	0.0	2.6	3.1	1.3
1209	Portland <7>........................	41 34	72 38	+3 50	+4 28	-0.4	0.0	2.2	2.6	1.1
1211	Rocky Hill <7>......................	41 39	72 38	+4 43	+5 44	-0.6	0.0	2.0	2.4	1.0
1213	Hartford <7>........................	41 46	72 40	+5 29	+6 52	-0.7	0.0	1.9	2.3	1.0
				on BRIDGEPORT, p.48						
1214	Westbrook, Duck Island Roads............	41 16	72 28	-0 23	-0 34	-2.6	0.0	4.1	4.7	2.0
1215	Duck Island.............................	41 15	72 29	-0 25	-0 37	-2.2	0.0	4.5	5.2	2.2
1217	Madison.................................	41 16	72 36	-0 20	-0 32	-1.8	0.0	4.9	5.6	2.4
1219	Falkner Island..........................	41 13	72 39	-0 13	-0 27	-1.3	0.0	5.4	6.2	2.7
1220	Sachem Head.............................	41 15	72 42	-0 10	-0 17	-1.3	0.0	5.4	6.2	2.7
1221	Money Island............................	41 15	72 45	-0 11	-0 25	-1.1	0.0	5.6	6.4	2.8
1223	Branford Harbor.........................	41 16	72 49	-0 07	-0 20	-0.8	0.0	5.9	6.8	2.9
1225	New Haven Harbor entrance...............	41 14	72 55	-0 08	-0 16	-0.5	0.0	6.2	7.1	3.1
1227	New Haven (city dock)...................	41 18	72 55	+0 02	-0 03	-0.7	0.0	6.0	6.9	3.0
1229	Milford Harbor..........................	41 13	73 03	-0 07	-0 12	-0.1	0.0	6.6	7.6	3.3
1231	Stratford, Housatonic River.............	41 11	73 07	+0 27	+0 59	-1.2	0.0	5.5	6.3	2.7
1233	Shelton, Housatonic River...............	41 19	73 05	+1 36	+2 42	-1.7	0.0	5.0	5.8	2.5
1235	BRIDGEPORT..............................	41 10	73 11	Daily predictions				6.7	7.7	3.4
1237	Black Rock Harbor entrance..............	41 09	73 13	-0 03	-0 05	+0.2	0.0	6.9	7.9	3.4
1239	Saugatuck River entrance................	41 06	73 22	-0 01	-0 01	+0.3	0.0	7.0	8.0	3.5
1241	South Norwalk...........................	41 06	73 25	+0 10	+0 13	+0.4	0.0	7.1	8.2	3.5
1243	Greens Ledge............................	41 03	73 27	-0 01	-0 03	+0.5	0.0	7.2	8.3	3.6
1245	Stamford................................	41 02	73 33	+0 04	+0 06	+0.5	0.0	7.2	8.3	3.6
1247	Cos Cob Harbor..........................	41 01	73 36	+0 06	+0 09	+0.5	0.0	7.2	8.3	3.6
1249	Greenwich...............................	41 01	73 37	+0 02	-0 01	+0.7	0.0	7.4	8.5	3.7
1251	Great Captain Island....................	40 59	73 37	+0 01	-0 01	+0.6	0.0	7.3	8.4	3.6
	NEW YORK Long Island Sound, North Side			on WILLETS POINT, p.52						
1253	Port Chester............................	41 00	73 40	-0 09	-0 12	+0.1	0.0	7.2	8.5	3.6
1254	Rye Beach...............................	40 58	73 40	-0 28	-0 29	+0.1	0.0	7.2	8.4	3.6
1255	Mamaroneck..............................	40 56	73 44	-0 08	-0 11	+0.2	0.0	7.3	8.6	3.6
1257	New Rochelle............................	40 54	73 47	-0 24	-0 17	+0.1	0.0	7.2	8.6	3.6
1259	Davids Island...........................	40 53	73 46	-0 02	-0 07	+0.1	0.0	7.2	8.5	3.6
1261	City Island.............................	40 51	73 47	-0 03	-0 03	+0.1	0.0	7.2	8.5	3.6
1263	Throgs Neck.............................	40 48	73 48	+0 02	+0 14	-0.1	0.0	7.0	8.2	3.5
	East River									
1265	Whitestone..............................	40 48	73 49	+0 02	+0 14	0.0	0.0	7.1	8.3	3.5
1267	Old Ferry Point.........................	40 48	73 50	+0 04	+0 16	0.0	0.0	7.1	8.3	3.5
1269	College Point, Flushing Bay.............	40 47	73 51	+0 20	+0 28	-0.6	0.0	6.5	7.6	3.2
1271	Northern Blvd. Bridge, Flushing Creek...	40 46	73 50	+0 23	+0 37	-0.3	0.0	6.8	8.0	3.4
1273	Westchester, Westchester Creek..........	40 50	73 50	+0 10	+0 16	-0.1	0.0	7.0	8.3	3.5
1275	Hunts Point.............................	40 48	73 52	+0 08	+0 15	-0.2	0.0	6.9	8.1	3.4
1277	Westchester Ave. Bridge, Bronx River....	40 50	73 53	+0 10	+0 17	-0.2	0.0	6.9	8.1	3.4
1279	North Brother Island....................	40 48	73 54	+0 09	+0 17	-0.5	0.0	6.6	7.8	3.3
1281	Port Morris (Stony Point)...............	40 48	73 54	+0 13	+0 16	-0.8	0.0	6.3	7.4	3.1

Endnotes can be found at the end of table 2.

NO.	PLACE	POSITION Lat.	POSITION Long.	DIFFERENCES Time High Water	DIFFERENCES Time Low Water	DIFFERENCES Height High Water	DIFFERENCES Height Low Water	RANGES Mean	RANGES Spring	Mean Tide Level
		° ' N	° ' W	h. m.	h. m.	ft	ft	ft	ft	ft
	New York, East River Time meridian, 75°W			on WILLETS POINT, p.52						
1283	Lawrence Point...........................	40 47	73 55	-0 03	+0 13	-0.7	0.0	6.4	7.6	3.2
1285	Wolcott Avenue...........................	40 47	73 55	-0 03	+0 13	-1.0	0.0	6.1	7.2	3.0
				on NEW YORK, p.56						
1287	Pot Cove, Astoria........................	40 47	73 56	+2 20	+2 29	+0.8	0.0	5.3	6.3	2.6
1289	Hell Gate, Hallets Point.................	40 47	73 56	+2 00	+2 04	+0.6	0.0	5.1	6.1	2.5
1291	Horns Hook, East 90th Street.............	40 47	73 57	+1 50	+1 30	+0.3	0.0	4.8	5.8	2.4
1293	Welfare Island, north end................	40 46	73 56	+1 45	+1 25	+0.3	0.0	4.8	5.8	2.4
1295	37th Avenue, Long Island City............	40 46	73 57	+1 30	+1 10	0.0	0.0	4.5	5.5	2.2
1297	East 41st Street, New York City..........	40 45	73 58	+1 20	+0 56	-0.2	0.0	4.3	5.2	2.1
1299	Hunters Point, Newtown Creek.............	40 44	73 57	+1 18	+0 53	-0.4	0.0	4.1	4.9	2.0
1301	English Kills entrance, Newtown Creek....	40 43	73 55	+1 30	+1 04	-0.3	0.0	4.2	5.0	2.1
1303	East 27th Street, Bellevue Hospital......	40 44	73 58	+1 08	+1 03	-0.3	0.0	4.2	5.0	2.1
1305	East 19th Street, New York City..........	40 44	73 58	+1 02	+0 58	-0.4	0.0	4.1	4.9	2.0
1307	North 3d Street, Brooklyn................	40 43	73 58	+0 55	+0 42	-0.4	0.0	4.1	4.9	2.0
1309	Williamsburg Bridge......................	40 43	73 58	+0 52	+0 38	-0.4	0.0	4.1	4.9	2.0
1311	Wallabout Bay............................	40 42	73 59	+0 50	+0 35	-0.4	0.0	4.1	4.9	2.0
1313	Brooklyn Bridge..........................	40 42	74 00	+0 13	+0 07	-0.2	0.0	4.3	5.2	2.1
	Harlem River									
1315	East 110th Street, New York City....	40 47	73 56	+1 52	+1 35	+0.6	0.0	5.1	6.1	2.6
1317	Willis Avenue Bridge................	40 48	73 56	+1 47	+1 30	+0.5	0.0	5.0	6.0	2.5
1319	Madison Avenue Bridge...............	40 49	73 56	+1 52	+1 35	+0.4	0.0	4.9	5.9	2.4
1321	Central Bridge......................	40 50	73 56	+1 52	+1 35	+0.2	0.0	4.7	5.7	2.3
1323	Washington Bridge...................	40 51	73 56	+1 52	+1 35	-0.1	0.0	4.4	5.2	2.2
1325	University Heights Bridge...........	40 52	73 55	+1 40	+1 30	-0.5	0.0	4.0	4.8	2.0
1327	Broadway Bridge.....................	40 52	73 55	+1 20	+1 20	-0.7	0.0	3.8	4.6	1.9
1329	Spuyten Duyvil Bridge...............	40 53	73 56	+1 01	+1 03	-0.9	0.0	3.6	4.3	1.8
	Long Island Sound, South Side			on WILLETS POINT, p.52						
1331	WILLETS POINT............................	40 48	73 47	Daily predictions				7.1	8.3	3.5
1333	Hewlett Point............................	40 50	73 45	-0 03	-0 03	0.0	0.0	7.1	8.3	3.5
1335	Port Washington, Manhasset Bay...........	40 50	73 42	-0 01	+0 11	+0.2	0.0	7.3	8.6	3.6
1337	Execution Rocks..........................	40 53	73 44	-0 06	-0 08	+0.2	0.0	7.3	8.6	3.6
1339	Glen Cove, Hempstead Harbor..............	40 52	73 39	-0 11	-0 06	+0.2	0.0	7.3	8.6	3.6
				on BRIDGEPORT, p.48						
	Oyster Bay									
1341	Oyster Bay Harbor...................	40 53	73 32	+0 08	+0 11	+0.6	0.0	7.3	8.4	3.6
1343	Bayville Bridge.....................	40 54	73 33	+0 13	+0 18	+0.7	0.0	7.4	8.5	3.7
1345	Cold Spring Harbor..................	40 52	73 28	+0 08	+0 06	+0.7	0.0	7.4	8.5	3.7
1347	Eatons Neck Point........................	40 57	73 24	+0 03	+0 06	+0.4	0.0	7.1	8.2	3.6
1349	Lloyd Harbor entrance, Huntington Bay....	40 55	73 26	+0 03	+0 01	+0.7	0.0	7.4	8.5	3.7
1351	Northport, Northport Bay.................	40 54	73 21	+0 03	+0 06	+0.6	0.0	7.3	8.4	3.6
1353	Nissequogue River entrance...............	40 54	73 14	-0 03	-0 06	+0.3	0.0	7.0	8.0	3.5
1355	Stony Brook, Smithtown Bay...............	40 55	73 09	+0 08	+0 08	-0.6	0.0	6.1	7.0	3.0
1357	Stratford Shoal..........................	41 04	73 06	-0 05	-0 09	-0.1	0.0	6.6	7.6	3.3
1359	Port Jefferson Harbor entrance...........	40 58	73 05	+0 03	-0 01	-0.1	0.0	6.6	7.6	3.3
1361	Port Jefferson...........................	40 57	73 05	+0 06	+0 03	-0.1	0.0	6.6	7.6	3.3
1363	Setauket Harbor..........................	40 57	73 06	+0 04	+0 09	0.0	0.0	6.7	7.7	3.3
1365	Conscience Bay entrance (Narrows)........	40 58	73 07	+0 02	+0 02	0.0	0.0	6.7	7.7	3.3
1367	Mount Sinai Harbor.......................	40 58	73 02	+0 05	+0 16	-0.7	0.0	6.0	6.9	3.0
1369	Herod Point..............................	40 58	72 50	-0 07	-0 16	-0.8	0.0	5.9	6.8	2.9
1370	Northville...............................	40 59	72 39	-0 02	-0 05	-1.3	0.0	5.4	6.2	2.7
1371	Mattituck Inlet..........................	41 01	72 34	+0 05	-0 06	-1.5	0.0	5.2	6.0	2.6
1373	Horton Point.............................	41 05	72 27	-0 20	-0 35	*0.60	*0.60	4.0	4.6	2.0
1374	Hashamomuck Beach........................	41 06	72 24	+0 04	-0 15	*0.63	*0.63	4.2	4.8	2.1
1375	Truman Beach.............................	41 08	72 19	-0 42	-0 52	*0.51	*0.51	3.4	3.9	1.7
				on NEW LONDON, p.44						
1377	Plum Gut Harbor, Plum Island.............	41 10	72 12	+0 27	+0 16	0.0	0.0	2.6	3.1	1.3
1379	Little Gull Island.......................	41 12	72 06	+0 12	-0 22	-0.4	0.0	2.2	2.6	1.1
	Shelter Island Sound									
1381	Orient..............................	41 08	72 18	+0 36	+0 36	-0.1	0.0	2.5	3.0	1.2
1383	Greenport...........................	41 06	72 22	+1 04	+0 49	-0.2	0.0	2.4	2.9	1.2
1385	Southhold...........................	41 04	72 25	+1 43	+1 33	-0.3	0.0	2.3	2.7	1.1
1387	Noyack Bay..........................	41 00	72 20	+2 05	+1 44	-0.3	0.0	2.3	2.7	1.1
1389	Sag Harbor..........................	41 00	72 18	+0 59	+0 48	-0.1	0.0	2.5	3.0	1.2
1391	Cedar Point.........................	41 02	72 16	+0 44	+0 27	-0.1	0.0	2.5	3.0	1.2
	Peconic Bays									
1393	New Suffolk.........................	41 00	72 28	+2 26	+2 11	0.0	0.0	2.6	3.1	1.3
1395	South Jamesport.....................	40 56	72 35	+2 32	+2 40	+0.1	0.0	2.7	3.2	1.3
1397	Shinnecock Canal....................	40 54	72 30	+2 33	+2 31	-0.2	0.0	2.4	2.9	1.2
1399	Threemile Harbor ent., Gardiners Bay....	41 02	72 11	+0 21	+0 02	-0.2	0.0	2.4	2.9	1.2
1401	Promised Land, Napeague Bay..............	41 00	72 05	-0 14	-0 08	-0.3	0.0	2.3	2.7	1.1
1403	Montauk Harbor entrance..................	41 04	71 56	-0 25	-0 16	-0.7	0.0	1.9	2.3	0.9
1405	Montauk, Fort Pond Bay...................	41 03	71 58	-0 29	-0 24	-0.5	0.0	2.1	2.5	1.1
1407	Montauk Point, north side................	41 04	71 52	-1 13	-1 31	-0.6	0.0	2.0	2.4	1.0

Endnotes can be found at the end of table 2.

NO.	PLACE	POSITION Lat.	POSITION Long.	DIFFERENCES Time High Water	DIFFERENCES Time Low Water	DIFFERENCES Height High Water	DIFFERENCES Height Low Water	RANGES Mean	RANGES Spring	Mean Tide Level
		° ' N	° ' W	h. m.	h. m.	ft	ft	ft	ft	ft
	Long Island, South Side Time meridian, 75°W			on SANDY HOOK, p.64						
1409	Shinnecock inlet (ocean)...............	40 50	72 28	-0 50	-1 08	*0.63	*0.63	2.9	3.5	1.4
1411	Ponquogue Bridge, Shinnecock Bay........	40 51	72 30	+0 29	+0 14	-2.3	0.0	2.3	2.8	1.2
1413	Potunk Point, Moriches Bay.............	40 48	72 39	+3 35	+3 35	*0.11	*0.11	0.5	0.6	0.2
1415	Moriches Inlet.........................	40 46	72 45	-0 56	-1 11	*0.63	*0.63	2.9	3.5	1.4
1417	Mastic Beach, Moriches Bay.............	40 45	72 50	+3 28	+3 39	*0.11	*0.11	0.5	0.6	0.2
1419	Fire Island Breakwater.................	40 37	73 18	-0 39	-0 51	-0.5	0.0	4.1	5.0	2.0
1421	Democrat Point, Fire Island Inlet.......	40 38	73 18	-0 38	-0 29	*0.57	*0.57	2.6	3.1	1.3
	Great South Bay									
1422	Fire Island Coast Guard Station.....	40 38	73 16	-0 19	-0 17	*0.41	*0.41	1.9	2.3	0.9
1423	Fire Island Radiobeacon............	40 38	73 13	+0 47	+1 20	*0.15	*0.15	0.7	0.8	0.3
1425	West Fire Island...................	40 39	73 12	+2 11	+2 16	*0.13	*0.13	0.6	0.7	0.3
1427	Point o' Woods.....................	40 39	73 08	+2 28	+2 33	*0.15	*0.15	0.7	0.8	0.3
1429	Bellport, Bellport Bay.............	40 45	72 56	+3 44	+4 14	*0.17	*0.17	0.8	1.0	0.4
1431	Patchogue..........................	40 45	73 01	+3 23	+3 47	*0.15	*0.15	0.7	0.8	0.3
1433	Sayville (Brown Creek).............	40 44	73 04	+3 39	+3 44	*0.13	*0.13	0.6	0.7	0.3
1435	Great River, Connetquot River.......	40 43	73 09	+3 20	+3 30	*0.15	*0.15	0.7	0.8	0.3
1437	Bay Shore..........................	40 43	73 14	+2 23	+2 39	*0.13	*0.13	0.6	0.7	0.3
1439	Oakbeach...........................	40 38	73 17	+2 24	+2 56	*0.15	*0.15	0.7	0.8	0.3
1441	Babylon............................	40 41	73 19	+2 12	+2 39	*0.13	*0.13	0.6	0.7	0.3
1443	Gilgo Heading......................	40 37	73 24	+2 23	+2 56	*0.24	*0.24	1.1	1.3	0.5
1445	Amityville.............................	40 39	73 25	+2 21	+3 03	*0.26	*0.26	1.2	1.4	0.6
1447	Biltmore Shores, South Oyster Bay.......	40 40	73 28	+2 05	+2 30	*0.30	*0.30	1.4	1.7	0.7
1449	Jones Inlet (Point Lookout)............	40 35	73 35	-0 19	-0 27	*0.78	*0.78	3.6	4.3	1.8
	Hempstead Bay									
1451	Deep Creek Meadow..................	40 36	73 32	+1 02	+1 09	*0.52	*0.52	2.4	2.9	1.2
1453	Green Island.......................	40 37	73 30	+1 22	+1 29	*0.41	*0.41	1.9	2.3	0.9
1455	Cuba Island........................	40 37	73 31	+1 08	+1 20	*0.50	*0.50	2.3	2.8	1.1
1457	Bellmore, Bellmore Creek............	40 40	73 31	+1 29	+1 56	*0.43	*0.43	2.0	2.4	1.0
1459	Neds Creek.........................	40 37	73 33	+0 50	+0 52	-1.9	0.0	2.7	3.3	1.3
1461	Freeport Creek.....................	40 38	73 34	+0 34	+0 27	-1.5	0.0	3.1	3.8	1.5
1463	Freeport, Baldwin Bay..............	40 38	73 35	+0 38	+0 53	-1.6	0.0	3.0	3.6	1.5
1465	Long Beach.........................	40 36	73 39	+0 19	0 00	-0.7	0.0	3.9	4.7	1.9
1467	Long Beach (outer coast)...............	40 35	73 39	-0 29	-0 35	-0.1	0.0	4.5	5.4	2.2
	Hempstead Bay-Continued									
1469	East Rockaway......................	40 38	73 40	+0 42	+0 45	-0.7	0.0	3.9	4.7	1.9
1471	Woodmere, Brosewere Bay............	40 37	73 42	+0 35	+0 48	-0.7	0.0	3.9	4.7	1.9
1473	East Rockaway Inlet....................	40 36	73 44	-0 06	-0 16	-0.5	0.0	4.1	5.0	2.0
	Jamaica Bay									
1475	Plumb Beach Channel................	40 35	73 55	+0 03	-0 05	+0.3	0.0	4.9	5.9	2.4
1477	Barren Island, Rockaway Inlet.......	40 35	73 53	0 00	-0 06	+0.4	0.0	5.0	6.0	2.5
1479	Beach Channel (bridge).............	40 35	73 49	+0 38	+0 22	+0.5	0.0	5.1	6.2	2.5
1481	Motts Basin........................	40 37	73 46	+0 40	+0 46	+0.8	0.0	5.4	6.5	2.7
1483	Norton Point, Head of Bay..........	40 38	73 45	+0 39	+0 43	+0.8	0.0	5.4	6.5	2.7
1485	J. F. K. International Airport......	40 37	73 47	+0 26	+0 43	+0.7	0.0	5.3	6.4	2.6
1487	Grassy Bay (bridge)................	40 39	73 50	+0 44	+0 45	+0.6	0.0	5.2	6.3	2.6
1489	Canarsie...........................	40 38	73 53	+0 28	+0 06	+0.6	0.0	5.2	6.3	2.6
1491	Mill Basin.........................	40 37	73 55	+0 29	+0 02	+0.6	0.0	5.2	6.3	2.6
	NEW YORK and NEW JERSEY New York Harbor									
1493	Coney Island...........................	40 34	73 59	-0 03	-0 19	+0.1	0.0	4.7	5.7	2.3
1495	Norton Point, Gravesend Bay............	40 35	74 00	-0 03	+0 01	+0.1	0.0	4.7	5.7	2.3
1497	Fort Wadsworth, The Narrows............	40 36	74 03	+0 02	+0 12	-0.3	0.0	4.3	5.2	2.1
1499	Fort Hamilton, The Narrows.............	40 37	74 02	+0 03	+0 05	+0.1	0.0	4.7	5.7	2.3
				on NEW YORK, p.56						
1501	Bay Ridge..............................	40 38	74 02	-0 24	-0 24	+0.1	0.0	4.6	5.5	2.3
1503	St. George, Staten Island..............	40 39	74 04	-0 21	-0 18	0.0	0.0	4.5	5.4	2.2
1505	Bayonne, New Jersey....................	40 41	74 06	-0 19	-0 08	0.0	0.0	4.5	5.4	2.2
1507	Gowanus Bay............................	40 40	74 01	-0 19	-0 15	-0.1	0.0	4.4	5.3	2.2
1509	Governors Island.......................	40 42	74 01	-0 11	-0 06	-0.1	0.0	4.4	5.3	2.2
1511	NEW YORK (The Battery).................	40 42	74 01	Daily Predictions				4.5	5.4	2.2
	Hudson River <8>									
1513	Jersey City, Con Rail RR. Ferry, N. J...	40 43	74 02	+0 07	+0 07	-0.1	0.0	4.4	5.3	2.2
1515	New York, Desbrosses Street............	40 43	74 01	+0 10	+0 10	-0.1	0.0	4.4	5.3	2.2
1517	New York, Chelsea Docks................	40 45	74 01	+0 17	+0 16	-0.2	0.0	4.3	5.2	2.1
1519	Hoboken, Castle Point, N. J............	40 45	74 01	+0 17	+0 16	-0.2	0.0	4.3	5.2	2.1
1521	Weehawken, Days Point, N. J............	40 46	74 01	+0 24	+0 23	-0.3	0.0	4.2	5.0	2.1
1523	New York, Union Stock Yards............	40 47	74 00	+0 27	+0 26	-0.3	0.0	4.2	5.0	2.1
1525	New York, 130th Street.................	40 49	73 58	+0 37	+0 35	-0.5	0.0	4.0	4.8	2.0
1527	George Washington Bridge...............	40 51	73 57	+0 46	+0 43	-0.6	0.0	3.9	4.6	1.9
1529	Spuyten Duyvil, west of RR. bridge......	40 53	73 56	+0 58	+0 53	-0.7	0.0	3.8	4.5	1.9
1531	Yonkers................................	40 56	73 54	+1 09	+1 10	-0.8	0.0	3.7	4.4	1.8

Endnotes can be found at the end of table 2.

NO.	PLACE	POSITION Lat.	POSITION Long.	DIFFERENCES Time High Water	DIFFERENCES Time Low Water	DIFFERENCES Height High Water	DIFFERENCES Height Low Water	RANGES Mean	RANGES Spring	Mean Tide Level
		° ′ N	° ′ W	h. m.	h. m.	ft	ft	ft	ft	ft
	Hudson River <8> Time meridian, 75°W			on NEW YORK, p.56						
1533	Dobbs Ferry	41 01	73 53	+1 29	+1 40	-1.1	0.0	3.4	4.0	1.7
1535	Tarrytown	41 05	73 52	+1 45	+1 54	-1.3	0.0	3.2	3.7	1.6
1537	Ossining	41 10	73 52	+1 53	+2 14	-1.4	0.0	3.1	3.6	1.5
1539	Haverstraw	41 12	73 58	+1 59	+2 25	-1.6	0.0	2.9	3.4	1.4
1541	Peekskill	41 17	73 56	+2 24	+3 00	-1.3	+0.3	2.9	3.4	1.7
1543	West Point	41 24	73 57	+3 16	+3 37	-1.5	+0.3	2.7	3.1	1.6
1545	Newburgh	41 30	74 00	+3 42	+4 00	-1.5	+0.2	2.8	3.2	1.6
1547	New Hamburg	41 35	73 57	+4 00	+4 25	-1.5	+0.1	2.9	3.3	1.5
1549	Poughkeepsie	41 42	73 57	+4 30	+4 43	-1.3	+0.1	3.1	3.5	1.6
1551	Hyde Park	41 47	73 57	+4 56	+5 09	-1.3	0.0	3.2	3.6	1.6
1553	Kingston Point	41 56	73 58	+5 16	+5 31	-0.9	-0.1	3.7	4.2	1.7
1555	Tivoli	42 04	73 56	+5 46	+6 01	-0.8	-0.2	3.9	4.4	1.7
1557	Catskill	42 13	73 51	+6 37	+6 55	-0.7	-0.3	4.1	4.6	1.7
1559	Hudson	42 15	73 48	+6 54	+7 09	-0.9	-0.4	4.0	4.4	1.6
				on ALBANY, p.60						
1561	Coxsackie	42 21	73 48	-1 01	-1 38	-0.5	+0.2	3.9	4.3	2.1
1563	New Baltimore	42 27	73 47	-0 34	-0 56	-0.1	+0.4	4.1	4.5	2.4
1565	Castleton-on-Hudson	42 32	73 46	-0 17	-0 29	-0.2	+0.1	4.3	4.7	2.2
1567	ALBANY	42 39	73 45	Daily predictions				4.6	5.0	2.5
1569	Troy	42 44	73 42	+0 08	+0 10	+0.1	0.0	4.7	5.1	2.3
	The Kills and Newark Bay			on NEW YORK, p.56						
	Kill Van Kull									
1571	Constable Hook	40 39	74 05	-0 34	-0 21	0.0	0.0	4.5	5.4	2.2
1573	New Brighton	40 39	74 05	-0 12	-0 18	0.0	0.0	4.5	5.4	2.2
1575	Port Richmond	40 38	74 08	-0 03	+0 05	0.0	0.0	4.5	5.4	2.2
1577	Bergen Point	40 39	74 08	+0 03	+0 03	+0.1	0.0	4.6	5.5	2.3
1579	Shooters Island	40 39	74 10	+0 06	+0 18	+0.1	0.0	4.6	5.5	2.3
1581	Port Newark Terminal	40 41	74 08	-0 01	+0 18	+0.6	0.0	5.1	6.1	2.5
1583	Newark, Passaic River	40 44	74 10	+0 22	+0 52	+0.6	0.0	5.1	6.1	2.5
1585	Passaic, Gregory Ave. bridge	40 51	74 07	+0 49	+1 57	+0.6	0.0	5.1	6.1	2.5
	Hackensack River									
1586	Kearny Point	40 44	74 06	+0 09	+0 33	+0.5	0.0	5.0	6.0	2.5
1587	Secaucus	40 48	74 04	+1 13	+1 09	+0.6	0.0	5.1	6.1	2.6
1588	Little Ferry	40 51	74 02	+1 22	+1 14	+0.8	0.0	5.3	6.4	2.7
1589	Hackensack	40 53	74 02	+1 33	+1 58	+0.8	0.0	5.3	6.4	2.6
				on SANDY HOOK, p.64						
	Arthur Kill									
1591	Elizabethport	40 39	74 11	+0 25	+0 39	+0.3	0.0	4.9	5.9	2.4
1593	Chelsea	40 36	74 12	+0 24	+0 35	+0.4	0.0	5.0	6.0	2.5
1595	Carteret	40 35	74 13	+0 23	+0 31	+0.5	0.0	5.1	6.2	2.6
1597	Rossville	40 33	74 13	+0 17	+0 25	+0.7	0.0	5.3	6.4	2.6
1599	Tottenville	40 31	74 15	+0 03	+0 13	+0.7	0.0	5.3	6.4	2.6
1601	Perth Amboy	40 30	74 16	+0 13	+0 19	+0.6	0.0	5.2	6.3	2.6
	Lower New York Bay, Raritan Bay, etc.									
1603	New Dorp Beach	40 34	74 06	-0 04	+0 04	+0.3	0.0	4.9	5.9	2.4
1605	Great Kills Harbor	40 33	74 08	+0 07	+0 19	+0.1	0.0	4.7	5.7	2.4
1607	Princes Bay	40 31	74 12	+0 01	+0 04	+0.3	0.0	4.9	5.9	2.4
	Raritan River									
1609	South Amboy	40 29	74 17	+0 05	+0 15	+0.4	0.0	5.0	6.0	2.5
1611	Washington Canal	40 28	74 22	+0 34	+0 50	+1.0	0.0	5.6	6.8	2.8
1613	South River highway bridge	40 27	74 22	+0 55	+1 02	+0.9	0.0	5.5	6.7	2.8
1615	New Brunswick	40 29	74 26	+0 46	+1 26	+1.2	0.0	5.8	7.0	2.9
1617	Keyport	40 26	74 12	+0 08	+0 19	+0.4	0.0	5.0	6.0	2.5
1619	Keansburg	40 27	74 09	-0 03	-0 01	+0.3	0.0	4.9	5.9	2.4
1621	Port Monmouth	40 26	74 05	-0 02	-0 02	+0.2	0.0	4.8	5.8	2.4
1623	Atlantic Highlands	40 25	74 02	-0 01	0 00	+0.1	0.0	4.7	5.7	2.3
1625	SANDY HOOK	40 28	74 01	Daily predictions				4.6	5.6	2.3
	Sandy Hook Bay									
	Shrewsbury River									
1627	Highlands	40 24	73 59	+0 35	+0 55	-0.8	0.0	3.8	4.6	1.9
1629	Red Bank, Navesink River	40 21	74 04	+1 48	+2 23	*0.65	*0.65	3.0	3.6	1.5
1631	Normandie	40 23	73 59	+1 09	+1 45	*0.63	*0.63	2.9	3.5	1.4
1633	Sea Bright	40 21	73 59	+2 10	+2 38	*0.37	*0.37	1.7	2.1	0.8
1635	Branchport, Pleasure Bay	40 19	74 00	+3 00	+3 26	*0.37	*0.37	1.7	2.1	0.8
	NEW JERSEY, Outer Coast									
1637	Sea Bright	40 22	73 58	-0 34	-0 45	-0.2	0.0	4.4	5.3	2.2
1639	Long Branch	40 18	73 59	-0 34	-0 45	-0.2	0.0	4.4	5.3	2.2

Endnotes can be found at the end of table 2.

NO.	PLACE	POSITION Lat.	POSITION Long.	DIFFERENCES Time High Water	DIFFERENCES Time Low Water	DIFFERENCES Height High Water	DIFFERENCES Height Low Water	RANGES Mean	RANGES Spring	Mean Tide Level
		° ' N	° ' W	h. m.	h. m.	ft	ft	ft	ft	ft
	NEW JERSEY, Outer Coast Time meridian, 75°W			on SANDY HOOK, p.64						
1641	Asbury Park	40 13	74 00	-0 34	-0 45	-0.3	0.0	4.3	5.2	2.1
1643	Shark River Inlet (entrance)	40 11	74 01	-0 18	-0 36	-0.6	0.0	4.0	4.8	2.0
1645	Municipal Boat Basin, Shark River	40 11	74 02	+0 27	+0 36	-0.9	0.0	3.7	4.4	1.8
1647	Sea Girt	40 08	74 02	-0 34	-0 45	-0.3	0.0	4.3	5.2	2.1
1649	Manasquan Inlet	40 06	74 02	-0 12	-0 36	-0.6	0.0	4.0	4.8	2.0
	Manasquan River									
1651	Railroad bridge	40 06	74 03	+0 20	+0 05	-1.1	0.0	3.5	4.2	1.7
1653	Riviera Beach	40 06	74 05	+0 51	+1 25	-1.5	0.0	3.1	3.8	1.5
1655	Seaside Park (ocean)	39 55	74 05	-0 33	-0 44	-0.4	0.0	4.2	5.1	2.1
	Barnegat Bay									
1657	Mantoloking	40 02	74 03	+5 34	+5 34	*0.11	*0.11	0.5	0.6	0.2
1659	Coates Point, highway bridge	39 57	74 07	+4 19	+4 28	*0.11	*0.11	0.5	0.6	0.2
1661	Toms River (town)	39 57	74 12	+4 37	+4 47	*0.13	*0.13	0.6	0.7	0.3
1663	Waretown	39 47	74 11	+2 33	+2 49	*0.13	*0.13	0.6	0.7	0.3
1665	Oyster Cr. Chan. (off Sedge Island)	39 47	74 08	+2 16	+2 17	*0.13	*0.13	0.6	0.7	0.3
1667	Barnegat Inlet	39 46	74 06	-0 20	-0 21	-1.5	0.0	3.1	3.8	1.5
1669	Harvey Cedars	39 42	74 08	+3 15	+4 02	*0.17	*0.17	0.8	1.0	0.4
	Little Egg Harbor									
1671	Manahawkin Bridge	39 39	74 11	+2 33	+3 20	*0.33	*0.33	1.5	1.8	0.7
1673	Long Point	39 36	74 16	+1 48	+1 56	*0.48	*0.48	2.2	2.7	1.1
1675	Tuckerton Creek entrance	39 35	74 20	+1 40	+1 54	*0.52	*0.52	2.4	2.9	1.2
1677	Beach Haven	39 34	74 15	+1 47	+2 01	*0.48	*0.48	2.2	2.7	1.1
1679	Holgate	39 32	74 16	+1 11	+1 07	*0.57	*0.57	2.6	3.1	1.3
	Great Bay									
1681	Little Egg Inlet	39 30	74 18	-0 01	-0 03	-0.9	0.0	3.7	4.5	1.8
1683	Seven Islands	39 31	74 20	+0 12	+0 16	-1.2	0.0	3.4	4.1	1.7
1685	Graveling Point	39 32	74 24	+1 05	+1 18	-1.2	0.0	3.4	4.1	1.7
1687	Mullica River, highway bridge	39 33	74 28	+1 55	+2 12	-1.3	0.0	3.3	4.0	1.6
1689	Main Marsh Thorofare	39 29	74 23	+1 04	+1 30	-1.3	0.0	3.3	4.0	1.6
1691	Brigantine Channel	39 27	74 21	+0 01	+0 03	-1.1	0.0	3.5	4.2	1.7
1693	Grassy Bay	39 26	74 24	+1 08	+1 11	-1.2	0.0	3.4	4.1	1.7
1695	Absecon Creek entrance, Absecon Bay	39 25	74 29	+1 04	+1 17	-1.0	0.0	3.6	4.4	1.8
1697	Broad Creek, Middle Thorofare	39 24	74 26	+0 55	+0 33	-1.2	0.0	3.4	4.1	1.7
1699	Absecon Inlet (Gardner Basin)	39 23	74 25	+0 14	-0 01	-1.0	0.0	3.6	4.4	1.8
1701	Beach Thorofare (railroad bridges)	39 22	74 27	+0 52	+0 40	-0.8	0.0	3.8	4.6	1.9
1703	Atlantic City, Steel Pier	39 21	74 25	-0 26	-0 35	-0.5	0.0	4.1	5.0	2.0
1705	Chelsea (highway bridge)	39 21	74 28	+0 49	+0 45	-0.6	0.0	4.0	4.8	2.0
1707	Beach Thorofare (Shelter Island)	39 21	74 30	+0 39	+0 32	-0.7	0.0	3.9	4.7	1.9
1709	Dock Thorofare (bridge)	39 21	74 32	+0 48	+0 32	-0.8	0.0	3.8	4.6	1.9
1711	Longport (inside)	39 18	74 32	+0 05	-0 01	-0.7	0.0	3.9	4.7	2.0
1713	Great Egg Harbor Inlet	39 18	74 34	+0 12	-0 05	-0.8	0.0	3.8	4.6	1.9
1715	Ocean City (9th Street bridge)	39 17	74 35	+0 24	+0 19	-0.9	0.0	3.7	4.5	1.8
1717	Great Egg Harbor Bay	39 18	74 38	+0 44	+0 57	-1.0	0.0	3.6	4.4	1.8
	Great Egg Harbor River									
1719	Scull Landing	39 22	74 43	+1 43	+1 54	-0.9	0.0	3.7	4.5	1.8
1721	Mays Landing	39 27	74 44	+2 34	+2 39	-0.6	0.0	4.0	4.8	2.0
1723	Peck Bay (34th Street bridge)	39 15	74 38	+0 51	+1 02	-0.9	0.0	3.7	4.5	1.8
1725	Devils Island, Crook Horn Creek	39 14	74 39	+0 37	+0 22	-1.0	0.0	3.6	4.4	1.8
1727	Corson Inlet (bridges)	39 13	74 39	+0 09	+0 04	-0.7	0.0	3.9	4.7	1.9
1729	Ben Hands Thorofare	39 12	74 40	+0 48	+0 32	-0.9	0.0	3.7	4.5	1.8
1731	Sea Isle City (Ludlam Thoro. bridge)	39 09	74 42	+0 45	+0 49	-0.8	0.0	3.8	4.6	1.9
1733	Sea Isle City (beach)	39 09	74 41	-0 19	-0 19	-0.5	0.0	4.1	5.0	2.0
1735	Townsends Inlet	39 07	74 43	+0 06	+0 04	-0.8	0.0	3.8	4.6	1.9
1737	Long Reach	39 06	74 45	+0 53	+0 53	-0.8	0.0	3.8	4.6	1.9
1739	Great Sound (ent. to Cresse Thoro.)	39 05	74 47	+1 03	+1 05	-0.5	0.0	4.1	5.0	2.0
1741	Stone Harbor (Great Chan. bridge)	39 03	74 46	+0 42	+0 26	-0.5	0.0	4.1	5.0	2.0
1743	Hereford Inlet (North Wildwood)	39 01	74 48	+0 02	+0 02	-0.5	0.0	4.1	5.0	2.0
1745	Wildwood (beach)	38 59	74 48	-0 15	-0 19	-0.5	0.0	4.1	5.0	2.0
1747	Grassy Sound Channel (hwy. bridge)	39 02	74 49	+0 40	+0 28	-0.5	0.0	4.1	5.0	2.0
1749	West Wildwood (Grassy Sound bridge)	39 00	74 50	+0 45	+0 29	-0.3	0.0	4.3	5.2	2.1
1751	Swain Channel	38 59	74 52	+0 54	+0 27	-0.2	0.0	4.4	5.3	2.2
1753	Cape May Harbor	38 57	74 53	-0 02	-0 16	-0.2	0.0	4.4	5.3	2.2
1755	Cape May, Municipal Pier	38 56	74 55	+0 02	-0 17	-0.3	0.0	4.3	5.2	2.1
	NEW JERSEY and DELAWARE Delaware Bay, Eastern Shore			on BREAKWATER HARBOR, p.68						
1757	Five Fathom Bank	38 51	74 38	-0 43	-0 38	0.0	0.0	4.1	4.9	2.0
1759	McCrie Shoal	38 51	74 51	-0 22	-0 21	+0.2	0.0	4.3	5.2	2.1
1761	Cape May Point	38 56	74 58	-0 10	-0 04	+0.6	0.0	4.7	5.6	2.3
1762	Cape May, ferry terminal	38 58	74 58	-0 04	-0 01	+0.8	0.0	4.9	5.8	2.4
1763	Bay Shore Channel	38 58	74 58	-0 09	-0 03	+0.8	0.0	4.9	5.8	2.4
1765	Miami Beach	39 02	74 56	+0 17	+0 26	+1.0	0.0	5.1	6.1	2.5
1767	Dennis Creek entrance	39 10	74 54	+0 48	+1 04	+1.5	0.0	5.6	6.6	2.8
1769	East Point, Maurice River Cove	39 12	75 02	+0 53	+1 12	+1.6	0.0	5.7	6.7	2.8
	Maurice River									
1771	Port Norris	39 14	75 02	+1 14	+1 38	+1.6	0.0	5.7	6.7	2.8
1773	Mauricetown	39 17	75 00	+1 48	+2 21	+1.7	0.0	5.8	6.8	2.9
1775	Millville	39 24	75 02	+2 37	+3 23	+1.9	0.0	6.0	7.0	3.0
1777	Egg Island Point	39 11	75 08	+0 33	+1 02	+1.6	0.0	5.7	6.7	2.8

Endnotes can be found at the end of table 2.

NO.	PLACE	POSITION Lat.	POSITION Long.	DIFFERENCES Time High Water	DIFFERENCES Time Low Water	DIFFERENCES Height High Water	DIFFERENCES Height Low Water	RANGES Mean	RANGES Spring	Mean Tide Level
		° ′ N	° ′ W	h. m.	h. m.	ft	ft	ft	ft	ft
	NEW JERSEY and DELAWARE Delaware Bay, Eastern Shore Time meridian, 75°W			on REEDY POINT, p.72						
1779	Fortescue	39 14	75 10	-2 05	-2 19	+0.4	0.0	5.9	7.0	2.9
1781	Ben Davis Point	39 17	75 17	-1 40	-1 49	+0.5	0.0	6.0	6.9	3.0
	Cohansey River									
1783	Entrance	39 21	75 22	-1 30	-1 29	+0.5	0.0	6.0	6.9	3.0
1785	Laning Wharf	39 23	75 20	-1 10	-1 14	+0.5	0.0	6.0	6.8	3.0
1787	Fairton	39 23	75 14	+0 05	-0 24	+0.7	0.0	6.2	7.0	3.1
1789	Bridgeton	39 25	75 14	+0 27	-0 13	+1.0	0.0	6.5	7.3	3.2
1791	Bay Side	39 23	75 24	-1 23	-1 22	+0.6	0.0	6.1	6.9	3.0
	DEL., N.J., and PA. Delaware Bay, Central Lighthouses			on BREAKWATER HARBOR, p.68						
1793	Brandywine Shoal Light	38 59	75 07	+0 09	+0 28	+0.8	0.0	4.9	5.9	2.4
1795	Fourteen Foot Bank Light	39 03	75 11	+0 18	+0 48	+1.1	0.0	5.2	6.2	2.6
1797	Miah Maull Shoal Light	39 08	75 13	+0 28	+1 08	+1.4	0.0	5.5	6.5	2.7
1799	Elbow of Cross Ledge Light	39 11	75 16	+0 40	+1 21	+1.5	0.0	5.6	6.5	2.8
				on REEDY POINT, p.72						
1801	Ship John Shoal Light	39 18	75 23	-1 32	-1 36	+0.2	0.0	5.7	6.6	2.8
	Delaware Bay, Western Shore			on BREAKWATER HARBOR, p.68						
1803	Cape Henlopen	38 48	75 05	-0 05	-0 05	0.0	0.0	4.1	4.9	2.0
1805	BREAKWATER HARBOR	38 47	75 06	Daily predictions				4.1	4.9	2.1
1807	Roosevelt Inlet	38 49	75 12	+0 09	+0 13	+0.3	0.0	4.4	5.2	2.2
1809	Mispillion River entrance	38 57	75 19	+0 33	+1 00	+0.5	0.0	4.6	5.4	2.3
1811	Murderkill River entrance	39 04	75 24	+0 56	+1 32	+0.7	0.0	4.8	5.7	2.4
1813	St. Jones River entrance	39 04	75 24	+0 57	+1 33	+0.7	0.0	4.8	5.7	2.4
1815	Mahon River entrance	39 11	75 24	+1 13	+1 52	+1.3	0.0	5.4	6.3	2.7
1817	Leipsic River entrance	39 15	75 24	+1 18	+1 59	+1.4	0.0	5.5	6.4	2.7
1819	Leipsic, Leipsic River	39 15	75 31	+3 42	+3 50	-0.6	0.0	3.5	4.0	1.7
				on REEDY POINT, p.72						
1821	Woodland Beach	39 20	75 28	-1 15	-1 14	+0.4	0.0	5.9	6.8	2.9
	Delaware River									
1823	Liston Point	39 25	75 32	-0 55	-0 59	+0.2	0.0	5.7	6.4	2.8
1825	Taylors Bridge, Blackbird Creek	39 24	75 36	+1 47	+0 54	-2.6	0.0	2.9	3.3	1.4
1827	Reedy Island	39 31	75 34	-0 16	-0 16	+0.1	0.0	5.6	6.2	2.8
1831	Salem, Salem River	39 35	75 28	+0 19	+0 20	+0.1	0.0	5.6	6.1	2.8
1833	REEDY POINT	39 34	75 34	Daily predictions				5.5	6.0	2.7
	Chesapeake and Delaware Canal									
1835	Biddle Point, Delaware	39 33	75 37	-0 05	+0 01	-0.4	0.0	5.1	5.5	2.5
1837	Summit Bridge, Delaware	39 33	75 44	-0 34	-0 55	*0.64	*0.64	3.5	3.9	1.7
1839	Chesapeake City, Maryland	39 32	75 49	-0 30	-1 06	*0.49	*0.49	2.7	3.0	1.4
1841	Pea Patch Island, Delaware	39 35	75 34	+0 08	+0 12	0.0	0.0	5.5	6.0	2.7
1843	New Castle, Delaware	39 39	75 34	+0 30	+0 49	+0.1	0.0	5.6	6.0	2.8
1845	Deepwater Point, N. J.	39 42	75 31	+0 46	+1 11	+0.1	0.0	5.6	6.0	2.8
1847	Christina River entrance, Del	39 43	75 31	+0 51	+1 16	+0.1	0.0	5.6	5.9	2.8
1849	Wilmington, Christina River, Del	39 44	75 33	+0 56	+1 27	+0.2	0.0	5.7	6.0	2.8
1851	Edgemoor, Del	39 45	75 30	+0 56	+1 27	+0.1	0.0	5.6	5.9	2.8
1853	Oldmans Point, N. J.	39 46	75 28	+1 03	+1 34	+0.1	0.0	5.6	5.9	2.8
				on PHILADELPHIA, p.76						
1855	Marcus Hook, Pa	39 49	75 25	-1 12	-1 06	-0.6	0.0	5.6	5.9	2.8
1857	Chester, Pa	39 51	75 21	-0 51	-0 45	-0.5	0.0	5.7	6.0	2.8
1859	Billingsport, N. J.	39 51	75 14	-0 31	-0 25	-0.5	0.0	5.7	6.0	2.8
1861	Fort Mifflin, Pa	39 52	75 13	-0 21	-0 15	-0.5	0.0	5.7	6.0	2.8
	Schuylkill River									
1863	Girard Point, Pa	39 54	75 12	-0 17	-0 10	-0.5	0.0	5.7	6.0	2.8
1865	Point Breeze, Pa	39 55	75 12	-0 13	-0 05	-0.5	0.0	5.7	6.0	2.8
1867	Grays Ferry Bridge, Pa	39 57	75 12	-0 07	+0 01	-0.4	0.0	5.8	6.1	2.9
1869	Fairmount Bridge, Pa	39 58	75 11	+0 02	+0 11	-0.4	0.0	5.8	6.1	2.9
1871	Philadelphia, South Broad St., Pa	39 53	75 11	-0 17	-0 11	-0.4	0.0	5.8	6.1	2.9
1873	Gloucester City, N. J.	39 54	75 08	-0 05	+0 02	-0.4	0.0	5.8	6.1	2.9
1875	Philadelphia, Washington Ave., Pa	39 56	75 08	+0 04	+0 11	-0.3	0.0	5.9	6.2	3.0
1877	PHILADELPHIA, Pier 11 North, Pa	39 57	75 08	Daily predictions				6.2	6.6	3.1
1879	Camden, Cooper Point, N. J.	39 57	75 08	+0 12	+0 19	-0.3	0.0	5.9	6.2	3.0
1881	Philadelphia, Pier 80 N (old site), Pa	39 58	75 07	+0 18	+0 26	-0.3	0.0	5.9	6.2	3.0
1883	Philadelphia, Bridesburg, Pa	40 00	75 04	+0 34	+0 43	-0.2	0.0	6.0	6.3	3.0
1885	Torresdale, Pa	40 03	74 59	+1 06	+1 17	0.0	0.0	6.2	6.5	3.1

Endnotes can be found at the end of table 2.

NO.	*PLACE	POSITION Lat.	POSITION Long.	DIFFERENCES Time High Water	DIFFERENCES Time Low Water	DIFFERENCES Height High Water	DIFFERENCES Height Low Water	RANGES Mean	RANGES Spring	Mean Tide Level
		° ' N	° ' W	h. m.	h. m.	ft	ft	ft	ft	ft
	NEW JERSEY and PENNSYLVANIA Delaware River-Continued Time meridian, 75°W			on PHILADELPHIA, p.76						
1887	Burlington, N. J.	40 05	74 52	+1 30	+1 43	+0.2	0.0	6.4	6.7	3.2
1889	Bristol, Pa.	40 06	74 51	+1 37	+1 51	+0.3	0.0	6.5	6.8	3.3
1891	Florence, N. J.	40 07	74 48	+1 47	+2 05	+0.4	0.0	6.6	6.9	3.3
1893	Bordentown, N. J.	40 09	74 43	+1 49	+2 15	+0.5	0.0	6.7	7.0	3.3
1895	Trenton, N. J.	40 11	74 45	+1 55	+2 40	+0.6	0.0	6.8	7.1	3.4
	DELAWARE, Outer Coast			on SANDY HOOK, p.64						
1897	Rehoboth Beach	38 43	75 05	-0 07	-0 21	-0.7	0.0	3.9	4.7	1.9
	Indian River									
1899	Inlet (bridge)	38 37	75 04	+0 34	-0 18	*0.59	*0.59	2.7	3.2	1.3
1900	Inlet (Coast Guard Station)	38 37	75 04	+0 41	+0 18	*0.46	*0.46	2.1	2.5	1.1
1901	Oak Orchard	38 36	75 10	+2 44	+3 11	*0.20	*0.20	0.9	1.1	0.5
1903	Possum Point	38 35	75 16	+3 09	+4 00	*0.22	*0.22	1.0	1.2	0.5
1905	Rehoboth Bay	- - -	- - -	- - -	- - -	- -	- -	0.5	0.6	0.2
1907	Fenwick Island Light	38 27	75 03	-0 13	-0 19	-0.9	0.0	3.7	4.5	1.8
	MARYLAND, Outer Coast									
1909	Ocean City (outer coast)	38 20	75 05	-0 28	-0 30	-1.2	0.0	3.4	4.1	1.7
1910	Ocean City (Isle of Wight Bay)	38 20	75 05	-0 14	-0 25	-2.4	0.0	2.2	2.7	1.1
1911	North Beach Coast Guard Station	38 12	75 09	-0 28	-0 29	-1.2	0.0	3.4	4.1	1.7
	MARYLAND and VIRGINIA Chincoteague Bay									
1913	Assateague Beach, Toms Cove	37 52	75 22	+0 06	+0 16	-1.0	0.0	3.6	4.4	1.8
1915	Chincoteague Point	37 54	75 25	+0 05	+0 11	*0.57	*0.57	2.6	3.1	1.3
1917	Bogues Bay, Chincoteague Inlet	37 53	75 30	+0 38	+0 57	-1.6	0.0	3.0	3.6	1.5
1918	Wishart Point, Bogues Bay	37 53	75 30	+0 20	+0 42	-2.0	0.0	2.6	3.1	1.3
1919	Chincoteague, Chincoteague Channel	37 56	75 23	+0 40	+0 47	*0.37	*0.37	1.7	2.1	0.9
1921	Piney Island, Assateague Channel	37 56	75 21	+1 05	+1 13	*0.46	*0.46	2.1	2.5	1.0
1923	Greenbackville	38 00	75 23	+2 19	+2 48	*0.13	*0.13	0.6	0.7	0.3
1925	George Island Landing	38 02	75 22	+2 53	+3 02	*0.13	*0.13	0.6	0.7	0.3
1927	Assacorkin Island	38 04	75 19	+3 33	+3 42	*0.09	*0.09	0.4	0.5	0.2
1928	Public Landing	38 09	75 17	+4 58	+5 27	*0.09	*0.09	0.4	0.5	0.2
	VIRGINIA, Outer Coast									
1929	Wallops Island	37 50	75 29	-0 23	-0 32	-1.0	0.0	3.6	4.4	1.8
1930	Gargathy Neck	37 47	75 34	+1 05	+0 56	-1.6	0.0	3.0	3.6	1.5
1931	Metomkin Inlet	37 40	75 36	+0 35	+0 12	-1.0	0.0	3.6	4.4	1.8
1932	Folly Creek, Metomkin Inlet	37 42	75 38	+0 58	+0 41	-1.3	0.0	3.3	4.0	1.7
1933	Wachapreague Inlet (inside)	37 35	75 37	+0 09	+0 03	-0.7	0.0	3.9	4.7	1.9
1935	Quinby Inlet entrance	37 28	75 40	+0 04	-0 12	-0.6	0.0	4.0	4.8	2.0
1937	The Swash, south end	37 30	75 40	+0 19	+0 14	-0.7	0.0	3.9	4.7	1.9
1939	Great Machipongo Inlet (inside)	37 24	75 43	+0 36	+0 23	-0.7	0.0	3.9	4.7	1.9
1941	Upshur Neck, south end	37 28	75 48	+0 50	+0 52	-0.2	0.0	4.4	5.3	2.2
1943	Sand Shoal Inlet (Coast Guard Station)	37 18	75 47	+0 08	-0 11	-0.5	0.0	4.1	4.9	2.0
1945	Ship Shoal Inlet	37 13	75 48	+0 26	+0 09	-0.6	0.0	4.0	4.8	2.0
1947	Smith Island (Coast Guard Station)	37 07	75 55	+0 23	+0 59	-1.1	0.0	3.5	4.2	1.7
	Chesapeake Bay, Eastern Shore			on HAMPTON ROADS, p.88						
1949	Fishermans Island	37 06	75 59	-0 43	-0 55	+0.5	0.0	3.0	3.6	1.5
1951	Kiptopeke Beach (ferry)	37 10	75 59	-0 36	-0 30	+0.2	0.0	2.7	3.2	1.4
1953	Old Plantation Flats	37 14	76 03	-0 23	-0 10	-0.1	0.0	2.4	2.9	1.2
1955	Cape Charles Harbor	37 16	76 01	-0 14	+0 02	-0.1	0.0	2.4	2.9	1.2
1957	Nassawadox Creek	37 28	75 58	+1 00	+0 53	-0.7	0.0	1.8	2.2	0.9
1959	Gaskins Point, Occohannock Creek	37 33	75 55	+1 36	+2 08	-0.8	0.0	1.7	2.0	0.9
1961	Pungoteague Creek	37 40	75 50	+2 26	+2 42	-0.8	0.0	1.7	2.0	0.8
1963	Onancock, Onancock Creek	37 43	75 45	+2 56	+3 14	-0.7	0.0	1.8	2.2	0.9
1965	Watts Island	37 48	75 54	+3 03	+3 07	-0.9	0.0	1.6	1.9	0.8
1967	Tangier Sound Light	37 47	75 58	+2 55	+2 53	*0.64	*0.64	1.6	1.9	0.8
1969	Muddy Creek Entrance	37 51	75 40	+3 18	+3 48	-0.3	0.0	2.2	2.6	1.1
1970	Guard Shore	37 51	75 42	+3 07	+3 42	-0.2	0.0	2.3	2.7	1.2
	MARYLAND Chesapeake Bay, Eastern Shore									
1971	Ape Hole Creek, Pocomoke Sound	37 58	75 49	+3 28	+3 53	-0.2	0.0	2.3	2.8	1.1
	Pocomoke River									
1973	Shelltown	37 59	75 38	+3 33	+4 11	-0.1	0.0	2.4	2.9	1.2
1975	Pocomoke City	38 05	75 34	+5 50	+6 10	-0.9	0.0	1.6	2.0	0.8
1976	Snowhill, city park	38 10	75 24	+7 36	+7 48	-0.6	0.0	1.9	2.3	1.0
1977	Janes Island Light	37 58	75 55	+3 55	+3 55	-0.7	0.0	1.8	2.2	0.9
1979	Crisfield, Little Annemessex River	37 59	75 52	+3 51	+4 00	-0.5	0.0	2.0	2.4	1.0

Endnotes can be found at the end of table 2.

NO.	PLACE	POSITION Lat.	Long.	DIFFERENCES Time High Water	Low Water	Height High Water	Low Water	RANGES Mean	Spring	Mean Tide Level
		° ′ N	° ′ W	h. m.	h. m.	ft	ft	ft	ft	ft
	MARYLAND Chesapeake Bay, Eastern Shore Time meridian, 75°W			on HAMPTON ROADS, p.88						
1981	Long Point, Big Annemessex River........	38 03	75 48	+4 20	+4 41	-0.4	0.0	2.1	2.5	1.0
1983	Teague Creek, Manokin River............	38 06	75 50	+4 39	+5 00	-0.4	0.0	2.1	2.5	1.0
1985	Ewell, Smith Island.....................	38 00	76 02	+4 00	+4 26	*0.64	*0.64	1.6	1.9	0.8
1987	Solomons Lump Light.....................	38 03	76 01	+4 17	+4 20	-0.8	0.0	1.7	2.0	0.8
1989	Holland Island Bar Light................	38 04	76 06	+4 17	+4 25	*0.56	*0.56	1.4	1.7	0.7
1990	Chance..................................	38 10	75 57	+4 41	+4 53	-0.3	0.0	2.2	2.6	1.1
1991	Sharkfin Shoal Light....................	38 12	75 59	+4 47	+5 01	-0.3	0.0	2.2	2.6	1.1
1993	Great Shoals Light, Monie Bay...........	38 13	75 53	+5 01	+5 17	-0.2	0.0	2.3	2.8	1.2
	Wicomico River									
1995	Whitehaven..........................	38 16	75 47	+5 28	+5 42	-0.1	0.0	2.4	2.9	1.2
1997	Salisbury...........................	38 22	75 36	+6 22	+6 19	+0.5	0.0	3.0	3.6	1.5
	Nanticoke River									
1999	Roaring Point.......................	38 16	75 55	+5 01	+5 30	-0.2	0.0	2.3	2.8	1.2
2001	Vienna..............................	38 29	75 49	+7 42	+7 45	-0.3	0.0	2.2	2.6	1.1
2003	Sharptown...........................	38 32	75 43	+8 20	+8 23	0.0	0.0	2.5	3.0	1.3
2005	Fishing Point, Fishing Bay..............	38 18	76 01	+5 05	+5 29	0.0	0.0	2.5	3.0	1.2
2007	Hooper Strait Light.....................	38 14	76 05	+4 56	+5 02	-0.8	0.0	1.7	2.0	0.8
				on BALTIMORE, p.80						
2009	Hooper Island Light.....................	38 15	76 15	-5 07	-5 23	+0.4	0.0	1.5	1.8	0.7
2010	Hooper Island...........................	38 18	76 12	-5 00	-4 51	+0.4	0.0	1.5	1.7	0.8
2011	Barren Island...........................	38 20	76 16	-4 52	-5 07	+0.2	0.0	1.3	1.5	0.6
	Little Choptank River									
2013	Taylors Island, Slaughter Creek.....	38 28	76 18	-3 09	-3 25	+0.1	0.0	1.2	1.4	0.6
2015	Woolford, Church Creek..............	38 30	76 10	-3 25	-3 10	+0.3	0.0	1.4	1.6	0.7
2017	Cherry Island, Beckwiths Creek......	38 34	76 13	-3 21	-3 11	+0.2	0.0	1.3	1.5	0.6
2019	Hudson Creek........................	38 35	76 15	-3 49	-3 31	+0.3	0.0	1.4	1.6	0.7
2021	Sharps Island Light.....................	38 38	76 23	-3 51	-4 00	+0.2	0.0	1.3	1.5	0.6
	Choptank River									
2023	Choptank River Light................	38 39	76 11	-3 17	-3 18	+0.3	0.0	1.4	1.6	0.7
2025	Cambridge...........................	38 34	76 04	-2 44	-2 39	+0.5	0.0	1.6	1.8	0.8
2027	Choptank............................	38 41	75 57	-2 13	-1 58	+0.5	0.0	1.6	1.8	0.8
2029	Dover Bridge........................	38 45	76 00	-0 38	-0 53	+0.6	0.0	1.7	1.9	0.9
2031	Denton..............................	38 53	75 50	+0 13	+0 22	+1.1	0.0	2.2	2.5	1.1
2033	Greensboro..........................	38 58	75 49	+1 18	+1 08	+1.4	0.0	2.5	2.9	1.2
2035	Wayman Wharf, Tuckahoe Creek........	38 53	75 57	+0 53	+0 25	+1.3	0.0	2.4	2.8	1.2
	Tred Avon River									
2037	Oxford..............................	38 42	76 10	-3 05	-3 00	+0.3	0.0	1.4	1.6	0.7
2039	Easton Point........................	38 46	76 06	-2 59	-2 50	+0.5	0.0	1.6	1.8	0.8
2041	Deep Neck Point, Broad Creek............	38 44	76 14	-3 10	-3 01	+0.3	0.0	1.4	1.6	0.7
2043	St. Michaels, San Domingo Creek.........	38 46	76 14	-3 08	-3 06	+0.3	0.0	1.4	1.6	0.7
2045	Avalon, Dogwood Harbor..................	38 42	76 20	-3 08	-3 03	+0.2	0.0	1.3	1.5	0.6
2047	Poplar Island...........................	38 46	76 23	-3 12	-3 18	+0.1	0.0	1.2	1.3	0.6
2049	Ferry Cove, Eastern Bay.................	38 46	76 20	-3 01	-3 04	-0.1	0.0	1.0	1.2	0.5
2051	Claiborne, Eastern Bay..................	38 50	76 17	-2 40	-2 43	0.0	0.0	1.1	1.3	0.5
2053	St. Michaels, Miles River...............	38 47	76 13	-2 18	-2 08	+0.1	0.0	1.2	1.4	0.6
2055	Wye Landing, Wye East River.............	38 54	76 06	-2 05	-1 51	+0.2	0.0	1.3	1.5	0.6
2057	Kent Island Narrows.....................	38 58	76 15	-1 44	-1 38	+0.1	0.0	1.2	1.4	0.6
2058	Matapeake, Kent Island..................	38 58	76 21	-1 24	-1 49	-0.1	0.0	1.0	1.2	0.5
2059	Bloody Point Bar Light..................	38 50	76 24	-2 46	-2 54	0.0	0.0	1.1	1.3	0.5
	Chester River									
2061	Love Point..........................	39 02	76 18	-0 24	-0 46	0.0	0.0	1.1	1.3	0.6
2063	Queenstown..........................	39 00	76 10	-0 08	-0 24	+0.2	0.0	1.3	1.5	0.6
2065	Shipyard Landing, Langford Creek....	39 10	76 11	+0 14	+0 05	+0.4	0.0	1.5	1.7	0.7
2067	Centreville Landing, Corsica River..	39 03	76 04	+0 06	-0 01	+0.5	0.0	1.6	1.8	0.8
2069	Cliffs Point........................	39 06	76 08	-0 02	-0 17	+0.4	0.0	1.5	1.7	0.7
2070	Cliffs Wharf........................	39 07	76 08	-0 02	-0 14	+0.4	0.0	1.5	1.7	0.8
2071	Chestertown.........................	39 12	76 04	+0 43	+0 24	+0.7	0.0	1.8	2.1	0.9
2073	Crumpton............................	39 15	75 56	+1 18	+1 13	+1.3	0.0	2.4	2.8	1.2
2075	Millington..........................	39 15	75 50	+2 03	+2 30	+0.9	0.0	2.0	2.3	1.0
2077	Deep Landing, Swan Creek................	39 09	76 16	-0 12	-0 19	0.0	0.0	1.1	1.3	0.5
2079	Tolchester..............................	39 13	76 15	+0 24	+0 13	+0.1	0.0	1.2	1.4	0.6
2081	Worton Creek entrance...................	39 18	76 10	+1 07	+1 03	+0.2	0.0	1.3	1.5	0.6
	Sassafras River									
2083	Betterton...........................	39 22	76 04	+2 27	+2 08	+0.5	0.0	1.6	1.8	0.8
2085	Georgetown..........................	39 22	75 53	+2 01	+1 55	+0.9	0.0	2.0	2.3	1.0
	Elk River									
2087	Town Point Neck.....................	39 30	75 55	+3 16	+3 00	+1.0	0.0	2.1	2.4	1.0
2089	Courthouse Point....................	39 31	75 53	+2 49	+2 38	+1.1	0.0	2.2	2.5	1.1
	C & D Canal (See Delaware River)....	- - -	- - -	- - -	- - -	- -	- -	- -	- -	- -
2091	Old Frenchtown Wharf................	39 34	75 51	+3 00	+2 45	+1.2	0.0	2.3	2.6	1.1
2093	Charlestown, Northeast River............	39 34	75 58	+3 38	+3 48	+0.8	0.0	1.9	2.2	0.9
	Chesapeake Bay, Western Shore									
	Susquehanna River									
2095	Havre de Grace......................	39 32	76 05	+3 10	+3 30	+0.7	0.0	1.8	2.0	0.9
2097	Port Deposit........................	39 36	76 07	+4 00	+4 48	+1.0	0.0	2.1	2.4	1.0

Endnotes can be found at the end of table 2.

NO.	PLACE	POSITION Lat.	Long.	DIFFERENCES Time High Water	Low Water	Height High Water	Low Water	RANGES Mean	Spring	Mean Tide Level
		° ′ N	° ′ W	h. m.	h. m.	ft	ft	ft	ft	ft
	Virginia, York River Time meridian, 75°W			on HAMPTON ROADS, p.88						
2321	Mumfort Islands	37 16	76 31	+0 19	+0 12	0.0	0.0	2.5	3.0	1.2
2323	Penniman Spit	37 17	76 35	+0 41	+0 44	0.0	0.0	2.5	3.0	1.2
2324	Cheatham Annex	37 18	76 35	+0 43	+0 35	0.0	0.0	2.5	3.0	1.2
2325	Queen Creek (2 miles upstream)	37 18	76 39	+1 00	+0 59	-0.1	0.0	2.4	2.9	1.2
2327	Clay Bank	37 21	76 37	+0 50	+0 49	+0.3	0.0	2.8	3.4	1.4
2329	Allmondsville	37 23	76 39	+0 59	+1 02	+0.3	0.0	2.8	3.3	1.4
2330	Roane Point	37 27	76 42	+1 42	+1 45	+0.3	0.0	2.8	3.4	1.4
2331	West Point	37 32	76 48	+2 07	+2 33	+0.3	0.0	2.8	3.4	1.4
	Mattaponi River									
2333	Wakema	37 39	76 54	+3 29	+3 52	+0.9	0.0	3.4	3.9	1.7
2335	Walkerton	37 43	77 02	+4 26	+4 54	+1.4	0.0	3.9	4.5	1.9
	Pamunkey River									
2337	Sweet Hall Landing	37 34	76 54	+3 48	+4 06	+0.2	0.0	2.7	3.1	1.3
2339	Lester Manor	37 35	76 59	+4 40	+4 55	+0.3	0.0	2.8	3.2	1.4
2341	White House	37 35	77 01	+5 09	+5 24	+0.5	0.0	3.0	3.4	1.5
2343	Northbury	37 37	77 07	+5 58	+6 13	+0.8	0.0	3.3	3.8	1.6
	Chesapeake Bay, Western Shore-Con.									
2345	York Point, Poquoson River	37 10	76 24	-0 07	+0 01	-0.1	0.0	2.4	2.9	1.2
2347	Messick Point, Back River	37 06	76 19	-0 26	-0 05	-0.2	0.0	2.3	2.8	1.2
	Hampton Roads									
2349	Old Point Comfort	37 00	76 19	-0 04	-0 14	0.0	0.0	2.5	3.0	1.3
2351	Hampton River	37 01	76 20	+0 02	-0 07	+0.1	0.0	2.6	3.1	1.3
2353	HAMPTON ROADS (Sewells Pt.)	36 57	76 20	Daily predictions				2.5	2.9	1.2
2355	Lafayette River	36 54	76 18	+0 11	+0 20	+0.1	0.0	2.6	3.1	1.3
2357	Lafayette River, Granby St. Bridge	36 53	76 17	+0 26	+0 32	+0.2	0.0	2.7	3.2	1.3
	Elizabeth River									
2359	Craney Island	36 54	76 20	+0 13	-0 01	+0.1	0.0	2.6	3.1	1 3
2361	Port Norfolk, Western Branch	36 51	76 20	+0 17	+0 24	+0.1	0.0	2.6	3 1	1.3
2363	Norfolk	36 51	76 18	+0 18	+0 15	+0.3	0.0	2.8	3.4	1.4
2365	Portsmouth, Southern Branch	36 49	76 18	+0 20	+0 20	+0.3	0.0	2.8	3.4	1.4
	Nansemond River									
2367	Pig Point	36 55	76 26	+0 37	+0 35	+0.3	0.0	2.8	3.4	1.4
2369	Town Point	36 53	76 30	+0 33	+0 39	+0.5	0.0	3.0	3.6	1.5
2371	Hollidays Point (bridge)	36 50	76 33	+0 51	+0 58	+0.5	0.0	3.0	3.6	1.5
2373	Suffolk	36 44	76 35	+1 37	+1 30	+1.3	0.0	3.8	4.6	1.9
	James River									
2375	Chuckatuck Creek entrance	36 55	76 30	+0 45	+0 52	+0.3	0.0	2.8	3.4	1.4
2377	Newport News	36 58	76 26	+0 24	+0 23	+0.1	0.0	2.6	3.1	1.3
2378	Huntington Park	37 01	76 28	+0 40	+0 39	+0.1	0.0	2.6	3.1	1.3
2379	Menchville	37 05	76 32	+0 58	+1 14	+0.1	0.0	2.6	3.1	1.3
2381	Smithfield, Pagan River	36 59	76 38	+1 29	+1 23	+0.3	0.0	2.8	3.4	1.4
2383	Burwell Bay	37 03	76 40	+1 20	+1 39	-0.1	0.0	2.4	2.9	1.2
2385	Mulberry Point	37 08	76 38	+2 00	+2 21	-0.1	0.0	2.4	2.9	1.2
2387	Hog Point	37 12	76 41	+2 15	+2 33	-0.4	0.0	2.1	2.5	1.0
2388	Scotland	37 11	76 47	+2 51	+3 20	-0.6	0.0	1.9	2.1	1.0
2389	Jamestown Island	37 12	76 47	+2 58	+3 31	-0.5	0.0	2.0	2.4	1.0
2391	Dillard Wharf	37 12	76 52	+3 33	+4 10	-0.6	0.0	1.9	2.3	0.9
	Chickahominy River									
2393	Ferry Point (bridge)	37 16	76 53	+3 56	+4 21	-0.6	0.0	1.9	2.3	1.0
2395	Wright Island Landing	37 21	76 52	+4 39	+4 58	-0.3	0.0	2.2	2.6	1.1
2397	Mount Airy	37 21	76 55	+5 05	+5 33	-0.3	0.0	2.2	2.6	1.1
2399	Lanexa	37 24	76 54	+5 35	+6 03	+0.1	0.0	2.6	3.1	1.3
2401	Claremont	37 14	76 57	+3 58	+4 30	-0.7	0.0	1.8	2.0	0.9
2403	Sturgeon Point	37 18	77 00	+4 32	+5 04	-0.4	0.0	2.1	2.5	1.0
2405	Windmill Point	37 18	77 06	+5 26	+5 51	-0.2	0.0	2.3	2.7	1.1
2406	Willcox Wharf, Charles City	37 19	77 06	+5 25	+5 45	-0.3	0.0	2.2	2.4	1.1
2407	Westover	37 19	77 09	+5 47	+6 12	-0.1	0.0	2.4	2.8	1.2
2409	Jordon Point	37 19	77 13	+6 11	+6 34	0.0	0.0	2.5	2.9	1.2
				on WASHINGTON, p.84						
2411	City Point (Hopewell)	37 19	77 16	-4 55	-5 12	-0.3	0.0	2.6	3.0	1.3
2413	Petersburg, Appomattox River	37 14	77 24	-4 25	-4 00	0.0	0.0	2.9	3.3	1.4
2415	Bermuda Hundred	37 20	77 16	-4 50	-5 05	-0.3	0.0	2.6	3.0	1.3
2417	Haxall	37 22	77 15	-4 43	-4 52	-0.2	0.0	2.7	3.1	1.4
2419	Curles, 1 mile north of	37 24	77 18	-4 25	-4 26	-0.1	0.0	2.8	3.2	1.4
2420	Chester	37 23	77 23	-4 12	-3 59	0.0	0.0	2.9	3.2	1.5
2421	Meadowville	37 23	77 19	-4 34	-4 33	0.0	0.0	2.9	3.3	1.4
2423	Kingsland Reach	37 24	77 23	-4 32	-4 28	+0.1	0.0	3.0	3.5	1.5
2425	Falling Creek entrance	37 26	77 26	-4 21	-4 08	+0.3	0.0	3.2	3.7	1.6
2427	Richmond Deepwater Terminal	37 27	77 25	-4 18	-4 01	+0.4	0.0	3.3	3.8	1.6
2429	Lower Rocketts	37 30	77 25	-3 52	-3 32	+0.3	0.0	3.2	3.6	1.6
2431	Richmond (river locks)	37 32	77 25	-3 49	-3 26	+0.3	0.0	3.2	3.6	1.6

Endnotes can be found at the end of table 2.

NO.	PLACE	POSITION		DIFFERENCES				RANGES		Mean Tide Level
		Lat.	Long.	Time		Height		Mean	Spring	
				High Water	Low Water	High Water	Low Water			
		° ' N	° ' W	h. m.	h. m.	ft	ft	ft	ft	ft
	Chesapeake Bay, Southern Shore Time meridian, 75°W			on HAMPTON ROADS, p.88						
2433	Little Creek (RR. Terminal)............	36 55	76 11	-0 48	-0 50	+0.1	0.0	2.6	3.1	1.3
	Lynnhaven Inlet									
2435	Highway bridge, east of............	36 54	76 05	-0 09	+0 06	-0.5	0.0	2.0	2.4	1.0
	Lynnhaven Bay									
2436	Bayville............	36 54	76 06	+0 50	+1 43	-0.8	0.0	1.7	2.0	0.9
2437	Buchanan Creek entrance............	36 52	76 07	+1 00	+1 51	-0.6	0.0	1.9	2.3	0.9
2438	Long Creek............	36 54	76 04	+0 48	+1 19	*0.32	*0.32	0.8	1.0	0.4
2439	Brown Cove............	36 52	76 04	+0 46	+1 43	-0.8	0.0	1.7	2.0	0.8
2440	Cape Henry............	36 56	76 00	-0 48	-1 10	+0.3	0.0	2.8	3.4	1.4
	VIRGINIA, Outer Coast									
2441	Virginia Beach............	36 51	75 58	-1 26	-1 30	+0.9	0.0	3.4	4.1	1.7
2442	False Cape............	36 36	75 53	-1 41	-1 40	+1.1	0.0	3.6	4.3	1.8
	NORTH CAROLINA, Outer Coast									
2443	Currituck Beach Light............	36 23	75 50	-1 46	-1 45	+1.1	0.0	3.6	4.3	1.8
2444	Albemarle and Pamlico Sounds <9>........	- - -	- - -	- - -	- - -	- -	- -	- -	- -	- -
2445	Kitty Hawk (ocean)............	36 06	75 43	-1 50	-1 49	+0.7	0.0	3.2	3.8	1.6
2446	Jennetts Pier (ocean)............	35 55	75 36	-1 54	-1 50	+0.8	0.0	3.3	3.9	1.6
2447	Roanoke Sound Channel............	35 48	75 35	+0 27	+0 37	-2.0	0.0	0.5	0.6	0.3
2448	Oregon Inlet Marina............	35 48	75 33	-0 38	+0 26	-1.9	0.0	0.6	0.7	0.3
2449	Oregon Inlet............	35 46	75 31	-1 13	-1 07	-0.5	0.0	2.0	2.4	1.0
2450	Oregon Inlet Bridge............	35 46	75 32	-1 27	-1 35	-0.6	0.0	1.9	2.3	1.0
2451	Oregon Inlet Channel............	35 46	75 34	-1 19	-1 14	-1.3	0.0	1.2	1.4	0.6
2452	Old House Channel............	35 46	75 35	-0 36	-0 12	-1.8	0.0	0.7	0.8	0.4
2453	Oregon Inlet (USCG Station)............	35 46	75 32	-1 40	-1 31	-0.8	0.0	1.7	2.0	0.9
2454	Davis Slough............	35 45	75 33	-1 01	-0 41	-1.6	0.0	0.9	1.1	0.5
2455	Cape Hatteras............	35 14	75 31	-1 54	-2 05	+1.1	0.0	3.6	4.3	1.8
2456	Hatteras (ocean)............	35 12	75 42	-2 02	-2 05	+0.9	0.0	3.4	4.1	1.7
2457	Hatteras Inlet............	35 12	75 44	-1 39	-1 39	-0.5	0.0	2.0	2.4	1.0
2458	Ocracoke Inlet............	35 04	76 01	-1 38	-1 41	-0.6	0.0	1.9	2.3	0.9
2459	Ocracoke, Ocracoke Inlet............	35 07	75 59	-1 23	-1 00	*0.40	*0.40	1.0	1.2	0.5
2461	Cape Lookout............	34 37	76 32	-2 04	-2 13	+1.2	0.0	3.7	4.4	1.9
2463	Shell Point, Harkers Island............	34 41	76 32	+0 12	+0 45	-1.2	0.0	1.3	1.6	0.6
2465	Beaufort (Pivers Island)............	34 43	76 40	-1 01	-1 09	+0.5	0.0	3.0	3.6	1.5
2467	Morehead City............	34 43	76 42	-0 58	-1 05	+0.4	0.0	2.9	3.5	1.4
2469	Atlantic Beach............	34 42	76 43	-2 02	-2 03	+1.1	0.0	3.6	4.3	1.8
2471	Bogue Inlet............	34 39	77 06	-1 34	-1 37	-0.3	0.0	2.2	2.6	1.1
2473	New River Inlet............	34 32	77 20	-1 31	-1 35	+0.5	0.0	3.0	3.6	1.5
2475	New Topsail Inlet............	34 22	77 38	-1 27	-0 52	+0.5	0.0	3.0	3.5	1.5
				on CHARLESTON, p.96						
2477	Masonboro Inlet............	34 11	77 49	-0 14	+0 05	-1.4	0.0	3.8	4.5	1.9
2479	Wilmington Beach............	34 02	77 54	-0 48	-0 38	-1.2	0.0	4.0	4.7	2.0
2481	Cape Fear............	33 51	77 58	-0 33	-0 28	-0.7	0.0	4.5	5.1	2.2
	Cape Fear River									
2483	Bald Head............	33 52	78 00	-0 17	-0 11	-0.9	0.0	4.3	4.9	2.2
2485	Fort Caswell............	33 54	78 01	-0 12	-0 05	-1.0	0.0	4.2	4.8	2.1
2487	Southport............	33 55	78 01	0 00	+0 11	-1.1	0.0	4.1	4.6	2.0
2489	Reaves Point............	34 00	77 57	+0 15	+0 45	-1.3	0.0	3.9	4.3	2.0
				on WILMINGTON, p.92						
2491	Campbell Island............	34 07	77 56	-0 49	-0 44	-0.4	0.0	3.8	4.0	1.9
2493	WILMINGTON............	34 14	77 57	Daily predictions				4.2	4.5	2.1
2495	Castle Hayne, Northeast River.......	34 21	77 56	+2 40	+2 55	*0.40	*0.40	1.7	1.9	0.8
2497	Bannermans Br., Northeast River.....	34 35	77 46	+5 54	+6 09	*0.31	*0.31	1.3	1.4	0.6
				on CHARLESTON, p.96						
2500	Yaupon Beach............	33 54	78 05	-0 39	-0 49	-0.3	0.0	4.9	5.8	2.4
2501	Lockwoods Folly Inlet............	33 55	78 14	-0 29	-0 12	-1.0	0.0	4.2	4.8	2.1
2503	Shallotte Inlet (Bowen Point)............	33 55	78 22	+0 10	+0 28	-0.6	0.0	4.6	5.4	2.3
2505	Tubbs Inlet............	33 53	78 29	-0 19	-0 12	-0.7	0.0	4.5	5.1	2.2
	SOUTH CAROLINA, Outer Coast									
2507	Little River, 1 mile above mouth........	33 51	78 34	0 00	+0 03	-0.2	0.0	5.0	5.9	2.5
2509	Little River (town), Little River.......	33 52	78 37	+0 29	+0 02	0.0	0.0	5.2	6.1	2.6
2511	Myrtle Beach............	33 41	78 53	-0 27	-0 27	-0.1	0.0	5.1	6.0	2.5
2513	Murrells Inlet............	33 32	79 02	-0 09	+0 20	-0.7	0.0	4.5	5.3	2.2
2514	Pawleys Island............	33 26	79 07	-0 29	-0 30	-0.4	0.0	4.8	5.6	2.4
2515	North Inlet............	33 20	79 10	-0 18	0 00	-0.7	0.0	4.5	5.3	2.2
	Winyah Bay									
2517	Entrance (south jetty)............	33 11	79 09	-0 28	-0 28	-0.6	0.0	4.6	5.4	2.3
2519	Georgetown Lighthouse............	33 13	79 11	+0 26	+0 25	-1.4	0.0	3.8	4.4	1.9
2521	Esterville-Minim Creek Canal (ferry)...	33 15	79 16	+0 31	+1 04	*0.63	*0.63	3.3	3.9	1.6

Endnotes can be found at the end of table 2.

NO.	PLACE	POSITION Lat.	POSITION Long.	DIFFERENCES Time High Water	DIFFERENCES Time Low Water	DIFFERENCES Height High Water	DIFFERENCES Height Low Water	RANGES Mean	RANGES Spring	Mean Tide Level
		° ' N	° ' W	h. m.	h. m.	ft	ft	ft	ft	ft
	South Carolina, Winyah Bay Time meridian, 75°W			on CHARLESTON, p.96						
2523	Frazier Point	33 19	79 17	+1 19	+2 03	-1.7	0.0	3.5	4.1	1.7
2525	Georgetown, Sampit River	33 22	79 17	+1 27	+2 25	*0.63	*0.63	3.3	3.9	1.6
2527	Georgetown, Pee Dee River bridge	33 22	79 16	+1 34	+2 35	*0.63	*0.63	3.3	3.9	1.6
	Waccamaw River									
2529	Schooner Creek entrance	33 27	79 10	+2 21	+3 18	*0.62	*0.62	3.2	3.8	1.6
2531	Wachesaw Ldg., 1 mile south of	33 33	79 06	+3 06	+4 08	*0.56	*0.56	2.9	3.4	1.4
2533	Bull Creek entrance	33 36	79 06	+3 38	+4 41	*0.44	*0.44	2.3	2.7	1.1
2535	Enterprise Landing	33 40	79 04	+4 54	+5 31	*0.38	*0.38	2.0	2.4	1.0
2537	Toddville	33 45	79 04	+7 10	+7 07	*0.25	*0.25	1.3	1.5	0.6
2539	Conway	33 50	79 02	+7 47	+7 56	*0.23	*0.23	1.2	1.4	0.6
	SOUTH CAROLINA, Outer Coast-Con.									
2541	North Santee River Inlet	33 08	79 15	-0 16	0 00	-0.7	0.0	4.5	5.3	2.2
2543	Minim Creek ent., North Santee River	33 12	79 16	-0 02	+1 02	-1.3	0.0	3.9	4.6	1.9
2544	Cedar Island Point, South Santee River	33 07	79 16	-0 23	+0 04	-1.1	0.0	4.1	4.8	2.0
2545	Brown Island, South Santee River	33 09	79 20	+0 20	+1 27	-1.1	0.0	4.1	4.8	2.0
2547	Cape Romain	33 01	79 21	-0 29	-0 21	-0.5	0.0	4.7	5.5	2.3
2549	Cape Romain, 46 miles east of	33 05	78 26	-1 12	-1 17	-1.1	0.0	4.1	4.8	2.0
	Bull Bay									
2551	Five Fathom Creek entrance	33 00	79 30	-0 13	-0 11	-0.3	0.0	4.9	5.8	2.4
2553	McClellanville, Jeremy Creek	33 05	79 28	+0 20	+0 21	-0.1	0.0	5.1	6.0	2.5
2555	Harbor River entrance	33 02	79 32	-0 04	+0 32	-0.3	0.0	4.9	5.8	2.4
2557	Jack Creek entrance	32 56	79 35	-0 21	-0 19	-0.2	0.0	5.0	5.9	2.5
2559	Wharf Creek entrance	32 55	79 37	+0 05	-0 12	-0.1	0.0	5.1	6.0	2.5
2561	Sewee Bay	32 56	79 39	+0 06	+0 07	-0.2	0.0	5.0	5.9	2.5
2563	Capers Inlet	32 51	79 42	-0 16	-0 14	0.0	0.0	5.2	6.1	2.6
2565	Dewees Inlet	32 50	79 44	-0 09	-0 16	-0.2	0.0	5.0	5.9	2.5
2567	Isle of Palms (outer coast)	32 47	79 47	-0 16	-0 17	0.0	0.0	5.2	6.1	2.6
2569	Sullivans Island (outer coast)	32 46	79 50	-0 15	-0 16	0.0	0.0	5.2	6.1	2.6
	Charleston Harbor									
2571	Entrance (north jetty)	32 44	79 48	-0 16	-0 19	0.0	0.0	5.2	6.1	2.6
2573	Fort Sumter	32 45	79 52	-0 09	-0 13	-0.2	0.0	5.0	5.9	2.5
2575	The Cove	32 46	79 52	-0 08	-0 06	-0.1	0.0	5.1	6.0	2.6
2577	CHARLESTON (Customhouse Wharf)	32 47	79 55	Daily predictions				5.2	6.1	2.6
2579	Shipyard Creek, 0.8 mile above entrance.	32 50	79 57	+0 27	+0 16	+0.1	0.0	5.3	6.3	2.6
	Cooper River									
2581	North Charleston	32 52	79 58	+0 40	+0 36	0.0	0.0	5.2	6.1	2.6
2583	Goose Creek entrance	32 54	79 57	+0 50	+0 40	0.0	0.0	5.2	6.1	2.6
2585	Yeamans Hall, Goose Creek	32 56	79 59	+2 36	+2 03	-0.2	0.0	5.0	5.9	2.5
2587	Snow Point, north of	32 57	79 56	+1 27	+1 14	-0.3	0.0	4.9	5.8	2.4
2589	Dean Hall	33 03	79 56	+2 46	+2 27	-1.1	0.0	4.1	4.8	2.0
2591	Quimby Creek, East Branch	33 06	79 49	+4 08	+3 47	-0.9	0.0	4.3	5.1	2.1
2593	RR. bridge, West Branch	33 06	79 57	+3 18	+3 05	-1.0	0.0	4.2	5.0	2.1
	Wando River									
2597	Cainhoy	32 55	79 50	+0 57	+0 39	+0.8	0.0	6.0	7.1	3.0
2599	Woodville	32 55	79 44	+2 07	+1 22	+1.1	0.0	6.3	7.4	3.2
	Ashley River									
2601	Wappoo Creek (highway bridge)	32 46	79 58	+0 22	+0 22	0.0	0.0	5.2	6.1	2.6
2603	Highway bridge	32 47	79 58	+0 22	+0 15	0.0	0.0	5.2	6.1	2.6
2605	Highway bridge (2 miles above)	32 50	79 58	+0 25	+0 17	+0.3	0.0	5.5	6.5	2.8
2607	Bees Ferry bridge	32 51	80 03	+1 14	+1 07	+0.3	0.0	5.5	6.4	2.8
2609	Magnolia Gardens	32 53	80 05	+1 16	+1 06	+0.4	0.0	5.6	6.6	2.8
2611	Greggs Landing	32 56	80 09	+1 47	+1 35	+0.9	0.0	6.1	7.2	3.0
	SOUTH CAROLINA, Outer Coast-Con.									
2613	Folly Island (outer coast)	32 39	79 56	-0 15	-0 18	0.0	0.0	5.2	6.1	2.6
2615	Folly River (below bridge)	32 39	79 58	+0 13	-0 09	+0.2	0.0	5.4	6.4	2.7
2617	Legareville, 1 mile above, Stono River	32 41	80 00	+0 13	+0 06	0.0	0.0	5.2	6.1	2.6
2619	Elliott Cut, Stono River	32 46	80 00	+0 48	+0 49	0.0	0.0	5.2	6.1	2.6
2621	Church Flats, RR. bridge, Stono River	32 45	80 08	+2 06	+1 47	+0.5	0.0	5.7	6.7	2.8
	North Edisto River									
2623	Rockville, Bohicket Creek	32 36	80 12	+0 20	+0 05	+0.6	0.0	5.8	6.8	2.9
2624	Point of Pines	32 35	80 14	+0 16	+0 11	+0.4	0.0	5.6	6.5	2.8
2625	Dawho River entrance	32 38	80 16	+0 46	+0 27	+0.9	0.0	6.1	7.2	3.0
2627	Dawho Ferry, Dawho River	32 38	80 20	+1 18	+1 00	+1.3	0.0	6.5	7.7	3.2
2629	Toogoodoo Creek, 2 miles above ent.	32 40	80 18	+1 11	+0 35	+1.2	0.0	6.4	7.6	3.2
2631	Yonges Island, Wadmalaw River	32 41	80 14	+1 19	+0 34	+1.4	0.0	6.6	7.8	3.3
2633	Ravens Point, Church Creek	32 42	80 09	+1 43	+0 49	+1.8	0.0	7.0	8.3	3.5
				on SAVANNAH RIVER ENT., p.100						
2635	Edisto Beach, Edisto Island	32 30	80 18	-0 35	-0 41	-1.0	0.0	5.9	6.9	2.9
	South Edisto River									
2637	Big Bay Creek entrance	32 30	80 20	0 00	-0 09	-0.8	0.0	6.1	7.2	3.0
2639	Peters Point, St. Pierre Creek	32 32	80 21	+0 17	+0 04	-0.7	0.0	6.2	7.3	3.1
2641	Watts Cut ent., 0.8 mile south of	32 36	80 23	+0 38	+0 55	-0.6	0.0	6.3	7.4	3.1
2643	Dawho River entrance	32 39	80 23	+1 28	+1 42	-0.6	0.0	6.3	7.4	3.1
2645	Jacksonboro	32 46	80 27	+3 16	+4 21	*0.28	*0.28	1.9	2.2	0.9

Endnotes can be found at the end of table 2.

NO.	PLACE	POSITION Lat.	POSITION Long.	DIFFERENCES Time High Water	DIFFERENCES Time Low Water	DIFFERENCES Height High Water	DIFFERENCES Height Low Water	RANGES Mean	RANGES Spring	Mean Tide Level
		° ′ N	° ′ W	h. m.	h. m.	ft	ft	ft	ft	ft
	St. Helena Sound Time meridian, 75°W			on SAVANNAH RIVER ENT., p.100						
2647	Harbor River entrance	32 24	80 27	-0 01	-0 05	-0.8	0.0	6.1	7.1	3.0
2649	Combahee Bank	32 29	80 26	+0 04	+0 05	-0.7	0.0	6.2	7.3	3.1
2651	Seabrook, Ashepoo River	32 31	80 25	+0 13	+0 15	-0.7	0.0	6.2	7.3	3.1
2653	Hutchinson Island, Ashepoo River	32 33	80 29	+0 41	+0 52	-0.6	0.0	6.3	7.4	3.1
2655	Fields Point, Combahee River	32 34	80 33	+0 48	+0 58	-0.5	0.0	6.4	7.5	3.2
2657	Highway Bridge, Combahee River	32 39	80 41	+2 50	+2 51	*0.64	*0.64	4.4	5.1	2.2
2659	Lucy Point Creek ent., Morgan River	32 27	80 37	+0 58	+0 27	-0.1	0.0	6.8	8.0	3.4
2661	Summerhouse Point, Bull River	32 32	80 34	+1 03	+0 33	-0.3	0.0	6.6	7.8	3.3
2663	Brickyard Point, Coosaw River	32 30	80 40	+1 20	+1 07	+0.4	0.0	7.3	8.5	3.6
2665	Coosaw River	32 32	80 41	+1 25	+1 09	+0.3	0.0	7.2	8.4	3.6
2667	Fripp Inlet, Hunting Island	32 21	80 28	+0 01	-0 22	-0.7	0.0	6.2	7.3	3.1
	Port Royal Sound									
2669	Martins Industry	32 07	80 35	-0 30	-0 41	-0.5	0.0	6.4	7.6	3.2
2671	Hilton Head	32 14	80 40	-0 08	-0 16	-0.3	0.0	6.6	7.8	3.3
2673	Club Bridge Creek entrance	32 20	80 33	+0 30	-0 20	-0.1	0.0	6.8	8.0	3.4
2675	Station Creek	32 19	80 36	+0 28	-0 19	0.0	0.0	6.9	8.1	3.4
2677	Chowan Creek, Distant Island	32 23	80 38	+1 03	+0 30	+0.2	0.0	7.1	8.3	3.5
2679	Parris Island, Beaufort River	32 21	80 40	+0 35	+0 17	+0.2	0.0	7.1	8.3	3.5
2681	Port Royal, Battery Creek	32 22	80 41	+0 37	+0 24	+0.3	0.0	7.2	8.5	3.6
2683	Beaufort, Beaufort River	32 26	80 40	+1 13	+0 46	+0.5	0.0	7.4	8.7	3.7
2684	Colleton River Mouth	32 19	80 48	+0 46	+0 34	+0.4	0.0	7.3	8.5	3.7
2685	Victoria Bluff, Colleton River	32 18	80 48	+1 03	+0 37	+0.6	0.0	7.5	8.8	3.7
2687	Baileys Landing, Okatee River	32 21	80 54	+1 33	+0 59	+1.2	0.0	8.1	9.5	4.0
2689	Lemon Island, Chechessee River	32 22	80 50	+1 04	+0 45	+0.7	0.0	7.6	8.9	3.8
2691	Archers Creek entrance, Broad River	32 21	80 44	+0 41	+0 27	+0.2	0.0	7.1	8.3	3.5
2693	Corning Landing, Whale Branch	32 30	80 47	+1 29	+1 13	+1.0	0.0	7.9	9.2	3.9
2695	Skull Creek, north entrance	32 16	80 44	+0 26	+0 20	+0.1	0.0	7.0	8.3	3.5
2697	Skull Creek, south entrance	32 13	80 47	+0 33	+0 08	+0.7	0.0	7.6	9.0	3.8
2699	Haig Point, Daufuskie Island	32 09	80 50	+0 09	-0 07	+0.3	0.0	7.2	8.4	3.6
2701	Bluffton, May River	32 14	80 52	+0 54	+0 21	+1.2	0.0	8.1	9.5	4.0
2703	Daufuskie Landing, New River	32 06	80 54	+0 23	+0 24	+0.3	0.0	7.2	8.5	3.6
2705	Walls Cut, Turtle Island	32 05	80 55	+0 08	+0 16	+0.2	0.0	7.1	8.3	3.6
	GEORGIA Savannah River									
2707	Tybee Light	32 02	80 51	-0 08	-0 15	-0.1	0.0	6.8	8.0	3.4
2709	SAVANNAH RIVER ENTRANCE	32 02	80 54	Daily predictions				6.9	8.1	3.5
				on SAVANNAH, p.104						
2711	Fort Jackson	32 05	81 02	-0 07	-0 14	+0.1	0.0	7.5	8.7	3.8
2713	SAVANNAH	32 05	81 05	Daily predictions				7.4	8.6	3.7
2715	Port Wentworth	32 09	81 08	+0 33	+0 41	-0.4	0.0	7.0	8.1	3.5
2717	S.C.L. RR. bridge	32 14	81 09	+1 15	+2 12	-1.2	0.0	6.2	7.2	3.1
	Tybee Creek and Wassaw Sound			on SAVANNAH RIVER ENT., p.100						
2719	Tybee Creek entrance	31 59	80 51	-0 07	+0 02	-0.1	0.0	6.8	8.0	3.4
2721	Beach Hammock	31 57	80 56	+0 01	-0 10	0.0	0.0	6.9	8.1	3.4
2723	Romerly Marsh Creek	31 56	81 00	+0 10	-0 06	+0.2	0.0	7.1	8.3	3.5
	Wilmington River									
2725	Savannah-Oglethorpe Hotel	32 00	81 00	+0 16	+0 03	+0.9	0.0	7.8	9.1	3.9
2727	Thunderbolt	32 02	81 03	+0 34	+0 09	+1.0	0.0	7.9	9.2	3.9
2729	North entrance	32 04	81 00	+0 42	+0 41	+0.7	0.0	7.6	8.9	3.8
2731	Isle of Hope, Skidaway River	31 59	81 03	+0 52	+0 25	+0.9	0.0	7.8	9.1	3.9
	Ossabaw Sound									
2733	Egg Islands	31 50	81 05	+0 06	+0 07	+0.3	0.0	7.2	8.4	3.6
2735	Vernon View, Burnside River	31 56	81 06	+0 42	+0 28	+0.6	0.0	7.5	8.8	3.8
2737	Coffee Bluff, Forest River	31 56	81 09	+1 07	+0 39	+0.6	0.0	7.5	8.8	3.7
2739	Fort McAllister, Ogeechee River	31 53	81 13	+0 50	+1 13	0.0	0.0	6.9	8.1	3.4
2741	Highway bridge, Ogeechee River	31 59	81 17	+3 21	+4 22	*0.14	*0.14	1.0	1.2	0.5
2743	Cane Patch Creek entrance	31 49	81 09	+0 57	+0 40	+0.3	0.0	7.2	8.4	3.6
	St. Catherines and Sapelo Sounds									
2745	Walburg Creek entrance	31 42	81 09	+0 25	+0 20	+0.2	0.0	7.1	8.3	3.6
2747	Kilkenny Club, Kilkenny Creek	31 47	81 12	+0 31	+0 13	+1.0	0.0	7.9	9.2	3.9
2749	Sunbury, Medway River	31 46	81 17	+0 56	+0 42	+0.6	0.0	7.5	8.8	3.8
2751	Belfast, Belfast River	31 49	81 18	+1 25	+1 07	+0.9	0.0	7.8	9.1	3.9

Endnotes can be found at the end of table 2.

NO.	PLACE	POSITION Lat.	POSITION Long.	DIFFERENCES Time High Water	DIFFERENCES Time Low Water	DIFFERENCES Height High Water	DIFFERENCES Height Low Water	RANGES Mean	RANGES Spring	Mean Tide Level
		° ′ N	° ′ W	h. m.	h. m.	ft	ft	ft	ft	ft
	St. Catherines and Sapelo Sounds Time meridian, 75°W			on SAVANNAH RIVER ENT., p.100						
2753	North Newport River	31 40	81 16	+0 58	+0 33	+0.7	0.0	7.6	8.9	3.8
2755	South Newport River	31 38	81 16	+0 39	+0 44	+0.5	0.0	7.4	8.7	3.7
2756	Dallas Bluff, Julienton River	31 35	81 19	+0 50	+1 01	+0.7	0.0	7.6	8.9	3.8
2757	Blackbeard Island	31 32	81 12	+0 20	+0 19	0.0	0.0	6.9	8.1	3.4
2758	Dog Hammock, Sapelo River	31 32	81 16	+0 31	+0 23	+0.2	0.0	7.1	8.3	3.6
2759	Pine Harbor, Sapelo River	31 33	81 22	+1 05	+1 01	+0.3	0.0	7.2	8.4	3.6
2760	Eagle Creek, Mud River	31 31	81 17	+0 23	+0 16	+0.3	0.0	7.2	8.4	3.6
2761	Mud River, at Old Teakettle Creek	31 29	81 19	+0 47	+0 43	+0.5	0.0	7.4	8.7	3.7
	Doboy and Altamaha Sounds									
2762	Blackbeard Creek, Blackbeard Island	31 29	81 13	+0 21	+0 44	-0.4	0.0	6.5	7.6	3.3
2763	Sapelo Island	31 23	81 17	0 00	+0 02	-0.1	0.0	6.8	8.0	3.4
2765	Hudson Creek entrance	31 27	81 21	+0 39	+0 28	+0.3	0.0	7.2	8.4	3.6
2767	Threemile Cut entrance, Darien River	31 21	81 23	+0 46	+0 52	+0.2	0.0	7.1	8.3	3.5
2769	Darien, Darien River	31 22	81 26	+1 10	+1 12	+0.4	0.0	7.3	8.5	3.6
2771	Wolf Island	31 20	81 19	+0 06	+0 35	-0.3	0.0	6.6	7.7	3.3
2773	Champney Island, South Altamaha River	31 20	81 28	+1 12	+2 30	-1.7	0.0	5.2	6.1	2.6
2775	Hampton River entrance	31 13	81 19	+0 18	+0 01	-0.3	0.0	6.6	7.8	3.3
2777	Jones Creek entrance, Hampton River	31 18	81 20	+1 05	+0 10	+0.3	0.0	7.2	8.5	3.6
	St. Simons Sound									
2779	St. Simons Sound Bar	31 06	81 19	+0 01	-0 05	-0.4	0.0	6.5	7.6	3.2
2781	St. Simons Light	31 08	81 24	+0 24	+0 28	-0.3	0.0	6.6	7.7	3.3
2783	Frederica River	31 13	81 24	+0 50	+0 53	+0.3	0.0	7.2	8.4	3.6
2785	Troup Creek entrance, Mackay River	31 13	81 26	+0 54	+0 49	+0.3	0.0	7.2	8.4	3.6
2787	Brunswick, East River	31 09	81 30	+0 55	+0 40	+0.4	0.0	7.3	8.5	3.6
	Turtle River									
2789	Allied Chemical Corp. docks	31 11	81 31	+1 05	+0 39	+0.7	0.0	7.6	8.9	3.8
2791	Dillard Creek	31 14	81 34	+1 34	+0 59	+1.1	0.0	8.0	9.4	4.0
2793	Buffalo River entrance	31 13	81 35	+1 39	+0 55	+1.1	0.0	8.0	9.4	4.0
2795	Highway bridge, South Brunswick River	31 09	81 34	+1 09	+0 46	+0.7	0.0	7.6	8.9	3.8
2797	Jekyll Point	31 01	81 26	+0 28	+0 28	-0.3	0.0	6.6	7.7	3.3
2799	Jointer Island, Jointer Creek	31 06	81 30	+1 02	+0 49	+0.3	0.0	7.2	8.4	3.6
	Little Satilla River									
2801	2.5 miles above mouth	31 04	81 30	+0 47	+0 49	-0.1	0.0	6.8	8.0	3.4
2803	8 miles above mouth	31 06	81 34	+1 15	+1 20	+0.4	0.0	7.3	8.5	3.6
2805	Below Spring Bluff	31 10	81 37	+2 00	+1 49	+0.6	0.0	7.5	8.8	3.7
2807	Dover Bluff, Dover Creek	31 01	81 32	+0 57	+0 49	+0.1	0.0	7.0	8.2	3.5
	Satilla River									
2809	Todd Creek entrance	30 58	81 31	+0 43	+0 59	-0.2	0.0	6.7	7.8	3.3
2811	Bailey Cut, 0.8 mile west of	30 59	81 36	+0 57	+1 20	0.0	0.0	6.9	8.1	3.4
2813	Ceylon	30 58	81 39	+1 25	+1 53	-0.3	0.0	6.6	7.7	3.3
2815	Burnt Fort	30 57	81 54	+4 46	+5 23	*0.46	*0.46	3.2	3.7	1.6
2817	Cumberland Wharf, Cumberland River	30 56	81 27	+0 40	+0 42	-0.1	0.0	6.8	8.0	3.4
2819	Floyd Creek, 2.8 miles above entrance	30 56	81 30	+0 59	+0 39	+0.2	0.0	7.1	8.3	3.5
	GEORGIA and FLORIDA Cumberland Sound									
2821	St. Marys Entrance, north jetty	30 43	81 26	+0 15	+0 15	-1.1	0.0	5.8	6.8	2.9
2823	Crooked River entrance	30 51	81 29	+1 23	+1 12	-0.1	0.0	6.8	8.0	3.4
2825	Harrietts Bluff, Crooked River	30 52	81 35	+2 09	+2 12	-0.5	0.0	6.4	7.5	3.2
2827	St. Marys, St. Marys River	30 43	81 33	+1 21	+1 13	-0.9	0.0	6.0	7.0	3.0
2829	Crandall, St. Marys River	30 43	81 37	+2 10	+1 59	-1.8	0.0	5.1	6.0	2.5
				on MAYPORT, p.108						
2831	Fernandina Beach (outer coast)	30 38	81 26	-0 18	-0 01	+1.2	0.0	5.7	6.7	2.8
2833	Fernandina Beach, Amelia River	30 40	81 28	+0 32	+0 16	+1.5	0.0	6.0	7.0	3.0
2835	Chester, Bells River	30 41	81 32	+0 49	+0 41	+1.9	0.0	6.4	7.5	3.2
2837	S.C.L. RR. bridge, Kingsley Creek	30 38	81 29	+0 59	+0 43	+1.5	0.0	6.0	7.0	3.0
	FLORIDA Nassau Sound and Fort George River									
2839	Nassau Sound	30 31	81 27	-0 03	+0 06	+0.9	0.0	5.4	6.3	2.7
2841	Amelia City, South Amelia River	30 35	81 28	+0 54	+1 03	+1.1	0.0	5.6	6.6	2.8
2843	Nassauville, Nassau River	30 34	81 31	+1 04	+1 37	+0.3	0.0	4.8	5.6	2.4
2845	Mink Creek entrance, Nassau River	30 32	81 34	+1 58	+2 32	-0.6	0.0	3.9	4.6	1.9
2847	Halfmoon Island, highway bridge	30 34	81 36	+3 00	+3 21	-1.0	0.0	3.5	4.1	1.7
2849	Sawpit Creek entrance	30 31	81 27	-0 02	+0 30	+0.5	0.0	5.0	5.8	2.5
2851	Fort George Island, Fort George River	30 26	81 26	+0 29	+0 39	+0.3	0.0	4.8	5.6	2.4
	FLORIDA, St. Johns River									
2853	South Jetty	30 24	81 23	-0 23	-0 17	+0.4	0.0	4.9	5.7	2.4
2855	MAYPORT	30 24	81 26	Daily predictions				4.5	5.3	2.3

Endnotes can be found at the end of table 2.

NO.	PLACE	POSITION		DIFFERENCES				RANGES		Mean Tide Level
		Lat.	Long.	Time		Height		Mean	Spring	
				High Water	Low Water	High Water	Low Water			
		° ' N	° ' W	h. m.	h. m.	ft	ft	ft	ft	ft
	FLORIDA, St. Johns River Time meridian, 75°W			on MAYPORT, p.108						
2857	Pablo Creek bascule bridge	30 19	81 26	+1 39	+1 15	*0.64	*0.64	2.9	3.4	1.4
2859	Fulton	30 23	81 30	+0 29	+0 42	-1.1	0.0	3.4	4.0	1.7
2861	Dame Point	30 23	81 33	+0 46	+0 55	*0.67	*0.67	3.0	3.5	1.5
2863	Phoenix Park (Cummers Mill)	30 23	81 38	+0 58	+1 25	*0.44	*0.44	2.0	2.3	1.0
2865	Jacksonville (Dredge Depot)	30 21	81 37	+1 24	+1 50	*0.44	*0.44	2.0	2.3	1.0
2867	Jacksonville (RR. bridge)	30 19	81 40	+2 06	+2 13	*0.27	*0.27	1.2	1.4	0.6
2869	Ortega River entrance	30 17	81 42	+2 27	+2 50	*0.20	*0.20	0.9	1.1	0.5
2871	Orange Park	30 10	81 42	+3 49	+4 14	*0.16	*0.16	0.7	0.8	0.3
2873	Green Cove Springs	30 00	81 40	+5 26	+6 13	*0.18	*0.18	0.8	0.9	0.4
2875	East Tocoi	29 51	81 34	+6 47	+7 18	*0.22	*0.22	1.0	1.2	0.5
2877	Bridgeport	29 45	81 34	+6 58	+7 32	*0.24	*0.24	1.1	1.3	0.5
2879	Palatka	29 39	81 38	+7 26	+8 21	*0.27	*0.27	1.2	1.4	0.6
2881	Welaka	29 29	81 40	+7 46	+8 25	*0.11	*0.11	0.5	0.6	0.2
	FLORIDA, East Coast									
2883	Atlantic Beach	30 20	81 24	-0 25	-0 18	+0.7	0.0	5.2	6.0	2.6
2885	St. Augustine Inlet	29 53	81 17	-0 21	-0 01	0.0	0.0	4.5	5.3	2.2
2887	St. Augustine	29 54	81 18	+0 14	+0 43	-0.3	0.0	4.2	5.0	2.1
2889	Daytona Beach (ocean)	29 14	81 00	-0 33	-0 32	-0.4	0.0	4.1	4.9	2.0
				on MIAMI HARBOR ENT., p.112						
2891	Ponce de Leon Inlet	29 04	80 55	+0 06	+0 20	-0.2	0.0	2.3	2.7	1.2
2893	Cape Canaveral	28 26	80 34	-0 41	-0 41	+1.0	0.0	3.5	4.1	1.8
2894	Oak Hill, Mosquito Lagoon <21>	28 52	80 50	- - -	- - -	- -	- -	- -	- -	- -
	Indian River									
2895	Melbourne <22>	28 06	80 37	- - -	- - -	- -	- -	- -	- -	- -
2896	Palm Bay	28 02	80 35	+3 40	+4 19	*0.10	*0.10	0.2	0.2	0.1
2897	Wabasso	27 45	80 26	+2 48	+3 19	*0.16	*0.16	0.4	0.5	0.2
2898	Vero Beach	27 38	80 22	+3 21	+3 50	*0.32	*0.32	0.8	1.0	0.4
2900	Fort Pierce	27 27	80 19	+1 08	+1 01	*0.48	*0.48	1.2	1.4	0.6
2901	Jensen Beach	27 14	80 13	+2 40	+3 06	*0.40	*0.40	1.0	1.2	0.5
2902	Sebastian Inlet	27 52	80 27	-0 24	-0 20	-0.4	0.0	2.1	2.5	1.0
2903	Vero Beach (ocean)	27 40	80 22	-0 31	-0 25	+0.9	0.0	3.4	4.0	1.7
2905	Fort Pierce Inlet, south jetty	27 28	80 17	-0 09	-0 14	+0.1	0.0	2.6	3.1	1.3
	St. Lucie River									
2907	North Fork	27 15	80 19	+2 50	+3 29	*0.40	*0.40	1.0	1.2	0.5
2908	Stuart	27 12	80 16	+2 37	+3 33	*0.36	*0.36	0.9	1.1	0.4
2909	South Fork	27 10	80 15	+2 54	+3 34	*0.36	*0.36	0.9	1.1	0.4
2911	Sewall Point	27 10	80 11	+1 35	+2 11	*0.36	*0.36	0.9	1.1	0.4
2912	Seminole Shores	27 11	80 10	-0 30	-0 14	+0.5	0.0	3.0	3.6	1.5
2913	Great Pocket	27 09	80 10	+1 18	+1 51	*0.44	*0.44	1.1	1.3	0.6
2914	Gomez, South Jupiter Narrows	27 06	80 08	+1 56	+2 41	*0.52	*0.52	1.3	1.6	0.6
2916	Hobe Sound - State Park	27 02	80 06	+1 46	+2 22	-0.9	0.0	1.6	1.9	0.8
2917	Conch Bar, Jupiter Sound	26 59	80 06	+1 19	+1 38	-0.8	0.0	1.7	2.0	0.8
2918	Jupiter Sound, south end	26 57	80 05	+0 46	+0 49	-0.5	0.0	2.0	2.4	1.0
2919	Jupiter Inlet	26 57	80 04	+0 15	+0 01	0.0	0.0	2.5	3.0	1.2
	Loxahatchee River									
2921	Tequesta	26 57	80 06	+1 18	+2 02	-0.7	0.0	1.8	2.2	0.9
2922	North Fork	26 58	80 07	+1 27	+1 59	-0.6	0.0	1.9	2.3	1.0
2923	Southwest Fork (spillway)	26 56	80 09	+1 15	+1 49	-0.5	0.0	2.0	2.4	1.0
2924	Northwest Fork	26 59	80 08	+1 34	+2 10	-0.5	0.0	2.0	2.4	1.0
2926	Southwest Fork	26 57	80 07	+1 15	+1 47	-0.6	0.0	1.9	2.3	1.0
2927	Jupiter, Lake Worth Creek	26 56	80 05	+0 57	+1 16	-0.4	0.0	2.1	2.5	1.0
2928	Donald Ross Bridge	26 53	80 04	+0 43	+0 54	-0.2	0.0	2.3	2.8	1.2
2929	North Palm Beach, Lake Worth Creek	26 50	80 03	+0 05	+0 17	+0.4	0.0	2.9	3.4	1.4
2931	Port of Palm Beach, Lake Worth	26 46	80 03	0 00	+0 12	+0.1	0.0	2.6	3.1	1.3
2932	Palm Beach (ocean)	26 43	80 02	-0 21	-0 18	+0.3	0.0	2.8	3.3	1.4
2933	West Palm Beach Canal	26 39	80 03	+1 08	+1 36	0.0	0.0	2.5	2.8	1.2
2934	Lake Worth Pier (ocean)	26 37	80 02	-0 19	-0 17	+0.3	0.0	2.8	3.3	1.4
2936	Boynton Beach	26 33	80 03	+1 26	+2 09	0.0	0.0	2.5	2.8	1.2
2937	Delray Beach	26 28	80 04	+1 45	+2 09	0.0	0.0	2.5	2.9	1.2
2938	Yamato	26 24	80 04	+1 43	+1 59	-0.1	0.0	2.4	2.8	1.2
2939	Boca Raton	26 21	80 05	+0 47	+1 13	-0.3	0.0	2.2	2.5	1.1
2941	Deerfield Beach	26 19	80 05	+0 51	+1 07	-0.1	0.0	2.4	2.9	1.2
2942	Hillsboro Beach, Intracoastal waterway	26 16	80 05	+0 26	+0 38	+0.3	0.0	2.8	3.2	1.4
2943	Hillsboro Inlet (inside)	26 16	80 05	+0 08	+0 06	0.0	0.0	2.5	2.9	1.2
2944	Lauderdale-by-the-sea	26 11	80 06	-0 08	-0 08	+0.1	0.0	2.6	3.1	1.3
	Fort Lauderdale									
2946	Bahia Mar Yacht Club	26 07	80 06	+0 19	+0 38	-0.1	0.0	2.4	2.8	1.2
2947	Andrews Ave. bridge, New River	26 07	80 09	+0 39	+0 56	-0.4	0.0	2.1	2.4	1.0
2948	Port Everglades	26 06	80 07	-0 06	-0 06	+0.1	0.0	2.6	3.1	1.3
2949	South Port Everglades	26 05	80 07	0 00	+0 01	0.0	0.0	2.5	2.9	1.3
2951	Hollywood Beach	26 02	80 07	+1 00	+1 08	-0.4	0.0	2.1	2.4	1.0
2952	Golden Beach	25 58	80 08	+1 36	+2 04	-0.4	0.0	2.1	2.4	1.0
2953	Sunny Isles, Biscayne Creek	25 56	80 08	+2 23	+2 27	-0.7	0.0	1.8	2.2	0.9
2954	North Miami Beach	25 56	80 07	-0 04	0 00	0.0	0.0	2.5	3.0	1.2
2956	Bakers Haulover Inlet (inside)	25 54	80 08	+1 17	+1 35	-0.5	0.0	2.0	2.4	1.0
2957	Indian Creek	25 52	80 09	+1 36	+1 50	-0.4	0.0	2.1	2.5	1.1
2958	Miami Beach	25 46	80 08	0 00	0 00	0.0	0.0	2.5	3.0	1.3
2959	MIAMI HARBOR ENTRANCE	25 46	80 08	Daily predictions				2.5	3.0	1.3

Endnotes can be found at the end of table 2.

NO.	PLACE	POSITION Lat.	POSITION Long.	DIFFERENCES Time High Water	DIFFERENCES Time Low Water	DIFFERENCES Height High Water	DIFFERENCES Height Low Water	RANGES Mean	RANGES Spring	Mean Tide Level
		° ' N	° ' W	h. m.	h. m.	ft	ft	ft	ft	ft
	VENEZUELA Time meridian, 60°W			on ISLA ZAPARA, p.152						
3551	ISLA ZAPARA, Lake Maracaibo.............	11 00	71 35	Daily predictions				2.8	3.0	2.7
3552	Bahia de Tablazos, Lake Maracaibo........	10 53	71 35	+0 30	+0 11	*0.61	*0.31	2.1	2.3	1.5
3553	Punta de Palmas..........................	10 48	71 37	+0 35	+0 16	*0.49	*0.31	1.6	1.8	1.2
				on AMUAY, p.156				Mean	Diurnal	
3554	AMUAY..................................	11 45	70 13	Daily predictions				- -	1.2	0.6
3555	La Guaira †............................	10 36	66 56	-2 29	-1 59	+0.8	+1.0	- -	1.0	1.5
3557	Carenero †.............................	10 32	66 07	-1 51	-1 59	+0.8	+1.0	- -	1.0	1.5
3559	Cumana †...............................	10 28	64 11	-2 37	-1 02	-0.1	0.0	- -	1.1	0.5
3561	Porlamar, Isla de Margarita †..........	10 57	63 51	-1 19	-0 59	+0.6	0.0	- -	1.8	0.9
3563	Carupano †.............................	10 40	63 15	-1 17	-0 42	+0.2	0.0	- -	1.4	0.7
				on PUNTA GORDA, p.160				Mean	Spring	
	Gulf of Paria									
3565	Macuro................................	10 39	61 56	-1 15	-2 05	*0.38	*0.38	2.2	2.7	1.4
3567	Puerto de Hierro......................	10 37	62 05	-0 46	-1 19	*0.59	*0.59	3.3	4.2	2.0
3569	Barra de Maturin, channel entrance..	10 18	62 31	-0 22	-0 45	-1.0	+0.2	4.6	5.7	2.8
3571	PUNTA GORDA, Rio San Juan...........	10 10	62 38	Daily predictions				5.8	7.1	3.2
3573	Boca Pedernales entrance............	10 01	62 12	-0 03	-0 34	-1.3	+0.2	4.3	5.4	2.6
3575	Rio Orinoco ent., Isla Ramon Isidro.....	8 39	60 35	+0 07	-0 12	+0.2	+1.0	5.0	6.7	3.8
	TRINIDAD									
3577	Staubles Bay............................	10 41	61 39	-1 07	-2 02	(*0.33+1.7)		1.9	2.5	2.8
3579	Carenage Bay............................	10 41	61 36	-0 58	-1 40	(*0.34+1.6)		2.0	2.6	2.7
3581	Port of Spain...........................	10 39	61 31	-0 44	-1 12	(*0.31+1.4)		1.8	2.3	2.4
3583	Bonasse pier............................	10 05	61 52	-0 43	-1 15	-1.0	+1.4	3.4	4.4	3.4
3585	Erin Bay................................	10 04	61 39	-0 50	-1 41	-0.3	+1.2	4.3	5.6	3.6
3587	Guayaguayare Bay........................	10 09	61 01	-1 32	-2 09	(*0.53+1.3)		3.1	3.8	3.0
3588	Nariva River............................	10 24	61 02	-1 06	-2 16	(*0.41+1.3)		2.4	3.1	2.5
	GUYANA Time meridian, 56°15'W			on SURINAME RIVIER, p.164						
3589	Parika, Essequibo River.................	6 52	58 25	+0 37	+1 01	+1.6	+1.0	6.6	8.3	5.6
3591	Georgetown..............................	6 48	58 10	+0 17	+0 01	+0.9	+1.1	5.8	8.0	5.3
	SURINAM Time meridian, 52°30'W									
3593	Nickerie River..........................	5 57	56 59	+0 09	+0 21	+1.1	0.0	7.1	9.2	4.9
3595	SURINAME RIVIER ENTRANCE................	6 00	55 14	Daily predictions				6.0	7.6	4.3
3597	Paramaribo, Suriname Rivier.............	5 49	55 09	+1 09	+1 42	0.0	0.0	6.0	7.3	4.3
	FRENCH GUIANA Time meridian, 60°W									
3599	Rio Maroni entrance.....................	5 45	53 58	+0 48	+0 54	+0.7	+1.2	5.5	7.2	5.2
3601	Iles du Salut...........................	5 17	52 35	+0 23	+0 23	+1.7	+2.2	5.5	7.2	6.2
3603	Cayenne.................................	4 56	52 20	+0 45	+0 45	+2.4	+1.8	6.6	7.8	6.4
	BRAZIL <16> Time meridian, 45°W.									
3605	Cape Cassipore..........................	3 49	51 01	+1 54	+1 49	+1.5	+0.3	7.2	9.5	5.2
3607	Rio Cunani entrance.....................	2 50	50 53	+2 40	+2 54	(*2.42-0.2)		14.5	19.0	10.1
3609	Ilha de Maraca anchorage................	2 09	50 30	+2 10	+2 22	(*2.42-0.2)		14.5	19.0	10.1
3611	Ilha do Brigue, Amazon River............	0 55	50 05	+7 39	+8 10	+8.3	+1.1	13.2	15.7	9.0
3613	Ponta Pedreira, Amazon River............	0 11	50 43	+7 01	+7 13	*2.08	*2.23	12.3	16.2	9.0
3615	Macapa, Amazon River....................	0 03	51 11	+11 27	+12 43	+2.8	+0.4	8.4	9.5	5.9
		S	W							
3617	Canal de Braganca, Rio Para entrance....	0 23	47 55	+6 39	+6 39	+1.8	-0.1	7.9	10.4	5.1
3619	Salinopolis.............................	0 39	47 23	+3 08	+3 22	*1.99	*1.54	12.5	15.9	8.3
3621	Belem (Para)............................	1 27	48 30	+7 04	+8 07	+2.9	+0.7	8.2	10.1	6.1
3623	Ilhas de Sao Joao.......................	1 17	44 55	+2 01	+2 01	*1.70	*1.31	10.7	14.1	7.0
3625	Sao Luiz................................	2 32	44 18	+2 58	+2 55	(*2.35-0.7)		14.1	17.1	9.3
3627	Santana, Recifes de.....................	2 16	43 36	+1 16	+1 15	*1.58	*1.15	10.0	13.1	6.5
3629	Tutoia, Baia da.........................	2 46	42 14	+0 41	+0 40	+2.4	+0.4	8.0	10.0	5.7
3631	Luis Correia............................	2 53	41 40	+0 31	+0 43	+1.8	+0.4	7.4	9.4	5.4
3633	Camocim.................................	2 53	40 52	+1 37	+1 36	+2.0	+0.4	7.6	9.7	5.5
3635	Rio Ceara (bar).........................	3 41	38 37	+0 17	+0 09	+0.2	-0.1	6.3	8.3	4.3
3637	Fortaleza...............................	3 43	38 29	+0 22	+0 18	+0.2	-0.3	6.5	8.5	4.2
	Time meridian, 30°W			on RECIFE, p.168						
3639	Fernando de Noronha.....................	3 50	32 25	+1 32	+1 33	-1.2	-0.5	4.5	6.0	2.9
3641	Rocas, Atol das.........................	3 51	33 49	+1 43	+1 44	+2.3	0.0	7.5	10.0	4.9

Endnotes can be found at the end of table 2.

NO.	PLACE	POSITION Lat.	POSITION Long.	DIFFERENCES Time High Water	DIFFERENCES Time Low Water	DIFFERENCES Height High Water	DIFFERENCES Height Low Water	RANGES Mean	RANGES Spring	Mean Tide Level
		° ' S	° ' W	h. m.	h. m.	ft	ft	ft	ft	ft
	BRAZIL <16> Time meridian, 45°W			on RECIFE, p.168						
3643	Macau, Rio Acu	5 06	36 41	+1 29	+1 58	+0.6	-0.1	5.9	7.6	4.1
3645	Natal	5 47	35 12	+0 28	+0 30	+0.1	-0.2	5.5	7.3	3.7
3647	Cabedelo	6 58	34 50	+0 36	+0 37	+0.1	-0.2	5.5	7.2	3.7
3649	Tambau	7 06	34 50	-0 04	-0 03	+0.7	-0.1	6.0	7.6	4.1
3651	RECIFE	8 03	34 52	Daily predictions				5.3	7.1	3.8
3653	Maceio	9 40	35 43	+0 10	+0 14	-0.3	-0.2	5.1	6.8	3.6
3655	Rio Sao Francisco (bar)	10 31	36 24	+0 06	+0 14	-0.7	0.0	4.5	6.0	3.5
3657	Aracaju	10 56	37 03	+0 33	+0 48	-0.8	-0.3	4.7	6.1	3.3
3659	Salvador	12 58	38 31	-0 02	-0 08	+0.6	+0.4	5.5	7.4	4.3
3661	Ponta da Areia	12 47	38 30	+0 10	+0 06	+0.6	-0.1	5.9	7.6	4.0
3663	Morro de Sao Paulo	13 21	38 54	-0 11	-0 13	-0.6	0.0	4.6	6.0	3.5
3665	Camamu	13 54	38 58	-0 08	-0 04	-0.2	+0.1	4.9	6.5	3.8
3667	Ilheus	14 48	39 02	-0 33	-0 32	-0.9	-0.3	4.6	5.8	3.2
3669	Canavieiras	15 40	38 56	+0 16	+0 22	-1.0	-0.2	4.5	5.8	3.1
3671	Santa Cruz Cabralia	16 17	39 02	-0 35	-0 35	-1.2	-0.5	4.5	6.0	2.9
3673	Cumuruxatiba	17 06	39 11	-0 23	-0 09	+0.4	+0.3	5.3	7.2	4.2
3675	Caravelas	17 43	39 09	-0 50	-0 49	-0.8	-0.5	4.9	6.4	3.1
3677	Abrolhos Anchorage	17 58	38 42	-0 01	+0 04	+0.6	+0.1	5.7	7.6	4.2
3679	Vitoria	20 19	40 19	-0 34	-0 35	*0.66	*0.75	3.3	4.6	2.6
3681	Guarapari	20 40	40 30	+0 12	+0 17	*0.62	*0.75	3.1	4.2	2.5
				on RIO DE JANEIRO, p.172						
3683	Sao Joao da Barra	21 38	41 03	+0 34	-0 42	-0.1	-0.2	2.6	3.6	2.1
3685	Macae (Imbitiba Bay)	22 23	41 46	-0 23	-1 08	0.0	-0.2	2.7	3.6	2.1
3687	Armacao dos Buzios	22 45	41 53	-0 01	-0 55	-0.1	-0.1	2.5	3.4	2.1
3689	Cabo Frio	23 00	42 03	-0 03	-0 05	*0.91	*0.90	2.3	3.2	2.0
3691	RIO DE JANEIRO	22 54	43 10	Daily predictions				2.5	3.5	2.2
3693	Itacurussa	22 56	43 55	+0 50	-0 26	0.0	-0.1	2.6	3.3	2.2
3695	Angra dos Reis	23 01	44 19	-0 35	-0 40	*0.86	*0.86	2.1	3.0	1.9
3697	Parati	23 14	44 43	-0 09	-1 25	-0.1	0.0	2.4	3.4	2.2
3699	Sao Sebastiao	23 49	45 24	-0 28	-1 24	*0.94	*1.00	2.3	3.3	2.2
3701	SANTOS	23 56	46 19	Daily predictions				2.6	3.8	2.4
3703	Cananeia	25 01	47 56	+1 09	-1 09	+0.4	+0.2	2.7	4.1	2.6
3705	Paranagua	25 31	48 27	+1 51	-1 32	+1.8	+0.2	4.1	6.0	3.2
3707	Sao Francisco do Sul	26 15	48 38	+0 38	- - -	+0.8	-0.1	3.4	4.8	2.6
3709	Itajai	26 54	48 39	-0 08	-0 16	(*0.76+0.4)		1.9	2.8	2.1
3711	Porto Belo	27 09	48 33	-0 38	-0 28	*0.74	*0.74	1.8	2.5	1.7
3713	Florianopolis	27 36	48 34	-0 14	+0 15	*0.69	*0.70	1.7	2.4	1.6
3715	Imbituba	28 14	48 39	-0 17	-1 10	*0.54	*0.50	1.4	2.0	1.2
3717	Laguna	28 30	48 47	+1 10	-1 31	(*0.32+0.4)		0.8	1.2	1.1
3719	Barra do Rio Grande <18> †	32 10	52 05	- - -	- - -	- -	- -	- -	0.8	0.3
	URUGUAY			on BUENOS AIRES, p.180						
3721	Montevideo	34 55	56 13	-5 10	-7 11	(*0.52+1.6)		1.1	1.4	3.0
3723	Colonia, Rio de la Plata	34 28	57 51	+0 17	-0 33	(*0.52+1.2)		1.1	1.3	2.6
	ARGENTINA									
	Rio de la Plata									
3725	BUENOS AIRES	34 36	58 22	Daily predictions				2.1	2.5	2.6
3727	La Plata	34 50	57 53	-1 50	-2 04	+0.2	+0.6	1.7	2.0	3.0
3729	Banco Chico	34 50	57 30	-3 00	-3 24	+0.8	+0.8	2.1	2.5	3.4
3731	Banco Cuirassier	35 06	57 08	-5 25	-5 39	+0.8	+0.8	2.1	2.5	3.4
3733	Punta Piedras	35 26	57 07	-7 10	-7 23	+2.2	+1.1	3.2	3.8	4.2
3735	Punta Norte del Cabo San Antonio <17>	36 18	56 47	-8 50	-9 26	+1.2	+0.3	3.0	3.7	3.3
3737	Mar del Plata <17>	38 03	57 33	-0 02	+0 14	+0.7	+0.2	2.6	3.0	3.0
3739	Quequen <17>	38 35	58 42	-0 18	-0 22	+1.5	-0.3	3.9	4.2	3.2
				on PUERTO BELGRANO, p.184						
3741	Faro Recalada	39 00	61 16	-0 20	-0 15	-4.1	-0.7	6.5	7.1	5.6
3743	Monte Hermoso	38 59	61 41	-0 18	-0 27	-2.8	-0.8	7.9	9.1	6.2
	Bahia Blanca									
3745	Punta Ancla	38 57	62 00	-0 15	+0 06	-1.1	-0.3	9.1	9.9	7.2
3747	Puerto Rosales	38 55	62 04	0 00	+0 07	+0.1	-0.1	10.1	11.0	8.0
3749	PUERTO BELGRANO	38 53	62 06	Daily predictions				9.9	10.8	8.0
3751	Ingeniero White	38 47	62 16	+0 33	+0 18	+0.6	+0.4	10.1	11.0	8.5
3753	General Daniel Cerri	38 45	62 23	+0 47	+0 36	*1.19	*1.20	11.8	12.9	9.5
3755	Canal del Sur, Isla Bermejo	39 01	61 58	-0 28	-0 12	-1.3	-0.2	8.8	9.6	7.2
3757	Canal Bermejo, Isla Trinidad	39 05	61 58	-0 30	-0 14	-1.9	-0.4	8.4	9.2	6.8
3759	Punta Lobos, Isla Trinidad	39 14	61 53	-0 48	-0 46	-2.5	-0.6	8.0	8.8	6.4
3761	Punta Laberinto	39 26	62 03	-0 49	-0 58	-2.1	-0.9	8.7	9.6	6.5
3763	Bahia Anegada, Islote NW	40 01	62 10	-1 39	-1 47	(*0.66-0.5)		6.5	7.2	4.8
3765	Bahia San Blas	40 33	62 14	-3 19	-3 28	*0.53	*0.40	5.6	6.0	4.0
3767	Segunda Barranca	40 47	62 17	-4 49	-4 57	(*0.55-0.4)		5.4	5.9	4.0
3769	Punta Redonda, Rio Negro entrance	41 02	62 46	-5 48	-5 57	-1.0	-1.0	9.9	11.2	7.0

Endnotes can be found at the end of table 2.

NO.	PLACE	POSITION Lat.	POSITION Long.	DIFFERENCES Time High Water	DIFFERENCES Time Low Water	DIFFERENCES Height High Water	DIFFERENCES Height Low Water	RANGES Mean	RANGES Spring	Mean Tide Level
		° ′	° ′	h. m.	h. m.	ft	ft	ft	ft	ft
		S	W							
	ARGENTINA Time meridian, 45°W			on COMODORO RIVADAVIA, p.188						
	Golfo San Matias									
3771	Caleta de los Loros	41 02	64 06	+7 14	+7 08	*1.45	*1.39	20.3	24.0	14.8
3773	Puerto San Antonio	40 48	64 52	+7 30	+7 23	(*1.57-1.6)		21.9	25.6	14.6
	Golfo San Jose									
3775	San Roman	42 15	64 14	+7 15	+7 18	(*1.42-1.1)		19.8	23.4	13.5
3777	Pueyrredon (Fondeadero)	42 24	64 09	+7 46	+7 40	(*1.52-2.2)		21.2	24.6	13.5
3779	La Argentina (Fondeadero)	42 23	64 34	+7 04	+6 58	*1.31	*1.36	18.0	23.3	13.5
3781	Punta Norte	42 05	63 46	+6 50	+6 44	-0.8	-1.4	14.5	17.0	9.5
3783	Caleta Valdes	42 31	63 36	+5 04	+4 58	-5.2	-1.9	10.6	12.4	6.7
3785	Punta Delgada	42 46	63 38	+4 08	+4 02	-5.8	-2.0	10.1	11.7	6.4
	Golfo Nuevo									
3787	Punta Ninfas (Fondeadero)	42 57	64 25	+2 48	+3 31	-2.3	-1.0	12.6	15.4	8.6
3789	Puerto Piramides	42 35	64 17	+2 56	+3 33	-2.7	-1.3	12.5	15.0	8.3
3791	Puerto Madryn	42 46	65 02	+3 08	+3 42	-0.8	-0.1	13.2	16.0	9.8
3793	Bahia Engano	43 20	65 04	+2 06	+2 00	-2.7	-1.3	12.5	15.2	8.2
3795	Isla Escondida	43 43	65 17	+2 10	+2 05	-3.3	-0.3	10.9	13.1	8.5
3797	Bahia Janssen	44 02	65 14	+1 48	+2 03	-4.1	-1.9	11.7	13.9	7.3
3799	Cabo Raso	44 20	65 14	+1 41	+1 26	-4.8	-1.6	10.7	12.4	7.0
3801	Bahia Cruz	44 27	65 19	+2 13	+2 07	-6.1	-2.1	9.9	11.5	6.2
3803	Santa Elena, Puerto	44 31	65 22	+1 45	+1 40	-3.1	-0.4	11.2	13.6	8.5
3805	Bahia Camarones	44 54	65 36	+1 10	+1 14	-2.3	+0.1	11.5	13.7	9.2
	Golfo San Jorge									
3807	Caleta Leones	45 03	65 37	+1 11	+1 05	-0.7	-0.2	13.4	14.7	9.8
3809	Bahia Gil (Caleta Horno)	45 02	65 41	+0 42	+0 36	-1.7	+0.3	11.9	14.1	9.6
3811	Puerto Melo	45 01	65 50	+0 27	+0 24	-1.5	+0.1	12.3	14.6	9.6
3813	Isla Tova	45 06	65 59	+0 27	+0 24	-1.5	+0.1	12.3	14.6	9.6
3815	Bahia Bustamante	45 07	66 32	+0 28	+0 23	-0.8	+0.7	12.4	14.7	10.2
3817	COMODORO RIVADAVIA	45 52	67 29	Daily predictions				14.0	16.3	10.3
3819	Cabo Blanco	47 12	65 45	-1 15	-1 20	-2.3	-0.3	11.9	13.2	9.0
3821	Puerto Deseado	47 45	65 55	-2 52	-2 44	-0.6	+1.0	12.4	14.5	10.5
3823	Bahia Oso Marino	47 56	65 48	-3 35	-3 40	-1.2	+1.2	11.5	14.1	10.3
3825	Bahia de los Nodales	48 01	65 57	-3 01	-3 06	-1.2	+0.1	12.6	15.3	9.7
3827	Bahia Laura	48 23	66 29	-5 28	-5 28	+6.7	-1.9	22.5	25.4	12.7
3829	Bahia San Julian (Punta Pena)	49 15	67 40	-4 58	-5 04	(*1.40-1.4)		19.5	23.6	13.0
				on PUNTA LOYOLA, p.192						
3831	Santa Cruz (Punta Quilla)	50 07	68 25	+0 43	+0 44	+0.2	+0.1	26.0	32.4	20.4
3833	Ria Coig	50 57	69 10	-0 05	-0 04	0.0	-0.7	26.6	32.2	19.9
3835	PUNTA LOYOLA	51 36	69 01	Daily predictions				25.9	32.4	20.3
3837	Rio Gallegos (Reduccion Beacon)	51 37	69 13	+0 21	+0 30	+4.2	+1.1	29.0	36.2	22.9
3839	Cabo Virgenes	52 21	68 22	-0 36	-0 55	-2.1	0.0	23.8	29.8	19.2
	Tierra del Fuego <19>			on COMODORO RIVADAVIA, p.188						
3841	Bahia San Sebastian	53 10	68 30	-7 50	-7 55	*1.69	*1.91	22.8	28.6	17.7
3843	Rio Grande (Muelle)	53 48	67 41	-7 50	-7 55	*1.15	*1.18	15.8	19.2	11.8
3845	Cabo San Pablo	54 17	66 42	-8 48	-8 53	*1.17	*1.27	16.0	19.3	12.2
				on PUERTO BELGRANO, p.184						
3847	Bahia Thetis	54 38	65 15	+1 28	+1 20	-1.4	-0.2	8.7	10.6	7.2
	SOUTH ATLANTIC OCEAN ISLANDS Time meridian, 60°W			on PICTOU, p.8						
	Falkland Islands									
3849	Port Louis (Berkeley Sound)	51 33	58 09	+7 50	+7 47	-0.9	-1.0	3.3	4.2	3.0
3851	Stanley Harbor	51 42	57 51	+7 51	+7 48	-1.0	-1.0	3.2	4.2	2.9
	Time meridian, 31°45′W									
	South Georgia									
3853	Royal Bay (Moltke Harbor)	54 31	36 01	+9 58	+10 19	*0.36	*0.13	1.7	2.3	1.2
3855	Leith Harbor	54 08	36 41	+9 15	+9 35	*0.64	*0.65	2.0	2.7	2.5
	Time meridian, local									
	South Orkneys									
3857	Scotia Bay, Laurie Island	60 44	44 39	+8 21	+8 32	-0.3	-0.6	3.5	5.0	3.5
	South Shetlands									
3859	Port Foster, Deception Island	62 58	60 34	+8 26	+8 38	0.0	-0.1	3.3	4.3	3.9
	Time meridian, 45°W									
3860	Admiralty Bay	62 03	58 24	+9 49	+10 05	-0.5	-0.4	3.1	4.4	3.5

Endnotes can be found at the end of table 2.

ENDNOTES

* RATIO. If the ratio is accompanied by a correction factor multiply the heights of the high and low waters at the reference station by the ratio and then apply the correction factor. See note and example on pages 197 and 198.

† The tide at this location is chiefly diurnal. SEE CAUTION NOTE ON PAGE 197.

< 1> Neap low water falls lower than spring low water.

< 2> Wharves are dry at low water.

< 3> There is a bore in the Petitcodiac River. It arrives at Moncton about 2h 30m before high water at St. John; its height is about 3 to 3 1/2 feet on average spring tides, but it sometimes exceeds 5 feet on highest tides. On small tides it is not much more than a large ripple.

< 4> The Reversing Falls at St. John. -- The most turbulence in the gorge occurs on days when the tides are largest. On largest tides the outward fall is between 15 and 16 1/2 feet and is accompanied by a greater turbulence than the inward fall which is between 11 and 12 1/2 feet. The outward fall is at its greatest between 2 hours before and 1 hour after low water at St John: the inward fall is greater just before the time of high water.

< 5> For Eastern Standard time subtract one hour from the predictions obtained using these differences.

< 6> Low water time difference is +2h 47m. SEE CAUTION NOTE ON PAGE 210.

< 7> Tidal information applies only during low river stages.

< 8> Values for the Hudson River above the George Washington Bridge are based upon averages for the six months May to October, when the freshwater discharge is at a minimum.

< 9> In Albermarle and Pamlico Sounds, except near the inlets, the periodic tide has a mean range of less than 0.5 foot.

<10> In the eastern part of Florida Bay the periodic tide has a mean range of less than 0.5 foot.

<11> In Choctawhatchee and Perdido Bays the periodic tide has a mean range of less than 0.5 foot.

<12> At New Orleans the diurnal range of the tide during low river stages averages 0.8 foot. There is no periodic tide at high river stages.

<13> For places on the Pacific coast, see "Tide Tables, West Coast of North and South America."

<14> Inside, in the various bays, except near the inlets, the periodic tide has a mean range of less than 0.5 foot.

<15> Spring range is given instead of diurnal range.

<16> A "Pororoca", a bore, reported to vary from 5 to 15 feet at spring tides, occurs in the Araguary, Guama and Guajara Rivers.

<17> Predictions will be approximate.

<18> Diurnal range is given instead of spring range.

<19> For places in Magellan Strait, on the south coast of Tierra del Fuego and on the Pacific coast, see "Tide Tables, West Coast of North and South America."

<20> The time differences should be applied only to the higher high and the lower low water times of the reference station.

<21> From Oak Hill southward in Mosquito Lagoon the periodic tide is negligible.

<22> In Indian River north of Melbourne, in Banana River and in Banana Creek, the periodic tides are negligible.

<23> Nearby tidal surveys suggest that the tides may actually occur 1/2 to 3/4 of an hour later than these time differences indicate.

TABLE 3.—HEIGHT OF TIDE AT ANY TIME

EXPLANATION OF TABLE

Although the footnote of table 3 may be sufficient explanation, two examples are given here to illustrate its use.

Example 1.—Find the height of the tide at 0755 at New York (The Battery), N.Y., on a day when the predicted tides from table 1 are given as:

Low Water		High Water	
Time	Height	Time	Height
h.m.	ft	h.m.	ft
0522	0.1	1114	4.2
1741	0.6	2310	4.1

An inspection of the above example shows that the desired time falls between the two morning tides.

The duration of rise is $11^h\ 14^m - 5^h\ 22^m = 5^h\ 52^m$.
The time after low water for which the height is required is $7^h\ 55^m - 5^h\ 22^m = 2^h\ 33^m$.
The range of tide is 4.2 —0.1=4.1 feet.

The duration of rise or fall in table 3 is given in heavy-faced type for each 20 minutes from $4^h\ 00^m$ to $10^h\ 40^m$. The nearest tabular value to $5^h\ 52^m$, the above duration of rise, is $6^h\ 00^m$; and on the horizontal line of $6^h\ 00^m$ the nearest tabular time to $2^h\ 33^m$ after low water for which the height is required is $2^h\ 36^m$. Following down the column in which this $2^h\ 36^m$ is found to its intersection with the line of the range 4.0 feet (which is the nearest tabular value to the above range of 4.1 feet) the correction is found to be 1.6 feet, which being reckoned from low water must be added, making 0.1+1.6=1.7 feet, or 0.5 meter which is the required height above mean low water, the datum for New York.

Example 2.—Find the height of the tide at 0300 at Portland, Maine, on a day when the predicted tides from table 1 are given as:

High Water		Low Water	
Time	Height	Time	Height
h.m.	ft	h.m.	ft
0012	11.3	0638	—2.0
1251	10.0	1853	—0.8

The duration of fall is $6^h\ 38^m - 00^h\ 12^m = 6^h\ 26^m$.
The time after high water for which the height is required is $3^h\ 00^m - 00^h\ 12^m = 2^h\ 48^m$.
The range of tide is 11.3 —(—2.0)=13.3 feet.

Entering table 3 at the duration of fall of $6^h\ 20^m$, which is the nearest value to $6^h\ 26^m$, the nearest value on the horizontal line to $2^h\ 48^m$ is $2^h\ 45^m$ after high water. Following down this column to its intersection with a range of 13.5 feet which is the nearest tabular value to 13.3 feet, one obtains 5.3 which, being calculated from high water, must be subtracted from it. The approximate height at $03^h\ 00^m$ is, therefore, 11.3 —5.3=6.0 feet or 1.8 meters.

When the duration of rise or fall is greater than $10^h\ 40^m$, enter the table with one-half the given duration and with one-half the time from the nearest high or low water; but if the duration of rise or fall is less than 4 hours, enter the table with double the given duration and with double the time from the nearest high or low water.

Similarly, when the range of tide is greater than 20 feet, enter the table with one-half the given range. The tabular correction should then be doubled before applying it to the given high or low water height. If the range of tide is greater than 40 feet, take one-third of the range and multiply the tabular correction by 3.

If the height at any time is desired for a place listed in table 2, predictions of the high and low waters for the day in question should be obtained by the use of the differences given for the place in that table. Having obtained these predictions, the height for any intermediate time is obtained in the same manner as illustrated in the foregoing examples.

Graphical Method

If the height of the tide is required for a number of times on a certain day the full tide curve for the day may be obtained by the *one-quarter, one-tenth rule*. The procedure is as follows:

1. On cross-section paper plot the high and low water points in the order of their occurrence for the day, measuring time horizontally and height vertically. These are the basic points for the curve.
2. Draw light straight lines connecting the points representing successive high and low waters.
3. Divide each of these straight lines into four equal parts. The halfway point of each line gives another point for the curve.
4. At the quarter point adjacent to high water draw a vertical line above the point and at the quarter point adjacent to low water draw a vertical line below the point, making the length of these lines equal to one-tenth of the range between the high and low waters used. The points marking the ends of these vertical lines give two additional intermediate points for the curve.
5. Draw a smooth curve through the points of high and low waters and the intermediate points, making the curve well rounded near high and low waters. This curve will approximate the actual tide curve and heights for any time of the day may be readily scaled from it.

Caution.—Both methods presented are based on the assumption that the rise and fall conform to simple cosine curves. Therefore the heights obtained will be approximate. The roughness of approximation will vary as the tide curve differs from a cosine curve.

An example of the use of the graphical method is illustrated below. Using the same predicted tides as in example 2, the approximate height at $03^h\ 00^m$ could be determined as shown below.

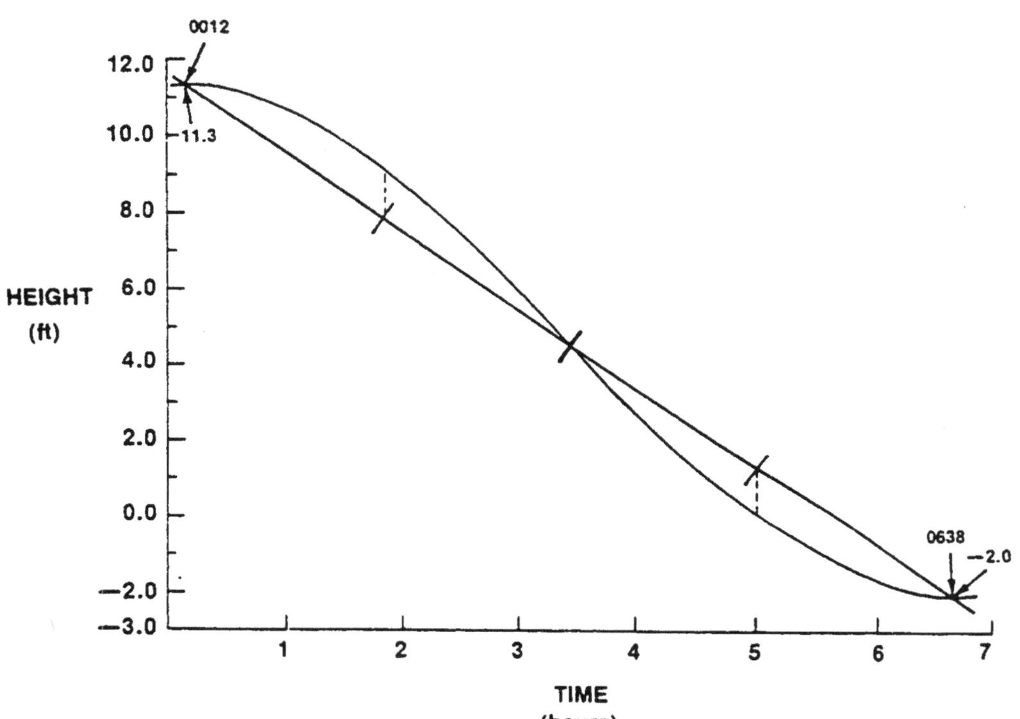

Duration of rise or fall, see footnote	Time from the nearest high water or low water														
h. m.	h. m.	h. m.	h. m.	h. m.	h. m.	h. m.	h. m.	h. m.	h. m.	h. m.	h. m.	h. m.	h. m.	h. m.	h. m.
4 00	0 08	0 16	0 24	0 32	0 40	0 48	0 56	1 04	1 12	1 20	1 28	1 36	1 44	1 52	2 00
4 20	0 09	0 17	0 26	0 35	0 43	0 52	1 01	1 09	1 18	1 27	1 35	1 44	1 53	2 01	2 10
4 40	0 09	0 19	0 28	0 37	0 47	0 56	1 05	1 15	1 24	1 33	1 43	1 52	2 01	2 11	2 20
5 00	0 10	0 20	0 30	0 40	0 50	1 00	1 10	1 20	1 30	1 40	1 50	2 00	2 10	2 20	2 30
5 20	0 11	0 21	0 32	0 43	0 53	1 04	1 15	1 25	1 36	1 47	1 57	2 08	2 19	2 29	2 40
5 40	0 11	0 23	0 34	0 45	0 57	1 08	1 19	1 31	1 42	1 53	2 05	2 16	2 27	2 39	2 50
6 00	0 12	0 24	0 36	0 48	1 00	1 12	1 24	1 36	1 48	2 00	2 12	2 24	2 36	2 48	3 00
6 20	0 13	0 25	0 38	0 51	1 03	1 16	1 29	1 41	1 54	2 07	2 19	2 32	2 45	2 57	3 10
6 40	0 13	0 27	0 40	0 53	1 07	1 20	1 33	1 47	2 00	2 13	2 27	2 40	2 53	3 07	3 20
7 00	0 14	0 28	0 42	0 56	1 10	1 24	1 38	1 52	2 06	2 20	2 34	2 48	3 02	3 16	3 30
7 20	0 15	0 29	0 44	0 59	1 13	1 28	1 43	1 57	2 12	2 27	2 41	2 56	3 11	3 25	3 40
7 40	0 15	0 31	0 46	1 01	1 17	1 32	1 47	2 03	2 18	2 33	2 49	3 04	3 19	3 35	3 50
8 00	0 16	0 32	0 48	1 04	1 20	1 36	1 52	2 08	2 24	2 40	2 56	3 12	3 28	3 44	4 00
8 20	0 17	0 33	0 50	1 07	1 23	1 40	1 57	2 13	2 30	2 47	3 03	3 20	3 37	3 53	4 10
8 40	0 17	0 35	0 52	1 09	1 27	1 44	2 01	2 19	2 36	2 53	3 11	3 28	3 45	4 03	4 20
9 00	0 18	0 36	0 54	1 12	1 30	1 48	2 06	2 24	2 42	3 00	3 18	3 36	3 54	4 12	4 30
9 20	0 19	0 37	0 56	1 15	1 33	1 52	2 11	2 29	2 48	3 07	3 25	3 44	4 03	4 21	4 40
9 40	0 19	0 39	0 58	1 17	1 37	1 56	2 15	2 35	2 54	3 13	3 33	3 52	4 11	4 31	4 50
10 00	0 20	0 40	1 00	1 20	1 40	2 00	2 20	2 40	3 00	3 20	3 40	4 00	4 20	4 40	5 00
10 20	0 21	0 41	1 02	1 23	1 43	2 04	2 25	2 45	3 06	3 27	3 47	4 08	4 29	4 49	5 10
10 40	0 21	0 43	1 04	1 25	1 47	2 08	2 29	2 51	3 12	3 33	3 55	4 16	4 37	4 59	5 20

Range of tide, see footnote	Correction to height														
Ft.	Ft.	Ft.	Ft.	Ft.	Ft.	Ft.	Ft.	Ft.	Ft.	Ft.	Ft.	Ft.	Ft.	Ft.	Ft.
0.5	0.0	0.0	0.0	0.0	0.0	0.0	0.1	0.1	0.1	0.1	0.1	0.2	0.2	0.2	0.2
1.0	0.0	0.0	0.0	0.0	0.1	0.1	0.1	0.2	0.2	0.2	0.3	0.3	0.4	0.4	0.5
1.5	0.0	0.0	0.0	0.1	0.1	0.1	0.2	0.2	0.3	0.4	0.4	0.5	0.6	0.7	0.8
2.0	0.0	0.0	0.0	0.1	0.1	0.2	0.3	0.3	0.4	0.5	0.6	0.7	0.8	0.9	1.0
2.5	0.0	0.0	0.1	0.1	0.2	0.2	0.3	0.4	0.5	0.6	0.7	0.9	1.0	1.1	1.2
3.0	0.0	0.0	0.1	0.1	0.2	0.3	0.4	0.5	0.6	0.8	0.9	1.0	1.2	1.3	1.5
3.5	0.0	0.0	0.1	0.2	0.2	0.3	0.4	0.6	0.7	0.9	1.0	1.2	1.4	1.6	1.8
4.0	0.0	0.0	0.1	0.2	0.3	0.4	0.5	0.7	0.8	1.0	1.2	1.4	1.6	1.8	2.0
4.5	0.0	0.0	0.1	0.2	0.3	0.4	0.6	0.7	0.9	1.1	1.3	1.6	1.8	2.0	2.2
5.0	0.0	0.1	0.1	0.2	0.3	0.5	0.6	0.8	1.0	1.2	1.5	1.7	2.0	2.2	2.5
5.5	0.0	0.1	0.1	0.2	0.4	0.5	0.7	0.9	1.1	1.4	1.6	1.9	2.2	2.5	2.8
6.0	0.0	0.1	0.1	0.3	0.4	0.6	0.8	1.0	1.2	1.5	1.8	2.1	2.4	2.7	3.0
6.5	0.0	0.1	0.2	0.3	0.4	0.6	0.8	1.1	1.3	1.6	1.9	2.2	2.6	2.9	3.2
7.0	0.0	0.1	0.2	0.3	0.5	0.7	0.9	1.2	1.4	1.8	2.1	2.4	2.8	3.1	3.5
7.5	0.0	0.1	0.2	0.3	0.5	0.7	1.0	1.2	1.5	1.9	2.2	2.6	3.0	3.4	3.8
8.0	0.0	0.1	0.2	0.3	0.5	0.8	1.0	1.3	1.6	2.0	2.4	2.8	3.2	3.6	4.0
8.5	0.0	0.1	0.2	0.4	0.6	0.8	1.1	1.4	1.8	2.1	2.5	2.9	3.4	3.8	4.2
9.0	0.0	0.1	0.2	0.4	0.6	0.9	1.2	1.5	1.9	2.2	2.7	3.1	3.6	4.0	4.5
9.5	0.0	0.1	0.2	0.4	0.6	0.9	1.2	1.6	2.0	2.4	2.8	3.3	3.8	4.3	4.8
10.0	0.0	0.1	0.2	0.4	0.7	1.0	1.3	1.7	2.1	2.5	3.0	3.5	4.0	4.5	5.0
10.5	0.0	0.1	0.3	0.5	0.7	1.0	1.3	1.7	2.2	2.6	3.1	3.6	4.2	4.7	5.2
11.0	0.0	0.1	0.3	0.5	0.7	1.1	1.4	1.8	2.3	2.8	3.3	3.8	4.4	4.9	5.5
11.5	0.0	0.1	0.3	0.5	0.8	1.1	1.5	1.9	2.4	2.9	3.4	4.0	4.6	5.1	5.8
12.0	0.0	0.1	0.3	0.5	0.8	1.1	1.5	2.0	2.5	3.0	3.6	4.1	4.8	5.4	6.0
12.5	0.0	0.1	0.3	0.5	0.8	1.2	1.6	2.1	2.6	3.1	3.7	4.3	5.0	5.6	6.2
13.0	0.0	0.1	0.3	0.6	0.9	1.2	1.7	2.2	2.7	3.2	3.9	4.5	5.1	5.8	6.5
13.5	0.0	0.1	0.3	0.6	0.9	1.3	1.7	2.2	2.8	3.4	4.0	4.7	5.3	6.0	6.8
14.0	0.0	0.2	0.3	0.6	0.9	1.3	1.8	2.3	2.9	3.5	4.2	4.8	5.5	6.3	7.0
14.5	0.0	0.2	0.4	0.6	1.0	1.4	1.9	2.4	3.0	3.6	4.3	5.0	5.7	6.5	7.2
15.0	0.0	0.2	0.4	0.6	1.0	1.4	1.9	2.5	3.1	3.8	4.4	5.2	5.9	6.7	7.5
15.5	0.0	0.2	0.4	0.7	1.0	1.5	2.0	2.6	3.2	3.9	4.6	5.4	6.1	6.9	7.8
16.0	0.0	0.2	0.4	0.7	1.1	1.5	2.1	2.6	3.3	4.0	4.7	5.5	6.3	7.2	8.0
16.5	0.0	0.2	0.4	0.7	1.1	1.6	2.1	2.7	3.4	4.1	4.9	5.7	6.5	7.4	8.2
17.0	0.0	0.2	0.4	0.7	1.1	1.6	2.2	2.8	3.5	4.2	5.0	5.9	6.7	7.6	8.5
17.5	0.0	0.2	0.4	0.8	1.2	1.7	2.2	2.9	3.6	4.4	5.2	6.0	6.9	7.8	8.8
18.0	0.0	0.2	0.4	0.8	1.2	1.7	2.3	3.0	3.7	4.5	5.3	6.2	7.1	8.1	9.0
18.5	0.1	0.2	0.5	0.8	1.2	1.8	2.4	3.1	3.8	4.6	5.5	6.4	7.3	8.3	9.2
19.0	0.1	0.2	0.5	0.8	1.3	1.8	2.4	3.1	3.9	4.8	5.6	6.6	7.5	8.5	9.5
19.5	0.1	0.2	0.5	0.8	1.3	1.9	2.5	3.2	4.0	4.9	5.8	6.7	7.7	8.7	9.8
20.0	0.1	0.2	0.5	0.9	1.3	1.9	2.6	3.3	4.1	5.0	5.9	6.9	7.9	9.0	10.0

Obtain from the predictions the high water and low water, one of which is before and the other after the time for which the height is required. The difference between the times of occurrence of these tides is the duration of rise or fall, and the difference between their heights is the range of tide for the above table. Find the difference between the nearest high or low water and the time for which the height is required.

Enter the table with the duration of rise or fall, printed in heavy-faced type, which most nearly agrees with the actual value, and on that horizontal line find the time from the nearest high or low water which agrees most nearly with the corresponding actual difference. The correction sought is in the column directly below, on the line with the range of tide.

When the nearest tide is high water, subtract the correction.

When the nearest tide is low water, add the correction.

Feet	0.0	0.1	0.2	0.3	0.4	0.5	0.6	0.7	0.8	0.9	Feet
	Tenths of a Foot										
0	0.00	0.03	0.06	0.09	0.12	0.15	0.18	0.21	0.24	0.27	0
1	0.30	0.34	0.37	0.40	0.43	0.46	0.49	0.52	0.55	0.58	1
2	0.61	0.64	0.67	0.70	0.73	0.76	0.79	0.82	0.85	0.88	2
3	0.91	0.94	0.98	1.01	1.04	1.07	1.10	1.13	1.16	1.19	3
4	1.22	1.25	1.28	1.31	1.34	1.37	1.40	1.43	1.46	1.49	4
5	1.52	1.55	1.58	1.62	1.65	1.68	1.71	1.74	1.77	1.80	5
6	1.83	1.86	1.89	1.92	1.95	1.98	2.01	2.04	2.07	2.10	6
7	2.13	2.16	2.19	2.23	2.26	2.29	2.32	2.35	2.38	2.41	7
8	2.44	2.47	2.50	2.53	2.56	2.59	2.62	2.65	2.68	2.71	8
9	2.74	2.77	2.80	2.83	2.87	2.90	2.93	2.96	2.99	3.02	9
10	3.05	3.08	3.11	3.14	3.17	3.20	3.23	3.26	3.29	3.32	10
11	3.35	3.38	3.41	3.44	3.47	3.51	3.54	3.57	3.60	3.63	11
12	3.66	3.69	3.72	3.75	3.78	3.81	3.84	3.87	3.90	3.93	12
13	3.96	3.99	4.02	4.05	4.08	4.11	4.15	4.18	4.21	4.24	13
14	4.27	4.30	4.33	4.36	4.39	4.42	4.45	4.48	4.51	4.54	14
15	4.57	4.60	4.63	4.66	4.69	4.72	4.75	4.79	4.82	4.85	15
16	4.88	4.91	4.94	4.97	5.00	5.03	5.06	5.09	5.12	5.15	16
17	5.18	5.21	5.24	5.27	5.30	5.33	5.36	5.39	5.43	5.46	17
18	5.49	5.52	5.55	5.58	5.61	5.64	5.67	5.70	5.73	5.76	18
19	5.79	5.82	5.85	5.88	5.91	5.94	5.97	6.00	6.04	6.07	19
20	6.10	6.13	6.16	6.19	6.22	6.25	6.28	6.31	6.34	6.37	20
21	6.40	6.43	6.46	6.49	6.52	6.55	6.58	6.61	6.64	6.68	21
22	6.71	6.74	6.77	6.80	6.83	6.86	6.89	6.92	6.95	6.98	22
23	7.01	7.04	7.07	7.10	7.13	7.16	7.19	7.22	7.25	7.28	23
24	7.32	7.35	7.38	7.41	7.44	7.47	7.50	7.53	7.56	7.59	24
25	7.62	7.65	7.68	7.71	7.74	7.77	7.80	7.83	7.86	7.89	25
26	7.92	7.96	7.99	8.02	8.05	8.08	8.11	8.14	8.17	8.20	26
27	8.23	8.26	8.29	8.32	8.35	8.38	8.41	8.44	8.47	8.50	27
28	8.53	8.56	8.60	8.63	8.66	8.69	8.72	8.75	8.78	8.81	28
29	8.84	8.87	8.90	8.93	8.96	8.99	9.02	9.05	9.08	9.11	29
30	9.14	9.17	9.20	9.24	9.27	9.30	9.33	9.36	9.39	9.42	30
31	9.45	9.48	9.51	9.54	9.57	9.60	9.63	9.66	9.69	9.72	31
32	9.75	9.78	9.81	9.85	9.88	9.91	9.94	9.97	10.00	10.03	32
33	10.06	10.09	10.12	10.15	10.18	10.21	10.24	10.27	10.30	10.33	33
34	10.36	10.39	10.42	10.45	10.49	10.52	10.55	10.58	10.61	10.64	34
35	10.67	10.70	10.73	10.76	10.79	10.82	10.85	10.88	10.91	10.94	35
36	10.97	11.00	11.03	11.06	11.09	11.13	11.16	11.19	11.22	11.25	36
37	11.28	11.31	11.34	11.37	11.40	11.43	11.46	11.49	11.52	11.55	37
38	11.58	11.61	11.64	11.67	11.70	11.73	11.77	11.80	11.83	11.86	38
39	11.89	11.92	11.95	11.98	12.01	12.04	12.07	12.10	12.13	12.16	39
40	12.19	12.22	12.25	12.28	12.31	12.34	12.37	12.41	12.44	12.47	40
41	12.50	12.53	12.56	12.59	12.62	12.65	12.68	12.71	12.74	12.77	41
42	12.80	12.83	12.86	12.89	12.92	12.95	12.98	13.01	13.05	13.08	42
43	13.11	13.14	13.17	13.20	13.23	13.26	13.29	13.32	13.35	13.38	43
44	13.41	13.44	13.47	13.50	13.53	13.56	13.59	13.62	13.66	13.69	44
45	13.72	13.75	13.78	13.81	13.84	13.87	13.90	13.93	13.96	13.99	45
46	14.02	14.05	14.08	14.11	14.14	14.17	14.20	14.23	14.26	14.30	46
47	14.33	14.36	14.39	14.42	14.45	14.48	14.51	14.54	14.57	14.60	47
48	14.63	14.66	14.69	14.72	14.75	14.78	14.81	14.84	14.87	14.90	48
49	14.94	14.97	15.00	15.03	15.06	15.09	15.12	15.15	15.18	15.21	49
50	15.24	15.27	15.30	15.33	15.36	15.39	15.42	15.45	15.48	15.51	50

TIDE TABLES

Advance information relative to the rise and fall of the tide is given in annual tide tables. These tables include the predicted times and heights of high and low waters for every day in the year for a number of reference stations and differences for obtaining similar predictions for numerous other places.

Tide Tables, Central and Western Pacific Ocean and Indian Ocean.
Tide Tables, East Coast of North and South America (Including Greenland).
Tide Tables, Europe and West Coast of Africa (Including the Mediterranean Sea).
Tide Tables, West Coast of North and South America (Including the Hawaiian Islands).

TIDAL BENCH MARKS

To provide permanent points for the observed heights of the tide and the tidal datum planes determined therefrom, a system of bench marks is established at each tide station. The descriptions and elevations of these bench marks along our coast are compiled, published, and available for distribution. Requests for such bench mark data should specify the coastal locality for which the information is desired.

TIDAL CURRENT TABLES

Accompanying the rise and fall of the tide is a periodic horizontal flow of the water known as the tidal current. Advance information relative to these currents is made available in annual tidal current tables which include daily predictions of the times of slack water and the times and velocities of strength of flood and ebb currents for a number of waterways together with differences for obtaining predictions for numerous other places.

Tidal Current Tables, Atlantic Coast of North America.
Tidal Current Tables, Pacific Coast of North America and Asia.

TIDAL CURRENT CHARTS

Each publication consists of a set of 12 charts which depict, by means of arrows and figures, the direction and speed of the tidal current for each hour of the tidal cycle. The charts, which may be used for any year, present a comprehensive view of the tidal current movement in the respective waterways as a whole and also supply a means for readily determining for any time the direction and speed of the current at various localities throughout the water areas covered. The Narragansett Bay tidal current chart is to be used with the annual tide tables. The other charts require the annual tidal current tables.

Tidal Current Charts, Boston Harbor.
Tidal Current Charts, Charleston Harbor, S.C.
Tidal Current Charts, Delaware Bay and River.
Tidal Current Charts, Long Island Sound and Block Island Sound.
Tidal Current Charts, Narragansett Bay.
Tidal Current Charts, Narragansett Bay to Nantucket Sound.
Tidal Current Charts, New York Harbor.
Tidal Current Charts, Puget Sound, Northern Part.
Tidal Current Charts, Puget Sound, Southern Part.
Tidal Current Charts, San Francisco Bay.
Tidal Current Charts, Upper Chesapeake Bay.
Tidal Current Charts, Tampa Bay.

TIDAL CURRENT DIAGRAMS

The tidal current diagrams are a series of 12 monthly diagrams to be used with the tidal current charts to give the user a convenient method to determine the current flow on a particular day.

Tidal Current Diagrams for Long Island Sound and Block Island Sound.
Tidal Current Diagrams for Boston Harbor.
Tidal Current Diagrams for New York Harbor.
Tidal Current Diagrams for Upper Chesapeake Bay.

INDEX TO STATIONS, 1983 (Numbers refer to table 2)

[Stations marked with an asterisk (*) are reference stations for which daily predictions are given in table 1. Page numbers of reference stations are given-in parentheses.]

A

B

C

D

E

F

G

H

I

J

K

L

M

N

O

P

Q

R

S

T

U

V

W

Y

MERCHANT MARINE DECK EXAMINATION REFERENCE MATERIAL

PART TWO

1983 TIDAL CURRENT TABLES

ATLANTIC COAST of NORTH AMERICA

CONTENTS

IMPORTANT NOTICES

Daylight saving time is not used in this publication. All daily tidal current predictions and predictions compiled by the use of Table 2 data are based on the standard time meridian indicated for each location. Predicted times may be converted to daylight saving times, where necessary, by adding 1 hour to these data. In converting times from the Astronomical Data page, it should be remembered that daylight saving time is based on a meridian 15° east of the normal standard meridian for a particular place.

Current data have been presented in a different format in Table 2. The new manner of presentation will enable the user to approximate more accurately the times and speeds of the various current phases. Slight changes in terminology also have been made. A full explanation of the proper use of the new table is given on the pages immediately preceding the data.

TIDAL CURRENT TABLES

INTRODUCTION

Current tables for the use of mariners have been published by the National Ocean Survey (formerly the Coast and Geodetic Survey) since 1890. Tables for the Atlantic coast first appeared as a part of the tide tables and consisted of brief directions for obtaining the times of the current for a few locations from the times of high and low waters. Daily predictions of slack water for five stations were given for the year 1916, and by 1923 the tables had so expanded that they were then issued as a separate publication entitled *Current Tables, Atlantic Coast*. A companion volume, *Current Tables, Pacific Coast*, was also issued that year. In 1930 the predictions for the Atlantic coast were extended to include the times and velocities of maximum current.

In the preparation of these tables, all available observations were used. In some cases, however, the observations were insufficient for obtaining final results, and as further information becomes available it will be included in subsequent editions. All persons using these tables are invited to send information or suggestions for increasing their usefulness to the Director, National Ocean Survey, Rockville, Md. 20852, U.S.A. The data for lightship stations are based on observations obtained through the cooperation of the U.S. Coast Guard. By cooperative arrangements, full predictions for Bay of Fundy Entrance (Grand Manan Channel) were furnished by the Canadian Hydrographic Service.

Daily predicted times of slack water and predicted times and velocities of maximum current (flood and ebb) are presented in table 1 for a number of reference stations. Similar predictions for many other locations may be obtained by applying the correction factors listed in table 2 to the predictions of the appropriate reference station. The velocity of a current at times between slack water and maximum current may be approximated by the use of table 3. The duration of weak current near the time of slack water may be computed by the use of table 4.

LIST OF REFERENCE STATIONS

TABLE 1.—DAILY CURRENT PREDICTIONS

EXPLANATION OF TABLE

This table gives the predicted times of slack water and the predicted times and velocities of maximum current—flood and ebb—for each day of the year at a number of stations on the Atlantic coast of North America. The times are given in hours and minutes and the velocities in knots.

Time.—The kind of time used for the predictions at each reference station is indicated by the time meridian at the bottom of each page.

Slack water and maximum current.—The columns headed "Slack water" contain the predicted times at which there is no current; or, in other words, the times at which the current has stopped setting in a given direction and is about to begin to set in the opposite direction. Offshore, where the current is rotary, slack water denotes the time of minimum current. Beginning with the slack water before flood the current increases in velocity until the strength or maximum velocity of the flood current is reached; it then decreases until the following slack water or slack before ebb. The ebb current now begins, increases to a maximum velocity, and then decreases to the next slack. The predicted times and velocities of maximum current are given in the columns headed "Maximum Current." Flood velocities are marked with an "F," the ebb velocities with an "E." An entry in the "Slack Water" column will be *slack, flood begins* if the maximum current which follows it is marked "F." Otherwise the entry will be *slack, ebb begins.*

Directions of set.—As the terms flood and ebb do not in all cases clearly indicate the direction of the current, the approximate directions toward which the currents flow are given at the top of each page to distinguish the two streams.

Number of slacks and strengths.—There are usually four slacks and four maximums each day. When a vacancy occurs in any day, the slack or maximum that seems to be missing will be found to occur soon after midnight as the first slack or maximum of the following day. At some stations where the diurnal inequality is large, there may be on certain days a continuous flood or ebb current with varying velocity throughout half the day giving only two slacks and two maximums on that particular day.

Current and tide.—It is important to notice that the predicted slacks and strengths given in this table refer to the horizontal motion of the water and not to the vertical rise and fall of the tide. The relation of current to tide is not constant, but varies from place to place, and the time of slack water does not generally coincide with the time of high or low water, nor does the time of maximum velocity of the current usually coincide with the time of most rapid change in the vertical height of the tide. At stations located on a tidal river or bay the time of slack water may differ from 1 to 3 hours from the time of high or low water. The times of high and low waters are given in the tide tables published by the National Ocean Survey.

Variations from predictions.—In using this table it should be borne in mind that actual times of slack or maximum occasionally differ from the predicted times by as much as half an hour and in rare instances the difference may be as much as an hour. Comparisons of predicted with observed times of slack water indicate that more than 90 percent of the slack waters occurred within half an hour of the predicted times. To make sure, therefore, of getting the full advantage of a favorable current or slack water, the navigator should reach the entrance or strait at least half an hour before the predicted time of the desired condition of current. Currents are frequently disturbed by wind or variations in river discharge. On days when the current is affected by such disturbing influences the times and velocities will differ from those given in the table, but local knowledge will enable one to make proper allowance for these effects.

Typical current curves.—The variations in the tidal current from day to day and from place to place are illustrated on the opposite page by the current curves for representative ports along the Atlantic and Gulf Coasts of the United States. Flood current is represented by the solid line curve above the zero velocity (slack water) line and the ebb current by the broken line curve below the slack water line. The curves show clearly that the currents along the Atlantic coast are semi-daily (two floods and two ebbs in a day) in character with their principal variations following changes in the Moon's distance and phase. In the Gulf of Mexico, however, the currents are daily in character. As the dominant factor is the change in the Moon's declination the currents in the Gulf tend to become semi-daily when the Moon is near the equator. By reference to the curves it will be noted that with this daily type of current there are times when the current may be erratic (marked with an asterisk), or one flood or ebb current of the day may be quite weak. Therefore in using the predictions of the current it is essential to carefully note the velocities as well as the times.

F-Flood, Dir. 032° True   E-Ebb, Dir. 212° True

NOVEMBER

Day	Slack Water Time h.m.	Maximum Current Time h.m.	Vel. knots
1	0225	0535	2.1F
Tu	0855	1205	2.3E
	1510	1810	1.9F
	2110		
2		0025	2.5E
W	0330	0635	2.5F
	0950	1300	2.7E
	1610	1905	2.4F
	2205		
3		0120	2.8E
Th	0420	0725	2.9F
	1035	1350	3.1E
	1655	1955	2.7F
	2255		
4		0205	3.1E
F	0505	0810	3.1F
	1120	1430	3.4E
	1740	2035	3.0F
	2340		
5		0250	3.2E
Sa	0545	0850	3.3F
	1155	1510	3.5E
	1820	2115	3.1F
6	0020	0330	3.1E
Su	0625	0925	3.2F
	1230	1550	3.5E
	1900	2150	3.0F
7	0100	0405	3.0E
M	0705	1000	3.0F
	1305	1625	3.3E
	1935	2225	2.9F
8	0135	0445	2.7E
Tu	0740	1035	2.8F
	1340	1700	3.0E
	2010	2300	2.6F
9	0215	0520	2.3E
W	0815	1110	2.4F
	1410	1740	2.6E
	2050	2340	2.2F
10	0250	0600	1.9E
Th	0855	1145	2.0F
	1440	1815	2.2E
	2130		
11		0015	1.9F
F	0330	0645	1.5E
	0940	1225	1.5F
	1515	1900	1.8E
	2215		
12		0100	1.5F
Sa	0420	0740	1.1E
	1030	1310	1.1F
	1600	1955	1.4E
	2310		
13		0155	1.2F
Su	0530	0855	0.9E
	1145	1410	0.8F
	1705	2110	1.2E
14	0015	0310	1.1F
M	0655	1015	1.0E
	1310	1535	0.7F
	1835	2230	1.2E
15	0125	0430	1.2F
Tu	0805	1120	1.3E
	1425	1705	0.9F
	2000	2330	1.4E

Day	Slack Water Time h.m.	Maximum Current Time h.m.	Vel. knots
16	0225	0535	1.5F
W	0855	1210	1.6E
	1515	1805	1.3F
	2105		
17		0025	1.7E
Th	0315	0625	1.8F
	0935	1255	2.1E
	1600	1850	1.7F
	2150		
18		0105	2.0E
F	0400	0705	2.2F
	1015	1335	2.5E
	1640	1930	2.2F
	2235		
19		0145	2.4E
Sa	0440	0745	2.6F
	1050	1410	2.9E
	1715	2010	2.6F
	2315		
20		0225	2.6E
Su	0520	0820	2.9F
	1125	1445	3.2E
	1755	2050	2.9F
	2355		
21		0300	2.8E
M	0600	0900	3.1F
	1200	1525	3.4E
	1835	2125	3.1F
22	0035	0340	2.9E
Tu	0640	0940	3.2F
	1240	1600	3.4E
	1915	2210	3.2F
23	0115	0425	2.9E
W	0720	1020	3.1F
	1320	1645	3.4E
	1955	2250	3.1F
24	0200	0505	2.8E
Th	0810	1105	2.9F
	1405	1730	3.2E
	2040	2335	2.9F
25	0245	0555	2.5E
F	0900	1150	2.6F
	1450	1820	2.9E
	2130		
26		0030	2.7F
Sa	0340	0655	2.3E
	0955	1245	2.3F
	1545	1920	2.5E
	2230		
27		0125	2.4F
Su	0445	0800	2.1E
	1100	1350	1.9F
	1650	2025	2.3E
	2335		
28		0230	2.2F
M	0555	0915	2.0E
	1215	1500	1.7F
	1810	2140	2.1E
29	0040	0345	2.1F
Tu	0710	1025	2.1E
	1330	1620	1.7F
	1930	2250	2.2E
30	0150	0455	2.2F
W	0815	1130	2.4E
	1440	1735	1.9F
	2040	2355	2.3E

DECEMBER

Day	Slack Water Time h.m.	Maximum Current Time h.m.	Vel. knots
1	0250	0600	2.4F
Th	0915	1230	2.7E
	1540	1835	2.2F
	2140		
2		0050	2.5E
F	0345	0655	2.6F
	1005	1320	2.9E
	1630	1925	2.5F
	2235		
3		0140	2.6E
Sa	0435	0740	2.7F
	1050	1405	3.1E
	1715	2010	2.6F
	2320		
4		0225	2.7E
Su	0520	0825	2.7F
	1130	1450	3.2E
	1755	2055	2.7F
5	0005	0310	2.7E
M	0605	0900	2.7F
	1205	1530	3.1E
	1835	2130	2.7F
6	0045	0350	2.6E
Tu	0645	0940	2.6F
	1240	1605	3.0E
	1915	2210	2.6F
7	0120	0430	2.4E
W	0725	1015	2.4F
	1315	1645	2.8E
	1950	2245	2.4F
8	0200	0510	2.1E
Th	0800	1050	2.1F
	1350	1720	2.5E
	2030	2320	2.2F
9	0235	0545	1.9E
F	0845	1130	1.9F
	1425	1800	2.2E
	2110		
10		0000	2.0F
Sa	0315	0630	1.7E
	0925	1210	1.6F
	1500	1840	1.9E
	2150		
11		0040	1.8F
Su	0400	0715	1.5E
	1015	1255	1.4F
	1545	1925	1.7E
	2235		
12		0125	1.6F
M	0445	0810	1.4E
	1110	1345	1.2F
	1640	2020	1.5E
	2325		
13		0220	1.5F
Tu	0545	0910	1.4E
	1215	1445	1.1F
	1745	2125	1.4E
14	0025	0320	1.5F
W	0645	1015	1.5E
	1320	1555	1.2F
	1900	2230	1.4E
15	0125	0425	1.6F
Th	0740	1110	1.7E
	1420	1705	1.4F
	2005	2330	1.6E

Day	Slack Water Time h.m.	Maximum Current Time h.m.	Vel. knots
16	0220	0525	1.8F
F	0835	1205	2.1E
	1510	1800	1.7F
	2110		
17		0020	1.8E
Sa	0315	0615	2.0F
	0925	1250	2.4E
	1600	1855	2.1F
	2200		
18		0110	2.1E
Su	0405	0705	2.3F
	1010	1335	2.7E
	1645	1940	2.4F
	2250		
19		0200	2.4E
M	0455	0755	2.6F
	1055	1420	3.0E
	1730	2025	2.7F
	2335		
20		0245	2.6E
Tu	0540	0840	2.8F
	1140	1505	3.2E
	1815	2110	3.0F
21	0020	0330	2.8E
W	0630	0925	2.9F
	1225	1550	3.3E
	1900	2155	3.1F
22	0105	0415	2.9E
Th	0715	1010	3.0F
	1310	1635	3.3E
	1945	2240	3.2F
23	0155	0505	2.9E
F	0805	1055	2.9F
	1355	1720	3.2E
	2030	2330	3.1F
24	0240	0555	2.8E
Sa	0855	1145	2.7F
	1445	1810	3.0E
	2120		
25		0015	3.0F
Su	0330	0645	2.7E
	0950	1235	2.5F
	1540	1905	2.8E
	2210		
26		0110	2.7F
M	0425	0745	2.5E
	1045	1335	2.2F
	1635	2005	2.5E
	2305		
27		0205	2.5F
Tu	0525	0845	2.4E
	1150	1435	2.0F
	1740	2105	2.3E
28	0005	0305	2.3F
W	0625	0945	2.3E
	1255	1540	1.8F
	1850	2210	2.1E
29	0105	0410	2.1F
Th	0730	1050	2.3E
	1400	1655	1.8F
	2005	2315	2.0E
30	0210	0515	2.0F
F	0830	1150	2.4E
	1505	1800	1.9F
	2110		
31		0020	2.0E
Sa	0315	0620	2.1F
	0925	1250	2.5E
	1600	1900	2.1F
	2210		

Time meridian 60° W. 0000 is midnight. 1200 is noon.

F-Flood, Dir. 355° True E-Ebb, Dir. 195° True

JANUARY

Day	Slack Water Time h.m.	Maximum Current Time h.m.	Vel. knots
1	0139	0424	2.2E
Sa	0800	1017	1.8F
	1352	1654	2.6E
	2046	2253	1.6F
2	0234	0517	2.1E
Su	0855	1110	1.7F
	1444	1745	2.5E
	2138	2346	1.6F
3	0329	0611	2.1E
M	0951	1201	1.6F
	1538	1838	2.4E
	2231		
4		0039	1.5F
Tu	0426	0706	2.0E
	1050	1254	1.4F
	1634	1932	2.2E
	2326		
5		0132	1.4F
W	0523	0803	1.8E
	1151	1348	1.2F
	1732	2027	2.1E
6	0022	0227	1.3F
Th	0621	0902	1.7E
	1253	1445	1.0F
	1832	2122	1.9E
7	0118	0319	1.1F
F	0719	1008	1.7E
	1356	1544	0.8F
	1932	2221	1.7E
8	0213	0417	1.0F
Sa	0815	1124	1.7E
	1458	1744	0.7F
	2032	2323	1.6E
9	0308	0612	1.0F
Su	0908	1246	1.7E
	1556	1947	0.7F
	2129		
10		0023	1.5E
M	0359	0657	1.0F
	0959	1341	1.7E
	1650	2040	0.8F
	2222		
11		0115	1.5E
Tu	0448	0758	1.0F
	1046	1420	1.8E
	1739	2129	0.8F
	2312		
12		0200	1.4E
W	0534	0734	1.0F
	1129	1443	1.8E
	1823	2057	0.8F
	2359		
13		0236	1.4E
Th	0617	0816	1.0F
	1211	1510	1.9E
	1905	2051	0.8F
14	0042	0314	1.5E
F	0700	0858	1.1F
	1249	1542	1.9E
	1945	2131	0.9F
15	0124	0355	1.5E
Sa	0741	0940	1.1F
	1326	1619	1.9E
	2025	2212	1.0F

Day	Slack Water Time h.m.	Maximum Current Time h.m.	Vel. knots
16	0203	0435	1.5E
Su	0822	1023	1.2F
	1400	1658	1.9E
	2103	2253	1.0F
17	0240	0518	1.5E
M	0904	1106	1.2F
	1430	1741	1.9E
	2142	2338	1.1F
18	0316	0602	1.6E
Tu	0948	1149	1.1F
	1456	1822	1.9E
	2222		
19		0021	1.1F
W	0352	0648	1.6E
	1034	1235	1.1F
	1523	1908	1.8E
	2303		
20		0106	1.2F
Th	0429	0733	1.6E
	1123	1324	1.1F
	1558	1955	1.8E
	2346		
21		0153	1.2F
F	0513	0824	1.6E
	1217	1415	1.0F
	1644	2044	1.7E
22	0034	0243	1.2F
Sa	0605	0916	1.6E
	1315	1508	1.0F
	1743	2135	1.7E
23	0125	0336	1.2F
Su	0705	1011	1.7E
	1414	1603	1.0F
	1901	2232	1.7E
24	0219	0431	1.3F
M	0808	1110	1.8E
	1512	1701	1.0F
	2023	2328	1.7E
25	0315	0528	1.4F
Tu	0909	1207	2.0E
	1609	1800	1.1F
	2134		
26		0027	1.8E
W	0411	0623	1.5F
	1007	1305	2.1E
	1703	1859	1.2F
	2238		
27		0124	1.9E
Th	0506	0721	1.6F
	1102	1400	2.3E
	1755	1956	1.4F
	2336		
28		0220	2.0E
F	0600	0816	1.7F
	1156	1455	2.5E
	1846	2052	1.5F
29	0031	0315	2.1E
Sa	0653	0909	1.8F
	1248	1546	2.6E
	1936	2143	1.6F
30	0125	0408	2.2E
Su	0746	1002	1.8F
	1339	1637	2.6E
	2026	2236	1.6F
31	0217	0501	2.2E
M	0839	1052	1.7F
	1429	1727	2.5E
	2115	2325	1.6F

FEBRUARY

Day	Slack Water Time h.m.	Maximum Current Time h.m.	Vel. knots
1	0309	0552	2.2E
Tu	0933	1143	1.6F
	1520	1815	2.4E
	2206		
2		0014	1.6F
W	0401	0643	2.1E
	1028	1232	1.4F
	1612	1905	2.2E
	2257		
3		0103	1.4F
Th	0454	0737	1.9E
	1125	1323	1.2F
	1706	1957	2.0E
	2350		
4		0153	1.3F
F	0548	0830	1.8E
	1225	1414	1.0F
	1802	2049	1.8E
5	0044	0242	1.1F
Sa	0643	0926	1.7E
	1326	1506	0.8F
	1901	2144	1.6E
6	0140	0335	1.0F
Su	0739	1031	1.6E
	1428	1725	0.6F
	2001	2241	1.4E
7	0236	0427	0.9F
M	0834	1147	1.5E
	1528	1800	0.6F
	2100	2339	1.3E
8	0330	0520	0.8F
Tu	0926	1308	1.6E
	1623	2019	0.7F
	2155		
9		0043	1.3E
W	0422	0614	0.8F
	1016	1357	1.6E
	1713	2105	0.7F
	2247		
10		0134	1.3E
Th	0510	0704	0.9F
	1102	1420	1.7E
	1757	2150	0.8F
	2334		
11		0212	1.4E
F	0555	0751	1.0F
	1145	1445	1.8E
	1838	2026	0.8F
12	0018	0253	1.5E
Sa	0638	0834	1.0F
	1226	1519	1.9E
	1917	2106	0.9F
13	0058	0333	1.6E
Su	0719	0917	1.1F
	1303	1556	1.9E
	1955	2147	1.1F
14	0136	0412	1.6E
M	0800	0959	1.2F
	1337	1634	2.0E
	2032	2228	1.2F
15	0211	0453	1.7E
Tu	0840	1042	1.2F
	1407	1713	2.0E
	2108	2309	1.3F

Day	Slack Water Time h.m.	Maximum Current Time h.m.	Vel. knots
16	0243	0534	1.8E
W	0921	1127	1.2F
	1434	1756	2.0E
	2146	2352	1.3F
17	0314	0619	1.8E
Th	1005	1210	1.2F
	1501	1839	1.9E
	2225		
18		0036	1.3F
F	0347	0705	1.8E
	1052	1257	1.2F
	1535	1924	1.8E
	2307		
19		0123	1.3F
Sa	0427	0754	1.8E
	1144	1348	1.1F
	1620	2015	1.8E
	2356		
20		0214	1.3F
Su	0518	0847	1.8E
	1242	1440	1.0F
	1718	2106	1.7E
21	0051	0305	1.3F
M	0623	0942	1.8E
	1344	1537	1.0F
	1839	2206	1.7E
22	0151	0402	1.3F
Tu	0735	1041	1.8E
	1446	1636	1.0F
	2007	2305	1.7E
23	0253	0502	1.3F
W	0844	1143	1.9E
	1546	1737	1.1F
	2120		
24		0006	1.7E
Th	0354	0601	1.4F
	0948	1242	2.1E
	1642	1837	1.2F
	2224		
25		0106	1.9E
F	0451	0702	1.5F
	1046	1341	2.3E
	1735	1938	1.3F
	2322		
26		0206	2.0E
Sa	0546	0759	1.6F
	1141	1439	2.4E
	1826	2035	1.5F
27	0016	0300	2.2E
Su	0639	0851	1.6F
	1233	1529	2.5E
	1915	2127	1.6F
28	0107	0352	2.2E
M	0731	0944	1.7F
	1323	1618	2.5E
	2003	2216	1.7F

Time meridian 75° W. 0000 is midnight. 1200 is noon.

F-Flood, Dir. 355° True E-Ebb, Dir. 195° True

MARCH

Day	Slack Water Time h.m.	Maximum Current Time h.m.	Vel. knots
1	0156	0442	2.3E
Tu	0822	1033	1.6F
	1411	1705	2.4E
	2050	2302	1.6F
2	0244	0531	2.2E
W	0913	1120	1.5F
	1500	1751	2.3E
	2138	2346	1.5F
3	0332	0617	2.1E
Th	1005	1207	1.4F
	1548	1838	2.1E
	2227		
4		0031	1.4F
F	0420	0705	2.0E
	1058	1254	1.2F
	1638	1923	1.9E
	2317		
5		0116	1.2F
Sa	0510	0755	1.8E
	1155	1342	1.0F
	1731	2014	1.6E
6	0010	0205	1.1F
Su	0603	0847	1.7E
	1254	1433	0.8F
	1829	2106	1.4E
7	0106	0254	0.9F
M	0658	0944	1.5E
	1354	1713	0.6F
	1929	2201	1.3E
8	0203	0348	0.8F
Tu	0754	1040	1.5E
	1454	1744	0.5F
	2029	2300	1.2E
9	0300	0441	0.7F
W	0850	1151	1.5E
	1549	1822	0.6F
	2126		
10		0004	1.2E
Th	0354	0713	0.7F
	0942	1250	1.6E
	1639	1910	0.7F
	2218		
11		0101	1.3E
F	0444	0633	0.8F
	1031	1334	1.6E
	1724	2012	0.7F
	2305		
12		0147	1.4E
Sa	0531	0721	0.9F
	1116	1411	1.7E
	1805	1954	0.9F
	2348		
13		0226	1.6E
Su	0614	0807	1.0F
	1158	1448	1.8E
	1843	2037	1.0F
14	0028	0307	1.7E
M	0655	0853	1.1F
	1236	1525	1.9E
	1921	2116	1.2F
15	0104	0345	1.8E
Tu	0735	0934	1.2F
	1311	1605	2.0E
	1957	2158	1.3F

Day	Slack Water Time h.m.	Maximum Current Time h.m.	Vel. knots
16	0138	0427	1.9E
W	0815	1017	1.3F
	1343	1646	2.0E
	2033	2239	1.4F
17	0210	0508	2.0E
Th	0856	1100	1.3F
	1414	1727	2.0E
	2111	2324	1.5F
18	0241	0553	2.0E
F	0939	1145	1.3F
	1445	1812	1.9E
	2150		
19		0009	1.5F
Sa	0315	0638	2.0E
	1027	1233	1.3F
	1523	1857	1.9E
	2235		
20		0056	1.4F
Su	0356	0729	1.9E
	1119	1324	1.2F
	1611	1949	1.8E
	2328		
21		0145	1.4F
M	0449	0820	1.9E
	1218	1417	1.1F
	1717	2044	1.7E
22	0027	0241	1.3F
Tu	0557	0918	1.9E
	1320	1514	1.1F
	1841	2143	1.6E
23	0132	0338	1.2F
W	0713	1019	1.9E
	1423	1614	1.0F
	2000	2246	1.6E
24	0238	0441	1.2F
Th	0825	1122	1.9E
	1524	1717	1.1F
	2109	2350	1.7E
25	0340	0542	1.2F
F	0930	1224	2.0E
	1621	1822	1.2F
	2210		
26		0053	1.9E
Sa	0439	0643	1.3F
	1029	1325	2.2E
	1714	1922	1.3F
	2306		
27		0154	2.0E
Su	0533	0743	1.4F
	1124	1420	2.3E
	1804	2016	1.5F
	2357		
28		0249	2.2E
M	0625	0836	1.5F
	1215	1510	2.3E
	1851	2106	1.6F
29	0046	0338	2.2E
Tu	0715	0926	1.5F
	1304	1557	2.3E
	1938	2151	1.6F
30	0132	0421	2.3E
W	0804	1013	1.5F
	1351	1639	2.2E
	2023	2234	1.6F
31	0217	0507	2.2E
Th	0853	1056	1.4F
	1437	1723	2.1E
	2109	2317	1.5F

APRIL

Day	Slack Water Time h.m.	Maximum Current Time h.m.	Vel. knots
1	0301	0550	2.1E
F	0942	1139	1.3F
	1524	1808	1.9E
	2155		
2		0000	1.3F
Sa	0346	0634	2.0E
	1032	1226	1.1F
	1612	1854	1.7E
	2244		
3		0041	1.2F
Su	0431	0720	1.8E
	1125	1311	0.9F
	1702	1940	1.5E
	2336		
4		0129	1.0F
M	0520	0811	1.7E
	1221	1402	0.8F
	1758	2031	1.4E
5	0031	0218	0.9F
Tu	0613	0903	1.6E
	1319	1451	0.7F
	1857	2125	1.2E
6	0129	0311	0.8F
W	0710	0958	1.5E
	1416	1547	0.6F
	1956	2224	1.2E
7	0228	0406	0.7F
Th	0808	1057	1.5E
	1510	1813	0.6F
	2053	2323	1.2E
8	0323	0502	0.7F
F	0903	1154	1.5E
	1559	1904	0.7F
	2144		
9		0021	1.3E
Sa	0415	0557	0.8F
	0955	1243	1.6E
	1644	1832	0.8F
	2231		
10		0111	1.5E
Su	0502	0650	0.9F
	1041	1331	1.7E
	1726	1918	1.0F
	2314		
11		0154	1.7E
M	0546	0737	1.0F
	1125	1410	1.8E
	1805	2003	1.2F
	2353		
12		0238	1.8E
Tu	0628	0824	1.1F
	1205	1453	1.9E
	1843	2046	1.3F
13	0030	0319	2.0E
W	0709	0907	1.3F
	1242	1534	2.0E
	1921	2129	1.5F
14	0105	0400	2.1E
Th	0751	0951	1.3F
	1318	1617	2.0E
	1959	2212	1.5F
15	0138	0443	2.1E
F	0833	1036	1.4F
	1355	1701	2.0E
	2039	2257	1.6F

Day	Slack Water Time h.m.	Maximum Current Time h.m.	Vel. knots
16	0214	0528	2.2E
Sa	0918	1123	1.4F
	1435	1746	1.9E
	2123	2344	1.6F
17	0253	0615	2.2E
Su	1007	1212	1.3F
	1521	1835	1.9E
	2212		
18		0032	1.5F
M	0339	0705	2.1E
	1100	1303	1.3F
	1619	1930	1.8E
	2308		
19		0123	1.4F
Tu	0436	0758	2.0E
	1159	1356	1.2F
	1728	2025	1.7E
20	0011	0218	1.3F
W	0544	0857	2.0E
	1300	1456	1.1F
	1842	2127	1.6E
21	0118	0319	1.2F
Th	0658	0958	1.9E
	1402	1557	1.1F
	1951	2230	1.6E
22	0224	0421	1.1F
F	0808	1103	1.9E
	1502	1700	1.1F
	2055	2338	1.7E
23	0326	0524	1.1F
Sa	0912	1205	2.0E
	1558	1805	1.2F
	2153		
24		0044	1.9E
Su	0425	0627	1.2F
	1011	1306	2.1E
	1650	1905	1.3F
	2247		
25		0141	2.0E
M	0519	0725	1.2F
	1105	1400	2.1E
	1739	1956	1.4F
	2336		
26		0234	2.1E
Tu	0610	0819	1.3F
	1156	1449	2.1E
	1826	2042	1.5F
27	0023	0319	2.2E
W	0659	0905	1.3F
	1244	1532	2.1E
	1912	2123	1.5F
28	0107	0400	2.2E
Th	0746	0946	1.3F
	1330	1615	2.0E
	1956	2203	1.4F
29	0150	0441	2.1E
F	0833	1031	1.2F
	1415	1656	1.9E
	2040	2245	1.4F
30	0231	0524	2.1E
Sa	0920	1114	1.1F
	1500	1737	1.7E
	2125	2326	1.3F

Time meridian 75° W. 0000 is midnight. 1200 is noon.

BOSTON HARBOR (Deer Island Light), MASSACHUSETTS, 1983

F-Flood, Dir. 254° True   E-Ebb, Dir. 111° True

JANUARY

Day	Slack Water Time h.m.	Maximum Current Time h.m.	Vel. knots
1		0309	1.3E
Sa	0606	0839	1.4F
	1153	1536	1.4E
	1838	2125	1.4F
2	0027	0420	1.3E
Su	0659	0934	1.3F
	1245	1648	1.4E
	1930	2228	1.3F
3	0120	0532	1.2E
M	0755	1045	1.2F
	1340	1800	1.3E
	2026	2337	1.2F
4	0216	0637	1.2E
Tu	0852	1205	1.1F
	1437	1905	1.2E
	2122		
5		0043	1.1F
W	0314	0739	1.2E
	0953	1313	1.0F
	1537	2007	1.2E
	2221		
6		0146	1.1F
Th	0413	0839	1.2E
	1056	1417	1.0F
	1640	2107	1.2E
	2321		
7		0247	1.1F
F	0514	0938	1.3E
	1158	1518	1.0F
	1743	2205	1.2E
8	0020	0344	1.1F
Sa	0615	1034	1.4E
	1258	1615	1.1F
	1850	2300	1.3E
9	0116	0439	1.1F
Su	0715	1127	1.4E
	1353	1709	1.1F
	1956	2352	1.3E
10	0209	0530	1.2F
M	0810	1218	1.5E
	1444	1759	1.2F
	2053		
11		0042	1.3E
Tu	0258	0617	1.2F
	0857	1306	1.5E
	1530	1846	1.2F
	2136		
12		0129	1.3E
W	0341	0703	1.2F
	0938	1351	1.5E
	1613	1930	1.2F
	2212		
13		0214	1.3E
Th	0425	0745	1.2F
	1017	1435	1.4E
	1654	2012	1.2F
	2248		
14		0257	1.2E
F	0507	0826	1.2F
	1054	1516	1.3E
	1734	2051	1.2F
	2323		
15		0338	1.1E
Sa	0547	0902	1.2F
	1131	1555	1.2E
	1812	2126	1.2F
16	0000	0416	1.1E
Su	0628	0927	1.1F
	1208	1627	1.2E
	1852	2148	1.2F
17	0036	0446	1.0E
M	0709	0930	1.2F
	1247	1606	1.1E
	1932	2153	1.2F
18	0115	0418	1.0E
Tu	0751	1005	1.2F
	1328	1626	1.1E
	2014	2229	1.2F
19	0156	0447	1.0E
W	0838	1048	1.2F
	1412	1703	1.1E
	2059	2313	1.2F
20	0241	0528	1.1E
Th	0927	1135	1.2F
	1500	1747	1.1E
	2147		
21		0000	1.3F
F	0329	0618	1.1E
	1018	1226	1.2F
	1551	1838	1.0E
	2238		
22		0051	1.3F
Sa	0421	0714	1.1E
	1111	1320	1.1F
	1646	1937	1.0E
	2330		
23		0145	1.3F
Su	0515	0818	1.1E
	1207	1417	1.1F
	1744	2043	1.0E
24	0025	0242	1.3F
M	0611	0930	1.2E
	1301	1519	1.2F
	1842	2158	1.1E
25	0120	0342	1.3F
Tu	0707	1052	1.3E
	1358	1631	1.2F
	1941	2330	1.2E
26	0216	0447	1.3F
W	0804	1204	1.4E
	1451	1746	1.3F
	2038		
27		0036	1.3E
Th	0310	0556	1.4F
	0859	1259	1.5E
	1544	1846	1.4F
	2133		
28		0130	1.3E
F	0402	0659	1.4F
	0952	1352	1.5E
	1636	1941	1.5F
	2227		
29		0223	1.4E
Sa	0456	0756	1.5F
	1045	1445	1.5E
	1727	2034	1.5F
	2319		
30		0316	1.4E
Su	0549	0850	1.5F
	1137	1538	1.5E
	1818	2126	1.5F
31	0010	0411	1.4E
M	0641	0946	1.4F
	1229	1635	1.5E
	1909	2219	1.4F

FEBRUARY

Day	Slack Water Time h.m.	Maximum Current Time h.m.	Vel. knots
1	0102	0509	1.4E
Tu	0735	1042	1.3F
	1321	1734	1.4E
	2000	2315	1.3F
2	0154	0608	1.3E
W	0830	1142	1.2F
	1416	1836	1.3E
	2054		
3		0012	1.2F
Th	0248	0709	1.3E
	0928	1244	1.1F
	1513	1937	1.2E
	2150		
4		0112	1.2F
F	0343	0809	1.3E
	1027	1346	1.0F
	1613	2038	1.2E
	2248		
5		0212	1.1F
Sa	0441	0909	1.3E
	1127	1446	1.0F
	1715	2137	1.1E
	2347		
6		0311	1.0F
Su	0541	1006	1.3E
	1228	1545	1.0F
	1820	2233	1.2E
7	0044	0408	1.0F
M	0640	1101	1.3E
	1325	1641	1.0F
	1932	2327	1.2E
8	0140	0502	1.1F
Tu	0738	1153	1.4E
	1419	1734	1.1F
	2043		
9		0018	1.2E
W	0231	0552	1.1F
	0830	1242	1.4E
	1507	1822	1.1F
	2123		
10		0106	1.2E
Th	0319	0639	1.1F
	0914	1329	1.4E
	1550	1907	1.2F
	2154		
11		0152	1.2E
F	0402	0723	1.2F
	0954	1412	1.4E
	1630	1949	1.2F
	2227		
12		0234	1.2E
Sa	0444	0804	1.2F
	1031	1452	1.3E
	1709	2028	1.2F
	2300		
13		0314	1.2E
Su	0524	0841	1.2F
	1108	1528	1.3E
	1746	2102	1.3F
	2334		
14		0348	1.1E
M	0603	0909	1.2F
	1144	1550	1.2E
	1823	2123	1.3F
15	0010	0354	1.1E
Tu	0642	0912	1.2F
	1222	1533	1.2E
	1901	2127	1.3F
16	0047	0348	1.1E
W	0724	0942	1.3F
	1302	1556	1.2E
	1941	2201	1.4F
17	0126	0417	1.2E
Th	0808	1021	1.3F
	1344	1629	1.2E
	2024	2242	1.4F
18	0209	0456	1.2E
F	0855	1106	1.3F
	1429	1712	1.1E
	2110	2328	1.4F
19	0255	0542	1.2E
Sa	0946	1154	1.2F
	1519	1801	1.1E
	2202		
20		0017	1.3F
Su	0345	0633	1.2E
	1040	1246	1.2F
	1613	1857	1.0E
	2258		
21		0110	1.3F
M	0440	0737	1.1E
	1138	1342	1.1F
	1712	2004	1.0E
	2356		
22		0207	1.2F
Tu	0538	0853	1.1E
	1236	1445	1.1F
	1814	2228	1.0E
23	0055	0310	1.2F
W	0639	1100	1.2E
	1333	1613	1.1F
	1918	2336	1.1E
24	0153	0430	1.2F
Th	0740	1201	1.3E
	1430	1741	1.2F
	2018		
25		0031	1.3E
F	0251	0559	1.3F
	0839	1255	1.5E
	1524	1839	1.3F
	2116		
26		0124	1.4E
Sa	0347	0659	1.4F
	0935	1346	1.5E
	1617	1932	1.5F
	2210		
27		0214	1.5E
Su	0439	0753	1.4F
	1029	1435	1.6E
	1707	2022	1.5F
	2301		
28		0304	1.5E
M	0531	0844	1.5F
	1120	1525	1.6E
	1757	2111	1.5F
	2351		

Time meridian 75° W. 0000 is midnight. 1200 is noon.
At times of slack water before maximum ebb, the velocity actually averages 0.3 knot in a direction of 184° true.

F-Flood, Dir. 254° True E-Ebb, Dir. 111° True

MARCH

Day	Slack Water Time h.m.	Maximum Current Time h.m.	Maximum Current Vel. knots
1		0354	1.5E
Tu	0622	0933	1.5F
	1211	1615	1.5E
	1845	2159	1.5F
2	0040	0445	1.5E
W	0713	1024	1.4F
	1301	1709	1.4E
	1934	2248	1.4F
3	0129	0540	1.4E
Th	0805	1117	1.3F
	1352	1806	1.3E
	2026	2340	1.3F
4	0219	0638	1.3E
F	0859	1212	1.2F
	1446	1906	1.2E
	2118		
5		0035	1.2F
Sa	0310	0737	1.3E
	0954	1311	1.1F
	1542	2007	1.1E
	2212		
6		0134	1.1F
Su	0405	0837	1.2E
	1051	1411	1.0F
	1641	2106	1.1E
	2310		
7		0234	1.0F
M	0502	0935	1.2E
	1151	1511	0.9F
	1743	2204	1.1E
8	0009	0333	1.0F
Tu	0600	1031	1.2E
	1250	1609	0.9F
	1847	2259	1.1E
9	0107	0430	1.0F
W	0658	1125	1.3E
	1344	1703	1.0F
	1951	2351	1.1E
10	0200	0522	1.0F
Th	0753	1215	1.3E
	1435	1753	1.1F
	2043		
11		0040	1.2E
F	0250	0611	1.1F
	0842	1301	1.3E
	1520	1838	1.2F
	2122		
12		0125	1.2E
Sa	0337	0656	1.1F
	0925	1344	1.3E
	1600	1921	1.2F
	2157		
13		0207	1.2E
Su	0418	0737	1.2F
	1004	1424	1.3E
	1639	1959	1.3F
	2232		
14		0245	1.2E
M	0458	0814	1.2F
	1042	1458	1.3E
	1717	2033	1.3F
	2306		
15		0316	1.2E
Tu	0538	0845	1.3F
	1119	1509	1.2E
	1753	2053	1.4F
	2342		

Day	Slack Water Time h.m.	Maximum Current Time h.m.	Maximum Current Vel. knots
16		0313	1.2E
W	0617	0853	1.3F
	1157	1506	1.2E
	1831	2101	1.4F
17	0020	0324	1.3E
Th	0658	0918	1.3F
	1237	1531	1.2E
	1911	2134	1.5F
18	0059	0352	1.3E
F	0740	0957	1.4F
	1319	1604	1.2E
	1955	2216	1.5F
19	0141	0430	1.3E
Sa	0828	1040	1.3F
	1403	1645	1.1E
	2042	2300	1.4F
20	0226	0515	1.2E
Su	0919	1127	1.2F
	1452	1733	1.1E
	2135	2349	1.3F
21	0316	0607	1.2E
M	1013	1219	1.2F
	1547	1830	1.0E
	2231		
22		0041	1.2F
Tu	0411	0710	1.1E
	1111	1315	1.1F
	1647	1941	0.9E
	2332		
23		0139	1.1F
W	0511	0941	1.1E
	1211	1420	1.0F
	1752	2224	1.0E
24	0034	0245	1.0F
Th	0615	1051	1.2E
	1311	1625	1.0F
	1857	2323	1.1E
25	0136	0448	1.1F
F	0719	1148	1.3E
	1410	1730	1.2F
	1959		
26		0017	1.3E
Sa	0234	0553	1.2F
	0820	1241	1.4E
	1505	1826	1.3F
	2057		
27		0109	1.4E
Su	0330	0648	1.3F
	0918	1332	1.5E
	1557	1917	1.4F
	2151		
28		0158	1.5E
M	0422	0740	1.4F
	1011	1420	1.6E
	1646	2005	1.5F
	2241		
29		0247	1.6E
Tu	0512	0828	1.5F
	1102	1508	1.6E
	1734	2052	1.5F
	2329		
30		0334	1.6E
W	0602	0916	1.5F
	1151	1556	1.5E
	1821	2137	1.5F
31	0016	0423	1.6E
Th	0650	1003	1.4F
	1240	1645	1.4E
	1909	2222	1.4F

APRIL

Day	Slack Water Time h.m.	Maximum Current Time h.m.	Maximum Current Vel. knots
1	0102	0514	1.5E
F	0740	1051	1.3F
	1328	1739	1.3E
	1958	2309	1.3F
2	0149	0608	1.4E
Sa	0830	1142	1.2F
	1418	1836	1.2E
	2048	2359	1.2F
3	0237	0706	1.3E
Su	0922	1237	1.1F
	1510	1935	1.1E
	2140		
4		0055	1.1F
M	0328	0804	1.2E
	1018	1335	1.0F
	1605	2034	1.0E
	2235		
5		0155	1.0F
Tu	0422	0902	1.1E
	1113	1434	0.9F
	1703	2131	1.0E
	2331		
6		0255	0.9F
W	0518	0958	1.1E
	1210	1532	0.9F
	1801	2226	1.0E
7	0029	0352	0.9F
Th	0615	1051	1.2E
	1304	1626	1.0F
	1858	2318	1.1E
8	0124	0447	1.0F
F	0710	1141	1.2E
	1355	1716	1.0F
	1950		
9		0007	1.1E
Sa	0216	0536	1.0F
	0801	1228	1.2E
	1441	1803	1.1F
	2036		
10		0052	1.2E
Su	0302	0622	1.1F
	0848	1311	1.2E
	1524	1845	1.2F
	2118		
11		0134	1.2E
M	0347	0704	1.2F
	0931	1351	1.2E
	1604	1925	1.3F
	2157		
12		0211	1.3E
Tu	0428	0742	1.3F
	1012	1422	1.2E
	1644	1957	1.4F
	2235		
13		0238	1.3E
W	0509	0813	1.3F
	1052	1427	1.2E
	1723	2016	1.4F
	2313		
14		0240	1.3E
Th	0550	0826	1.4F
	1132	1440	1.2E
	1803	2034	1.5F
	2353		
15		0301	1.3E
F	0632	0856	1.4F
	1214	1509	1.2E
	1846	2110	1.5F

Day	Slack Water Time h.m.	Maximum Current Time h.m.	Maximum Current Vel. knots
16	0034	0333	1.3E
Sa	0718	0934	1.4F
	1257	1546	1.2E
	1930	2152	1.5F
17	0117	0412	1.3E
Su	0806	1019	1.3F
	1343	1628	1.1E
	2020	2237	1.4F
18	0204	0457	1.2E
M	0858	1106	1.2F
	1433	1717	1.0E
	2114	2325	1.3F
19	0255	0551	1.1E
Tu	0952	1158	1.1F
	1529	1817	0.9E
	2212		
20		0020	1.1F
W	0351	0659	1.1E
	1050	1256	1.0F
	1630	2104	0.9E
	2314		
21		0120	1.0F
Th	0452	0933	1.1E
	1151	1454	0.9F
	1734	2207	1.0E
22	0018	0325	0.9F
F	0557	1035	1.2E
	1251	1614	1.0F
	1839	2306	1.2E
23	0119	0440	1.0F
Sa	0701	1131	1.3E
	1350	1714	1.1F
	1940		
24		0000	1.3E
Su	0218	0539	1.1F
	0802	1225	1.4E
	1444	1808	1.3F
	2037		
25		0051	1.4E
M	0313	0633	1.3F
	0900	1314	1.5E
	1536	1858	1.4F
	2130		
26		0141	1.5E
Tu	0405	0723	1.3F
	0953	1403	1.5E
	1624	1945	1.5F
	2220		
27		0228	1.6E
W	0453	0811	1.4F
	1043	1450	1.5E
	1711	2031	1.5F
	2306		
28		0315	1.6E
Th	0541	0857	1.4F
	1131	1537	1.5E
	1758	2115	1.4F
	2351		
29		0402	1.5E
F	0629	0943	1.4F
	1218	1625	1.4E
	1843	2159	1.4F
30	0036	0450	1.5E
Sa	0716	1028	1.3F
	1304	1716	1.2E
	1930	2242	1.3F

Time meridian 75° W. 0000 is midnight. 1200 is noon.
At times of slack water before maximum ebb, the velocity actually averages 0.3 knot in a direction of 184° true.

F-Flood, Dir. 254° True   E-Ebb, Dir. 111° True

MAY

Day	Slack Water Time h.m.	Maximum Current Time h.m.	Vel. knots	Day	Slack Water Time h.m.	Maximum Current Time h.m.	Vel. knots
1	0120	0541	1.4E	16	0057	0402	1.3E
Su	0803	1116	1.2F	M	0747	1002	1.3F
	1350	1808	1.1E		1327	1621	1.1E
	2019	2326	1.2F		2002	2219	1.3F
2	0206	0634	1.3E	17	0146	0452	1.2E
M	0852	1205	1.1F	Tu	0839	1051	1.2F
	1439	1904	1.0E		1420	1717	1.0E
	2109				2059	2311	1.2F
3		0016	1.1F	18	0239	0553	1.1E
Tu	0253	0730	1.2E	W	0934	1147	1.1F
	0943	1258	1.0F		1516	1939	1.0E
	1529	2000	1.0E		2158		
	2201						
4		0113	1.0F	19		0007	1.1F
W	0344	0826	1.1E	Th	0337	0810	1.1E
	1037	1354	1.0F		1032	1304	1.0F
	1622	2055	1.0E		1616	2048	1.0E
	2256				2259		
5		0212	0.9F	20		0157	0.9F
Th	0437	0920	1.1E	F	0438	0917	1.1E
	1129	1449	1.0F		1132	1453	1.0F
	1716	2148	1.0E		1718	2149	1.1E
	2350						
6		0309	0.9F	21	0001	0322	1.0F
F	0531	1012	1.1E	Sa	0541	1016	1.2E
	1220	1542	1.0F		1231	1557	1.1F
	1809	2240	1.0E		1820	2246	1.2E
7	0043	0404	1.0F	22	0102	0425	1.0F
Sa	0625	1102	1.1E	Su	0644	1112	1.3E
	1310	1633	1.1F		1329	1654	1.1F
	1901	2328	1.1E		1919	2341	1.3E
8	0135	0454	1.0F	23	0200	0521	1.1F
Su	0718	1149	1.1E	M	0745	1205	1.3E
	1358	1719	1.2F		1422	1747	1.2F
	1949				2016		
9		0013	1.2E	24		0032	1.4E
M	0223	0541	1.1F	Tu	0255	0614	1.2F
	0807	1231	1.2E		0842	1256	1.4E
	1442	1802	1.2F		1513	1837	1.3F
	2034				2109		
10		0055	1.2E	25		0122	1.5E
Tu	0310	0624	1.2F	W	0346	0704	1.3F
	0854	1309	1.2E		0935	1345	1.4E
	1527	1841	1.3F		1602	1924	1.3F
	2118				2157		
11		0130	1.3E	26		0210	1.5E
W	0355	0702	1.3F	Th	0434	0752	1.3F
	0939	1337	1.2E		1025	1433	1.4E
	1610	1912	1.4F		1649	2010	1.4F
	2201				2243		
12		0153	1.3E	27		0257	1.5E
Th	0439	0735	1.3F	F	0521	0838	1.3F
	1023	1348	1.2E		1111	1520	1.4E
	1653	1935	1.4F		1734	2054	1.3F
	2243				2327		
13		0209	1.3E	28		0343	1.5E
F	0523	0800	1.4F	Sa	0607	0923	1.3F
	1107	1416	1.2E		1156	1607	1.3E
	1738	2008	1.5F		1820	2137	1.3F
	2326						
14		0240	1.4E	29	0010	0429	1.4E
Sa	0609	0834	1.4F	Su	0651	1007	1.2F
	1152	1452	1.2E		1240	1654	1.2E
	1822	2047	1.5F		1906	2219	1.2F
15	0011	0318	1.4E	30	0053	0517	1.3E
Su	0657	0916	1.4F	M	0738	1051	1.1F
	1238	1534	1.2E		1324	1743	1.1E
	1911	2132	1.4F		1951	2301	1.1F
				31	0136	0605	1.2E
				Tu	0823	1136	1.1F
					1409	1833	1.0E
					2040	2340	1.1F

JUNE

Day	Slack Water Time h.m.	Maximum Current Time h.m.	Vel. knots	Day	Slack Water Time h.m.	Maximum Current Time h.m.	Vel. knots
1	0221	0655	1.1E	16	0226	0647	1.2E
W	0910	1221	1.0F	Th	0917	1221	1.1F
	1455	1925	1.0E		1503	1927	1.1E
	2129				2142		
2		0018	1.0F	17		0048	1.1F
Th	0309	0745	1.1E	F	0324	0755	1.2E
	0959	1308	1.0F		1013	1332	1.1F
	1543	2015	1.0E		1601	2029	1.1E
	2220				2242		
3		0109	1.0F	18		0201	1.0F
F	0358	0836	1.0E	Sa	0424	0857	1.2E
	1048	1357	1.0F		1111	1435	1.1F
	1632	2105	1.0E		1701	2129	1.2E
	2311				2343		
4		0210	1.0F	19		0305	1.0F
Sa	0450	0927	1.0E	Su	0526	0955	1.2E
	1137	1447	1.1F		1209	1535	1.1F
	1723	2155	1.0E		1800	2226	1.3E
5	0002	0306	1.0F	20	0043	0404	1.0F
Su	0542	1014	1.0E	M	0628	1051	1.2E
	1226	1535	1.1F		1306	1631	1.1F
	1813	2242	1.1E		1859	2320	1.4E
6	0054	0358	1.1F	21	0141	0500	1.1F
M	0634	1059	1.0E	Tu	0728	1145	1.3E
	1313	1619	1.2F		1400	1724	1.2F
	1903	2325	1.1E		1954		
7	0144	0446	1.1F	22		0012	1.4E
Tu	0725	1139	1.1E	W	0235	0553	1.1F
	1401	1700	1.3F		0826	1237	1.3E
	1951				1451	1814	1.2F
					2047		
8		0005	1.2E	23		0102	1.5E
W	0233	0530	1.2F	Th	0327	0643	1.2F
	0816	1210	1.1E		0919	1326	1.3E
	1449	1738	1.3F		1540	1903	1.2F
	2039				2135		
9		0036	1.3E	24		0151	1.5E
Th	0321	0612	1.3F	F	0414	0732	1.2F
	0905	1235	1.2E		1008	1414	1.3E
	1537	1816	1.4F		1628	1949	1.2F
	2126				2220		
10		0106	1.3E	25		0238	1.5E
F	0409	0651	1.3F	Sa	0500	0818	1.2F
	0953	1314	1.2E		1052	1501	1.3E
	1624	1858	1.4F		1712	2034	1.2F
	2213				2303		
11		0142	1.4E	26		0324	1.4E
Sa	0458	0733	1.4F	Su	0544	0902	1.2F
	1042	1357	1.2E		1134	1547	1.2E
	1712	1942	1.5F		1758	2117	1.2F
	2301				2345		
12		0224	1.4E	27		0408	1.4E
Su	0547	0816	1.4F	M	0628	0946	1.2F
	1131	1444	1.2E		1216	1633	1.2E
	1802	2029	1.4F		1841	2158	1.1F
	2350						
13		0312	1.4E	28	0026	0452	1.3E
M	0637	0904	1.3F	Tu	0710	1027	1.1F
	1221	1535	1.2E		1257	1717	1.1E
	1854	2118	1.4F		1927	2236	1.1F
14	0040	0404	1.3E	29	0108	0535	1.2E
Tu	0728	0955	1.3F	W	0753	1105	1.1F
	1313	1637	1.1E		1338	1800	1.0E
	1948	2210	1.3F		2011	2301	1.1F
15	0132	0513	1.2E	30	0150	0616	1.1E
W	0821	1054	1.2F	Th	0838	1135	1.1F
	1407	1817	1.1E		1421	1843	1.0E
	2044	2309	1.2F		2058	2320	1.1F

Time meridian 75° W. 0000 is midnight. 1200 is noon.
At times of slack water before maximum ebb, the velocity actually averages 0.3 knot in a direction of 184° true.

F-Flood, Dir. 254° True E-Ebb, Dir. 111° True

JULY

Day	Slack Water Time (h.m.)	Maximum Current Time (h.m.)	Vel. (knots)
1	0235	0650	1.0E
F	0921	1149	1.1F
	1505	1921	1.0E
	2145		
2		0002	1.1F
Sa	0322	0637	1.0E
	1008	1229	1.1F
	1552	1909	1.0E
	2234		
3		0050	1.1F
Su	0411	0717	1.0E
	1054	1315	1.2F
	1640	1953	1.0E
	2324		
4		0140	1.1F
M	0502	0806	1.0E
	1142	1405	1.2F
	1730	2045	1.1E
5	0016	0234	1.1F
Tu	0554	0901	1.0E
	1232	1456	1.3F
	1821	2142	1.1E
6	0108	0329	1.2F
W	0647	0959	1.1E
	1323	1549	1.3F
	1912	2237	1.2E
7	0159	0424	1.2F
Th	0740	1056	1.1E
	1415	1642	1.4F
	2003	2335	1.3E
8	0250	0520	1.3F
F	0833	1154	1.2E
	1507	1735	1.4F
	2055		
9		0029	1.4E
Sa	0341	0617	1.3F
	0927	1253	1.2E
	1559	1829	1.4F
	2147		
10		0123	1.4E
Su	0432	0713	1.4F
	1019	1352	1.2E
	1650	1923	1.4F
	2238		
11		0218	1.4E
M	0523	0808	1.4F
	1111	1453	1.3E
	1742	2018	1.4F
	2330		
12		0316	1.4E
Tu	0616	0907	1.4F
	1204	1557	1.3E
	1837	2117	1.3F
13	0022	0419	1.4E
W	0708	1007	1.3F
	1257	1701	1.3E
	1931	2224	1.3F
14	0116	0526	1.3E
Th	0800	1109	1.3F
	1351	1804	1.2E
	2027	2335	1.2F
15	0211	0631	1.3E
F	0855	1211	1.2F
	1446	1906	1.2E
	2124		

Day	Slack Water Time (h.m.)	Maximum Current Time (h.m.)	Vel. (knots)
16		0040	1.1F
Sa	0309	0733	1.2E
	0950	1312	1.2F
	1542	2006	1.2E
	2223		
17		0143	1.1F
Su	0408	0834	1.2E
	1048	1412	1.2F
	1640	2106	1.3E
	2322		
18		0243	1.1F
M	0509	0933	1.2E
	1145	1510	1.1F
	1738	2203	1.3E
19	0022	0341	1.1F
Tu	0611	1029	1.2E
	1241	1606	1.1F
	1836	2258	1.4E
20	0120	0438	1.1F
W	0713	1124	1.2E
	1337	1700	1.1F
	1933	2351	1.4E
21	0214	0531	1.1F
Th	0812	1216	1.2E
	1429	1751	1.1F
	2025		
22		0041	1.4E
F	0306	0622	1.1F
	0905	1306	1.3E
	1519	1840	1.1F
	2114		
23		0130	1.4E
Sa	0352	0710	1.1F
	0952	1355	1.3E
	1607	1928	1.1F
	2158		
24		0217	1.4E
Su	0439	0756	1.2F
	1033	1440	1.2E
	1651	2012	1.1F
	2240		
25		0302	1.4E
M	0520	0839	1.2F
	1112	1525	1.2E
	1735	2055	1.1F
	2320		
26		0345	1.3E
Tu	0601	0921	1.2F
	1150	1607	1.2E
	1818	2134	1.1F
27	0000	0425	1.2E
W	0641	0958	1.1F
	1228	1648	1.1E
	1859	2207	1.1F
28	0039	0502	1.1E
Th	0721	1029	1.1F
	1306	1724	1.1E
	1941	2212	1.1F
29	0119	0503	1.1E
F	0802	1030	1.2F
	1347	1710	1.0E
	2026	2242	1.1F
30	0202	0505	1.1E
Sa	0845	1104	1.2F
	1429	1728	1.1E
	2111	2323	1.2F
31	0247	0540	1.1E
Su	0929	1146	1.3F
	1514	1808	1.1E
	2159		

AUGUST

Day	Slack Water Time (h.m.)	Maximum Current Time (h.m.)	Vel. (knots)
1		0011	1.2F
M	0335	0624	1.1E
	1017	1233	1.3F
	1601	1855	1.1E
	2249		
2		0101	1.2F
Tu	0425	0714	1.1E
	1106	1323	1.3F
	1651	1950	1.2E
	2340		
3		0153	1.2F
W	0518	0811	1.0E
	1158	1416	1.3F
	1744	2049	1.2E
4	0035	0249	1.2F
Th	0614	0913	1.1E
	1251	1511	1.3F
	1838	2154	1.2E
5	0129	0347	1.2F
F	0710	1021	1.1E
	1347	1608	1.3F
	1933	2303	1.3E
6	0222	0450	1.3F
Sa	0807	1138	1.2E
	1440	1708	1.4F
	2028		
7		0015	1.4E
Su	0317	0558	1.3F
	0903	1254	1.2E
	1536	1809	1.4F
	2123		
8		0118	1.4E
M	0409	0703	1.4F
	0958	1355	1.3E
	1630	1915	1.4F
	2217		
9		0216	1.5E
Tu	0500	0802	1.4F
	1051	1451	1.4E
	1723	2018	1.4F
	2310		
10		0311	1.5E
W	0552	0858	1.4F
	1144	1546	1.4E
	1818	2118	1.4F
11	0004	0408	1.4E
Th	0644	0954	1.4F
	1237	1643	1.4E
	1911	2218	1.3F
12	0058	0507	1.4E
F	0737	1050	1.4F
	1329	1741	1.4E
	2006	2318	1.3F
13	0152	0607	1.3E
Sa	0830	1147	1.3F
	1423	1841	1.3E
	2102		
14		0018	1.2F
Su	0248	0708	1.3E
	0924	1246	1.2F
	1518	1941	1.3E
	2200		
15		0118	1.1F
M	0347	0809	1.2E
	1020	1344	1.2F
	1614	2040	1.3E
	2259		

Day	Slack Water Time (h.m.)	Maximum Current Time (h.m.)	Vel. (knots)
16		0218	1.1F
Tu	0447	0908	1.2E
	1119	1443	1.1F
	1712	2138	1.3E
	2358		
17		0317	1.0F
W	0550	1006	1.2E
	1216	1539	1.1F
	1811	2234	1.3E
18	0056	0414	1.0F
Th	0654	1101	1.2E
	1311	1635	1.1F
	1909	2327	1.4E
19	0150	0508	1.1F
F	0801	1154	1.2E
	1407	1727	1.1F
	2003		
20		0019	1.4E
Sa	0241	0558	1.1F
	0856	1244	1.2E
	1457	1817	1.1F
	2052		
21		0107	1.4E
Su	0329	0646	1.1F
	0935	1331	1.2E
	1543	1903	1.1F
	2135		
22		0153	1.4E
M	0412	0731	1.2F
	1011	1416	1.2E
	1628	1947	1.1F
	2215		
23		0236	1.3E
Tu	0452	0812	1.2F
	1046	1459	1.2E
	1710	2028	1.1F
	2253		
24		0317	1.3E
W	0531	0851	1.2F
	1121	1539	1.2E
	1750	2105	1.1F
	2331		
25		0354	1.2E
Th	0610	0925	1.2F
	1157	1614	1.1E
	1830	2132	1.1F
26	0009	0418	1.1E
F	0648	0936	1.2F
	1233	1624	1.1E
	1911	2134	1.2F
27	0049	0353	1.1E
Sa	0728	0950	1.3F
	1312	1614	1.1E
	1954	2208	1.2F
28	0130	0421	1.1E
Su	0809	1027	1.3F
	1354	1646	1.2E
	2039	2250	1.2F
29	0214	0459	1.1E
M	0853	1111	1.3F
	1438	1728	1.2E
	2128	2337	1.2F
30	0302	0544	1.1E
Tu	0941	1159	1.3F
	1526	1817	1.2E
	2219		
31		0027	1.2F
W	0353	0637	1.0E
	1034	1249	1.3F
	1618	1913	1.2E
	2311		

Time meridian 75° W. 0000 is midnight. 1200 is noon.
At times of slack water before maximum ebb, the velocity actually averages 0.3 knot in a direction of 184° true.

F-Flood, Dir. 254° True E-Ebb, Dir. 111° True

SEPTEMBER

Day	Slack Water Time h.m.	Maximum Current Time h.m.	Vel. knots
1		0121	1.2F
Th	0448	0736	1.0E
	1129	1343	1.3F
	1712	2016	1.2E
2	0008	0218	1.2F
F	0546	0845	1.0E
	1227	1441	1.3F
	1810	2131	1.2E
3	0103	0321	1.2F
Sa	0646	1016	1.1E
	1323	1543	1.3F
	1908	2306	1.3E
4	0159	0438	1.2F
Su	0745	1153	1.2E
	1420	1654	1.3F
	2006		
5		0015	1.4E
M	0253	0556	1.3F
	0843	1248	1.3E
	1516	1812	1.3F
	2102		
6		0110	1.5E
Tu	0347	0655	1.4F
	0938	1342	1.4E
	1610	1914	1.4F
	2158		
7		0203	1.5E
W	0438	0748	1.5F
	1031	1433	1.5E
	1702	2009	1.4F
	2251		
8		0254	1.5E
Th	0529	0839	1.5F
	1122	1525	1.5E
	1756	2104	1.4F
	2343		
9		0347	1.5E
F	0619	0930	1.5F
	1213	1619	1.5E
	1849	2157	1.4F
10	0036	0443	1.4E
Sa	0710	1023	1.4F
	1304	1715	1.4E
	1941	2253	1.3F
11	0129	0541	1.3E
Su	0801	1118	1.3F
	1355	1813	1.4E
	2037	2351	1.2F
12	0224	0642	1.2E
M	0857	1215	1.2F
	1448	1913	1.3E
	2132		
13		0051	1.1F
Tu	0321	0742	1.2E
	0951	1315	1.1F
	1544	2013	1.3E
	2231		
14		0151	1.0F
W	0421	0842	1.1E
	1050	1414	1.1F
	1642	2111	1.3E
	2330		
15		0250	1.0F
Th	0524	0940	1.1E
	1149	1512	1.0F
	1741	2208	1.3E

Day	Slack Water Time h.m.	Maximum Current Time h.m.	Vel. knots
16	0029	0347	1.0F
F	0630	1036	1.2E
	1247	1608	1.0F
	1840	2302	1.3E
17	0122	0441	1.1F
Sa	0740	1128	1.2E
	1340	1701	1.1F
	1936	2353	1.4E
18	0213	0531	1.1F
Su	0833	1218	1.2E
	1430	1750	1.1F
	2026		
19		0040	1.4E
M	0300	0617	1.2F
	0909	1305	1.3E
	1518	1836	1.1F
	2109		
20		0125	1.3E
Tu	0341	0701	1.2F
	0942	1349	1.3E
	1600	1918	1.2F
	2148		
21		0207	1.3E
W	0421	0741	1.2F
	1015	1429	1.2E
	1641	1958	1.2F
	2225		
22		0245	1.2E
Th	0459	0817	1.3F
	1049	1506	1.2E
	1720	2032	1.2F
	2302		
23		0316	1.2E
F	0537	0845	1.3F
	1124	1531	1.2E
	1800	2048	1.2F
	2339		
24		0302	1.1E
Sa	0614	0845	1.3F
	1201	1514	1.2E
	1840	2101	1.2F
25	0018	0315	1.1E
Su	0654	0914	1.3F
	1240	1537	1.2E
	1923	2137	1.2F
26	0100	0346	1.1E
M	0737	0955	1.4F
	1321	1611	1.2E
	2009	2220	1.2F
27	0144	0426	1.1E
Tu	0822	1039	1.3F
	1406	1655	1.2E
	2059	2307	1.2F
28	0232	0513	1.0E
W	0913	1128	1.3F
	1455	1745	1.2E
	2150	2358	1.2F
29	0326	0607	1.0E
Th	1008	1220	1.2F
	1549	1844	1.1E
	2248		
30		0053	1.1F
F	0423	0712	1.0E
	1107	1316	1.2F
	1646	1955	1.1E
	2344		

OCTOBER

Day	Slack Water Time h.m.	Maximum Current Time h.m.	Vel. knots
1		0154	1.1F
Sa	0524	0841	1.0E
	1206	1418	1.1F
	1747	2206	1.2E
2	0041	0313	1.1F
Su	0627	1046	1.1E
	1305	1535	1.1F
	1848	2311	1.3E
3	0139	0449	1.2F
M	0727	1142	1.2E
	1402	1710	1.2F
	1948		
4		0005	1.4E
Tu	0232	0548	1.3F
	0824	1235	1.4E
	1458	1810	1.3F
	2045		
5		0056	1.5E
W	0325	0640	1.4F
	0918	1326	1.5E
	1551	1904	1.4F
	2139		
6		0146	1.5E
Th	0415	0730	1.5F
	1009	1414	1.5E
	1642	1954	1.4F
	2231		
7		0236	1.5E
F	0504	0818	1.5F
	1059	1504	1.6E
	1733	2044	1.4F
	2322		
8		0326	1.5E
Sa	0553	0906	1.5F
	1148	1555	1.5E
	1824	2134	1.4F
9	0012	0419	1.4E
Su	0642	0954	1.4F
	1236	1649	1.5E
	1917	2226	1.3F
10	0104	0516	1.3E
M	0733	1046	1.3F
	1326	1746	1.4E
	2009	2322	1.2F
11	0156	0615	1.2E
Tu	0827	1142	1.2F
	1417	1845	1.3E
	2103		
12		0020	1.1F
W	0252	0715	1.1E
	0921	1242	1.1F
	1511	1944	1.3E
	2200		
13		0121	1.0F
Th	0350	0814	1.1E
	1019	1343	1.0F
	1607	2042	1.2E
	2259		
14		0220	1.0F
F	0450	0911	1.1E
	1119	1442	1.0F
	1706	2138	1.2E
	2357		
15		0317	1.0F
Sa	0551	1007	1.1E
	1216	1538	1.0F
	1804	2232	1.3E

Day	Slack Water Time h.m.	Maximum Current Time h.m.	Vel. knots
16	0050	0413	1.1F
Su	0651	1059	1.2E
	1310	1631	1.0F
	1900	2322	1.3E
17	0139	0459	1.1F
M	0744	1148	1.2E
	1400	1719	1.1F
	1951		
18		0009	1.3E
Tu	0224	0545	1.2F
	0827	1234	1.3E
	1446	1804	1.2F
	2036		
19		0053	1.3E
W	0307	0627	1.3F
	0904	1316	1.3E
	1529	1846	1.2F
	2116		
20		0133	1.3E
Th	0346	0706	1.3F
	0940	1355	1.3E
	1609	1924	1.2F
	2154		
21		0209	1.2E
F	0424	0739	1.3F
	1016	1426	1.2E
	1649	1955	1.3F
	2232		
22		0224	1.1E
Sa	0502	0757	1.4F
	1052	1429	1.2E
	1730	2007	1.3F
	2311		
23		0220	1.1E
Su	0541	0811	1.4F
	1130	1439	1.2E
	1811	2032	1.3F
	2350		
24		0245	1.1E
M	0623	0845	1.4F
	1210	1508	1.3E
	1856	2110	1.3F
25	0033	0319	1.1E
Tu	0708	0927	1.4F
	1252	1545	1.2E
	1942	2153	1.3F
26	0119	0401	1.1E
W	0757	1012	1.3F
	1339	1630	1.2E
	2033	2241	1.2F
27	0208	0450	1.0E
Th	0850	1101	1.2F
	1429	1723	1.1E
	2128	2333	1.1F
28	0303	0548	1.0E
F	0948	1154	1.1F
	1525	1826	1.1E
	2225		
29		0030	1.0F
Sa	0403	0701	0.9E
	1048	1254	1.0F
	1625	2056	1.1E
	2323		
30		0139	1.0F
Su	0506	0935	1.0E
	1149	1406	1.0F
	1729	2202	1.2E
31	0022	0339	1.1F
M	0608	1035	1.2E
	1249	1605	1.1F
	1831	2258	1.3E

Time meridian 75° W. 0000 is midnight. 1200 is noon.
At times of slack water before maximum ebb, the velocity actually averages 0.3 knot in a direction of 184° true.

F-Flood, Dir. 254° True E-Ebb, Dir. 111° True

NOVEMBER

Day	Slack Water Time h.m.	Maximum Current Time h.m.	Vel. knots
1	0119	0440	1.2F
Tu	0708	1128	1.3E
	1347	1706	1.2F
	1931	2351	1.4E
2	0212	0534	1.3F
W	0805	1219	1.4E
	1441	1759	1.3F
	2028		
3		0041	1.5E
Th	0304	0625	1.4F
	0858	1309	1.5E
	1533	1850	1.4F
	2122		
4		0130	1.5E
F	0353	0712	1.5F
	0948	1357	1.6E
	1623	1938	1.4F
	2213		
5		0219	1.5E
Sa	0441	0758	1.5F
	1036	1445	1.6E
	1712	2026	1.4F
	2302		
6		0307	1.4E
Su	0529	0844	1.5F
	1123	1534	1.5E
	1801	2113	1.4F
	2350		
7		0358	1.4E
M	0618	0929	1.4F
	1210	1625	1.5E
	1850	2202	1.3F
8	0039	0452	1.3E
Tu	0708	1017	1.3F
	1257	1719	1.4E
	1941	2254	1.2F
9	0129	0548	1.2E
W	0759	1109	1.1F
	1346	1815	1.3E
	2033	2349	1.1F
10	0221	0646	1.1E
Th	0851	1207	1.0F
	1437	1913	1.2E
	2128		
11		0047	1.0F
F	0315	0742	1.0E
	0948	1307	1.0F
	1531	2009	1.2E
	2222		
12		0145	1.0F
Sa	0411	0838	1.0E
	1043	1406	0.9F
	1626	2104	1.2E
	2318		
13		0240	1.0F
Su	0506	0933	1.1E
	1140	1502	0.9F
	1722	2157	1.2E
14	0010	0333	1.0F
M	0601	1024	1.1E
	1233	1555	1.0F
	1818	2247	1.2E
15	0059	0421	1.1F
Tu	0653	1113	1.2E
	1323	1643	1.1F
	1909	2335	1.2E

Day	Slack Water Time h.m.	Maximum Current Time h.m.	Vel. knots
16	0144	0507	1.2F
W	0739	1158	1.2E
	1410	1728	1.2F
	1956		
17		0017	1.2E
Th	0228	0549	1.3F
	0822	1239	1.3E
	1454	1810	1.2F
	2040		
18		0056	1.2E
F	0309	0627	1.3F
	0902	1316	1.3E
	1537	1847	1.3F
	2122		
19		0126	1.2E
Sa	0350	0658	1.4F
	0941	1341	1.3E
	1619	1918	1.3F
	2203		
20		0131	1.2E
Su	0431	0716	1.4F
	1021	1347	1.3E
	1701	1937	1.4F
	2244		
21		0151	1.2E
M	0513	0742	1.5F
	1102	1413	1.3E
	1746	2007	1.4F
	2326		
22		0224	1.2E
Tu	0558	0821	1.5F
	1144	1448	1.3E
	1830	2048	1.3F
23	0011	0302	1.1E
W	0645	0903	1.4F
	1229	1528	1.3E
	1919	2132	1.3F
24	0058	0347	1.1E
Th	0736	0950	1.3F
	1317	1615	1.2E
	2010	2221	1.2F
25	0150	0438	1.0E
F	0830	1040	1.2F
	1409	1711	1.1E
	2107	2313	1.1F
26	0245	0541	0.9E
Sa	0929	1135	1.1F
	1506	1823	1.1E
	2203		
27		0013	1.0F
Su	0345	0817	1.0E
	1030	1239	1.0F
	1608	2045	1.1E
	2302		
28		0218	1.0F
M	0447	0919	1.1E
	1132	1449	1.0F
	1711	2146	1.2E
29	0002	0326	1.1F
Tu	0549	1017	1.2E
	1233	1555	1.0F
	1814	2243	1.2E
30	0059	0425	1.2F
W	0649	1112	1.3E
	1331	1652	1.1F
	1915	2336	1.3E

DECEMBER

Day	Slack Water Time h.m.	Maximum Current Time h.m.	Vel. knots
1	0153	0518	1.3F
Th	0746	1204	1.4E
	1426	1745	1.2F
	2013		
2		0027	1.4E
F	0245	0608	1.3F
	0839	1253	1.5E
	1518	1835	1.3F
	2107		
3		0116	1.4E
Sa	0334	0655	1.4F
	0929	1341	1.6E
	1607	1923	1.3F
	2157		
4		0204	1.4E
Su	0421	0741	1.4F
	1016	1428	1.6E
	1653	2009	1.3F
	2245		
5		0252	1.4E
M	0509	0826	1.4F
	1101	1516	1.5E
	1740	2056	1.3F
	2331		
6		0341	1.3E
Tu	0556	0910	1.3F
	1146	1604	1.4E
	1828	2142	1.2F
7	0017	0430	1.2E
W	0642	0955	1.2F
	1230	1654	1.4E
	1915	2228	1.2F
8	0103	0521	1.2E
Th	0731	1040	1.1F
	1316	1745	1.3E
	2003	2317	1.1F
9	0150	0614	1.1E
F	0821	1129	1.0F
	1403	1838	1.2E
	2052		
10		0008	1.0F
Sa	0238	0707	1.0E
	0912	1224	1.0F
	1453	1931	1.1E
	2142		
11		0101	1.0F
Su	0329	0801	1.0E
	1007	1321	0.9F
	1544	2025	1.1E
	2233		
12		0154	1.0F
M	0420	0853	1.0E
	1059	1417	0.9F
	1638	2117	1.0E
	2323		
13		0246	1.0F
Tu	0511	0944	1.0E
	1151	1510	1.0F
	1731	2206	1.0E
14	0013	0335	1.1F
W	0602	1033	1.1E
	1242	1600	1.0F
	1824	2253	1.1E
15	0101	0421	1.2F
Th	0651	1118	1.2E
	1331	1646	1.1F
	1914	2336	1.1E

Day	Slack Water Time h.m.	Maximum Current Time h.m.	Vel. knots
16	0148	0504	1.3F
F	0739	1200	1.2E
	1419	1730	1.2F
	2002		
17		0015	1.1E
Sa	0232	0542	1.3F
	0824	1234	1.3E
	1504	1809	1.3F
	2049		
18		0041	1.2E
Su	0318	0613	1.4F
	0908	1258	1.3E
	1550	1843	1.3F
	2134		
19		0059	1.2E
M	0402	0642	1.5F
	0953	1320	1.4E
	1636	1913	1.4F
	2220		
20		0132	1.2E
Tu	0449	0720	1.5F
	1037	1356	1.4E
	1721	1950	1.4F
	2306		
21		0211	1.2E
W	0537	0802	1.5F
	1123	1436	1.4E
	1809	2031	1.4F
	2353		
22		0255	1.2E
Th	0627	0847	1.4F
	1210	1521	1.3E
	1859	2118	1.3F
23	0042	0344	1.1E
F	0718	0934	1.3F
	1300	1611	1.2E
	1950	2207	1.2F
24	0134	0441	1.1E
Sa	0812	1026	1.2F
	1353	1712	1.2E
	2044	2301	1.1F
25	0229	0647	1.0E
Su	0910	1123	1.1F
	1450	1917	1.1E
	2140		
26		0014	1.1F
M	0327	0757	1.1E
	1011	1316	1.0F
	1550	2026	1.1E
	2240		
27		0200	1.0F
Tu	0427	0859	1.1E
	1113	1434	1.0F
	1653	2126	1.1E
	2339		
28		0305	1.1F
W	0527	0957	1.2E
	1215	1537	1.0F
	1756	2224	1.2E
29	0038	0404	1.1F
Th	0628	1053	1.3E
	1314	1635	1.1F
	1859	2319	1.3E
30	0133	0459	1.2F
F	0726	1147	1.4E
	1410	1729	1.2F
	1959		
31		0011	1.3E
Sa	0227	0550	1.2F
	0821	1237	1.5E
	1502	1820	1.2F
	2054		

Time meridian 75° W. 0000 is midnight. 1200 is noon.
At times of slack water before maximum ebb, the velocity actually averages 0.3 knot in a direction of 184° true.

F-Flood, Dir. 070° True E-Ebb, Dir. 250° True

JANUARY

Day	Slack Water Time	Maximum Current Time	Maximum Current Vel.
	h.m.	h.m.	knots
1		0118	4.8E
Sa	0419	0718	4.6F
	1029	1337	5.1E
	1646	1952	4.9F
	2322		
2		0209	4.7E
Su	0511	0807	4.5F
	1120	1427	5.1E
	1737	2045	4.9F
3	0015	0300	4.7E
M	0604	0859	4.4F
	1214	1519	5.0E
	1830	2138	4.7F
4	0109	0354	4.6E
Tu	0659	0956	4.3F
	1311	1613	4.8E
	1926	2233	4.6F
5	0205	0449	4.4E
W	0757	1055	4.1F
	1411	1709	4.6E
	2023	2333	4.3F
6	0302	0547	4.3E
Th	0857	1159	3.9F
	1515	1809	4.4E
	2123		
7		0035	4.1F
F	0400	0644	4.2E
	1000	1305	3.8F
	1621	1909	4.2E
	2224		
8		0140	4.0F
Sa	0457	0743	4.1E
	1102	1418	3.8F
	1725	2009	4.0E
	2325		
9		0242	3.9F
Su	0551	0842	4.1E
	1201	1521	3.9F
	1826	2108	4.0E
10	0022	0343	3.8F
M	0643	0934	4.2E
	1254	1619	4.0F
	1921	2203	4.0E
11	0115	0432	3.8F
Tu	0730	1023	4.3E
	1343	1706	4.1F
	2011	2248	4.0E
12	0202	0513	3.9F
W	0815	1106	4.3E
	1427	1747	4.1F
	2057	2336	4.0E
13	0244	0548	3.9F
Th	0856	1149	4.4E
	1508	1824	4.2F
	2139		
14		0018	4.1E
F	0324	0627	3.9F
	0935	1231	4.5E
	1546	1857	4.2F
	2219		
15		0058	4.1E
Sa	0402	0700	3.9F
	1013	1310	4.5E
	1623	1928	4.2F
	2257		
16		0137	4.1E
Su	0438	0733	3.9F
	1049	1349	4.5E
	1700	2003	4.2F
	2335		
17		0216	4.1E
M	0515	0810	3.9F
	1126	1431	4.4E
	1737	2039	4.2F
18	0012	0258	4.1E
Tu	0553	0847	3.9F
	1204	1512	4.4E
	1815	2116	4.1F
19	0050	0341	4.0E
W	0633	0928	3.8F
	1244	1555	4.3E
	1856	2158	4.0F
20	0131	0426	4.0E
Th	0717	1013	3.8F
	1329	1642	4.1E
	1940	2239	3.9F
21	0214	0512	3.9E
F	0805	1102	3.7F
	1421	1733	4.0E
	2029	2330	3.9F
22	0303	0603	3.9E
Sa	0858	1153	3.7F
	1521	1828	4.0E
	2124		
23		0025	3.8F
Su	0357	0658	4.0E
	0957	1255	3.7F
	1626	1926	3.9E
	2224		
24		0124	3.8F
M	0454	0756	4.1E
	1059	1400	3.9F
	1734	2027	4.0E
	2326		
25		0226	3.9F
Tu	0551	0855	4.3E
	1201	1505	4.1F
	1838	2127	4.1E
26	0028	0327	4.0F
W	0648	0950	4.5E
	1301	1609	4.3F
	1938	2222	4.3E
27	0126	0427	4.2F
Th	0742	1047	4.8E
	1357	1706	4.6F
	2033	2317	4.5E
28	0222	0522	4.4F
F	0835	1138	5.0E
	1450	1800	4.8F
	2125		
29		0011	4.7E
Sa	0314	0613	4.5F
	0926	1229	5.1E
	1541	1850	4.9F
	2216		
30		0101	4.8E
Su	0405	0704	4.6F
	1016	1320	5.2E
	1632	1939	5.0F
	2305		
31		0151	4.8E
M	0455	0755	4.7F
	1107	1409	5.2E
	1721	2029	4.9F
	2354		

FEBRUARY

Day	Slack Water Time	Maximum Current Time	Maximum Current Vel.
	h.m.	h.m.	knots
1		0240	4.8E
Tu	0545	0844	4.6F
	1158	1459	5.1E
	1811	2117	4.8F
2	0043	0329	4.7E
W	0635	0935	4.4F
	1251	1549	4.8E
	1901	2207	4.6F
3	0133	0420	4.5E
Th	0727	1029	4.2F
	1347	1643	4.6E
	1954	2259	4.3F
4	0225	0511	4.3E
F	0823	1122	4.0F
	1447	1737	4.3E
	2049	2353	4.0F
5	0320	0607	4.1E
Sa	0922	1226	3.8F
	1550	1835	4.0E
	2148		
6		0054	3.7F
Su	0417	0706	4.0E
	1023	1335	3.7F
	1655	1936	3.8E
	2250		
7		0201	3.6F
M	0515	0804	3.9E
	1126	1449	3.7F
	1759	2035	3.7E
	2351		
8		0308	3.5F
Tu	0611	0901	4.0E
	1224	1552	3.8F
	1857	2137	3.7E
9	0048	0406	3.6F
W	0703	0954	4.1E
	1317	1641	3.9F
	1949	2227	3.8E
10	0138	0451	3.7F
Th	0750	1043	4.2E
	1404	1728	4.0F
	2035	2313	3.9E
11	0223	0532	3.8F
F	0834	1129	4.3E
	1446	1805	4.1F
	2116	2354	4.1E
12	0303	0607	3.9F
Sa	0914	1208	4.4E
	1524	1837	4.2F
	2155		
13		0033	4.2E
Su	0340	0640	4.0F
	0952	1248	4.5E
	1601	1906	4.3F
	2231		
14		0112	4.2E
M	0415	0714	4.1F
	1028	1327	4.6E
	1636	1939	4.3F
	2306		
15		0150	4.3E
Tu	0450	0747	4.1F
	1104	1406	4.6E
	1711	2011	4.3F
	2340		
16		0230	4.3E
W	0526	0822	4.1F
	1140	1447	4.5E
	1747	2048	4.3F
17	0015	0309	4.3E
Th	0603	0901	4.1F
	1218	1528	4.4E
	1826	2125	4.2F
18	0051	0352	4.2E
F	0644	0942	4.1F
	1301	1613	4.3E
	1908	2208	4.1F
19	0132	0439	4.1E
Sa	0730	1030	4.0F
	1351	1703	4.1E
	1956	2255	3.9F
20	0219	0530	4.1E
Su	0823	1121	3.9F
	1451	1758	4.0E
	2051	2350	3.8F
21	0314	0625	4.0E
M	0923	1226	3.8F
	1600	1857	3.9E
	2154		
22		0052	3.7F
Tu	0417	0725	4.1E
	1030	1335	3.9F
	1713	2001	3.9E
	2302		
23		0201	3.7F
W	0523	0828	4.3E
	1138	1445	4.1F
	1821	2105	4.1E
24	0009	0308	3.9F
Th	0627	0931	4.5E
	1242	1553	4.3F
	1922	2206	4.3E
25	0112	0412	4.1F
F	0726	1028	4.7E
	1341	1654	4.6F
	2018	2301	4.5E
26	0208	0510	4.4F
Sa	0821	1123	5.0E
	1435	1746	4.8F
	2109	2354	4.7E
27	0300	0602	4.6F
Su	0912	1213	5.1E
	1526	1836	4.9F
	2157		
28		0042	4.9E
M	0349	0651	4.7F
	1002	1303	5.2E
	1614	1922	5.0F
	2243		

Time meridian 75° W. 0000 is midnight. 1200 is noon.

F-Flood, Dir. 070° True E-Ebb, Dir. 250° True

MARCH

Day	Slack Water Time h.m.	Maximum Current Time h.m.	Vel. knots
1		0129	4.9E
Tu	0436	0737	4.7F
	1051	1349	5.1E
	1701	2008	4.9F
	2328		
2		0215	4.9E
W	0522	0824	4.7F
	1140	1437	5.0E
	1747	2051	4.7F
3	0013	0303	4.8E
Th	0608	0909	4.5F
	1229	1523	4.8E
	1834	2135	4.5F
4	0058	0349	4.6E
F	0656	0957	4.3F
	1321	1613	4.5E
	1922	2223	4.1F
5	0146	0437	4.3E
Sa	0746	1049	4.0F
	1417	1705	4.1E
	2013	2311	3.8F
6	0238	0530	4.1E
Su	0841	1145	3.8F
	1518	1801	3.8E
	2109		
7		0009	3.5F
M	0334	0625	3.9E
	0942	1253	3.6F
	1623	1900	3.6E
	2212		
8		0114	3.3F
Tu	0435	0725	3.8E
	1046	1408	3.5F
	1728	2001	3.5E
	2317		
9		0228	3.2F
W	0536	0826	3.8E
	1149	1521	3.6F
	1827	2102	3.6E
10	0018	0333	3.4F
Th	0632	0924	3.9E
	1245	1615	3.8F
	1919	2156	3.7E
11	0110	0424	3.6F
F	0723	1015	4.1E
	1334	1658	3.9F
	2006	2244	3.9E
12	0156	0507	3.7F
Sa	0808	1100	4.3E
	1417	1733	4.1F
	2047	2326	4.1E
13	0236	0542	3.9F
Su	0849	1142	4.4E
	1456	1808	4.2F
	2124		
14		0005	4.3E
M	0313	0614	4.1F
	0927	1222	4.6E
	1533	1837	4.3F
	2200		
15		0045	4.4E
Tu	0348	0647	4.2F
	1004	1301	4.6E
	1608	1909	4.4F
	2234		

Day	Slack Water Time h.m.	Maximum Current Time h.m.	Vel. knots
16		0122	4.5E
W	0423	0721	4.3F
	1040	1339	4.6E
	1643	1942	4.4F
	2307		
17		0200	4.5E
Th	0458	0756	4.3F
	1117	1418	4.6E
	1720	2019	4.4F
	2341		
18		0240	4.5E
F	0535	0835	4.3F
	1156	1500	4.5E
	1759	2056	4.3F
19	0017	0323	4.4E
Sa	0617	0918	4.3F
	1240	1545	4.4E
	1842	2139	4.1F
20	0057	0410	4.3E
Su	0703	1005	4.2F
	1332	1636	4.2E
	1931	2227	3.9F
21	0146	0500	4.2E
M	0757	1100	4.1F
	1434	1735	4.0E
	2028	2324	3.8F
22	0244	0559	4.1E
Tu	0900	1204	4.0F
	1545	1835	3.9E
	2134		
23		0029	3.6F
W	0352	0702	4.2E
	1009	1317	4.0F
	1658	1942	3.9E
	2246		
24		0141	3.6F
Th	0504	0807	4.3E
	1119	1432	4.1F
	1806	2049	4.1E
	2356		
25		0255	3.8F
F	0611	0911	4.5E
	1226	1543	4.3F
	1906	2149	4.3E
26	0058	0402	4.1F
Sa	0712	1009	4.7E
	1325	1640	4.6F
	1959	2244	4.5E
27	0153	0457	4.4F
Su	0807	1104	4.9E
	1418	1733	4.7F
	2048	2336	4.8E
28	0243	0549	4.6F
M	0858	1155	5.0E
	1508	1818	4.8F
	2134		
29		0021	4.9E
Tu	0330	0634	4.7F
	0947	1241	5.1E
	1554	1901	4.8F
	2217		
30		0107	4.9E
W	0415	0719	4.7F
	1034	1327	5.0E
	1638	1941	4.7F
	2259		
31		0150	4.9E
Th	0458	0802	4.7F
	1121	1413	4.8E
	1722	2022	4.5F
	2341		

APRIL

Day	Slack Water Time h.m.	Maximum Current Time h.m.	Vel. knots
1		0234	4.8E
F	0541	0843	4.5F
	1208	1459	4.6E
	1805	2103	4.3F
2	0023	0317	4.6E
Sa	0625	0929	4.3F
	1257	1544	4.3E
	1850	2145	4.0F
3	0107	0404	4.3E
Su	0712	1015	4.0F
	1349	1633	4.0E
	1938	2232	3.7F
4	0156	0455	4.1E
M	0804	1108	3.8F
	1447	1727	3.7E
	2032	2327	3.4F
5	0252	0550	3.9E
Tu	0901	1209	3.6F
	1549	1826	3.5E
	2133		
6		0028	3.2F
W	0354	0647	3.7E
	1004	1319	3.5F
	1652	1927	3.4E
	2239		
7		0141	3.1F
Th	0457	0748	3.7E
	1107	1433	3.5F
	1751	2026	3.5E
	2341		
8		0248	3.3F
F	0557	0846	3.8E
	1205	1530	3.7F
	1843	2121	3.7E
9	0035	0345	3.5F
Sa	0649	0940	4.0E
	1256	1615	3.9F
	1929	2210	3.9E
10	0122	0431	3.7F
Su	0736	1025	4.2E
	1341	1654	4.1F
	2011	2253	4.2E
11	0203	0506	4.0F
M	0819	1110	4.4E
	1422	1729	4.2F
	2049	2333	4.4E
12	0241	0543	4.2F
Tu	0859	1152	4.5E
	1500	1803	4.3F
	2124		
13		0014	4.5E
W	0317	0618	4.3F
	0937	1232	4.6E
	1537	1836	4.4F
	2159		
14		0053	4.6E
Th	0354	0654	4.4F
	1016	1313	4.7E
	1615	1912	4.4F
	2233		
15		0131	4.6E
F	0431	0733	4.5F
	1056	1354	4.6E
	1654	1949	4.4F
	2309		

Day	Slack Water Time h.m.	Maximum Current Time h.m.	Vel. knots
16		0214	4.6E
Sa	0511	0814	4.5F
	1139	1437	4.5E
	1736	2030	4.3F
	2348		
17		0257	4.6E
Su	0556	0859	4.5F
	1227	1526	4.4E
	1822	2117	4.1F
18	0032	0346	4.5E
M	0645	0949	4.3F
	1322	1617	4.2E
	1914	2208	4.0F
19	0124	0439	4.4E
Tu	0741	1046	4.2F
	1425	1718	4.0E
	2014	2307	3.8F
20	0226	0540	4.3E
W	0844	1153	4.1F
	1534	1820	4.0E
	2122		
21		0015	3.7F
Th	0336	0644	4.3E
	0953	1304	4.1F
	1643	1926	4.0E
	2234		
22		0130	3.7F
F	0448	0749	4.3E
	1102	1419	4.2F
	1747	2032	4.1E
	2342		
23		0244	3.9F
Sa	0555	0852	4.5E
	1207	1524	4.4F
	1845	2131	4.4E
24	0042	0350	4.1F
Su	0656	0950	4.6E
	1306	1621	4.5F
	1937	2224	4.6E
25	0136	0443	4.4F
M	0751	1046	4.8E
	1358	1713	4.6F
	2024	2313	4.7E
26	0224	0533	4.5F
Tu	0842	1133	4.8E
	1447	1756	4.6F
	2108	2358	4.8E
27	0309	0617	4.6F
W	0930	1220	4.8E
	1532	1837	4.6F
	2150		
28		0041	4.8E
Th	0352	0700	4.6F
	1017	1305	4.7E
	1614	1916	4.5F
	2230		
29		0124	4.8E
F	0434	0741	4.6F
	1102	1347	4.6E
	1656	1953	4.3F
	2310		
30		0205	4.7E
Sa	0515	0819	4.4F
	1147	1430	4.4E
	1737	2032	4.1F
	2350		

Time meridian 75° W. 0000 is midnight. 1200 is noon.

CAPE COD CANAL (RR. Bridge), MASSACHUSETTS, 1983

F-Flood, Dir. 070° True   E-Ebb, Dir. 250° True

MAY

Day	Slack Water Time h.m.	Maximum Current Time h.m.	Vel. knots
1		0248	4.5E
Su	0558	0903	4.2F
	1234	1516	4.1E
	1820	2115	3.8F
2	0033	0335	4.3E
M	0642	0946	4.0F
	1323	1605	3.9E
	1906	2157	3.6F
3	0119	0423	4.1E
Tu	0730	1033	3.8F
	1417	1656	3.7E
	1957	2249	3.3F
4	0212	0514	3.9E
W	0823	1130	3.6F
	1514	1750	3.5E
	2055	2348	3.2F
5	0312	0610	3.8E
Th	0921	1230	3.5F
	1613	1848	3.5E
	2157		
6		0051	3.1F
F	0415	0708	3.8E
	1021	1334	3.6F
	1709	1947	3.6E
	2258		
7		0157	3.3F
Sa	0515	0806	3.8E
	1119	1433	3.7F
	1800	2042	3.8E
	2352		
8		0255	3.5F
Su	0609	0858	4.0E
	1211	1524	3.8F
	1847	2131	4.0E
9	0041	0343	3.7F
M	0659	0950	4.2E
	1259	1609	4.0F
	1930	2216	4.2E
10	0125	0425	4.0F
Tu	0744	1035	4.3E
	1343	1648	4.2F
	2009	2300	4.4E
11	0206	0507	4.2F
W	0828	1120	4.5E
	1425	1727	4.3F
	2047	2341	4.6E
12	0246	0546	4.4F
Th	0910	1203	4.6E
	1506	1804	4.4F
	2124		
13		0022	4.7E
F	0326	0627	4.5F
	0953	1247	4.6E
	1547	1845	4.4F
	2202		
14		0105	4.8E
Sa	0408	0711	4.6F
	1038	1333	4.6E
	1631	1926	4.4F
	2242		
15		0151	4.8E
Su	0452	0756	4.6F
	1125	1419	4.5E
	1717	2013	4.3F
	2326		
16		0237	4.8E
M	0539	0843	4.6F
	1217	1510	4.4E
	1807	2100	4.2F
17	0015	0328	4.7E
Tu	0632	0938	4.5F
	1314	1604	4.3E
	1902	2154	4.0F
18	0110	0423	4.6E
W	0729	1036	4.4F
	1415	1702	4.2E
	2003	2255	3.9F
19	0213	0522	4.5E
Th	0831	1141	4.3F
	1520	1804	4.1E
	2110		
20		0004	3.8F
F	0322	0625	4.4E
	0937	1250	4.2F
	1624	1907	4.1E
	2218		
21		0116	3.8F
Sa	0431	0728	4.4E
	1043	1400	4.3F
	1724	2009	4.2E
	2322		
22		0228	4.0F
Su	0537	0831	4.4E
	1146	1504	4.3F
	1820	2108	4.4E
23	0021	0331	4.1F
M	0638	0930	4.5E
	1244	1559	4.4F
	1911	2159	4.5E
24	0115	0426	4.3F
Tu	0734	1022	4.5E
	1336	1648	4.4F
	1958	2248	4.6E
25	0203	0516	4.4F
W	0826	1112	4.6E
	1424	1733	4.4F
	2042	2334	4.7E
26	0249	0601	4.5F
Th	0914	1159	4.5E
	1509	1814	4.3F
	2124		
27		0017	4.7E
F	0331	0642	4.5F
	1000	1243	4.4E
	1551	1851	4.2F
	2204		
28		0100	4.7E
Sa	0412	0719	4.4F
	1044	1326	4.3E
	1632	1927	4.1F
	2243		
29		0141	4.6E
Su	0453	0800	4.3F
	1128	1409	4.2E
	1712	2008	3.9F
	2322		
30		0222	4.5E
M	0533	0837	4.2F
	1212	1453	4.0E
	1753	2046	3.7F
31	0003	0307	4.3E
Tu	0616	0919	4.0F
	1258	1538	3.9E
	1837	2129	3.6F

JUNE

Day	Slack Water Time h.m.	Maximum Current Time h.m.	Vel. knots
1	0048	0354	4.2E
W	0700	1002	3.9F
	1346	1627	3.7E
	1925	2216	3.4F
2	0136	0443	4.0E
Th	0748	1052	3.8F
	1437	1717	3.7E
	2017	2309	3.3F
3	0231	0534	3.9E
F	0840	1147	3.7F
	1529	1810	3.6E
	2113		
4		0006	3.3F
Sa	0329	0629	3.8E
	0935	1240	3.7F
	1622	1905	3.7E
	2210		
5		0104	3.3F
Su	0428	0725	3.9E
	1030	1335	3.7F
	1713	1957	3.8E
	2305		
6		0201	3.5F
M	0525	0818	4.0E
	1123	1429	3.8F
	1800	2049	4.0E
	2356		
7		0255	3.7F
Tu	0618	0911	4.1E
	1214	1518	3.9F
	1845	2137	4.2E
8	0044	0346	3.9F
W	0709	0958	4.2E
	1303	1606	4.1F
	1928	2225	4.4E
9	0130	0432	4.2F
Th	0757	1048	4.4E
	1350	1648	4.2F
	2010	2309	4.6E
10	0216	0520	4.4F
F	0845	1135	4.5E
	1437	1736	4.3F
	2053	2355	4.8E
11	0301	0607	4.6F
Sa	0933	1223	4.6E
	1523	1820	4.4F
	2136		
12		0041	4.9E
Su	0348	0653	4.7F
	1022	1311	4.6E
	1611	1908	4.4F
	2221		
13		0130	4.9E
M	0436	0741	4.7F
	1113	1402	4.6E
	1701	1957	4.4F
	2309		
14		0218	4.9E
Tu	0526	0832	4.7F
	1206	1453	4.5E
	1753	2048	4.3F
15	0001	0312	4.9E
W	0619	0926	4.7F
	1301	1548	4.5E
	1849	2144	4.2F
16	0058	0407	4.8E
Th	0715	1023	4.6F
	1359	1645	4.4E
	1948	2242	4.1F
17	0200	0505	4.6E
F	0815	1124	4.4F
	1458	1743	4.3E
	2051	2348	4.0F
18	0305	0604	4.5E
Sa	0917	1228	4.3F
	1558	1843	4.3E
	2155		
19		0056	3.9F
Su	0412	0707	4.4E
	1020	1334	4.2F
	1656	1943	4.3E
	2258		
20		0207	4.0F
M	0517	0806	4.3E
	1121	1439	4.2F
	1752	2039	4.3E
	2357		
21		0311	4.1F
Tu	0619	0905	4.3E
	1220	1534	4.2F
	1844	2133	4.4E
22	0052	0406	4.2F
W	0716	1001	4.3E
	1313	1627	4.1F
	1932	2224	4.5E
23	0142	0501	4.3F
Th	0809	1050	4.3E
	1402	1713	4.1F
	2017	2310	4.5E
24	0229	0544	4.3F
F	0857	1139	4.2E
	1448	1754	4.0F
	2100	2354	4.5E
25	0312	0625	4.3F
Sa	0943	1221	4.2E
	1530	1833	4.0F
	2141		
26		0037	4.5E
Su	0353	0705	4.3F
	1026	1305	4.1E
	1610	1909	3.9F
	2220		
27		0118	4.5E
M	0432	0742	4.2F
	1108	1346	4.1E
	1649	1944	3.8F
	2259		
28		0159	4.4E
Tu	0511	0817	4.2F
	1149	1428	4.0E
	1728	2021	3.8F
	2339		
29		0240	4.4E
W	0551	0853	4.1F
	1230	1512	3.9E
	1609	2100	3.7F
30	0020	0325	4.3E
Th	0631	0936	4.0F
	1312	1555	3.9E
	1852	2145	3.6F

Time meridian 75° W. 0000 is midnight. 1200 is noon.

F-Flood, Dir. 070° True E-Ebb, Dir. 250° True

JULY

Day	Slack Water Time h.m.	Maximum Current Time h.m.	Vel. knots
1	0103	0410	4.1E
F	0715	1017	3.9F
	1357	1642	3.8E
	1939	2229	3.6F
2	0151	0459	4.0E
Sa	0801	1104	3.8F
	1443	1731	3.8E
	2028	2318	3.5F
3	0244	0550	4.0E
Su	0850	1153	3.8F
	1532	1822	3.8E
	2121		
4		0015	3.5F
M	0340	0642	3.9E
	0943	1245	3.7F
	1622	1913	3.9E
	2216		
5		0110	3.6F
Tu	0440	0737	3.9E
	1037	1340	3.8F
	1712	2007	4.0E
	2311		
6		0209	3.7F
W	0539	0833	4.0E
	1133	1433	3.8F
	1802	2100	4.2E
7	0006	0307	3.9F
Th	0636	0927	4.1E
	1227	1528	4.0F
	1851	2151	4.4E
8	0058	0403	4.2F
F	0731	1019	4.3E
	1320	1619	4.1F
	1939	2241	4.6E
9	0150	0455	4.4F
Sa	0824	1110	4.4E
	1412	1712	4.3F
	2027	2332	4.8E
10	0240	0546	4.6F
Su	0916	1202	4.6E
	1503	1802	4.4F
	2115		
11		0023	5.0E
M	0330	0637	4.8F
	1006	1253	4.6E
	1554	1851	4.5F
	2204		
12		0112	5.1E
Tu	0421	0727	4.9F
	1057	1344	4.7E
	1645	1942	4.5F
	2255		
13		0203	5.1E
W	0512	0818	4.9F
	1149	1435	4.7E
	1737	2035	4.5F
	2348		
14		0254	5.0E
Th	0604	0911	4.8F
	1241	1528	4.6E
	1831	2129	4.4F
15	0043	0348	4.9E
F	0658	1004	4.7F
	1335	1623	4.5E
	1927	2226	4.3F

Day	Slack Water Time h.m.	Maximum Current Time h.m.	Vel. knots
16	0142	0442	4.7E
Sa	0754	1102	4.5F
	1430	1717	4.4E
	2026	2325	4.1F
17	0244	0540	4.5E
Su	0852	1159	4.3F
	1527	1813	4.3E
	2127		
18		0030	4.0F
M	0349	0640	4.3E
	0953	1303	4.1F
	1625	1912	4.2E
	2229		
19		0139	3.9F
Tu	0454	0740	4.1E
	1054	1408	3.9F
	1721	2010	4.2E
	2330		
20		0248	4.0F
W	0558	0839	4.0E
	1155	1510	3.9F
	1816	2108	4.2E
21	0028	0349	4.0F
Th	0657	0937	4.0E
	1251	1605	3.8F
	1907	2200	4.3E
22	0121	0443	4.1F
F	0751	1031	4.0E
	1342	1654	3.8F
	1954	2249	4.3E
23	0209	0532	4.1F
Sa	0839	1117	4.0E
	1428	1739	3.9F
	2039	2333	4.4E
24	0252	0609	4.2F
Su	0924	1200	4.1E
	1510	1814	3.9F
	2120		
25		0015	4.5E
M	0333	0648	4.2F
	1005	1241	4.1E
	1549	1847	3.9F
	2159		
26		0056	4.5E
Tu	0411	0719	4.2F
	1044	1322	4.1E
	1626	1923	3.9F
	2237		
27		0136	4.5E
W	0448	0752	4.2F
	1122	1402	4.1E
	1703	1959	3.9F
	2315		
28		0215	4.4E
Th	0525	0827	4.2F
	1159	1443	4.1E
	1740	2034	3.9F
	2353		
29		0257	4.4E
F	0602	0903	4.1F
	1236	1522	4.1E
	1819	2115	3.8F
30	0032	0340	4.3E
Sa	0641	0942	4.0F
	1315	1607	4.0E
	1901	2154	3.8F
31	0115	0425	4.2E
Su	0723	1021	3.9F
	1356	1652	3.9E
	1946	2239	3.7F

AUGUST

Day	Slack Water Time h.m.	Maximum Current Time h.m.	Vel. knots
1	0203	0514	4.0E
M	0809	1111	3.8F
	1441	1740	3.9E
	2036	2332	3.7F
2	0258	0607	3.9E
Tu	0901	1200	3.7F
	1532	1835	3.9E
	2132		
3		0029	3.7F
W	0401	0700	3.9E
	0957	1257	3.7F
	1626	1930	4.0E
	2231		
4		0131	3.8F
Th	0506	0800	3.9E
	1057	1358	3.7F
	1723	2027	4.1E
	2332		
5		0236	3.9F
F	0610	0858	4.0E
	1158	1458	3.9F
	1820	2123	4.4E
6	0032	0337	4.2F
Sa	0710	0956	4.2E
	1258	1557	4.0F
	1914	2219	4.6E
7	0129	0438	4.4F
Su	0806	1051	4.4E
	1354	1654	4.3F
	2007	2313	4.9E
8	0222	0532	4.7F
M	0858	1144	4.6E
	1447	1745	4.4F
	2059		
9		0004	5.0E
Tu	0314	0621	4.9F
	0949	1234	4.8E
	1538	1837	4.6F
	2150		
10		0055	5.2E
W	0405	0713	5.0F
	1038	1325	4.8E
	1628	1928	4.7F
	2240		
11		0144	5.2E
Th	0455	0802	5.0F
	1126	1414	4.9E
	1718	2017	4.7F
	2332		
12		0234	5.1E
F	0545	0850	4.9F
	1215	1503	4.8E
	1808	2108	4.6F
13	0025	0325	5.0E
Sa	0635	0941	4.7F
	1305	1554	4.7E
	1901	2201	4.4F
14	0121	0418	4.7E
Su	0728	1033	4.4F
	1358	1646	4.5E
	1956	2258	4.2F
15	0220	0514	4.4E
M	0824	1128	4.1F
	1452	1743	4.3E
	2054	2359	4.0F

Day	Slack Water Time h.m.	Maximum Current Time h.m.	Vel. knots
16	0324	0610	4.1E
Tu	0923	1229	3.9F
	1550	1840	4.1E
	2157		
17		0108	3.8F
W	0430	0711	3.9E
	1025	1338	3.7F
	1649	1939	4.0E
	2300		
18		0222	3.8F
Th	0535	0812	3.8E
	1129	1445	3.6F
	1747	2038	4.0E
19	0001	0327	3.8F
F	0635	0913	3.8E
	1228	1546	3.6F
	1842	2134	4.1E
20	0057	0424	3.9F
Sa	0729	1007	3.8E
	1321	1636	3.7F
	1932	2225	4.2E
21	0146	0513	4.1F
Su	0817	1056	3.9E
	1407	1717	3.8F
	2017	2311	4.3E
22	0230	0550	4.1F
M	0859	1139	4.1E
	1448	1754	3.9F
	2058	2353	4.4E
23	0309	0621	4.2F
Tu	0939	1217	4.2E
	1525	1827	4.0F
	2137		
24		0031	4.5E
W	0346	0654	4.2F
	1015	1256	4.2E
	1601	1900	4.0F
	2214		
25		0110	4.5E
Th	0421	0726	4.3F
	1050	1334	4.3E
	1635	1932	4.1F
	2250		
26		0149	4.5E
F	0456	0756	4.3F
	1124	1412	4.3E
	1710	2007	4.1F
	2326		
27		0228	4.5E
Sa	0531	0831	4.2F
	1158	1452	4.2E
	1746	2044	4.1F
28	0003	0309	4.4E
Su	0609	0906	4.1F
	1233	1533	4.2E
	1825	2123	4.0F
29	0044	0354	4.2E
M	0649	0947	4.0F
	1311	1618	4.1E
	1909	2208	3.9F
30	0131	0439	4.1E
Tu	0734	1030	3.9F
	1355	1705	4.0E
	1958	2258	3.8F
31	0227	0533	3.9E
W	0826	1123	3.7F
	1447	1800	4.0E
	2055	2357	3.8F

Time meridian 75° W. 0000 is midnight. 1200 is noon.

CAPE COD CANAL (RR. Bridge), MASSACHUSETTS, 1983

F-Flood, Dir. 070° True   E-Ebb, Dir. 250° True

SEPTEMBER

Day	Slack Water Time h.m.	Maximum Current Time h.m.	Vel. knots
1	0332	0632	3.8E
Th	0925	1222	3.6F
	1547	1857	4.0E
	2159		
2		0106	3.8F
F	0443	0733	3.8E
	1031	1328	3.6F
	1652	2001	4.1E
	2306		
3		0212	3.9F
Sa	0551	0836	4.0E
	1138	1435	3.8F
	1756	2100	4.4E
4	0011	0321	4.2F
Su	0652	0937	4.2E
	1241	1540	4.0F
	1856	2158	4.6E
5	0111	0422	4.5F
M	0748	1034	4.4E
	1338	1640	4.3F
	1952	2254	4.9E
6	0206	0516	4.7F
Tu	0839	1126	4.7E
	1431	1733	4.5F
	2044	2345	5.1E
7	0257	0605	4.9F
W	0928	1215	4.9E
	1520	1821	4.7F
	2135		
8		0034	5.2E
Th	0346	0653	5.0F
	1014	1303	5.0E
	1608	1910	4.8F
	2225		
9		0123	5.2E
F	0434	0739	4.9F
	1100	1349	5.0E
	1656	1958	4.8F
	2314		
10		0212	5.1E
Sa	0522	0824	4.8F
	1146	1437	4.9E
	1743	2046	4.7F
11	0005	0300	4.9E
Su	0610	0909	4.6F
	1233	1526	4.7E
	1832	2135	4.5F
12	0059	0351	4.6E
M	0659	1000	4.3F
	1322	1614	4.5E
	1924	2228	4.2F
13	0156	0442	4.3E
Tu	0752	1052	3.9F
	1415	1708	4.2E
	2020	2327	3.9F
14	0258	0541	3.9E
W	0851	1150	3.6F
	1512	1804	4.0E
	2121		
15		0036	3.7F
Th	0403	0642	3.7E
	0954	1259	3.4F
	1614	1905	3.9E
	2226		

Day	Slack Water Time h.m.	Maximum Current Time h.m.	Vel. knots
16		0151	3.6F
F	0509	0744	3.6E
	1100	1413	3.3F
	1716	2007	3.9E
	2330		
17		0302	3.7F
Sa	0609	0845	3.6E
	1202	1518	3.4F
	1814	2105	4.0E
18	0027	0358	3.8F
Su	0702	0940	3.8E
	1255	1611	3.6F
	1905	2158	4.1E
19	0117	0441	4.0F
M	0748	1027	3.9E
	1340	1654	3.8F
	1952	2243	4.3E
20	0201	0520	4.1F
Tu	0829	1110	4.1E
	1421	1729	3.9F
	2033	2326	4.4E
21	0240	0553	4.2F
W	0907	1148	4.3E
	1457	1800	4.1F
	2112		
22		0005	4.5E
Th	0316	0623	4.3F
	0942	1227	4.4E
	1532	1832	4.2F
	2149		
23		0043	4.6E
F	0351	0653	4.3F
	1016	1304	4.4E
	1606	1905	4.3F
	2225		
24		0122	4.6E
Sa	0426	0725	4.3F
	1048	1342	4.4E
	1640	1938	4.3F
	2300		
25		0200	4.5E
Su	0501	0758	4.3F
	1121	1421	4.4E
	1716	2016	4.3F
	2338		
26		0240	4.4E
M	0539	0835	4.2F
	1155	1500	4.3E
	1755	2055	4.2F
27	0020	0326	4.3E
Tu	0619	0916	4.0F
	1233	1545	4.2E
	1839	2140	4.1F
28	0109	0413	4.1E
W	0706	1001	3.9F
	1318	1636	4.1E
	1930	2233	4.0F
29	0207	0508	3.9E
Th	0800	1055	3.7F
	1413	1730	4.1E
	2029	2334	3.9F
30	0314	0609	3.8E
F	0903	1158	3.6F
	1519	1833	4.1E
	2136		

OCTOBER

Day	Slack Water Time h.m.	Maximum Current Time h.m.	Vel. knots
1		0042	3.9F
Sa	0426	0712	3.8E
	1013	1309	3.6F
	1630	1938	4.2E
	2246		
2		0157	4.0F
Su	0534	0817	4.0E
	1123	1421	3.7F
	1738	2041	4.4E
	2352		
3		0305	4.2F
M	0635	0918	4.2E
	1226	1527	4.0F
	1841	2140	4.6E
4	0053	0406	4.5F
Tu	0729	1015	4.5E
	1323	1624	4.3F
	1937	2235	4.9E
5	0147	0459	4.7F
W	0818	1107	4.8E
	1414	1717	4.6F
	2029	2326	5.0E
6	0238	0546	4.8F
Th	0905	1154	4.9E
	1502	1805	4.8F
	2119		
7		0016	5.1E
F	0326	0631	4.9F
	0949	1240	5.0E
	1548	1853	4.8F
	2208		
8		0102	5.1E
Sa	0412	0714	4.8F
	1032	1325	5.0E
	1633	1937	4.8F
	2257		
9		0149	4.9E
Su	0458	0757	4.6F
	1116	1411	4.9E
	1718	2021	4.7F
	2346		
10		0234	4.7E
M	0543	0843	4.4F
	1200	1457	4.7E
	1804	2109	4.4F
11	0037	0325	4.4E
Tu	0630	0926	4.1F
	1246	1544	4.5E
	1853	2157	4.2F
12	0131	0414	4.1E
W	0720	1015	3.7F
	1337	1634	4.2E
	1946	2253	3.9F
13	0230	0510	3.8E
Th	0817	1111	3.4F
	1434	1730	4.0E
	2044	2357	3.7F
14	0333	0608	3.6E
F	0919	1215	3.2F
	1536	1829	3.8E
	2148		
15		0108	3.6F
Sa	0436	0710	3.5E
	1025	1330	3.2F
	1640	1931	3.8E
	2251		

Day	Slack Water Time h.m.	Maximum Current Time h.m.	Vel. knots
16		0220	3.6F
Su	0535	0810	3.6E
	1127	1439	3.3F
	1740	2030	3.9E
	2349		
17		0321	3.7F
M	0627	0905	3.7E
	1221	1534	3.5F
	1834	2123	4.0E
18	0040	0404	3.9F
Tu	0712	0953	4.0E
	1307	1616	3.7F
	1921	2212	4.2E
19	0125	0441	4.1F
W	0754	1038	4.2E
	1348	1657	4.0F
	2004	2253	4.4E
20	0206	0516	4.2F
Th	0831	1117	4.3E
	1426	1729	4.1F
	2044	2334	4.5E
21	0243	0549	4.3F
F	0907	1154	4.5E
	1502	1802	4.3F
	2122		
22		0014	4.5E
Sa	0320	0621	4.3F
	0941	1234	4.6E
	1537	1837	4.4F
	2159		
23		0054	4.6E
Su	0356	0654	4.3F
	1014	1311	4.6E
	1613	1912	4.4F
	2238		
24		0134	4.5E
M	0433	0729	4.3F
	1048	1352	4.6E
	1650	1951	4.4F
	2318		
25		0216	4.4E
Tu	0513	0809	4.2F
	1124	1435	4.5E
	1732	2034	4.4F
26	0003	0301	4.3E
W	0556	0852	4.1F
	1205	1519	4.4E
	1818	2123	4.3F
27	0055	0352	4.1E
Th	0645	0939	3.9F
	1253	1610	4.3E
	1911	2217	4.2F
28	0154	0449	4.0E
F	0742	1036	3.7F
	1351	1711	4.2E
	2011	2318	4.1F
29	0301	0549	3.9E
Sa	0848	1143	3.6F
	1459	1812	4.2E
	2118		
30		0029	4.0F
Su	0410	0654	3.9E
	0958	1253	3.6F
	1612	1916	4.3E
	2227		
31		0140	4.1F
M	0515	0757	4.1E
	1107	1407	3.8F
	1722	2020	4.4E
	2333		

Time meridian 75° W. 0000 is midnight. 1200 is noon.

F-Flood, Dir. 070° True E-Ebb, Dir. 250° True

NOVEMBER

Day	Slack Water Time h.m.	Maximum Current Time h.m.	Vel. knots	Day	Slack Water Time h.m.	Maximum Current Time h.m.	Vel. knots
1		0249	4.3F	16		0311	3.8F
Tu	0613	0858	4.3E	W	0631	0914	3.9E
	1210	1514	4.1F		1227	1531	3.7F
	1825	2121	4.6E		1845	2131	4.1E
2	0034	0347	4.5F	17	0044	0356	3.9F
W	0706	0953	4.6E	Th	0714	0959	4.2E
	1305	1612	4.4F		1311	1616	3.9F
	1922	2216	4.8E		1930	2219	4.2E
3	0128	0441	4.6F	18	0127	0435	4.1F
Th	0755	1044	4.8E	F	0753	1044	4.3E
	1356	1703	4.6F		1351	1654	4.1F
	2015	2307	4.9E		2013	2303	4.4E
4	0218	0526	4.7F	19	0209	0510	4.2F
F	0841	1133	4.9E	Sa	0831	1123	4.5E
	1443	1751	4.7F		1430	1733	4.3F
	2105	2355	4.9E		2055	2346	4.5E
5	0306	0610	4.7F	20	0248	0547	4.3F
Sa	0924	1218	5.0E	Su	0907	1204	4.6E
	1528	1835	4.7F		1509	1810	4.4F
	2153				2136		
6		0041	4.8E	21		0027	4.5E
Su	0350	0652	4.6F	M	0328	0626	4.3F
	1006	1301	4.9E		0943	1245	4.7E
	1612	1918	4.7F		1548	1851	4.5F
	2240				2218		
7		0127	4.7E	22		0110	4.5E
M	0434	0733	4.4F	Tu	0409	0707	4.3F
	1048	1345	4.8E		1020	1328	4.7E
	1655	2001	4.6F		1630	1932	4.6F
	2328				2303		
8		0213	4.5E	23		0155	4.5E
Tu	0518	0814	4.2F	W	0452	0746	4.2F
	1130	1428	4.6E		1101	1413	4.7E
	1739	2045	4.4F		1714	2018	4.5F
					2351		
9	0016	0259	4.2E	24		0243	4.4E
W	0602	0859	3.9F	Th	0539	0835	4.2F
	1214	1514	4.4E		1146	1500	4.6E
	1825	2128	4.1F		1803	2109	4.5F
10	0106	0348	4.0E	25	0044	0336	4.3E
Th	0650	0942	3.7F	F	0631	0924	4.0F
	1301	1603	4.2E		1237	1555	4.6E
	1914	2220	3.9F		1857	2202	4.4F
11	0200	0439	3.7E	26	0142	0429	4.1E
F	0742	1033	3.4F	Sa	0728	1022	3.9F
	1355	1656	4.0E		1337	1649	4.5E
	2007	2315	3.7F		1956	2305	4.3F
12	0258	0532	3.6E	27	0245	0530	4.1E
Sa	0840	1131	3.2F	Su	0832	1127	3.8F
	1455	1753	3.8E		1444	1753	4.4E
	2105				2100		
13		0017	3.6F	28		0011	4.2F
Su	0356	0633	3.5E	M	0349	0633	4.1E
	0942	1237	3.1F		0940	1236	3.8F
	1558	1851	3.8E		1555	1855	4.4E
	2205				2207		
14		0123	3.6F	29		0119	4.2F
M	0452	0730	3.6E	Tu	0451	0736	4.2E
	1043	1346	3.2F		1047	1348	3.9F
	1659	1948	3.8E		1703	1959	4.4E
	2303				2312		
15		0222	3.7F	30		0226	4.3F
Tu	0544	0823	3.7E	W	0549	0835	4.4E
	1138	1442	3.4F		1149	1456	4.1F
	1754	2042	3.9E		1807	2058	4.5E
	2356						

DECEMBER

Day	Slack Water Time h.m.	Maximum Current Time h.m.	Vel. knots	Day	Slack Water Time h.m.	Maximum Current Time h.m.	Vel. knots
1	0012	0326	4.4F	16		0305	3.8F
Th	0642	0930	4.5E	F	0630	0920	4.1E
	1246	1555	4.3F		1229	1531	3.8F
	1906	2156	4.6E		1855	2143	4.1E
2	0108	0419	4.4F	17	0047	0350	3.9F
F	0731	1022	4.7E	Sa	0713	1006	4.3E
	1337	1648	4.5F		1316	1619	4.0F
	2000	2248	4.6E		1943	2231	4.2E
3	0159	0508	4.4F	18	0134	0435	4.1F
Sa	0817	1113	4.8E	Su	0755	1051	4.5E
	1425	1736	4.6F		1400	1703	4.3F
	2051	2336	4.6E		2030	2317	4.4E
4	0247	0553	4.4F	19	0219	0516	4.2F
Su	0901	1155	4.8E	M	0836	1137	4.7E
	1510	1821	4.6F		1444	1748	4.5F
	2139				2115		
5		0023	4.5E	20		0003	4.5E
M	0331	0634	4.3F	Tu	0304	0602	4.3F
	0943	1240	4.8E		0917	1221	4.8E
	1554	1904	4.5F		1528	1833	4.6F
	2225				2202		
6		0108	4.4E	21		0049	4.5E
Tu	0414	0712	4.2F	W	0349	0645	4.3F
	1024	1321	4.7E		0959	1307	4.9E
	1636	1945	4.4F		1613	1919	4.7F
	2311				2249		
7		0152	4.3E	22		0137	4.5E
W	0455	0753	4.0F	Th	0436	0729	4.4F
	1105	1405	4.6E		1044	1356	4.9E
	1718	2024	4.3F		1700	2007	4.7F
	2355				2338		
8		0235	4.1E	23		0226	4.5E
Th	0537	0831	3.9F	F	0525	0819	4.3F
	1147	1450	4.4E		1132	1444	4.9E
	1800	2104	4.1F		1750	2056	4.7F
9	0041	0319	4.0E	24	0030	0317	4.5E
F	0621	0912	3.7F	Sa	0617	0912	4.2F
	1231	1535	4.3E		1225	1535	4.8E
	1844	2151	4.0F		1843	2148	4.6F
10	0128	0407	3.8E	25	0125	0413	4.4E
Sa	0708	1001	3.5F	Su	0713	1007	4.1F
	1319	1623	4.1E		1323	1632	4.7E
	1931	2236	3.8F		1940	2247	4.5F
11	0218	0458	3.7E	26	0222	0508	4.3E
Su	0759	1050	3.4F	M	0813	1108	4.0F
	1412	1715	3.9E		1427	1730	4.5E
	2022	2327	3.7F		2040	2348	4.3F
12	0310	0550	3.6E	27	0322	0609	4.3E
M	0854	1147	3.3F	Tu	0916	1215	4.0F
	1510	1808	3.8E		1535	1832	4.4E
	2116				2143		
13		0023	3.6F	28		0054	4.2F
Tu	0403	0644	3.7E	W	0422	0709	4.3E
	0951	1245	3.3F		1022	1325	4.0F
	1610	1905	3.8E		1643	1934	4.3E
	2211				2247		
14		0118	3.6F	29		0200	4.1F
W	0455	0738	3.7E	Th	0520	0809	4.3E
	1047	1344	3.4F		1125	1433	4.0F
	1708	1959	3.8E		1749	2036	4.3E
	2306				2350		
15		0213	3.7F	30		0301	4.1F
Th	0544	0829	3.9E	F	0616	0908	4.4E
	1140	1439	3.6F		1224	1539	4.2F
	1803	2052	4.0E		1850	2134	4.3E
	2358						
				31	0048	0402	4.1F
				Sa	0708	0959	4.5E
					1319	1638	4.3F
					1946	2229	4.3E

Time meridian 75° W. 0000 is midnight. 1200 is noon.

POLLOCK RIP CHANNEL, MASSACHUSETTS, 1983

F-Flood, Dir. 035° True   E-Ebb, Dir. 225° True

JANUARY

Day	Slack Water Time h.m.	Maximum Current Time h.m.	Vel. knots
1		0053	1.9E
Sa	0402	0712	1.9F
	1021	1307	2.0E
	1618	1944	2.4F
	2308		
2		0145	1.9E
Su	0456	0805	1.9F
	1115	1400	2.0E
	1712	2039	2.3F
3	0002	0242	1.9E
M	0552	0905	1.9F
	1212	1457	1.9E
	1808	2137	2.3F
4	0057	0337	1.8E
Tu	0650	1007	1.9F
	1311	1557	1.8E
	1907	2241	2.2F
5	0155	0438	1.7E
W	0750	1113	1.8F
	1413	1659	1.7E
	2008	2344	2.1F
6	0253	0542	1.7E
Th	0851	1222	1.8F
	1518	1805	1.6E
	2112		
7		0051	2.0F
F	0352	0646	1.6E
	0953	1327	1.9F
	1622	1914	1.6E
	2216		
8		0153	2.0F
Sa	0450	0747	1.6E
	1054	1428	2.0F
	1725	2021	1.5E
	2319		
9		0254	1.9F
Su	0546	0851	1.7E
	1151	1528	2.1F
	1824	2122	1.5E
10	0017	0349	1.9F
M	0639	0942	1.7E
	1243	1617	2.1F
	1918	2215	1.6E
11	0111	0438	1.9F
Tu	0727	1029	1.7E
	1330	1706	2.2F
	2007	2305	1.6E
12	0159	0525	1.9F
W	0812	1112	1.7E
	1414	1751	2.2F
	2051	2344	1.6E
13	0242	0607	1.9F
Th	0854	1150	1.7E
	1453	1830	2.2F
	2133		
14		0023	1.6E
F	0322	0644	1.8F
	0934	1225	1.8E
	1530	1905	2.2F
	2211		
15		0056	1.6E
Sa	0359	0719	1.8F
	1012	1259	1.8E
	1606	1938	2.2F
	2249		

Day	Slack Water Time h.m.	Maximum Current Time h.m.	Vel. knots
16		0129	1.7E
Su	0435	0752	1.8F
	1050	1333	1.8E
	1641	2010	2.2F
	2326		
17		0203	1.7E
M	0512	0824	1.8F
	1129	1410	1.8E
	1718	2043	2.1F
18	0005	0242	1.8E
Tu	0550	0859	1.8F
	1211	1450	1.8E
	1757	2118	2.1F
19	0045	0321	1.8E
W	0630	0936	1.8F
	1254	1533	1.8E
	1839	2158	2.1F
20	0128	0404	1.8E
Th	0712	1019	1.8F
	1342	1620	1.7E
	1925	2241	2.0F
21	0213	0449	1.7E
F	0759	1106	1.8F
	1433	1709	1.7E
	2014	2330	1.9F
22	0302	0539	1.7E
Sa	0848	1158	1.7F
	1528	1804	1.6E
	2108		
23		0023	1.8F
Su	0353	0630	1.6E
	0942	1257	1.7F
	1626	1857	1.5E
	2205		
24		0122	1.7F
M	0447	0727	1.6E
	1038	1358	1.8F
	1726	1959	1.5E
	2306		
25		0222	1.7F
Tu	0542	0824	1.7E
	1136	1503	1.9F
	1826	2100	1.5E
26	0008	0325	1.7F
W	0638	0922	1.7E
	1233	1603	2.0F
	1923	2201	1.6E
27	0108	0426	1.7F
Th	0732	1017	1.8E
	1329	1659	2.1F
	2018	2256	1.7E
28	0205	0522	1.8F
F	0825	1112	1.9E
	1423	1754	2.3F
	2111	2352	1.8E
29	0259	0616	1.9F
Sa	0918	1205	2.0E
	1516	1845	2.4F
	2202		
30		0045	1.9E
Su	0352	0708	2.0F
	1010	1259	2.1E
	1608	1938	2.4F
	2253		
31		0135	1.9E
M	0443	0800	2.1F
	1102	1350	2.1E
	1700	2029	2.4F
	2343		

FEBRUARY

Day	Slack Water Time h.m.	Maximum Current Time h.m.	Vel. knots
1		0225	1.9E
Tu	0534	0852	2.1F
	1155	1443	2.0E
	1752	2121	2.3F
2	0034	0317	1.9E
W	0627	0946	2.0F
	1251	1537	1.9E
	1846	2216	2.2F
3	0127	0412	1.8E
Th	0721	1046	2.0F
	1348	1633	1.8E
	1943	2315	2.0F
4	0221	0507	1.7E
F	0817	1149	1.9F
	1449	1736	1.6E
	2042		
5		0017	1.9F
Sa	0318	0607	1.6E
	0916	1252	1.9F
	1551	1839	1.5E
	2144		
6		0120	1.8F
Su	0415	0711	1.5E
	1017	1354	1.9F
	1654	1946	1.4E
	2247		
7		0221	1.8F
M	0513	0812	1.5E
	1116	1457	2.0F
	1755	2052	1.4E
	2348		
8		0321	1.8F
Tu	0608	0909	1.6E
	1211	1550	2.0F
	1850	2149	1.5E
9	0044	0414	1.8F
W	0700	1002	1.6E
	1302	1639	2.1F
	1941	2238	1.5E
10	0133	0459	1.8F
Th	0747	1050	1.7E
	1347	1722	2.2F
	2025	2319	1.6E
11	0217	0542	1.9F
F	0830	1127	1.7E
	1428	1804	2.2F
	2106	2356	1.7E
12	0257	0621	1.9F
Sa	0909	1202	1.8E
	1505	1839	2.2F
	2144		
13		0029	1.7E
Su	0333	0654	1.9F
	0947	1234	1.8E
	1541	1910	2.2F
	2220		
14		0101	1.8E
M	0407	0724	1.9F
	1024	1307	1.9E
	1615	1939	2.2F
	2255		
15		0134	1.8E
Tu	0441	0753	1.9F
	1102	1344	1.9E
	1650	2011	2.2F
	2331		

Day	Slack Water Time h.m.	Maximum Current Time h.m.	Vel. knots
16		0209	1.9E
W	0516	0824	2.0F
	1140	1421	1.9E
	1727	2042	2.2F
17	0009	0247	1.9E
Th	0553	0901	2.0F
	1222	1502	1.9E
	1807	2119	2.1F
18	0049	0328	1.9E
F	0633	0938	2.0F
	1307	1547	1.8E
	1851	2202	2.0F
19	0133	0413	1.8E
Sa	0717	1026	1.9F
	1358	1636	1.7E
	1939	2251	1.9F
20	0222	0500	1.7E
Su	0807	1119	1.8F
	1454	1730	1.6E
	2034	2344	1.7F
21	0316	0555	1.6E
M	0903	1220	1.8F
	1557	1829	1.5E
	2136		
22		0048	1.6F
Tu	0416	0652	1.6E
	1006	1329	1.7F
	1702	1934	1.4E
	2244		
23		0157	1.5F
W	0518	0758	1.5E
	1111	1444	1.8F
	1807	2044	1.4E
	2352		
24		0313	1.6F
Th	0620	0904	1.6E
	1216	1552	2.0F
	1908	2149	1.5E
25	0056	0421	1.7F
F	0719	1008	1.7E
	1317	1653	2.1F
	2005	2249	1.7E
26	0155	0518	1.9F
Sa	0814	1104	1.9E
	1413	1748	2.3F
	2057	2342	1.8E
27	0248	0609	2.0F
Su	0907	1157	2.0E
	1506	1837	2.4F
	2146		
28		0032	1.9E
M	0338	0700	2.1F
	0957	1248	2.1E
	1556	1925	2.4F
	2234		

Time meridian 75° W. 0000 is midnight. 1200 is noon.

F-Flood, Dir. 035° True E-Ebb, Dir. 225° True

MARCH

Day	Slack Water Time h.m.	Maximum Current Time h.m.	Vel. knots
1		0119	2.0E
Tu	0425	0748	2.2F
	1047	1336	2.1E
	1645	2011	2.4F
	2320		
2		0205	2.0E
W	0512	0833	2.2F
	1137	1424	2.0E
	1734	2059	2.3F
3	0007	0252	1.9E
Th	0600	0924	2.1F
	1229	1515	1.9E
	1823	2147	2.1F
4	0056	0341	1.8E
F	0649	1015	2.0F
	1322	1606	1.7E
	1915	2241	1.9F
5	0147	0432	1.7E
Sa	0741	1114	1.9F
	1419	1701	1.6E
	2011	2342	1.8F
6	0242	0527	1.6E
Su	0837	1216	1.9F
	1520	1804	1.4E
	2111		
7		0043	1.7F
M	0339	0628	1.5E
	0937	1321	1.8F
	1621	1910	1.3E
	2213		
8		0147	1.6F
Tu	0438	0733	1.4E
	1037	1420	1.9F
	1721	2015	1.4E
	2315		
9		0248	1.6F
W	0535	0832	1.5E
	1135	1518	2.0F
	1817	2112	1.4E
10	0012	0339	1.7F
Th	0629	0930	1.5E
	1228	1607	2.0F
	1908	2205	1.5E
11	0102	0430	1.8F
F	0717	1014	1.6E
	1315	1652	2.1F
	1953	2249	1.6E
12	0146	0511	1.9F
Sa	0802	1056	1.7E
	1357	1731	2.2F
	2033	2324	1.7E
13	0226	0551	2.0F
Su	0842	1131	1.8E
	1435	1808	2.2F
	2111	2357	1.8E
14	0301	0622	2.0F
M	0920	1205	1.9E
	1511	1837	2.2F
	2146		
15		0029	1.9E
Tu	0335	0652	2.0F
	0957	1238	2.0E
	1546	1905	2.2F
	2221		

Day	Slack Water Time h.m.	Maximum Current Time h.m.	Vel. knots
16		0100	1.9E
W	0408	0719	2.1F
	1033	1315	2.0E
	1621	1936	2.2F
	2257		
17		0135	2.0E
Th	0442	0754	2.1F
	1112	1352	2.0E
	1658	2009	2.2F
	2334		
18		0214	2.0E
F	0518	0827	2.1F
	1153	1436	2.0E
	1738	2046	2.1F
19	0014	0255	1.9E
Sa	0558	0908	2.1F
	1239	1517	1.9E
	1823	2131	2.0F
20	0058	0340	1.9E
Su	0643	0957	2.0F
	1331	1608	1.7E
	1913	2219	1.8F
21	0149	0431	1.7E
M	0735	1052	1.9F
	1430	1705	1.6E
	2011	2316	1.6F
22	0248	0529	1.6E
Tu	0836	1156	1.8F
	1536	1808	1.4E
	2118		
23		0029	1.5F
W	0353	0632	1.5E
	0943	1315	1.8F
	1644	1916	1.4E
	2231		
24		0153	1.5F
Th	0501	0743	1.5E
	1055	1435	1.8F
	1751	2031	1.4E
	2342		
25		0310	1.6F
F	0607	0853	1.6E
	1203	1545	2.0F
	1852	2139	1.6E
26	0046	0414	1.8F
Sa	0707	0957	1.7E
	1305	1644	2.2F
	1948	2237	1.7E
27	0143	0510	2.0F
Su	0803	1056	1.9E
	1402	1735	2.3F
	2039	2330	1.9E
28	0233	0559	2.1F
M	0854	1147	2.0E
	1453	1824	2.4F
	2126		
29		0016	2.0E
Tu	0320	0646	2.2F
	0943	1236	2.0E
	1541	1908	2.3F
	2211		
30		0100	2.0E
W	0405	0729	2.3F
	1031	1320	2.0E
	1627	1951	2.3F
	2255		
31		0143	2.0E
Th	0448	0812	2.2F
	1118	1403	1.9E
	1713	2036	2.1F
	2339		

APRIL

Day	Slack Water Time h.m.	Maximum Current Time h.m.	Vel. knots
1		0226	1.9E
F	0532	0858	2.2F
	1207	1449	1.8E
	1759	2121	2.0F
2	0025	0309	1.8E
Sa	0618	0946	2.1F
	1257	1538	1.7E
	1848	2210	1.8F
3	0114	0356	1.6E
Su	0706	1040	1.9F
	1351	1631	1.5E
	1940	2303	1.6F
4	0206	0447	1.5E
M	0759	1139	1.8F
	1447	1727	1.4E
	2038		
5		0009	1.6F
Tu	0303	0546	1.4E
	0856	1240	1.8F
	1546	1831	1.3E
	2138		
6		0112	1.5F
W	0401	0649	1.4E
	0955	1340	1.8F
	1644	1932	1.4E
	2238		
7		0209	1.6F
Th	0459	0750	1.4E
	1053	1437	1.9F
	1739	2034	1.4E
	2334		
8		0306	1.7F
F	0554	0847	1.5E
	1147	1528	2.0F
	1828	2123	1.6E
9	0025	0354	1.8F
Sa	0643	0936	1.6E
	1236	1613	2.1F
	1914	2208	1.7E
10	0109	0437	1.9F
Su	0729	1017	1.7E
	1320	1654	2.1F
	1955	2243	1.8E
11	0149	0512	2.0F
M	0810	1056	1.8E
	1401	1729	2.2F
	2034	2319	1.9E
12	0225	0547	2.1F
Tu	0849	1131	1.9E
	1438	1800	2.2F
	2110	2352	1.9E
13	0259	0616	2.1F
W	0927	1206	1.9E
	1515	1831	2.2F
	2146		
14		0025	2.0E
Th	0333	0647	2.2F
	1006	1245	2.0E
	1552	1904	2.1F
	2222		
15		0104	2.0E
F	0409	0721	2.2F
	1046	1326	2.0E
	1631	1939	2.1F
	2301		

Day	Slack Water Time h.m.	Maximum Current Time h.m.	Vel. knots
16		0141	2.0E
Sa	0447	0800	2.2F
	1130	1409	2.0E
	1714	2020	2.0F
	2343		
17		0226	2.0E
Su	0530	0845	2.2F
	1218	1456	1.9E
	1802	2105	1.9F
18	0031	0314	1.9E
M	0618	0932	2.1F
	1313	1547	1.7E
	1856	2200	1.7F
19	0126	0409	1.7E
Tu	0714	1034	2.0F
	1414	1647	1.6E
	1958	2307	1.6F
20	0229	0508	1.6E
W	0818	1145	1.9F
	1520	1752	1.5E
	2108		
21		0023	1.5F
Th	0338	0617	1.5E
	0929	1307	1.8F
	1628	1905	1.4E
	2221		
22		0149	1.5F
F	0447	0730	1.5E
	1041	1425	1.9F
	1733	2021	1.5E
	2330		
23		0259	1.7F
Sa	0553	0843	1.6E
	1149	1532	2.1F
	1833	2127	1.6E
24	0031	0400	1.9F
Su	0654	0949	1.7E
	1251	1628	2.2F
	1928	2224	1.8E
25	0126	0453	2.1F
M	0749	1044	1.8E
	1346	1719	2.3F
	2017	2311	1.9E
26	0215	0544	2.2F
Tu	0840	1135	1.9E
	1437	1806	2.3F
	2103	2357	1.9E
27	0300	0629	2.3F
W	0928	1220	1.9E
	1524	1851	2.2F
	2147		
28		0038	1.9E
Th	0342	0711	2.3F
	1014	1304	1.9E
	1608	1931	2.1F
	2229		
29		0116	1.9E
F	0424	0753	2.2F
	1100	1345	1.8E
	1652	2013	2.0F
	2312		
30		0157	1.8E
Sa	0505	0837	2.1F
	1146	1428	1.7E
	1736	2055	1.8F
	2356		

Time meridian 75° W. 0000 is midnight. 1200 is noon.

POLLOCK RIP CHANNEL, MASSACHUSETTS, 1983

F-Flood, Dir. 035° True   E-Ebb, Dir. 225° True

MAY

Day	Slack Water Time h.m.	Maximum Current Time h.m.	Vel. knots
1		0239	1.7E
Su	0548	0921	2.0F
	1233	1511	1.6E
	1822	2143	1.7F
2	0043	0325	1.6E
M	0634	1009	2.0F
	1323	1602	1.5E
	1911	2231	1.6F
3	0133	0412	1.5E
Tu	0723	1100	1.9F
	1415	1654	1.4E
	2005	2330	1.5F
4	0227	0506	1.5E
W	0817	1158	1.8F
	1509	1749	1.4E
	2101		
5		0029	1.5F
Th	0323	0603	1.4E
	0913	1255	1.8F
	1603	1848	1.4E
	2158		
6		0127	1.6F
F	0420	0703	1.4E
	1009	1350	1.9F
	1656	1943	1.5E
	2252		
7		0222	1.7F
Sa	0514	0759	1.5E
	1103	1441	1.9F
	1745	2034	1.6E
	2341		
8		0309	1.8F
Su	0605	0850	1.6E
	1153	1528	2.0F
	1831	2118	1.7E
9	0027	0352	1.9F
M	0652	0936	1.7E
	1239	1610	2.0F
	1914	2159	1.8E
10	0108	0433	2.0F
Tu	0736	1017	1.7E
	1322	1646	2.1F
	1954	2237	1.9E
11	0146	0506	2.1F
W	0817	1058	1.8E
	1403	1722	2.1F
	2033	2315	1.9E
12	0224	0542	2.1F
Th	0859	1137	1.9E
	1444	1756	2.0F
	2111	2353	2.0E
13	0301	0617	2.2F
F	0940	1218	1.9E
	1525	1833	2.0F
	2151		
14		0034	2.0E
Sa	0340	0656	2.3F
	1024	1303	1.9E
	1608	1914	2.0F
	2233		
15		0117	2.0E
Su	0423	0740	2.3F
	1111	1348	1.9E
	1655	1957	1.9F
	2319		
16		0204	2.0E
M	0509	0827	2.2F
	1202	1438	1.8E
	1747	2050	1.8F
17	0011	0255	1.9E
Tu	0602	0924	2.1F
	1259	1533	1.7E
	1845	2150	1.7F
18	0110	0352	1.8E
W	0700	1025	2.0F
	1400	1636	1.6E
	1949	2301	1.6F
19	0214	0454	1.6E
Th	0806	1139	2.0F
	1505	1743	1.5E
	2057		
20		0017	1.6F
F	0323	0605	1.6E
	0915	1255	2.0F
	1610	1854	1.5E
	2206		
21		0137	1.7F
Sa	0431	0718	1.6E
	1025	1408	2.0F
	1712	2005	1.6E
	2312		
22		0244	1.8F
Su	0536	0827	1.6E
	1132	1510	2.1F
	1810	2106	1.7E
23	0011	0343	2.0F
M	0637	0934	1.7E
	1233	1607	2.1F
	1904	2202	1.8E
24	0105	0437	2.2F
Tu	0733	1027	1.8E
	1328	1700	2.1F
	1953	2253	1.9E
25	0154	0526	2.2F
W	0824	1118	1.8E
	1419	1747	2.1F
	2040	2336	1.9E
26	0239	0611	2.3F
Th	0912	1204	1.8E
	1506	1833	2.0F
	2123		
27		0017	1.8E
F	0321	0654	2.2F
	0958	1247	1.7E
	1549	1914	1.9F
	2205		
28		0056	1.8E
Sa	0401	0735	2.2F
	1042	1328	1.7E
	1631	1953	1.8F
	2247		
29		0134	1.7E
Su	0441	0816	2.1F
	1125	1407	1.6E
	1713	2034	1.7F
	2329		
30		0214	1.7E
M	0522	0855	2.1F
	1209	1448	1.6E
	1756	2114	1.6F
31	0013	0255	1.6E
Tu	0604	0940	2.0F
	1255	1531	1.5E
	1842	2200	1.6F

JUNE

Day	Slack Water Time h.m.	Maximum Current Time h.m.	Vel. knots
1	0101	0340	1.6E
W	0650	1023	1.9F
	1342	1619	1.5E
	1931	2247	1.6F
2	0151	0431	1.5E
Th	0739	1113	1.9F
	1431	1710	1.5E
	2022	2342	1.6F
3	0244	0522	1.5E
F	0830	1205	1.9F
	1521	1800	1.5E
	2114		
4		0036	1.6F
Sa	0338	0617	1.5E
	0923	1257	1.9F
	1611	1852	1.6E
	2205		
5		0127	1.7F
Su	0431	0709	1.5E
	1016	1349	1.9F
	1700	1943	1.6E
	2254		
6		0220	1.8F
M	0523	0802	1.6E
	1107	1435	1.9F
	1747	2031	1.7E
	2341		
7		0305	1.8F
Tu	0613	0851	1.6E
	1156	1520	1.9F
	1832	2114	1.8E
8	0026	0349	1.9F
W	0700	0938	1.7E
	1244	1605	1.9F
	1915	2158	1.8E
9	0108	0430	2.0F
Th	0746	1023	1.7E
	1330	1645	1.9F
	1958	2241	1.9E
10	0150	0510	2.1F
F	0832	1109	1.8E
	1415	1725	1.9F
	2041	2324	2.0E
11	0233	0552	2.2F
Sa	0918	1154	1.8E
	1502	1812	1.9F
	2125		
12		0009	2.0E
Su	0317	0638	2.3F
	1006	1241	1.9E
	1550	1854	1.9F
	2211		
13		0056	2.0E
M	0404	0726	2.3F
	1056	1332	1.9E
	1641	1945	1.9F
	2302		
14		0147	2.0E
Tu	0455	0816	2.3F
	1149	1425	1.8E
	1735	2042	1.8F
	2356		
15		0239	1.9E
W	0550	0914	2.2F
	1245	1522	1.8E
	1834	2143	1.8F
16	0056	0338	1.8E
Th	0649	1019	2.1F
	1344	1622	1.7E
	1936	2251	1.7F
17	0159	0441	1.7E
F	0753	1126	2.1F
	1445	1727	1.7E
	2040		
18		0005	1.7F
Sa	0305	0548	1.6E
	0859	1237	2.0F
	1546	1834	1.7E
	2145		
19		0114	1.8F
Su	0411	0659	1.6E
	1006	1344	2.0F
	1647	1943	1.7E
	2248		
20		0220	1.9F
M	0516	0809	1.6E
	1111	1449	2.0F
	1744	2044	1.7E
	2347		
21		0321	2.1F
Tu	0617	0915	1.6E
	1212	1544	2.0F
	1839	2139	1.8E
22	0042	0416	2.2F
W	0714	1011	1.7E
	1309	1638	2.0F
	1929	2232	1.8E
23	0132	0505	2.2F
Th	0807	1106	1.7E
	1400	1727	2.0F
	2017	2315	1.8E
24	0218	0554	2.2F
F	0855	1149	1.6E
	1447	1812	1.9F
	2101	2357	1.8E
25	0301	0638	2.2F
Sa	0940	1232	1.6E
	1531	1853	1.8F
	2143		
26		0036	1.7E
Su	0340	0719	2.2F
	1022	1310	1.6E
	1611	1934	1.8F
	2223		
27		0112	1.7E
M	0419	0754	2.1F
	1103	1346	1.6E
	1650	2013	1.7F
	2304		
28		0149	1.7E
Tu	0457	0833	2.1F
	1143	1423	1.6E
	1730	2048	1.7F
	2346		
29		0230	1.7E
W	0536	0909	2.1F
	1224	1502	1.6E
	1811	2124	1.7F
30	0030	0311	1.7E
Th	0618	0947	2.0F
	1307	1543	1.6E
	1854	2206	1.7F

Time meridian 75° W. 0000 is midnight. 1200 is noon.

POLLOCK RIP CHANNEL, MASSACHUSETTS, 1983

F-Flood, Dir. 035° True   E-Ebb, Dir. 225° True

JULY

Day	Slack Water Time h.m.	Maximum Current Time h.m.	Maximum Current Vel. knots
1	0116	0356	1.7E
F	0702	1029	2.0F
	1352	1628	1.6E
	1940	2251	1.7F
2	0205	0441	1.6E
Sa	0749	1114	2.0F
	1438	1717	1.7E
	2028	2342	1.7F
3	0256	0533	1.6E
Su	0838	1200	1.9F
	1526	1804	1.7E
	2116		
4		0031	1.7F
M	0348	0624	1.6E
	0929	1251	1.8F
	1614	1853	1.7E
	2206		
5		0122	1.7F
Tu	0442	0715	1.5E
	1022	1343	1.8F
	1703	1943	1.7E
	2256		
6		0218	1.8F
W	0535	0808	1.5E
	1115	1434	1.8F
	1752	2032	1.7E
	2345		
7		0307	1.9F
Th	0627	0901	1.6E
	1208	1522	1.8F
	1840	2123	1.8E
8	0033	0356	2.0F
F	0719	0955	1.6E
	1301	1616	1.8F
	1928	2210	1.8E
9	0122	0447	2.1F
Sa	0810	1044	1.7E
	1352	1705	1.8F
	2016	2301	1.9E
10	0211	0535	2.2F
Su	0900	1137	1.8E
	1444	1754	1.9F
	2105	2351	2.0E
11	0300	0623	2.3F
M	0950	1228	1.8E
	1535	1845	1.9F
	2155		
12		0042	2.0E
Tu	0351	0715	2.3F
	1041	1319	1.9E
	1628	1938	1.9F
	2247		
13		0135	2.0E
W	0444	0810	2.3F
	1133	1411	1.9E
	1722	2033	1.9F
	2342		
14		0228	2.0E
Th	0538	0905	2.3F
	1227	1508	1.9E
	1817	2131	1.9F
15	0040	0325	1.9E
F	0635	1006	2.2F
	1323	1603	1.8E
	1916	2235	1.9F

Day	Slack Water Time h.m.	Maximum Current Time h.m.	Maximum Current Vel. knots
16	0140	0425	1.8E
Sa	0735	1107	2.1F
	1420	1704	1.7E
	2016	2342	1.9F
17	0243	0530	1.7E
Su	0838	1212	2.0F
	1519	1807	1.7E
	2118		
18		0048	1.9F
M	0348	0636	1.6E
	0943	1321	2.0F
	1618	1914	1.7E
	2220		
19		0155	2.0F
Tu	0453	0746	1.5E
	1047	1423	1.9F
	1717	2015	1.7E
	2320		
20		0256	2.0F
W	0556	0851	1.5E
	1150	1522	1.9F
	1813	2115	1.7E
21	0017	0354	2.1F
Th	0654	0952	1.6E
	1248	1617	1.9F
	1905	2208	1.7E
22	0109	0445	2.2F
F	0747	1045	1.6E
	1341	1708	1.9F
	1954	2255	1.7E
23	0156	0534	2.2F
Sa	0835	1131	1.6E
	1428	1751	1.9F
	2039	2338	1.7E
24	0239	0617	2.2F
Su	0919	1210	1.6E
	1510	1833	1.8F
	2120		
25		0016	1.7E
M	0318	0656	2.2F
	0959	1247	1.6E
	1548	1910	1.8F
	2200		
26		0049	1.8E
Tu	0355	0731	2.2F
	1037	1320	1.7E
	1624	1945	1.8F
	2239		
27		0124	1.8E
W	0431	0803	2.2F
	1114	1354	1.7E
	1701	2016	1.8F
	2318		
28		0201	1.8E
Th	0508	0836	2.1F
	1151	1429	1.7E
	1737	2050	1.8F
	2358		
29		0238	1.8E
F	0546	0909	2.1F
	1231	1508	1.8E
	1816	2125	1.8F
30	0041	0318	1.8E
Sa	0626	0944	2.1F
	1312	1547	1.8E
	1857	2206	1.8F
31	0126	0403	1.7E
Su	0710	1026	2.0F
	1355	1632	1.7E
	1941	2251	1.8F

AUGUST

Day	Slack Water Time h.m.	Maximum Current Time h.m.	Maximum Current Vel. knots
1	0215	0452	1.7E
M	0756	1111	1.9F
	1442	1720	1.7E
	2029	2340	1.8F
2	0307	0543	1.6E
Tu	0847	1202	1.8F
	1531	1809	1.7E
	2119		
3		0034	1.8F
W	0403	0638	1.5E
	0942	1257	1.7F
	1623	1902	1.6E
	2213		
4		0131	1.8F
Th	0501	0734	1.5E
	1041	1352	1.6F
	1717	1957	1.6E
	2309		
5		0234	1.8F
F	0559	0831	1.5E
	1140	1454	1.6F
	1811	2052	1.7E
6	0005	0332	1.9F
Sa	0656	0931	1.5E
	1239	1555	1.7F
	1905	2148	1.8E
7	0100	0430	2.1F
Su	0751	1027	1.6E
	1336	1651	1.8F
	1958	2243	1.9E
8	0154	0525	2.2F
M	0843	1121	1.8E
	1430	1744	1.9F
	2050	2336	2.0E
9	0247	0615	2.3F
Tu	0934	1214	1.9E
	1522	1836	2.0F
	2141		
10		0029	2.1E
W	0339	0706	2.4F
	1024	1305	1.9E
	1613	1928	2.1F
	2233		
11		0120	2.1E
Th	0431	0757	2.4F
	1114	1354	2.0E
	1704	2020	2.1F
	2326		
12		0214	2.1E
F	0523	0848	2.3F
	1205	1448	1.9E
	1756	2114	2.1F
13	0021	0305	2.0E
Sa	0617	0943	2.2F
	1257	1540	1.9E
	1850	2212	2.0F
14	0119	0403	1.8E
Su	0714	1044	2.1F
	1352	1636	1.8E
	1947	2314	2.0F
15	0220	0504	1.7E
M	0814	1145	1.9F
	1449	1737	1.7E
	2046		

Day	Slack Water Time h.m.	Maximum Current Time h.m.	Maximum Current Vel. knots
16		0021	1.9F
Tu	0323	0612	1.5E
	0917	1251	1.8F
	1548	1841	1.6E
	2149		
17		0128	1.9F
W	0428	0721	1.5E
	1022	1356	1.8F
	1648	1949	1.5E
	2251		
18		0230	2.0F
Th	0531	0828	1.4E
	1126	1457	1.8F
	1746	2048	1.6E
	2349		
19		0329	2.1F
F	0630	0928	1.5E
	1225	1553	1.8F
	1841	2145	1.6E
20	0043	0422	2.1F
Sa	0723	1021	1.6E
	1317	1644	1.9F
	1930	2230	1.7E
21	0131	0507	2.2F
Su	0809	1106	1.6E
	1403	1727	1.9F
	2015	2315	1.7E
22	0214	0550	2.2F
M	0851	1145	1.7E
	1444	1808	1.9F
	2056	2351	1.8E
23	0253	0628	2.2F
Tu	0929	1220	1.7E
	1520	1843	1.9F
	2135		
24		0025	1.8E
W	0329	0701	2.2F
	1005	1251	1.8E
	1554	1915	1.9F
	2212		
25		0056	1.9E
Th	0403	0730	2.2F
	1041	1321	1.8E
	1628	1944	2.0F
	2249		
26		0131	1.9E
F	0438	0800	2.2F
	1116	1354	1.9E
	1702	2013	2.0F
	2327		
27		0208	1.9E
Sa	0514	0829	2.1F
	1153	1429	1.9E
	1737	2048	2.0F
28	0007	0245	1.9E
Su	0552	0906	2.1F
	1232	1509	1.8E
	1816	2127	1.9F
29	0050	0330	1.8E
M	0633	0945	2.0F
	1314	1552	1.8E
	1858	2206	1.9F
30	0139	0415	1.7E
Tu	0720	1028	1.8F
	1400	1639	1.7E
	1945	2258	1.8F
31	0232	0508	1.6E
W	0812	1121	1.7F
	1452	1732	1.6E
	2038	2355	1.8F

Time meridian 75° W. 0000 is midnight. 1200 is noon.

F-Flood, Dir. 295° True E-Ebb, Dir. 100° True

JANUARY

Day	Slack Water Time h.m.	Maximum Current Time h.m.	Maximum Current Vel. knots
1	0025	0341	4.1E
Sa	0643	0937	4.1F
	1241	1606	4.7E
	1923	2211	4.0F
2	0119	0435	4.1E
Su	0741	1029	3.9F
	1336	1702	4.5E
	2017	2304	3.9F
3	0214	0533	4.0E
M	0841	1128	3.6F
	1432	1759	4.2E
	2113		
4		0002	3.6F
Tu	0311	0631	3.9E
	0944	1228	3.3F
	1531	1855	3.9E
	2211		
5		0101	3.4F
W	0409	0731	3.7E
	1050	1333	3.0F
	1633	1956	3.5E
	2311		
6		0205	3.2F
Th	0509	0832	3.6E
	1155	1443	2.7F
	1736	2057	3.3E
7	0011	0306	3.0F
F	0608	0933	3.5E
	1259	1552	2.6F
	1840	2155	3.1E
8	0110	0410	2.9F
Sa	0706	1028	3.5E
	1358	1653	2.6F
	1941	2252	3.0E
9	0205	0509	2.8F
Su	0800	1124	3.6E
	1453	1751	2.6F
	2037	2345	2.9E
10	0257	0558	2.8F
M	0848	1211	3.6E
	1542	1838	2.6F
	2127		
11		0032	2.9E
Tu	0345	0643	2.7F
	0933	1258	3.6E
	1627	1921	2.7F
	2211		
12		0118	2.9E
W	0428	0724	2.7F
	1013	1341	3.6E
	1708	2000	2.7F
	2251		
13		0201	2.9E
Th	0509	0757	2.7F
	1052	1422	3.5E
	1746	2033	2.6F
	2329		
14		0242	2.8E
F	0548	0828	2.6F
	1129	1459	3.5E
	1822	2101	2.6F
15	0005	0321	2.8E
Sa	0625	0904	2.6F
	1205	1538	3.4E
	1856	2134	2.6F
16	0040	0400	2.8E
Su	0701	0942	2.5F
	1242	1616	3.2E
	1930	2209	2.6F
17	0117	0438	2.7E
M	0738	1022	2.5F
	1320	1651	3.1E
	2003	2248	2.6F
18	0154	0514	2.7E
Tu	0818	1104	2.4F
	1400	1727	2.9E
	2039	2331	2.6F
19	0234	0552	2.7E
W	0903	1149	2.3F
	1444	1802	2.7E
	2119		
20		0015	2.5F
Th	0317	0637	2.7E
	0952	1240	2.2F
	1532	1849	2.6E
	2203		
21		0102	2.5F
F	0405	0729	2.7E
	1048	1331	2.2F
	1627	1942	2.5E
	2254		
22		0155	2.6F
Sa	0458	0828	2.9E
	1148	1429	2.2F
	1726	2049	2.5E
	2350		
23		0250	2.7F
Su	0555	0929	3.1E
	1250	1528	2.4F
	1829	2152	2.7E
24	0050	0349	2.9F
M	0654	1031	3.5E
	1350	1627	2.7F
	1932	2254	2.9E
25	0150	0447	3.2F
Tu	0754	1129	3.8E
	1447	1728	3.0F
	2032	2351	3.3E
26	0250	0544	3.5F
W	0851	1223	4.2E
	1542	1824	3.4F
	2129		
27		0046	3.7E
Th	0347	0640	3.8F
	0947	1315	4.6E
	1634	1918	3.8F
	2224		
28		0141	4.0E
F	0443	0736	4.1F
	1041	1409	4.8E
	1724	2012	4.0F
	2317		
29		0233	4.3E
Sa	0537	0829	4.2F
	1134	1459	4.9E
	1814	2103	4.2F
30	0009	0325	4.4E
Su	0631	0921	4.2F
	1227	1551	4.8E
	1905	2153	4.2F
31	0100	0417	4.4E
M	0726	1014	4.0F
	1319	1642	4.6E
	1955	2245	4.0F

FEBRUARY

Day	Slack Water Time h.m.	Maximum Current Time h.m.	Maximum Current Vel. knots
1	0152	0511	4.3E
Tu	0822	1108	3.7F
	1412	1735	4.2E
	2047	2336	3.7F
2	0244	0605	4.0E
W	0921	1205	3.3F
	1507	1828	3.8E
	2141		
3		0031	3.4F
Th	0338	0702	3.8E
	1022	1303	2.9F
	1603	1926	3.4E
	2238		
4		0129	3.0F
F	0434	0759	3.5E
	1125	1407	2.5F
	1704	2025	3.0E
	2337		
5		0230	2.7F
Sa	0532	0859	3.3E
	1229	1517	2.3F
	1806	2122	2.7E
6	0038	0335	2.5F
Su	0631	0958	3.2E
	1330	1625	2.2F
	1909	2223	2.6E
7	0137	0437	2.4F
M	0727	1053	3.2E
	1426	1726	2.3F
	2009	2317	2.6E
8	0232	0535	2.4F
Tu	0820	1148	3.2E
	1517	1815	2.4F
	2101		
9		0008	2.7E
W	0322	0623	2.5F
	0907	1233	3.3E
	1602	1900	2.5F
	2146		
10		0055	2.8E
Th	0407	0700	2.5F
	0950	1317	3.4E
	1643	1937	2.6F
	2226		
11		0137	2.9E
F	0448	0737	2.6F
	1029	1358	3.5E
	1720	2008	2.7F
	2303		
12		0217	3.0E
Sa	0526	0808	2.7F
	1107	1435	3.5E
	1755	2035	2.8F
	2338		
13		0256	3.0E
Su	0602	0842	2.7F
	1143	1513	3.4E
	1827	2105	2.8F
14	0011	0331	3.1E
M	0637	0919	2.8F
	1219	1549	3.3E
	1858	2141	2.9F
15	0046	0407	3.1E
Tu	0712	0956	2.8F
	1256	1622	3.2E
	1929	2216	2.9F
16	0121	0443	3.1E
W	0749	1037	2.7F
	1334	1651	3.1E
	2003	2257	2.8F
17	0158	0516	3.1E
Th	0831	1120	2.6F
	1416	1723	2.9E
	2041	2340	2.8F
18	0240	0557	3.1E
F	0918	1208	2.5F
	1502	1808	2.8E
	2125		
19		0029	2.7F
Sa	0328	0648	3.0E
	1013	1301	2.4F
	1556	1903	2.6E
	2218		
20		0122	2.7F
Su	0423	0751	3.0E
	1115	1358	2.3F
	1657	2015	2.6E
	2318		
21		0221	2.7F
M	0525	0901	3.2E
	1221	1501	2.4F
	1804	2126	2.7E
22	0026	0323	2.8F
Tu	0630	1007	3.4E
	1327	1605	2.6F
	1910	2235	3.0E
23	0133	0426	3.1F
W	0734	1108	3.8E
	1428	1709	3.0F
	2014	2334	3.4E
24	0238	0529	3.4F
Th	0836	1207	4.2E
	1524	1809	3.4F
	2113		
25		0032	3.8E
F	0337	0629	3.8F
	0934	1259	4.5E
	1617	1905	3.8F
	2207		
26		0126	4.2E
Sa	0432	0725	4.0F
	1028	1352	4.7E
	1707	1955	4.1F
	2259		
27		0217	4.5E
Su	0526	0817	4.2F
	1120	1441	4.8E
	1755	2045	4.2F
	2349		
28		0307	4.6E
M	0617	0906	4.2F
	1211	1530	4.7E
	1843	2133	4.2F

Time meridian 75° W. 0000 is midnight. 1200 is noon.

F-Flood, Dir. 295° True E-Ebb, Dir. 100° True

MARCH

Day	Slack Water Time h.m.	Maximum Current Time h.m.	Vel. knots	Day	Slack Water Time h.m.	Maximum Current Time h.m.	Vel. knots
1	0037	0357	4.6E	16	0013	0338	3.5E
Tu	0708	0957	4.0F	W	0645	0932	3.0F
	1300	1619	4.4E		1232	1554	3.3E
	1930	2219	4.0F		1856	2147	3.1F
2	0125	0446	4.4E	17	0049	0412	3.5E
W	0800	1045	3.6F	Th	0723	1013	3.0F
	1349	1709	4.0E		1311	1627	3.2E
	2019	2308	3.6F		1931	2228	3.1F
3	0214	0536	4.0E	18	0128	0445	3.5E
Th	0854	1136	3.2F	F	0805	1056	2.9F
	1439	1802	3.6E		1353	1703	3.0E
	2109	2356	3.2F		2011	2311	3.0F
4	0304	0631	3.7E	19	0211	0530	3.4E
F	0951	1229	2.8F	Sa	0853	1143	2.7F
	1532	1854	3.1E		1441	1746	2.9E
	2203				2059		
5		0047	2.8F	20		0003	2.9F
Sa	0356	0727	3.3E	Su	0301	0621	3.3E
	1051	1326	2.3F		0948	1238	2.6F
	1629	1950	2.7E		1536	1847	2.7E
	2302				2155		
6		0146	2.4F	21		0058	2.8F
Su	0451	0823	3.0E	M	0359	0729	3.2E
	1153	1435	2.1F		1052	1335	2.5F
	1730	2051	2.4E		1639	1958	2.7E
					2301		
7	0004	0250	2.1F	22		0159	2.7F
M	0550	0921	2.8E	Tu	0504	0842	3.2E
	1255	1548	2.0F		1201	1441	2.5F
	1833	2151	2.3E		1747	2113	2.8E
8	0106	0358	2.0F	23	0014	0304	2.8F
Tu	0649	1020	2.8E	W	0613	0948	3.4E
	1353	1649	2.0F		1308	1549	2.7F
	1934	2248	2.4E		1854	2218	3.1E
9	0204	0503	2.1F	24	0125	0412	3.0F
W	0745	1114	2.9E	Th	0720	1052	3.7E
	1444	1741	2.2F		1410	1654	3.1F
	2027	2339	2.5E		1958	2319	3.5E
10	0255	0554	2.3F	25	0229	0519	3.3F
Th	0836	1203	3.1E	F	0823	1151	4.1E
	1530	1826	2.4F		1506	1755	3.5F
	2113				2056		
11		0026	2.8E	26		0017	4.0E
F	0341	0633	2.4F	Sa	0327	0617	3.7F
	0921	1248	3.3E		0921	1243	4.4E
	1610	1901	2.6F		1558	1849	3.8F
	2153				2150		
12		0109	3.0E	27		0109	4.4E
Sa	0422	0710	2.6F	Su	0421	0712	3.9F
	1002	1327	3.4E		1014	1333	4.5E
	1647	1934	2.7F		1647	1938	4.0F
	2230				2239		
13		0149	3.2E	28		0159	4.6E
Su	0500	0742	2.8F	M	0512	0804	4.0F
	1041	1406	3.5E		1104	1422	4.5E
	1721	2003	2.9F		1733	2024	4.1F
	2305				2327		
14		0226	3.3E	29		0248	4.7E
M	0535	0815	2.9F	Tu	0601	0849	4.0F
	1118	1443	3.5E		1152	1510	4.4E
	1753	2035	3.0F		1819	2110	4.0F
	2339						
15		0303	3.4E	30	0012	0334	4.5E
Tu	0610	0854	3.0F	W	0650	0935	3.8F
	1155	1518	3.4E		1239	1557	4.1E
	1824	2112	3.1F		1904	2153	3.7F
				31	0057	0420	4.3E
				Th	0738	1021	3.4F
					1325	1642	3.7E
					1950	2236	3.4F

APRIL

Day	Slack Water Time h.m.	Maximum Current Time h.m.	Vel. knots	Day	Slack Water Time h.m.	Maximum Current Time h.m.	Vel. knots
1	0142	0508	3.9E	16	0103	0424	3.8E
F	0827	1107	3.0F	Sa	0745	1035	3.1F
	1412	1731	3.2E		1336	1646	3.2E
	2038	2323	2.9F		1950	2251	3.2F
2	0228	0559	3.5E	17	0150	0514	3.7E
Sa	0919	1156	2.6F	Su	0835	1124	3.0F
	1501	1822	2.8E		1427	1737	3.0E
	2129				2043	2344	3.0F
3		0012	2.5F	18	0243	0611	3.5E
Su	0317	0650	3.1E	M	0932	1220	2.8F
	1015	1247	2.2F		1524	1841	2.9E
	1554	1916	2.4E		2144		
	2226						
4		0104	2.2F	19		0041	2.9F
M	0409	0746	2.8E	Tu	0344	0716	3.4E
	1114	1348	2.0F		1036	1321	2.7F
	1652	2017	2.2E		1628	1950	2.9E
	2329				2254		
5		0203	1.9F	20		0145	2.8F
Tu	0506	0844	2.6E	W	0450	0826	3.4E
	1214	1455	1.9F		1143	1426	2.8F
	1753	2116	2.2E		1734	2059	3.1E
6	0032	0310	1.8F	21	0008	0252	2.8F
W	0606	0942	2.6E	Th	0559	0932	3.5E
	1311	1601	1.9F		1249	1533	2.9F
	1852	2213	2.3E		1840	2204	3.4E
7	0131	0418	1.9F	22	0117	0404	3.0F
Th	0705	1037	2.7E	F	0706	1033	3.7E
	1403	1656	2.1F		1350	1640	3.2F
	1946	2305	2.5E		1942	2303	3.8E
8	0223	0509	2.1F	23	0219	0510	3.3F
F	0758	1126	2.9E	Sa	0809	1132	3.9E
	1449	1739	2.3F		1446	1739	3.5F
	2032	2351	2.8E		2038	2358	4.1E
9	0309	0554	2.4F	24	0316	0609	3.5F
Sa	0846	1211	3.1E	Su	0906	1224	4.1E
	1530	1816	2.6F		1537	1830	3.7F
	2113				2130		
10		0033	3.1E	25		0051	4.4E
Su	0350	0633	2.6F	M	0408	0702	3.7F
	0930	1254	3.2E		0958	1315	4.2E
	1608	1850	2.8F		1625	1920	3.8F
	2151				2218		
11		0115	3.4E	26		0138	4.5E
M	0429	0711	2.8F	Tu	0457	0747	3.7F
	1011	1334	3.4E		1047	1402	4.1E
	1642	1925	3.0F		1711	2003	3.8F
	2228				2303		
12		0153	3.6E	27		0224	4.5E
Tu	0506	0747	3.0F	W	0545	0834	3.6F
	1050	1411	3.4E		1133	1447	3.9E
	1716	2002	3.2F		1755	2046	3.6F
	2304				2347		
13		0231	3.7E	28		0310	4.3E
W	0542	0824	3.2F	Th	0631	0916	3.4F
	1129	1447	3.4E		1218	1530	3.6E
	1749	2039	3.3F		1839	2124	3.4F
	2341						
14		0307	3.8E	29	0029	0356	4.0E
Th	0620	0905	3.2F	F	0716	0957	3.1F
	1209	1522	3.4E		1301	1616	3.3E
	1825	2120	3.3F		1922	2205	3.0F
15	0020	0345	3.9E	30	0111	0439	3.7E
F	0700	0948	3.2F	Sa	0801	1039	2.8F
	1251	1603	3.3E		1346	1705	2.9E
	1904	2204	3.3F		2008	2248	2.7F

Time meridian 75° W. 0000 is midnight. 1200 is noon.

THE RACE, LONG ISLAND SOUND, 1983

F-Flood, Dir. 295° True E-Ebb, Dir. 100° True

MAY

Day	Slack Water Time h.m.	Maximum Current Time h.m.	Vel. knots
1	0154	0528	3.3E
Su	0849	1124	2.5F
	1432	1753	2.6E
	2057	2337	2.3F
2	0239	0616	3.0E
M	0939	1215	2.2F
	1521	1844	2.3E
	2151		
3		0025	2.0F
Tu	0329	0707	2.7E
	1032	1306	2.0F
	1615	1939	2.2E
	2251		
4		0122	1.8F
W	0423	0804	2.5E
	1128	1402	1.9F
	1711	2037	2.2E
	2352		
5		0221	1.8F
Th	0521	0901	2.5E
	1223	1501	2.0F
	1806	2133	2.3E
6	0051	0322	1.8F
F	0619	0956	2.6E
	1314	1555	2.1F
	1858	2224	2.6E
7	0143	0418	2.0F
Sa	0715	1045	2.7E
	1400	1644	2.3F
	1945	2313	2.9E
8	0231	0508	2.3F
Su	0805	1132	2.9E
	1443	1725	2.6F
	2029	2358	3.2E
9	0314	0551	2.6F
M	0852	1217	3.1E
	1522	1807	2.9F
	2110		
10		0039	3.5E
Tu	0355	0633	2.8F
	0937	1259	3.2E
	1600	1846	3.1F
	2151		
11		0121	3.8E
W	0435	0715	3.1F
	1019	1337	3.3E
	1637	1928	3.3F
	2231		
12		0200	4.0E
Th	0514	0759	3.3F
	1102	1418	3.4E
	1716	2011	3.5F
	2312		
13		0241	4.1E
F	0556	0842	3.4F
	1146	1459	3.4E
	1758	2054	3.5F
	2356		
14		0322	4.2E
Sa	0641	0928	3.4F
	1232	1544	3.4E
	1844	2141	3.5F
15	0043	0410	4.1E
Su	0729	1017	3.4F
	1322	1636	3.4E
	1935	2232	3.4F

Day	Slack Water Time h.m.	Maximum Current Time h.m.	Vel. knots
16	0135	0504	4.0E
M	0821	1110	3.3F
	1416	1733	3.3E
	2033	2327	3.2F
17	0231	0602	3.8E
Tu	0919	1205	3.2F
	1514	1834	3.2E
	2138		
18		0029	3.1F
W	0332	0706	3.7E
	1021	1306	3.1F
	1616	1939	3.3E
	2248		
19		0132	2.9F
Th	0437	0810	3.6E
	1125	1411	3.1F
	1720	2044	3.4E
	2358		
20		0241	2.9F
F	0545	0913	3.6E
	1228	1517	3.1F
	1823	2145	3.6E
21	0104	0352	3.0F
Sa	0650	1013	3.7E
	1328	1621	3.3F
	1923	2244	3.9E
22	0205	0457	3.2F
Su	0752	1110	3.7E
	1423	1719	3.4F
	2018	2339	4.1E
23	0302	0554	3.3F
M	0849	1203	3.8E
	1515	1814	3.5F
	2109		
24		0031	4.3E
Tu	0354	0648	3.4F
	0941	1252	3.7E
	1603	1901	3.5F
	2156		
25		0118	4.3E
W	0442	0737	3.3F
	1029	1341	3.6E
	1649	1944	3.4F
	2240		
26		0205	4.2E
Th	0528	0818	3.2F
	1114	1426	3.4E
	1733	2022	3.2F
	2322		
27		0249	4.0E
F	0612	0858	3.0F
	1157	1509	3.2E
	1816	2100	3.0F
28	0003	0332	3.8E
Sa	0655	0936	2.8F
	1239	1553	3.0E
	1858	2141	2.8F
29	0042	0416	3.5E
Su	0737	1014	2.6F
	1321	1639	2.7E
	1941	2220	2.5F
30	0123	0459	3.2E
M	0820	1055	2.4F
	1404	1723	2.5E
	2027	2305	2.3F
31	0206	0543	2.9E
Tu	0904	1136	2.3F
	1449	1812	2.3E
	2117	2352	2.0F

JUNE

Day	Slack Water Time h.m.	Maximum Current Time h.m.	Vel. knots
1	0252	0633	2.7E
W	0950	1226	2.2F
	1537	1904	2.3E
	2211		
2		0043	1.9F
Th	0342	0722	2.6E
	1039	1317	2.1F
	1627	1957	2.3E
	2308		
3		0138	1.8F
F	0436	0815	2.5E
	1129	1408	2.1F
	1718	2048	2.4E
4	0004	0232	1.9F
Sa	0532	0908	2.5E
	1219	1459	2.2F
	1809	2141	2.6E
5	0058	0327	2.0F
Su	0628	0959	2.6E
	1306	1550	2.4F
	1857	2230	2.9E
6	0148	0421	2.2F
M	0721	1050	2.7E
	1352	1639	2.6F
	1944	2316	3.2E
7	0235	0509	2.5F
Tu	0813	1134	2.9E
	1435	1725	2.9F
	2030		
8		0002	3.6E
W	0320	0558	2.8F
	0902	1222	3.1E
	1519	1811	3.2F
	2115		
9		0048	3.9E
Th	0404	0646	3.1F
	0949	1308	3.3E
	1603	1857	3.4F
	2201		
10		0131	4.1E
F	0449	0731	3.3F
	1037	1354	3.5E
	1649	1944	3.6F
	2248		
11		0217	4.3E
Sa	0535	0820	3.5F
	1125	1440	3.6E
	1737	2034	3.7F
	2337		
12		0308	4.4E
Su	0623	0909	3.6F
	1216	1530	3.7E
	1829	2125	3.7F
13	0028	0356	4.4E
M	0713	1000	3.7F
	1308	1622	3.7E
	1924	2218	3.7F
14	0122	0451	4.3E
Tu	0807	1055	3.6F
	1402	1720	3.7E
	2024	2315	3.5F
15	0219	0549	4.1E
W	0903	1149	3.5F
	1500	1821	3.7E
	2128		

Day	Slack Water Time h.m.	Maximum Current Time h.m.	Vel. knots
16		0012	3.3F
Th	0319	0647	3.9E
	1002	1250	3.4F
	1600	1922	3.7E
	2235		
17		0118	3.1F
F	0422	0748	3.7E
	1103	1353	3.3F
	1701	2025	3.7E
	2342		
18		0227	3.0F
Sa	0526	0849	3.6E
	1204	1458	3.3F
	1802	2124	3.8E
19	0047	0335	3.0F
Su	0631	0950	3.5E
	1303	1601	3.3F
	1901	2224	3.9E
20	0148	0441	3.0F
M	0733	1047	3.4E
	1400	1700	3.3F
	1956	2319	4.0E
21	0245	0540	3.0F
Tu	0830	1141	3.4E
	1453	1753	3.2F
	2048		
22		0010	4.0E
W	0337	0631	3.0F
	0923	1230	3.3E
	1543	1842	3.2F
	2135		
23		0059	4.0E
Th	0426	0720	3.0F
	1012	1321	3.2E
	1630	1925	3.0F
	2219		
24		0144	3.9E
F	0511	0803	2.9F
	1056	1406	3.1E
	1714	2003	2.9F
	2300		
25		0228	3.8E
Sa	0554	0842	2.8F
	1138	1449	2.9E
	1756	2039	2.7F
	2339		
26		0309	3.6E
Su	0634	0917	2.7F
	1217	1531	2.8E
	1837	2116	2.6F
27	0017	0350	3.4E
M	0712	0951	2.6F
	1256	1613	2.7E
	1917	2153	2.4F
28	0056	0430	3.2E
Tu	0750	1029	2.5F
	1336	1655	2.6E
	1959	2236	2.3F
29	0136	0511	3.0E
W	0829	1107	2.4F
	1416	1737	2.5E
	2042	2321	2.2F
30	0219	0554	2.8E
Th	0908	1149	2.4F
	1459	1825	2.4E
	2130		

Time meridian 75° W. 0000 is midnight. 1200 is noon.

F-Flood, Dir. 295° True E-Ebb, Dir. 100° True

JULY

Day	Slack Water Time h.m.	Maximum Current Time h.m.	Vel. knots
1		0008	2.1F
F	0304	0639	2.6E
	0950	1234	2.3F
	1543	1913	2.4E
	2221		
2		0056	2.0F
Sa	0353	0727	2.5E
	1035	1323	2.3F
	1631	2002	2.5E
	2315		
3		0149	2.0F
Su	0446	0816	2.4E
	1122	1412	2.4F
	1720	2055	2.7E
4	0010	0242	2.1F
M	0542	0913	2.5E
	1212	1504	2.5F
	1811	2146	2.9E
5	0104	0337	2.2F
Tu	0639	1004	2.6E
	1302	1555	2.7F
	1902	2237	3.2E
6	0157	0433	2.5F
W	0735	1057	2.8E
	1353	1648	2.9F
	1954	2328	3.6E
7	0248	0526	2.8F
Th	0829	1151	3.0E
	1445	1739	3.2F
	2046		
8		0019	3.9E
F	0338	0617	3.1F
	0922	1239	3.3E
	1536	1832	3.5F
	2137		
9		0109	4.2E
Sa	0427	0709	3.4F
	1015	1330	3.6E
	1628	1924	3.8F
	2229		
10		0158	4.5E
Su	0516	0801	3.7F
	1106	1424	3.8E
	1722	2015	3.9F
	2321		
11		0249	4.6E
M	0605	0851	3.9F
	1158	1515	4.0E
	1816	2108	4.0F
12	0014	0341	4.7E
Tu	0656	0944	4.0F
	1251	1607	4.1E
	1912	2203	3.9F
13	0108	0435	4.6E
W	0748	1035	3.9F
	1345	1704	4.1E
	2011	2259	3.8F
14	0204	0530	4.4E
Th	0843	1130	3.8F
	1440	1802	4.0E
	2112	2357	3.5F
15	0301	0625	4.1E
F	0939	1228	3.6F
	1537	1900	3.9E
	2215		

Day	Slack Water Time h.m.	Maximum Current Time h.m.	Vel. knots
16		0057	3.2F
Sa	0401	0726	3.8E
	1037	1327	3.4F
	1636	1959	3.8E
	2320		
17		0205	3.0F
Su	0504	0824	3.5E
	1138	1431	3.2F
	1736	2100	3.7E
18	0025	0315	2.8F
M	0607	0923	3.3E
	1238	1536	3.0F
	1835	2159	3.7E
19	0127	0418	2.7F
Tu	0710	1025	3.1E
	1336	1638	2.9F
	1932	2256	3.7E
20	0226	0521	2.7F
W	0810	1118	3.0E
	1432	1735	2.9F
	2025	2350	3.7E
21	0319	0617	2.7F
Th	0905	1211	3.0E
	1524	1824	2.8F
	2114		
22		0037	3.7E
F	0407	0704	2.7F
	0953	1300	2.9E
	1611	1909	2.8F
	2158		
23		0124	3.6E
Sa	0451	0747	2.7F
	1036	1346	2.9E
	1655	1947	2.7F
	2239		
24		0207	3.6E
Su	0532	0824	2.7F
	1116	1427	2.9E
	1736	2021	2.6F
	2317		
25		0247	3.5E
M	0609	0851	2.7F
	1153	1508	2.9E
	1815	2056	2.6F
	2354		
26		0325	3.4E
Tu	0645	0925	2.6F
	1228	1547	2.8E
	1852	2132	2.5F
27	0031	0403	3.2E
W	0719	0958	2.6F
	1304	1626	2.8E
	1930	2208	2.5F
28	0109	0440	3.1E
Th	0753	1035	2.6F
	1341	1704	2.7E
	2009	2249	2.4F
29	0148	0517	2.9E
F	0827	1114	2.5F
	1419	1743	2.7E
	2050	2334	2.3F
30	0229	0553	2.7E
Sa	0904	1157	2.5F
	1500	1826	2.7E
	2137		
31		0021	2.2F
Su	0315	0634	2.6E
	0945	1243	2.5F
	1545	1909	2.7E
	2228		

AUGUST

Day	Slack Water Time h.m.	Maximum Current Time h.m.	Vel. knots
1		0110	2.1F
M	0405	0725	2.4E
	1032	1332	2.5F
	1634	2003	2.8E
	2325		
2		0203	2.1F
Tu	0501	0818	2.4E
	1125	1425	2.5F
	1729	2104	2.9E
3	0024	0303	2.2F
W	0602	0924	2.5E
	1222	1520	2.7F
	1826	2203	3.2E
4	0123	0402	2.4F
Th	0703	1025	2.7E
	1321	1617	2.9F
	1925	2300	3.5E
5	0220	0457	2.7F
F	0803	1122	3.0E
	1421	1716	3.2F
	2022	2355	3.9E
6	0314	0554	3.1F
Sa	0900	1220	3.4E
	1518	1812	3.6F
	2118		
7		0049	4.3E
Su	0406	0650	3.5F
	0955	1312	3.8E
	1614	1907	3.9F
	2213		
8		0140	4.6E
M	0456	0741	3.9F
	1048	1405	4.2E
	1708	2000	4.1F
	2306		
9		0232	4.8E
Tu	0546	0834	4.1F
	1139	1458	4.4E
	1802	2054	4.2F
	2359		
10		0324	4.8E
W	0636	0925	4.2F
	1231	1550	4.5E
	1857	2147	4.1F
11	0052	0413	4.7E
Th	0726	1016	4.1F
	1323	1642	4.5E
	1953	2239	3.9F
12	0145	0507	4.4E
F	0818	1107	3.9F
	1415	1736	4.3E
	2051	2336	3.6F
13	0240	0602	4.0E
Sa	0912	1202	3.6F
	1510	1834	4.0E
	2151		
14		0035	3.2F
Su	0337	0657	3.6E
	1009	1258	3.3F
	1606	1930	3.7E
	2255		
15		0139	2.8F
M	0437	0758	3.2E
	1110	1402	2.9F
	1705	2031	3.5E

Day	Slack Water Time h.m.	Maximum Current Time h.m.	Vel. knots
16	0000	0248	2.5F
Tu	0540	0857	2.9E
	1212	1506	2.7F
	1806	2133	3.4E
17	0103	0359	2.4F
W	0645	0958	2.8E
	1313	1615	2.6F
	1905	2231	3.3E
18	0202	0503	2.4F
Th	0747	1057	2.7E
	1411	1712	2.5F
	2001	2325	3.3E
19	0256	0554	2.5F
F	0842	1151	2.8E
	1504	1807	2.6F
	2051		
20		0016	3.4E
Sa	0343	0643	2.6F
	0930	1236	2.9E
	1551	1849	2.6F
	2136		
21		0059	3.4E
Su	0426	0724	2.6F
	1011	1321	3.0E
	1634	1926	2.6F
	2216		
22		0141	3.5E
M	0505	0757	2.7F
	1048	1402	3.0E
	1713	1959	2.7F
	2254		
23		0220	3.5E
Tu	0540	0824	2.7F
	1123	1441	3.1E
	1750	2031	2.7F
	2330		
24		0257	3.4E
W	0613	0853	2.8F
	1157	1518	3.1E
	1825	2104	2.7F
25	0006	0334	3.3E
Th	0645	0925	2.8F
	1231	1554	3.1E
	1900	2141	2.7F
26	0042	0408	3.1E
F	0715	1001	2.8F
	1305	1629	3.0E
	1936	2220	2.6F
27	0119	0441	3.0E
Sa	0748	1042	2.7F
	1341	1702	3.0E
	2015	2301	2.5F
28	0159	0514	2.8E
Su	0823	1123	2.7F
	1420	1736	2.9E
	2059	2346	2.4F
29	0242	0549	2.6E
M	0905	1206	2.6F
	1505	1823	2.9E
	2150		
30		0038	2.3F
Tu	0332	0636	2.5E
	0953	1257	2.5F
	1556	1924	2.9E
	2248		
31		0133	2.2F
W	0430	0742	2.4E
	1050	1352	2.5F
	1655	2027	3.0E
	2352		

Time meridian 75° W. 0000 is midnight. 1200 is noon.

THE RACE, LONG ISLAND SOUND, 1983

F-Flood, Dir. 295° True E-Ebb, Dir. 100° True

SEPTEMBER

Day	Slack Water Time h.m.	Maximum Current Time h.m.	Vel. knots
1		0232	2.3F
Th	0533	0855	2.5E
	1155	1454	2.6F
	1758	2137	3.2E
2	0056	0335	2.5F
F	0639	1002	2.7E
	1302	1555	2.9F
	1903	2237	3.5E
3	0157	0437	2.8F
Sa	0742	1106	3.2E
	1406	1700	3.2F
	2005	2336	3.9E
4	0253	0538	3.2F
Su	0841	1201	3.6E
	1506	1758	3.6F
	2103		
5		0030	4.3E
M	0346	0633	3.7F
	0936	1256	4.1E
	1602	1852	4.0F
	2158		
6		0123	4.6E
Tu	0436	0725	4.0F
	1028	1347	4.5E
	1655	1946	4.2F
	2251		
7		0212	4.8E
W	0525	0814	4.2F
	1119	1439	4.7E
	1748	2037	4.3F
	2342		
8		0302	4.8E
Th	0613	0903	4.3F
	1208	1528	4.7E
	1840	2128	4.2F
9	0033	0353	4.6E
F	0702	0951	4.2F
	1258	1619	4.6E
	1933	2219	3.9F
10	0124	0443	4.2E
Sa	0752	1042	3.9F
	1348	1712	4.3E
	2027	2311	3.5F
11	0216	0536	3.8E
Su	0844	1133	3.5F
	1439	1805	3.9E
	2125		
12		0005	3.0F
M	0310	0631	3.3E
	0940	1227	3.0F
	1533	1901	3.6E
	2226		
13		0106	2.6F
Tu	0409	0729	2.9E
	1040	1326	2.6F
	1631	2001	3.2E
	2330		
14		0217	2.3F
W	0511	0828	2.6E
	1144	1432	2.3F
	1731	2102	3.0E
15	0033	0329	2.2F
Th	0615	0930	2.5E
	1248	1546	2.2F
	1833	2201	3.0E

Day	Slack Water Time h.m.	Maximum Current Time h.m.	Vel. knots
16	0132	0432	2.2F
F	0718	1031	2.5E
	1347	1650	2.2F
	1930	2256	3.0E
17	0225	0525	2.3F
Sa	0812	1122	2.7E
	1440	1739	2.4F
	2022	2345	3.2E
18	0312	0611	2.5F
Su	0858	1211	2.9E
	1526	1824	2.5F
	2108		
19		0031	3.3E
M	0353	0650	2.6F
	0939	1252	3.1E
	1608	1859	2.6F
	2149		
20		0112	3.4E
Tu	0431	0721	2.8F
	1015	1333	3.2E
	1647	1931	2.8F
	2227		
21		0149	3.4E
W	0506	0750	2.9F
	1049	1409	3.3E
	1723	2003	2.8F
	2304		
22		0228	3.4E
Th	0538	0818	2.9F
	1123	1447	3.4E
	1757	2037	2.9F
	2340		
23		0303	3.3E
F	0609	0853	3.0F
	1156	1521	3.4E
	1831	2112	2.9F
24	0016	0337	3.2E
Sa	0639	0930	3.0F
	1230	1553	3.4E
	1906	2153	2.8F
25	0053	0406	3.0E
Su	0712	1007	2.9F
	1307	1630	3.3E
	1946	2235	2.7F
26	0133	0439	2.9E
M	0749	1050	2.8F
	1347	1705	3.2E
	2030	2320	2.6F
27	0217	0520	2.7E
Tu	0833	1137	2.7F
	1433	1754	3.1E
	2122		
28		0011	2.5F
W	0309	0612	2.6E
	0926	1231	2.6F
	1528	1853	3.0E
	2221		
29		0106	2.4F
Th	0409	0723	2.5E
	1029	1330	2.5F
	1631	2007	3.0E
	2327		
30		0209	2.4F
F	0514	0840	2.6E
	1140	1433	2.6F
	1738	2115	3.2E

OCTOBER

Day	Slack Water Time h.m.	Maximum Current Time h.m.	Vel. knots
1	0034	0314	2.6F
Sa	0621	0949	2.9E
	1251	1540	2.9F
	1846	2218	3.5E
2	0136	0418	2.9F
Su	0725	1050	3.4E
	1356	1644	3.2F
	1950	2318	3.9E
3	0233	0519	3.4F
M	0823	1145	3.9E
	1456	1745	3.6F
	2049		
4		0013	4.2E
Tu	0325	0614	3.8F
	0918	1239	4.4E
	1550	1840	3.9F
	2144		
5		0104	4.5E
W	0415	0705	4.1F
	1009	1330	4.7E
	1642	1931	4.1F
	2235		
6		0153	4.6E
Th	0503	0753	4.2F
	1057	1419	4.8E
	1733	2021	4.1F
	2325		
7		0242	4.5E
F	0550	0840	4.2F
	1145	1508	4.8E
	1822	2110	4.0F
8	0013	0331	4.3E
Sa	0637	0925	4.0F
	1232	1554	4.6E
	1912	2157	3.7F
9	0102	0417	3.9E
Su	0725	1014	3.6F
	1319	1645	4.2E
	2004	2245	3.3F
10	0151	0508	3.5E
M	0815	1102	3.2F
	1407	1736	3.8E
	2057	2336	2.9F
11	0243	0602	3.0E
Tu	0910	1153	2.7F
	1458	1831	3.3E
	2155		
12		0034	2.4F
W	0338	0658	2.6E
	1009	1250	2.3F
	1553	1929	3.0E
	2255		
13		0135	2.1F
Th	0437	0759	2.4E
	1113	1353	2.0F
	1652	2027	2.8E
	2356		
14		0248	2.0F
F	0540	0859	2.3E
	1218	1502	1.9F
	1753	2127	2.7E
15	0054	0351	2.1F
Sa	0639	0956	2.4E
	1317	1609	2.0F
	1852	2220	2.8E

Day	Slack Water Time h.m.	Maximum Current Time h.m.	Vel. knots
16	0146	0447	2.2F
Su	0733	1049	2.6E
	1410	1702	2.2F
	1946	2311	2.9E
17	0233	0532	2.4F
M	0819	1139	2.9E
	1456	1745	2.4F
	2033	2354	3.1E
18	0315	0607	2.6F
Tu	0900	1220	3.2E
	1538	1824	2.6F
	2117		
19		0039	3.2E
W	0352	0639	2.8F
	0937	1259	3.4E
	1616	1858	2.8F
	2157		
20		0118	3.3E
Th	0427	0711	2.9F
	1013	1338	3.6E
	1653	1931	2.9F
	2235		
21		0155	3.3E
F	0500	0744	3.1F
	1048	1414	3.7E
	1728	2009	3.0F
	2312		
22		0231	3.3E
Sa	0532	0820	3.1F
	1123	1449	3.7E
	1804	2046	3.1F
	2350		
23		0305	3.2E
Su	0606	0859	3.2F
	1159	1526	3.7E
	1841	2127	3.0F
24	0030	0340	3.1E
M	0642	0942	3.1F
	1239	1603	3.6E
	1922	2210	3.0F
25	0112	0419	3.0E
Tu	0724	1026	3.0F
	1322	1642	3.5E
	2009	2301	2.8F
26	0200	0504	2.8E
W	0813	1115	2.9F
	1412	1738	3.4E
	2102	2352	2.7F
27	0254	0605	2.7E
Th	0911	1210	2.7F
	1510	1841	3.3E
	2202		
28		0050	2.6F
F	0354	0715	2.7E
	1018	1313	2.7F
	1614	1950	3.2E
	2307		
29		0151	2.7F
Sa	0459	0826	2.9E
	1131	1417	2.7F
	1723	2057	3.3E
30	0013	0256	2.8F
Su	0605	0930	3.2E
	1242	1526	2.9F
	1831	2201	3.5E
31	0115	0402	3.1F
M	0707	1031	3.6E
	1346	1633	3.2F
	1935	2259	3.8E

Time meridian 75° W. 0000 is midnight. 1200 is noon.

F-Flood, Dir. 295° True E-Ebb, Dir. 100° True

NOVEMBER

Day	Slack Water Time h.m.	Maximum Current Time h.m.	Vel. knots
1	0212	0503	3.5F
Tu	0805	1129	4.1E
	1444	1735	3.5F
	2034	2354	4.1E
2	0305	0557	3.8F
W	0859	1222	4.4E
	1538	1829	3.7F
	2128		
3		0045	4.2E
Th	0354	0646	3.9F
	0949	1311	4.7E
	1629	1918	3.9F
	2219		
4		0133	4.2E
F	0442	0735	4.0F
	1036	1400	4.7E
	1718	2005	3.8F
	2308		
5		0222	4.1E
Sa	0528	0818	3.9F
	1122	1447	4.6E
	1806	2052	3.7F
	2355		
6		0308	3.9E
Su	0614	0904	3.6F
	1207	1533	4.3E
	1853	2137	3.4F
7	0041	0356	3.5E
M	0701	0947	3.3F
	1251	1619	4.0E
	1941	2223	3.1F
8	0127	0445	3.2E
Tu	0749	1033	2.9F
	1336	1708	3.6E
	2030	2309	2.7F
9	0216	0533	2.8E
W	0840	1120	2.5F
	1424	1759	3.2E
	2122	2357	2.4F
10	0306	0629	2.5E
Th	0936	1210	2.1F
	1514	1853	2.9E
	2216		
11		0051	2.1F
F	0401	0723	2.3E
	1037	1306	1.9F
	1609	1948	2.6E
	2312		
12		0150	2.0F
Sa	0457	0822	2.3E
	1139	1408	1.8F
	1707	2042	2.6E
13	0007	0251	2.0F
Su	0553	0916	2.4E
	1238	1514	1.8F
	1805	2139	2.6E
14	0059	0346	2.1F
M	0645	1009	2.6E
	1331	1609	2.0F
	1901	2228	2.7E
15	0146	0433	2.3F
Tu	0733	1100	2.9E
	1419	1659	2.2F
	1952	2315	2.8E

Day	Slack Water Time h.m.	Maximum Current Time h.m.	Vel. knots
16	0230	0513	2.5F
W	0816	1143	3.2E
	1503	1742	2.5F
	2039		
17		0001	3.0E
Th	0309	0554	2.8F
	0856	1226	3.4E
	1543	1822	2.7F
	2122		
18		0043	3.1E
F	0346	0630	3.0F
	0935	1304	3.7E
	1622	1859	2.9F
	2204		
19		0124	3.2E
Sa	0422	0710	3.1F
	1014	1345	3.8E
	1700	1941	3.1F
	2245		
20		0203	3.2E
Su	0459	0751	3.3F
	1053	1421	3.9E
	1739	2021	3.2F
	2327		
21		0240	3.2E
M	0537	0833	3.3F
	1134	1504	4.0E
	1820	2105	3.2F
22	0010	0321	3.2E
Tu	0620	0918	3.4F
	1218	1545	4.0E
	1904	2152	3.2F
23	0056	0408	3.2E
W	0707	1007	3.3F
	1306	1632	3.9E
	1952	2239	3.2F
24	0146	0458	3.1E
Th	0801	1058	3.2F
	1358	1727	3.7E
	2046	2336	3.1F
25	0241	0559	3.1E
F	0901	1153	3.0F
	1457	1828	3.6E
	2145		
26		0031	3.0F
Sa	0341	0704	3.1E
	1009	1257	2.9F
	1600	1933	3.5E
	2247		
27		0134	3.0F
Su	0443	0808	3.3E
	1120	1402	2.8F
	1707	2038	3.5E
	2351		
28		0238	3.1F
M	0547	0912	3.5E
	1229	1512	2.9F
	1814	2139	3.5E
29	0052	0343	3.2F
Tu	0648	1013	3.8E
	1332	1620	3.1F
	1918	2239	3.7E
30	0150	0443	3.4F
W	0746	1110	4.1E
	1431	1721	3.3F
	2018	2334	3.8E

DECEMBER

Day	Slack Water Time h.m.	Maximum Current Time h.m.	Vel. knots
1	0244	0539	3.6F
Th	0840	1203	4.3E
	1525	1816	3.4F
	2113		
2		0027	3.8E
F	0335	0630	3.7F
	0930	1255	4.5E
	1616	1909	3.5F
	2204		
3		0116	3.8E
Sa	0424	0717	3.6F
	1017	1340	4.4E
	1704	1955	3.4F
	2252		
4		0203	3.7E
Su	0510	0802	3.5F
	1102	1427	4.3E
	1751	2038	3.3F
	2338		
5		0249	3.5E
M	0555	0845	3.3F
	1145	1512	4.1E
	1835	2121	3.1F
6	0022	0335	3.2E
Tu	0640	0926	3.0F
	1227	1555	3.8E
	1919	2159	2.9F
7	0105	0419	3.0E
W	0725	1007	2.7F
	1309	1642	3.5E
	2003	2240	2.6F
8	0149	0507	2.7E
Th	0812	1050	2.4F
	1351	1727	3.1E
	2047	2323	2.4F
9	0234	0556	2.5E
F	0902	1136	2.2F
	1437	1816	2.9E
	2134		
10		0012	2.3F
Sa	0321	0646	2.4E
	0956	1226	2.0F
	1526	1906	2.6E
	2222		
11		0100	2.1F
Su	0411	0738	2.3E
	1053	1319	1.8F
	1619	1958	2.5E
	2313		
12		0151	2.1F
M	0502	0831	2.4E
	1150	1416	1.8F
	1715	2052	2.4E
13	0003	0242	2.2F
Tu	0553	0924	2.6E
	1245	1512	1.9F
	1811	2144	2.5E
14	0052	0333	2.3F
W	0642	1015	2.8E
	1337	1605	2.1F
	1906	2233	2.6E
15	0139	0424	2.5F
Th	0729	1103	3.1E
	1424	1657	2.3F
	1958	2321	2.7E

Day	Slack Water Time h.m.	Maximum Current Time h.m.	Vel. knots
16	0223	0510	2.7F
F	0815	1147	3.4E
	1509	1745	2.6F
	2046		
17		0007	2.9E
Sa	0305	0555	2.9F
	0859	1233	3.7E
	1552	1830	2.8F
	2133		
18		0050	3.1E
Su	0348	0640	3.2F
	0943	1316	3.9E
	1634	1915	3.1F
	2219		
19		0134	3.2E
M	0431	0725	3.4F
	1028	1359	4.1E
	1717	2001	3.3F
	2304		
20		0220	3.4E
Tu	0516	0810	3.6F
	1114	1443	4.3E
	1801	2046	3.5F
	2351		
21		0305	3.5E
W	0603	0859	3.6F
	1202	1530	4.3E
	1847	2135	3.6F
22	0040	0354	3.6E
Th	0655	0949	3.6F
	1253	1619	4.3E
	1936	2224	3.6F
23	0132	0448	3.6E
F	0750	1044	3.5F
	1346	1715	4.1E
	2029	2317	3.5F
24	0226	0546	3.6E
Sa	0851	1139	3.4F
	1444	1812	3.9E
	2125		
25		0013	3.4F
Su	0323	0647	3.6E
	0955	1240	3.2F
	1545	1913	3.7E
	2225		
26		0114	3.3F
M	0423	0748	3.6E
	1103	1344	3.0F
	1649	2016	3.6E
	2326		
27		0217	3.3F
Tu	0525	0851	3.7E
	1211	1454	2.9F
	1754	2117	3.5E
28	0028	0322	3.2F
W	0626	0952	3.8E
	1315	1605	2.9F
	1859	2216	3.4E
29	0128	0425	3.3F
Th	0725	1050	4.0E
	1416	1709	3.0F
	2001	2313	3.4E
30	0225	0526	3.3F
F	0821	1145	4.1E
	1512	1806	3.1F
	2058		
31		0009	3.4E
Sa	0318	0617	3.3F
	0913	1236	4.1E
	1603	1857	3.1F
	2151		

Time meridian 75° W. 0000 is midnight. 1200 is noon.

HELL GATE (off Mill Rock), EAST RIVER, NEW YORK, 1983

F-Flood, Dir. 050° True E-Ebb, Dir. 230° True

JANUARY

Day	Slack Water Time h.m.	Maximum Current Time h.m.	Vel. knots
1		0141	5.1E
Sa	0509	0806	3.9F
	1112	1411	5.2E
	1747	2039	3.7F
	2341		
2		0235	5.0E
Su	0605	0903	3.8F
	1207	1506	5.1E
	1842	2135	3.6F
3	0036	0330	4.9E
M	0703	1001	3.6F
	1304	1601	4.9E
	1939	2233	3.5F
4	0132	0427	4.8E
Tu	0803	1059	3.4F
	1402	1700	4.7E
	2038	2333	3.3F
5	0230	0528	4.6E
W	0906	1204	3.3F
	1501	1801	4.5E
	2138		
6		0036	3.2F
Th	0329	0635	4.5E
	1009	1308	3.1F
	1601	1908	4.4E
	2237		
7		0139	3.1F
F	0428	0740	4.4E
	1110	1411	3.1F
	1659	2014	4.3E
	2334		
8		0239	3.1F
Sa	0524	0845	4.4E
	1207	1510	3.1F
	1754	2111	4.3E
9	0027	0330	3.1F
Su	0617	0941	4.4E
	1300	1559	3.1F
	1845	2200	4.3E
10	0116	0419	3.2F
M	0706	1026	4.5E
	1347	1645	3.2F
	1933	2245	4.4E
11	0201	0504	3.2F
Tu	0752	1107	4.6E
	1431	1730	3.2F
	2016	2322	4.5E
12	0243	0543	3.3F
W	0835	1140	4.7E
	1512	1807	3.3F
	2058	2356	4.5E
13	0323	0620	3.4F
Th	0916	1217	4.7E
	1551	1844	3.3F
	2138		
14		0031	4.6E
F	0401	0657	3.4F
	0956	1253	4.8E
	1629	1919	3.3F
	2217		
15		0107	4.7E
Sa	0439	0733	3.4F
	1035	1328	4.8E
	1707	1956	3.3F
	2255		

Day	Slack Water Time h.m.	Maximum Current Time h.m.	Vel. knots
16		0144	4.7E
Su	0516	0809	3.4F
	1114	1405	4.8E
	1744	2032	3.3F
	2333		
17		0223	4.7E
M	0554	0848	3.4F
	1153	1446	4.8E
	1822	2109	3.2F
18	0011	0302	4.7E
Tu	0632	0927	3.3F
	1232	1527	4.7E
	1900	2148	3.2F
19	0051	0345	4.6E
W	0713	1008	3.2F
	1314	1609	4.6E
	1940	2231	3.1F
20	0133	0430	4.6E
Th	0758	1055	3.1F
	1359	1654	4.5E
	2024	2319	3.0F
21	0219	0519	4.5E
F	0848	1144	3.1F
	1450	1745	4.5E
	2113		
22		0008	3.0F
Sa	0312	0613	4.5E
	0945	1239	3.0F
	1545	1838	4.4E
	2208		
		0105	3.0F
Su	0410	0708	4.5E
	1048	1339	3.0F
	1646	1937	4.4E
	2309		
24		0204	3.1F
M	0512	0809	4.6E
	1152	1442	3.1F
	1749	2039	4.5E
25	0011	0308	3.3F
Tu	0615	0912	4.7E
	1255	1547	3.3F
	1851	2140	4.6E
26	0112	0409	3.5F
W	0717	1014	4.9E
	1355	1647	3.4F
	1950	2241	4.8E
27	0211	0510	3.7F
Th	0816	1114	5.1E
	1452	1745	3.6F
	2047	2340	4.9E
28	0308	0608	3.8F
F	0913	1212	5.2E
	1546	1840	3.8F
	2141		
29		0036	5.1E
Sa	0402	0703	3.9F
	1008	1307	5.2E
	1639	1934	3.8F
	2234		
30		0130	5.1E
Su	0456	0757	4.0F
	1101	1400	5.2E
	1730	2025	3.8F
	2327		
31		0223	5.1E
M	0550	0850	3.9F
	1154	1451	5.1E
	1822	2118	3.8F

FEBRUARY

Day	Slack Water Time h.m.	Maximum Current Time h.m.	Vel. knots
1	0018	0314	5.0E
Tu	0644	0942	3.8F
	1247	1542	5.0E
	1915	2211	3.6F
2	0111	0408	4.9E
W	0739	1037	3.6F
	1340	1636	4.7E
	2008	2305	3.4F
3	0204	0502	4.7E
Th	0836	1134	3.4F
	1434	1730	4.5E
	2103		
4		0001	3.2F
F	0259	0558	4.4E
	0934	1233	3.1F
	1530	1826	4.3E
	2159		
5		0101	3.0F
Sa	0355	0657	4.3E
	1033	1334	3.0F
	1626	1927	4.1E
	2256		
6		0200	2.9F
Su	0451	0801	4.2E
	1131	1436	2.9F
	1722	2028	4.0E
	2352		
7		0259	2.9F
M	0546	0902	4.1E
	1226	1531	2.9F
	1815	2125	4.0E
8	0044	0350	3.0F
Tu	0638	0957	4.2E
	1316	1618	3.0F
	1905	2213	4.1E
9	0131	0435	3.1F
W	0726	1038	4.3E
	1401	1701	3.1F
	1951	2254	4.3E
10	0214	0517	3.2F
Th	0811	1117	4.5E
	1443	1742	3.2F
	2033	2330	4.4E
11	0255	0556	3.4F
F	0853	1152	4.6E
	1523	1819	3.3F
	2114		
12		0005	4.5E
Sa	0333	0631	3.5F
	0934	1228	4.7E
	1600	1854	3.4F
	2153		
13		0043	4.7E
Su	0410	0709	3.5F
	1013	1305	4.8E
	1636	1927	3.5F
	2230		
14		0119	4.8E
M	0447	0743	3.6F
	1051	1339	4.8E
	1712	2002	3.5F
	2307		
15		0156	4.8E
Tu	0523	0821	3.6F
	1129	1418	4.8E
	1747	2039	3.5F
	2344		

Day	Slack Water Time h.m.	Maximum Current Time h.m.	Vel. knots
16		0235	4.8E
W	0600	0858	3.6F
	1207	1457	4.8E
	1822	2116	3.4F
17	0022	0316	4.8E
Th	0639	0939	3.5F
	1248	1539	4.7E
	1900	2159	3.4F
18	0103	0358	4.8E
F	0722	1024	3.4F
	1332	1625	4.6E
	1942	2244	3.3F
19	0149	0447	4.7E
Sa	0811	1112	3.2F
	1421	1712	4.5E
	2031	2335	3.2F
20	0242	0540	4.6E
Su	0909	1207	3.1F
	1518	1806	4.4E
	2129		
21		0034	3.1F
M	0344	0639	4.5E
	1015	1312	3.0F
	1622	1909	4.3E
	2236		
22		0138	3.1F
Tu	0451	0744	4.5E
	1126	1417	3.1F
	1729	2014	4.3E
	2346		
23		0249	3.2F
W	0600	0852	4.6E
	1234	1531	3.2F
	1836	2121	4.5E
24	0054	0357	3.4F
Th	0706	1000	4.7E
	1337	1635	3.4F
	1937	2229	4.7E
25	0156	0501	3.7F
F	0807	1104	4.9E
	1435	1736	3.7F
	2035	2330	4.9E
26	0254	0600	3.9F
Sa	0903	1202	5.1E
	1528	1828	3.9F
	2128		
27		0026	5.1E
Su	0348	0653	4.0F
	0957	1256	5.1E
	1619	1919	4.0F
	2219		
28		0119	5.2E
M	0440	0743	4.1F
	1048	1345	5.2E
	1708	2006	4.0F
	2309		

Time meridian 75° W. 0000 is midnight. 1200 is noon.

HELL GATE (off Mill Rock), EAST RIVER, NEW YORK, 1983

F-Flood, Dir. 050° True E-Ebb, Dir. 230° True

MARCH

Day	Slack Water Time h.m.	Maximum Current Time h.m.	Vel. knots
1		0207	5.2E
Tu	0530	0832	4.0F
	1137	1431	5.1E
	1756	2055	3.9F
	2357		
2		0254	5.1E
W	0620	0921	3.9F
	1226	1519	4.9E
	1844	2143	3.7F
3	0046	0342	4.9E
Th	0710	1011	3.7F
	1315	1607	4.7E
	1933	2231	3.5F
4	0135	0430	4.6E
F	0801	1102	3.4F
	1405	1653	4.4E
	2023	2321	3.3F
5	0226	0516	4.4E
Sa	0855	1154	3.1F
	1457	1742	4.1E
	2117		
6		0016	3.0F
Su	0320	0610	4.1E
	0951	1252	2.9F
	1552	1835	3.9E
	2213		
7		0117	2.9F
M	0416	0708	4.0E
	1049	1351	2.8F
	1648	1936	3.8E
	2310		
8		0216	2.8F
Tu	0513	0811	3.9E
	1146	1452	2.8F
	1743	2039	3.8E
9	0005	0312	2.9F
W	0608	0912	4.0E
	1238	1543	2.9F
	1835	2134	3.9E
10	0056	0403	3.0F
Th	0658	1000	4.1E
	1326	1632	3.0F
	1923	2219	4.1E
11	0141	0448	3.2F
F	0745	1045	4.3E
	1409	1710	3.2F
	2006	2258	4.3E
12	0223	0527	3.4F
Sa	0828	1122	4.5E
	1449	1749	3.3F
	2047	2336	4.5E
13	0302	0605	3.5F
Su	0909	1159	4.6E
	1527	1823	3.5F
	2125		
14		0014	4.7E
M	0339	0640	3.6F
	0948	1237	4.8E
	1602	1858	3.6F
	2203		
15		0050	4.8E
Tu	0416	0716	3.7F
	1026	1312	4.8E
	1637	1933	3.6F
	2239		
16		0128	4.9E
W	0453	0752	3.8F
	1104	1351	4.9E
	1712	2010	3.7F
	2317		
17		0209	5.0E
Th	0530	0832	3.7F
	1143	1432	4.8E
	1748	2047	3.6F
	2356		
18		0250	4.9E
F	0611	0913	3.6F
	1224	1513	4.8E
	1827	2132	3.6F
19	0038	0335	4.9E
Sa	0655	0958	3.5F
	1309	1559	4.6E
	1910	2217	3.4F
20	0127	0424	4.7E
Su	0746	1049	3.3F
	1400	1646	4.5E
	2002	2309	3.3F
21	0222	0517	4.6E
M	0845	1146	3.2F
	1500	1745	4.3E
	2104		
22		0010	3.2F
Tu	0327	0619	4.4E
	0954	1252	3.1F
	1607	1848	4.2E
	2217		
23		0121	3.1F
W	0438	0726	4.4E
	1108	1405	3.1F
	1716	1958	4.2E
	2332		
24		0237	3.2F
Th	0549	0839	4.4E
	1217	1518	3.2F
	1824	2111	4.4E
25	0041	0349	3.5F
F	0655	0952	4.6E
	1320	1623	3.5F
	1925	2219	4.6E
26	0143	0451	3.7F
Sa	0755	1055	4.8E
	1416	1722	3.7F
	2020	2319	4.9E
27	0239	0547	3.9F
Su	0850	1149	4.9E
	1508	1811	3.9F
	2111		
28		0014	5.1E
M	0331	0637	4.0F
	0941	1239	5.0E
	1556	1900	4.0F
	2200		
29		0101	5.1E
Tu	0420	0726	4.1F
	1029	1323	5.0E
	1643	1945	4.0F
	2247		
30		0146	5.1E
W	0507	0811	4.0F
	1115	1409	5.0E
	1728	2028	3.9F
	2333		
31		0227	5.0E
Th	0554	0854	3.9F
	1201	1450	4.8E
	1813	2114	3.7F

APRIL

Day	Slack Water Time h.m.	Maximum Current Time h.m.	Vel. knots
1	0018	0310	4.8E
F	0640	0940	3.6F
	1247	1532	4.6E
	1858	2158	3.5F
2	0104	0351	4.6E
Sa	0727	1026	3.4F
	1334	1617	4.3E
	1945	2244	3.2F
3	0152	0437	4.3E
Su	0817	1114	3.1F
	1423	1703	4.1E
	2036	2335	3.0F
4	0243	0528	4.1E
M	0910	1206	2.9F
	1515	1754	3.9E
	2130		
5		0031	2.8F
Tu	0338	0620	3.9E
	1006	1306	2.7F
	1610	1848	3.7E
	2228		
6		0132	2.7F
W	0434	0719	3.8E
	1103	1405	2.7F
	1706	1947	3.7E
	2325		
7		0229	2.8F
Th	0530	0819	3.9E
	1158	1501	2.8F
	1759	2045	3.8E
8	0017	0324	2.9F
F	0623	0915	4.0E
	1247	1550	3.0F
	1847	2137	4.1E
9	0105	0409	3.1F
Sa	0711	1003	4.2E
	1331	1631	3.2F
	1932	2221	4.3E
10	0148	0451	3.3F
Su	0755	1044	4.4E
	1412	1710	3.3F
	2013	2302	4.5E
11	0229	0530	3.5F
M	0837	1124	4.6E
	1451	1749	3.5F
	2053	2341	4.7E
12	0308	0608	3.7F
Tu	0918	1202	4.8E
	1528	1824	3.6F
	2131		
13		0021	4.9E
W	0347	0647	3.8F
	0957	1241	4.9E
	1604	1902	3.7F
	2210		
14		0101	5.0E
Th	0427	0726	3.8F
	1037	1321	4.9E
	1641	1941	3.8F
	2250		
15		0142	5.1E
F	0507	0807	3.8F
	1119	1404	4.9E
	1721	2023	3.7F
	2332		
16		0225	5.0E
Sa	0551	0850	3.7F
	1203	1449	4.8E
	1804	2108	3.6F
17	0018	0314	4.9E
Su	0639	0939	3.5F
	1251	1536	4.6E
	1852	2159	3.5F
18	0110	0404	4.8E
M	0733	1031	3.4F
	1345	1631	4.5E
	1949	2256	3.3F
19	0209	0501	4.6E
Tu	0835	1132	3.2F
	1447	1728	4.3E
	2056		
20		0001	3.2F
W	0315	0604	4.4E
	0945	1242	3.1F
	1555	1836	4.2E
	2210		
21		0113	3.2F
Th	0426	0715	4.3E
	1057	1356	3.1F
	1703	1949	4.2E
	2324		
22		0229	3.2F
F	0536	0830	4.4E
	1203	1507	3.3F
	1808	2104	4.4E
23	0031	0338	3.4F
Sa	0640	0941	4.5E
	1304	1610	3.5F
	1907	2211	4.7E
24	0130	0438	3.7F
Su	0738	1042	4.7E
	1357	1703	3.7F
	2000	2308	4.9E
25	0224	0531	3.8F
M	0830	1132	4.8E
	1447	1753	3.8F
	2050	2353	5.0E
26	0314	0618	3.9F
Tu	0919	1217	4.9E
	1533	1838	3.9F
	2136		
27		0040	5.1E
W	0400	0703	3.9F
	1004	1300	4.9E
	1618	1921	3.9F
	2221		
28		0122	5.1E
Th	0445	0747	3.9F
	1049	1341	4.8E
	1701	2002	3.8F
	2304		
29		0203	5.0E
F	0529	0828	3.7F
	1132	1421	4.7E
	1744	2043	3.6F
	2348		
30		0239	4.8E
Sa	0613	0911	3.5F
	1215	1500	4.5E
	1827	2126	3.4F

Time meridian 75° W. 0000 is midnight. 1200 is noon.

HELL GATE (off Mill Rock), EAST RIVER, NEW YORK, 1983

F-Flood, Dir. 050° True   E-Ebb, Dir. 230° True

MAY

Day	Slack Water Time h.m.	Maximum Current Time h.m.	Vel. knots
1	0032	0322	4.6E
Su	0657	0952	3.3F
	1300	1543	4.3E
	1912	2210	3.2F
2	0117	0404	4.4E
M	0744	1036	3.1F
	1346	1627	4.1E
	2000	2256	3.0F
3	0205	0450	4.2E
Tu	0834	1126	2.9F
	1435	1712	4.0E
	2052	2347	2.8F
4	0256	0541	4.0E
W	0927	1220	2.7F
	1528	1805	3.9E
	2147		
5		0043	2.7F
Th	0351	0635	4.0E
	1022	1316	2.7F
	1621	1900	3.9E
	2243		
6		0140	2.8F
F	0446	0730	4.0E
	1115	1411	2.8F
	1714	1955	4.0E
	2336		
7		0233	2.9F
Sa	0539	0823	4.1E
	1205	1502	2.9F
	1803	2049	4.1E
8	0026	0325	3.0F
Su	0629	0915	4.2E
	1251	1547	3.1F
	1849	2138	4.4E
9	0112	0410	3.2F
M	0715	1000	4.4E
	1333	1629	3.3F
	1933	2223	4.6E
10	0156	0454	3.4F
Tu	0800	1045	4.6E
	1414	1710	3.5F
	2016	2306	4.8E
11	0238	0533	3.6F
W	0843	1130	4.8E
	1454	1753	3.6F
	2058	2351	5.0E
12	0321	0616	3.7F
Th	0926	1213	4.9E
	1535	1834	3.7F
	2141		
13		0036	5.1E
F	0405	0659	3.8F
	1010	1256	4.9E
	1617	1917	3.8F
	2225		
14		0120	5.1E
Sa	0450	0746	3.7F
	1056	1343	4.9E
	1702	2004	3.8F
	2312		
15		0209	5.1E
Su	0539	0834	3.7F
	1144	1430	4.8E
	1751	2053	3.7F

Day	Slack Water Time h.m.	Maximum Current Time h.m.	Vel. knots
16	0003	0258	5.0E
M	0631	0927	3.5F
	1236	1522	4.7E
	1845	2148	3.5F
17	0058	0351	4.8E
Tu	0728	1024	3.4F
	1333	1617	4.5E
	1946	2246	3.4F
18	0158	0450	4.6E
W	0831	1125	3.2F
	1435	1718	4.4E
	2054	2354	3.2F
19	0304	0554	4.5E
Th	0938	1233	3.1F
	1540	1829	4.3E
	2205		
20		0107	3.2F
F	0412	0707	4.4E
	1045	1345	3.2F
	1645	1941	4.4E
	2314		
21		0217	3.3F
Sa	0518	0817	4.4E
	1148	1452	3.3F
	1747	2053	4.5E
22	0018	0324	3.4F
Su	0619	0925	4.5E
	1245	1550	3.5F
	1844	2154	4.7E
23	0115	0419	3.5F
M	0715	1022	4.6E
	1337	1641	3.6F
	1936	2248	4.8E
24	0207	0510	3.6F
Tu	0806	1111	4.7E
	1425	1730	3.7F
	2025	2335	4.9E
25	0255	0558	3.7F
W	0853	1156	4.8E
	1510	1815	3.7F
	2110		
26		0018	5.0E
Th	0340	0641	3.7F
	0937	1233	4.8E
	1554	1857	3.7F
	2154		
27		0057	4.9E
F	0423	0722	3.6F
	1020	1314	4.7E
	1636	1936	3.6F
	2236		
28		0134	4.9E
Sa	0505	0801	3.5F
	1102	1350	4.6E
	1717	2015	3.5F
	2318		
29		0213	4.8E
Su	0548	0842	3.4F
	1144	1428	4.5E
	1759	2057	3.4F
30	0000	0251	4.6E
M	0630	0922	3.2F
	1226	1509	4.4E
	1842	2136	3.2F
31	0043	0332	4.5E
Tu	0714	1004	3.1F
	1310	1552	4.3E
	1927	2221	3.1F

JUNE

Day	Slack Water Time h.m.	Maximum Current Time h.m.	Vel. knots
1	0128	0416	4.4E
W	0800	1049	2.9F
	1356	1637	4.2E
	2015	2306	2.9F
2	0216	0503	4.2E
Th	0848	1138	2.8F
	1444	1726	4.1E
	2106	2357	2.8F
3	0306	0554	4.2E
F	0938	1227	2.8F
	1534	1817	4.1E
	2158		
4		0051	2.8F
Sa	0358	0645	4.1E
	1029	1317	2.8F
	1625	1909	4.1E
	2251		
5		0144	2.9F
Su	0451	0738	4.2E
	1118	1410	2.9F
	1715	2002	4.3E
	2343		
6		0235	3.0F
M	0543	0830	4.3E
	1206	1459	3.1F
	1804	2053	4.5E
7	0033	0327	3.2F
Tu	0633	0921	4.5E
	1252	1547	3.2F
	1852	2146	4.7E
8	0122	0415	3.3F
W	0722	1010	4.6E
	1338	1635	3.4F
	1940	2234	4.9E
9	0210	0504	3.5F
Th	0810	1058	4.8E
	1423	1722	3.6F
	2028	2323	5.0E
10	0258	0552	3.6F
F	0858	1146	4.9E
	1510	1809	3.7F
	2116		
11		0012	5.1E
Sa	0346	0641	3.7F
	0946	1235	4.9E
	1558	1858	3.8F
	2206		
12		0103	5.2E
Su	0436	0730	3.7F
	1036	1325	4.9E
	1649	1950	3.8F
	2257		
13		0154	5.1E
M	0528	0821	3.7F
	1128	1418	4.9E
	1742	2041	3.7F
	2351		
14		0247	5.1E
Tu	0623	0916	3.6F
	1223	1511	4.8E
	1840	2140	3.6F
15	0048	0343	4.9E
W	0721	1014	3.4F
	1320	1608	4.7E
	1941	2240	3.5F

Day	Slack Water Time h.m.	Maximum Current Time h.m.	Vel. knots
16	0148	0440	4.7E
Th	0821	1115	3.3F
	1420	1710	4.6E
	2047	2345	3.3F
17	0251	0544	4.6E
F	0924	1221	3.3F
	1522	1816	4.5E
	2153		
18		0055	3.3F
Sa	0354	0652	4.5E
	1026	1327	3.2F
	1624	1927	4.5E
	2258		
19		0200	3.3F
Su	0457	0801	4.4E
	1126	1430	3.3F
	1724	2035	4.5E
	2359		
20		0306	3.3F
M	0556	0904	4.4E
	1222	1527	3.4F
	1820	2136	4.6E
21	0055	0359	3.4F
Tu	0650	0959	4.5E
	1314	1618	3.4F
	1912	2227	4.7E
22	0146	0450	3.4F
W	0740	1051	4.5E
	1402	1707	3.5F
	2000	2314	4.7E
23	0234	0535	3.5F
Th	0827	1130	4.6E
	1447	1751	3.5F
	2045	2355	4.8E
24	0318	0618	3.5F
F	0911	1209	4.6E
	1530	1831	3.5F
	2128		
25		0032	4.8E
Sa	0400	0657	3.5F
	0953	1248	4.6E
	1611	1909	3.5F
	2210		
26		0108	4.8E
Su	0441	0735	3.4F
	1034	1324	4.6E
	1651	1950	3.5F
	2251		
27		0146	4.7E
M	0521	0813	3.4F
	1114	1402	4.6E
	1731	2029	3.4F
	2332		
28		0223	4.7E
Tu	0601	0852	3.3F
	1155	1440	4.5E
	1812	2107	3.3F
29	0013	0302	4.6E
W	0642	0932	3.2F
	1236	1521	4.4E
	1853	2148	3.2F
30	0056	0345	4.5E
Th	0723	1014	3.1F
	1319	1602	4.4E
	1936	2233	3.1F

Time meridian 75° W. 0000 is midnight. 1200 is noon.

F-Flood, Dir. 050° True E-Ebb, Dir. 230° True

JULY

Day	Slack Water Time h.m.	Maximum Current Time h.m.	Vel. knots
1	0140	0428	4.4E
F	0806	1056	3.0F
	1402	1648	4.3E
	2021	2315	3.0F
2	0226	0515	4.3E
Sa	0851	1142	2.9F
	1449	1737	4.3E
	2110		
3		0006	3.0F
Su	0315	0602	4.3E
	0938	1233	2.9F
	1538	1826	4.3E
	2202		
4		0057	3.0F
M	0406	0652	4.3E
	1027	1321	3.0F
	1629	1919	4.4E
	2257		
5		0152	3.0F
Tu	0500	0747	4.3E
	1118	1414	3.1F
	1723	2014	4.5E
	2352		
6		0245	3.1F
W	0555	0842	4.4E
	1210	1509	3.2F
	1817	2110	4.6E
7	0047	0341	3.3F
Th	0649	0937	4.5E
	1303	1602	3.4F
	1911	2206	4.8E
8	0142	0438	3.4F
F	0743	1028	4.7E
	1356	1655	3.6F
	2005	2300	5.0E
9	0236	0529	3.6F
Sa	0836	1124	4.8E
	1449	1749	3.8F
	2059	2353	5.1E
10	0329	0622	3.7F
Su	0929	1217	4.9E
	1542	1844	3.9F
	2153		
11		0047	5.1E
M	0421	0715	3.8F
	1022	1312	5.0E
	1636	1939	3.9F
	2247		
12		0142	5.1E
Tu	0515	0809	3.8F
	1116	1405	5.0E
	1731	2032	3.9F
	2342		
13		0237	5.1E
W	0609	0903	3.7F
	1210	1501	4.9E
	1828	2129	3.8F
14	0038	0332	4.9E
Th	0704	1001	3.6F
	1306	1556	4.8E
	1927	2227	3.6F
15	0135	0427	4.8E
F	0801	1059	3.5F
	1403	1656	4.7E
	2028	2329	3.5F

Day	Slack Water Time h.m.	Maximum Current Time h.m.	Vel. knots
16	0234	0528	4.6E
Sa	0900	1201	3.4F
	1502	1757	4.5E
	2130		
17		0033	3.3F
Su	0334	0629	4.4E
	0959	1302	3.3F
	1601	1903	4.4E
	2233		
18		0138	3.2F
M	0434	0736	4.3E
	1058	1405	3.2F
	1700	2010	4.4E
	2333		
19		0239	3.2F
Tu	0532	0840	4.2E
	1154	1505	3.2F
	1756	2113	4.4E
20	0029	0334	3.2F
W	0626	0937	4.2E
	1247	1556	3.3F
	1849	2206	4.4E
21	0121	0425	3.2F
Th	0717	1024	4.3E
	1336	1645	3.3F
	1938	2252	4.5E
22	0208	0511	3.3F
F	0804	1107	4.3E
	1421	1730	3.4F
	2024	2333	4.5E
23	0252	0552	3.3F
Sa	0848	1146	4.4E
	1503	1809	3.5F
	2107		
24		0009	4.6E
Su	0333	0633	3.4F
	0929	1222	4.5E
	1544	1846	3.5F
	2148		
25		0044	4.6E
M	0412	0710	3.4F
	1009	1257	4.5E
	1622	1923	3.5F
	2228		
26		0119	4.7E
Tu	0450	0745	3.4F
	1048	1333	4.6E
	1700	1959	3.5F
	2308		
27		0156	4.7E
W	0528	0821	3.4F
	1127	1412	4.6E
	1738	2037	3.5F
	2347		
28		0233	4.7E
Th	0605	0858	3.4F
	1206	1451	4.6E
	1816	2116	3.4F
29	0027	0312	4.6E
F	0642	0935	3.3F
	1245	1530	4.5E
	1855	2155	3.3F
30	0108	0355	4.5E
Sa	0720	1017	3.2F
	1326	1613	4.5E
	1936	2236	3.3F
31	0151	0437	4.4E
Su	0800	1059	3.1F
	1409	1700	4.4E
	2022	2325	3.2F

AUGUST

Day	Slack Water Time h.m.	Maximum Current Time h.m.	Vel. knots
1	0238	0522	4.3E
M	0845	1149	3.1F
	1458	1747	4.4E
	2113		
2		0016	3.1F
Tu	0329	0613	4.3E
	0935	1240	3.1F
	1551	1843	4.4E
	2211		
3		0113	3.1F
W	0425	0712	4.3E
	1031	1337	3.2F
	1650	1940	4.4E
	2313		
4		0211	3.1F
Th	0525	0807	4.3E
	1131	1436	3.3F
	1751	2041	4.5E
5	0016	0312	3.2F
F	0625	0909	4.4E
	1233	1538	3.4F
	1851	2140	4.7E
6	0117	0413	3.4F
Sa	0724	1008	4.6E
	1333	1639	3.6F
	1950	2242	4.8E
7	0215	0513	3.6F
Su	0821	1107	4.8E
	1431	1736	3.8F
	2048	2339	5.0E
8	0310	0609	3.8F
M	0916	1204	4.9E
	1527	1831	4.0F
	2143		
9		0036	5.1E
Tu	0403	0702	3.9F
	1009	1300	5.0E
	1621	1927	4.0F
	2237		
10		0129	5.1E
W	0456	0756	3.9F
	1102	1353	5.1E
	1716	2021	4.0F
	2330		
11		0221	5.1E
Th	0548	0847	3.9F
	1155	1447	5.0E
	1810	2114	4.0F
12	0024	0313	4.9E
F	0640	0942	3.8F
	1248	1539	4.9E
	1905	2209	3.8F
13	0118	0407	4.7E
Sa	0733	1036	3.7F
	1342	1636	4.7E
	2002	2306	3.6F
14	0214	0502	4.5E
Su	0828	1132	3.5F
	1438	1731	4.5E
	2100		
15		0006	3.4F
M	0311	0603	4.3E
	0925	1232	3.3F
	1536	1834	4.3E
	2201		

Day	Slack Water Time h.m.	Maximum Current Time h.m.	Vel. knots
16		0109	3.2F
Tu	0409	0702	4.1E
	1024	1335	3.2F
	1635	1937	4.1E
	2301		
17		0212	3.1F
W	0508	0809	4.0E
	1122	1436	3.1F
	1732	2041	4.1E
	2358		
18		0310	3.1F
Th	0603	0912	3.9E
	1217	1531	3.2F
	1827	2140	4.1E
19	0051	0403	3.1F
F	0655	1003	4.0E
	1307	1620	3.2F
	1917	2229	4.2E
20	0138	0448	3.2F
Sa	0742	1045	4.1E
	1353	1708	3.4F
	2003	2308	4.3E
21	0222	0529	3.3F
Su	0825	1122	4.3E
	1434	1743	3.5F
	2045	2343	4.4E
22	0302	0604	3.4F
M	0905	1155	4.4E
	1514	1820	3.6F
	2126		
23		0018	4.5E
Tu	0340	0641	3.5F
	0944	1231	4.5E
	1551	1856	3.6F
	2205		
24		0052	4.6E
W	0416	0715	3.6F
	1022	1306	4.6E
	1628	1931	3.7F
	2243		
25		0126	4.7E
Th	0452	0750	3.6F
	1058	1341	4.7E
	1703	2006	3.7F
	2321		
26		0203	4.7E
F	0526	0825	3.6F
	1135	1420	4.7E
	1739	2042	3.6F
	2359		
27		0240	4.6E
Sa	0600	0901	3.5F
	1212	1501	4.7E
	1816	2122	3.6F
28	0038	0319	4.6E
Su	0636	0940	3.4F
	1252	1542	4.6E
	1856	2203	3.5F
29	0120	0404	4.5E
M	0714	1021	3.4F
	1335	1624	4.5E
	1941	2250	3.3F
30	0206	0451	4.3E
Tu	0758	1110	3.3F
	1425	1715	4.4E
	2033	2342	3.2F
31	0259	0542	4.2E
W	0851	1203	3.2F
	1522	1810	4.4E
	2134		

Time meridian 75° W. 0000 is midnight. 1200 is noon.

THE NARROWS, NEW YORK HARBOR, NEW YORK, 1983

F-Flood, Dir. 340° True E-Ebb, Dir. 160° True

JANUARY

Day	Slack Water Time h.m.	Maximum Current Time h.m.	Maximum Current Vel. knots
1		0152	2.3E
Sa	0509	0754	2.4F
	1112	1429	2.6E
	1807	2028	1.8F
	2330		
2		0243	2.3E
Su	0604	0850	2.3F
	1204	1519	2.6E
	1859	2127	1.8F
3	0026	0336	2.2E
M	0703	0945	2.1F
	1256	1609	2.4E
	1953	2227	1.8F
4	0123	0431	2.1E
Tu	0807	1044	1.9F
	1347	1703	2.2E
	2049	2325	1.8F
5	0220	0531	1.9E
W	0911	1144	1.7F
	1440	1802	2.1E
	2143		
6		0023	1.8F
Th	0320	0637	1.9E
	1014	1242	1.5F
	1535	1900	2.0E
	2237		
7		0121	1.7F
F	0422	0742	1.8E
	1115	1345	1.4F
	1632	1958	1.9E
	2329		
8		0227	1.7F
Sa	0524	0839	1.9E
	1214	1502	1.3F
	1729	2049	1.9E
9	0020	0330	1.8F
Su	0620	0931	1.9E
	1312	1606	1.2F
	1823	2138	1.8E
10	0111	0423	1.8F
M	0710	1020	1.9E
	1406	1655	1.3F
	1912	2223	1.8E
11	0159	0510	1.9F
Tu	0755	1109	2.0E
	1455	1740	1.3F
	1958	2310	1.8E
12	0245	0545	1.9F
W	0837	1156	2.0E
	1540	1815	1.3F
	2042	2359	1.7E
13	0328	0618	1.9F
Th	0918	1238	2.0E
	1622	1846	1.3F
	2125		
14		0042	1.7E
F	0409	0646	1.9F
	0958	1320	2.1E
	1702	1915	1.4F
	2208		
15		0127	1.8E
Sa	0448	0722	1.9F
	1038	1359	2.1E
	1741	1951	1.4F
	2252		

Day	Slack Water Time h.m.	Maximum Current Time h.m.	Maximum Current Vel. knots
16		0206	1.8E
Su	0528	0801	1.8F
	1118	1438	2.1E
	1821	2032	1.4F
	2336		
17		0247	1.8E
M	0609	0846	1.7F
	1159	1515	2.0E
	1901	2117	1.4F
18	0019	0326	1.7E
Tu	0653	0933	1.6F
	1239	1552	2.0E
	1942	2201	1.4F
19	0104	0409	1.7E
W	0744	1020	1.5F
	1320	1633	1.9E
	2025	2250	1.5F
20	0151	0457	1.6E
Th	0841	1107	1.4F
	1404	1720	1.8E
	2109	2335	1.5F
21	0241	0552	1.6E
F	0940	1156	1.3F
	1451	1813	1.7E
	2154		
22		0024	1.6F
Sa	0337	0657	1.6E
	1039	1250	1.3F
	1544	1911	1.7E
	2242		
23		0117	1.7F
Su	0436	0756	1.8E
	1138	1345	1.2F
	1643	2008	1.8E
	2333		
24		0213	1.8F
M	0536	0854	1.9E
	1238	1446	1.2F
	1743	2101	1.9E
25	0028	0314	1.9F
Tu	0634	0947	2.1E
	1335	1547	1.4F
	1841	2154	2.0E
26	0124	0413	2.1F
W	0728	1041	2.2E
	1430	1648	1.5F
	1936	2251	2.1E
27	0220	0508	2.3F
Th	0820	1137	2.4E
	1520	1740	1.7F
	2030	2347	2.2E
28	0313	0559	2.4F
F	0912	1229	2.5E
	1608	1831	1.9F
	2124		
29		0043	2.4E
Sa	0406	0649	2.5F
	1003	1321	2.6E
	1655	1918	2.0F
	2218		
30		0137	2.4E
Su	0457	0738	2.4F
	1053	1410	2.6E
	1742	2010	2.0F
	2313		
31		0228	2.4E
M	0550	0831	2.3F
	1143	1457	2.6E
	1831	2104	2.0F

FEBRUARY

Day	Slack Water Time h.m.	Maximum Current Time h.m.	Maximum Current Vel. knots
1	0007	0316	2.4E
Tu	0646	0924	2.1F
	1232	1545	2.4E
	1922	2201	1.9F
2	0100	0409	2.2E
W	0745	1020	1.9F
	1320	1634	2.2E
	2015	2253	1.9F
3	0154	0505	2.0E
Th	0846	1116	1.6F
	1409	1725	2.0E
	2109	2347	1.8F
4	0249	0604	1.8E
F	0947	1210	1.4F
	1500	1824	1.8E
	2203		
5		0043	1.7F
Sa	0348	0708	1.7E
	1048	1309	1.2F
	1555	1923	1.7E
	2256		
6		0142	1.6F
Su	0449	0809	1.7E
	1147	1424	1.1F
	1654	2020	1.7E
	2350		
7		0253	1.6F
M	0548	0904	1.7E
	1245	1537	1.1F
	1752	2112	1.6E
8	0042	0357	1.6F
Tu	0641	0953	1.8E
	1340	1632	1.1F
	1846	2157	1.6E
9	0134	0448	1.7F
W	0728	1042	1.9E
	1430	1717	1.2F
	1935	2246	1.7E
10	0222	0527	1.8F
Th	0811	1126	1.9E
	1514	1759	1.3F
	2020	2333	1.7E
11	0307	0558	1.8F
F	0852	1211	2.0E
	1555	1828	1.4F
	2103		
12		0021	1.8E
Sa	0349	0628	1.9F
	0932	1254	2.1E
	1634	1853	1.5F
	2145		
13		0104	1.8E
Su	0429	0659	1.9F
	1012	1333	2.1E
	1710	1925	1.5F
	2227		
14		0145	1.9E
M	0508	0738	1.8F
	1051	1410	2.1E
	1746	2002	1.6F
	2309		
15		0223	1.9E
Tu	0548	0819	1.8F
	1130	1446	2.1E
	1822	2045	1.6F
	2351		

Day	Slack Water Time h.m.	Maximum Current Time h.m.	Maximum Current Vel. knots
16		0300	1.9E
W	0630	0904	1.7F
	1210	1521	2.0E
	1858	2130	1.6F
17	0035	0339	1.9E
Th	0717	0950	1.6F
	1250	1558	1.9E
	1937	2217	1.7F
18	0120	0424	1.8E
F	0811	1039	1.5F
	1332	1637	1.8E
	2021	2304	1.7F
19	0210	0519	1.8E
Sa	0911	1128	1.4F
	1419	1731	1.7E
	2112	2353	1.7F
20	0304	0622	1.7E
Su	1012	1221	1.3F
	1512	1836	1.7E
	2207		
21		0047	1.7F
M	0405	0728	1.8E
	1113	1318	1.2F
	1614	1941	1.7E
	2306		
22		0146	1.8F
Tu	0509	0828	1.9E
	1214	1420	1.2F
	1719	2040	1.8E
23	0007	0249	1.9F
W	0611	0924	2.1E
	1312	1528	1.3F
	1822	2138	2.0E
24	0108	0357	2.0F
Th	0708	1019	2.2E
	1407	1635	1.6F
	1921	2235	2.1E
25	0207	0457	2.2F
F	0802	1116	2.4E
	1458	1730	1.8F
	2016	2330	2.3E
26	0302	0548	2.3F
Sa	0853	1209	2.5E
	1545	1815	2.0F
	2109		
27		0027	2.4E
Su	0354	0636	2.4F
	0942	1300	2.6E
	1631	1901	2.1F
	2201		
28		0120	2.5E
M	0445	0723	2.3F
	1031	1348	2.6E
	1716	1947	2.1F
	2253		

Time meridian 75° W. 0000 is midnight. 1200 is noon.

F-Flood, Dir. 340° True E-Ebb, Dir. 160° True

MARCH

Day	Slack Water Time h.m.	Maximum Current Time h.m.	Vel. knots
1		0209	2.5E
Tu	0535	0809	2.2F
	1118	1434	2.5E
	1802	2036	2.1F
	2344		
2		0257	2.4E
W	0627	0900	2.0F
	1205	1517	2.4E
	1849	2129	2.0F
3	0035	0345	2.3E
Th	0722	0951	1.7F
	1251	1603	2.2E
	1939	2220	1.9F
4	0125	0434	2.1E
F	0820	1045	1.5F
	1338	1651	1.9E
	2033	2311	1.8F
5	0216	0528	1.8E
Sa	0920	1136	1.3F
	1427	1746	1.7E
	2128		
6		0002	1.6F
Su	0310	0631	1.7E
	1019	1232	1.1F
	1520	1846	1.5E
	2223		
7		0055	1.5F
M	0409	0733	1.6E
	1117	1333	1.0F
	1619	1947	1.5E
	2318		
8		0201	1.4F
Tu	0509	0831	1.6E
	1214	1500	1.0F
	1721	2041	1.5E
9	0013	0318	1.4F
W	0605	0921	1.7E
	1308	1602	1.1F
	1819	2132	1.6E
10	0106	0415	1.5F
Th	0655	1008	1.8E
	1357	1651	1.2F
	1910	2219	1.6E
11	0157	0458	1.6F
F	0740	1055	1.9E
	1442	1730	1.4F
	1955	2308	1.7E
12	0243	0533	1.7F
Sa	0822	1138	2.0E
	1522	1759	1.5F
	2038	2353	1.8E
13	0327	0605	1.8F
Su	0902	1221	2.0E
	1600	1824	1.6F
	2119		
14		0036	2.0E
M	0408	0636	1.8F
	0942	1302	2.1E
	1635	1857	1.7F
	2200		
15		0120	2.0E
Tu	0447	0712	1.8F
	1021	1339	2.1E
	1709	1933	1.8F
	2242		

Day	Slack Water Time h.m.	Maximum Current Time h.m.	Vel. knots
16		0159	2.1E
W	0527	0753	1.8F
	1101	1416	2.1E
	1742	2012	1.8F
	2324		
17		0239	2.1E
Th	0609	0836	1.7F
	1141	1453	2.1E
	1816	2057	1.8F
18	0008	0318	2.1E
F	0656	0925	1.6F
	1222	1530	2.0E
	1855	2145	1.8F
19	0054	0401	2.0E
Sa	0750	1014	1.5F
	1307	1609	1.9E
	1942	2236	1.8F
20	0144	0453	1.9E
Su	0850	1105	1.4F
	1355	1702	1.7E
	2040	2329	1.8F
21	0239	0556	1.8E
M	0952	1159	1.3F
	1451	1811	1.7E
	2143		
22		0026	1.8F
Tu	0340	0705	1.8E
	1052	1256	1.3F
	1555	1921	1.7E
	2248		
23		0123	1.8F
W	0445	0809	1.9E
	1152	1401	1.3F
	1703	2024	1.8E
	2353		
24		0229	1.8F
Th	0549	0905	2.1E
	1249	1512	1.4F
	1808	2125	2.0E
25	0055	0344	1.9F
F	0648	1000	2.2E
	1343	1623	1.7F
	1907	2219	2.2E
26	0155	0448	2.1F
Sa	0742	1052	2.3E
	1433	1718	1.9F
	2001	2316	2.3E
27	0250	0538	2.2F
Su	0831	1146	2.4E
	1520	1801	2.1F
	2053		
28		0009	2.4E
M	0342	0624	2.2F
	0919	1235	2.4E
	1604	1844	2.2F
	2143		
29		0101	2.5E
Tu	0431	0705	2.1F
	1006	1321	2.4E
	1648	1925	2.2F
	2232		
30		0149	2.5E
W	0519	0748	2.0F
	1051	1407	2.4E
	1732	2009	2.1F
	2320		
31		0235	2.4E
Th	0608	0834	1.8F
	1137	1448	2.2E
	1816	2055	2.0F

APRIL

Day	Slack Water Time h.m.	Maximum Current Time h.m.	Vel. knots
1	0007	0319	2.3E
F	0700	0923	1.6F
	1222	1533	2.0E
	1904	2143	1.9F
2	0055	0405	2.1E
Sa	0755	1014	1.4F
	1307	1618	1.8E
	1956	2234	1.7F
3	0143	0456	1.8E
Su	0852	1105	1.2F
	1355	1709	1.6E
	2052	2323	1.6F
4	0233	0554	1.7E
M	0949	1158	1.1F
	1448	1810	1.4E
	2149		
5		0014	1.4F
Tu	0327	0654	1.6E
	1045	1252	1.0F
	1546	1912	1.4E
	2246		
6		0111	1.3F
W	0425	0755	1.6E
	1139	1404	1.0F
	1649	2010	1.4E
	2342		
7		0214	1.3F
Th	0523	0846	1.7E
	1230	1517	1.1F
	1748	2101	1.5E
8	0036	0330	1.4F
F	0616	0933	1.8E
	1318	1612	1.3F
	1840	2150	1.7E
9	0128	0422	1.5F
Sa	0704	1016	1.9E
	1403	1655	1.5F
	1927	2236	1.8E
10	0216	0501	1.6F
Su	0747	1101	1.9E
	1444	1723	1.6F
	2009	2323	1.9E
11	0302	0536	1.7F
M	0828	1143	2.0E
	1522	1752	1.8F
	2051		
12		0009	2.1E
Tu	0345	0609	1.8F
	0909	1226	2.1E
	1557	1825	1.9F
	2132		
13		0052	2.2E
W	0426	0647	1.8F
	0949	1307	2.1E
	1631	1902	2.0F
	2214		
14		0133	2.2E
Th	0507	0726	1.7F
	1030	1347	2.1E
	1705	1944	2.1F
	2258		
15		0217	2.3E
F	0551	0811	1.7F
	1113	1426	2.1E
	1742	2031	2.0F
	2344		

Day	Slack Water Time h.m.	Maximum Current Time h.m.	Vel. knots
16		0300	2.3E
Sa	0639	0900	1.6F
	1158	1505	2.0E
	1824	2120	2.0F
17	0033	0345	2.2E
Su	0733	0952	1.5F
	1247	1550	1.9E
	1916	2215	1.9F
18	0124	0436	2.1E
M	0832	1047	1.4F
	1339	1646	1.8E
	2019	2308	1.9F
19	0219	0537	2.0E
Tu	0933	1142	1.4F
	1437	1755	1.7E
	2128		
20		0006	1.8F
W	0319	0645	1.9E
	1032	1241	1.4F
	1542	1906	1.7E
	2235		
21		0107	1.7F
Th	0423	0748	2.0E
	1128	1345	1.4F
	1650	2011	1.9E
	2340		
22		0214	1.7F
F	0527	0846	2.1E
	1223	1501	1.6F
	1755	2109	2.0E
23	0042	0331	1.8F
Sa	0625	0938	2.2E
	1316	1607	1.8F
	1853	2203	2.2E
24	0141	0434	1.9F
Su	0718	1029	2.3E
	1406	1700	2.0F
	1946	2258	2.3E
25	0236	0524	2.0F
M	0807	1120	2.3E
	1453	1745	2.2F
	2035	2351	2.4E
26	0327	0608	2.0F
Tu	0853	1209	2.3E
	1538	1824	2.2F
	2123		
27		0040	2.4E
W	0416	0647	1.9F
	0938	1255	2.2E
	1621	1901	2.2F
	2209		
28		0128	2.4E
Th	0503	0727	1.7F
	1023	1341	2.2E
	1703	1940	2.1F
	2255		
29		0212	2.3E
F	0550	0809	1.6F
	1108	1422	2.0E
	1746	2023	2.0F
	2340		
30		0255	2.2E
Sa	0638	0854	1.4F
	1153	1505	1.9E
	1831	2109	1.8F

Time meridian 75° W. 0000 is midnight. 1200 is noon.

THE NARROWS, NEW YORK HARBOR, NEW YORK, 1983

F-Flood, Dir. 340° True   E-Ebb, Dir. 160° True

MAY

Day	Slack Water Time h.m.	Maximum Current Time h.m.	Maximum Current Vel. knots
1	0025	0338	2.0E
Su	0730	0945	1.3F
	1239	1546	1.7E
	1921	2158	1.7F
2	0111	0427	1.9E
M	0824	1036	1.2F
	1327	1637	1.5E
	2016	2249	1.5F
3	0158	0515	1.7E
Tu	0918	1127	1.1F
	1418	1732	1.4E
	2114	2339	1.4F
4	0248	0614	1.6E
W	1011	1219	1.1F
	1514	1833	1.3E
	2211		
5		0030	1.3F
Th	0341	0713	1.6E
	1101	1312	1.1F
	1614	1936	1.4E
	2307		
6		0123	1.3F
F	0437	0805	1.7E
	1149	1411	1.2F
	1712	2030	1.5E
7	0002	0223	1.3F
Sa	0532	0854	1.8E
	1235	1509	1.3F
	1806	2118	1.7E
8	0055	0325	1.4F
Su	0622	0938	1.9E
	1319	1600	1.5F
	1854	2203	1.8E
9	0146	0416	1.5F
M	0708	1021	1.9E
	1401	1639	1.7F
	1938	2251	2.0E
10	0234	0458	1.6F
Tu	0752	1104	2.0E
	1441	1716	1.9F
	2021	2337	2.1E
11	0320	0539	1.6F
W	0834	1150	2.0E
	1518	1755	2.1F
	2104		
12		0022	2.2E
Th	0404	0620	1.7F
	0917	1233	2.0E
	1555	1836	2.2F
	2149		
13		0109	2.3E
F	0448	0702	1.7F
	1001	1318	2.1E
	1634	1919	2.2F
	2235		
14		0156	2.4E
Sa	0533	0749	1.6F
	1048	1403	2.1E
	1716	2006	2.2F
	2324		
15		0241	2.4E
Su	0622	0838	1.6F
	1138	1449	2.0E
	1804	2057	2.1F
16	0015	0329	2.3E
M	0716	0933	1.5F
	1231	1538	2.0E
	1900	2153	2.0F
17	0107	0420	2.2E
Tu	0814	1030	1.5F
	1326	1633	1.9E
	2006	2252	1.9F
18	0201	0519	2.1E
W	0912	1128	1.5F
	1426	1740	1.8E
	2115	2351	1.8F
19	0259	0623	2.1E
Th	1009	1227	1.6F
	1529	1850	1.8E
	2221		
20		0050	1.7F
F	0400	0726	2.1E
	1103	1330	1.6F
	1635	1954	1.9E
	2325		
21		0156	1.7F
Sa	0501	0824	2.1E
	1156	1440	1.7F
	1739	2053	2.1E
22	0026	0312	1.6F
Su	0600	0915	2.2E
	1248	1550	1.9F
	1837	2146	2.2E
23	0125	0419	1.7F
M	0653	1006	2.2E
	1338	1641	2.0F
	1929	2239	2.2E
24	0220	0511	1.7F
Tu	0741	1052	2.1E
	1426	1726	2.1F
	2017	2330	2.3E
25	0312	0552	1.7F
W	0827	1140	2.1E
	1512	1805	2.2F
	2103		
26		0021	2.3E
Th	0400	0633	1.6F
	0911	1229	2.0E
	1555	1840	2.1F
	2147		
27		0107	2.2E
F	0446	0708	1.5F
	0956	1315	1.9E
	1637	1916	2.0F
	2231		
28		0151	2.2E
Sa	0531	0745	1.4F
	1040	1358	1.9E
	1719	1954	1.9F
	2314		
29		0234	2.1E
Su	0617	0828	1.3F
	1126	1439	1.8E
	1802	2039	1.8F
	2358		
30		0313	2.0E
M	0704	0916	1.2F
	1213	1521	1.6E
	1849	2126	1.6F
31	0041	0358	1.9E
Tu	0754	1008	1.2F
	1300	1608	1.5E
	1941	2217	1.5F

JUNE

Day	Slack Water Time h.m.	Maximum Current Time h.m.	Maximum Current Vel. knots
1	0125	0444	1.8E
W	0844	1055	1.2F
	1350	1659	1.4E
	2038	2306	1.4F
2	0211	0534	1.7E
Th	0933	1144	1.2F
	1441	1755	1.4E
	2135	2355	1.4F
3	0300	0630	1.7E
F	1020	1229	1.3F
	1536	1856	1.4E
	2231		
4		0045	1.3F
Sa	0352	0724	1.7E
	1106	1320	1.3F
	1633	1951	1.5E
	2326		
5		0138	1.3F
Su	0445	0812	1.8E
	1150	1411	1.4F
	1728	2043	1.7E
6	0020	0233	1.3F
M	0538	0858	1.8E
	1234	1505	1.6F
	1818	2131	1.8E
7	0113	0330	1.3F
Tu	0628	0941	1.9E
	1317	1556	1.8F
	1906	2217	2.0E
8	0205	0424	1.4F
W	0715	1028	1.9E
	1400	1642	2.0F
	1952	2306	2.1E
9	0254	0510	1.5F
Th	0801	1111	2.0E
	1442	1728	2.2F
	2038	2357	2.3E
10	0342	0556	1.6F
F	0847	1202	2.0E
	1526	1811	2.3F
	2126		
11		0048	2.4E
Sa	0428	0641	1.7F
	0936	1252	2.1E
	1610	1857	2.4F
	2215		
12		0136	2.5E
Su	0515	0728	1.7F
	1027	1343	2.1E
	1658	1946	2.3F
	2305		
13		0225	2.5E
M	0604	0819	1.7F
	1121	1434	2.2E
	1750	2039	2.2F
	2357		
14		0313	2.5E
Tu	0656	0915	1.7F
	1216	1525	2.1E
	1848	2136	2.1F
15	0050	0404	2.4E
W	0751	1015	1.7F
	1313	1621	2.0E
	1953	2233	2.0F
16	0143	0458	2.3E
Th	0847	1113	1.7F
	1411	1722	1.9E
	2059	2333	1.9F
17	0237	0558	2.2E
F	0942	1212	1.7F
	1512	1829	1.9E
	2204		
18		0032	1.7F
Sa	0334	0700	2.1E
	1036	1311	1.8F
	1616	1935	1.9E
	2306		
19		0138	1.6F
Su	0433	0757	2.1E
	1129	1418	1.8F
	1719	2033	2.0E
20	0007	0250	1.5F
M	0531	0849	2.1E
	1220	1525	1.9F
	1817	2128	2.1E
21	0106	0357	1.5F
Tu	0625	0941	2.0E
	1311	1622	2.0F
	1910	2219	2.1E
22	0202	0452	1.5F
W	0715	1026	2.0E
	1401	1708	2.0F
	1957	2308	2.1E
23	0255	0539	1.5F
Th	0802	1114	1.9E
	1448	1749	2.0F
	2042		
24		0000	2.1E
F	0342	0618	1.4F
	0847	1203	1.9E
	1532	1822	2.0F
	2125		
25		0046	2.1E
Sa	0427	0653	1.4F
	0931	1249	1.8E
	1615	1855	2.0F
	2207		
26		0129	2.1E
Su	0510	0726	1.3F
	1016	1334	1.8E
	1656	1931	1.9F
	2249		
27		0210	2.1E
M	0553	0805	1.3F
	1101	1418	1.7E
	1738	2012	1.8F
	2331		
28		0250	2.1E
Tu	0636	0848	1.3F
	1147	1457	1.7E
	1822	2057	1.7F
29	0012	0329	2.0E
W	0721	0935	1.3F
	1233	1540	1.6E
	1909	2144	1.6F
30	0054	0411	1.9E
Th	0806	1020	1.3F
	1320	1625	1.5E
	2002	2234	1.5F

Time meridian 75° W. 0000 is midnight. 1200 is noon.

F-Flood, Dir. 340° True E-Ebb, Dir. 160° True

JULY

Day	Slack Water Time h.m.	Maximum Current Time h.m.	Vel. knots
1	0137	0456	1.8E
F	0852	1107	1.3F
	1408	1716	1.5E
	2058	2321	1.4F
2	0222	0544	1.7E
Sa	0937	1152	1.4F
	1458	1813	1.5E
	2155		
3		0010	1.3F
Su	0309	0637	1.7E
	1021	1240	1.5F
	1552	1913	1.6E
	2250		
4		0059	1.3F
M	0401	0730	1.7E
	1104	1327	1.5F
	1648	2006	1.7E
	2346		
5		0152	1.2F
Tu	0455	0819	1.8E
	1149	1422	1.7F
	1743	2058	1.8E
6	0042	0249	1.2F
W	0549	0908	1.8E
	1235	1517	1.8F
	1835	2146	2.0E
7	0136	0347	1.3F
Th	0641	0954	1.9E
	1323	1610	2.0F
	1926	2239	2.1E
8	0229	0442	1.4F
F	0732	1045	2.0E
	1413	1702	2.2F
	2015	2331	2.3E
9	0319	0533	1.6F
Sa	0823	1138	2.1E
	1503	1751	2.4F
	2105		
10		0024	2.4E
Su	0406	0620	1.7F
	0914	1231	2.2E
	1553	1838	2.4F
	2155		
11		0117	2.5E
M	0453	0710	1.8F
	1008	1326	2.3E
	1644	1927	2.4F
	2247		
12		0206	2.6E
Tu	0541	0801	1.8F
	1103	1418	2.3E
	1738	2020	2.3F
	2338		
13		0255	2.6E
W	0631	0856	1.9F
	1159	1511	2.3E
	1835	2116	2.2F
14	0030	0343	2.5E
Th	0724	0953	1.9F
	1255	1604	2.2E
	1936	2215	2.0F
15	0121	0436	2.3E
F	0818	1053	1.9F
	1352	1701	2.1E
	2040	2315	1.8F
16	0213	0531	2.2E
Sa	0913	1150	1.9F
	1450	1803	2.0E
	2144		
17		0011	1.7F
Su	0306	0630	2.0E
	1007	1246	1.8F
	1551	1909	1.9E
	2245		
18		0112	1.5F
M	0403	0730	2.0E
	1100	1348	1.8F
	1653	2012	1.9E
	2346		
19		0221	1.3F
Tu	0501	0822	1.9E
	1153	1455	1.8F
	1753	2107	1.9E
20	0045	0336	1.3F
W	0558	0915	1.9E
	1246	1600	1.8F
	1847	2159	2.0E
21	0142	0434	1.3F
Th	0651	1003	1.8E
	1337	1649	1.9F
	1936	2248	2.0E
22	0234	0523	1.3F
F	0739	1051	1.8E
	1426	1732	1.9F
	2020	2335	2.0E
23	0322	0602	1.3F
Sa	0825	1139	1.8E
	1512	1809	1.9F
	2102		
24		0022	2.0E
Su	0405	0637	1.4F
	0909	1227	1.8E
	1555	1836	1.9F
	2143		
25		0103	2.0E
M	0445	0706	1.4F
	0953	1313	1.8E
	1636	1910	1.8F
	2223		
26		0144	2.1E
Tu	0525	0738	1.4F
	1037	1353	1.8E
	1716	1946	1.8F
	2303		
27		0225	2.1E
W	0604	0815	1.4F
	1121	1434	1.8E
	1757	2029	1.7F
	2343		
28		0300	2.0E
Th	0644	0858	1.4F
	1204	1513	1.8E
	1841	2114	1.6F
29	0023	0337	2.0E
F	0724	0945	1.4F
	1248	1552	1.7E
	1930	2201	1.5F
30	0104	0416	1.9E
Sa	0806	1033	1.5F
	1333	1637	1.6E
	2023	2250	1.4F
31	0146	0459	1.8E
Su	0849	1118	1.5F
	1421	1733	1.6E
	2120	2337	1.3F

AUGUST

Day	Slack Water Time h.m.	Maximum Current Time h.m.	Vel. knots
1	0231	0550	1.7E
M	0934	1205	1.6F
	1513	1832	1.6E
	2218		
2		0027	1.2F
Tu	0320	0647	1.7E
	1020	1254	1.6F
	1610	1933	1.7E
	2315		
3		0118	1.2F
W	0416	0743	1.7E
	1109	1347	1.7F
	1709	2028	1.8E
4	0013	0217	1.2F
Th	0515	0836	1.8E
	1201	1445	1.8F
	1807	2122	2.0E
5	0109	0318	1.3F
F	0614	0931	1.9E
	1257	1546	2.0F
	1902	2213	2.1E
6	0204	0420	1.4F
Sa	0709	1024	2.0E
	1353	1642	2.2F
	1954	2307	2.3E
7	0255	0513	1.6F
Su	0803	1117	2.2E
	1447	1734	2.3F
	2045		
8		0002	2.4E
M	0343	0604	1.8F
	0857	1215	2.3E
	1540	1824	2.4F
	2136		
9		0054	2.5E
Tu	0429	0653	2.0F
	0951	1309	2.4E
	1632	1913	2.4F
	2226		
10		0144	2.6E
W	0516	0742	2.0F
	1045	1403	2.5E
	1725	2002	2.3F
	2317		
11		0232	2.6E
Th	0603	0834	2.1F
	1140	1452	2.5E
	1819	2057	2.2F
12	0007	0319	2.5E
F	0653	0929	2.0F
	1234	1544	2.3E
	1917	2152	2.0F
13	0056	0409	2.3E
Sa	0746	1027	2.0F
	1328	1637	2.2E
	2018	2249	1.8F
14	0145	0500	2.1E
Su	0841	1119	1.9F
	1423	1736	2.0E
	2121	2347	1.5F
15	0237	0557	1.9E
M	0936	1216	1.8F
	1522	1840	1.9E
	2222		
16		0043	1.3F
Tu	0332	0658	1.8E
	1032	1314	1.7F
	1623	1944	1.8E
	2322		
17		0152	1.2F
W	0431	0757	1.7E
	1126	1426	1.6F
	1724	2043	1.8E
18	0021	0310	1.1F
Th	0531	0850	1.7E
	1221	1531	1.6F
	1820	2134	1.8E
19	0117	0411	1.2F
F	0627	0941	1.7E
	1314	1629	1.7F
	1910	2221	1.9E
20	0208	0500	1.3F
Sa	0718	1029	1.7E
	1404	1714	1.8F
	1954	2308	1.9E
21	0255	0543	1.4F
Su	0804	1116	1.7E
	1451	1749	1.8F
	2035	2353	2.0E
22	0337	0618	1.4F
M	0847	1201	1.8E
	1534	1818	1.8F
	2115		
23		0035	2.0E
Tu	0415	0643	1.5F
	0929	1247	1.8E
	1615	1848	1.8F
	2154		
24		0116	2.1E
W	0452	0709	1.5F
	1011	1328	1.9E
	1655	1921	1.8F
	2234		
25		0154	2.1E
Th	0528	0746	1.6F
	1052	1409	1.9E
	1735	2000	1.7F
	2313		
26		0231	2.1E
F	0604	0826	1.6F
	1134	1447	1.9E
	1816	2045	1.6F
	2352		
27		0306	2.0E
Sa	0640	0909	1.6F
	1217	1526	1.9E
	1901	2130	1.5F
28	0032	0339	1.9E
Su	0717	0956	1.6F
	1301	1605	1.8E
	1953	2218	1.4F
29	0113	0418	1.8E
M	0800	1043	1.6F
	1348	1656	1.7E
	2050	2307	1.3F
30	0157	0503	1.7E
Tu	0848	1132	1.7F
	1440	1755	1.7E
	2150	2358	1.2F
31	0248	0605	1.6E
W	0942	1224	1.7F
	1537	1901	1.7E
	2249		

Time meridian 75° W. 0000 is midnight. 1200 is noon.

DELAWARE BAY ENTRANCE, 1983

F-Flood, Dir. 305° True E-Ebb, Dir. 140° True

JANUARY

Day	Slack Water Time h.m.	Maximum Current Time h.m.	Vel. knots
1 Sa		0127	1.8E
	0442	0746	2.0F
	1056	1403	2.0E
	1733	2020	1.7F
	2321		
2 Su		0222	1.8E
	0539	0841	1.9F
	1151	1458	1.9E
	1829	2116	1.7F
3 M	0020	0320	1.7E
	0640	0940	1.8F
	1249	1557	1.9E
	1927	2214	1.6F
4 Tu	0122	0423	1.7E
	0745	1039	1.7F
	1349	1656	1.8E
	2026	2315	1.6F
5 W	0226	0527	1.6E
	0851	1143	1.6F
	1451	1759	1.8E
	2126		
6 Th		0018	1.7F
	0330	0635	1.7E
	0957	1245	1.6F
	1552	1900	1.7E
	2224		
7 F		0117	1.7F
	0432	0740	1.7E
	1059	1345	1.6F
	1652	1959	1.8E
	2319		
8 Sa		0216	1.8F
	0529	0839	1.8E
	1158	1444	1.6F
	1748	2059	1.8E
9 Su	0011	0309	1.9F
	0622	0934	1.9E
	1252	1537	1.6F
	1839	2146	1.8E
10 M	0100	0359	1.9F
	0711	1022	1.9E
	1341	1626	1.6F
	1927	2231	1.7E
11 Tu	0145	0444	1.9F
	0755	1105	1.9E
	1427	1707	1.6F
	2011	2314	1.7E
12 W	0226	0523	1.9F
	0836	1144	1.9E
	1508	1750	1.5F
	2051	2349	1.7E
13 Th	0305	0600	1.8F
	0913	1217	1.8E
	1547	1826	1.5F
	2128		
14 F		0025	1.6E
	0341	0639	1.8F
	0948	1251	1.8E
	1623	1904	1.5F
	2203		
15 Sa		0100	1.6E
	0416	0715	1.7F
	1022	1326	1.8E
	1657	1939	1.5F
	2238		
16 Su		0137	1.6E
	0451	0752	1.7F
	1056	1401	1.8E
	1731	2018	1.5F
	2315		
17 M		0215	1.6E
	0528	0833	1.7F
	1133	1442	1.8E
	1807	2101	1.5F
	2355		
18 Tu		0258	1.6E
	0610	0915	1.6F
	1213	1525	1.8E
	1846	2142	1.6F
19 W	0040	0343	1.6E
	0656	1002	1.6F
	1257	1608	1.8E
	1930	2233	1.6F
20 Th	0129	0434	1.6E
	0748	1053	1.5F
	1346	1658	1.7E
	2017	2321	1.6F
21 F	0222	0527	1.6E
	0845	1146	1.5F
	1439	1751	1.7E
	2109		
22 Sa		0016	1.6F
	0318	0624	1.6E
	0947	1243	1.5F
	1536	1846	1.7E
	2205		
23 Su		0111	1.7F
	0418	0724	1.7E
	1050	1341	1.5F
	1636	1945	1.7E
	2302		
24 M		0210	1.7F
	0518	0823	1.7E
	1153	1442	1.5F
	1736	2041	1.7E
25 Tu	0000	0305	1.8F
	0617	0924	1.8E
	1254	1539	1.5F
	1836	2140	1.7E
26 W	0058	0403	1.9F
	0714	1020	1.9E
	1352	1635	1.6F
	1934	2237	1.8E
27 Th	0154	0457	2.0F
	0810	1116	2.0E
	1446	1730	1.7F
	2031	2332	1.8E
28 F	0249	0551	2.0F
	0903	1210	2.0E
	1539	1823	1.7F
	2126		
29 Sa		0026	1.9E
	0343	0644	2.0F
	0955	1301	2.1E
	1630	1917	1.8F
	2219		
30 Su		0120	1.9E
	0438	0737	2.0F
	1047	1353	2.1E
	1720	2008	1.8F
	2313		
31 M		0213	1.9E
	0532	0828	1.9F
	1138	1442	2.0E
	1811	2101	1.8F

FEBRUARY

Day	Slack Water Time h.m.	Maximum Current Time h.m.	Vel. knots
1 Tu	0007	0306	1.8E
	0628	0922	1.8F
	1230	1535	1.9E
	1902	2152	1.8F
2 W	0102	0401	1.8E
	0725	1017	1.7F
	1323	1630	1.9E
	1955	2246	1.8F
3 Th	0158	0459	1.7E
	0824	1111	1.6F
	1418	1725	1.8E
	2049	2343	1.7F
4 F	0256	0600	1.7E
	0925	1209	1.5F
	1515	1821	1.7E
	2144		
5 Sa		0038	1.7F
	0354	0657	1.7E
	1025	1306	1.5F
	1612	1919	1.6E
	2239		
6 Su		0134	1.7F
	0451	0758	1.7E
	1124	1407	1.5F
	1710	2014	1.6E
	2333		
7 M		0229	1.7F
	0545	0856	1.7E
	1219	1502	1.5F
	1805	2111	1.6E
8 Tu	0025	0324	1.7F
	0637	0947	1.8E
	1311	1552	1.5F
	1856	2158	1.6E
9 W	0114	0412	1.7F
	0724	1034	1.8E
	1359	1641	1.5F
	1944	2245	1.6E
10 Th	0200	0456	1.8F
	0808	1117	1.8E
	1442	1724	1.5F
	2027	2325	1.6E
11 F	0242	0539	1.7F
	0848	1154	1.8E
	1521	1802	1.5F
	2106		
12 Sa		0003	1.6E
	0320	0615	1.7F
	0924	1228	1.8E
	1557	1840	1.6F
	2142		
13 Su		0040	1.6E
	0356	0651	1.7F
	0958	1301	1.8E
	1630	1915	1.6F
	2216		
14 M		0115	1.7E
	0430	0728	1.7F
	1031	1336	1.8E
	1701	1953	1.6F
	2251		
15 Tu		0152	1.7E
	0506	0807	1.7F
	1105	1412	1.9E
	1733	2032	1.7F
	2328		
16 W		0231	1.8E
	0545	0850	1.7F
	1143	1451	1.9E
	1809	2112	1.7F
17 Th	0008	0312	1.8E
	0628	0931	1.7F
	1224	1534	1.8E
	1849	2155	1.7F
18 F	0054	0401	1.8E
	0716	1020	1.6F
	1310	1623	1.8E
	1935	2246	1.7F
19 Sa	0145	0453	1.8E
	0812	1113	1.5F
	1402	1714	1.7E
	2027	2339	1.7F
20 Su	0242	0550	1.7E
	0914	1209	1.4F
	1500	1813	1.6E
	2126		
21 M		0038	1.7F
	0344	0651	1.7E
	1022	1312	1.4F
	1605	1913	1.6E
	2231		
22 Tu		0140	1.7F
	0450	0756	1.7E
	1131	1417	1.4F
	1714	2020	1.6E
	2339		
23 W		0245	1.7F
	0556	0904	1.7E
	1238	1521	1.5F
	1822	2124	1.6E
24 Th	0045	0346	1.8F
	0700	1006	1.8E
	1339	1625	1.6F
	1926	2229	1.7E
25 F	0147	0448	1.9F
	0759	1107	1.9E
	1435	1720	1.7F
	2025	2326	1.8E
26 Sa	0245	0542	2.0F
	0854	1201	2.0E
	1527	1815	1.8F
	2119		
27 Su		0021	1.9E
	0339	0636	2.0F
	0945	1250	2.1E
	1615	1903	1.9F
	2210		
28 M		0112	2.0E
	0430	0726	2.0F
	1033	1339	2.1E
	1701	1952	1.9F
	2259		

Time meridian 75° W. 0000 is midnight. 1200 is noon.

DELAWARE BAY ENTRANCE, 1983

F-Flood, Dir. 305° True E-Ebb, Dir. 140° True

MARCH

Day	Slack Water Time h.m.	Maximum Current Time h.m.	Vel. knots
1		0200	2.0E
Tu	0521	0812	1.9F
	1120	1424	2.0E
	1746	2037	1.9F
	2347		
2		0248	2.0E
W	0610	0900	1.9F
	1206	1509	1.9E
	1832	2126	1.9F
3	0035	0335	1.9E
Th	0701	0949	1.7F
	1253	1555	1.8E
	1918	2213	1.8F
4	0124	0426	1.8E
F	0753	1037	1.6F
	1342	1644	1.7E
	2008	2303	1.7F
5	0216	0518	1.7E
Sa	0848	1131	1.5F
	1435	1737	1.6E
	2100	2356	1.7F
6	0310	0613	1.6E
Su	0946	1227	1.4F
	1531	1832	1.5E
	2156		
7		0053	1.6F
M	0407	0714	1.6E
	1045	1326	1.3F
	1630	1933	1.5E
	2253		
8		0150	1.6F
Tu	0504	0813	1.6E
	1143	1424	1.4F
	1729	2033	1.5E
	2350		
9		0245	1.6F
W	0559	0910	1.6E
	1237	1521	1.4F
	1824	2124	1.5E
10	0043	0337	1.6F
Th	0650	0959	1.7E
	1326	1612	1.5F
	1915	2216	1.5E
11	0132	0426	1.7F
F	0736	1045	1.8E
	1411	1654	1.5F
	2000	2300	1.6E
12	0217	0509	1.7F
Sa	0818	1126	1.8E
	1450	1736	1.6F
	2040	2339	1.7E
13	0257	0549	1.7F
Su	0856	1159	1.8E
	1525	1812	1.7F
	2116		
14		0015	1.7E
M	0334	0626	1.7F
	0931	1233	1.9E
	1557	1848	1.7F
	2150		
15		0050	1.8E
Tu	0409	0703	1.8F
	1004	1308	1.9E
	1628	1925	1.8F
	2224		

Day	Slack Water Time h.m.	Maximum Current Time h.m.	Vel. knots
16		0127	1.9E
W	0444	0740	1.8F
	1037	1343	1.9E
	1659	2000	1.8F
	2259		
17		0205	1.9E
Th	0521	0821	1.7F
	1114	1422	1.9E
	1733	2041	1.9F
	2339		
18		0248	1.9E
F	0603	0902	1.7F
	1155	1503	1.9E
	1813	2125	1.9F
19	0023	0333	1.9E
Sa	0651	0950	1.6F
	1241	1550	1.8E
	1900	2213	1.8F
20	0114	0424	1.8E
Su	0746	1043	1.5F
	1334	1644	1.7E
	1954	2310	1.7F
21	0212	0523	1.7E
M	0850	1144	1.4F
	1436	1745	1.6E
	2059		
22		0012	1.6F
Tu	0318	0627	1.7E
	1002	1251	1.3F
	1547	1852	1.5E
	2212		
23		0119	1.6F
W	0430	0738	1.6E
	1116	1401	1.4F
	1703	2004	1.5E
	2328		
24		0230	1.6F
Th	0541	0849	1.7E
	1224	1511	1.5F
	1815	2118	1.6E
25	0039	0337	1.7F
F	0648	0958	1.8E
	1325	1612	1.6F
	1919	2225	1.7E
26	0142	0438	1.8F
Sa	0748	1057	1.9E
	1419	1710	1.8F
	2016	2322	1.9E
27	0239	0533	1.9F
Su	0841	1148	2.0E
	1508	1759	1.9F
	2107		
28		0012	2.0E
M	0330	0624	2.0F
	0930	1235	2.1E
	1554	1846	2.0F
	2154		
29		0059	2.1E
Tu	0418	0707	2.0F
	1014	1316	2.0E
	1636	1929	2.0F
	2239		
30		0142	2.1E
W	0504	0753	1.9F
	1057	1357	2.0E
	1717	2012	2.0F
	2321		
31		0224	2.0E
Th	0549	0834	1.8F
	1139	1438	1.9E
	1758	2053	1.9F

APRIL

Day	Slack Water Time h.m.	Maximum Current Time h.m.	Vel. knots
1	0004	0306	1.9E
F	0634	0919	1.7F
	1221	1521	1.8E
	1840	2138	1.8F
2	0048	0351	1.8E
Sa	0721	1004	1.5F
	1306	1607	1.6E
	1926	2224	1.7F
3	0134	0438	1.7E
Su	0812	1055	1.4F
	1356	1657	1.5E
	2016	2316	1.6F
4	0225	0532	1.6E
M	0906	1148	1.3F
	1451	1750	1.4E
	2112		
5		0009	1.5F
Tu	0321	0628	1.6E
	1004	1247	1.3F
	1551	1848	1.4E
	2213		
6		0107	1.5F
W	0419	0727	1.6E
	1102	1345	1.3F
	1652	1951	1.4E
	2313		
7		0207	1.5F
Th	0516	0826	1.6E
	1157	1442	1.4F
	1750	2049	1.4E
8	0010	0302	1.5F
F	0610	0919	1.7E
	1247	1534	1.5F
	1842	2144	1.5E
9	0102	0353	1.6F
Sa	0659	1006	1.7E
	1332	1621	1.6F
	1929	2229	1.6E
10	0149	0438	1.6F
Su	0744	1048	1.8E
	1412	1702	1.7F
	2009	2309	1.7E
11	0231	0519	1.7F
M	0823	1125	1.8E
	1448	1739	1.8F
	2046	2346	1.8E
12	0309	0559	1.7F
Tu	0859	1201	1.9E
	1520	1817	1.9F
	2121		
13		0022	1.9E
W	0345	0637	1.8F
	0934	1237	1.9E
	1552	1854	1.9F
	2155		
14		0101	2.0E
Th	0421	0714	1.8F
	1009	1312	1.9E
	1624	1931	2.0F
	2232		
15		0138	2.0E
F	0500	0755	1.7F
	1047	1353	1.9E
	1701	2012	2.0F
	2313		

Day	Slack Water Time h.m.	Maximum Current Time h.m.	Vel. knots
16		0221	2.0E
Sa	0543	0840	1.7F
	1130	1437	1.8E
	1744	2059	1.9F
	2359		
17		0310	2.0E
Su	0632	0929	1.6F
	1219	1526	1.7E
	1833	2149	1.8F
18	0051	0401	1.9E
M	0730	1026	1.5F
	1317	1623	1.6E
	1933	2246	1.7F
19	0151	0503	1.8E
Tu	0836	1128	1.4F
	1424	1728	1.5E
	2045	2353	1.6F
20	0300	0612	1.7E
W	0949	1238	1.4F
	1540	1842	1.4E
	2204		
21		0105	1.5F
Th	0415	0725	1.7E
	1101	1349	1.4F
	1658	2000	1.5E
	2322		
22		0217	1.6F
F	0527	0838	1.7E
	1207	1459	1.6F
	1807	2111	1.6E
23	0032	0324	1.7F
Sa	0633	0943	1.8E
	1306	1600	1.8F
	1909	2215	1.8E
24	0133	0422	1.8F
Su	0731	1040	1.9E
	1357	1651	1.9F
	2002	2310	2.0E
25	0227	0517	1.9F
M	0823	1130	2.0E
	1444	1740	2.0F
	2050	2359	2.1E
26	0317	0604	1.9F
Tu	0909	1213	2.0E
	1528	1823	2.1F
	2134		
27		0040	2.1E
W	0402	0649	1.9F
	0952	1254	1.9E
	1608	1904	2.1F
	2215		
28		0121	2.1E
Th	0445	0728	1.8F
	1032	1331	1.9E
	1646	1942	2.0F
	2254		
29		0159	2.0E
F	0526	0808	1.7F
	1110	1409	1.7E
	1724	2024	1.9F
	2332		
30		0237	1.9E
Sa	0608	0849	1.6F
	1150	1448	1.6E
	1803	2103	1.8F

Time meridian 75° W. 0000 is midnight. 1200 is noon.

F-Flood, Dir. 305° True E-Ebb, Dir. 140° True

MAY

Day	Slack Water Time h.m.	Maximum Current Time h.m.	Vel. knots
1 Su	0012	0316	1.8E
	0651	0932	1.5F
	1233	1529	1.5E
	1846	2148	1.7F
2 M	0055	0403	1.7E
	0737	1020	1.4F
	1321	1618	1.4E
	1935	2236	1.6F
3 Tu	0143	0452	1.7E
	0828	1113	1.3F
	1415	1712	1.4E
	2030	2330	1.5F
4 W	0235	0547	1.6E
	0923	1208	1.3F
	1514	1809	1.3E
	2131		
5 Th		0028	1.4F
	0332	0643	1.6E
	1019	1304	1.4F
	1615	1911	1.4E
	2234		
6 F		0125	1.4F
	0430	0741	1.6E
	1113	1401	1.5F
	1712	2010	1.4E
	2333		
7 Sa		0222	1.5F
	0526	0834	1.7E
	1203	1455	1.6F
	1805	2104	1.6E
8 Su	0027	0315	1.5F
	0617	0922	1.7E
	1248	1542	1.7F
	1852	2153	1.7E
9 M	0115	0402	1.6F
	0703	1008	1.8E
	1329	1625	1.8F
	1934	2234	1.8E
10 Tu	0200	0445	1.6F
	0745	1048	1.8E
	1406	1705	1.9F
	2013	2314	1.9E
11 W	0241	0528	1.7F
	0825	1127	1.9E
	1441	1744	2.0F
	2050	2355	2.0E
12 Th	0321	0608	1.7F
	0903	1205	1.9E
	1516	1823	2.0F
	2128		
13 F		0034	2.1E
	0400	0650	1.7F
	0942	1246	1.9E
	1553	1905	2.0F
	2208		
14 Sa		0117	2.1E
	0443	0734	1.7F
	1025	1329	1.8E
	1635	1950	2.0F
	2252		
15 Su		0203	2.1E
	0529	0821	1.6F
	1112	1416	1.8E
	1722	2037	1.9F
	2340		
16 M		0254	2.0E
	0621	0913	1.6F
	1206	1509	1.7E
	1818	2132	1.8F
17 Tu	0035	0348	1.9E
	0721	1010	1.5F
	1309	1611	1.5E
	1923	2233	1.7F
18 W	0138	0450	1.8E
	0827	1115	1.5F
	1420	1720	1.5E
	2039	2341	1.6F
19 Th	0247	0600	1.7E
	0937	1225	1.5F
	1536	1835	1.5E
	2158		
20 F		0052	1.5F
	0400	0712	1.7E
	1044	1335	1.6F
	1649	1950	1.6E
	2313		
21 Sa		0202	1.6F
	0509	0821	1.8E
	1145	1440	1.8F
	1754	2101	1.7E
22 Su	0019	0308	1.7F
	0612	0923	1.9E
	1241	1537	1.9F
	1851	2200	1.9E
23 M	0118	0405	1.7F
	0708	1016	1.9E
	1331	1629	2.0F
	1943	2251	2.0E
24 Tu	0211	0456	1.8F
	0759	1105	1.9E
	1417	1716	2.1F
	2029	2339	2.1E
25 W	0259	0542	1.8F
	0845	1148	1.9E
	1459	1757	2.1F
	2111		
26 Th		0020	2.1E
	0343	0625	1.7F
	0927	1227	1.8E
	1539	1838	2.0F
	2150		
27 F		0057	2.0E
	0425	0703	1.6F
	1006	1302	1.7E
	1616	1914	1.9F
	2227		
28 Sa		0133	1.9E
	0504	0742	1.5F
	1043	1338	1.6E
	1652	1952	1.8F
	2303		
29 Su		0208	1.9E
	0543	0822	1.5F
	1122	1416	1.5E
	1729	2032	1.7F
	2339		
30 M		0247	1.8E
	0623	0903	1.4F
	1203	1457	1.4E
	1811	2114	1.6F
31 Tu	0019	0328	1.8E
	0705	0949	1.4F
	1250	1546	1.4E
	1858	2201	1.5F

JUNE

Day	Slack Water Time h.m.	Maximum Current Time h.m.	Vel. knots
1 W	0104	0415	1.7E
	0752	1038	1.4F
	1342	1637	1.4E
	1951	2252	1.5F
2 Th	0153	0505	1.7E
	0842	1132	1.4F
	1437	1732	1.4E
	2050	2347	1.4F
3 F	0246	0600	1.7E
	0933	1225	1.5F
	1535	1829	1.4E
	2151		
4 Sa		0044	1.4F
	0342	0653	1.7E
	1025	1318	1.6F
	1630	1927	1.5E
	2251		
5 Su		0140	1.4F
	0437	0747	1.7E
	1114	1411	1.7F
	1723	2020	1.6E
	2347		
6 M		0233	1.5F
	0530	0837	1.7E
	1200	1459	1.8F
	1812	2111	1.7E
7 Tu	0039	0323	1.5F
	0619	0923	1.8E
	1244	1546	1.9F
	1857	2159	1.8E
8 W	0127	0411	1.6F
	0706	1010	1.8E
	1325	1629	2.0F
	1940	2245	2.0E
9 Th	0213	0457	1.6F
	0750	1053	1.8E
	1405	1714	2.0F
	2022	2329	2.0E
10 F	0257	0543	1.6F
	0835	1136	1.8E
	1446	1757	2.1F
	2104		
11 Sa		0012	2.1E
	0342	0629	1.6F
	0920	1223	1.8E
	1530	1842	2.1F
	2149		
12 Su		0059	2.1E
	0429	0716	1.6F
	1009	1310	1.8E
	1617	1933	2.0F
	2237		
13 M		0146	2.1E
	0519	0807	1.6F
	1102	1402	1.7E
	1710	2024	1.9F
	2328		
14 Tu		0241	2.0E
	0613	0900	1.6F
	1200	1459	1.6E
	1810	2120	1.8F
15 W	0025	0337	1.9E
	0712	1001	1.6F
	1305	1602	1.6E
	1918	2221	1.7F
16 Th	0126	0439	1.9E
	0815	1105	1.6F
	1414	1711	1.5E
	2032	2327	1.6F
17 F	0232	0543	1.8E
	0918	1209	1.7F
	1524	1822	1.6E
	2146		
18 Sa		0037	1.6F
	0340	0651	1.8E
	1019	1314	1.8F
	1631	1935	1.7E
	2255		
19 Su		0140	1.6F
	0445	0757	1.8E
	1117	1416	1.9F
	1732	2042	1.8E
	2359		
20 M		0245	1.6F
	0546	0856	1.9E
	1212	1511	2.0F
	1828	2138	1.9E
21 Tu	0057	0340	1.6F
	0641	0947	1.9E
	1302	1604	2.0F
	1918	2229	2.0E
22 W	0150	0432	1.6F
	0732	1038	1.8E
	1348	1647	2.1F
	2005	2316	2.0E
23 Th	0238	0519	1.6F
	0819	1122	1.8E
	1431	1733	2.0F
	2047	2357	2.0E
24 F	0323	0602	1.6F
	0902	1200	1.7E
	1511	1809	1.9F
	2125		
25 Sa		0034	2.0E
	0404	0641	1.5F
	0942	1238	1.6E
	1549	1850	1.9F
	2201		
26 Su		0107	1.9E
	0442	0718	1.5F
	1020	1314	1.5E
	1625	1926	1.8F
	2236		
27 M		0142	1.8E
	0519	0759	1.4F
	1058	1351	1.5E
	1702	2004	1.7F
	2311		
28 Tu		0218	1.8E
	0556	0837	1.4F
	1138	1432	1.4E
	1741	2045	1.6F
	2348		
29 W		0300	1.8E
	0634	0919	1.4F
	1221	1515	1.4E
	1825	2132	1.6F
30 Th	0029	0341	1.8E
	0716	1006	1.5F
	1308	1604	1.4E
	1915	2217	1.5F

Time meridian 75° W. 0000 is midnight. 1200 is noon.

F-Flood, Dir. 305° True E-Ebb, Dir. 140° True

JULY

Day	Slack Water Time h.m.	Maximum Current Time h.m.	Vel. knots
1	0114	0430	1.8E
F	0800	1055	1.5F
	1359	1654	1.4E
	2009	2309	1.5F
2	0203	0517	1.8E
Sa	0847	1144	1.6F
	1452	1749	1.5E
	2107		
3		0002	1.4F
Su	0255	0610	1.7E
	0935	1236	1.7F
	1546	1844	1.5E
	2207		
4		0057	1.4F
M	0348	0700	1.7E
	1024	1329	1.7F
	1639	1939	1.6E
	2305		
5		0153	1.4F
Tu	0443	0753	1.7E
	1112	1420	1.8F
	1731	2032	1.7E
6	0002	0246	1.4F
W	0536	0844	1.7E
	1201	1511	1.9F
	1821	2126	1.8E
7	0056	0337	1.5F
Th	0629	0933	1.7E
	1248	1558	2.0F
	1910	2215	1.9E
8	0148	0428	1.5F
F	0721	1024	1.7E
	1336	1647	2.0F
	1958	2304	2.0E
9	0238	0519	1.6F
Sa	0812	1114	1.8E
	1424	1736	2.1F
	2046	2353	2.1E
10	0328	0610	1.6F
Su	0905	1205	1.8E
	1515	1826	2.0F
	2135		
11		0044	2.1E
M	0418	0701	1.6F
	0959	1258	1.7E
	1608	1919	2.0F
	2226		
12		0136	2.1E
Tu	0509	0755	1.7F
	1055	1353	1.7E
	1705	2012	1.9F
	2318		
13		0227	2.1E
W	0603	0850	1.7F
	1154	1450	1.7E
	1805	2107	1.8F
14	0013	0325	2.0E
Th	0658	0948	1.7F
	1256	1551	1.6E
	1910	2207	1.7F
15	0111	0423	1.9E
F	0754	1047	1.7F
	1359	1656	1.6E
	2017	2309	1.6F

Day	Slack Water Time h.m.	Maximum Current Time h.m.	Vel. knots
16	0212	0521	1.9E
Sa	0852	1148	1.8F
	1503	1803	1.7E
	2125		
17		0012	1.6F
Su	0313	0625	1.8E
	0950	1248	1.8F
	1605	1909	1.7E
	2231		
18		0113	1.5F
M	0415	0726	1.8E
	1046	1345	1.9F
	1704	2014	1.8E
	2334		
19		0213	1.5F
Tu	0515	0823	1.8E
	1140	1442	1.9F
	1800	2111	1.9E
20	0032	0312	1.5F
W	0611	0921	1.7E
	1231	1533	2.0F
	1851	2204	1.9E
21	0126	0403	1.5F
Th	0704	1012	1.7E
	1320	1621	2.0F
	1938	2250	1.9E
22	0215	0454	1.5F
F	0753	1053	1.6E
	1405	1704	1.9F
	2022	2335	1.9E
23	0300	0539	1.5F
Sa	0838	1136	1.6E
	1447	1745	1.9F
	2101		
24		0010	1.9E
Su	0341	0618	1.5F
	0919	1215	1.5E
	1525	1824	1.8F
	2137		
25		0045	1.9E
M	0419	0654	1.4F
	0957	1251	1.5E
	1602	1902	1.7F
	2211		
26		0120	1.9E
Tu	0454	0733	1.5F
	1034	1326	1.5E
	1638	1939	1.7F
	2244		
27		0152	1.9E
W	0528	0811	1.5F
	1112	1405	1.5E
	1715	2018	1.7F
	2319		
28		0229	1.9E
Th	0602	0850	1.5F
	1151	1447	1.5E
	1756	2101	1.6F
	2356		
29		0310	1.9E
F	0638	0933	1.6F
	1233	1530	1.5E
	1840	2145	1.6F
30	0037	0351	1.9E
Sa	0717	1018	1.6F
	1319	1617	1.6E
	1930	2230	1.5F
31	0121	0436	1.8E
Su	0800	1103	1.7F
	1409	1708	1.6E
	2024	2321	1.5F

AUGUST

Day	Slack Water Time h.m.	Maximum Current Time h.m.	Vel. knots
1	0210	0524	1.8E
M	0846	1155	1.7F
	1502	1803	1.6E
	2123		
2		0016	1.4F
Tu	0303	0619	1.7E
	0936	1248	1.8F
	1557	1859	1.6E
	2225		
3		0113	1.4F
W	0400	0712	1.7E
	1030	1341	1.8F
	1654	1958	1.7E
	2328		
4		0211	1.4F
Th	0459	0809	1.7E
	1125	1438	1.9F
	1750	2057	1.8E
5	0029	0310	1.4F
F	0600	0907	1.7E
	1221	1533	1.9F
	1846	2153	1.9E
6	0127	0405	1.4F
Sa	0700	1004	1.7E
	1317	1629	2.0F
	1941	2248	2.0E
7	0223	0503	1.5F
Su	0759	1059	1.7E
	1412	1722	2.0F
	2033	2341	2.0E
8	0315	0557	1.6F
M	0856	1156	1.8E
	1508	1815	2.0F
	2125		
9		0034	2.1E
Tu	0406	0649	1.7F
	0951	1249	1.8E
	1603	1907	2.0F
	2216		
10		0124	2.1E
W	0456	0742	1.8F
	1046	1345	1.8E
	1659	1958	2.0F
	2306		
11		0215	2.1E
Th	0545	0834	1.8F
	1142	1437	1.8E
	1756	2053	1.9F
	2357		
12		0306	2.1E
F	0636	0927	1.9F
	1238	1535	1.8E
	1854	2148	1.8F
13	0050	0401	2.0E
Sa	0727	1023	1.9F
	1335	1633	1.7E
	1955	2242	1.6F
14	0145	0455	1.9E
Su	0821	1118	1.9F
	1434	1733	1.7E
	2058	2340	1.5F
15	0242	0551	1.8E
M	0916	1215	1.8F
	1533	1836	1.7E
	2201		

Day	Slack Water Time h.m.	Maximum Current Time h.m.	Vel. knots
16		0043	1.4F
Tu	0341	0647	1.7E
	1011	1312	1.8F
	1631	1937	1.7E
	2304		
17		0142	1.4F
W	0441	0749	1.6E
	1107	1408	1.8F
	1728	2039	1.7E
18	0003	0241	1.4F
Th	0540	0846	1.6E
	1201	1503	1.8F
	1821	2134	1.8E
19	0058	0334	1.4F
F	0635	0941	1.6E
	1252	1552	1.8F
	1910	2225	1.8E
20	0148	0428	1.4F
Sa	0727	1029	1.6E
	1339	1641	1.8F
	1955	2306	1.9E
21	0233	0513	1.5F
Su	0813	1114	1.6E
	1423	1722	1.8F
	2035	2345	1.9E
22	0314	0552	1.5F
M	0855	1151	1.6E
	1503	1801	1.8F
	2112		
23		0020	1.9E
Tu	0351	0631	1.5F
	0933	1227	1.6E
	1541	1838	1.8F
	2145		
24		0052	1.9E
W	0424	0706	1.6F
	1009	1302	1.6E
	1616	1913	1.7F
	2217		
25		0125	1.9E
Th	0455	0742	1.6F
	1043	1339	1.6E
	1651	1951	1.7F
	2249		
26		0158	1.9E
F	0526	0819	1.7F
	1119	1416	1.6E
	1727	2029	1.7F
	2324		
27		0236	1.9E
Sa	0558	0858	1.7F
	1158	1457	1.7E
	1808	2112	1.6F
28	0001	0313	1.9E
Su	0634	0938	1.8F
	1240	1542	1.7E
	1854	2157	1.6F
29	0044	0358	1.9E
M	0715	1027	1.8F
	1328	1631	1.7E
	1946	2244	1.5F
30	0131	0449	1.8E
Tu	0802	1116	1.8F
	1421	1727	1.6E
	2046	2341	1.4F
31	0225	0540	1.7E
W	0856	1209	1.7F
	1520	1824	1.6E
	2152		

Time meridian 75° W. 0000 is midnight. 1200 is noon.

F-Flood, Dir. 305° True E-Ebb, Dir. 140° True

SEPTEMBER

Day	Slack Water Time h.m.	Maximum Current Time h.m.	Vel. knots
1		0041	1.3F
Th	0326	0641	1.6E
	0955	1310	1.7F
	1622	1929	1.6E
	2301		
2		0144	1.3F
F	0433	0743	1.6E
	1059	1412	1.8F
	1727	2033	1.7E
3	0009	0249	1.3F
Sa	0542	0849	1.6E
	1205	1515	1.8F
	1829	2136	1.8E
4	0111	0351	1.4F
Su	0648	0953	1.6E
	1308	1614	1.9F
	1928	2235	1.9E
5	0208	0451	1.6F
M	0751	1051	1.7E
	1407	1710	2.0F
	2022	2330	2.1E
6	0300	0545	1.7F
Tu	0848	1147	1.8E
	1503	1803	2.0F
	2114		
7		0022	2.1E
W	0349	0637	1.9F
	0941	1240	1.9E
	1557	1855	2.0F
	2202		
8		0110	2.2E
Th	0436	0724	1.9F
	1033	1331	1.9E
	1649	1944	2.0F
	2250		
9		0156	2.1E
F	0522	0812	2.0F
	1123	1421	1.9E
	1741	2031	1.9F
	2336		
10		0243	2.1E
Sa	0608	0903	2.0F
	1213	1512	1.9E
	1833	2122	1.8F
11	0024	0330	2.0E
Su	0656	0952	1.9F
	1305	1604	1.8E
	1928	2213	1.6F
12	0114	0421	1.8E
M	0746	1043	1.8F
	1359	1659	1.7E
	2027	2308	1.5F
13	0207	0512	1.7E
Tu	0839	1136	1.8F
	1456	1758	1.6E
	2128		
14		0007	1.3F
W	0305	0611	1.6E
	0935	1235	1.7F
	1554	1859	1.6E
	2230		
15		0106	1.3F
Th	0406	0712	1.5E
	1033	1331	1.7F
	1652	2000	1.6E
	2330		

Day	Slack Water Time h.m.	Maximum Current Time h.m.	Vel. knots
16		0209	1.3F
F	0507	0813	1.5E
	1130	1430	1.7F
	1747	2059	1.7E
17	0025	0304	1.3F
Sa	0606	0909	1.5E
	1224	1521	1.7F
	1838	2150	1.8E
18	0116	0357	1.4F
Su	0659	1000	1.5E
	1313	1609	1.8F
	1924	2235	1.8E
19	0201	0444	1.5F
M	0746	1045	1.6E
	1359	1654	1.8F
	2006	2314	1.9E
20	0241	0523	1.6F
Tu	0828	1126	1.6E
	1440	1733	1.8F
	2043	2349	1.9E
21	0317	0600	1.7F
W	0905	1202	1.7E
	1517	1811	1.8F
	2117		
22		0021	1.9E
Th	0349	0636	1.7F
	0939	1235	1.7E
	1552	1847	1.8F
	2148		
23		0055	1.9E
F	0419	0710	1.8F
	1012	1310	1.8E
	1625	1923	1.8F
	2219		
24		0126	2.0E
Sa	0448	0747	1.8F
	1046	1347	1.8E
	1701	1958	1.7F
	2253		
25		0203	1.9E
Su	0519	0824	1.8F
	1123	1424	1.8E
	1739	2041	1.7F
	2329		
26		0240	1.9E
M	0555	0905	1.8F
	1205	1510	1.8E
	1824	2124	1.6F
27	0011	0325	1.8E
Tu	0637	0951	1.8F
	1253	1557	1.7E
	1916	2216	1.5F
28	0100	0414	1.7E
W	0726	1043	1.8F
	1347	1656	1.7E
	2017	2311	1.3F
29	0157	0510	1.6E
Th	0825	1143	1.7F
	1450	1757	1.6E
	2127		
30		0016	1.3F
F	0303	0617	1.5E
	0932	1246	1.6F
	1559	1905	1.6E
	2242		

OCTOBER

Day	Slack Water Time h.m.	Maximum Current Time h.m.	Vel. knots
1		0124	1.3F
Sa	0418	0726	1.5E
	1046	1353	1.7F
	1709	2016	1.7E
	2352		
2		0234	1.4F
Su	0533	0838	1.6E
	1158	1502	1.8F
	1815	2124	1.8E
3	0055	0337	1.5F
M	0642	0944	1.7E
	1303	1603	1.9F
	1915	2222	1.9E
4	0151	0438	1.7F
Tu	0742	1045	1.8E
	1402	1700	2.0F
	2010	2317	2.1E
5	0241	0530	1.9F
W	0837	1139	2.0E
	1456	1751	2.0F
	2059		
6		0004	2.1E
Th	0328	0619	2.0F
	0927	1228	2.0E
	1546	1837	2.0F
	2145		
7		0051	2.1E
F	0412	0704	2.1F
	1014	1315	2.0E
	1634	1923	2.0F
	2229		
8		0135	2.1E
Sa	0455	0749	2.0F
	1100	1400	2.0E
	1722	2009	1.8F
	2312		
9		0215	2.0E
Su	0538	0834	2.0F
	1145	1443	1.9E
	1810	2056	1.7F
	2356		
10		0301	1.9E
M	0622	0920	1.9F
	1232	1532	1.8E
	1900	2141	1.5F
11	0042	0347	1.7E
Tu	0709	1006	1.8F
	1322	1623	1.7E
	1954	2233	1.4F
12	0133	0436	1.6E
W	0800	1058	1.7F
	1415	1719	1.6E
	2051	2331	1.3F
13	0229	0532	1.5E
Th	0856	1156	1.6F
	1512	1816	1.5E
	2152		
14		0029	1.2F
F	0331	0633	1.4E
	0956	1252	1.5F
	1611	1919	1.5E
	2251		
15		0130	1.3F
Sa	0433	0735	1.4E
	1056	1353	1.6F
	1707	2018	1.6E
	2347		

Day	Slack Water Time h.m.	Maximum Current Time h.m.	Vel. knots
16		0229	1.4F
Su	0533	0836	1.5E
	1152	1447	1.6F
	1800	2110	1.7E
17	0037	0320	1.5F
M	0626	0927	1.6E
	1244	1536	1.7F
	1848	2159	1.8E
18	0122	0406	1.6F
Tu	0713	1014	1.7E
	1330	1625	1.7F
	1931	2238	1.9E
19	0202	0447	1.7F
W	0755	1054	1.7E
	1412	1704	1.8F
	2010	2313	1.9E
20	0238	0528	1.8F
Th	0833	1130	1.8E
	1450	1742	1.8F
	2045	2349	1.9E
21	0311	0603	1.8F
F	0907	1206	1.9E
	1526	1817	1.8F
	2117		
22		0022	1.9E
Sa	0341	0637	1.9F
	0941	1242	1.9E
	1600	1853	1.8F
	2149		
23		0055	1.9E
Su	0411	0714	1.9F
	1015	1319	1.9E
	1636	1932	1.7F
	2224		
24		0130	1.9E
M	0444	0755	1.9F
	1053	1358	1.9E
	1716	2013	1.7F
	2302		
25		0211	1.9E
Tu	0522	0836	1.9F
	1136	1443	1.9E
	1801	2100	1.6F
	2346		
26		0257	1.8E
W	0607	0925	1.8F
	1225	1534	1.8E
	1855	2151	1.4F
27	0038	0348	1.7E
Th	0701	1017	1.7F
	1322	1629	1.7E
	1959	2252	1.3F
28	0140	0451	1.5E
F	0806	1122	1.6F
	1428	1737	1.6E
	2111		
29		0000	1.3F
Sa	0253	0600	1.5E
	0921	1231	1.6F
	1541	1850	1.6E
	2226		
30		0111	1.3F
Su	0412	0716	1.5E
	1039	1341	1.6F
	1654	2001	1.7E
	2335		
31		0220	1.5F
M	0526	0830	1.6E
	1152	1449	1.7F
	1800	2110	1.8E

Time meridian 75° W. 0000 is midnight. 1200 is noon.

F-Flood, Dir. 305° True E-Ebb, Dir. 140° True

NOVEMBER

Day	Slack Water Time h.m.	Maximum Current Time h.m.	Maximum Current Vel. knots
1	0036	0324	1.7F
Tu	0632	0937	1.8E
	1256	1550	1.8F
	1900	2209	2.0E
2	0130	0422	1.9F
W	0730	1035	1.9E
	1352	1646	1.9F
	1953	2300	2.1E
3	0219	0513	2.0F
Th	0821	1126	2.1E
	1444	1735	2.0F
	2041	2349	2.1E
4	0305	0558	2.1F
F	0909	1213	2.1E
	1532	1820	1.9F
	2126		
5		0031	2.1E
Sa	0347	0641	2.1F
	0953	1256	2.1E
	1618	1903	1.9F
	2207		
6		0110	2.0E
Su	0428	0725	2.0F
	1036	1339	2.0E
	1702	1946	1.7F
	2248		
7		0149	1.9E
M	0508	0808	1.9F
	1117	1417	1.9E
	1746	2029	1.6F
	2329		
8		0231	1.7E
Tu	0550	0847	1.8F
	1200	1503	1.8E
	1832	2112	1.5F
9	0012	0312	1.6E
W	0634	0935	1.7F
	1245	1548	1.7E
	1921	2203	1.4F
10	0100	0401	1.5E
Th	0723	1024	1.6F
	1334	1639	1.6E
	2014	2255	1.3F
11	0154	0455	1.4E
F	0818	1115	1.5F
	1428	1734	1.5E
	2110	2350	1.3F
12	0254	0554	1.4E
Sa	0917	1213	1.5F
	1525	1832	1.5E
	2207		
13		0049	1.3F
Su	0355	0654	1.4E
	1018	1313	1.5F
	1622	1929	1.6E
	2302		
14		0145	1.4F
M	0454	0753	1.5E
	1115	1408	1.5F
	1716	2023	1.7E
	2352		
15		0239	1.5F
Tu	0547	0849	1.6E
	1208	1459	1.6F
	1806	2112	1.8E

Day	Slack Water Time h.m.	Maximum Current Time h.m.	Maximum Current Vel. knots
16	0038	0327	1.7F
W	0635	0936	1.7E
	1257	1546	1.7F
	1851	2155	1.8E
17	0119	0412	1.8F
Th	0718	1019	1.8E
	1341	1629	1.7F
	1932	2235	1.9E
18	0157	0451	1.9F
F	0758	1057	1.9E
	1421	1710	1.7F
	2010	2312	1.9E
19	0231	0529	1.9F
Sa	0835	1138	1.9E
	1459	1749	1.7F
	2046	2348	1.9E
20	0304	0607	2.0F
Su	0911	1213	2.0E
	1537	1828	1.7F
	2121		
21		0025	1.9E
M	0338	0645	2.0F
	0949	1254	2.0E
	1616	1909	1.7F
	2159		
22		0106	1.9E
Tu	0415	0725	2.0F
	1029	1337	2.0E
	1658	1952	1.6F
	2241		
23		0149	1.8E
W	0458	0812	1.9F
	1115	1423	1.9E
	1746	2043	1.6F
	2330		
24		0240	1.7E
Th	0548	0903	1.8F
	1207	1516	1.8E
	1842	2135	1.5F
25	0027	0335	1.6E
F	0647	1002	1.7F
	1306	1617	1.7E
	1947	2238	1.4F
26	0133	0439	1.5E
Sa	0757	1105	1.6F
	1413	1722	1.7E
	2057	2345	1.4F
27	0247	0550	1.5E
Su	0915	1215	1.6F
	1525	1834	1.6E
	2207		
28		0055	1.5F
M	0403	0706	1.5E
	1031	1325	1.6F
	1636	1944	1.7E
	2313		
29		0203	1.6F
Tu	0513	0820	1.7E
	1140	1432	1.7F
	1741	2049	1.8E
30	0012	0304	1.8F
W	0616	0923	1.9E
	1243	1534	1.8F
	1840	2147	1.9E

DECEMBER

Day	Slack Water Time h.m.	Maximum Current Time h.m.	Maximum Current Vel. knots
1	0106	0403	2.0F
Th	0712	1020	2.0E
	1339	1629	1.8F
	1933	2240	2.0E
2	0155	0451	2.0F
F	0803	1110	2.1E
	1430	1716	1.9F
	2021	2325	2.0E
3	0240	0538	2.1F
Sa	0849	1155	2.1E
	1517	1803	1.8F
	2105		
4		0006	1.9E
Su	0323	0619	2.0F
	0932	1238	2.0E
	1601	1844	1.7F
	2146		
5		0047	1.8E
M	0403	0700	2.0F
	1012	1317	1.9E
	1643	1924	1.6F
	2226		
6		0125	1.7E
Tu	0442	0739	1.9F
	1051	1355	1.8E
	1724	2005	1.5F
	2305		
7		0204	1.6E
W	0521	0821	1.8F
	1130	1434	1.8E
	1806	2047	1.4F
	2346		
8		0243	1.5E
Th	0603	0901	1.7F
	1211	1516	1.7E
	1849	2132	1.4F
9	0031	0329	1.5E
F	0648	0948	1.6F
	1256	1601	1.6E
	1936	2220	1.4F
10	0120	0420	1.4E
Sa	0739	1039	1.5F
	1345	1652	1.6E
	2026	2312	1.4F
11	0215	0515	1.4E
Su	0836	1132	1.5F
	1437	1747	1.6E
	2118		
12		0006	1.4F
M	0312	0612	1.4E
	0934	1227	1.5F
	1532	1840	1.6E
	2211		
13		0101	1.5F
Tu	0408	0708	1.5E
	1032	1323	1.5F
	1626	1935	1.7E
	2301		
14		0154	1.6F
W	0502	0801	1.6E
	1127	1417	1.5F
	1718	2023	1.7E
	2349		
15		0242	1.7F
Th	0552	0854	1.7E
	1219	1507	1.6F
	1807	2111	1.7E

Day	Slack Water Time h.m.	Maximum Current Time h.m.	Maximum Current Vel. knots
16	0033	0331	1.8F
F	0639	0942	1.8E
	1306	1554	1.6F
	1852	2155	1.8E
17	0114	0414	1.9F
Sa	0722	1025	1.9E
	1351	1637	1.6F
	1935	2238	1.8E
18	0154	0457	1.9F
Su	0804	1107	1.9E
	1434	1720	1.7F
	2016	2319	1.8E
19	0233	0538	2.0F
M	0845	1149	2.0E
	1516	1804	1.7F
	2058		
20		0002	1.8E
Tu	0313	0622	2.0F
	0927	1234	2.0E
	1600	1849	1.7F
	2142		
21		0045	1.8E
W	0357	0708	2.0F
	1012	1319	2.0E
	1646	1938	1.6F
	2229		
22		0134	1.8E
Th	0445	0757	1.9F
	1101	1410	2.0E
	1737	2027	1.6F
	2322		
23		0228	1.7E
F	0540	0850	1.8F
	1155	1503	1.9E
	1833	2122	1.6F
24	0021	0325	1.7E
Sa	0642	0948	1.7F
	1254	1601	1.8E
	1934	2224	1.6F
25	0127	0430	1.6E
Su	0751	1051	1.7F
	1358	1706	1.8E
	2038	2329	1.6F
26	0237	0540	1.6E
M	0904	1157	1.6F
	1506	1813	1.7E
	2143		
27		0035	1.6F
Tu	0347	0650	1.7E
	1015	1305	1.6F
	1613	1921	1.8E
	2246		
28		0140	1.7F
W	0453	0801	1.8E
	1123	1412	1.6F
	1717	2023	1.8E
	2345		
29		0240	1.9F
Th	0555	0904	1.9E
	1224	1511	1.7F
	1816	2126	1.8E
30	0040	0337	1.9F
F	0651	1000	2.0E
	1321	1606	1.7F
	1910	2219	1.9E
31	0130	0428	2.0F
Sa	0742	1051	2.0E
	1412	1700	1.7F
	2000	2304	1.8E

Time meridian 75° W. 0000 is midnight. 1200 is noon.

CHESAPEAKE BAY ENTRANCE, VIRGINIA, 1983

F-Flood, Dir. 305° True   E-Ebb, Dir. 125° True

JANUARY

Day	Slack Water Time h.m.	Maximum Current Time h.m.	Vel. knots
1	0002	0355	2.0E
Sa	0717	1015	1.7F
	1332	1648	1.7E
	2006	2227	1.0F
2	0056	0449	1.9E
Su	0811	1107	1.6F
	1422	1741	1.6E
	2100	2322	0.9F
3	0153	0545	1.8E
M	0907	1200	1.4F
	1512	1836	1.5E
	2156		
4		0019	0.9F
Tu	0254	0645	1.6E
	1007	1255	1.2F
	1602	1932	1.5E
	2255		
5		0121	0.8F
W	0400	0747	1.5E
	1110	1351	1.0F
	1652	2029	1.4E
	2355		
6		0225	0.8F
Th	0511	0854	1.3E
	1217	1452	0.8F
	1742	2127	1.4E
7	0055	0333	0.8F
F	0626	1002	1.2E
	1326	1554	0.7F
	1833	2225	1.4E
8	0153	0436	0.8F
Sa	0737	1105	1.2E
	1433	1652	0.6F
	1922	2320	1.4E
9	0247	0537	0.9F
Su	0842	1206	1.2E
	1533	1746	0.5F
	2008		
10		0008	1.4E
M	0336	0627	0.9F
	0938	1257	1.2E
	1625	1834	0.5F
	2052		
11		0053	1.4E
Tu	0420	0716	1.0F
	1026	1345	1.2E
	1710	1915	0.5F
	2132		
12		0138	1.4E
W	0501	0755	1.0F
	1108	1424	1.2E
	1750	1954	0.5F
	2209		
13		0217	1.5E
Th	0540	0832	1.0F
	1145	1503	1.2E
	1825	2030	0.5F
	2245		
14		0253	1.5E
F	0616	0905	1.1F
	1218	1540	1.2E
	1859	2105	0.6F
	2320		
15		0329	1.5E
Sa	0653	0939	1.1F
	1250	1615	1.2E
	1933	2140	0.6F
	2356		

Day	Slack Water Time h.m.	Maximum Current Time h.m.	Vel. knots
16		0404	1.4E
Su	0729	1014	1.0F
	1320	1646	1.2E
	2007	2216	0.6F
17	0033	0438	1.4E
M	0807	1049	1.0F
	1351	1721	1.2E
	2043	2253	0.6F
18	0113	0515	1.4E
Tu	0847	1126	1.0F
	1422	1759	1.1E
	2121	2334	0.7F
19	0158	0559	1.3E
W	0931	1207	0.9F
	1456	1836	1.1E
	2204		
20		0023	0.7F
Th	0249	0645	1.2E
	1020	1251	0.8F
	1533	1921	1.1E
	2251		
21		0116	0.7F
F	0348	0741	1.2E
	1115	1340	0.7F
	1615	2009	1.2E
	2344		
22		0213	0.8F
Sa	0457	0848	1.1E
	1217	1435	0.6F
	1704	2108	1.3E
23	0042	0317	0.8F
Su	0614	0956	1.1E
	1323	1536	0.6F
	1759	2209	1.4E
24	0141	0426	1.0F
M	0732	1105	1.2E
	1428	1642	0.6F
	1900	2310	1.5E
25	0239	0529	1.2F
Tu	0844	1209	1.3E
	1530	1743	0.7F
	2003		
26		0009	1.7E
W	0335	0631	1.4F
	0948	1309	1.4E
	1626	1843	0.8F
	2105		
27		0108	1.8E
Th	0429	0729	1.5F
	1045	1402	1.6E
	1718	1939	0.9F
	2205		
28		0201	2.0E
F	0522	0820	1.6F
	1137	1453	1.7E
	1808	2032	1.0F
	2302		
29		0254	2.1E
Sa	0614	0911	1.7F
	1226	1542	1.7E
	1856	2124	1.1F
	2358		
30		0345	2.1E
Su	0706	1001	1.6F
	1312	1631	1.7E
	1944	2214	1.1F
31	0052	0437	2.0E
M	0758	1049	1.5F
	1357	1718	1.7E
	2033	2304	1.1F

FEBRUARY

Day	Slack Water Time h.m.	Maximum Current Time h.m.	Vel. knots
1	0147	0529	1.9E
Tu	0850	1138	1.3F
	1440	1804	1.6E
	2124	2355	1.0F
2	0243	0623	1.7E
W	0945	1226	1.1F
	1522	1856	1.5E
	2217		
3		0049	1.0F
Th	0341	0721	1.4E
	1043	1317	0.9F
	1604	1949	1.4E
	2313		
4		0150	0.9F
F	0444	0822	1.3E
	1147	1411	0.7F
	1648	2045	1.3E
5	0013	0252	0.8F
Sa	0553	0927	1.1E
	1256	1507	0.5F
	1734	2141	1.2E
6	0114	0357	0.7F
Su	0705	1036	1.0E
	1406	1609	0.4F
	1825	2242	1.2E
7	0214	0503	0.7F
M	0813	1136	1.0E
	1512	1714	0.3F
	1921	2339	1.3E
8	0309	0602	0.8F
Tu	0912	1231	1.0E
	1606	1809	0.4F
	2016		
9		0028	1.3E
W	0358	0651	0.9F
	1002	1320	1.1E
	1650	1851	0.4F
	2106		
10		0115	1.4E
Th	0441	0736	0.9F
	1043	1403	1.2E
	1727	1936	0.5F
	2151		
11		0157	1.4E
F	0520	0811	1.0F
	1120	1440	1.2E
	1800	2011	0.6F
	2231		
12		0234	1.5E
Sa	0557	0844	1.0F
	1152	1515	1.2E
	1831	2045	0.6F
	2309		
13		0310	1.5E
Su	0633	0916	1.1F
	1222	1545	1.3E
	1901	2120	0.7F
	2345		
14		0343	1.5E
M	0708	0948	1.1F
	1249	1617	1.3E
	1932	2152	0.8F
15	0023	0418	1.5E
Tu	0744	1021	1.0F
	1317	1647	1.3E
	2005	2230	0.8F

Day	Slack Water Time h.m.	Maximum Current Time h.m.	Vel. knots
16	0103	0453	1.5E
W	0823	1058	1.0F
	1345	1719	1.3E
	2040	2311	0.9F
17	0146	0532	1.4E
Th	0904	1135	0.9F
	1416	1756	1.3E
	2121	2354	0.9F
18	0235	0619	1.3E
F	0951	1216	0.8F
	1450	1837	1.3E
	2208		
19		0046	0.9F
Sa	0332	0714	1.2E
	1046	1305	0.7F
	1531	1928	1.3E
	2304		
20		0141	0.9F
Su	0438	0818	1.1E
	1149	1402	0.6F
	1619	2031	1.3E
21	0006	0250	0.9F
M	0555	0931	1.1E
	1300	1506	0.5F
	1719	2139	1.4E
22	0112	0359	1.0F
Tu	0715	1048	1.1E
	1411	1619	0.5F
	1830	2248	1.5E
23	0218	0511	1.1F
W	0830	1153	1.2E
	1515	1726	0.6F
	1945	2356	1.6E
24	0320	0617	1.3F
Th	0934	1254	1.4E
	1612	1830	0.8F
	2056		
25		0056	1.8E
F	0418	0715	1.5F
	1029	1347	1.6E
	1702	1929	1.0F
	2200		
26		0151	2.0E
Sa	0512	0808	1.5F
	1118	1436	1.7E
	1749	2020	1.1F
	2259		
27		0242	2.0E
Su	0603	0855	1.6F
	1203	1520	1.8E
	1834	2109	1.2F
	2353		
28		0333	2.0E
M	0653	0942	1.5F
	1245	1605	1.8E
	1918	2155	1.3F

Time meridian 75° W. 0000 is midnight. 1200 is noon.
* Current weak and variable.

F-Flood, Dir. 305° True E-Ebb, Dir. 125° True

MARCH

Day	Slack Water Time h.m.	Maximum Current Time h.m.	Vel. knots	Day	Slack Water Time h.m.	Maximum Current Time h.m.	Vel. knots
1	0045	0422	2.0E	16	0011	0355	1.6E
Tu	0742	1024	1.4F	W	0721	0954	1.0F
	1324	1650	1.8E		1238	1613	1.4E
	2003	2243	1.3F		1929	2205	1.1F
2	0135	0510	1.8E	17	0052	0433	1.5E
W	0831	1109	1.2F	Th	0800	1027	1.0F
	1401	1733	1.7E		1307	1646	1.4E
	2050	2329	1.2F		2006	2247	1.1F
3	0226	0601	1.6E	18	0137	0514	1.5E
Th	0922	1151	1.0F	F	0842	1106	0.9F
	1437	1819	1.5E		1338	1722	1.4E
	2138				2048	2332	1.1F
4		0016	1.1F	19	0226	0603	1.3E
F	0317	0650	1.4E	Sa	0931	1151	0.8F
	1016	1237	0.7F		1414	1808	1.4E
	1513	1905	1.4E		2138		
	2231						
5		0111	0.9F	20		0023	1.1F
Sa	0413	0748	1.2E	Su	0323	0656	1.2E
	1115	1327	0.5F		1027	1238	0.7F
	1550	1959	1.2E		1457	1859	1.4E
	2329				2235		
6		0208	0.8F	21		0122	1.1F
Su	0514	0852	1.0E	M	0428	0803	1.1E
	1223	1420	0.4F		1133	1338	0.5F
	1632	2100	1.1E		1549	2003	1.4E
					2341		
7	0032	0311	0.7F	22		0232	1.0F
M	0623	0958	0.9E	Tu	0544	0918	1.1E
	1336	1524	0.3F		1247	1447	0.5F
	1726	2203	1.1E		1655	2120	1.4E
8	0137	0420	0.6F	23	0052	0343	1.0F
Tu	0733	1105	0.9E	W	0702	1033	1.1E
	1444	1636	0.3F		1359	1603	0.5F
	1833	2308	1.1E		1817	2235	1.5E
9	0237	0527	0.7F	24	0203	0457	1.1F
W	0834	1202	1.0E	Th	0814	1140	1.3E
	1538	1737	0.3F		1502	1717	0.6F
	1942				1940	2343	1.6E
10		0002	1.2E	25	0308	0602	1.2F
Th	0329	0621	0.8F	F	0914	1238	1.5E
	0925	1249	1.1E		1555	1820	0.8F
	1620	1825	0.4F		2054		
	2041						
11		0049	1.3E	26		0044	1.8E
F	0415	0704	0.9F	Sa	0406	0700	1.3F
	1008	1331	1.2E		1006	1327	1.6E
	1655	1907	0.5F		1642	1917	1.0F
	2131				2158		
12		0132	1.4E	27		0140	1.9E
Sa	0455	0739	0.9F	Su	0500	0749	1.4F
	1044	1408	1.2E		1052	1414	1.7E
	1726	1945	0.7F		1727	2007	1.2F
	2215				2254		
13		0210	1.5E	28		0229	1.9E
Su	0533	0814	1.0F	M	0550	0835	1.4F
	1116	1441	1.3E		1133	1457	1.8E
	1756	2021	0.8F		1809	2053	1.3F
	2254				2346		
14		0246	1.5E	29		0317	1.9E
M	0609	0849	1.0F	Tu	0638	0918	1.3F
	1144	1512	1.4E		1211	1538	1.8E
	1826	2055	0.9F		1851	2136	1.4F
	2333						
15		0322	1.6E	30	0034	0404	1.8E
Tu	0644	0918	1.0F	W	0724	0959	1.1F
	1211	1542	1.4E		1245	1619	1.7E
	1856	2128	1.0F		1934	2220	1.3F
				31	0121	0449	1.7E
				Th	0811	1038	1.0F
					1318	1659	1.6E
					2017	2303	1.2F

APRIL

Day	Slack Water Time h.m.	Maximum Current Time h.m.	Vel. knots	Day	Slack Water Time h.m.	Maximum Current Time h.m.	Vel. knots
1	0206	0534	1.5E	16	0130	0459	1.5E
F	0858	1118	0.8F	Sa	0826	1044	0.8F
	1350	1741	1.5E		1307	1700	1.6E
	2102	2346	1.1F		2025	2315	1.3F
2	0252	0623	1.3E	17	0222	0548	1.4E
Sa	0948	1159	0.6F	Su	0917	1129	0.7F
	1422	1826	1.3E		1348	1746	1.5E
	2151				2117		
3		0032	0.9F	18		0008	1.3F
Su	0341	0714	1.1E	M	0319	0648	1.3E
	1045	1246	0.4F		1017	1224	0.6F
	1456	1915	1.2E		1436	1843	1.5E
	2246				2217		
4		0126	0.8F	19		0110	1.2F
M	0435	0814	1.0E	Tu	0424	0757	1.2E
	1149	1337	0.3F		1125	1327	0.5F
	1538	2015	1.1E		1535	1954	1.4E
	2348				2325		
5		0225	0.7F	20		0218	1.1F
Tu	0537	0919	0.9E	W	0535	0908	1.2E
		1440	*		1237	1439	0.5F
		2120	1.0E		1650	2110	1.4E
6	0053	0331	0.6F	21	0037	0329	1.1F
W	0643	1026	0.9E	Th	0646	1019	1.2E
		1551	*		1344	1555	0.6F
		2226	1.1E		1817	2226	1.4E
7	0156	0439	0.6F	22	0148	0441	1.1F
Th	0745	1122	1.0E	F	0751	1120	1.4E
	1458	1655	0.3F		1443	1706	0.7F
	1905	2323	1.1E		1940	2333	1.6E
8	0252	0536	0.7F	23	0254	0544	1.1F
F	0837	1209	1.1E	Sa	0847	1215	1.5E
	1539	1750	0.5F		1534	1806	0.9F
	2011				2051		
9		0018	1.2E	24		0031	1.7E
Sa	0340	0621	0.8F	Su	0353	0638	1.1F
	0920	1254	1.2E		0936	1304	1.6E
	1614	1834	0.6F		1620	1903	1.1F
	2105				2153		
10		0059	1.4E	25		0126	1.7E
Su	0423	0700	0.9F	M	0447	0729	1.1F
	0957	1329	1.3E		1019	1347	1.7E
	1646	1912	0.8F		1703	1948	1.3F
	2152				2247		
11		0142	1.5E	26		0215	1.8E
M	0503	0739	0.9F	Tu	0536	0810	1.1F
	1030	1402	1.4E		1057	1430	1.8E
	1717	1950	0.9F		1745	2035	1.3F
	2235				2336		
12		0220	1.5E	27		0302	1.7E
Tu	0541	0811	1.0F	W	0622	0850	1.0F
	1100	1435	1.5E		1132	1511	1.7E
	1749	2026	1.1F		1825	2116	1.3F
	2317						
13		0255	1.6E	28	0021	0345	1.6E
W	0619	0846	1.0F	Th	0707	0930	0.9F
	1129	1507	1.5E		1204	1548	1.7E
	1822	2104	1.2F		1906	2156	1.3F
	2359						
14		0336	1.6E	29	0105	0428	1.5E
Th	0658	0925	1.0F	F	0751	1006	0.8F
	1159	1540	1.6E		1235	1628	1.6E
	1858	2145	1.3F		1947	2237	1.2F
15	0043	0414	1.6E	30	0146	0512	1.3E
F	0740	1001	0.9F	Sa	0835	1045	0.6F
	1232	1617	1.6E		1305	1706	1.5E
	1939	2228	1.3F		2030	2318	1.1F

Time meridian 75° W. 0000 is midnight. 1200 is noon.
* Current weak and variable.

CHESAPEAKE BAY ENTRANCE, VIRGINIA, 1983

F-Flood, Dir. 305° True   E-Ebb, Dir. 125° True

MAY

Day	Slack Water Time h.m.	Maximum Current Time h.m.	Vel. knots
1 Su	0228	0557	1.2E
	0923	1125	0.5F
	1337	1747	1.3E
	2117		
2 M		0000	0.9F
	0311	0646	1.1E
	1015	1211	0.4F
	1413	1836	1.2E
	2208		
3 Tu		0049	0.8F
	0359	0741	1.0E
	1114	1258	0.3F
	1457	1933	1.1E
	2305		
4 W		0144	0.7F
	0452	0838	0.9E
	1217	1402	0.3F
	1554	2038	1.0E
5 Th	0007	0242	0.6F
	0549	0940	0.9E
	1317	1505	0.3F
	1707	2141	1.0E
6 F	0109	0345	0.6F
	0646	1035	1.0E
	1407	1608	0.4F
	1824	2242	1.1E
7 Sa	0206	0441	0.7F
	0738	1124	1.1E
	1450	1705	0.5F
	1933	2336	1.2E
8 Su	0258	0530	0.7F
	0822	1206	1.2E
	1527	1752	0.7F
	2033		
9 M		0021	1.3E
	0345	0615	0.8F
	0902	1244	1.3E
	1603	1835	0.9F
	2125		
10 Tu		0107	1.4E
	0429	0657	0.9F
	0938	1320	1.4E
	1638	1919	1.1F
	2213		
11 W		0151	1.5E
	0511	0737	0.9F
	1013	1359	1.6E
	1714	2000	1.2F
	2300		
12 Th		0232	1.5E
	0553	0818	0.9F
	1048	1433	1.6E
	1752	2041	1.4F
	2347		
13 F		0313	1.6E
	0637	0855	0.9F
	1124	1514	1.7E
	1833	2126	1.5F
14 Sa	0035	0401	1.5E
	0722	0942	0.9F
	1203	1555	1.7E
	1919	2212	1.5F
15 Su	0125	0450	1.5E
	0812	1025	0.8F
	1245	1644	1.7E
	2009	2303	1.5F
16 M	0219	0541	1.4E
	0907	1118	0.7F
	1333	1735	1.7E
	2104		
17 Tu		0000	1.4F
	0316	0642	1.3E
	1007	1214	0.6F
	1429	1836	1.6E
	2205		
18 W		0101	1.3F
	0417	0745	1.3E
	1112	1319	0.6F
	1535	1946	1.5E
	2312		
19 Th		0203	1.1F
	0520	0851	1.3E
	1219	1430	0.6F
	1653	2100	1.4E
20 F	0022	0312	1.1F
	0623	0956	1.3E
	1322	1543	0.7F
	1817	2209	1.4E
21 Sa	0132	0418	1.0F
	0721	1055	1.4E
	1419	1652	0.8F
	1936	2317	1.5E
22 Su	0238	0520	1.0F
	0814	1150	1.5E
	1510	1753	1.0F
	2045		
23 M		0018	1.5E
	0338	0613	0.9F
	0900	1238	1.6E
	1557	1844	1.1F
	2144		
24 Tu		0109	1.6E
	0432	0702	0.9F
	0942	1323	1.7E
	1640	1932	1.2F
	2237		
25 W		0158	1.5E
	0521	0745	0.8F
	1019	1404	1.7E
	1722	2016	1.3F
	2325		
26 Th		0244	1.5E
	0607	0826	0.8F
	1053	1445	1.6E
	1803	2056	1.3F
27 F	0008	0328	1.4E
	0650	0902	0.7F
	1125	1523	1.6E
	1843	2135	1.2F
28 Sa	0048	0409	1.3E
	0732	0940	0.6F
	1156	1600	1.5E
	1923	2211	1.1F
29 Su	0127	0449	1.2E
	0814	1018	0.5F
	1228	1637	1.4E
	2004	2251	1.1F
30 M	0205	0532	1.1E
	0858	1056	0.5F
	1303	1718	1.3E
	2048	2331	1.0F
31 Tu	0243	0616	1.1E
	0945	1141	0.4F
	1342	1802	1.2E
	2135		

JUNE

Day	Slack Water Time h.m.	Maximum Current Time h.m.	Vel. knots
1 W		0016	0.9F
	0325	0704	1.0E
	1036	1228	0.4F
	1429	1856	1.1E
	2226		
2 Th		0106	0.8F
	0409	0756	1.0E
	1129	1321	0.4F
	1524	1953	1.1E
	2322		
3 F		0157	0.7F
	0456	0849	1.0E
	1222	1420	0.4F
	1629	2054	1.0E
4 Sa	0020	0252	0.7F
	0545	0940	1.0E
	1311	1520	0.5F
	1741	2153	1.1E
5 Su	0118	0349	0.7F
	0634	1031	1.1E
	1356	1615	0.6F
	1852	2251	1.1E
6 M	0213	0440	0.7F
	0720	1114	1.2E
	1439	1708	0.8F
	1957	2342	1.2E
7 Tu	0305	0529	0.7F
	0804	1158	1.4E
	1520	1759	1.0F
	2057		
8 W		0034	1.3E
	0354	0615	0.8F
	0847	1241	1.5E
	1601	1848	1.2F
	2152		
9 Th		0122	1.4E
	0442	0700	0.8F
	0929	1325	1.6E
	1644	1936	1.3F
	2244		
10 F		0210	1.5E
	0529	0747	0.8F
	1012	1408	1.8E
	1728	2023	1.5F
	2336		
11 Sa		0256	1.5E
	0617	0835	0.9F
	1057	1451	1.8E
	1815	2112	1.6F
12 Su	0027	0347	1.6E
	0706	0923	0.9F
	1144	1540	1.9E
	1904	2201	1.6F
13 M	0119	0437	1.5E
	0758	1013	0.8F
	1234	1631	1.8E
	1957	2254	1.6F
14 Tu	0211	0531	1.5E
	0852	1106	0.8F
	1329	1729	1.8E
	2053	2347	1.5F
15 W	0305	0629	1.5E
	0950	1203	0.8F
	1429	1829	1.7E
	2153		
16 Th		0045	1.3F
	0400	0727	1.4E
	1051	1308	0.7F
	1537	1933	1.5E
	2257		
17 F		0147	1.2F
	0455	0826	1.4E
	1152	1415	0.8F
	1652	2044	1.5E
18 Sa	0005	0248	1.0F
	0551	0927	1.4E
	1253	1524	0.8F
	1810	2151	1.4E
19 Su	0113	0352	0.9F
	0644	1025	1.5E
	1350	1629	0.9F
	1925	2258	1.4E
20 M	0220	0453	0.8F
	0735	1120	1.5E
	1444	1729	1.0F
	2033	2358	1.4E
21 Tu	0322	0546	0.7F
	0821	1209	1.5E
	1533	1825	1.1F
	2132		
22 W		0051	1.4E
	0418	0635	0.7F
	0904	1254	1.6E
	1619	1915	1.1F
	2225		
23 Th		0142	1.3E
	0508	0722	0.6F
	0943	1339	1.6E
	1702	1958	1.1F
	2312		
24 F		0227	1.3E
	0552	0800	0.6F
	1019	1421	1.5E
	1743	2039	1.1F
	2353		
25 Sa		0310	1.3E
	0633	0838	0.5F
	1054	1500	1.5E
	1823	2114	1.1F
26 Su	0031	0349	1.2E
	0712	0916	0.5F
	1128	1538	1.5E
	1902	2152	1.1F
27 M	0106	0427	1.2E
	0750	0952	0.5F
	1203	1615	1.4E
	1941	2228	1.0F
28 Tu	0140	0507	1.1E
	0829	1031	0.5F
	1241	1656	1.3E
	2022	2306	1.0F
29 W	0214	0544	1.1E
	0909	1112	0.5F
	1321	1735	1.3E
	2105	2346	0.9F
30 Th	0249	0626	1.1E
	0952	1157	0.5F
	1406	1820	1.2E
	2151		

Time meridian 75° W. 0000 is midnight. 1200 is noon.
* Current weak and variable.

F-Flood, Dir. 305° True E-Ebb, Dir. 125° True

JULY

Day	Slack Water Time h.m.	Maximum Current Time h.m.	Vel. knots
1		0029	0.8F
F	0325	0708	1.0E
	1037	1242	0.5F
	1457	1909	1.1E
	2241		
2		0114	0.8F
Sa	0405	0755	1.1E
	1125	1336	0.5F
	1556	2005	1.1E
	2334		
3		0201	0.7F
Su	0446	0842	1.1E
	1214	1429	0.6F
	1702	2104	1.1E
4	0032	0256	0.7F
M	0532	0933	1.2E
	1303	1530	0.7F
	1813	2205	1.1E
5	0131	0350	0.6F
Tu	0619	1025	1.3E
	1352	1627	0.8F
	1924	2305	1.2E
6	0228	0444	0.6F
W	0710	1116	1.4E
	1441	1727	1.0F
	2031		
7		0005	1.2E
Th	0324	0538	0.7F
	0801	1205	1.6E
	1531	1821	1.2F
	2132		
8		0058	1.3E
F	0417	0631	0.7F
	0854	1256	1.7E
	1620	1915	1.4F
	2230		
9		0151	1.5E
Sa	0508	0723	0.8F
	0947	1347	1.8E
	1710	2008	1.5F
	2324		
10		0242	1.5E
Su	0558	0816	0.9F
	1040	1437	1.9E
	1800	2057	1.6F
11	0015	0331	1.6E
M	0648	0909	0.9F
	1134	1530	2.0E
	1852	2149	1.7F
12	0105	0421	1.6E
Tu	0739	1001	1.0F
	1230	1621	2.0E
	1945	2240	1.6F
13	0155	0514	1.6E
W	0831	1055	1.0F
	1327	1718	1.9E
	2040	2333	1.5F
14	0243	0605	1.6E
Th	0925	1151	1.0F
	1427	1816	1.7E
	2138		
15		0026	1.3F
F	0332	0701	1.6E
	1021	1250	0.9F
	1531	1917	1.6E
	2239		

Day	Slack Water Time h.m.	Maximum Current Time h.m.	Vel. knots
16		0121	1.1F
Sa	0421	0756	1.5E
	1119	1351	0.9F
	1640	2021	1.4E
	2344		
17		0219	0.9F
Su	0511	0855	1.4E
	1219	1457	0.9F
	1753	2128	1.3E
18	0052	0319	0.7F
M	0601	0954	1.4E
	1319	1601	0.9F
	1907	2236	1.2E
19	0200	0420	0.6F
Tu	0652	1051	1.4E
	1417	1708	0.9F
	2015	2337	1.2E
20	0306	0521	0.5F
W	0741	1142	1.4E
	1511	1805	1.0F
	2116		
21		0034	1.2E
Th	0403	0612	0.5F
	0829	1234	1.4E
	1600	1857	1.0F
	2209		
22		0125	1.2E
F	0453	0700	0.5F
	0914	1319	1.5E
	1645	1942	1.0F
	2254		
23		0208	1.2E
Sa	0535	0741	0.5F
	0955	1400	1.5E
	1726	2019	1.0F
	2333		
24		0250	1.2E
Su	0613	0819	0.5F
	1034	1443	1.5E
	1805	2056	1.0F
25	0008	0325	1.2E
M	0647	0856	0.5F
	1111	1518	1.5E
	1843	2131	1.0F
26	0040	0401	1.2E
Tu	0721	0929	0.6F
	1148	1555	1.4E
	1920	2203	1.0F
27	0110	0435	1.2E
W	0755	1006	0.6F
	1225	1630	1.4E
	1957	2236	1.0F
28	0139	0511	1.2E
Th	0830	1044	0.6F
	1305	1706	1.4E
	2036	2315	0.9F
29	0209	0544	1.2E
F	0907	1125	0.7F
	1347	1748	1.3E
	2118	2350	0.9F
30	0240	0621	1.1E
Sa	0947	1206	0.7F
	1434	1829	1.2E
	2204		
31		0033	0.8F
Su	0314	0702	1.1E
	1031	1255	0.7F
	1528	1922	1.1E
	2255		

AUGUST

Day	Slack Water Time h.m.	Maximum Current Time h.m.	Vel. knots
1		0117	0.7F
M	0352	0749	1.2E
	1121	1350	0.7F
	1631	2025	1.1E
	2353		
2		0210	0.6F
Tu	0435	0843	1.2E
	1215	1449	0.8F
	1742	2128	1.1E
3	0055	0307	0.6F
W	0526	0939	1.3E
	1312	1555	0.9F
	1857	2235	1.1E
4	0159	0408	0.6F
Th	0625	1039	1.4E
	1410	1658	1.1F
	2010	2340	1.2E
5	0301	0512	0.6F
F	0728	1140	1.6E
	1507	1759	1.2F
	2116		
6		0039	1.3E
Sa	0357	0609	0.7F
	0832	1238	1.7E
	1602	1859	1.4F
	2214		
7		0135	1.5E
Su	0449	0709	0.8F
	0933	1334	1.9E
	1655	1952	1.6F
	2308		
8		0224	1.6E
M	0539	0803	1.0F
	1033	1426	2.0E
	1748	2043	1.6F
	2357		
9		0313	1.7E
Tu	0627	0855	1.1F
	1130	1518	2.1E
	1839	2133	1.6F
10	0044	0402	1.8E
W	0715	0947	1.2F
	1226	1610	2.0E
	1931	2221	1.6F
11	0129	0449	1.8E
Th	0804	1039	1.2F
	1322	1703	1.9E
	2024	2310	1.4F
12	0213	0538	1.7E
F	0865	1130	1.2F
	1419	1758	1.8E
	2119	2358	1.2F
13	0256	0628	1.6E
Sa	0947	1224	1.1F
	1518	1855	1.6E
	2218		
14		0049	1.0F
Su	0339	0721	1.5E
	1043	1321	1.0F
	1621	1957	1.4E
	2321		
15		0143	0.7F
M	0424	0818	1.4E
	1143	1425	0.9F
	1730	2102	1.2E

Day	Slack Water Time h.m.	Maximum Current Time h.m.	Vel. knots
16	0029	0244	0.6F
Tu	0512	0917	1.3E
	1246	1530	0.8F
	1842	2211	1.1E
17	0141	0348	0.4F
W	0605	1017	1.3E
	1348	1642	0.8F
	1951	2314	1.1E
18	0249	0452	0.4F
Th	0702	1116	1.3E
	1447	1743	0.8F
	2053		
19		0012	1.1E
F	0347	0550	0.4F
	0759	1211	1.3E
	1539	1834	0.9F
	2145		
20		0103	1.1E
Sa	0433	0639	0.4F
	0852	1300	1.4E
	1625	1919	0.9F
	2228		
21		0144	1.2E
Su	0511	0721	0.5F
	0939	1341	1.4E
	1707	1956	1.0F
	2305		
22		0223	1.2E
M	0545	0758	0.6F
	1021	1421	1.5E
	1745	2031	1.0F
	2338		
23		0258	1.2E
Tu	0616	0833	0.7F
	1059	1458	1.5E
	1821	2102	1.0F
24	0007	0331	1.3E
W	0647	0905	0.7F
	1135	1533	1.5E
	1856	2134	1.0F
25	0034	0401	1.3E
Th	0717	0940	0.8F
	1212	1605	1.5E
	1932	2207	1.0F
26	0059	0432	1.3E
F	0749	1015	0.8F
	1249	1642	1.4E
	2009	2241	0.9F
27	0126	0501	1.3E
Sa	0823	1052	0.9F
	1330	1719	1.4E
	2048	2316	0.9F
28	0154	0536	1.3E
Su	0901	1133	0.9F
	1415	1800	1.3E
	2133	2355	0.8F
29	0226	0614	1.2E
M	0945	1220	0.9F
	1507	1849	1.2E
	2224		
30		0042	0.7F
Tu	0303	0701	1.2E
	1037	1316	0.9F
	1608	1946	1.1E
	2323		
31		0133	0.6F
W	0348	0758	1.3E
	1136	1419	0.9F
	1720	2100	1.0E

Time meridian 75° W. 0000 is midnight. 1200 is noon.
* Current weak and variable.

SAVANNAH RIVER ENTRANCE (between jetties), GEORGIA, 1983

F-Flood, Dir. 260° True   E-Ebb, Dir. 080° True

JANUARY

Day	Slack Water Time h.m.	Maximum Current Time h.m.	Maximum Current Vel. knots
1 Sa		0121	2.9E
	0434	0711	2.4F
	1021	1355	3.3E
	1723	1943	2.0F
	2246		
2 Su		0214	2.9E
	0529	0803	2.3F
	1114	1447	3.2E
	1816	2037	1.9F
	2342		
3 M		0310	2.8E
	0625	0857	2.1F
	1206	1541	3.1E
	1909	2131	1.8F
4 Tu	0039	0403	2.7E
	0724	0949	1.9F
	1300	1634	2.9E
	2004	2223	1.7F
5 W	0138	0502	2.6E
	0826	1045	1.6F
	1355	1730	2.7E
	2059	2321	1.6F
6 Th	0239	0602	2.5E
	0929	1141	1.4F
	1452	1826	2.5E
	2155		
7 F		0015	1.5F
	0339	0659	2.4E
	1032	1240	1.2F
	1549	1922	2.4E
	2250		
8 Sa		0111	1.4F
	0438	0800	2.3E
	1134	1337	1.0F
	1647	2018	2.3E
	2343		
9 Su		0204	1.3F
	0534	0857	2.3E
	1233	1435	0.9F
	1742	2111	2.2E
10 M	0034	0258	1.3F
	0625	0950	2.4E
	1326	1527	0.9F
	1833	2200	2.2E
11 Tu	0121	0344	1.4F
	0711	1036	2.4E
	1414	1614	0.9F
	1920	2247	2.2E
12 W	0206	0428	1.4F
	0753	1119	2.4E
	1458	1700	1.0F
	2003	2330	2.2E
13 Th	0248	0510	1.5F
	0831	1200	2.5E
	1539	1739	1.1F
	2041		
14 F		0011	2.2E
	0328	0551	1.5F
	0906	1241	2.5E
	1617	1819	1.1F
	2117		
15 Sa		0051	2.2E
	0408	0630	1.6F
	0938	1320	2.5E
	1655	1858	1.2F
	2151		
16 Su		0132	2.2E
	0448	0711	1.6F
	1009	1359	2.5E
	1732	1939	1.3F
	2225		
17 M		0214	2.2E
	0528	0752	1.6F
	1041	1438	2.5E
	1810	2020	1.4F
	2301		
18 Tu		0256	2.1E
	0610	0837	1.5F
	1115	1519	2.4E
	1848	2105	1.4F
	2341		
19 W		0341	2.1E
	0656	0919	1.5F
	1153	1602	2.4E
	1929	2148	1.4F
20 Th	0024	0427	2.1E
	0745	1006	1.4F
	1235	1648	2.3E
	2013	2237	1.5F
21 F	0113	0518	2.1E
	0838	1057	1.4F
	1323	1738	2.3E
	2101	2327	1.5F
22 Sa	0208	0612	2.2E
	0936	1152	1.3F
	1416	1833	2.2E
	2153		
23 Su		0022	1.6F
	0309	0709	2.3E
	1037	1249	1.3F
	1517	1928	2.3E
	2248		
24 M		0117	1.7F
	0415	0807	2.4E
	1139	1349	1.3F
	1624	2026	2.4E
	2344		
25 Tu		0216	1.8F
	0521	0908	2.6E
	1239	1449	1.4F
	1734	2126	2.5E
26 W	0041	0314	2.0F
	0626	1006	2.8E
	1336	1549	1.6F
	1842	2222	2.7E
27 Th	0138	0413	2.1F
	0726	1059	3.0E
	1430	1646	1.7F
	1945	2318	2.8E
28 F	0233	0509	2.3F
	0823	1154	3.2E
	1522	1742	1.9F
	2044		
29 Sa		0013	3.0E
	0327	0601	2.3F
	0917	1245	3.3E
	1613	1835	2.0F
	2139		
30 Su		0105	3.0E
	0420	0654	2.3F
	1008	1336	3.3E
	1703	1926	2.0F
	2233		
31 M		0157	3.0E
	0514	0746	2.3F
	1058	1426	3.3E
	1752	2017	2.0F
	2325		

FEBRUARY

Day	Slack Water Time h.m.	Maximum Current Time h.m.	Maximum Current Vel. knots
1 Tu		0248	3.0E
	0608	0837	2.1F
	1147	1517	3.1E
	1842	2106	1.9F
2 W	0017	0342	2.8E
	0703	0926	1.8F
	1235	1608	2.9E
	1933	2154	1.8F
3 Th	0110	0436	2.6E
	0800	1017	1.6F
	1323	1659	2.6E
	2025	2245	1.6F
4 F	0204	0529	2.5E
	0859	1108	1.3F
	1414	1752	2.4E
	2119	2338	1.4F
5 Sa	0300	0628	2.3E
	1001	1202	1.0F
	1507	1846	2.2E
	2214		
6 Su		0029	1.3F
	0358	0725	2.2E
	1104	1257	0.9F
	1604	1943	2.1E
	2309		
7 M		0125	1.2F
	0455	0823	2.2E
	1204	1356	0.8F
	1703	2038	2.0E
8 Tu	0003	0219	1.2F
	0549	0916	2.2E
	1259	1452	0.8F
	1800	2129	2.0E
9 W	0054	0311	1.2F
	0640	1009	2.3E
	1348	1546	0.8F
	1852	2219	2.0E
10 Th	0141	0359	1.3F
	0725	1054	2.3E
	1432	1631	0.9F
	1939	2306	2.1E
11 F	0225	0444	1.4F
	0805	1137	2.4E
	1512	1713	1.1F
	2020	2349	2.2E
12 Sa	0307	0526	1.5F
	0842	1216	2.5E
	1549	1755	1.2F
	2057		
13 Su		0030	2.2E
	0347	0608	1.5F
	0915	1255	2.5E
	1625	1833	1.3F
	2130		
14 M		0108	2.3E
	0426	0649	1.6F
	0946	1333	2.6E
	1701	1912	1.5F
	2204		
15 Tu		0148	2.3E
	0505	0728	1.6F
	1018	1411	2.6E
	1736	1955	1.6F
	2238		
16 W		0230	2.4E
	0546	0811	1.6F
	1052	1450	2.5E
	1813	2036	1.6F
	2316		
17 Th		0313	2.4E
	0630	0854	1.6F
	1129	1531	2.5E
	1852	2118	1.7F
	2358		
18 F		0357	2.4E
	0717	0941	1.5F
	1210	1616	2.4E
	1936	2205	1.7F
19 Sa	0046	0446	2.3E
	0810	1030	1.5F
	1256	1705	2.3E
	2025	2256	1.7F
20 Su	0139	0541	2.3E
	0908	1124	1.4F
	1350	1801	2.2E
	2120	2351	1.7F
21 M	0240	0642	2.4E
	1011	1223	1.3F
	1452	1902	2.2E
	2220		
22 Tu		0050	1.7F
	0348	0744	2.4E
	1116	1324	1.3F
	1603	2004	2.3E
	2322		
23 W		0152	1.8F
	0500	0847	2.6E
	1218	1429	1.4F
	1719	2105	2.5E
24 Th	0024	0255	1.9F
	0609	0946	2.8E
	1317	1530	1.5F
	1831	2206	2.7E
25 F	0123	0356	2.0F
	0712	1044	3.0E
	1411	1628	1.7F
	1935	2302	2.9E
26 Sa	0220	0453	2.1F
	0809	1136	3.2E
	1502	1725	1.9F
	2032	2357	3.0E
27 Su	0314	0545	2.2F
	0901	1227	3.2E
	1551	1816	2.0F
	2125		
28 M		0048	3.1E
	0406	0637	2.2F
	0951	1316	3.3E
	1639	1904	2.1F
	2215		

Time meridian 75° W. 0000 is midnight. 1200 is noon.

F-Flood, Dir. 260° True E-Ebb, Dir. 080° True

MARCH

Day	Slack Water Time h.m.	Maximum Current Time h.m.	Vel. knots
1		0137	3.1E
Tu	0457	0725	2.1F
	1037	1402	3.2E
	1725	1951	2.1F
	2303		
2		0227	3.0E
W	0548	0813	2.0F
	1122	1450	3.0E
	1812	2036	2.0F
	2350		
3		0316	2.9E
Th	0640	0859	1.7F
	1205	1536	2.8E
	1900	2122	1.8F
4	0036	0404	2.7E
F	0733	0945	1.5F
	1248	1623	2.5E
	1949	2210	1.6F
5	0124	0458	2.4E
Sa	0829	1036	1.2F
	1332	1716	2.3E
	2040	2259	1.4F
6	0214	0551	2.2E
Su	0927	1125	1.0F
	1421	1809	2.0E
	2136	2350	1.2F
7	0309	0649	2.1E
M	1029	1218	0.8F
	1517	1905	1.9E
	2233		
8		0044	1.1F
Tu	0407	0746	2.0E
	1129	1317	0.7F
	1621	2004	1.8E
	2330		
9		0141	1.0F
W	0505	0842	2.1E
	1225	1416	0.7F
	1725	2101	1.9E
10	0025	0236	1.1F
Th	0600	0934	2.2E
	1315	1511	0.8F
	1822	2152	2.0E
11	0115	0327	1.2F
F	0649	1022	2.3E
	1359	1601	1.0F
	1911	2237	2.1E
12	0201	0415	1.3F
Sa	0733	1107	2.4E
	1438	1644	1.2F
	1953	2322	2.2E
13	0243	0500	1.4F
Su	0811	1146	2.5E
	1515	1726	1.3F
	2031		
14		0003	2.4E
M	0323	0541	1.5F
	0846	1226	2.6E
	1551	1807	1.5F
	2105		
15		0044	2.5E
Tu	0403	0624	1.6F
	0919	1304	2.6E
	1626	1846	1.7F
	2139		
16		0122	2.5E
W	0442	0703	1.7F
	0953	1340	2.6E
	1701	1925	1.8F
	2215		
17		0203	2.6E
Th	0523	0746	1.7F
	1028	1421	2.6E
	1739	2008	1.9F
	2253		
18		0246	2.6E
F	0607	0829	1.7F
	1107	1504	2.5E
	1820	2053	1.9F
	2336		
19		0332	2.6E
Sa	0656	0917	1.6F
	1149	1550	2.4E
	1906	2140	1.9F
20	0024	0423	2.5E
Su	0749	1008	1.5F
	1238	1641	2.3E
	1958	2231	1.8F
21	0118	0518	2.5E
M	0848	1103	1.4F
	1334	1740	2.3E
	2056	2327	1.7F
22	0220	0618	2.4E
Tu	0952	1202	1.3F
	1439	1841	2.2E
	2201		
23		0030	1.7F
W	0330	0722	2.5E
	1057	1306	1.3F
	1556	1947	2.3E
	2307		
24		0133	1.7F
Th	0444	0826	2.6E
	1159	1411	1.4F
	1713	2051	2.5E
25	0011	0239	1.7F
F	0554	0927	2.8E
	1257	1514	1.5F
	1823	2152	2.7E
26	0112	0340	1.8F
Sa	0656	1024	2.9E
	1350	1612	1.7F
	1923	2247	2.9E
27	0208	0438	1.9F
Su	0752	1115	3.0E
	1440	1704	1.9F
	2018	2339	3.0E
28	0301	0529	2.0F
M	0842	1204	3.1E
	1527	1755	2.0F
	2107		
29		0030	3.1E
Tu	0351	0616	2.0F
	0929	1251	3.1E
	1612	1839	2.1F
	2153		
30		0115	3.1E
W	0440	0701	1.9F
	1012	1335	3.0E
	1656	1924	2.0F
	2237		
31		0201	3.0E
Th	0528	0747	1.8F
	1053	1421	2.8E
	1740	2007	1.9F
	2319		

APRIL

Day	Slack Water Time h.m.	Maximum Current Time h.m.	Vel. knots
1		0249	2.8E
F	0616	0830	1.6F
	1132	1505	2.6E
	1825	2048	1.8F
2	0000	0335	2.6E
Sa	0705	0914	1.4F
	1211	1551	2.3E
	1912	2134	1.6F
3	0042	0424	2.4E
Su	0758	1000	1.2F
	1252	1639	2.1E
	2003	2221	1.4F
4	0126	0515	2.2E
M	0853	1048	1.0F
	1337	1733	1.9E
	2057	2310	1.2F
5	0215	0609	2.1E
Tu	0951	1144	0.8F
	1433	1830	1.8E
	2155		
6		0005	1.1F
W	0311	0707	2.0E
	1049	1239	0.8F
	1538	1927	1.8E
	2255		
7		0100	1.0F
Th	0412	0803	2.0E
	1144	1338	0.8F
	1645	2026	1.8E
	2351		
8		0158	1.0F
F	0511	0854	2.1E
	1233	1433	0.9F
	1745	2117	2.0E
9	0044	0251	1.1F
Sa	0604	0943	2.2E
	1318	1524	1.1F
	1835	2206	2.1E
10	0131	0342	1.2F
Su	0651	1028	2.3E
	1358	1609	1.3F
	1919	2251	2.3E
11	0215	0427	1.4F
M	0733	1113	2.5E
	1436	1651	1.5F
	1958	2335	2.5E
12	0257	0513	1.5F
Tu	0812	1152	2.5E
	1513	1736	1.7F
	2035		
13		0015	2.6E
W	0338	0555	1.6F
	0849	1232	2.6E
	1550	1817	1.9F
	2113		
14		0056	2.7E
Th	0419	0639	1.7F
	0926	1314	2.6E
	1628	1900	2.0F
	2152		
15		0139	2.8E
F	0503	0722	1.8F
	1006	1355	2.6E
	1709	1943	2.0F
	2234		
16		0224	2.8E
Sa	0549	0809	1.7F
	1048	1440	2.6E
	1753	2028	2.0F
	2319		
17		0311	2.8E
Su	0639	0858	1.7F
	1135	1529	2.5E
	1843	2118	2.0F
18	0009	0405	2.7E
M	0733	0951	1.6F
	1228	1624	2.4E
	1939	2213	1.9F
19	0105	0501	2.6E
Tu	0833	1047	1.5F
	1328	1724	2.3E
	2041	2312	1.7F
20	0208	0602	2.6E
W	0935	1146	1.4F
	1439	1828	2.3E
	2147		
21		0013	1.6F
Th	0318	0706	2.6E
	1038	1251	1.4F
	1555	1933	2.4E
	2255		
22		0117	1.6F
F	0429	0807	2.6E
	1139	1354	1.5F
	1707	2036	2.5E
	2359		
23		0220	1.6F
Sa	0536	0908	2.7E
	1235	1455	1.6F
	1812	2136	2.7E
24	0059	0321	1.6F
Su	0637	1001	2.8E
	1327	1552	1.7F
	1908	2231	2.8E
25	0155	0418	1.7F
M	0730	1054	2.9E
	1415	1643	1.9F
	2000	2320	2.9E
26	0246	0509	1.7F
Tu	0819	1142	2.9E
	1501	1729	1.9F
	2046		
27		0009	3.0E
W	0335	0554	1.7F
	0903	1223	2.8E
	1544	1814	1.9F
	2130		
28		0054	3.0E
Th	0421	0637	1.6F
	0944	1309	2.7E
	1627	1855	1.9F
	2210		
29		0137	2.9E
F	0507	0721	1.5F
	1023	1353	2.5E
	1709	1936	1.8F
	2248		
30		0221	2.7E
Sa	0553	0802	1.4F
	1100	1436	2.4E
	1753	2018	1.7F
	2325		

Time meridian 75° W. 0000 is midnight. 1200 is noon.

MOBILE BAY ENTRANCE, ALABAMA, 1983

F-Flood, Dir. 025° True E-Ebb, Dir. 190° True

JANUARY

Day	Slack Water Time h.m.	Maximum Current Time h.m.	Maximum Current Vel. knots
1 Sa	1220	0552 1845	3.1E 2.9F
2 Su	0051 1314	0643 1933	2.8E 2.5F
3 M	0142 1401	0724 2017	2.3E 1.9F
4 Tu	0225 1432	0759 2046	1.7E 1.3F
5 W	0252 1417	0808 1945	1.0E 0.6F
6 Th	0213 1157 2109	0654 1621	0.5E 0.4F
7 F	0840 1949	0251 1453	0.4E 0.8F
8 Sa	0744 1959	0125 1437	1.0E 1.2F
9 Su	0756 2028	0138 1450	1.5E 1.6F
10 M	0825 2103	0215 1519	1.9E 1.8F
11 Tu	0900 2143	0244 1548	2.1E 2.0F
12 W	0940 2224	0328 1631	2.2E 2.1F
13 Th	1023 2306	0408 1707	2.3E 2.1F
14 F	1106 2348	0451 1749	2.3E 2.1F
15 Sa	1149	0533 1826	2.2E 2.0F

Day	Slack Water Time h.m.	Maximum Current Time h.m.	Maximum Current Vel. knots
16 Su	0028 1230	0616 1901	2.1E 1.9F
17 M	0106 1308	0657 1930	1.9E 1.7F
18 Tu	0141 1342	0732 1950	1.6E 1.4F
19 W	0211 1409	0755 2000	1.3E 1.0F
20 Th	0233 1417	0816 1913	0.8E 0.5F
21 F	0150	0642 1624	0.3E *
22 Sa	0602 1821	0109 1240	0.4E 0.6F
23 Su	0601 1838	0031 1236	1.0E 1.2F
24 M	0640 1920	0057 1311	1.6E 1.8F
25 Tu	0730 2012	0135 1359	2.2E 2.3F
26 W	0826 2109	0221 1459	2.6E 2.6F
27 Th	0926 2207	0313 1600	2.9E 2.8F
28 F	1027 2305	0405 1702	3.0E 2.9F
29 Sa	1128	0500 1759	2.9E 2.7F
30 Su	0002 1226	0549 1900	2.5E 2.3F
31 M	0055 1320	0630 1945	2.0E 1.7F

FEBRUARY

Day	Slack Water Time h.m.	Maximum Current Time h.m.	Maximum Current Vel. knots
1 Tu	0143 1403	0707 2031	1.4E 1.0F
2 W	0221 1401	0700 2018	0.8E 0.3F
3 Th	1734	0554 1332 2314	* 0.3F 0.4E
4 F	0545 1738	1232 2329	0.7F 1.0E
5 Sa	0547 1816	1241	1.2F
6 Su	0621 1901	0012 1310	1.4E 1.5F
7 M	0703 1949	0055 1348	1.7E 1.7F
8 Tu	0748 2039	0136 1442	1.9E 1.8F
9 W	0837 2129	0227 1531	2.0E 1.9F
10 Th	0927 2218	0313 1623	2.1E 1.9F
11 F	1017 2304	0358 1715	2.1E 1.8F
12 Sa	1104 2348	0439 1757	2.0E 1.8F
13 Su	1149	0522 1839	1.9E 1.6F
14 M	0029 1231	0557 1915	1.6E 1.4F
15 Tu	0109 1314	0640 1938	1.3E 1.1F

Day	Slack Water Time h.m.	Maximum Current Time h.m.	Maximum Current Vel. knots
16 W	0151 1402	0720 2019	0.9E 0.6F
17 Th	0246	0733 2006	0.4E *
18 F		0308 0848 2126	* * 0.4E
19 Sa	0258 1538	0939 2223	0.7F 1.0E
20 Su	0406 1641	1028 2312	1.3F 1.6E
21 M	0505 1745	1128	1.8F
22 Tu	0606 1850	0012 1228	2.1E 2.1F
23 W	0709 1957	0104 1340	2.4E 2.4F
24 Th	0815 2102	0201 1446	2.6E 2.5F
25 F	0921 2207	0257 1556	2.6E 2.4F
26 Sa	1028 2309	0355 1710	2.4E 2.2F
27 Su	1137	0448 1813	2.1E 1.8F
28 M	0011 1252	0530 1935	1.5E 1.2F

Time meridian 90° W. 0000 is midnight. 1200 IS noon.
If three consecutive entries are marked (F) the middle one is not a true maximum but an intermediate value to show the current pattern.
* Current weak and variable.

F-Flood, Dir. 025° True E-Ebb, Dir. 190° True

MARCH

Day	Slack Water Time h.m.	Maximum Current Time h.m.	Vel. knots
1	0116	0613	0.9E
Tu	1449	2112	0.7F
2	0244	0600	0.3E
W		1048	*
		1559	0.3E
	2045		
3		0907	0.4F
Th	1331	1917	0.7E
4	0151	0922	0.9F
F	1453	2053	1.1E
5	0314	1006	1.2F
Sa	1558	2202	1.4E
6	0413	1054	1.4F
Su	1659	2305	1.6E
7	0509	1140	1.5F
M	1801		
8		0001	1.7E
Tu	0606	1243	1.6F
	1905		
9		0059	1.8E
W	0704	1352	1.6F
	2009		
10		0153	1.8E
Th	0803	1505	1.5F
	2109		
11		0243	1.8E
F	0902	1614	1.5F
	2205		
12		0339	1.7E
Sa	1000	1717	1.4F
	2258		
13		0422	1.5E
Su	1057	1812	1.2F
	2350		
14		0457	1.2E
M	1201	1857	1.0F
15	0050	0559	0.8E
Tu	1341	2025	0.7F
16	0223	0700	0.4E
W	1747	2340	0.4F
17	0904	1636	0.5E
Th	2233		
18		0612	0.7F
F	1209	1839	0.9E
19	0049	0730	1.2F
Sa	1332	2000	1.4E
20	0211	0839	1.6F
Su	1444	2111	1.8E
21	0321	0940	2.0F
M	1556	2224	2.1E
22	0429	1044	2.2F
Tu	1710	2329	2.3E
23	0537	1154	2.2F
W	1824		
24		0035	2.3E
Th	0646	1313	2.2F
	1938		
25		0135	2.2E
F	0755	1433	1.9F
	2050		
26		0232	1.9E
Sa	0907	1603	1.6F
	2202		
27		0327	1.5E
Su	1030	1745	1.1F
	2322		
28		0415	0.9E
M	1315	1948	0.7F
29	0123	0436	0.3E
Tu		0811	*
		1407	0.4E
	1840	2324	0.4F
30		0236	0.3F
W		0611	0.4F
	1037	1620	0.8E
	2214		
31		0637	0.9F
Th	1200	1736	1.2E

APRIL

Day	Slack Water Time h.m.	Maximum Current Time h.m.	Vel. knots
1	0001	0720	1.3F
F	1300	1851	1.5E
2	0111	0804	1.5F
Sa	1356	1954	1.7E
3	0211	0839	1.6F
Su	1454	2057	1.8E
4	0309	0933	1.7F
M	1556	2206	1.8E
5	0408	1024	1.6F
Tu	1702	2306	1.7E
6	0508	1128	1.5F
W	1813		
7		0013	1.6E
Th	0609	1238	1.3F
	1923		
8		0110	1.5E
F	0709	1406	1.2F
	2031		
9		0204	1.3E
Sa	0810	1542	1.0F
	2138		
10		0254	1.1E
Su	0918	1719	0.7F
	2256		
11		0348	0.7E
M	1139	1948	0.5F
12	0101	0437	0.3E
Tu		0905	*
		1329	0.3E
	1749	2312	0.4F
13	0833	1512	0.7E
W	2043		
14		0349	0.8F
Th	1016	1622	1.2E
	2225		
15		0520	1.3F
F	1119	1724	1.6E
	2340		
16		0621	1.7F
Sa	1219	1831	2.0E
17	0048	0715	2.1F
Su	1320	1936	2.2E
18	0154	0813	2.3F
M	1425	2043	2.4E
19	0259	0914	2.4F
Tu	1533	2147	2.4E
20	0404	1017	2.3F
W	1643	2253	2.2E
21	0507	1123	2.0F
Th	1753	2353	1.9E
22	0608	1225	1.6F
F	1904		
23		0044	1.5E
Sa	0706	1354	1.0F
	2020		
24		0125	0.9E
Su	0802	1624	0.5F
	2205		
25		0112	0.3E
M		0743	*
		1348	0.3E
	1801		
26		0536	0.4F
Tu	0938	1502	0.9E
	2055		
27		0511	1.0F
W	1025	1600	1.4E
	2210		
28		0531	1.4F
Th	1108	1648	1.8E
	2305		
29		0606	1.7F
F	1152	1737	2.0E
	2356		
30		0641	1.9F
Sa	1237	1826	2.1E

Time meridian 90° W. 0000 is midnight. 1200 IS noon.
If three consecutive entries are marked (F) the middle one is not a true maximum but an intermediate value to show the current pattern.
* Current weak and variable.

MOBILE BAY ENTRANCE, ALABAMA, 1983

F-Flood, Dir. 025° True E-Ebb, Dir. 190° True

MAY

Day	Slack Water Time h.m.	Maximum Current Time h.m.	Maximum Current Vel. knots
1 Su	0045 1324	0721 1921	2.0F 2.1E
2 M	0136 1415	0758 2016	1.9F 2.0E
3 Tu	0228 1511	0844 2117	1.8F 1.9E
4 W	0322 1610	0930 2217	1.6F 1.7E
5 Th	0414 1711	1016 2306	1.4F 1.5E
6 F	0503 1813	1051	1.1F
7 Sa	0547 1920	0003 1109	1.2E 0.8F
8 Su	0623 2100	0052 1039	0.8E 0.4F
9 M		0112 0828 1409 2142	0.4E * * *
10 Tu	1946	0102 0513 1429	* * 0.7E
11 W	0913 2056	0314 1518	0.7F 1.2E
12 Th	0951 2154	0351 1553	1.3F 1.7E
13 F	1036 2250	0438 1643	1.8F 2.1E
14 Sa	1126 2348	0526 1733	2.3F 2.5E
15 Su	1221	0615 1827	2.6F 2.7E

Day	Slack Water Time h.m.	Maximum Current Time h.m.	Maximum Current Vel. knots
16 M	0047 1318	0712 1927	2.7F 2.7E
17 Tu	0147 1417	0803 2027	2.7F 2.6E
18 W	0245 1516	0900 2121	2.4F 2.3E
19 Th	0340 1613	0949 2212	2.0F 1.9E
20 F	0426 1704	1021 2248	1.5F 1.3E
21 Sa	0452 1739	1025 2249	0.8F 0.7E
22 Su	0405	0748 2032	0.3F *
23 M	0928 2050	0527 1435	0.5F 0.7E
24 Tu	0925 2110	0429 1456	1.0F 1.3E
25 W	0952 2145	0430 1533	1.4F 1.8E
26 Th	1026 2223	0445 1608	1.8F 2.1E
27 F	1103 2303	0514 1651	2.1F 2.3E
28 Sa	1142 2346	0545 1732	2.2F 2.4E
29 Su	1224	0621 1815	2.2F 2.3E
30 M	0030 1309	0700 1903	2.1F 2.2E
31 Tu	0117 1355	0735 1954	2.0F 2.1E

JUNE

Day	Slack Water Time h.m.	Maximum Current Time h.m.	Maximum Current Vel. knots
1 W	0203 1441	0819 2043	1.8F 1.9E
2 Th	0246 1526	0848 2126	1.6F 1.6E
3 F	0325 1605	0903 2207	1.3F 1.2E
4 Sa	0353 1634	0910 2236	0.9F 0.8E
5 Su	0400 1542	0812 2212	0.5F 0.3E
6 M	0243 1030 1958	0645 1441	0.3F 0.4E
7 Tu	0847 1952	0413 1423	0.5F 0.9E
8 W	0843 2027	0253 1438	1.0F 1.5E
9 Th	0911 2112	0313 1518	1.6F 2.0E
10 F	0951 2202	0351 1556	2.1F 2.5E
11 Sa	1039 2257	0434 1639	2.6F 2.8E
12 Su	1131 2353	0529 1733	2.8F 3.0E
13 M	1225	0618 1827	3.0F 3.0E
14 Tu	0050 1320	0711 1920	2.9F 2.8E
15 W	0145 1412	0800 2009	2.6F 2.4E

Day	Slack Water Time h.m.	Maximum Current Time h.m.	Maximum Current Vel. knots
16 Th	0233 1459	0846 2048	2.1F 1.8E
17 F	0309 1532	0915 2106	1.4F 1.2E
18 Sa	0310 1514	0842 2027	0.8F 0.6E
19 Su	0125 1028 2144	0541 1554	0.5F 0.4E
20 M	0836 2025	0353 1408	0.8F 1.0E
21 Tu	0840 2036	0326 1421	1.3F 1.6E
22 W	0906 2105	0336 1450	1.7F 2.0E
23 Th	0940 2140	0356 1527	2.0F 2.3E
24 F	1018 2218	0428 1602	2.2F 2.4E
25 Sa	1057 2259	0500 1643	2.3F 2.4E
26 Su	1139 2342	0542 1724	2.3F 2.4E
27 M	1221	0620 1808	2.2F 2.3E
28 Tu	0025 1302	0655 1853	2.1F 2.2E
29 W	0106 1342	0730 1937	1.9F 2.0E
30 Th	0144 1419	0748 2012	1.7F 1.7E

Time meridian 90° W. 0000 is midnight. 1200 IS noon.
If three consecutive entries are marked (F) the middle one is not a true maximum but an intermediate value to show the current pattern.
* Current weak and variable.

F-Flood, Dir. 025° True E-Ebb, Dir. 190° True

JULY

Day	Slack Water Time h.m.	Maximum Current Time h.m.	Vel. knots
1 F	0217 1449	0808 2038	1.4F 1.3E
2 Sa	0241 1504	0815 2048	1.0F 0.8E
3 Su	0240 1354	0731 1939	0.6F 0.3E
4 M	0100 0937 1932	0536 1409	0.4F 0.4E
5 Tu	0750 1905	0253 1342	0.6F 1.0E
6 W	0745 1934	0147 1349	1.1F 1.6E
7 Th	0815 2017	0208 1418	1.7F 2.1E
8 F	0857 2108	0251 1501	2.2F 2.6E
9 Sa	0948 2204	0345 1550	2.6F 2.9E
10 Su	1041 2302	0437 1642	2.9F 3.1E
11 M	1137 2359	0533 1732	3.0F 3.0E
12 Tu	1231	0628 1826	2.8F 2.7E
13 W	0055 1323	0719 1909	2.5F 2.3E
14 Th	0145 1408	0800 1939	2.0F 1.7E
15 F	0222 1440	0834 1951	1.3F 1.0E

Day	Slack Water Time h.m.	Maximum Current Time h.m.	Vel. knots
16 Sa	0215 1408 2319	0748 1845	0.6F 0.4E
17 Su	0807 1937	0334 1352	0.4F 0.4E
18 M	0703 1905	0157 1254	0.8F 1.0E
19 Tu	0725 1929	0206 1315	1.3F 1.6E
20 W	0801 2004	0222 1350	1.7F 2.0E
21 Th	0842 2045	0251 1427	1.9F 2.2E
22 F	0926 2128	0331 1508	2.1F 2.3E
23 Sa	1011 2212	0417 1554	2.1F 2.3E
24 Su	1055 2257	0458 1635	2.1F 2.3E
25 M	1139 2340	0546 1716	2.1F 2.2E
26 Tu	1221	0623 1759	2.0F 2.0E
27 W	0022 1300	0658 1840	1.8F 1.8E
28 Th	0059 1336	0727 1909	1.5F 1.5E
29 F	0133 1408	0748 1947	1.2F 1.1E
30 Sa	0201 1433	0749 1951	0.8F 0.7E
31 Su	0208	0642 1813	0.4F *

AUGUST

Day	Slack Water Time h.m.	Maximum Current Time h.m.	Vel. knots
1 M	1713	0333 1221 2355	* 0.4E 0.5F
2 Tu	0547 1731	1200 2353	0.9E 1.1F
3 W	0611 1813	1229	1.5E
4 Th	0655 1905	0042 1312	1.6F 2.0E
5 F	0748 2002	0131 1358	2.1F 2.4E
6 Sa	0846 2102	0232 1447	2.5F 2.7E
7 Su	0945 2204	0336 1540	2.7F 2.9E
8 M	1045 2307	0438 1638	2.7F 2.8E
9 Tu	1143	0542 1727	2.6F 2.5E
10 W	0008 1239	0636 1815	2.2F 2.0E
11 Th	0109 1333	0739 1845	1.6F 1.3E
12 F	0210 1425	0842 1857	1.0F 0.6E
13 Sa		0931 1703 2348	* * 0.3F
14 Su	0334 1613	0930 2321	0.5E 0.8F
15 M	0437 1659	1038 2345	1.1E 1.3F

Day	Slack Water Time h.m.	Maximum Current Time h.m.	Vel. knots
16 Tu	0532 1747	1133	1.5E
17 W	0626 1836	0036 1224	1.6F 1.8E
18 Th	0721 1926	0120 1310	1.8F 2.0E
19 F	0816 2018	0214 1359	1.8F 2.0E
20 Sa	0910 2111	0314 1451	1.8F 2.0E
21 Su	1003 2203	0411 1539	1.8F 2.0E
22 M	1053 2252	0506 1622	1.8F 1.9E
23 Tu	1139 2340	0554 1711	1.6F 1.7E
24 W	1223	0637 1748	1.5F 1.5E
25 Th	0026 1307	0712 1829	1.2F 1.1E
26 F	0115 1358	0800 1912	0.9F 0.7E
27 Sa	0224 1525	0912 1933	0.5F 0.3E
28 Su		1838	*
29 M	1406	0824 2040	0.5E 0.7F
30 Tu	0251 1525	0933 2143	1.0E 1.2F
31 W	0401 1629	1036 2240	1.5E 1.7F

Time meridian 90° W. 0000 is midnight. 1200 IS noon.
If three consecutive entries are marked (F) the middle one is not a true maximum but an intermediate value to show the current pattern.
* Current weak and variable.

GALVESTON BAY ENTRANCE (between jetties), TEXAS, 1983

F-Flood, Dir. 300° True E-Ebb, Dir. 100° True

JANUARY

Day	Slack Water Time h.m.	Maximum Current Time h.m.	Vel. knots
1 Sa	0239	1013	3.9E
	1456	1827	2.9F
2 Su	0312	1107	3.4E
	1551	1918	2.5F
3 M	0251	1201	2.7E
	1647	2004	2.0F
4 Tu	0145	0455	0.4E
		0705	0.3E
		1317	1.9E
	1744	2045	1.6F
5 W	0119	0455	0.8E
		0845	*
		1445	1.1E
	1843	2125	1.1F
6 Th	0059	0500	1.3E
	0853	1035	0.4F
	1345	1639	0.5E
	1947	2203	0.7F
7 F	0034	0525	1.8E
	0926	1232	1.0F
	1647	1911	0.3E
	2100	2243	0.4F
8 Sa	0021	0552	2.2E
	1003	1346	1.6F
	1838	2043	0.3E
		2324	*
9 Su		0626	2.6E
	1040	1429	2.0F
	1949	2136	0.3E
10 M		0006	*
		0658	2.8E
	1118	1458	2.2F
	2047	2231	0.3E
11 Tu		0041	*
		0735	3.0E
	1156	1527	2.4F
		2327	*
12 W		0120	*
		0807	3.1E
	1234	1558	2.4F
13 Th		0021	*
		0152	*
		0845	3.1E
	1312	1633	2.4F
14 F	0018	0920	3.1E
	1350	1708	2.3F
15 Sa	0149	0949	3.0E
	1428	1743	2.1F

Day	Slack Water Time h.m.	Maximum Current Time h.m.	Vel. knots
16 Su	0242	1018	2.8E
	1506	1823	1.9F
17 M	0308	1049	2.5E
	1544	1901	1.7F
18 Tu	0310	1118	2.1E
	1623	1941	1.4F
19 W	0125	1144	1.6E
	1707	2018	1.1F
20 Th	0029	0321	0.4E
		0819	*
		1312	0.9E
	1803	2059	0.7F
	2326		
21 F		0336	0.8E
	0821	0950	0.3F
	1132	1537	0.4E
	1941	2135	0.3F
	2303		
22 Sa		0408	1.4E
	0839	1112	0.9F
		1948	*
		2210	*
23 Su		0448	1.9E
	0912	1221	1.6F
	1826	2113	0.4E
		2252	0.3E
24 M		0529	2.6E
	0952	1323	2.3F
	1942	2217	0.4E
		2327	0.4E
25 Tu		0615	3.2E
	1037	1413	2.8F
	2054	2319	0.3E
		2345	0.3E
26 W		0702	3.7E
	1125	1501	3.2F
	2217		
27 Th		0748	4.0E
	1215	1548	3.3F
28 F	0201	0837	4.1E
	1306	1631	3.2F
29 Sa		0100	*
		0217	*
		0928	4.0E
	1356	1715	2.9F
30 Su		0048	*
		0324	0.3F
	0447	1017	3.6E
	1446	1753	2.4F
31 M		0036	*
		0429	0.4F
	0555	1106	2.9E
	1535	1833	1.9F
	2326		

FEBRUARY

Day	Slack Water Time h.m.	Maximum Current Time h.m.	Vel. knots
1 Tu		0102	0.3E
	0340	0546	0.4F
	0707	1203	2.1E
	1624	1908	1.4F
	2301		
2 W		0139	0.7E
	0525	0704	0.4F
	0838	1312	1.2E
	1718	1946	0.9F
	2228		
3 Th		0225	1.1E
	0644	0833	0.5F
	1143	1449	0.5E
	1828	2025	0.4F
	2208		
4 F		0317	1.5E
	0746	1021	0.8F
		1822	*
		2108	*
5 Sa		0414	1.9E
	0840	1254	1.3F
	1752	1947	0.3E
		2156	*
6 Su		0501	2.2E
	0929	1343	1.8F
	1846	2049	0.4E
		2245	*
7 M		0555	2.4E
	1014	1418	2.1F
	1931	2124	0.4E
		2342	*
8 Tu		0638	2.7E
	1058	1452	2.2F
	2014	2211	0.4E
9 W		0025	*
		0718	2.9E
	1140	1515	2.3F
	2100	2242	0.3E
10 Th		0111	*
		0759	3.0E
	1220	1536	2.2F
		2322	*
11 F		0149	*
		0834	3.0E
	1258	1605	2.2F
		2339	*
12 Sa		0229	0.3F
	0338	0909	3.0E
	1335	1634	2.0F
		2319	*
13 Su		0304	0.3F
	0425	0944	2.8E
	1410	1706	1.8F
		2326	*
14 M		0342	0.3F
	0511	1014	2.5E
	1444	1738	1.6F
		2341	*
15 Tu		0428	0.3F
	0600	1048	2.1E
	1519	1810	1.2F
	2201		

Day	Slack Water Time h.m.	Maximum Current Time h.m.	Vel. knots
16 W		0010	0.3E
	0213	0529	0.3F
	0700	1123	1.6E
	1558	1842	0.8F
	2115		
17 Th		0031	0.6E
	0341	0639	0.4F
	0820	1218	1.0E
	1649	1911	0.4F
	2053		
18 F		0046	0.9E
	0512	0800	0.6F
	1026	1354	0.4E
		1941	*
19 Sa		0129	1.3E
	0628	0924	1.0F
	1602		
20 Su		0233	1.7E
	0733	1053	1.5F
	1743		
21 M		0346	2.2E
	0832	1209	2.1F
	1839		
22 Tu		0455	2.7E
	0928	1312	2.6F
	1932	2208	0.5E
		2302	0.5E
23 W		0555	3.2E
	1023	1400	2.9F
	2024	2228	0.4E
		2359	0.3E
24 Th		0652	3.6E
	1115	1443	3.0F
		2240	*
25 F		0059	*
		0745	3.7E
	1206	1524	2.9F
		2231	*
26 Sa		0151	0.4F
	0314	0834	3.7E
	1256	1601	2.6F
		2226	*
27 Su		0245	0.7F
	0431	0926	3.3E
	1343	1636	2.1F
	2108	2241	0.4E
28 M	0046	0345	0.9F
	0543	1015	2.7E
	1430	1705	1.6F
	2049	2309	0.7E

Time meridian 90° W. 0000 is midnight. 1200 is noon.
* Current weak and variable.
If three consecutive entries are marked (E) the middle one is not a true maximum but an intermediate value to show the current pattern.

F-Flood, Dir. 300° True E-Ebb, Dir. 100° True

MARCH

Day	Slack Water Time h.m.	Maximum Current Time h.m.	Vel. knots
1	0151	0445	1.0F
Tu	0657	1109	2.0E
	1517	1737	1.1F
	2021	2338	1.1E
2	0300	0548	1.1F
W	0824	1203	1.2E
	1610	1810	0.6F
	2000		
3		0013	1.4E
Th	0414	0657	1.1F
	1039	1321	0.5E
		1844	*
4		0053	1.6E
F	0529	0815	1.1F
	1423	1737	0.3E
		1914	*
5		0147	1.7E
Sa	0641	0956	1.3F
	1635	1910	0.5E
		1957	0.4E
6		0256	1.8E
Su	0748	1220	1.6F
	1726	1959	0.6E
		2111	0.6E
7		0415	2.0E
M	0848	1309	1.8F
	1807	2035	0.6E
		2226	0.5E
8		0521	2.2E
Tu	0942	1346	2.0F
	1843	2104	0.6E
		2323	0.3E
9		0615	2.4E
W	1031	1415	2.0F
	1916	2132	0.5E
10		0014	*
Th		0703	2.6E
	1116	1436	2.0F
	1942	2154	0.4E
11		0100	*
F		0745	2.7E
	1157	1459	1.9F
	2000	2157	0.3E
	2358		
12		0143	0.4F
Sa	0310	0821	2.7E
	1235	1523	1.8F
	2007	2145	0.3E
13	0004	0224	0.6F
Su	0407	0856	2.6E
	1311	1549	1.6F
	2006	2158	0.4E
14	0018	0307	0.8F
M	0502	0933	2.3E
	1347	1617	1.3F
	1947	2214	0.6E
15	0043	0353	0.9F
Tu	0558	1008	1.9E
	1425	1646	1.0F
	1917	2228	0.9E

Day	Slack Water Time h.m.	Maximum Current Time h.m.	Vel. knots
16	0120	0440	1.0F
W	0701	1052	1.5E
	1508	1715	0.6F
	1859	2243	1.2E
17	0205	0538	1.2F
Th	0819	1146	0.9E
		1736	*
		2250	1.5E
18	0259	0639	1.3F
F	1025	1303	0.4E
		1538	*
		2313	1.8E
19	0406	0756	1.5F
Sa	1456	2348	2.1E
20	0524	0912	1.7F
Su	1634		
21		0058	2.3E
M	0646	1035	2.0F
	1725		
22		0301	2.4E
Tu	0800	1156	2.4F
	1809		
23		0433	2.7E
W	0906	1251	2.6F
	1846	2119	0.6E
		2305	0.5E
24		0542	3.0E
Th	1005	1335	2.6F
	1907	2124	0.5E
25		0005	*
F		0645	3.1E
	1100	1412	2.5F
	1912	2117	0.5E
	2330		
26		0108	0.4F
Sa	0231	0742	3.0E
	1150	1444	2.2F
	1908	2111	0.7E
	2345		
27		0205	0.9F
Su	0403	0836	2.7E
	1239	1516	1.8F
	1856	2126	1.0E
28	0017	0257	1.3F
M	0526	0926	2.3E
	1326	1545	1.3F
	1835	2146	1.4E
29	0059	0352	1.5F
Tu	0648	1020	1.7E
	1414	1612	0.8F
	1814	2212	1.7E
30	0145	0449	1.7F
W	0820	1118	1.1E
	1511	1641	0.4F
	1800	2238	2.0E
31	0236	0545	1.7F
Th	1014	1226	0.5E
		1709	*
		2306	2.1E

APRIL

Day	Slack Water Time h.m.	Maximum Current Time h.m.	Vel. knots
1	0330	0646	1.7F
F	1250	2341	2.1E
2	0432	0756	1.6F
Sa	1508		
3		0017	2.0E
Su	0542	0912	1.6F
	1604		
4		0142	1.9E
M	0654	1107	1.7F
	1645		
5		0313	1.8E
Tu	0802	1218	1.8F
	1719	2009	0.8E
		2157	0.7E
6		0433	1.9E
W	0902	1251	1.8F
	1745	2033	0.8E
		2308	0.4E
7		0542	2.1E
Th	0954	1316	1.8F
	1803	2047	0.7E
8		0000	*
F		0633	2.2E
	1041	1339	1.7F
	1812	2052	0.7E
	2327		
9		0054	0.3F
Sa	0211	0720	2.2E
	1123	1406	1.6F
	1814	2044	0.7E
	2335		
10		0135	0.7F
Su	0331	0802	2.1E
	1204	1432	1.4F
	1805	2044	0.9E
	2350		
11		0221	1.0F
M	0440	0844	1.9E
	1244	1458	1.1F
	1740	2059	1.2E
12	0010	0305	1.3F
Tu	0549	0927	1.6E
	1328	1527	0.7F
	1721	2114	1.5E
13	0037	0353	1.6F
W	0703	1017	1.2E
	1422	1549	0.3F
	1705	2129	1.9E
14	0111	0443	1.8F
Th	0833	1106	0.7E
		1608	*
		2139	2.2E
15	0153	0538	2.0F
F	1037	1231	0.3E
		1356	0.3E
		2159	2.5E

Day	Slack Water Time h.m.	Maximum Current Time h.m.	Vel. knots
16	0244	0639	2.2F
Sa	1350	2237	2.7E
17	0346	0746	2.2F
Su	1524	2322	2.8E
18	0459	0900	2.3F
M	1615		
19		0033	2.7E
Tu	0618	1015	2.4F
	1654		
20		0239	2.5E
W	0733	1120	2.4F
	1720	2025	0.8E
		2142	0.8E
21		0415	2.5E
Th	0841	1215	2.4F
	1729	2021	0.8E
		2307	0.3E
22		0530	2.4E
F	0941	1252	2.1F
	1727	2015	0.9E
	2306		
23		0016	0.3F
Sa	0129	0640	2.3E
	1036	1327	1.8F
	1719	2004	1.1E
	2314		
24		0116	0.9F
Su	0335	0743	2.0E
	1127	1356	1.4F
	1704	2019	1.5E
	2342		
25		0210	1.4F
M	0518	0837	1.6E
	1217	1423	1.0F
	1643	2037	2.0E
26	0016	0305	1.8F
Tu	0650	0937	1.1E
	1309	1452	0.6F
	1628	2104	2.3E
27	0054	0355	2.1F
W	0820	1043	0.7E
		1519	*
		2127	2.5E
28	0133	0449	2.2F
Th	1000	1203	0.3E
		1541	*
		2156	2.6E
29	0216	0539	2.2F
F	1208	2217	2.6E
30	0302	0633	2.1F
Sa	1354	2243	2.5E

Time meridian 90° W. 0000 is midnight. 1200 is noon.
* Current weak and variable.
If three consecutive entries are marked (E) the middle one is not a true maximum but an intermediate value to show the current pattern.

GALVESTON BAY ENTRANCE (between jetties), TEXAS, 1983

F-Flood, Dir. 300° True   E-Ebb, Dir. 100° True

MAY

Day	Slack Water Time h.m.	Maximum Current Time h.m.	Vel. knots
1	0355	0731	2.0F
Su	1451	2313	2.3E
2	0457	0839	1.9F
M	1533		
3		0000	2.0E
Tu	0604	0956	1.8F
	1606		
4		0212	1.8E
W	0711	1055	1.8F
	1628	1936	0.9E
		2129	0.8E
5		0340	1.7E
Th	0811	1136	1.7F
	1640	1952	0.9E
		2240	0.4E
6		0456	1.7E
F	0906	1211	1.6F
	1643	2002	0.9E
		2340	*
7		0559	1.6E
Sa	0955	1240	1.4F
	1639	1943	1.0E
	2301		
8		0037	0.5F
Su	0226	0654	1.5E
	1042	1309	1.2F
	1622	1938	1.2E
	2311		
9		0129	1.0F
M	0409	0744	1.3E
	1129	1336	0.9F
	1556	1950	1.6E
	2329		
10		0212	1.4F
Tu	0538	0839	1.1E
	1221	1405	0.5F
	1539	2008	2.0E
	2353		
11		0301	1.9F
W	0705	0936	0.8E
		1433	*
		2029	2.4E
12	0024	0350	2.3F
Th	0838	1042	0.5E
		1448	*
		2045	2.8E
13	0102	0441	2.6F
F	1031	2113	3.1E
14	0147	0534	2.8F
Sa	1306	2145	3.3E
15	0240	0635	2.8F
Su	1426	2228	3.3E

Day	Slack Water Time h.m.	Maximum Current Time h.m.	Vel. knots
16	0340	0737	2.8F
M	1516	2325	3.2E
17	0447	0841	2.7F
Tu	1552		
18		0043	2.8E
W	0557	0946	2.5F
	1608		
19		0226	2.4E
Th	0706	1041	2.2F
	1604	1915	0.9E
		2150	0.5E
20		0357	2.0E
F	0810	1124	1.9F
	1554	1913	1.1E
		2310	*
21		0520	1.6E
Sa	0910	1159	1.5F
	1542	1902	1.4E
	2233		
22		0027	0.7F
Su	0306	0643	1.3E
	1006	1228	1.1F
	1523	1917	1.9E
	2259		
23		0130	1.3F
M	0511	0757	0.9E
	1101	1303	0.8F
	1503	1934	2.3E
	2331		
24		0224	1.8F
Tu	0650	0913	0.6E
	1158	1331	0.4F
	1454	2003	2.7E
25	0007	0313	2.2F
W	0823	1042	0.4E
		1358	*
		2027	2.9E
26	0044	0402	2.4F
Th	1001	1224	0.3E
		1421	*
		2056	3.0E
27	0122	0445	2.5F
F	1142	2125	3.0E
28	0202	0533	2.4F
Sa	1257	2154	2.9E
29	0245	0619	2.3F
Su	1352	2221	2.7E
30	0333	0711	2.2F
M	1436	2259	2.5E
31	0426	0805	2.0F
Tu	1509	2342	2.2E

JUNE

Day	Slack Water Time h.m.	Maximum Current Time h.m.	Vel. knots
1	0522	0900	1.9F
W	1529		
2		0105	1.9E
Th	0619	0946	1.7F
	1533	1905	0.8E
		2052	0.7E
3		0241	1.6E
F	0715	1029	1.5F
	1527	1913	0.9E
		2215	0.4E
4		0404	1.3E
Sa	0811	1104	1.3F
	1515	1854	1.0E
		2326	*
5		0521	1.0E
Su	0905	1140	1.0F
	1448	1830	1.3E
	2226		
6		0022	0.7F
M	0317	0630	0.8E
	1003	1215	0.7F
	1419	1839	1.7E
	2240		
7		0118	1.3F
Tu	0518	0739	0.6E
	1107	1242	0.4F
	1405	1900	2.2E
	2303		
8		0207	1.9F
W	0654	0859	0.4E
		1312	*
		1926	2.7E
	2334		
9		0256	2.4F
Th	0829	1112	0.3E
		1327	*
		1955	3.2E
10	0012	0344	2.8F
F	1026	2024	3.5E
11	0056	0438	3.1F
Sa	1225	2103	3.8E
12	0145	0529	3.2F
Su	1340	2151	3.8E
13	0239	0624	3.1F
M	1435	2240	3.6E
14	0336	0721	2.9F
Tu	1509	2335	3.2E
15	0436	0813	2.6F
W	1513		

Day	Slack Water Time h.m.	Maximum Current Time h.m.	Vel. knots
16		0046	2.6E
Th	0537	0904	2.2F
	1445	1805	0.7E
		2011	0.5E
17		0215	1.9E
F	0637	0947	1.8F
	1424	1756	1.0E
		2150	*
18		0350	1.3E
Sa	0737	1028	1.3F
	1405	1751	1.4E
	2137	2321	0.5F
19	0219	0526	0.8E
Su	0838	1103	0.9F
	1342	1808	2.0E
	2204		
20		0041	1.1F
M	0457	0716	0.4E
	0940	1137	0.6F
	1327	1831	2.5E
	2239		
21		0150	1.7F
Tu	0653	0901	0.3E
	1047	1212	0.3F
	1324	1900	2.8E
	2317		
22		0239	2.2F
W		1021	*
		1245	*
		1935	3.1E
	2355		
23		0322	2.4F
Th		1128	*
		1312	*
		2007	3.2E
24	0033	0403	2.5F
F		1243	*
		1302	*
		2042	3.2E
25	0112	0439	2.5F
Sa	1200	2111	3.1E
26	0152	0519	2.4F
Su	1300	2146	3.0E
27	0234	0602	2.3F
M	1351	2221	2.8E
28	0316	0642	2.1F
Tu	1429	2302	2.6E
29	0400	0726	1.9F
W	1451	2331	2.2E
30	0445	0809	1.7F
Th	1443		

Time meridian 90° W. 0000 is midnight. 1200 is noon.
* Current weak and variable.
If three consecutive entries are marked (E) the middle one is not a true maximum but an intermediate value to show the current pattern.

F-Flood, Dir. 300° True E-Ebb, Dir. 100° True

JULY

Day	Slack Water Time h.m.	Maximum Current Time h.m.	Vel. knots
1		0012	1.8E
F	0532	0852	1.5F
	1416	1820	0.6E
		2021	0.5E
2		0142	1.3E
Sa	0623	0930	1.2F
	1350	1806	0.8E
		2144	*
3		0320	0.8E
Su	0721	1012	0.9F
	1306	1712	1.1E
	2129	2301	0.4F
4	0131	0457	0.5E
M	0833	1047	0.5F
	1237	1730	1.6E
	2140		
5		0009	1.0F
Tu	0446	0656	0.3E
		1121	*
		1748	2.1E
	2205		
6		0106	1.7F
W	0637	0924	0.3E
		1150	*
		1820	2.6E
	2238		
7		0201	2.3F
Th	0813	1053	0.3E
		1211	*
		1852	3.2E
	2318		
8		0250	2.8F
F	0950	1935	3.6E
9	0003	0339	3.1F
Sa	1129	2016	4.0E
10	0051	0427	3.3F
Su	1308	2105	4.1E
11	0142	0518	3.2F
M	1434	2154	3.9E
12	0234	0604	2.9F
Tu	1534	2248	3.5E
13	0327	0650	2.6F
W	1508	2345	2.9E
14	0421	0733	2.1F
Th	1311	1557	0.3E
		1837	*
15		0046	2.1E
F	0515	0814	1.6F
	1238	1538	0.7E
		2009	*

Day	Slack Water Time h.m.	Maximum Current Time h.m.	Vel. knots
16		0209	1.2E
Sa	0611	0851	1.1F
	1210	1559	1.3E
	2005	2150	0.5F
17	0058	0352	0.5E
Su	0715	0932	0.7F
	1145	1642	1.8E
	2049	2341	1.0F
18		0650	*
M		1012	0.3F
	1137	1714	2.3E
	2133		
19		0117	1.6F
Tu		0820	*
		1054	*
		1758	2.6E
	2216		
20		0206	2.0F
W	0745	0924	0.3E
		1137	*
		1835	2.9E
	2259		
21		0249	2.3F
Th	0840	1021	0.3E
		1218	*
		1915	3.0E
	2340		
22		0324	2.4F
F		1118	*
		1300	*
		1953	3.1E
23	0021	0353	2.4F
Sa		1158	*
		1338	*
		2033	3.1E
24	0101	0424	2.4F
Su		1242	*
		1415	*
		2105	3.1E
25	0141	0454	2.2F
M		1344	*
		1444	*
		2142	3.0E
26	0219	0528	2.1F
Tu	1506	2215	2.7E
27	0257	0603	1.9F
W	1505	2250	2.4E
28	0334	0641	1.6F
Th	1446	2318	2.0E
29	0413	0715	1.3F
F		1410	*
		1512	*
		1648	*
		1833	*
30		0000	1.5E
Sa	0456	0756	1.0F
	1136	1430	0.4E
		1956	*
31		0109	0.9E
Su	0551	0836	0.6F
	1046	1459	0.8E
	1944	2118	0.3F
	2312		

AUGUST

Day	Slack Water Time h.m.	Maximum Current Time h.m.	Vel. knots
1		0309	0.4E
M		0912	*
		1542	1.3E
	2012	2242	0.8F
2		0739	*
Tu		0947	*
		1620	1.8E
	2048	2356	1.5F
3	0607	0900	0.4E
W		1022	0.3E
		1703	2.3E
	2130		
4		0054	2.1F
Th	0721	1002	0.4E
		1057	0.4E
		1750	2.9E
	2215		
5		0149	2.6F
F	0830	1835	3.4E
	2304		
6		0236	3.0F
Sa	0949	1924	3.8E
	2353		
7		0323	3.1F
Su		1214	*
		1238	*
		2016	4.0E
8	0044	0407	3.0F
M		1226	*
		1400	0.3F
	1521	2105	3.9E
9	0134	0447	2.8F
Tu		1144	*
		1503	0.4F
	1636	2154	3.6E
10	0224	0527	2.3F
W		1151	*
		1612	0.5F
	1748	2250	2.9E
11	0313	0605	1.8F
Th	1041	1220	0.3E
	1437	1724	0.6F
	1906	2346	2.1E
12	0404	0640	1.3F
F	1009	1255	0.8E
	1624	1840	0.6F
	2041		
13		0055	1.3E
Sa	0459	0715	0.8F
	0938	1340	1.2E
	1749	2003	0.8F
	2336		
14		0221	0.5E
Su	0612	0755	0.3F
	0922	1432	1.6E
	1901	2139	1.0F
15		0609	*
M		0837	*
		1532	2.0E
	2003		

Day	Slack Water Time h.m.	Maximum Current Time h.m.	Vel. knots
16		0003	1.5F
Tu	0530	0730	0.3E
		0926	*
		1629	2.3E
	2058		
17		0106	1.9F
W	0626	0831	0.4E
		1015	0.3E
		1727	2.5E
	2150		
18		0155	2.1F
Th	0711	0915	0.5E
		1117	0.3E
		1818	2.7E
	2237		
19		0230	2.2F
F	0753	0950	0.4E
		1206	*
		1902	2.8E
	2322		
20		0303	2.2F
Sa	0834	1025	0.3E
		1255	*
		1942	2.9E
21	0004	0324	2.2F
Su		1054	*
		1338	*
		2023	2.9E
22	0044	0351	2.0F
M		1109	*
		1415	0.3F
	1534	2058	2.9E
23	0122	0417	1.9F
Tu		1057	*
		1456	0.4F
	1624	2134	2.7E
24	0158	0449	1.7F
W		1058	*
		1539	0.5F
	1713	2204	2.4E
25	0234	0515	1.4F
Th		1119	*
		1624	0.5F
	1804	2240	2.0E
26	0311	0547	1.1F
F	0906	1139	0.4E
	1405	1720	0.5F
	1904	2321	1.5E
27	0353	0619	0.7F
Sa	0832	1157	0.7E
	1514	1826	0.5F
	2020		
28		0015	0.9E
Su	0459	0649	0.3F
	0812	1212	1.0E
	1632	1938	0.7F
	2221		
29		0149	0.4E
M		0724	*
		1236	1.3E
	1749	2059	1.0F
30	0309	1339	1.6E
Tu	1858	2220	1.4F
31	0506	1507	2.0E
W	2001	2339	1.9F

Time meridian 90° W. 0000 is midnight. 1200 is noon.
* Current weak and variable.
If three consecutive entries are marked (E) the middle one is not a true maximum but an intermediate value to show the current pattern.

GALVESTON BAY ENTRANCE (between jetties), TEXAS, 1983

F-Flood, Dir. 300° True E-Ebb, Dir. 100° True

SEPTEMBER

Day	Slack Water Time h.m.	Maximum Current Time h.m.	Vel. knots
1	0604	1624	2.5E
Th	2059		
2		0041	2.4F
F	0658	1724	2.9E
	2155		
3		0132	2.7F
Sa	0749	1006	0.4E
		1142	0.3E
		1827	3.3E
	2249		
4		0215	2.8F
Su		1017	*
		1237	*
		1918	3.5E
	2340		
5		0255	2.7F
M		0954	*
		1332	0.4F
	1453	2011	3.5E
6	0030	0333	2.5F
Tu		0954	*
		1423	0.8F
	1614	2100	3.2E
7	0119	0408	2.0F
W	0825	1011	0.5E
	1218	1523	1.1F
	1731	2155	2.7E
8	0208	0440	1.5F
Th	0801	1037	0.9E
	1319	1624	1.2F
	1851	2247	2.0E
9	0258	0512	1.0F
F	0733	1106	1.3E
	1426	1731	1.3F
	2026	2355	1.2E
10	0357	0541	0.5F
Sa	0715	1141	1.6E
	1536	1836	1.4F
	2248		
11		0115	0.5E
Su		0614	*
		1224	1.8E
	1650	1951	1.4F
12	0209	0527	0.3E
M		0643	0.3E
		1314	2.0E
	1804	2125	1.5F
13	0408	1427	2.0E
Tu	1915	2338	1.8F
14	0500	0742	0.7E
W		0840	0.6E
		1544	2.1E
	2020		
15		0040	2.0F
Th	0541	0812	0.7E
		1003	0.6E
		1656	2.2E
	2118		

Day	Slack Water Time h.m.	Maximum Current Time h.m.	Vel. knots
16		0123	2.0F
F	0615	0841	0.7E
		1105	0.4E
		1756	2.4E
	2209		
17		0152	2.0F
Sa	0645	0909	0.6E
		1201	*
		1847	2.5E
	2256		
18		0216	2.0F
Su	0706	0928	0.5E
		1246	*
		1929	2.6E
	2338		
19		0236	1.8F
M	0720	0927	0.4E
	1145	1332	0.5F
	1505	2005	2.5E
20	0018	0303	1.7F
Tu	0726	0922	0.5E
	1158	1412	0.7F
	1604	2042	2.4E
21	0055	0329	1.4F
W	0721	0930	0.6E
	1215	1456	0.9F
	1700	2122	2.1E
22	0133	0355	1.2F
Th	0659	0945	0.8E
	1238	1542	1.0F
	1758	2157	1.7E
23	0212	0424	0.8F
F	0634	1005	1.0E
	1310	1630	1.1F
	1901	2240	1.3E
24	0301	0451	0.4F
Sa	0618	1012	1.3E
	1349	1719	1.2F
	2019	2335	0.8E
25		0509	*
Su		1022	1.6E
	1437	1823	1.4F
	2231		
26		0057	0.3E
M		0256	*
		1042	1.9E
	1536	1926	1.5F
27	0222	1114	2.1E
Tu	1648	2042	1.7F
28	0359	1212	2.2E
W	1809	2205	2.0F
29	0451	1400	2.3E
Th	1925	2320	2.3F
30	0535	1556	2.5E
F	2032		

OCTOBER

Day	Slack Water Time h.m.	Maximum Current Time h.m.	Vel. knots
1		0015	2.5F
Sa	0611	0903	0.7E
		1040	0.6E
		1713	2.8E
	2133		
2		0100	2.5F
Su	0632	0904	0.5E
		1145	*
		1815	2.9E
	2229		
3		0141	2.4F
M	0635	0846	0.5E
	1113	1245	0.4F
	1404	1910	2.9E
	2321		
4		0213	2.1F
Tu	0630	0835	0.7E
	1122	1342	0.9F
	1543	2009	2.6E
5	0011	0245	1.7F
W	0614	0854	1.1E
	1152	1439	1.4F
	1712	2103	2.2E
6	0100	0317	1.2F
Th	0551	0918	1.6E
	1233	1532	1.7F
	1841	2158	1.6E
7	0151	0343	0.7F
F	0533	0939	2.0E
	1319	1631	1.9F
	2020	2301	1.0E
8	0255	0411	0.3F
Sa	0517	1013	2.3E
	1410	1728	2.0F
	2219		
9		0017	0.4E
Su		0432	*
		1043	2.4E
	1505	1829	2.0F
10	0105	1112	2.4E
M	1607	1937	1.9F
11	0253	1157	2.3E
Tu	1716	2101	1.9F
12	0344	1306	2.1E
W	1828	2239	1.9F
13	0423	1448	1.9E
Th	1937	2353	1.9F
14	0453	0747	0.9E
F		0940	0.7E
		1617	1.9E
	2038		
15		0030	1.9F
Sa	0516	0809	0.9E
		1051	0.4E
		1727	2.0E
	2132		

Day	Slack Water Time h.m.	Maximum Current Time h.m.	Vel. knots
16		0053	1.8F
Su	0531	0825	0.8E
		1146	*
		1821	2.0E
	2219		
17		0116	1.7F
M	0537	0825	0.8E
	1114	1237	0.4F
	1407	1903	2.0E
	2303		
18		0143	1.5F
Tu	0537	0820	0.9E
	1124	1323	0.7F
	1531	1947	1.9E
	2344		
19		0209	1.3F
W	0525	0821	1.1E
	1142	1409	1.1F
	1642	2028	1.7E
20	0025	0236	1.0F
Th	0502	0836	1.4E
	1203	1455	1.4F
	1752	2114	1.4E
21	0109	0302	0.6F
F	0446	0852	1.7E
	1228	1537	1.7F
	1906	2200	1.0E
22		0323	*
Sa		0906	2.0E
	1259	1627	1.9F
	2036	2257	0.6E
23		0339	*
Su		0922	2.3E
	1336	1715	2.0F
24		0019	*
M		0108	*
		0934	2.6E
	1422	1812	2.1F
25	0145	1005	2.7E
Tu	1518	1921	2.2F
26	0302	1046	2.8E
W	1625	2029	2.3F
27	0350	1146	2.7E
Th	1741	2144	2.4F
28	0428	1333	2.5E
F	1856	2249	2.4F
29	0454	0814	0.9E
Sa		0914	0.9E
		1533	2.4E
	2005	2340	2.3F
30	0501	0804	0.8E
Su		1042	0.4E
		1655	2.3E
	2107		
31		0021	2.1F
M	0457	0752	0.9E
		1150	*
		1809	2.1E
	2204		

Time meridian 90° W. 0000 is midnight. 1200 is noon.
* Current weak and variable.
If three consecutive entries are marked (E) the middle one is not a true maximum but an intermediate value to show the current pattern.

F-Flood, Dir. 300° True E-Ebb, Dir. 100° True

NOVEMBER

Day	Slack Water Time h.m.	Maximum Current Time h.m.	Vel. knots
1		0056	1.8F
Tu	0447	0739	1.2E
	1054	1253	0.8F
	1511	1912	1.9E
	2256		
2		0125	1.4F
W	0428	0748	1.7E
	1118	1353	1.4F
	1702	2014	1.5E
	2348		
3		0152	1.0F
Th	0406	0809	2.2E
	1152	1448	1.9F
	1840	2112	1.0E
4	0041	0221	0.5F
F	0354	0838	2.6E
	1230	1537	2.3F
	2016	2226	0.6E
5		0249	*
Sa		0904	2.9E
	1312	1632	2.5F
	2204		
6		0042	0.3E
Su		0306	*
		0936	3.0E
	1356	1723	2.5F
7	0027	0958	2.9E
M	1444	1817	2.4F
8	0152	1029	2.8E
Tu	1538	1921	2.2F
9	0242	1058	2.5E
W	1638	2027	2.1F
10	0320	1151	2.2E
Th	1744	2139	1.9F
11	0349	1349	1.9E
F	1849	2236	1.8F
12	0408	0716	0.9E
Sa		0912	0.8E
		1524	1.7E
	1950	2321	1.7F
13	0416	0731	0.9E
Su		1026	0.5E
		1636	1.6E
	2045	2346	1.6F
14	0416	0742	1.0E
M		1132	*
		1743	1.5E
	2135		
15		0018	1.4F
Tu	0410	0727	1.1E
	1051	1224	0.5F
	1430	1839	1.3E
	2222		

Day	Slack Water Time h.m.	Maximum Current Time h.m.	Vel. knots
16		0047	1.1F
W	0352	0721	1.4E
	1102	1313	1.0F
	1617	1933	1.2E
	2309		
17		0113	0.8F
Th	0328	0736	1.8E
	1121	1401	1.5F
	1744	2030	0.9E
18	0000	0142	0.5F
F	0314	0752	2.1E
	1145	1447	1.9F
	1906	2125	0.7E
19		0209	*
Sa		0812	2.5E
	1214	1533	2.3F
	2035	2228	0.4E
20		0225	*
Su		0830	2.8E
	1248	1622	2.5F
	2228		
21		0853	3.1E
M	1329	1715	2.7F
22	0104	0922	3.3E
Tu	1417	1806	2.7F
23	0214	1003	3.4E
W	1512	1909	2.7F
24	0303	1050	3.2E
Th	1615	2013	2.6F
25	0339	1153	2.9E
F	1722	2113	2.5F
26	0356	1329	2.4E
Sa	1830	2207	2.2F
27	0347	0704	0.8E
Su		0911	0.7E
		1515	2.0E
	1935	2253	1.9F
28	0332	0651	1.0E
M		1042	*
		1648	1.5E
	2037	2328	1.5F
29	0315	0639	1.4E
Tu	1014	1202	0.6F
	1435	1806	1.2E
	2136		
30		0003	1.1F
W	0252	0648	1.9E
	1036	1307	1.3F
	1655	1933	0.8E
	2233		

DECEMBER

Day	Slack Water Time h.m.	Maximum Current Time h.m.	Vel. knots
1		0035	0.7F
Th	0233	0709	2.5E
	1108	1407	1.9F
	1839	2051	0.5E
	2332		
2		0107	0.4F
F	0226	0738	2.9E
	1145	1457	2.4F
	2017	2225	0.3E
3		0135	*
Sa		0807	3.2E
	1224	1545	2.6F
4		0001	*
Su		0157	*
		0839	3.3E
	1304	1629	2.7F
	2343		
5		0914	3.3E
M	1346	1718	2.7F
6	0056	0945	3.2E
Tu	1430	1804	2.5F
7	0148	1016	2.9E
W	1518	1855	2.3F
8	0230	1052	2.6E
Th	1609	1948	2.1F
9	0301	1133	2.3E
F	1703	2037	1.9F
10	0318	1238	1.9E
Sa	1800	2123	1.7F
11	0317	0647	0.8E
Su		0832	0.7E
		1420	1.5E
	1856	2206	1.4F
12	0307	0654	0.9E
M		0952	0.4E
		1547	1.2E
	1953	2248	1.2F
13	0252	0645	1.0E
Tu		1109	*
		1710	0.9E
	2050	2323	0.9F
14	0225	0621	1.4E
W	1017	1212	0.6F
	1532	1827	0.7E
	2148	2353	0.6F
15	0157	0628	1.8E
Th	1032	1306	1.3F
	1723	1939	0.5E
	2252		

Day	Slack Water Time h.m.	Maximum Current Time h.m.	Vel. knots
16		0027	0.3F
F	0145	0651	2.2E
	1056	1355	1.8F
	1852	2107	0.4E
17		0054	*
Sa		0715	2.7E
	1125	1439	2.3F
	2020	2303	0.3E
18		0116	*
Su		0744	3.1E
	1200	1528	2.7F
	2208		
19		0813	3.5E
M	1240	1617	3.0F
20	0013	0850	3.7E
Tu	1325	1706	3.1F
21	0135	0929	3.8E
W	1415	1758	3.0F
22	0232	1013	3.7E
Th	1508	1850	2.8F
23	0312	1106	3.3E
F	1605	1942	2.5F
24	0322	1208	2.7E
Sa	1703	2028	2.1F
25	0238	0556	0.5E
Su		0720	0.5E
		1330	2.0E
	1803	2116	1.7F
26	0201	0537	0.8E
M		0911	*
		1501	1.3E
	1905	2154	1.3F
27	0135	0524	1.3E
Tu	0912	1050	0.4F
	1338	1652	0.7E
	2011	2236	0.8F
28	0106	0537	1.9E
W	0939	1224	1.1F
	1643	1907	0.4E
	2120	2311	0.5F
29	0053	0606	2.5E
Th	1016	1329	1.8F
	1844	2046	0.3E
		2346	*
30		0638	2.9E
F	1055	1424	2.3F
	2013	2201	0.3E
31		0022	*
Sa		0715	3.2E
	1135	1506	2.6F
		2307	*

Time meridian 90° W. 0000 is midnight. 1200 is noon.
* Current weak and variable.
If three consecutive entries are marked (E) the middle one is not a true maximum but an intermediate value to show the current pattern.

VIEQUES PASSAGE, PUERTO RICO, 1983

F-Flood, Dir. 250° True E-Ebb, Dir. 055° True

JANUARY

Day	Slack Water Time h.m.	Maximum Current Time h.m.	Vel. knots
1		0036	0.6F
Sa	0329	0610	0.5E
	0843	1214	0.9F
	1526	1859	1.1E
	2241		
2		0125	0.7F
Su	0427	0710	0.5E
	0949	1312	0.8F
	1617	1948	1.0E
	2324		
3		0216	0.7F
M	0524	0810	0.6E
	1058	1407	0.7F
	1708	2037	1.0E
4	0007	0307	0.7F
Tu	0620	0910	0.6E
	1209	1508	0.6F
	1800	2130	0.9E
5	0049	0359	0.8F
W	0717	1013	0.6E
	1324	1612	0.5F
	1853	2217	0.8E
6	0131	0448	0.8F
Th	0812	1117	0.7E
	1441	1713	0.4F
	1947	2307	0.6E
7	0212	0539	0.8F
F	0905	1216	0.7E
	1557	1817	0.3F
	2045	2358	0.5E
8	0254	0630	0.8F
Sa	0957	1317	0.7E
	1709	1923	0.3F
	2145		
9		0051	0.5E
Su	0335	0718	0.8F
	1045	1414	0.8E
	1813	2025	0.3F
	2247		
10		0140	0.4E
M	0416	0804	0.8F
	1130	1502	0.8E
	1908	2120	0.3F
	2350		
11		0235	0.3E
Tu	0458	0848	0.8F
	1212	1549	0.8E
	1956	2212	0.3F
12	0049	0322	0.3E
W	0541	0931	0.7F
	1252	1632	0.9E
	2036	2259	0.3F
13	0144	0411	0.3E
Th	0626	1013	0.7F
	1330	1711	0.9E
	2113	2342	0.4F
14	0234	0457	0.3E
F	0712	1054	0.7F
	1407	1748	0.9E
	2146		
15		0021	0.4F
Sa	0320	0543	0.3E
	0800	1135	0.6F
	1444	1823	0.9E
	2217		

Day	Slack Water Time h.m.	Maximum Current Time h.m.	Vel. knots
16		0100	0.5F
Su	0402	0629	0.3E
	0851	1218	0.6F
	1521	1901	0.8E
	2247		
17		0135	0.5F
M	0441	0713	0.3E
	0944	1301	0.6F
	1559	1936	0.8E
	2316		
18		0208	0.5F
Tu	0520	0802	0.4E
	1041	1348	0.5F
	1639	2015	0.7E
	2343		
19		0245	0.6F
W	0559	0847	0.4E
	1142	1434	0.4F
	1719	2051	0.7E
20	0012	0321	0.6F
Th	0640	0939	0.5E
	1248	1527	0.4F
	1803	2131	0.6E
21	0042	0403	0.7F
F	0724	1030	0.6E
	1357	1622	0.3F
	1851	2215	0.6E
22	0116	0444	0.7F
Sa	0812	1124	0.7E
	1507	1723	0.3F
	1945	2302	0.5E
23	0154	0533	0.8F
Su	0902	1224	0.7E
	1617	1826	0.3F
	2045	2353	0.5E
24	0239	0624	0.8F
M	0954	1321	0.8E
	1721	1932	0.3F
	2151		
25		0054	0.5E
Tu	0330	0719	0.9F
	1048	1418	0.9E
	1819	2034	0.3F
	2259		
26		0156	0.5E
W	0427	0815	0.9F
	1142	1513	1.0E
	1911	2132	0.4F
27	0006	0253	0.5E
Th	0529	0912	0.9F
	1236	1607	1.0E
	1959	2228	0.5F
28	0110	0358	0.5E
F	0633	1013	0.9F
	1329	1659	1.1E
	2044	2322	0.6F
29	0211	0459	0.6E
Sa	0739	1108	0.9F
	1421	1748	1.0E
	2127		
30		0011	0.6F
Su	0308	0559	0.6E
	0844	1204	0.9F
	1512	1838	1.0E
	2209		
31		0100	0.7F
M	0404	0659	0.7E
	0950	1300	0.8F
	1602	1925	1.0E
	2250		

FEBRUARY

Day	Slack Water Time h.m.	Maximum Current Time h.m.	Vel. knots
1		0148	0.8F
Tu	0458	0754	0.7E
	1056	1357	0.7F
	1651	2014	0.9E
	2330		
2		0237	0.8F
W	0551	0851	0.7E
	1203	1452	0.6F
	1740	2059	0.8E
3	0011	0326	0.8F
Th	0644	0951	0.7E
	1312	1548	0.5F
	1829	2146	0.7E
4	0051	0415	0.8F
F	0737	1048	0.7E
	1422	1647	0.4F
	1921	2234	0.6E
5	0132	0502	0.8F
Sa	0828	1145	0.7E
	1533	1748	0.3F
	2016	2324	0.5E
6	0213	0551	0.8F
Su	0919	1243	0.7E
	1640	1852	0.3F
	2115		
7		0018	0.4E
M	0257	0639	0.7F
	1007	1336	0.7E
	1741	1953	0.3F
	2219		
8		0111	0.3E
Tu	0343	0730	0.7F
	1054	1429	0.8E
	1833	2050	0.3F
	2323		
9		0203	0.3E
W	0431	0819	0.7F
	1139	1516	0.8E
	1918	2139	0.3F
10	0023	0257	0.3E
Th	0522	0904	0.7F
	1221	1557	0.8E
	1957	2226	0.4F
11	0116	0351	0.3E
F	0613	0953	0.6F
	1303	1640	0.8E
	2032	2309	0.4F
12	0202	0437	0.3E
Sa	0706	1035	0.6F
	1343	1720	0.8E
	2104	2345	0.5F
13	0243	0523	0.4E
Su	0758	1119	0.6F
	1422	1756	0.8E
	2133		
14		0020	0.5F
M	0321	0606	0.4E
	0850	1202	0.6F
	1502	1832	0.8E
	2201		
15		0056	0.5F
Tu	0358	0650	0.5E
	0943	1247	0.5F
	1541	1906	0.7E
	2228		

Day	Slack Water Time h.m.	Maximum Current Time h.m.	Vel. knots
16		0127	0.6F
W	0435	0736	0.5E
	1037	1332	0.5F
	1620	1941	0.7E
	2255		
17		0202	0.6F
Th	0514	0819	0.6E
	1134	1417	0.5F
	1701	2017	0.6E
	2324		
18		0241	0.7F
F	0557	0908	0.7E
	1234	1508	0.4F
	1744	2059	0.6E
	2357		
19		0324	0.7F
Sa	0643	0959	0.7E
	1338	1600	0.4F
	1832	2142	0.5E
20	0035	0409	0.8F
Su	0734	1052	0.7E
	1443	1701	0.3F
	1926	2231	0.5E
21	0120	0502	0.8F
M	0828	1153	0.8E
	1548	1800	0.3F
	2027	2333	0.5E
22	0213	0558	0.8F
Tu	0925	1255	0.8E
	1650	1909	0.3F
	2135		
23		0036	0.5E
W	0313	0701	0.8F
	1023	1353	0.9E
	1746	2010	0.4F
	2244		
24		0139	0.5E
Th	0420	0758	0.8F
	1122	1450	0.9E
	1837	2107	0.5F
	2351		
25		0247	0.5E
F	0529	0901	0.8F
	1219	1545	0.9E
	1924	2204	0.5F
26	0053	0350	0.6E
Sa	0638	1001	0.8F
	1314	1637	0.9E
	2008	2255	0.6F
27	0150	0450	0.7E
Su	0745	1059	0.8F
	1407	1725	0.9E
	2050	2345	0.7F
28	0245	0545	0.7E
M	0849	1154	0.8F
	1457	1813	0.9E
	2130		

Time meridian 60° W. 0000 is midnight. 1200 is noon.

TABLE 2.—CURRENT DIFFERENCES AND OTHER CONSTANTS AND ROTARY TIDAL CURRENTS

EXPLANATION OF TABLE

In this publication, reference stations are those for which daily predictions are listed in Table 1. Those stations appearing in Table 2 are called subordinate stations. The principal purpose of Table 2 is to present data that will enable one to determine the approximate times of minimum currents (slack waters) and the times and speeds of maximum currents at numerous subordinate stations on the Atlantic Coast of North America. By applying the specific corrections given in Table 2 to the predicted times and speeds of the current at the appropriate reference station, reasonable approximations of the current at the subordinate station may be compiled.

Locations and Depths

Because the latitude and longitude are listed according to the exactness recorded in the original survey records, the locations of the subordinate stations are presented in varying degrees of accuracy. Since a minute of latitude is nearly equivalent to a mile, a location given to the nearest minute may not indicate the exact position of the station. This should be remembered, especially in the case of a narrow stream, where the nearest minute of latitude or longitude may locate a station inland. In such cases, unless the description locates the station elsewhere, reference is made to the current in the center of the channel. In some instances, the charts may not present a convenient name for locating a station. In those cases, the position may be described by a bearing from some prominent place on the chart.

Although current measurements may have been recorded at various depths in the past, the data listed here for most of the subordinate stations are mean values determined to have been representative of the current at each location. For that reason, no specific current meter depths for those stations are given in Table 2. Beginning with the Boston Harbor tidal current survey in 1971, data for individual meter depths were published and subsequent new data may be presented in a similar manner.

Since most of the current data in Table 2 came from meters suspended from survey vessels or anchored buoys, the listed depths are those measured downward from the surface. Some later data have come from meters anchored at fixed depths from the bottom. Those meter positions were defined as depths below chart datum. Such defined depths in this and subsequent editions will be accompanied by the small letter "d".

Minimum Currents

The reader may note that at many locations the current may not diminish to a true slack water or zero speed stage. For that reason, the phrases, "minimum before flood" and "minimum before ebb" are used in Table 2 rather than "slack water" although either or both minimums may actually reach a zero speed value at some locations. Table 2 lists the average speeds and directions of the minimums.

Maximum Currents

Near the coast and in inland tidal waters, the current increases from minimum current (slack water) for a period of about 3 hours until the maximum speed or the strength of the current is reached. The speed then decreases for another period of about 3 hours when minimum current is again reached and the current begins a similar cycle in the opposite direction. The current that flows toward the coast or up a stream is known as the flood current; the opposite flow is known as the ebb current. Table 2 lists the average speeds and directions of the maximum floods and maximum ebbs. The directions are given in degrees, true, reading clockwise from 000° at north to 359° and are the directions toward which the currents flow.

Time Differences and Speed Ratios

Table 2 contains mean time differences by which the reader can compile approximate times for the minimum and maximum current phases at the subordinate stations. Time differences for those phases should be applied to the corresponding phases at the reference station. It will be seen upon inspection that some subordinate stations exhibit either a double flood or a double ebb stage or both. Explanations of these stages can be found in the glossary located elsewhere in this publication. In those cases, a separate time difference is listed for each of the three flood (or ebb) phases and these should be applied only to the daily maximum flood (or ebb) phase at the reference station. The results obtained by the application of the time differences will be based upon the time meridian shown above the name of the subordinate station. Differences of time meridians between a subordinate station and its reference station have been accounted for and no further adjustment by the reader is needed. Summer or daylight saving time is not used in this publication.

The speed ratios are used to compile approximations of the daily current speeds at the subordinate stations and refer only to the maximum floods and ebbs. No attempt is made to predict the speeds of the minimum currents. Normally, these ratios should be applied to the corresponding maximum current phases at the reference station. As mentioned above, however, some subordinate stations may exhibit either a double flood or a double ebb or both. As with the time differences, separate ratios are listed for each of the three flood (or ebb phases) and should be applied only to the daily maximum flood (or ebb) speed at the reference station. It should be noted that although the speed of a given current phase at a subordinate station is obtained by reference to the corresponding phase at the reference station, the directions of the current at the two places may differ considerably. Table 2 lists the average directions of the various current phases at the subordinate stations.

Rotary Tidal Currents

The last page of Table 2 is a listing of data for those stations which exhibited rotary current patterns. Briefly, a rotary current can be described as one which flows continually with the direction of flow changing through all points of the compass during the tidal period. A more complete description can be found in the glossary located elsewhere in this publication. The average speeds and directions are listed in half-hour increments as referred to the predicted times of "minimum before flood" at the reference station in Table 1. The Moon, at times of new, full, or perigee may increase these speeds 15 to 20 percent above average; or 30 to 40 percent if perigee occurs at or near the time of new or full Moon. Conversely, the Moon at times of quadrature or apogee may decrease the speeds 15 to 20 percent or 30 to 40 percent if they occur together. Near average speeds may be expected when apogee occurs near or at new or full Moon, or when perigee occurs at or near quadrature. The directions of the currents are given in degrees, true reading clockwise from 000° at north to 359° and are the direction toward which the water is flowing.

Example of The Use of Table 2

Suppose we wish to calculate the times of the minimum currents and the times and speeds of the maximum currents on a particular morning at the location listed as Winthrop Head, 1.1 nautical miles east of. From Table 2 we learn that the reference station is Boston

Harbor whose morning currents are listed below. Currents for Winthrop Head can be approximated by using the Table 2 corrections as indicated.

	Minimum before flood	Maximum flood		Minimum before ebb	Maximum ebb	
	h.m.	h.m.	kn	h.m.	h.m.	kn
Boston Harbor	0052	0419	1.2	0645	1109	1.4
Table 2 corrections	−0112	+0019	×0.4 ratio	+0031	−0146	×0.3 ratio
Winthrop Head	2340*	0438	0.5	0716	0923	0.4

* this minimum current phase is seen to occur just before midnight of the previous day.

Table 2 states that the average speeds and directions of the minimums before flood and ebb are 0.3 knots at 103° and 0.2 knots at 297°; respectively. The average directions of the maximum flood and maximum ebb are 205° and 019°; respectively.

TABLE 2. - CURRENT DIFFERENCES AND OTHER CONSTANTS, 1983

NO.	PLACE	METER DEPTH	POSITION Lat.	Long.	TIME DIFFERENCES Min. before Flood	Flood	Min. before Ebb	Ebb	SPEED RATIOS Flood	Ebb	AVERAGE SPEEDS AND DIRECTIONS Minimum before Flood	Maximum Flood	Minimum before Ebb	Maximum Ebb
		ft	° ' N	° ' W	h. m.	h. m.	h. m.	h. m.			knots deg.	knots deg.	knots deg.	knots deg.
	BAY OF FUNDY Time meridian, 60°W				on BAY OF FUNDY ENTRANCE, p.4									
1	Brazil Rock, 6 miles east of...........		43 22	65 18	-2 02	-2 00	-1 56	-2 00	0.4	0.4	0.0 - -	1.0 275	0.0 - -	1.0 050
6	Cape Sable, 3 miles south of...........		43 20	65 38	-3 02	-2 10	-1 21	-2 10	1.0	0.8	0.0 - -	2.2 275	0.0 - -	2.0 095
11	Cape Sable, 12 miles south of..........		43 11	65 37	-1 12	-1 00	-0 46	-1 00	0.7	0.7	0.0 - -	1.7 285	0.0 - -	1.6 090
16	Blonde Rock, 5 miles south of..........		43 15	65 59	-1 02	-0 50	-0 36	-0 50	0.9	0.8	0.0 - -	2.0 310	0.0 - -	2.0 125
21	Seal Island, 13 miles southwest of......		43 16	66 15	-0 17	+0 10	+0 39	+0 10	1.1	0.7	0.0 - -	2.6 325	0.0 - -	1.6 140
26	Cape Fourchu, 17 miles southwest of.....		43 34	66 24	+0 38	+0 45	+0 44	+0 45	0.5	0.5	0.0 - -	1.2 355	0.0 - -	1.2 145
31	Cape Fourchu, 4 miles west of..........		43 47	66 15	-0 12	0 00	+0 09	0 00	0.9	0.7	0.0 - -	2.0 000	0.0 - -	1.7 175
36	Lurcher Shoal, 6 miles east of.........		43 52	66 21	+0 08	+0 30	+0 39	+0 30	0.9	0.8	0.0 - -	2.0 355	0.0 - -	1.8 175
41	Lurcher Shoal, 10 miles west of........		43 46	66 42	+0 23	+0 30	-0 34	+0 30	0.6	0.7	0.0 - -	1.4 000	0.0 - -	1.6 160
46	Lurcher Shoal, 10 miles northwest of....		43 59	66 37	-0 02	+0 30	+0 49	+0 30	0.8	0.5	0.0 - -	1.8 005	0.0 - -	1.2 175
51	Brier Island, 5 miles west of..........		44 13	66 30	+0 43	+0 50	+0 54	+0 50	1.2	1.0	0.0 - -	2.7 005	0.0 - -	2.5 185
56	Brier Island, 15 miles west of.........		44 17	66 44	-0 42	-0 15	+0 14	-0 15	0.6	0.5	0.0 - -	1.4 060	0.0 - -	1.2 250
61	Gannet Rock, 5 miles southeast of.......		44 29	66 41	+0 38	+0 30	+0 09	+0 30	1.1	1.6	0.0 - -	2.6 040	0.0 - -	3.9 230
66	Boars Head, 10 miles northwest of.......		44 31	66 23	+0 48	+0 55	+0 59	+0 55	0.8	0.8	0.0 - -	1.9 020	0.0 - -	2.0 205
71	Prim Point, 20 miles west of...........		44 44	66 15	+0 38	+0 45	+0 54	+0 45	0.7	0.6	0.0 - -	1.6 040	0.0 - -	1.4 235
76	Cape Spencer, 14 miles south of.........		44 58	65 57	+0 51	+0 55	+0 57	+0 55	0.7	0.7	0.0 - -	1.7 050	0.0 - -	1.6 245
81	BAY OF FUNDY ENTRANCE..................		44 45.2	66 55.9	Daily predictions						0.0 - -	2.3 032	0.0 - -	2.4 212
	MAINE COAST Time meridian, 75°W													
86	Eastport, Friar Roads..................		44 54	66 59	0 00	0 00	0 00	0 00	1.2	1.2	0.0 - -	3.0 210	0.0 - -	3.0 040
91	Western Passage, off Kendall Head.......		44 55.9	67 00.0	+0 27	+0 11	+0 13	+0 40	1.4	1.3	0.0 - -	3.2 319	0.0 - -	3.1 142
96	Western Passage, off Frost Ledge........		44 57.9	67 01.9	+0 33	+0 04	-0 16	+0 15	0.9	0.7	0.0 - -	2.1 330	0.0 - -	1.7 150
101	Pond Point, 7.6 miles SSE of...........		44 20.1	67 30.2	+0 13	-0 20	-1 33	-0 05	0.2	0.5	0.0 - -	0.5 015	0.0 - -	1.2 215
106	Moosabec Reach, east end...............		44 31.71	67 34.36	-2 45	-3 08	-3 13	-3 39	0.4	0.4	0.0 - -	1.0 110	0.0 - -	1.0 258
111	Moosabec Reach, west end...............		44 31.25	67 39.00	-1 43	-1 43	-2 00	-1 44	0.4	0.5	0.0 - -	1.0 092	0.0 - -	1.2 253
116	Bar Harbor, 1.2 miles east of <1>.......		44 23.0	68 10.0	- - -	+0 30	- - -	+0 48	0.1	0.3	0.0 - -	0.2 328	0.0 - -	0.7 148
121	Casco Passage, east end, Blue Hill Bay..		44 11.7	68 27.9	-1 49	-1 44	-1 02	-1 58	0.3	0.3	0.0 - -	0.7 086	0.0 - -	0.7 284
126	Hat Island, SE of, Jericho Bay.........		44 08.0	68 29.7	-1 02	-0 35	-0 50	-1 20	0.4	0.5	0.0 - -	0.9 318	0.0 - -	1.3 124
					on PORTSMOUTH HARBOR ENTRANCE, p.10									
136	Isle Au Haut, 0.8 mi. east of Richs Pt..		44 05.0	68 35.0	-2 13	-1 47	-2 09	-1 47	1.2	0.8	0.0 - -	1.4 336	0.0 - -	1.5 139
146	West Penobscot Bay, off Monroe Island...		44 04.5	69 00.6	-1 09	-1 24	-2 20	-1 12	0.2	0.3	0.0 - -	0.3 006	0.0 - -	0.6 159
156	Muscongus Sound........................		43 56.5	69 26.9	Current weak and variable									
166	Damariscotta River, off Cavis Point.....		43 52.5	69 35.0	-0 49	-0 44	-1 24	-1 18	0.5	0.6	0.0 - -	0.6 350	0.0 - -	1.0 215
176	Sheepscot River, off Barter Island......		43 54.0	69 41.5	-0 48	-1 02	-1 15	-0 33	0.7	0.6	0.0 - -	0.8 005	0.0 - -	1.1 200
186	Lowe Point, NE of, Sasanoa River........		43 51.1	69 43.3	-0 48	+0 09	-0 46	-0 27	1.4	1.0	0.0 - -	1.7 327	0.0 - -	1.8 152
196	Lower Hell Gate, Knubble Bay <2>........		43 52.6	69 43.8	-0 23	+0 37	-0 46	+0 06	2.5	1.9	0.0 - -	3.0 290	0.0 - -	3.5 155
206	Upper Hell Gate, Sasanoa River..........		43 53.7	69 46.3	+3 31	+2 48	+1 20	+2 03	0.8	0.5	0.0 - -	1.0 307	0.0 - -	0.8 142
	KENNEBEC RIVER													
211	Hunniwell Point, northeast of...........		43 45.4	69 46.9	+0 05	+0 12	+0 05	+0 24	2.0	1.6	0.0 - -	2.4 332	0.0 - -	2.9 151
216	Bald Head, 0.3 mile southwest of........		43 48.1	69 47.6	+0 23	+0 28	-0 04	+0 23	1.3	1.3	0.0 - -	1.6 321	0.0 - -	2.3 153

Endnotes can be found at the end of Table 2.

TABLE 2. - CURRENT DIFFERENCES AND OTHER CONSTANTS, 1983

NO.	PLACE	METER DEPTH	POSITION Lat.	POSITION Long.	TIME DIFFERENCES Min. before Flood	TIME DIFFERENCES Flood	TIME DIFFERENCES Min. before Ebb	TIME DIFFERENCES Ebb	SPEED RATIOS Flood	SPEED RATIOS Ebb	Minimum before Flood knots	Minimum before Flood deg.	Maximum Flood knots	Maximum Flood deg.	Minimum before Ebb knots	Minimum before Ebb deg.	Maximum Ebb knots	Maximum Ebb deg.
		ft	° ' N	° ' W	h. m.	h. m.	h. m.	h. m.			knots	deg.	knots	deg.	knots	deg.	knots	deg.
	KENNEBEC RIVER Time meridian, 75°W			on	PORTSMOUTH HARBOR ENTRANCE, p.10													
221	Bluff Head, west of......................		43 51.3	69 47.8	+0 33	+0 53	+0 26	+0 24	1.9	1.9	0.0	- -	2.3	014	0.0	- -	3.4	184
226	Fiddler Ledge, north of..................		43 52.8	69 47.8	+0 47	+1 12	+0 22	+0 48	1.6	1.4	0.0	- -	1.9	267	0.0	- -	2.6	113
231	Doubling Point, south of.................		43 52.8	69 48.4	+0 28	+0 49	+0 23	+0 53	2.2	1.7	0.0	- -	2.6	300	0.0	- -	3.0	127
236	Lincoln Ledge, east of...................		43 53.8	69 48.6	+0 32	+0 45	+0 23	+0 34	1.6	1.6	0.0	- -	1.9	359	0.0	- -	2.8	174
241	Bath, 0.2 mile south of bridge <3>......		43 54.5	69 48.5	+0 29	+1 28	+0 43	+0 23	0.8	0.8	0.0	- -	1.0	003	0.0	- -	1.5	177
	CASCO BAY																	
251	Broad Sound, west of Eagle Island.......		43 42.7	70 03.8	-1 16	-1 05	-1 27	-0 59	0.8	0.7	0.0	- -	0.9	010	0.0	- -	1.3	168
261	Hussey Sound, SW of Overset Island......	15	43 40.27	70 10.52	-1 28	-1 18	-0 58	-1 30	0.9	0.6	0.0	- -	1.1	316	0.3	189	1.2	153
	...do................................	25	43 40.27	70 10.52	-1 39	-1 19	-1 06	-1 32	0.9	0.6	0.0	- -	1.1	318	0.3	211	1.1	155
	...do................................	40	43 40.27	70 10.52	-1 58	-1 16	-1 05	-1 32	0.9	0.5	0.1	228	1.1	314	0.3	200	1.0	154
271	Hussey Sound, SE of Pumpkin Nob.........	40	43 40.45	70 10.78	-2 21	-1 29	-1 32	-1 14	1.0	0.5	0.1	068	1.2	346	0.1	066	0.9	168
281	Hussey Sound, east of Crow Island.......	40	43 41.33	70 10.79	-2 18	-0 42	-0 55	-1 24	0.7	0.4	0.1	114	0.9	016	0.0	- -	0.8	197
291	Portland Hbr. ent., SW of Cushing I.....		43 37.9	70 12.7	-1 43	-1 11	-1 20	-0 58	0.8	0.6	0.0	- -	1.0	322	0.0	- -	1.1	154
301	Diamond I. Ledge, midchannel SW. of.....		43 39.6	70 13.5	-1 26	-1 12	-1 11	-1 06	0.8	0.5	0.0	- -	0.9	300	0.0	- -	0.9	150
311	Portland Breakwater Light 0.3 mi. NW of <1> <4>...............		43 39.5	70 14.5	- - -	-0 47	- - -	-1 07	0.3	0.3	0.0	- -	0.4		0.0	- -	0.5	048
321	Grand Trunk Wharves, off ends <1>......		43 39.5	70 14.7	- - -	-1 45	- - -	-1 50	0.5	0.2	0.0	- -	0.6	250	0.0	- -	0.4	040
331	Portland Bridge, center of draw.........		43 38.7	70 15.5	-1 06	-0 17	-0 38	-0 15	0.8	0.6	0.0	- -	0.9	225	0.0	- -	1.0	050
	MAINE COAST-Continued																	
341	Cape Elizabeth..........................		43 34	70 11	-1 35	-1 35	-1 35	-1 35	0.2	0.2	0.0	- -	0.3	340	0.0	- -	0.3	160
351	Cape Porpoise...........................		43 22	70 24	-0 55	-0 55	-0 55	-0 55	0.2	0.2	0.0	- -	0.3	035	0.0	- -	0.3	215
361	Cape Neddick............................		43 10	70 35	-0 20	-0 20	-0 20	-0 20	0.3	0.3	0.0	- -	0.4	025	0.0	- -	0.4	205
371	York Harbor entrance, 3 miles south of..		43 08	70 33	-0 15	-0 15	-0 15	-0 15	0.3	0.3	0.0	- -	0.4	025	0.0	- -	0.4	205
	PORTSMOUTH HARBOR																	
381	Kitts Rocks, 0.2 mile west of...........		43 03	70 42	0 00	0 00	0 00	0 00	0.7	0.9	0.0	- -	0.8	325	0.0	- -	1.6	175
391	Little Harbor entrance..................		43 03	70 43	-1 00	-1 00	-1 00	-1 00	0.6	0.6	0.0	- -	0.7	310	0.0	- -	1.1	130
401	PORTSMOUTH HARBOR ENT. (off Wood I.)....		43 03.8	70 42.3	Daily predictions						0.0	- -	1.2	355	0.0	- -	1.8	195
411	Fort Point..............................		43 04	70 42	+0 05	+0 05	+0 05	+0 05	1.2	1.1	0.0	- -	1.5	350	0.0	- -	2.0	130
421	Salamander Point........................		43 05	70 43	+0 10	+0 10	+0 10	+0 10	1.1	0.7	0.0	- -	1.3	260	0.0	- -	1.3	085
431	Hick Rocks and Clarks Island, between...		43 05	70 43	-0 35	-0 50	-0 35	-0 50	0.8	0.4	0.0	- -	0.9	335	0.0	- -	0.8	195
441	Kittery Point Bridge....................		43 05	70 43	-1 10	-1 10	-1 10	-1 10	0.7	0.6	0.0	- -	0.8	020	0.0	- -	1.1	200
451	Jamaica Island, northeast of............		43 05	70 43	-0 25	-0 25	-0 25	-0 25	0.8	0.7	0.0	- -	1.0	315	0.0	- -	1.0	135
461	Seavey Island, north of.................		43 05	70 44	+0 15	+0 15	+0 15	+0 15	1.2	1.0	0.0	- -	1.4	260	0.0	- -	1.8	080
471	Clarks I. and Seavey I., between <5>....		43 05	70 44					1.5		0.0	- -	1.8	200	0.0	- -		
481	Clarks Island, south of.................		43 04	70 44	+0 15	+0 15	+0 15	+0 15	1.7	1.7	0.0	- -	2.1	260	0.0	- -	3.1	080
491	Seavey Island, south of.................		43 04	70 44	+0 15	+0 15	+0 15	+0 15	2.5	2.1	0.0	- -	3.0	260	0.0	- -	3.8	090
501	Marvin Island and Goat Island, between..		43 04	70 44	-1 00	-1 00	-1 00	-1 00	1.0	0.4	0.0	- -	1.2	160	0.0	- -	0.8	340
511	Henderson Point, west of................		43 05	70 44	+0 30	+0 30	+0 30	+0 30	2.2	1.3	0.0	- -	2.6	340	0.0	- -	2.3	170
521	Off Gangway Rock........................		43 05	70 45	+0 30	+0 30	+0 30	+0 30	1.7	1.7	0.0	- -	2.1	280	0.0	- -	3.0	110
531	Badgers Island, east of.................		43 05	70 45	+0 25	+0 25	+0 25	+0 25	0.9	0.2	0.0	- -	1.1	240	0.0	- -	0.4	050

Endnotes can be found at the end of Table 2.

TABLE 2. - CURRENT DIFFERENCES AND OTHER CONSTANTS, 1983

NO.	PLACE	METER DEPTH	POSITION Lat.	POSITION Long.	TIME DIFFERENCES Min. before Flood	Flood	Min. before Ebb	Ebb	SPEED RATIOS Flood	Ebb	AVERAGE SPEEDS AND DIRECTIONS Minimum before Flood		Maximum Flood		Minimum before Ebb		Maximum Ebb	
		ft	° ' N	° ' W	h. m.	h. m.	h. m.	h. m.			knots	deg.	knots	deg.	knots	deg.	knots	deg.
	PORTSMOUTH HARBOR Time meridian, 75°W				on PORTSMOUTH HARBOR ENTRANCE, p.10													
541	Badgers Island, southwest of...........		43 05	70 45	+0 30	+0 30	+0 30	+0 30	2.7	2.0	0.0	- -	3.3	330	0.0	- -	3.7	125
	PISCATAQUA RIVER and TRIBUTARIES																	
546	NW of Nobles Island (RR. bridge)........		43 05	70 46	+0 35	+0 35	+0 35	+0 35	1.3	0.5	0.0	- -	1.6	050	0.0	- -	0.9	200
551	Nobles Island, north of................		43 06	70 46	+0 30	+0 30	+0 30	+0 30	3.0	2.4	0.0	- -	3.6	305	0.0	- -	4.4	140
556	Frankfort Island, south of.............		43 07	70 48	+0 30	+0 30	+0 30	+0 30	2.2	1.6	0.0	- -	2.6	310	0.0	- -	2.9	130
561	Little Bay entrance, Dover Point.......		43 07	70 50	+0 35	+0 35	+0 35	+0 35	3.2	2.3	0.0	- -	3.8	270	0.0	- -	4.2	095
566	Furber Strait..........................		43 05	70 52	+0 40	+0 40	+0 40	+0 40	1.7	1.2	0.0	- -	2.0	185	0.0	- -	2.1	010
	MASSACHUSETTS COAST																	
571	Gunboat Shoal..........................		43 01	70 42	+0 05	+0 05	+0 05	+0 05	0.4	0.3	0.0	- -	0.5	340	0.0	- -	0.5	160
576	Isles of Shoals Light, White Island.....		42 58	70 37	0 00	0 00	0 00	0 00	0.2	0.2	0.0	- -	0.3	020	0.0	- -	0.3	200
					on BOSTON HARBOR, p.16													
581	Merrimack River entrance...............		42 49.1	70 48.6	+1 04	+1 15	+1 13	-0 34	2.0	1.2	0.0	- -	2.2	285	0.0	- -	1.4	105
586	Newburyport, Merrimack River...........		42 48.8	70 52.1	+1 28	+1 48	+1 47	+0 35	1.4	1.2	0.0	- -	1.5	288	0.0	- -	1.4	098
591	Plum Island Sound entrance.............		42 42.3	70 47.3	+0 36	+0 50	+0 48	-0 07	1.5	1.2	0.0	- -	1.6	316	0.0	- -	1.5	184
596	Annisquam Harbor Light.................		42 40.1	70 41.1	+0 42	+0 49	+0 58	+0 03	0.9	1.1	0.0	- -	1.0	200	0.0	- -	1.3	013
601	Gloucester Harbor entrance.............		42 34.9	70 40.5	-0 28	+0 01	-0 29	-0 36	0.3	0.2	0.0	- -	0.3	340	0.0	- -	0.3	195
606	Blynman Canal ent., Gloucester Harbor...		42 36.6	70 40.4	-0 06	+0 05	-0 15	-0 39	2.7	2.8	0.0	- -	3.0	310	0.0	- -	3.3	130
611	Marblehead Channel.....................		42 30	70 49	+1 09	+1 09	+1 09	+1 09	0.4	0.3	0.0	- -	0.4	285	0.0	- -	0.4	105
616	Ram Island, 0.2 n.mi. NNE of............	10	42 28.75	70 51.68	See Rotary Tidal Currents, p.185													
621	Ram Island, 0.2 n.mi. southeast of......	10	42 28.45	70 51.55	See Rotary Tidal Currents, p.185													
626	Great Pig Rocks, southeast of...........	10	42 27.53	70 50.70	See Rotary Tidal Currents, p.185													
631	Galloupes Point, 0.4 n.mi. south of.....	10	42 27.24	70 53.70	See Rotary Tidal Currents, p.185													
636	Little Nahant, 0.9 n.mi. northeast of...	10	42 26.85	70 54.84	See Rotary Tidal Currents, p.185													
641	Egg Rock, 0.2 n.mi. north of............	10	42 26.25	70 53.93	See Rotary Tidal Currents, p.185													
646	Egg Rock, southwest of..................	10	42 25.85	70 54.20	See Rotary Tidal Currents, p.185													
651	Nahant, 1.8 n.mi. NE of East Point......	10	42 26.00	70 52.02	+0 32	+0 49	+0 15	+1 00	0.6	0.6	0.0	- -	0.7	252	0.1	291	0.7	144
	...do..................................	45	42 26.00	70 52.02	-0 21	+1 04	+1 14	-0 31	0.3	0.2	0.0	- -	0.3	250	0.0	- -	0.2	070
	...do..................................	80	42 26.00	70 52.02	-0 25	+1 04	+1 15	-0 31	0.2	0.1	0.1	329	0.2	238	0.0	- -	0.2	077
656	Nahant, 0.4 n.mi. east of East Point....	15	42 25.23	70 53.63	+0 04	-0 41	+0 15	+0 22	0.4	0.5	0.2	118	0.5	205	0.0	- -	0.6	045
	...do..................................	25	42 25.23	70 53.63	+0 03	-0 26	+0 08	+0 29	0.4	0.4	0.1	102	0.4	198	0.1	282	0.5	027
661	Nahant, 1 n.mi. SE of East Point........	45	42 23.83	70 51.17	+0 04	+1 04	+1 13	+0 14	0.3	0.2	0.0	- -	0.3	253	0.0	- -	0.3	074
	...do..................................	70	42 23.83	70 51.17	-0 22	-0 04	+0 19	-1 01	0.2	0.2	0.0	- -	0.2	261	0.0	- -	0.2	090
666	Pea Island, 0.4 n.mi. southeast of......	15	42 24.63	70 54.13	+0 53	+0 55	+0 42	-0 01	0.5	0.4	0.0	- -	0.5	239	0.1	161	0.5	063
	...do..................................	25	42 24.63	70 54.13	+0 34	+0 34	+0 57	+0 29	0.4	0.3	0.0	- -	0.5	224	0.0	- -	0.4	048
	...do..................................	65	42 24.63	70 54.13	-0 37	-0 59	+0 14	-0 31	0.3	0.3	0.1	332	0.4	271	0.0	- -	0.3	035
671	Bass Point, 1.2 n.mi. southeast of......	10	42 24.12	70 55.07	-0 22	+1 20	+0 58	-0 14	0.7	0.6	0.1	351	0.7	259	0.0	- -	0.7	066
	...do..................................	45	42 24.12	70 55.07	-0 29	-0 10	+0 52	-0 29	0.3	0.2	0.0	- -	0.4	251	0.0	- -	0.3	086
	...do..................................	60	42 24.12	70 55.07	-0 29	-0 10	+0 31	-0 59	0.2	0.2	0.0	- -	0.3	250	0.0	- -	0.2	091
676	Bass Point, 0.5 n.mi. SSW of............	15	42 24.57	70 56.53	See Rotary Tidal Currents, p.185													
681	Bass Point, 0.7 n.mi. west of...........	10	42 25.13	70 57.25	See Rotary Tidal Currents, p.185													

Endnotes can be found at the end of Table 2.

TABLE 2. - CURRENT DIFFERENCES AND OTHER CONSTANTS, 1983

NO.	PLACE	METER DEPTH	POSITION Lat.	Long.	TIME DIFFERENCES Min. before Flood	Flood	Min. before Ebb	Ebb	SPEED RATIOS Flood	Ebb	AVERAGE SPEEDS AND DIRECTIONS Minimum before Flood knots	deg.	Maximum Flood knots	deg.	Minimum before Ebb knots	deg.	Maximum Ebb knots	deg.
		ft	° ' N	° ' W	h. m.	h. m.	h. m.	h. m.			knots	deg.	knots	deg.	knots	deg.	knots	deg.
	CAPE COD BAY Time meridian, 75°W				on BOSTON HARBOR, p.16													
1231	Race Point, 7 miles north of		42 11	70 16	-0 01	-0 01	-0 01	-0 01	1.4	1.2	0.0	- -	1.5	290	0.0	- -	1.5	- -
1236	Race Point, 1 mile northwest of		42 05	70 15	-0 06	-0 06	-0 06	-0 06	0.9	0.8	0.0	- -	1.0	226	0.0	- -	0.9	061
1241	Provincetown Harbor		42 03	70 10	+0 04	+0 04	+0 04	+0 04	0.5	0.3	0.0	- -	0.6	315	0.0	- -	0.4	135
1246	Wellfleet Harbor		41 54	70 03	+0 09	+0 09	+0 09	+0 09	0.6	0.4	0.0	- -	0.7	020	0.0	- -	0.5	200
1251	Barnstable Harbor		41 43.6	70 16.4	+0 19	+0 58	+0 22	+0 29	1.1	1.2	0.0	- -	1.2	192	0.0	- -	1.4	004
1256	Sandwich Harbor		41 46	70 29	Current weak and variable													
	Cape Cod Canal (see Index)		- - - -	- - - -	- - -	- - -	- - -	- - -	- -	- -	- -	- -	- -	- -	- -	- -	- -	- -
1261	Sagamore Beach		41 48	70 31	Current weak and variable													
1266	Ellisville Harbor, 1 mile east of		41 51	70 30	+0 14	+0 14	+0 14	+0 14	0.3	0.2	0.0	- -	0.3	200	0.0	- -	0.3	020
1271	Manomet Point		41 56	70 32	+0 04	+0 04	+0 04	+0 04	1.0	0.7	0.0	- -	1.1	155	0.0	- -	0.9	010
1276	Gurnet Point, 1 mile east of		42 00	70 35	-0 06	-0 06	-0 06	-0 06	1.3	0.8	0.0	- -	1.4	250	0.0	- -	1.0	- -
1281	Plymouth Harbor		41 58	70 39	+0 04	+0 04	+0 04	+0 04	0.5	0.3	0.0	- -	0.5	245	0.0	- -	0.4	010
1286	Farnham Rock, 1 mile east of		42 06	70 35	-0 21	-0 21	-0 21	-0 21	1.0	0.8	0.0	- -	1.1	180	0.0	- -	0.9	010
	MASSACHUSETTS COAST-Continued				on POLLOCK RIP CHANNEL, p.28													
1291	Nauset Beach Light, 5 miles northeast of		41 56	69 54	See table 5.													
1296	Georges Bank and vicinity		- - - -	- - - -	See table 5.													
1301	Davis Bank		- - - -	- - - -	See table 5.													
1306	Monomoy Point, 23 miles east of		41 35	69 30	See table 5.													
1311	Nantucket Shoals		40 37	69 37	See table 5.													
1316	Nantucket Island, 28 miles east of		41 20	69 21	See table 5.													
1321	Old Man Shoal, Nantucket Shoals		41 13.6	69 59.0	+1 23	+1 03	+1 17	+1 14	0.9	0.9	0.0	- -	1.9	080	0.0	- -	1.6	225
1326	Miacomet Pond, 3.0 miles SSE of		41 11.4	70 05.8	+2 19	+2 03	+2 22	+2 16	0.6	0.8	0.0	- -	1.3	080	0.0	- -	1.4	280
1331	Tuckernuck Island, 4.2 miles SSW of		41 13.57	70 16.90	+4 08	+3 13	+2 17	+3 56	0.3	0.6	0.0	- -	0.5	090	0.0	- -	1.0	280
1336	Martha's Vineyard, 1.4 miles S of <1>		41 19.50	70 39.90	- - -	-2 53	- - -	-2 47	0.1	0.1	0.0	- -	0.3	230	0.0	- -	0.3	095
	NANTUCKET SOUND ENTRANCE																	
1341	Pollock Rip Channel, east end		41 33.9	69 55.4	-0 14	-0 39	-0 23	-0 38	1.0	1.1	0.0	- -	2.0	053	0.0	- -	1.8	212
1346	POLLOCK RIP CHANNEL (Butler Hole)		41 33	69 59	Daily predictions						0.0	- -	2.0	037	0.0	- -	1.8	226
1351	Great Round Shoal Channel		- - - -	- - - -	See table 5.													
	NANTUCKET SOUND																	
1356	Monomoy Pt., channel 0.2 mile west of		41 33.0	70 01.3	0 00	+0 39	+0 18	-0 23	0.8	1.2	0.0	- -	1.7	170	0.0	- -	2.0	346
1361	Chatham Roads		41 38.6	70 01.7	Current weak and variable													
1366	Stage Harbor, west of Morris Island		41 39.4	69 58.5	+3 07	+1 29	+2 24	+4 28	0.3	0.6	0.0	- -	0.5	335	0.0	- -	1.0	144
1371	Dennis Port, 2.2 miles south of		41 37.0	70 06.9	+1 28	+0 52	+0 27	+1 04	0.2	0.2	0.1	138	0.3	077	0.1	052	0.3	269
1376	Monomoy Point, 6 miles west of		41 33.5	70 09.0	+1 22	+1 52	+1 09	+1 22	0.2	0.3	0.1	194	0.5	090	0.1	256	0.5	275
1381	Handkerchief Lighted Whistle Buoy "H"		41 29.3	70 04.0	+1 08	+1 10	+0 49	+0 59	0.6	0.8	0.0	- -	1.3	080	0.0	- -	1.3	251
1386	Halfmoon Shoal, 1.9 miles northeast of		41 29.05	70 11.55	+1 42	+1 49	+1 24	+1 44	0.4	0.3	0.0	- -	0.8	110	0.0	- -	0.6	265
1391	Halfmoon Shoal, 3.5 miles east of		41 28.1	70 09.2	+1 13	+1 23	+1 06	+1 11	0.5	0.6	0.0	- -	1.1	088	0.0	- -	1.0	295
1396	Great Point, 0.5 mile west of		41 23.6	70 03.7	+0 25	+1 37	+1 13	+0 33	0.6	0.7	0.0	- -	1.1	029	0.0	- -	1.2	195
1401	Great Point, 3 miles west of		41 23.4	70 06.8	+1 15	+1 23	+0 51	+1 08	0.4	0.5	0.0	- -	0.8	066	0.0	- -	0.8	248
1406	Tuckernuck Shoal, off east end		41 24.3	70 10.4	+1 22	+1 34	+1 09	+1 10	0.5	0.5	0.3	000	0.9	113	0.3	186	0.9	287

Endnotes can be found at the end of Table 2.

TABLE 2. - CURRENT DIFFERENCES AND OTHER CONSTANTS, 1983

NO.	PLACE	METER DEPTH	POSITION Lat.	POSITION Long.	TIME DIFFERENCES Min. before Flood	TIME DIFFERENCES Flood	TIME DIFFERENCES Min. before Ebb	TIME DIFFERENCES Ebb	SPEED RATIOS Flood	SPEED RATIOS Ebb	AVERAGE SPEEDS AND DIRECTIONS Minimum before Flood	AVERAGE SPEEDS AND DIRECTIONS Maximum Flood	AVERAGE SPEEDS AND DIRECTIONS Minimum before Ebb	AVERAGE SPEEDS AND DIRECTIONS Maximum Ebb
		ft	° ' N	° ' W	h. m.	h. m.	h. m.	h. m.			knots deg.	knots deg.	knots deg.	knots deg.
	NANTUCKET SOUND Time meridian, 75°W				on POLLOCK RIP CHANNEL, p.28									
1411	Brant Point, 2 miles NNW of <1>........		41 19.25	70 06.30	- - -	+1 43	- - -	+2 36	0.2	0.2	0.0 - -	0.3 090	0.0 - -	0.3 275
1416	Nantucket Harbor entrance channel.......		41 18.4	70 06.0	+3 22	+1 55	+2 44	+3 58	0.6	0.9	0.0 - -	1.2 171	0.0 - -	1.5 350
1421	Eel Pt., Nantucket I. 2.5 miles NE of...		41 19.3	70 10.2	+1 13	+1 12	+1 02	+1 15	0.3	0.2	0.0 - -	0.6 094	0.0 - -	0.4 284
1426	Muskeget I., channel 1 mile northeast of		41 21.0	70 17.1	+1 29	+0 45	+0 57	+0 56	0.6	0.9	0.0 - -	1.1 108	0.0 - -	1.5 295
1431	Muskeget Rock, 1.3 miles southwest of...		41 19.2	70 23.6	+1 10	+0 23	+0 57	+0 18	0.6	0.6	0.0 - -	1.3 024	0.0 - -	1.0 192
1436	Muskeget Channel.......................		41 20.9	70 25.2	+1 40	+0 38	+1 29	+1 02	1.9	1.9	0.0 - -	3.8 021	0.0 - -	3.3 200
1441	Wasque Point, 2.0 miles southwest of....		41 19.90	70 29.25	+1 30	+1 04	+1 11	+0 32	0.6	0.6	0.0 - -	1.3 075	0.0 - -	1.2 280
								+1 15		0.5				0.9 280
								+1 53		0.6				1.1 280
1446	Long Shoal-Norton Shoal, between........		41 24.50	70 20.00	+1 31	+1 12	+1 26	+1 13	0.7	0.6	0.0 - -	1.4 100	0.0 - -	1.1 260
1451	Cape Page Lt., 1.7 miles SSE of.........		41 24.0	70 25.6	+0 58	-0 07	+0 49	+0 48	0.8	0.7	0.0 - -	1.6 025	0.0 - -	1.3 215
1456	Cross Rip Channel......................		41 26.9	70 17.5	+1 48	+1 48	+1 55	+1 59	0.6	0.5	0.0 - -	1.3 091	0.0 - -	0.9 272
1461	Cape Page Lt., 3.2 miles northeast of...		41 27.5	70 24.0	+2 42	+2 03	+2 33	+2 37	0.8	0.7	0.0 - -	1.6 095	0.0 - -	1.2 300
1466	Broken Ground-Horseshoe Shoal, between..		41 33.0	70 17.1	+1 46	+1 55	+1 15	+1 20	0.5	0.5	0.2 000	1.1 107	0.1 224	0.9 276
1471	Point Gammon, 1.2 miles south of........		41 35.3	70 15.4	+1 15	+1 03	+1 06	+1 02	0.5	0.6	0.0 - -	1.1 105	0.0 - -	1.0 260
1476	Hyannis Harbor, entrance off breakwater.		41 37.4	70 17.5	Current weak and variable									
1481	Lewis Bay entrance channel.............		41 37.9	70 16.4	+2 46	+0 53	+2 44	+4 22	0.5	0.8	0.0 - -	0.9 004	0.0 - -	1.3 184
1486	Cotuit Bay entrance (Bluff Point).......		41 36.6	70 25.8	+2 44	+2 33	+2 51	+3 35	0.3	0.4	0.0 - -	0.5 035	0.0 - -	0.7 218
1491	Wreck Shoal-Eldridge Shoal, between.....		41 32.0	70 25.7	+1 47	+1 32	+1 44	+1 45	0.8	0.8	0.0 - -	1.7 062	0.0 - -	1.4 245
1496	Hedge Fence Lighted Gong Buoy 22........		41 28.3	70 29.0	+2 48	+2 34	+2 38	+2 44	0.7	0.7	0.0 - -	1.4 108	0.0 - -	1.2 268
1501	Cape Page Light, 1.4 miles west of......		41 25.45	70 29.00	+2 13	+1 54	+1 26	+1 39	0.2	0.1	0.0 - -	0.3 095	0.0 - -	0.2 250
1506	Edgartown, Inner Harbor................		41 23.4	70 30.5	+0 25	-1 04	+0 35	-0 20	0.6	0.6	0.0 - -	1.1 075	0.0 - -	1.1 270
						+0 38		+1 08	0.3	0.3		0.6 070		0.5 265
						+1 58		+1 52	0.4	0.4		0.8 075		0.7 260
1511	Katama Pt., 0.6 mi. NNW of, Katama B....		41 21.9	70 30.3	+0 12	-0 43	+0 20	-0 31	0.3	0.3	0.0 - -	0.6 325	0.0 - -	0.5 180
						+0 47		+1 12	0.2	0.1		0.3 325		0.2 195
						+1 46		+1 57	0.2	0.2		0.4 325		0.3 175
1516	East Chop-Squash Meadow, between........		41 27.9	70 32.2	+2 07	+0 55	+1 43	+2 04	0.7	1.1	0.0 - -	1.4 131	0.0 - -	1.8 329
1521	East Chop, 1 mile north of.............		41 29.1	70 33.5	+2 40	+1 52	+2 17	+2 11	1.1	1.3	0.0 - -	2.2 116	0.0 - -	2.2 297
1526	Vineyard Haven.........................		41 28.1	70 35.2	Current weak and variable									
1531	West Chop, 0.8 mile north of...........		41 29.6	70 35.7	+2 49	+1 58	+2 20	+2 35	1.6	1.8	0.0 - -	3.1 096	0.0 - -	3.0 282
1536	Hedge Fence-L'Hommedieu Shoal, between..		41 30.3	70 32.2	+2 27	+1 38	+2 01	+1 52	1.0	1.3	0.0 - -	2.1 106	0.0 - -	2.2 276
1541	Waquoit Bay entrance...................		41 32.9	70 31.8	+3 21	+2 14	+3 40	+4 01	0.8	0.8	0.0 - -	1.5 348	0.0 - -	1.4 203
1546	L'Hommedieu Shoal, north of west end....		41 31.6	70 34.6	+2 30	+2 03	+2 12	+2 11	1.2	1.4	0.0 - -	2.3 080	0.0 - -	2.3 268
1551	Nobska Point, 1.8 miles east of.........		41 31.1	70 37.1	+2 13	+1 45	+1 55	+1 49	1.2	1.0	0.0 - -	2.3 063	0.0 - -	1.7 240
	VINEYARD SOUND													
1556	West Chop, 0.2 mile west of............		41 29.0	70 36.6	+1 19	+1 34	+1 50	+1 16	1.3	0.8	0.0 - -	2.7 059	0.0 - -	1.4 241
1561	Nobska Point, 1 mile southeast of.......		41 30.1	70 38.6	+2 33	+2 15	+2 25	+2 19	1.3	1.4	0.0 - -	2.6 071	0.0 - -	2.4 259
1566	Norton Point, 0.5 mile north of.........		41 28.1	70 39.9	+1 55	+1 44	+2 01	+1 12	1.7	1.4	0.0 - -	3.4 050	0.0 - -	2.4 240
1571	Tarpaulin Cove, 1.5 miles east of.......		41 28.3	70 43.5	+2 49	+2 07	+2 12	+2 33	1.0	1.4	0.0 - -	1.9 055	0.0 - -	2.3 232
1576	Robinsons Hole, 1.2 miles southeast of..		41 26.1	70 46.8	+2 30	+1 51	+2 11	+2 02	1.0	1.2	0.0 - -	1.9 060	0.0 - -	2.1 240
1581	Gay Head, 3 miles northeast of..........		41 23.1	70 47.0	+2 25	+1 50	+1 42	+2 11	0.5	0.8	0.0 - -	0.9 081	0.0 - -	1.3 238
1586	Menemsha Bight <6>.....................		41 21.3	70 46.3										
1591	Gay Head, 3 miles north of.............		41 24.1	70 51.2	+2 13	+1 24	+1 55	+1 17	0.6	0.7	0.0 - -	1.1 074	0.0 - -	1.2 255

Endnotes can be found at the end of Table 2.

TABLE 2. - CURRENT DIFFERENCES AND OTHER CONSTANTS, 1983

NO.	PLACE	METER DEPTH	POSITION Lat.	POSITION Long.	TIME DIFFERENCES Min. before Flood	TIME DIFFERENCES Flood	TIME DIFFERENCES Min. before Ebb	TIME DIFFERENCES Ebb	SPEED RATIOS Flood	SPEED RATIOS Ebb	AVERAGE SPEEDS AND DIRECTIONS Minimum before Flood	AVERAGE SPEEDS AND DIRECTIONS Maximum Flood	AVERAGE SPEEDS AND DIRECTIONS Minimum before Ebb	AVERAGE SPEEDS AND DIRECTIONS Maximum Ebb
		ft	° ' N	° ' W	h. m.	h. m.	h. m.	h. m.			knots deg.	knots deg.	knots deg.	knots deg.
	VINEYARD SOUND Time meridian, 75°W				on POLLOCK RIP CHANNEL, p.28									
1596	Gay Head, 1.5 miles northwest of........		41 21.8	70 51.8	+1 30	+0 54	+1 42	+1 16	1.0	1.2	0.0 - -	2.0 012	0.0 - -	2.0 249
1601	Cuttyhunk Island, 3.2 miles southwest of		41 23	71 00	See table 5.									
1606	Browns Ledge...........................		41 19.8	71 05.9	See table 5.									
	VINEYARD SOUND-BUZZARDS BAY				on CAPE COD CANAL, p.22									
	Woods Hole													
1611	South end...........................		41 30.8	70 40.2	+0 29	+1 40	+1 17	+0 08	0.4	0.2	0.0 - -	1.5 135	0.0 - -	1.1 318
1616	0.1 mile SW of Devils Foot Island....		41 31.2	70 41.1	+0 20	+1 41	+0 55	+0 31	0.9	0.8	0.0 - -	3.5 094	0.0 - -	3.6 276
1621	North end...........................		41 31.5	70 41.6	-0 29	+1 25	+1 09	-0 04	0.2	0.2	0.0 - -	0.8 160	0.0 - -	0.7 007
	Robinsons Hole													
1626	South end...........................		41 26.7	70 48.2	+1 14	+1 42	+1 20	+1 01	0.2	0.2	0.0 - -	0.8 162	0.0 - -	1.0 339
1631	Middle..............................		41 27.0	70 48.4	+1 30	+2 00	+1 02	+0 47	0.7	0.6	0.0 - -	2.8 146	0.0 - -	2.9 316
1636	North end...........................		41 27.4	70 48.7	+1 54	+2 00	+0 52	+1 17	0.2	0.3	0.0 - -	1.0 161	0.0 - -	1.2 338
	Quicks Hole													
1641	South end...........................		41 26.3	70 50.5	+2 18	+1 42	+1 17	+0 53	0.5	0.4	0.0 - -	1.9 140	0.0 - -	2.0 300
1646	Middle..............................		41 26.6	70 50.9	+2 21	+2 00	+1 26	+0 41	0.6	0.5	0.0 - -	2.5 167	0.0 - -	2.2 339
1651	North end...........................		41 27.1	70 51.0	+2 42	+2 06	+1 44	+0 23	0.5	0.6	0.0 - -	2.0 165	0.0 - -	2.6 002
1656	Canapitsit Channel.....................		41 25.4	70 54.5	+2 03	+2 27	+1 02	+0 26	0.6	0.4	0.0 - -	2.6 156	0.0 - -	1.7 312
					on POLLOCK RIP CHANNEL, p.28									
1661	Westport River entrance................		41 30.5	71 05.3	+0 09	-0 05	-0 26	-1 13	1.1	1.5	0.0 - -	2.2 290	0.0 - -	2.5 108
	BUZZARDS BAY <7>													
1666	Gooseberry Neck, 2 miles SSE of.........		41 27	71 01	See table 5.									
1671	Ribbon Reef-Sow & Pigs Reef, between....		41 25.3	70 58.2	-0 19	-1 31	-2 44	-1 54	0.4	0.7	0.0 - -	0.8 062	0.0 - -	1.2 237
1676	Penikese Island, 0.8 mile northwest of..		41 27.9	70 56.2	-1 37	-0 25	-0 55	-0 57	0.6	0.6	0.0 - -	1.2 050	0.0 - -	1.1 254
1681	Penikese Island, 0.2 mile south of......		41 26.6	70 55.5	-1 43	-0 15	-1 30	-2 39	0.4	0.5	0.0 - -	0.7 093	0.0 - -	0.9 287
1686	Gull I. and Nashawena I., between.......		41 26.2	70 54.2	-2 15	-0 57	-2 01	-2 41	0.5	0.6	0.0 - -	0.9 091	0.0 - -	1.1 247
1691	Weepecket Island, south of.............		41 30.4	70 44.3	-3 16	-1 07	-1 28	-2 27	0.4	0.4	0.0 - -	0.8 069	0.0 - -	0.6 255
1696	Quamquisset Harbor entrance............		41 32.4	70 39.8	Current weak and variable						0.0 - -	0.4 - -	0.0 - -	0.3 - -
1701	West Falmouth Harbor entrance...........		41 36.5	70 39.3	Current weak and variable									
1706	Megansett Harbor.......................		41 38.8	70 39.2	Current weak and variable									
1711	Abiels Ledge, 0.4 mile south of.........		41 41.1	70 40.4	+0 26	-0 36	-0 06	-0 23	0.4	0.6	0.0 - -	0.8 035	0.0 - -	1.0 216
1716	Dumpling Rocks, 0.2 mile southeast of...		41 32.0	70 55.1	-1 43	-1 03	-1 32	-2 09	0.4	0.6	0.0 - -	0.8 066	0.0 - -	1.1 190
1721	Apponaganset Bay.......................		41 35	70 57	Current weak and variable									
1726	Clarks Cove............................		41 36	70 55	Current weak and variable									
1731	New Bedford Harbor and approaches.......				Current weak and variable									
1736	West Island and Long Island, between....		41 35.6	70 50.4	Current weak and variable						0.0 - -	0.3 - -	0.0 - -	0.4 - -
1741	West Island, 1 mile southeast of........	6	41 34.0	70 48.6	-0 43	-0 43	-1 28	-1 42	0.4	0.5	0.0 - -	0.7 079	0.0 - -	0.8 203
1746	Nasketucket Bay........................		41 37.1	70 50.2	Current weak and variable						0.0 - -	0.3 - -	0.0 - -	0.3 - -
1751	Mattapoisett Harbor....................		41 38	70 47	Current weak and variable									
1756	Sippican Harbor........................		41 41	70 44	Current weak and variable						0.0 - -	0.3 - -	0.0 - -	0.4 - -
1761	Wareham River, off Long Beach Point.....		41 44.0	70 43.0	-1 41	-0 31	-1 22	-1 23	0.3	0.4	0.0 - -	0.6 022	0.0 - -	0.6 202

Endnotes can be found at the end of Table 2.

TABLE 2. - CURRENT DIFFERENCES AND OTHER CONSTANTS, 1983

NO.	PLACE	METER DEPTH	POSITION Lat.	Long.	TIME DIFFERENCES Min. before Flood	Flood	Min. before Ebb	Ebb	SPEED RATIOS Flood	Ebb	AVERAGE SPEEDS AND DIRECTIONS Minimum before Flood		Maximum Flood		Minimum before Ebb		Maximum Ebb	
		ft	° ' N	° ' W	h. m.	h. m.	h. m.	h. m.			knots	deg.	knots	deg.	knots	deg.	knots	deg.
	BUZZARDS BAY <7> Time meridian, 75°W				on POLLOCK RIP CHANNEL, p.28													
1766	Wareham River, off Barneys Point........		41 44.7	70 42.4	-1 49	-0 27	-1 22	-1 31	0.4	0.4	0.0	- -	0.7	010	0.0	- -	0.6	185
					on CAPE COD CANAL, p.22													
1771	Onset Bay, south of Onset Island........		41 43.9	70 38.7	Current weak and variable													
1776	Onset Bay, south of Wickets Island......		41 44.1	70 39.3	Current weak and variable													
	CAPE COD CANAL																	
1781	CAPE COD CANAL, railroad bridge.........		41 44.5	70 36.8	Daily predictions						0.0	- -	4.0	070	0.0	- -	4.5	250
1786	Bourne Highway bridge...................		41 45	70 35	-0 03	-0 01	-0 03	-0 04	0.8	0.9	0.0	- -	3.3	065	0.0	- -	4.0	245
1791	Bournedale..............................		41 46	70 34	-0 07	-0 03	-0 09	-0 10	0.8	0.8	0.0	- -	3.4	030	0.0	- -	3.6	210
1796	Sagamore Bridge.........................		41 46	70 33	-0 09	-0 04	-0 11	-0 13	0.7	0.6	0.0	- -	2.8	095	0.0	- -	2.5	275
1801	Cape Cod Canal, east end................	15	41 46.5	70 30.0	-0 13	-0 06	-0 17	-0 19	0.6	0.6	0.0	- -	2.4	065	0.0	- -	2.6	245
	NARRAGANSETT BAY <8>				on POLLOCK RIP CHANNEL, p.28													
1811	Sakonnet River (except Narrows).........		- - - -	- - - -	Current weak and variable													
1821	Tiverton, Stone bridge, Sakonnet R. <9>.		41 37.5	71 13.0	-2 58	-5 02	-2 26	-3 06	1.4	1.6	0.0	- -	2.7	010	0.0	- -	2.7	190
						-2 54			0.3				0.6	010				
						-0 36			1.3				2.5	010				
1831	Tiverton, RR. bridge, Sakonnet R. <10>..		41 38.3	71 12.9	-3 26	-5 06	-2 48	-3 41	1.2	1.4	0.0	- -	2.3	000	0.0	- -	2.4	180
						-3 04			- -				- -					
						-1 15			0.8				1.5	000				
1841	Brenton Point, 1.4 n.mi. southwest of...	7	41 25.9	71 22.6	-1 03	-0 38	-1 20	-1 04	0.2	0.4	0.0	- -	0.4	347	0.0	- -	0.6	170
1851	Castle Hill, west of....................	7	41 27.8	71 22.2	-1 22	-3 00	-1 31	-1 31	0.5	0.8	0.0	- -	1.0	000	0.0	- -	1.4	210
1861	Bull Point, east of.....................	10	41 28.8	71 21.0	-1 10	-0 47	-1 10	-1 33	0.6	0.8	0.0	- -	1.2	001	0.0	- -	1.5	206
1871	Mackerel Cove...........................		41 28.5	71 22.8	Current weak and variable													
1881	Newport Harbor, S and E of Goat Island..		41 29	71 20	Current weak and variable													
1891	Rose Island, northeast of...............		41 30.2	71 20.0	-1 58	-1 29	-1 24	-1 38	0.4	0.6	0.0	- -	0.8	340	0.0	- -	1.1	166
1901	Rose Island, west of....................		41 29.8	71 21.0	-0 42	-0 34	-1 20	-1 28	0.4	0.6	0.0	- -	0.7	001	0.0	- -	1.0	172
1911	Gould Island, southeast of..............	7	41 31.5	71 20.2	-1 40	-1 28	-1 14	-1 16	0.3	0.4	0.0	- -	0.5	033	0.0	- -	0.7	217
1921	Dyer Island-Carrs Point (between).......		41 34.5	71 17.8	-1 56	-1 13	-0 50	-1 37	0.4	0.4	0.0	- -	0.8	040	0.0	- -	0.6	236
1931	Dyer Island, west of....................	7	41 35.2	71 18.5	-1 04	-0 46	-0 53	-1 34	0.4	0.6	0.0	- -	0.8	023	0.0	- -	1.0	216
1941	Bristol Harbor..........................				Current weak and variable													
1951	Mount Hope Bridge.......................	7	41 38.4	71 15.5	-1 22	-1 34	-1 08	-0 58	0.6	0.8	0.0	- -	1.1	047	0.0	- -	1.4	230
1961	Mount Hope Bay..........................				Current weak and variable													
1971	Kickamuit R. (Narrows), Mt. Hope Bay....		41 41.9	71 14.7	-2 04	-3 34	-1 19	-0 48	0.7	1.0	0.0	- -	1.4	000	0.0	- -	1.7	191
						-1 40			0.5				0.9	000				
						-0 04			0.9				1.7	000				
1981	Beavertail Point, 0.8 mile northwest of.		41 27.5	71 24.7	-0 11	-0 54	-1 31	-0 19	0.3	0.6	0.0	- -	0.5	003	0.0	- -	1.0	188
1991	Dutch Island and Beaver Head, between...		41 29.8	71 24.2	-1 56	-1 32	-1 58	-1 47	0.5	0.6	0.0	- -	1.0	030	0.0	- -	1.0	233
2001	Dutch Island, west of...................	7	41 30.3	71 24.6	-1 33	-1 49	-1 21	-1 16	0.7	0.7	0.0	- -	1.3	014	0.0	- -	1.2	206
2011	Wickford Harbor.........................		41 34	71 26	Current weak and variable								0.3	- -			0.3	- -
2021	Prudence Island, west of................		- - - -	- - - -	Current weak and variable													
2031	Greenwich Bay entrance..................		41 40.0	71 23.6	Current weak and variable								0.3	- -			0.4	- -

Endnotes can be found at the end of Table 2.

TABLE 2. - CURRENT DIFFERENCES AND OTHER CONSTANTS, 1983

NO.	PLACE	METER DEPTH	POSITION Lat.	POSITION Long.	TIME DIFFERENCES Min. before Flood	Flood	Min. before Ebb	Ebb	SPEED RATIOS Flood	SPEED RATIOS Ebb	AVERAGE SPEEDS AND DIRECTIONS Minimum before Flood	Maximum Flood	Minimum before Ebb	Maximum Ebb
		ft	° ' N	° ' W	h. m.	h. m.	h. m.	h. m.			knots deg.	knots deg.	knots deg.	knots deg.
	NARRAGANSETT BAY <8> Time meridian, 75°W				on POLLOCK RIP CHANNEL, p.28									
2041	Patience Island, narrows east of........		41 39.5	71 21.2	-2 41	-2 29	-2 44	-2 37	0.4	0.5	0.0 - -	0.7 354	0.0 - -	0.9 157
2051	Patience I. and Warwick Neck, between...		41 39.8	71 22.4	-1 40	-1 21	-1 18	-1 13	0.3	0.5	0.0 - -	0.6 040	0.0 - -	0.8 224
2061	Warren River entrance..................		41 42.7	71 17.8	Current weak and variable						0.0 - -	0.4 020	0.0 - -	0.3 200
2071	Warren, Warren River....................		41 43.7	71 17.3	-0 14	+0 11	-0 22	-1 05	0.5	0.5	0.0 - -	1.0 358	0.0 - -	0.9 171
2081	Hog Island to Providence...............		- - - -	- - - -	Current weak and variable									
2091	India Point RR. Bridge, Seekonk R. <9>..		41 49.0	71 23.3	-1 48	-4 02	-1 31	-1 06	0.5	0.8	0.0 - -	1.0 020	0.0 - -	1.4 180
						-2 30			0.2			0.4 020		
						-0 12			0.7			1.3 020		
2101	Cold Spring Pt., Seekonk River <10>.....		41 49.6	71 22.8	-1 48	-4 14	-1 31	-1 02	0.4	0.8	0.0 - -	0.8 030	0.0 - -	1.4 210
						-2 24			0.1			0.2 030		
						-0 26			0.6			1.1 030		
	BLOCK ISLAND SOUND				on THE RACE, p.34									
	Point Judith													
2106	Harbor of Refuge, south entrance.....		41 21.48	71 29.75	-2 23	-2 52	-2 26	-3 59	0.2	0.2	0.0 - -	0.6 329	0.0 - -	0.8 141
								-2 41		0.1				0.4 141
								-1 56		0.2				0.7 141
2111	Harbor of Refuge, west entrance......		41 22	71 31	See table 5.									
2116	Pond entrance.........................		41 23	71 31	-3 23	-3 01	-3 16	-3 52	0.6	0.4	0.0 - -	1.8 351	0.0 - -	1.5 186
2121	2.4 miles southwest of...............		41 19.87	71 30.65	-0 48	-0 01	+0 18	-0 24	0.2	0.2	0.0 - -	0.7 258	0.0 - -	0.6 090
2126	4.5 miles southwest of...............		41 18	71 33	See table 5.									
	Block Island													
2131	four miles north of..................		41 18	71 32	-0 30	+0 03	+0 35	+0 21	0.2	0.2	0.0 - -	0.8 285	0.0 - -	0.8 076
2136	Sandy Point, 2.1 miles NNE of........	15	41 15.85	71 34.00	+0 09	-0 53	-0 30	-0 43	0.4	0.5	0.0 - -	1.0 296	0.0 - -	1.7 066
2141	Sandy Pt., 1.5 miles north of........	7	41 15	71 34	-0 22	-0 30	-1 03	-0 50	0.6	0.5	0.0 - -	1.9 315	0.0 - -	2.1 063
2146	Clay Head, 1.2 miles ENE of..........	15	41 13.35	71 31.85	-2 20	-1 32	-0 37	-0 55	0.2	0.1	0.5 220	0.7 298	0.0 - -	0.5 164
2151	Old Harbor Pt., 0.5 mile southeast of		41 09	71 32	-0 10	-0 29	-0 34	+0 09	0.1	0.1	0.0 - -	0.2 336	0.0 - -	0.6 175
2156	Lewis Pt., 1.0 mile southwest of.....		41 08.20	71 37.30	-1 37	-1 08	-0 34	-1 13	0.7	0.5	0.0 - -	1.9 298	0.0 - -	1.8 136
2161	Lewis Pt., 1.5 miles west of.........		41 09	71 38	-1 31	-1 15	-0 44	-0 57	0.4	0.4	0.0 - -	1.4 318	0.0 - -	1.7 170
2166	Great Salt Pond entrance.............		41 11.97	71 35.50	-4 18	-3 35	-3 34	-4 22	0.1	0.1	0.0 - -	0.3 165	0.0 - -	0.3 326
2171	Great Salt Pond ent., 1 mile NW of...	7	41 12	71 36	-0 52	-0 58	-1 50	-0 32	0.1	0.1	0.0 - -	0.4 158	0.0 - -	0.4 035
2176	Sandy Point, 0.4 mile west of <11>...		41 13.80	71 35.13	- - -	-1 24	- - -	-1 35	- -	0.2	0.0 - -	- - - -	0.0 - -	0.7 011
2181	Green Hill Point, 1.1 miles south of....		41 20.90	71 35.77	-1 06	-0 47	-0 34	-0 55	0.2	0.1	0.0 - -	0.6 258	0.0 - -	0.4 070
2186	Sandy Point, 4.1 miles northwest of.....	15	41 17.10	71 38.00	-0 04	+0 11	+0 22	+0 04	0.2	0.2	0.0 - -	0.7 270	0.0 - -	0.6 084
2191	Grace Point, 2.0 miles northwest of.....		41 12	71 38	See table 5.									
2196	Quonochontaug Beach, 1.1 miles S of.....		41 18.80	71 42.82	-0 52	+0 06	+0 37	-0 20	0.4	0.1	0.0 - -	1.1 248	0.0 - -	0.4 078
2201	Quonochontaug Beach, 3.8 miles S of.....	15	41 16.35	71 43.00	-0 05	-0 06	+0 29	+0 08	0.2	0.2	0.0 - -	0.7 243	0.0 - -	0.6 058
2206	Lewis Point, 6.0 miles WNW of..........	15	41 11.60	71 44.20	+0 51	+0 40	+0 06	+0 35	0.2	0.3	0.0 - -	0.6 286	0.0 - -	1.2 097
2211	Southwest Ledge........................		41 07	71 42	-0 33	-0 33	-0 10	-0 08	0.5	0.5	0.0 - -	1.5 321	0.0 - -	2.1 141
2216	Southwest Ledge, 2.0 miles west of......	15	41 06.80	71 43.00	+0 02	+0 10	+0 01	-0 41	0.5	0.5	0.0 - -	1.5 354	0.0 - -	1.9 168
2221	Watch Hill Point, 2.2 miles east of......		41 18.16	71 48.60	-0 37	-0 08	+0 35	-0 21	0.4	0.2	0.0 - -	1.2 260	0.0 - -	0.7 086
2226	Watch Hill Point, 5.2 miles SSE of......	15	41 13.20	71 49.00	+0 26	+0 18	+0 29	+0 12	0.4	0.3	0.0 - -	1.2 265	0.0 - -	1.2 064
2231	Montauk Point, 5.4 miles NNE of.........	15	41 09.55	71 49.48	+0 25	-0 03	-0 47	+0 08	0.4	0.5	0.0 - -	1.1 279	0.0 - -	1.6 079
2236	Montauk Point, 1.2 miles east of........		41 04.50	71 49.80	-1 30	-1 09	-0 48	-1 53	1.0	0.8	0.0 - -	2.8 346	0.0 - -	2.8 162
2241	Montauk Point, 1 mile northeast of......		41 05	71 51	-2 02	-1 29	-1 10	-1 41	0.7	0.4	0.0 - -	2.4 356	0.0 - -	1.9 145

Endnotes can be found at the end of Table 2.

TABLE 2. - CURRENT DIFFERENCES AND OTHER CONSTANTS, 1983

NO.	PLACE	METER DEPTH	POSITION Lat.	POSITION Long.	TIME DIFFERENCES Min. before Flood	Flood	Min. before Ebb	Ebb	SPEED RATIOS Flood	Ebb	AVERAGE SPEEDS AND DIRECTIONS Minimum before Flood		Maximum Flood		Minimum before Ebb		Maximum Ebb	
		ft	° ' N	° ' W	h. m.	h. m.	h. m.	h. m.			knots	deg.	knots	deg.	knots	deg.	knots	deg.
	BLOCK ISLAND SOUND Time meridian, 75°W				on THE RACE, p.34													
2246	Wicopesset Island, 1.1 miles SSE of.....		41 16.50	71 54.80	-1 02	-0 10	+0 39	-0 07	0.5	0.2	0.0	- -	1.5	250	0.0	- -	0.8	073
2251	East Pt., Fishers I., 4.1 miles S of....	15	41 13.40	71 55.50	+0 42	+0 32	+0 09	+0 12	0.3	0.5	0.0	- -	0.9	236	0.0	- -	1.8	073
2256	Cerberus Shoal, 1.5 miles east of.......	15	41 10.45	71 55.17	-0 23	-0 15	-0 33	-0 52	0.4	0.5	0.0	- -	1.1	256	0.0	- -	1.8	092
2261	Shagwong Reef & Cerberus Shoal, between.		41 07.90	71 55.50	-0 38	-0 47	-0 35	-0 57	0.6	0.5	0.0	- -	1.9	241	0.0	- -	1.8	056
2266	Montauk Harbor entrance................	6	41 04.78	71 56.35	-2 25	-2 47	-3 12	-4 49	0.4	0.2	0.0	- -	1.2	226	0.0	- -	0.6	033
								-2 32		0.1							0.2	024
								-0 44		0.2							0.5	353
2271	Mt. Prospect, 0.6 mile SSE of..........	15	41 14.75	71 59.80	-0 42	-0 06	0 00	-0 59	0.6	0.5	0.0	- -	1.7	275	0.0	- -	1.6	054
2276	Cerberus Shoal and Fishers I., between..	7	41 13	71 58	-0 57	-0 05	+0 11	-0 06	0.4	0.3	0.0	- -	1.3	264	0.0	- -	1.3	096
2281	Little Gull Island, 3.7 miles ESE of....		41 10.7	72 02.1	See table 5.													
2286	Gardiners Island, 3 miles northeast of..	10	41 07.9	72 02.0	-0 45	-0 56	-0 21	-0 26	0.3	0.2	0.0	- -	0.9	305	0.0	- -	1.0	138
2291	Eastern Plain Point, 1.2 miles N of.....		41 07.12	72 04.85	-2 53	-1 51	-1 18	-2 23	0.3	0.2	0.0	- -	1.0	290	0.0	- -	0.8	110
2296	Eastern Plain Pt., 3.9 miles ENE of.....		41 07.05	71 59.80	-1 09	-1 26	-0 32	-1 01	0.3	0.3	0.0	- -	1.0	246	0.0	- -	1.0	096
2301	Little Gull Island, 0.8 mile SSE of <51>		41 11.67	72 06.23	-2 18	-0 50	-0 33	-3 02	0.4	0.2	0.0	- -	1.3	331	0.0	- -	0.6	105
								-1 54		0.0							0.1	252
								-0 32		0.2							0.6	174
2306	Rocky Point, 2 miles WNW of............	15	41 03.55	72 01.80	-1 30	-1 01	-0 59	-0 59	0.1	0.1	0.1	192	0.3	255	0.2	340	0.3	065
	GARDINERS BAY, etc.																	
2311	Goff Point, 0.4 mile northwest of.......		41 01.49	72 03.75	-1 54	-2 25	-1 35	-2 31	0.4	0.5	0.0	- -	1.2	225	0.0	- -	1.6	010
2316	Acabonack Hbr. ent., 0.6 mile ESE of....		41 01.30	72 07.40	-1 42	-2 10	-1 15	-2 30	0.5	0.3	0.0	- -	1.4	345	0.0	- -	1.2	140
2321	Hog Creek Point, north of..............		41 04.10	72 09.70	-1 04	-0 49	-1 31	-1 52	0.1	0.1	0.0	- -	0.3	281	0.0	- -	0.3	067
2326	Ram Island, 2.2 miles east of..........		41 04.70	72 13.80	-0 27	-0 24	-0 24	-0 12	0.1	0.1	0.0	- -	0.2	250	0.0	- -	0.3	090
2331	Orient Point, 2.4 miles SSE of..........		41 07.50	72 12.30	+0 11	-0 34	+1 01	-0 31	0.1	0.1	0.0	- -	0.4	250	0.0	- -	0.3	025
2336	Gardiners Pt. Ruins, 1.1 miles N of.....		41 09.50	72 08.83	-0 20	-0 17	-0 19	+0 04	0.4	0.5	0.0	- -	1.2	270	0.0	- -	1.8	066
2341	Gardiners Point & Plum Island, between..	15	41 09.33	72 09.52	-0 26	-0 31	-0 42	-0 30	0.5	0.5	0.0	- -	1.4	288	0.0	- -	1.6	100
2346	Ram Island, 1.4 miles NNE of...........		41 05.8	72 15.8	-0 07	-0 02	-0 03	+0 17	0.1	0.2	0.0	- -	0.4	240	0.0	- -	0.6	075
2351	Long Beach Pt., 0.7 mile southwest of...	15	41 06.25	72 18.40	+0 25	-0 11	+0 34	0 00	0.5	0.5	0.0	- -	1.3	307	0.0	- -	1.8	101
2356	Hay Beach Point, 0.3 mile NW of <52>....		41 06.65	72 70.43	+0 12	+0 20	+0 51	-0 51	0.5	0.3	0.0	- -	1.5	210	0.0	- -	1.2	025
								+0 38		0.2							0.6	025
								+1 35		0.2							0.8	020
2361	Jennings Point, 0.2 mile NNW of.........	13	41 04.48	72 22.95	+0 24	+0 09	+0 27	+0 03	0.6	0.4	0.0	- -	1.6	290	0.0	- -	1.5	055
2366	Cedar Point, 0.2 mile west of..........		41 02.38	72 16.07	-0 19	-0 16	+0 19	-0 41	0.6	0.5	0.0	- -	1.8	195	0.0	- -	1.6	005
2371	North Haven Peninsula, north of.........		41 02.47	72 19.25	+0 04	-0 30	+0 29	-0 34	0.8	0.6	0.0	- -	2.4	230	0.0	- -	2.1	035
2376	Paradise Point, 0.4 mile east of........	13	41 02.88	72 22.57	+0 18	+0 03	+0 35	+0 06	0.5	0.4	0.0	- -	1.5	145	0.0	- -	1.5	345
2381	Little Peconic Bay entrance............	19	41 01.58	72 23.08	+0 27	+0 01	+0 43	+0 21	0.6	0.4	0.0	- -	1.6	240	0.0	- -	1.5	015
2386	Robins Island, 0.5 mile south of........		40 56.98	72 27.18	+0 24	-0 12	+0 46	+0 35	0.6	0.2	0.0	- -	1.7	245	0.0	- -	0.6	065
								-1 31		0.1							0.2	243
								-0 07		0.2							0.5	234
	FISHERS ISLAND SOUND																	
2391	Edwards Pt. and Sandy Pt., between......	4	41 19.90	71 53.88	-2 34	-3 17	-2 25	-3 41	0.4	0.3	0.0	- -	1.1	035	0.0	- -	1.0	227
2396	Napatree Point, 0.7 mile southwest of...		41 17.92	71 54.00	-0 56	-1 07	-0 57	-1 18	0.6	0.6	0.0	- -	1.7	284	0.0	- -	2.2	113
2401	Little Narragansett Bay entrance........		41 20	71 53	-1 56	-1 59	-2 09	-2 35	0.4	0.3	0.0	- -	1.3	092	0.0	- -	1.3	268

Endnotes can be found at the end of Table 2.

TABLE 2. - CURRENT DIFFERENCES AND OTHER CONSTANTS, 1983

NO.	PLACE	METER DEPTH	POSITION Lat.	POSITION Long.	TIME DIFFERENCES Min. before Flood	TIME DIFFERENCES Flood	TIME DIFFERENCES Min. before Ebb	TIME DIFFERENCES Ebb	SPEED RATIOS Flood	SPEED RATIOS Ebb	Minimum before Flood knots	Minimum before Flood deg.	Maximum Flood knots	Maximum Flood deg.	Minimum before Ebb knots	Minimum before Ebb deg.	Maximum Ebb knots	Maximum Ebb deg.
		ft	° ' N	° ' W	h. m.	h. m.	h. m.	h. m.			knots	deg.	knots	deg.	knots	deg.	knots	deg.
	FISHERS ISLAND SOUND Time meridian, 75°W				on THE RACE, p.34													
2406	Avondale, Pawcatuck River <51>..........	6	41 19.90	71 50.73	-1 56	-2 42	-2 17	-3 40	0.2	0.2	0.0	- -	0.6	058	0.0	- -	0.5	265
								-1 08		0.0							0.1	243
								+0 04		0.1							0.2	263
2411	Ram Island Reef, south of..............	7	41 18.1	71 58.5	-0 52	-0 47	-0 41	-0 50	0.4	0.4	0.0	- -	1.3	255	0.0	- -	1.6	088
2416	Noank <51>............................	4	41 19.12	71 59.30	-1 36	-3 16	-4 10	-4 30	0.2	0.1	0.0	- -	0.5	340	0.0	- -	0.3	173
								-1 24		0.0							0.0	- -
								+0 19		0.1							0.5	162
2421	Mystic, Highway Bridge, Mystic River....	6	41 21.25	71 58.18	-2 02	-2 50	-2 07	-3 39	0.2	0.1	0.0	- -	0.5	039	0.0	- -	0.4	231
								-1 40		0.0							0.2	234
								-0 20		0.1							0.3	232
2426	Clay Point, 1.3 miles NNE of...........	15	41 17.88	71 58.53	-0 42	-0 49	-0 40	-1 15	0.5	0.5	0.0	- -	1.4	264	0.0	- -	1.9	035
2431	North Hill Point, 1.1 miles NNW of......		41 17.57	72 01.68	-1 05	-0 26	-0 18	-1 37	0.5	0.4	0.0	- -	1.5	258	0.0	- -	1.2	082
	LONG ISLAND SOUND																	
	The Race																	
2436	Race Point, 0.4 mile southwest of....		41 14.70	72 02.60	-0 24	-0 35	-0 43	-0 44	0.9	1.0	0.0	- -	2.6	288	0.0	- -	3.5	135
2441	THE RACE, near Valiant Rock..........		41 14.20	72 03.60	Daily predictions						0.0	- -	2.9	295	0.0	- -	3.5	100
2446	0.5 mile NE of Little Gull Island....		41 13	72 06	-0 30	-0 14	-0 11	-0 26	1.0	0.7	0.0	- -	3.3	002	0.0	- -	3.1	107
2451	Little Gull I., 1.1 miles ENE of.....		41 13.10	72 05.10	-0 07	-0 11	+0 01	-0 45	1.4	1.3	0.0	- -	4.0	301	0.0	- -	4.7	130
2456	Great Gull Island, 0.7 mile WSW of......		41 11.67	72 08.02	-0 51	-0 33	-0 31	-1 42	0.9	0.9	0.0	- -	2.6	299	0.0	- -	3.2	133
2461	Plum Gut...............................		41 10.00	72 12.80	-1 22	-1 30	-1 01	-2 05	1.2	1.2	0.0	- -	3.5	323	0.0	- -	4.3	126
2466	Eastern Point, 1.5 miles south of.......		41 17.8	72 04.4	-1 57	-1 50	-1 03	-1 50	0.1	0.1	0.0	- -	0.4	249	0.0	- -	0.4	055
2471	New London Harbor entrance..............		41 19.08	72 05.02	-1 22	-1 51	-2 12	-1 15	0.1	0.1	0.0	- -	0.1	348	0.0	- -	0.2	211
	Thames River																	
2476	Winthrop Point.......................		41 21.63	72 05.30	-1 17	-1 59	-0 54	-2 35	0.1	0.1	0.0	- -	0.4	012	0.0	- -	0.4	180
								-1 08		0.0							0.2	186
								+0 04		0.1							0.3	185
2481	Off Smith Cove......................	5	41 23.98	72 05.18	-1 18	-2 20	-1 29	-1 54	0.2	0.1	0.0	- -	0.7	019	0.0	- -	0.5	199
								-1 30		0.1							0.2	202
								+0 13		0.2							0.6	198
2486	Off Stoddard Hill....................	15	41 27.65	72 04.12	-1 17	-2 23	-0 40	-2 29	0.2	0.1	0.0	- -	0.7	332	0.0	- -	0.4	164
								-1 11		0.0							0.2	165
								+0 26		0.2							0.5	161
2491	Lower Coal Dock.....................	15	41 30.88	72 04.72	Current weak and variable													
2496	Goshen Point, 1.9 miles SSE of.........	15	41 16.00	72 06.30	-1 05	-1 00	-1 03	-1 49	0.4	0.5	0.0	- -	1.2	285	0.0	- -	1.6	062
2501	Little Gull Island, 0.8 mile NNW of.....	15	41 13.10	72 06.93	+0 17	-1 19	-2 29	-0 46	0.7	0.8	0.0	- -	1.9	258	0.0	- -	2.9	043
2506	Bartlett Reef, 0.2 mile south of........		41 16.2	72 07.7	-2 01	-0 50	-1 00	-1 31	0.3	0.3	0.0	- -	1.4	255	0.0	- -	1.3	090
2511	Twotree Island Channel..................	11	41 17.87	72 08.47	-1 06	-1 27	-0 43	-1 42	0.4	0.4	0.0	- -	1.2	267	0.0	- -	1.6	099
2516	Niantic (Railroad Bridge)...............	5	41 19.40	72 10.62	-0 53	-1 03	-0 53	-0 40	0.6	0.2	0.0	- -	1.6	352	0.0	- -	0.8	178
2521	Black Point, 0.8 mile south of.........	15	41 16.40	72 12.50	-0 50	-1 11	-0 25	-1 10	0.4	0.4	0.0	- -	1.2	260	0.0	- -	1.4	073
2526	Black Point and Plum Island, between....	15	41 14.00	72 12.30	+0 25	+0 04	+0 29	+0 26	0.7	0.7	0.0	- -	2.1	236	0.0	- -	2.4	076
2531	Plum Island, 0.8 mile NNW of...........		41 11.87	72 11.92	+0 04	-0 16	-1 13	-0 41	0.6	0.7	0.0	- -	1.7	247	0.0	- -	2.4	065
2536	Branford Reef, 1.5 miles southwest of...	15	41 12.57	72 49.83	-0 13	-0 14	-0 09	-0 18	0.3	0.2	0.0	- -	0.8	272	0.0	- -	0.7	068
2541	Branford Reef, 5.0 miles south of.......	15	41 08.65	72 49.67	-0 01	+0 09	+0 11	+0 03	0.2	0.2	0.0	- -	0.7	260	0.0	- -	0.8	074
2546	Hatchett Point, 1.1 miles WSW of........		41 16.35	72 16.92	-2 37	-1 11	-0 52	-2 37	0.4	0.3	0.0	- -	1.3	240	0.0	- -	1.2	045

Endnotes can be found at the end of Table 2.

TABLE 2. - CURRENT DIFFERENCES AND OTHER CONSTANTS, 1983

NO.	PLACE	METER DEPTH	POSITION Lat.	POSITION Long.	TIME DIFFERENCES Min. before Flood	Flood	Min. before Ebb	Ebb	SPEED RATIOS Flood	Ebb	AVERAGE SPEEDS AND DIRECTIONS Minimum before Flood	Maximum Flood	Minimum before Ebb	Maximum Ebb
		ft	° ' N	° ' W	h. m.	h. m.	h. m.	h. m.			knots deg.	knots deg.	knots deg.	knots deg.
	LONG ISLAND SOUND Time meridian, 75°W				on THE RACE, p.34									
	Connecticut River													
2551	Lynde Point, channel east of.........		41 16	72 20	+0 42	+0 50	+0 18	+0 29	0.3	0.2	0.0 - -	0.9 344	0.0 - -	0.7 161
2556	Saybrook Point, 0.2 mile northeast of		41 17.02	72 20.87	+0 35	+0 51	+0 47	+0 30	0.5	0.4	0.0 - -	1.5 355	0.0 - -	1.5 160
2561	Railroad drawbridge.................	15	41 19.00	72 20.77	+0 27	-0 26	+0 54	+1 06	0.4	0.3	0.0 - -	1.0 360	0.0 - -	1.0 198
						+0 35			0.2			0.6 359		
						+1 31			0.3			0.9 356		
2566	Eustasia Island, 0.6 mile ESE of.....		41 23.30	72 24.23	+1 53	+1 38	+1 23	+1 26	0.4	0.4	0.0 - -	1.1 290	0.0 - -	1.4 070
2571	Eddy Rock Shoal, west of............	15	41 26.57	72 27.78	+1 41	+2 16	+2 01	+1 20	0.3	0.2	0.0 - -	0.8 350	0.0 - -	0.6 155
2576	Higganum Creek, 0.5 mile ESE of......		41 30.02	72 32.62	+3 06	+2 52	+2 35	+3 01	0.3	0.3	0.0 - -	0.8 270	0.0 - -	1.0 080
2581	Wilcox Island Park, east of..........		41 34.33	72 38.88	+4 06	+3 36	+3 07	+3 35	0.3	0.3	0.0 - -	0.9 355	0.0 - -	1.0 160
2586	Rocky Hill...........................	9	41 39.82	72 37.73	+4 41	+3 37	+3 21	+3 30	0.2	0.2	0.0 - -	0.6 335	0.0 - -	0.8 135
2591	Hartford Jetty <42>.................	9	41 45.07	72 39.02	+5 45	+4 39	+3 22	+4 29	0.0	0.2	0.0 - -	0.1 290	0.0 - -	0.7 095
2596	Saybrook Breakwater, 1.5 miles SE of....		41 14.78	72 19.05	-1 30	-1 11	-0 55	-1 57	0.7	0.6	0.0 - -	1.9 260	0.0 - -	2.0 070
2601	Mulford Point, 3.1 miles northwest of...	15	41 12.00	72 19.08	-0 06	-1 05	-0 05	-0 24	0.7	0.6	0.0 - -	1.9 269	0.0 - -	2.3 066
2606	Orient Point, 1 mile WNW of............		41 10.02	72 15.11	-1 09	-2 02	-0 33	-1 15	0.5	0.9	0.0 - -	1.4 245	0.0 - -	3.1 055
						-0 59			0.3			0.8 255		
						-0 09			0.7			2.1 245		
2611	Rocky Point, 0.3 mile north of..........	15	41 08.63	72 21.42	-0 27	-1 02	-1 01	-0 28	0.6	0.6	0.0 - -	1.8 279	0.0 - -	2.1 041
2616	Cornfield Point, 3 miles south of.......	7	41 12.9	72 22.4	-0 56	-0 17	-0 03	-0 20	0.6	0.4	0.0 - -	2.0 256	0.0 - -	1.7 094
2621	Cornfield Point, 1.1 miles south of.....	15	41 14.65	72 23.40	-1 01	-1 34	-1 02	-2 03	0.5	0.5	0.0 - -	1.4 293	0.0 - -	1.6 108
2626	Kesley Point, 2.1 miles southeast of....		41 14.10	72 27.93	-0 35	-1 02	-0 54	-1 00	0.5	0.5	0.0 - -	1.5 260	0.0 - -	1.8 070
2631	Six Mile Reef, 1.5 miles north of.......		41 12.66	72 28.87	-0 17	-0 12	-0 23	-0 41	0.3	0.4	0.0 - -	1.0 290	0.0 - -	1.3 095
2636	Six Mile Reef, 2 miles east of..........		41 10.83	72 26.90	-0 36	-0 12	-0 07	-0 35	0.6	0.6	0.0 - -	1.6 235	0.0 - -	2.1 040
2641	Horton Point, 1.4 miles NNW of..........		41 06.30	72 27.40	+0 04	+0 08	-0 03	-0 18	0.5	0.6	0.0 - -	1.4 260	0.0 - -	2.0 040
2646	Kelsey Point, 1 mile south of...........		41 14	72 30	-1 32	-1 00	-1 03	-1 51	0.6	0.3	0.0 - -	2.0 249	0.0 - -	1.5 118
2651	Hammonasset Point, 1.2 miles SW of......	15	41 14.22	72 34.00	-0 59	-1 15	-0 44	-1 31	0.3	0.3	0.0 - -	1.0 287	0.0 - -	1.0 106
2656	Hammonasset Point, 5 miles south of.....	15	41 09.80	72 34.17	-0 03	-0 03	-0 24	-0 06	0.5	0.4	0.0 - -	1.4 284	0.0 - -	1.5 090
2661	Mattituck Inlet, 1 mile northwest of....	15	41 01.68	72 34.22	-0 21	-0 15	-0 08	-0 26	0.3	0.3	0.0 - -	0.9 241	0.0 - -	1.0 053
2666	Sachem Head, 1 mile SSE of..............		41 13.65	72 42.30	-0 38	-0 36	-0 35	-1 02	0.4	0.3	0.0 - -	1.1 255	0.0 - -	1.0 065
2671	Sachem Head 6.2 miles south of.........	15	41 08.73	72 42.30	+0 29	+0 24	-0 12	-0 04	0.2	0.3	0.0 - -	0.6 260	0.0 - -	0.9 065
2676	Roanoke Point, 5.6 miles north of.......	15	41 04.37	72 42.53	-0 02	-0 02	-0 15	-0 24	0.2	0.3	0.0 - -	0.7 255	0.0 - -	0.9 050
2681	Roanoke Point, 2.3 miles NNW of.........		41 00.92	72 42.97	-1 19	-0 22	-0 10	-0 29	0.3	0.2	0.0 - -	0.9 270	0.0 - -	0.7 070
2686	Sachem Head, 1 mile south of............		41 14	72 43	-0 46	+0 03	-0 33	-0 38	0.3	0.3	0.0 - -	0.9 278	0.0 - -	1.2 084
2691	Herod Point, 2.8 miles north of.........	15	41 00.97	72 49.93	-0 29	-0 17	-0 27	-0 06	0.2	0.2	0.1 020	0.4 290	0.1 020	0.6 090
2696	Herod Point, 6.5 miles north of.........	15	41 04.65	72 49.80	-0 27	+0 06	+0 12	-0 07	0.3	0.2	0.0 - -	0.9 254	0.0 - -	0.7 070
2701	New Haven Harbor entrance <12>..........		41 14	72 55	-1 11	-1 34	-0 37	-1 15	0.4	0.2	0.0 - -	1.4 319	0.0 - -	0.9 152
2706	City Point, 1.3 miles northeast of......		41 17.83	72 54.42	+0 11	+0 30	+0 33	+0 08	0.1	0.1	0.0 - -	0.3 015	0.0 - -	0.4 215
2711	Oyster River Pt., 1.3 miles SSE of <1>..		41 12.87	72 58.00	- - -	-0 15	- - -	-0 47	0.1	0.1	0.0 - -	0.3 255	0.0 - -	0.3 060
2716	Pond Point, 4.2 miles SSE of...........		41 08.60	72 58.08	-0 20	+0 04	-0 04	-0 14	0.2	0.2	0.0 - -	0.6 265	0.0 - -	0.6 065
2721	Stratford Shoal, 6 miles east of........		41 04.52	72 58.43	+0 01	-0 02	-0 07	-0 09	0.2	0.2	0.0 - -	0.6 265	0.0 - -	0.6 060
2726	Sound Beach, 2.2 miles north of.........		41 00.33	72 58.45	-0 03	-0 06	-0 15	-0 25	0.3	0.3	0.0 - -	0.9 270	0.0 - -	0.9 075
2731	Charles Island, 0.8 mile SSE of.........		41 10.77	73 02.63	-0 51	-0 36	-0 30	-0 54	0.1	0.1	0.0 - -	0.4 250	0.0 - -	0.4 070
	Housatonic River													
2736	Milford Point, 0.2 mile west of......	10	41 10.35	73 06.82	-0 06	+0 01	+0 15	-0 55	0.4	0.3	0.0 - -	1.2 330	0.0 - -	1.2 135
2741	Railroad drawbridge, above...........	5	41 12.53	73 06.67	+0 34	+0 13	+0 29	-0 55	0.4	0.4	0.0 - -	1.1 350	0.0 - -	1.3 185
2746	Fowler Island, 0.1 mile NNW of.......	5	41 14.40	73 06.23	+0 48	+0 10	+0 30	+0 48	0.4	0.3	0.0 - -	1.1 040	0.0 - -	1.1 270

Endnotes can be found at the end of Table 2.

TABLE 2. - CURRENT DIFFERENCES AND OTHER CONSTANTS, 1983

NO.	PLACE	METER DEPTH	POSITION Lat.	POSITION Long.	TIME DIFFERENCES Min. before Flood	Flood	Min. before Ebb	Ebb	SPEED RATIOS Flood	Ebb	AVERAGE SPEEDS AND DIRECTIONS Minimum before Flood	Maximum Flood	Minimum before Ebb	Maximum Ebb
		ft	° ' N	° ' W	h. m.	h. m.	h. m.	h. m.			knots deg.	knots deg.	knots deg.	knots deg.
	LONG ISLAND SOUND Time meridian, 75°W				on THE RACE, p.34									
	Housatonic River													
2751	Wooster Island, 0.1 mile southwest of	5	41 16.67	73 05.20	+1 19	+0 33	+0 20	+0 22	0.2	0.2	0.0 - -	0.6 020	0.0 - -	0.7 220
2756	Derby-Shelton Bridge, below <13>.....		41 18.73	73 04.78	- - -	- - -	- - -	-0 06	- -	0.1	0.0 - -	- - - -	0.0 - -	0.4 095
2761	Point No Point, 2.1 miles south of......	15	41 06.75	73 07.13	-0 30	-0 06	-0 08	-0 01	0.4	0.3	0.0 - -	1.3 251	0.0 - -	1.2 074
2766	Old Field Point, 1 mile east of.........	15	40 58.47	73 05.80	+3 26	+2 31	+2 25	+1 56	0.1	0.2	0.0 - -	0.2 105	0.0 - -	0.6 308
	...do................................	22	40 58.47	73 05.80	+2 30	+1 54	+2 17	+1 44	0.1	0.2	0.0 - -	0.2 110	0.0 - -	0.5 297
2771	Old Field Point, 2 miles northeast of...	15	41 00.23	73 05.70	+0 33	+0 13	-0 11	+0 58	0.3	0.3	0.0 - -	1.0 266	0.0 - -	1.1 092
	...do................................	40	41 00.23	73 05.70	+0 22	+0 08	-0 12	+0 41	0.2	0.2	0.0 - -	0.5 236	0.0 - -	0.6 081
2776	Stratford Point, 4.3 miles south of.....	15	41 04.77	73 06.67	+0 12	+0 19	+0 05	+0 14	0.3	0.3	0.0 - -	1.0 254	0.0 - -	1.0 075
	...do................................	60	41 04.77	73 06.67	-0 36	-0 09	-0 23	+0 15	0.2	0.2	0.0 - -	0.6 291	0.0 - -	0.8 078
2781	Stratford Point, 6.1 miles south of.....	15	41 02.97	73 05.80	-0 18	+0 03	+0 16	+0 30	0.3	0.2	0.0 - -	1.0 267	0.0 - -	0.8 080
	...do................................	51	41 02.97	73 05.80	-0 43	-0 31	-0 34	-0 12	0.3	0.2	0.0 - -	0.9 279	0.0 - -	0.9 087
2786	Port Jefferson Harbor entrance..........		40 58	73 06	+0 11	+0 40	+0 32	+0 14	0.8	0.4	0.0 - -	2.6 151	0.0 - -	1.9 323
2791	Crane Neck Point, 0.5 mile northwest of.		40 58	73 10	-0 45	-1 24	-1 38	-1 34	0.4	0.3	0.0 - -	1.3 256	0.0 - -	1.5 016
2796	Bridgeport Hbr. ent., btn. jetties <14>.	4	41 09	73 11	-0 10	-0 22	+0 05	-0 03	0.2	0.1	0.0 - -	0.7 340	0.0 - -	0.6 176
2801	Crane Neck Point, 3.4 miles WNW of......	15	40 59.00	73 13.87	-0 12	+0 02	-0 25	+0 09	0.2	0.2	0.0 - -	0.5 261	0.0 - -	0.6 079
2806	Crane Neck Point, 3.7 miles WSW of......	15	40 56.30	73 13.87	-1 32	-0 31	-0 24	-0 18	0.1	0.1	0.0 - -	0.4 066	0.0 - -	0.4 232
2811	Shoal Point, 6 miles south of...........	15	41 01.70	73 14.03	+0 22	+0 28	+0 42	+0 55	0.1	0.1	0.0 - -	0.4 232	0.0 - -	0.4 047
2816	Pine Creek Point, 2.3 miles SSE of......	15	41 05.05	73 14.40	-0 20	+0 06	+0 21	+0 23	0.2	0.2	0.0 - -	0.7 272	0.0 - -	0.6 084
2821	Saugatuck River, 0.3 mi. NW of Bluff Pt.	15	41 06.27	73 21.92	-0 12	-0 41	+0 20	+0 10	0.2	0.1	0.0 - -	0.5 265	0.0 - -	0.4 080
2826	Saugatuck R., 0.5 mile above Bluff Pt...		41 06	73 23	Current weak and variable									
2831	Sheffield I. Tower, 1.1 miles SE of.....	15	41 01.97	73 24.33	+0 33	+0 39	+0 59	+0 33	0.3	0.2	0.0 - -	0.9 283	0.0 - -	0.8 081
	...do................................	60	41 01.97	73 24.33	-0 27	+0 24	+1 00	+0 36	0.2	0.2	0.0 - -	0.6 269	0.0 - -	0.5 076
2836	Sheffield I. Hbr., 0.5 mile southeast of	12	41 03.32	73 25.25	-2 41	-3 54	-3 36	-2 12	0.1	0.1	0.0 - -	0.2 229	0.0 - -	0.4 042
2841	Norwalk River, off Gregory Point........	15	41 05.20	73 24.22	-0 12	-0 21	+0 29	+0 30	0.2	0.2	0.0 - -	0.6 322	0.0 - -	0.5 155
2846	Eaton's Neck Pt., 1.3 miles north of....	15	40 58.60	73 23.77	+0 21	+0 21	+0 05	+0 21	0.5	0.4	0.0 - -	1.4 283	0.0 - -	1.4 075
2851	Eaton's Neck Pt., 1.8 miles west of.....		40 57	73 26	-1 09	-1 01	-0 28	-0 29	0.2	0.1	0.0 - -	0.5 199	0.0 - -	0.6 068
2856	Eaton's Neck Pt., 3 miles north of......	15	41 00.38	73 23.80	+0 40	+0 30	+0 36	+0 17	0.2	0.3	0.0 - -	0.7 253	0.0 - -	0.9 046
	...do................................	40	41 00.38	73 23.80	+0 17	+0 13	+0 26	+0 28	0.2	0.2	0.0 - -	0.6 264	0.0 - -	0.6 078
	...do................................	170	41 00.38	73 23.80	-0 38	-0 22	+1 26	+0 44	0.2	0.1	0.0 - -	0.6 188	0.0 - -	0.5 054
2861	Huntington Bay, off East Fort Point.....	15	40 55.60	73 25.05	-0 06	+0 14	+0 14	+0 51	0.2	0.1	0.0 - -	0.5 190	0.0 - -	0.5 014
	...do................................	30	40 55.60	73 25.05	-0 54	+0 10	+0 05	-0 16	0.1	0.1	0.0 - -	0.4 179	0.0 - -	0.3 007
2866	Northport Bay entrance (in channel).....	15	40 54.53	73 24.45	-0 11	+0 14	+0 12	+0 30	0.1	0.1	0.0 - -	0.4 100	0.0 - -	0.4 267
2871	Northport Bay, south of Duck I. Bluff...		40 55	73 23	+0 31	+0 54	+0 12	-0 05	0.1	0.1	0.0 - -	0.4 007	0.0 - -	0.3 286
2876	Long Neck Point, 0.6 mile south of......	15	41 01.58	73 28.68	-1 20	-0 05	+1 14	+0 11	0.3	0.1	0.0 - -	0.8 252	0.0 - -	0.5 073
	...do................................	27	41 01.58	73 28.68	-1 05	-0 08	+1 12	+0 09	0.3	0.1	0.0 - -	0.8 257	0.0 - -	0.5 080
2881	Lloyd Point, 1.3 miles NNW of...........	15	40 57.95	73 29.70	+1 16	+0 54	+1 20	+1 05	0.3	0.3	0.0 - -	1.0 255	0.0 - -	0.9 055
	...do................................	40	40 57.95	73 29.70	-0 08	+0 13	+1 07	+0 37	0.3	0.2	0.0 - -	1.0 269	0.0 - -	0.7 053
2886	Shippan Point, 1.3 miles SSE of.........	15	40 59.90	73 31.00	+0 28	+0 07	+0 13	+0 16	0.3	0.3	0.0 - -	0.9 239	0.0 - -	0.9 055
	...do................................	40	40 59.98	73 31.03	+0 10	+0 11	+0 46	-0 10	0.2	0.2	0.0 - -	0.7 247	0.0 - -	0.8 071
	Oyster Bay													
2891	Rocky Point, 1 mile east of..........	15	40 55.15	73 30.03	+0 11	+0 20	+0 14	+0 42	0.2	0.2	0.0 - -	0.6 117	0.0 - -	0.5 306
2896	Harbor ent., south of Plum Point.....		40 54	73 31	-0 04	+0 07	+0 04	+0 04	0.2	0.2	0.0 - -	0.7 244	0.0 - -	0.7 054
2901	Harbor, west of Soper Point..........		40 53	73 32	+0 26	+0 28	+0 01	+0 26	0.2	0.1	0.0 - -	0.6 333	0.0 - -	0.4 140
2906	Cold Spring Harbor...................		40 53	73 29	Current weak and variable									
2911	Stamford Harbor entrance................	12	41 00.88	73 32.20	-1 30	-1 17	-2 07	-0 22	0.1	0.2	0.0 - -	0.4 329	0.0 - -	0.8 134

Endnotes can be found at the end of Table 2.

TABLE 2. - CURRENT DIFFERENCES AND OTHER CONSTANTS, 1983

NO.	PLACE	METER DEPTH	POSITION Lat.	POSITION Long.	TIME DIFFERENCES Min. before Flood	TIME DIFFERENCES Flood	TIME DIFFERENCES Min. before Ebb	TIME DIFFERENCES Ebb	SPEED RATIOS Flood	SPEED RATIOS Ebb	AVERAGE SPEEDS AND DIRECTIONS Minimum before Flood	AVERAGE SPEEDS AND DIRECTIONS Maximum Flood	AVERAGE SPEEDS AND DIRECTIONS Minimum before Ebb	AVERAGE SPEEDS AND DIRECTIONS Maximum Ebb
		ft	° ' N	° ' W	h. m.	h. m.	h. m.	h. m.			knots deg.	knots deg.	knots deg.	knots deg.
	LONG ISLAND SOUND Time meridian, 75°W				on THE RACE, p.34									
2916	Greenwich Point, 1.1 miles south of.....	15	40 59.02	73 34.02	+1 13	+1 03	+1 39	+1 13	0.2	0.2	0.0 - -	0.7 258	0.0 - -	0.8 073
	...do................................	55	40 59.02	73 34.02	+1 16	+0 56	+0 41	+1 15	0.2	0.1	0.0 - -	0.6 265	0.0 - -	0.4 069
2921	Greenwich Point, 2.5 miles south of.....	15	40 57.60	73 33.68	+0 39	+0 15	+0 47	+0 41	0.2	0.2	0.0 - -	0.7 242	0.0 - -	0.7 052
	...do................................	55	40 57.60	73 33.68	-1 15	+0 01	-0 37	-0 05	0.2	0.1	0.0 - -	0.5 256	0.0 - -	0.4 079
2926	Oak Neck Point, 0.6 mile north of.......	15	40 55.50	73 34.02	+2 43	+2 03	+2 15	+2 23	0.2	0.2	0.0 - -	0.5 260	0.0 - -	0.6 072
	...do................................	30	40 55.50	73 34.02	+0 46	+1 40	+1 31	+2 03	0.2	0.1	0.0 - -	0.5 300	0.0 - -	0.5 090
2931	Captain Hbr. Ent., 0.6 mile southwest of	15	40 59.65	73 35.67	+1 24	+1 49	+1 39	+2 12	0.2	0.2	0.0 - -	0.6 312	0.0 - -	0.7 118
	...do................................	30	40 59.65	73 35.67	+1 14	+1 19	+0 48	+2 10	0.2	0.2	0.0 - -	0.5 319	0.0 - -	0.7 142
2936	Cos Cob Harbor, off Goose Island........		41 01	73 36	+0 13	-0 07	+0 04	-0 40	0.2	0.1	0.0 - -	0.5 013	0.0 - -	0.4 188
2941	Peningo Neck, 0.6 mi. off Parsonage Pt..	15	40 56.32	73 40.50	+1 01	+0 28	+1 06	+0 39	0.2	0.2	0.0 - -	0.7 226	0.0 - -	0.7 035
2946	Matinecock Point, 0.7 mile NNW of.......	15	40 54.80	73 38.40	+1 06	+0 32	+1 24	+0 48	0.2	0.2	0.0 - -	0.6 233	0.0 - -	0.6 046
	...do................................	40	40 54.80	73 38.40	+0 27	+0 12	+1 23	+0 32	0.2	0.1	0.0 - -	0.7 262	0.0 - -	0.5 053
2951	Matinecock Point, 1.7 miles northwest of	15	40 55.48	73 39.37	+1 12	+1 04	+0 57	+1 14	0.1	0.1	0.0 - -	0.4 234	0.0 - -	0.4 055
2956	Hempstead Harbor, 0.3 mile north of.....	15	40 51.72	73 40.47	Current weak and variable									
2961	Hempstead Harbor, 0.5 mile east of......	15	40 51.50	73 39.98	- - -	+0 05	- - -	-0 19	0.1	- -	0.0 - -	0.3 157	0.0 - -	0.1 331
2966	Old Town Wharf, 0.5 mile north of.......	5	40 48.78	73 39.08	- - -	-0 22	- - -	- - -	0.1	- -	0.0 - -	0.4 196	0.0 - -	- - - -
2971	Hempstead Harbor, off Glenwood Landing..	10	40 49.68	73 39.00	-0 46	-0 05	-0 07	-0 47	0.3	0.2	0.0 - -	0.9 138	0.0 - -	0.7 320
2976	Delancey Point, 1 mile southeast of.....	15	40 55.00	73 42.73	+0 37	+0 14	+1 04	+0 07	0.2	0.1	0.0 - -	0.5 244	0.0 - -	0.4 059
	...do................................	33	40 55.00	73 42.73	- - -	+0 11	+0 59	-0 27	0.1	0.1	0.0 - -	0.4 239	0.0 - -	0.3 069
2981	Mamaroneck Harbor.......................		40 56	73 43	Current weak and variable									
2986	Echo Bay entrance.......................		40 54	73 46	Current weak and variable									
					on THROGS NECK, p.40									
2991	Davids Island, channel 0.1 mile east of.		40 53	73 46	Current weak and variable									
2996	Huckleberry Island, 0.2 mile NW of......	15	40 53.43	73 45.43	-3 15	-4 07	-3 42	-3 53	0.4	0.3	0.0 - -	0.2 069	0.0 - -	0.2 234
3001	Huckleberry Island, 0.6 mile SE of......	15	40 52.80	73 44.75	-2 25	-0 24	-2 14	-2 37	0.6	0.4	0.0 - -	0.4 025	0.0 - -	0.3 226
3006	Execution Rocks, 0.4 mile southwest of..	15	40 52.40	73 44.00	-2 38	-3 03	-2 48	-2 51	1.0	0.5	0.0 - -	0.6 058	0.0 - -	0.4 246
3011	Manhasset Bay entrance..................	15	40 49.75	73 43.78	+2 58	+2 27	+2 27	+2 51	0.6	0.4	0.0 - -	0.4 115	0.0 - -	0.3 307
3016	Hart Island, 0.2 mile north of..........	15	40 51.82	73 46.27	-2 23	-3 55	-4 17	-3 23	0.3	0.3	0.0 - -	0.2 098	0.0 - -	0.3 264
								-0 48		0.2				0.1 283
								-0 36		0.2				0.2 283
3021	Hart Island, southeast of...............	15	40 50.62	73 45.77	-1 44	-0 07	-1 32	-0 18	0.9	0.5	0.0 - -	0.6 032	0.0 - -	0.4 216
3026	Hart Island and City Island, between....	15	40 51.37	73 46.73	-1 48	-2 51	-2 19	-2 40	0.4	0.3	0.0 - -	0.2 349	0.0 - -	0.2 143
						-2 39		- - -	0.3	- -		0.2 348		- - - -
						-0 28		-0 35	0.6	0.4		0.4 349		0.3 150
3031	City Island Bridge......................	10	40 51.47	73 47.60	-2 59	-4 52	-4 27	-4 26	0.3	0.6	0.0 - -	0.2 352	0.0 - -	0.5 198
						-2 30		-2 04	- -	- -		- - - -		- - - -
						-1 10		-0 40	0.2	0.2		0.1 327		0.2 196
3036	Eastchester Bay, near Big Tom...........	5	40 50.20	73 47.72	-3 05	-3 51	-4 07	-3 27	0.5	0.5	0.0 - -	0.3 097	0.0 - -	0.4 294
3041	Hutchinson R., Pelham Highway Bridge....	5	40 51.70	73 49.00	+2 41	+2 37	+1 51	+2 00	1.4	0.6	0.0 - -	0.8 305	0.0 - -	0.4 078
3046	City Island, 0.6 mile southeast of......	15	40 49.72	73 46.47	-1 17	-0 45	-2 59	-3 40	0.8	0.6	0.0 - -	0.5 038	0.0 - -	0.4 251
								-2 19		0.3				0.2 233
								-0 15		0.7				0.5 233

Endnotes can be found at the end of Table 2.

TABLE 2. - CURRENT DIFFERENCES AND OTHER CONSTANTS, 1983

NO.	PLACE	METER DEPTH	POSITION Lat.	POSITION Long.	TIME DIFFERENCES Min. before Flood	TIME DIFFERENCES Flood	TIME DIFFERENCES Min. before Ebb	TIME DIFFERENCES Ebb	SPEED RATIOS Flood	SPEED RATIOS Ebb	Minimum before Flood knots	Minimum before Flood deg.	Maximum Flood knots	Maximum Flood deg.	Minimum before Ebb knots	Minimum before Ebb deg.	Maximum Ebb knots	Maximum Ebb deg.
		ft	° ' N	° ' W	h. m.	h. m.	h. m.	h. m.			knots	deg.	knots	deg.	knots	deg.	knots	deg.
	LONG ISLAND SOUND Time meridian, 75°W				on THROGS NECK, p.40													
3051	Elm Point, 0.2 mile west of............	15	40 48.92	73 46.02	-1 33	-3 16	-1 48	-0 26	0.3	0.7	0.0	- -	0.2	026	0.0	- -	0.6	213
						-2 49			0.2				0.1	028				
						-0 09			1.0				0.6	024				
3056	Throgs Neck, 0.4 mile south of..........	15	40 47.90	73 47.45	+0 36	+0 18	+0 20	+0 06	1.3	0.8	0.0	- -	0.8	090	0.0	- -	0.6	278
3061	THROGS NECK, 0.2 mile south of..........	15	40 48.12	73 47.48	Daily predictions						0.0	- -	0.6	090	0.0	- -	0.8	289
	EAST RIVER				on HELL GATE, p.46													
3066	Cryders Point, 0.4 mile NNW of..........		40 48.02	73 47.92	-0 29	-0 43	-0 30	-1 00	0.4	0.2	0.0	- -	1.3	110	0.0	- -	1.1	285
3071	Old Ferry Point.........................		40 48	73 50	-1 23	-0 37	-0 02	-0 38	0.5	0.3	0.0	- -	1.7	076	0.0	- -	1.5	240
3076	Clason Point, 0.2 mile SSW of..........		40 48.04	73 51.07	-0 22	-0 46	0 00	-0 32	0.5	0.3	0.0	- -	1.8	070	0.0	- -	1.5	250
3081	Flushing Creek entrance................		40 45.9	73 50.7	Current weak and variable													
3086	Rikers I. chan., off La Guardia Field...		40 47	73 53	+0 04	-0 04	+0 04	-0 08	0.3	0.3	0.0	- -	1.1	088	0.0	- -	1.3	261
3091	Bronx River (1 mile north of Hunts Pt.).		40 48.9	73 52.5	Current weak and variable													
3096	Hunts Point, southwest of..............		40 48	73 53	+0 01	-0 10	+0 01	-0 05	0.5	0.3	0.0	- -	1.7	108	0.0	- -	1.3	280
3101	N. Brother I. & S. Brother I., between..		40 47.9	73 54.0	+0 10	+0 06	+0 20	-0 01	0.7	0.4	0.0	- -	2.5	066	0.0	- -	1.8	253
3106	Port Morris, channel off of............		40 47.94	73 54.36	-0 07	-0 32	+0 20	+0 03	0.4	0.4	0.0	- -	1.5	045	0.0	- -	1.7	220
3111	Off Winthrop Ave., Astoria.............		40 47.2	73 55.0	+0 04	+0 02	-0 01	-0 11	1.0	0.5	0.0	- -	3.4	040	0.0	- -	2.5	220
3116	Mill Rock, northeast of................		40 46.9	73 56.2	-0 23	+0 05	-0 29	-0 32	0.7	0.1	0.0	- -	2.3	103	0.0	- -	0.6	288
3121	Mill Rock, west of.....................		40 46.8	73 56.5	-0 26	+0 08	-0 02	-0 17	0.4	0.2	0.0	- -	1.2	000	0.0	- -	1.0	180
3126	HELL GATE (off Mill Rock)..............		40 46.7	73 56.3	Daily predictions						0.0	- -	3.4	050	0.0	- -	4.6	230
	Roosevelt Island																	
3131	west of, off 75th Street............		40 46	73 57	-0 02	-0 04	-0 08	+0 07	1.1	1.0	0.0	- -	3.8	037	0.0	- -	4.7	215
3136	east of, off 36th Avenue............		40 46	73 57	-0 08	-0 04	-0 08	-0 11	1.0	0.7	0.0	- -	3.5	030	0.0	- -	3.4	210
3141	west of, off 67th Street............		40 45.74	73 57.24	+0 13	-0 08	+0 06	+0 11	1.1	0.9	0.0	- -	3.6	011	0.0	- -	4.0	230
3146	west of, off 63rd Street............		40 45.58	73 57.27	-0 10	-0 08	0 00	+0 03	0.8	0.6	0.0	- -	2.8	036	0.0	- -	2.9	223
3151	east of.............................		40 45.49	73 57.08	0 00	-0 06	+0 02	+0 07	0.8	0.6	0.0	- -	2.8	028	0.0	- -	2.6	200
3156	Manhattan, off 31st Street.............		40 44.38	73 58.17	+0 09	-0 11	-0 02	+0 36	0.4	0.5	0.0	- -	1.5	000	0.0	- -	2.1	175
3161	Newtown Creek entrance.................		40 44	73 57	Current weak and variable													
3166	Pier 67, off 19th Street...............		40 44	73 58	-0 08	+0 08	-0 08	+0 07	0.5	0.4	0.0	- -	1.8	355	0.0	- -	1.9	179
3171	Williamsburg Bridge, 0.3 mile north of..		40 43.08	73 58.24	-0 05	+0 12	-0 01	+0 10	0.8	0.6	0.0	- -	2.7	020	0.0	- -	2.9	220
3176	Corlears Hook, south of, midstream <15>.		40 42.5	73 58.6	-0 12	+0 01	-0 09	-0 01	0.9	0.7	0.0	- -	3.0	058	0.0	- -	3.0	233
3181	Brooklyn Bridge, 0.1 mile southwest of..		40 42.2	74 00.0	-0 18	+0 08	-0 04	-0 07	0.9	0.8	0.0	- -	2.9	046	0.0	- -	3.5	222
3186	Governors I., N of (SEE CAUTION NOTE)...		40 41.8	74 01.0	-0 16	+0 16	-0 20	+0 17	0.4	0.4	0.0	- -	1.2	094	0.0	- -	1.7	269
3191	Buttermilk Channel.....................		40 41.15	74 00.81	-0 12	-0 18	-0 06	+0 18	0.5	0.5	0.0	- -	1.8	050	0.0	- -	2.4	220
	HARLEM RIVER																	
3196	East 105th Street......................		40 47	73 56	-0 20	+0 08	-0 02	-0 17	0.4	0.2	0.0	- -	1.2	035	0.0	- -	1.0	215
3201	East 117th Street (midchannel) <16>.....		40 47.6	73 55.8	-1 16	+0 10			0.4	- -	0.0	- -	1.3	197			- -	- -
3206	Willis Ave. Bridge, 0.1 mile NW of......		40 48.3	73 55.8	-0 30	0 00	-0 12	-0 13	0.4	0.3	0.0	- -	1.2	140	0.0	- -	1.3	330
3211	Madison Ave. Bridge....................		40 48.8	73 56.1	-0 20	+0 18	-0 21	-0 14	0.5	0.4	0.0	- -	1.8	180	0.0	- -	1.7	000
3216	Macombs Dam Bridge.....................		40 49.7	73 56.1	-0 20	+0 14	-0 22	-0 11	0.5	0.3	0.0	- -	1.7	180	0.0	- -	1.4	000
3221	High Bridge............................		40 50.5	73 55.9	-0 20	+0 08	-0 23	-0 08	0.6	0.4	0.0	- -	2.0	189	0.0	- -	2.0	015
3226	West 207th Street Bridge...............		40 51.8	73 54.9	-0 22	+0 05	-0 22	-0 02	0.6	0.4	0.0	- -	2.0	215	0.0	- -	2.0	035
3231	Broadway Bridge........................		40 52.4	73 54.7	-0 23	+0 08	-0 20	+0 04	0.6	0.5	0.0	- -	2.1	116	0.0	- -	2.3	299

Endnotes can be found at the end of Table 2.

TABLE 2. - CURRENT DIFFERENCES AND OTHER CONSTANTS, 1983

NO.	PLACE	METER DEPTH	POSITION Lat.	Long.	TIME DIFFERENCES Min. before Flood	Flood	Min. before Ebb	Ebb	SPEED RATIOS Flood	Ebb	AVERAGE SPEEDS AND DIRECTIONS Minimum before Flood	Maximum Flood	Minimum before Ebb	Maximum Ebb
		ft	° ' N	° ' W	h. m.	h. m.	h. m.	h. m.			knots deg.	knots deg.	knots deg.	knots deg.
	HARLEM RIVER Time meridian, 75°W				on HELL GATE, p.46									
3236	Spuyten Duyvil Creek entrance..........		40 52.68	73 55.46	-0 10	+0 12	-0 10	+0 17	0.4	0.3	0.0 - -	1.4 100	0.0 - -	1.5 285
	LONG ISLAND, South Coast				on THE NARROWS, p.52									
3241	Fire Island Lighted Whistle Bouy 2FI....		40 29	73 11	See table 5.									
3246	Fire Island Inlet, 22 miles S of <17>...		40 16	73 16	See table 5.									
3251	Shinnecock Canal, railroad bridge <18>..		40 53.2	72 30.1				-0 38	- -	0.8	- - - -	- - - -	- - - -	1.5 180
3256	Ponquogue bridge, Shinnecock Bay........		40 50.7	72 30.1	+0 54	+0 35	+0 27	+0 37	0.5	0.3	0.0 - -	0.8 250	0.0 - -	0.6 090
3261	Shinnecock Inlet........................		40 50.6	72 28.7	-0 06	-0 21	-0 30	-1 03	1.5	1.2	0.0 - -	2.5 350	0.0 - -	2.3 170
3266	Fire I. Inlet, 0.5 mi. S of Oak Beach...		40 37.78	73 18.40	-0 03	-0 01	+0 29	-0 01	1.4	1.2	0.0 - -	2.4 082	0.0 - -	2.4 244
3271	Jones Inlet.............................		40 35.5	73 34.0	-1 15	-0 49	-0 48	-1 05	1.8	1.3	0.0 - -	3.1 035	0.0 - -	2.6 217
3276	Long Beach, inside, between bridges.....		40 35.7	73 39.6	-0 54	+0 23	+0 32	0 00	0.3	0.3	0.0 - -	0.5 076	0.0 - -	0.6 277
3281	East Rockaway Inlet.....................		40 35.4	73 45.3	-1 46	-1 35	-1 03	-1 38	1.3	1.2	0.0 - -	2.2 042	0.0 - -	2.3 227
3286	Ambrose Light...........................		40 27	73 49	See table 5.									
3291	Sandy Hook App. Lighted Horn Bouy 2A....		40 27	73 55	See table 5.									
	JAMAICA BAY													
3296	Rockaway Inlet..........................		40 33.7	73 56.1	-1 55	-2 20	-1 33	-2 11	1.1	1.3	0.0 - -	1.8 085	0.0 - -	2.7 244
3301	Barren Island, east of..................		40 35	73 53	-1 59	-2 28	-2 03	-2 19	0.7	0.9	0.0 - -	1.2 004	0.0 - -	1.7 192
3306	Canarsie (midchannel, off pier).........		40 37.6	73 53.0	-1 54	-1 38	-1 18	-2 06	0.3	0.4	0.0 - -	0.5 045	0.0 - -	0.7 222
3311	Beach Channel (bridge)..................		40 35	73 49	-1 48	-1 13	-0 57	-1 25	1.1	1.0	0.0 - -	1.9 062	0.0 - -	2.0 225
3316	Grass Hassock Channel...................		40 36.6	73 47.1	-1 21	-1 02	-0 57	-0 54	0.6	0.5	0.0 - -	1.0 052	0.0 - -	1.0 228
	NEW YORK HARBOR ENTRANCE													
	Ambrose Channel													
3326	Entrance............................		40 30.4	73 58.4	-1 20	-1 30	-1 03	-0 38	1.0	1.2	0.0 - -	1.7 310	0.0 - -	2.3 110
3336	East of West Bank Light <19>.........		40 31.9	74 01.5	-0 04	-1 01	-0 53	+0 15	0.8	0.9	0.9 270	1.3 310	0.5 045	1.8 170
3346	Coney Island Lt., 1.6 miles SSW of......		40 33.04	74 01.4	+0 01	-0 48	-0 24	+0 56	0.5	0.8	0.0 - -	0.8 330	0.0 - -	1.5 145
3356	Ambrose Channel, north end..............		40 33.8	74 01.6	+0 15	-0 10	-0 09	+0 42	0.8	0.9	0.0 - -	1.3 332	0.0 - -	1.9 176
3366	Coney Island, 0.2 mile west of..........		40 34.6	74 01.1	-0 49	-1 43	-0 57	-0 07	0.9	1.0	0.0 - -	1.5 329	0.0 - -	2.0 170
3376	Ft. Lafayette, channel east of..........		40 36.5	74 02.2	-2 13	-0 06	+0 04	-1 50	0.6	0.5	0.0 - -	1.1 343	0.0 - -	0.9 194
3386	THE NARROWS, midchannel.................		40 36.6	74 02.8	Daily predictions						0.0 - -	1.7 340	0.0 - -	2.0 160
	NEW YORK HARBOR, Upper Bay													
3396	Tompkinsville...........................		40 38.1	74 03.6	-0 29	+0 20	+0 08	+0 20	0.9	1.0	0.0 - -	1.6 004	0.0 - -	2.0 172
3406	Bay Bridge Channel......................		40 39.0	74 02.0	-0 27	-0 50	-0 42	-0 36	0.6	0.6	0.0 - -	1.0 039	0.0 - -	1.1 218
3416	Red Hook Channel........................		40 40.0	74 01.2	-1 03	-0 44	-0 08	-0 30	0.6	0.4	0.0 - -	1.0 353	0.0 - -	0.7 170
3426	Robbins Reef Light, east of.............		40 39.45	74 03.48	+0 16	+0 16	+0 02	+0 24	0.8	0.8	0.0 - -	1.3 016	0.0 - -	1.6 204
3436	Red Hook, 1 mile west of................		40 40.5	74 02.5	+0 41	+1 06	+0 47	+0 52	0.8	1.2	0.0 - -	1.3 024	0.0 - -	2.3 206
3446	Statue of Liberty, east of..............		40 41.4	74 01.8	+0 57	+0 58	+0 56	+0 59	0.8	1.0	0.0 - -	1.4 031	0.0 - -	1.9 205

Endnotes can be found at the end of Table 2.

TABLE 2. - CURRENT DIFFERENCES AND OTHER CONSTANTS, 1983

NO.	PLACE	METER DEPTH	POSITION Lat.	POSITION Long.	TIME DIFFERENCES Min. before Flood	Flood	Min. before Ebb	Ebb	SPEED RATIOS Flood	SPEED RATIOS Ebb	AVERAGE SPEEDS AND DIRECTIONS Minimum before Flood		Maximum Flood		Minimum before Ebb		Maximum Ebb	
		ft	° ' N	° ' W	h. m.	h. m.	h. m.	h. m.			knots	deg.	knots	deg.	knots	deg.	knots	deg.
	HUDSON RIVER, Midchannel <20> Time meridian, 75°W				on THE NARROWS, p.52													
3456	The Battery, northwest of		40 43	74 02	+1 41	+1 26	+1 21	+1 46	0.9	1.2	0.0	- -	1.5	015	0.0	- -	2.3	194
3466	Desbrosses Street		40 43	74 01	+1 43	+1 30	+1 24	+1 52	0.9	1.2	0.0	- -	1.5	010	0.0	- -	2.3	- -
3476	Chelsea Docks		40 45	74 01	+1 27	+1 42	+1 32	+1 38	1.0	1.0	0.0	- -	1.7	018	0.0	- -	2.0	187
3486	Forty-second Street		40 46	74 00	+1 51	+1 41	+1 34	+2 00	1.0	1.2	0.0	- -	1.7	030	0.0	- -	2.3	- -
3496	Ninety-sixth Street		40 48	73 59	+1 57	+1 48	+1 42	+2 07	1.0	1.2	0.0	- -	1.7	030	0.0	- -	2.3	- -
3506	Grants Tomb, 123d Street		40 49	73 58	+1 59	+1 53	+1 45	+2 10	0.9	1.2	0.0	- -	1.6	025	0.0	- -	2.3	- -
3516	George Washington Bridge		40 51	73 57	+1 41	+1 55	+1 50	+2 08	0.9	1.1	0.0	- -	1.6	020	0.0	- -	2.2	200
3526	Spuyten Duyvil		40 53	73 56	+2 11	+2 08	+1 57	+2 24	0.9	1.1	0.0	- -	1.6	020	0.0	- -	2.1	- -
3536	Riverdale		40 54	73 55	+2 11	+2 07	+2 02	+2 32	0.8	1.0	0.0	- -	1.4	015	0.0	- -	2.0	200
3546	Dobbs Ferry		41 01	73 53	+2 30	+2 33	+2 24	+2 49	0.8	0.9	0.0	- -	1.3	010	0.0	- -	1.7	- -
3556	Tarrytown		41 05	73 53	+2 37	+2 46	+2 40	+3 02	0.6	0.8	0.0	- -	1.1	000	0.0	- -	1.5	- -
3566	Ossining		41 10	73 54	+2 50	+3 02	+3 05	+3 19	0.5	0.7	0.0	- -	0.9	320	0.0	- -	1.3	- -
3576	Haverstraw		41 12	73 57	+2 55	+3 08	+3 13	+3 26	0.5	0.7	0.0	- -	0.8	335	0.0	- -	1.3	- -
3586	Peekskill		41 17	73 57	+3 10	+3 24	+3 33	+3 42	0.5	0.6	0.0	- -	0.8	000	0.0	- -	1.2	- -
3596	Bear Mountain Bridge		41 19	73 59	+3 16	+3 31	+3 39	+3 48	0.5	0.6	0.0	- -	0.8	000	0.0	- -	1.1	- -
3606	Highland Falls		41 22	73 58	+3 24	+3 37	+3 44	+4 02	0.6	0.6	0.0	- -	1.0	005	0.0	- -	1.2	185
3616	West Point, off Duck Island		41 24	73 57	+3 32	+3 47	+3 51	+4 04	0.5	0.6	0.0	- -	1.0	010	0.0	- -	1.1	- -
3626	Newburgh		41 30	74 00	+3 50	+4 06	+4 03	+4 21	0.5	0.6	0.0	- -	0.9	005	0.0	- -	1.1	- -
3636	New Hamburg		41 35	73 57	+4 05	+4 20	+4 11	+4 33	0.6	0.6	0.0	- -	1.0	005	0.0	- -	1.1	- -
3646	Poughkeepsie		41 42	73 57	+4 26	+4 37	+4 21	+4 49	0.6	0.6	0.0	- -	1.1	005	0.0	- -	1.2	- -
3656	Hyde Park		41 47	73 57	+4 42	+4 48	+4 30	+5 00	0.7	0.7	0.0	- -	1.2	005	0.0	- -	1.3	- -
3666	Kingston Point <21>		41 56	73 57	+5 09	+5 09	+4 54	+5 19	0.8	0.8	0.0	- -	1.3	005	0.0	- -	1.6	- -
3676	Barrytown		42 00	73 56	+5 26	+5 21	+5 10	+5 26	0.8	0.9	0.0	- -	1.4	010	0.0	- -	1.7	- -
3686	Saugerties		42 04	73 56	+5 43	+5 42	+5 29	+5 36	0.9	1.0	0.0	- -	1.5	000	0.0	- -	1.9	- -
3696	Silver Point		42 09	73 54	+6 01	+6 14	+5 49	+5 50	0.9	1.0	0.0	- -	1.5	030	0.0	- -	2.0	- -
3706	Catskill		42 13	73 51	+6 16	+6 37	+6 09	+6 06	0.9	1.0	0.0	- -	1.6	355	0.0	- -	2.0	- -
3716	Hudson		42 15	73 48	+6 23	+6 45	+6 20	+6 15	0.9	1.0	0.0	- -	1.6	030	0.0	- -	2.0	- -
3726	Coxsackie		42 21	73 47	+6 45	+6 57	+6 55	+6 44	0.9	0.9	0.0	- -	1.6	350	0.0	- -	1.8	- -
3736	New Baltimore		42 27	73 47	+7 12	+7 04	+7 13	+7 09	0.8	0.8	0.0	- -	1.3	355	0.0	- -	1.5	- -
3746	Castleton-on-Hudson		42 32	73 46	+7 35	+7 11	+7 12	+7 29	0.5	0.6	0.0	- -	0.9	015	0.0	- -	1.2	- -
3756	Albany		42 39	73 45	+8 29	+7 32	+6 46	+7 47	0.2	0.4	0.0	- -	0.3	020	0.0	- -	0.8	- -
3766	Troy (below the locks) <22>		42 44	73 42	- - -	- - -	- - -	- - -	- -	- -	- -	- -	- -	- -	- -	- -	0.7	190
	NEW YORK HARBOR, Lower Bay																	
3776	False Hook Channel		40 28.4	74 00.0	-2 07	-1 36	-1 22	-1 28	1.1	0.7	0.0	- -	1.8	320	0.0	- -	1.4	135
3786	Sandy Hook, 1.7 miles ENE of north tip		40 29.7	73 59.0	-1 48	-1 38	-1 06	-1 48	0.9	0.8	0.0	- -	1.5	295	0.0	- -	1.7	100
3796	Sandy Hook & South Channels, junction		40 28.9	73 59.6	-1 28	-1 24	-1 13	-1 16	0.8	0.8	0.0	- -	1.3	300	0.0	- -	1.7	113
3806	Sandy Hook Chan., 0.4 mi. W of north tip		40 28.79	74 01.30	-1 51	-1 55	-1 30	-1 50	1.2	0.8	0.0	- -	2.0	235	0.0	- -	1.6	050
3816	Sandy Hook Pt., 2 mi. W of (channel)		40 28.8	74 03.6	-1 45	-2 00	-1 50	-1 42	0.4	0.3	0.0	- -	0.6	263	0.0	- -	0.6	086
3826	Chapel Hill South Channel		40 29.90	74 02.8	-2 12	-2 30	-1 40	-2 08	0.4	0.3	0.0	- -	0.7	255	0.0	- -	0.6	075
3836	New Dorp Beach, 1.2 miles south of		40 32.4	74 05.8	-4 19	-3 36	-4 35	-4 16	0.2	0.2	0.0	- -	0.4	225	0.0	- -	0.5	030
3846	Old Orchard Shoal Lt., 1.2 mi. ENE of		40 31.1	74 04.36	-2 19	-2 07	-1 23	-2 02	0.4	0.2	0.0	- -	0.7	270	0.0	- -	0.4	085
3856	New Dorp Beach, 1.8 miles SE of <23>		40 32.9	74 03.7	- - -	- - -	- - -	- - -	0.3	0.3	- -	- -	0.5	045	- -	- -	0.5	225
3866	Midland Beach, 2.6 miles SE of <24>		40 32.8	74 02.35	0 00	+0 07	0 00	+0 01	0.5	0.6	0.2	270	0.8	335	0.2	068	1.3	160
3876	Coney Island Lt., 1.5 miles SSE of		40 33.1	74 00.3	-1 27	-1 56	-0 58	-0 53	0.6	0.6	0.0	- -	1.1	310	0.0	- -	1.3	125

Endnotes can be found at the end of Table 2.

TABLE 2. - CURRENT DIFFERENCES AND OTHER CONSTANTS, 1983

NO.	PLACE	METER DEPTH	POSITION Lat.	POSITION Long.	TIME DIFFERENCES Min. before Flood	TIME DIFFERENCES Flood	TIME DIFFERENCES Min. before Ebb	TIME DIFFERENCES Ebb	SPEED RATIOS Flood	SPEED RATIOS Ebb	AVERAGE SPEEDS AND DIRECTIONS Minimum before Flood	Maximum Flood	Minimum before Ebb	Maximum Ebb
		ft	° ' N	° ' W	h. m.	h. m.	h. m.	h. m.			knots deg.	knots deg.	knots deg.	knots deg.
	DELAWARE BAY and RIVER Time meridian, 75°W				on DELAWARE BAY ENTRANCE, p.58									
4206	Ben Davis Point, 0.8 mile southwest of..		39 16.9	75 18.2	+0 56	+0 59	+1 21	+1 00	0.7	0.4	0.0 - -	1.2 308	0.0 - -	0.8 122
4211	Cohansey River, 0.5 mile above entrance.		39 20.9	75 21.6	+1 29	+1 21	+1 39	+1 28	0.7	0.7	0.0 - -	1.2 074	0.0 - -	1.4 254
4216	Bridgeton (Broad Street Bridge) <1>....		39 25.6	75 14.2	- - -	+2 28	- - -	+2 31	0.1	0.2	0.0 - -	0.2 000	0.0 - -	0.3 180
4221	Arnold Point, channel abreast of........		39 22.5	75 27.8	+2 25	+2 18	+2 03	+2 26	1.1	1.1	0.0 - -	2.0 336	0.0 - -	2.1 156
4226	Smyrna River entrance...................		39 21.9	75 30.8	+1 48	+1 42	+2 05	+2 07	0.7	0.8	0.0 - -	1.2 250	0.0 - -	1.5 070
4231	Stony Point, channel west of............		39 27.1	75 33.8	+3 23	+2 50	+2 38	+3 06	0.8	1.0	0.0 - -	1.5 324	0.0 - -	1.9 151
4236	Appoquinimink River entrance............		39 26.8	75 34.9	+2 33	+2 55	+2 22	+2 34	0.6	0.6	0.0 - -	1.0 231	0.0 - -	1.2 048
4241	Reedy Island (off end of pier)..........		39 30.7	75 33.4	+3 01	+3 01	+2 54	+3 23	1.3	1.4	0.0 - -	2.4 027	0.0 - -	2.6 194
4246	Alloway Creek ent., 0.2 mile above......		39 29.9	75 31.5	+2 21	+2 42	+2 19	+1 56	1.2	1.1	0.0 - -	2.1 129	0.0 - -	2.1 325
4251	New Bridge, Alloway Creek...............		39 31.6	75 27.1	+3 03	+3 57	+3 36	+3 36	0.7	0.7	0.0 - -	1.3 090	0.0 - -	1.4 270
4256	Reedy Point, 0.4 mile east of...........		39 33.53	75 33.13	+3 18	+3 02	+2 54	+4 00	1.0	1.2	0.0 - -	1.8 333	0.0 - -	2.3 166
4261	Reedy Point, 1.1 miles east of..........		39 33.58	75 32.47	+3 19	+3 11	+3 08	+3 36	1.0	0.9	0.0 - -	1.8 354	0.0 - -	1.7 179
4266	Salem River entrance....................		39 34.2	75 30.1	+3 46	+3 33	+3 37	+4 09	0.8	0.8	0.0 - -	1.5 062	0.0 - -	1.6 245
4271	Bulkhead Shoal Channel, off Del. City...		39 35.0	75 35.2	+3 16	+2 58	+3 03	+3 44	1.2	1.1	0.0 - -	2.1 308	0.0 - -	2.1 138
4276	Pea Patch Island, channel east of.......		39 36.0	75 33.9	+3 30	+3 13	+3 33	+4 09	1.3	1.2	0.0 - -	2.3 319	0.0 - -	2.3 148
4281	Penns Neck, 0.6 mile west of............		39 37.05	75 34.92	+3 38	+3 38	+3 14	+3 31	0.9	0.9	0.0 - -	1.7 002	0.0 - -	1.7 167
4286	Penns Neck, 0.3 mile west of............		39 37.07	75 34.58	+3 22	+3 07	+3 08	+3 37	1.0	0.9	0.0 - -	1.8 339	0.0 - -	1.7 152
4291	New Castle, channel abreast of..........		39 39.1	75 33.2	+4 04	+3 21	+3 34	+4 01	1.1	1.3	0.0 - -	1.9 051	0.0 - -	2.4 230
4296	Kelly Point, 0.2 mile northwest of......		39 38.9	75 32.8	+3 43	+3 55	+3 24	+3 31	0.9	0.8	0.0 - -	1.6 049	0.0 - -	1.5 230
4301	Deepwater Point, channel northwest of...		39 42.1	75 30.6	+3 44	+3 54	+3 45	+3 55	1.7	1.4	0.0 - -	3.0 029	0.0 - -	2.6 215
4306	Christina River, 1 mile above entrance..		39 43	75 32	+3 16	+3 01	+2 58	+2 44	0.4	0.5	0.0 - -	0.7 300	0.0 - -	0.9 050
4311	Cherry Island Flats, channel east of....		39 44.3	75 29.1	+4 09	+4 08	+4 02	+3 57	0.9	0.7	0.0 - -	1.6 027	0.0 - -	1.4 207
4316	Oldsmans Point..........................		39 45.9	75 28.4	+4 28	+3 42	+4 03	+4 40	0.9	0.8	0.0 - -	1.6 027	0.0 - -	1.5 210
4321	Marcus Hook.............................		39 48.2	75 24.6	+4 58	+4 19	+4 02	+4 51	0.9	0.8	0.0 - -	1.7 061	0.0 - -	1.6 232
4326	Eddystone...............................		39 50.8	75 20.5	+5 25	+4 41	+4 31	+4 55	0.9	1.2	0.0 - -	1.7 058	0.0 - -	2.2 242
4331	Essington Harbor........................		39 51.5	75 18.3	+4 09	+3 54	+4 04	+3 56	0.8	0.6	0.0 - -	1.4 096	0.0 - -	1.2 274
4336	Crab Point, 0.5 mile east of............		39 50.8	75 17.0	+4 48	+4 44	+4 44	+4 58	1.2	1.0	0.0 - -	2.1 094	0.0 - -	1.9 268
4341	Hog Island, channel southeast of........		39 52.0	75 12.9	+4 53	+4 53	+4 42	+4 52	1.1	1.2	0.0 - -	1.9 054	0.0 - -	2.2 231
4346	Schuylkill River entrance <1>.........		39 53.2	75 11.7	- - -	+3 20	- - -	+4 08	0.3	0.2	0.0 - -	0.5 356	0.0 - -	0.4 178
4351	Gloucester..............................		39 53.4	75 08.1	+5 13	+5 02	+4 53	+5 00	1.2	1.1	0.0 - -	2.2 020	0.0 - -	2.0 210
4356	Greenwich Point, northeast of...........		39 54.5	75 07.6	+5 18	+4 53	+4 54	+5 01	0.9	0.8	0.0 - -	1.6 002	0.0 - -	1.6 188
4361	Camden Marine Terminals, E of Chan. <29>		39 56.4	75 08.2	+5 52	+5 13	+5 16	+5 07	0.7	0.6	0.0 - -	1.3 005	0.0 - -	1.1 174
4366	Fisher Point............................		39 58.9	75 04.2	+6 07	+5 46	+5 23	+5 06	0.8	0.9	0.0 - -	1.4 041	0.0 - -	1.7 223
4371	Torresdale, west of channel.............		40 02.4	74 59.4	+6 54	+5 56	+4 59	+5 46	0.5	0.8	0.0 - -	0.9 044	0.0 - -	1.6 223
4376	Rancocas Creek, off Delanco.............		40 02.6	74 57.6	+6 36	+6 25	+5 51	+6 08	0.6	0.5	0.0 - -	1.0 090	0.0 - -	0.9 272
4381	Bristol, south of.......................	8	40 05.3	74 51.6	+6 55	+5 31	+4 57	+6 10	0.7	0.8	0.0 - -	1.3 024	0.0 - -	1.6 200
4386	Burlington Island, channel east of......		40 05.7	74 50.2	+7 32	+5 46	+4 16	+6 46	0.5	0.9	0.0 - -	0.9 018	0.0 - -	1.8 204
4391	Whitehill <30>..........................		40 08.2	74 44.2	- - -	- - -	- - -	+7 07	- -	0.7	0.0 - -	- - - -	0.0 - -	1.4 233
	DEL., MD. and VA. COAST													
4396	Indian River Inlet (bridge).............		38 37	75 04	- - -	+0 05	- - -	+0 10	1.0	1.1	0.0 - -	1.8 265	0.0 - -	2.1 085
4401	Fenwick Shoal Lighted Whistle Buoy 2....		38 25	74 46		See table 5.								
4406	Winter-Quarter Shoal Buoy 6WQS <31>.....		37 55	74 56		See table 5.								

Endnotes can be found at the end of Table 2.

TABLE 2. - CURRENT DIFFERENCES AND OTHER CONSTANTS, 1983

NO.	PLACE	METER DEPTH	POSITION Lat.	POSITION Long.	TIME DIFFERENCES Min. before Flood	Flood	Min. before Ebb	Ebb	SPEED RATIOS Flood	SPEED RATIOS Ebb	AVERAGE SPEEDS AND DIRECTIONS Minimum before Flood	Maximum Flood	Minimum before Ebb	Maximum Ebb
		ft	° ' N	° ' W	h. m.	h. m.	h. m.	h. m.			knots deg.	knots deg.	knots deg.	knots deg.
	DEL., MD. and VA. COAST Time meridian, 75°W				on CHESAPEAKE BAY ENTRANCE, p.64									
4411	Cape Charles, 70 miles east of..........		37 05	74 51	See table 5.									
4416	Smith Island Shoal, southeast of........	7	37 05.3	75 43.5	-2 14	-2 12	-2 04	-2 05	0.3	0.3	0.0 - -	0.3 298	0.0 - -	0.4 068
4421	Chesapeake Light, 4.4 miles northeast of		36 59	75 42	See table 5.									
4426	Cape Henry Light, 2.2 miles southeast of		36 53.9	75 58.7	-1 54	-1 18	-0 39	-1 41	1.0	0.6	0.0 - -	1.0 346	0.0 - -	0.9 165
	CHESAPEAKE BAY													
4431	Cape Henry Light, 1 mile north of.......		36 56.4	76 00.5	+0 04	-0 25	-0 08	-0 25	1.1	1.3	0.0 - -	1.1 280	0.0 - -	2.0 090
4436	Cape Henry Light, 1.8 miles north of....		36 57.4	76 00.1	-0 23	-0 11	+0 10	-0 17	1.2	1.0	0.0 - -	1.2 292	0.0 - -	1.5 099
4441	CHESAPEAKE BAY ENTRANCE................	7	36 58.8	76 00.4	Daily predictions						0.0 - -	1.0 306	0.0 - -	1.5 126
4446	Cape Henry Light, 4.6 miles north of....		37 00.1	75 59.3	-1 05	-0 46	-0 10	-0 54	1.3	0.9	0.0 - -	1.3 294	0.0 - -	1.3 104
4451	Cape Charles Light, 9.5 mi. WSW of......	7	37 03.7	76 05.4	-0 12	+0 08	+0 32	-0 05	1.5	0.9	0.0 - -	1.5 319	0.0 - -	1.4 126
4456	Cape Henry Light, 8.3 mi. northwest of..		37 02.2	76 06.6	-0 22	-0 12	+0 16	-0 05	1.0	0.7	0.0 - -	1.0 329	0.0 - -	1.1 133
4461	Lynnhaven Roads.........................		36 55.1	76 04.9	-0 58	-0 37	-0 14	-0 41	0.8	0.6	0.0 - -	0.8 280	0.0 - -	0.9 070
4466	Lynnhaven Inlet bridge..................		36 54.4	76 05.6	-1 56	-2 05	-2 12	-3 01	0.6	0.9	0.0 - -	0.6 180	0.0 - -	1.4 000
	Chesapeake Bay Bridge Tunnel													
4471	Chesapeake Beach, 1.5 miles north of.		36 56.69	76 07.33	-0 09	-0 07	-0 23	-0 31	0.8	0.6	0.0 - -	0.8 305	0.0 - -	0.9 100
4476	Thimble Shoal Channel...............		36 58.33	76 06.67	-0 53	-0 46	-0 24	-0 39	1.4	0.9	0.0 - -	1.4 310	0.0 - -	1.3 095
4481	Tail of the Horseshoe...............		36 59.57	76 06.20	-0 33	-0 25	-0 13	-0 59	0.9	0.7	0.0 - -	0.9 300	0.0 - -	1.0 110
4486	Middle Ground, channel west of.......		37 03.00	76 05.00	-0 10	-0 20	-0 36	+0 04	1.6	0.9	0.0 - -	1.6 335	0.0 - -	1.3 150
4491	Chesapeake Channel..................		37 02.50	76 04.33	-0 33	-0 17	+0 03	-0 12	1.8	1.0	0.0 - -	1.8 335	0.0 - -	1.5 145
4496	Fisherman Island, 3.2 miles WSW of...		37 04.00	76 02.25	-1 00	-1 07	-0 46	-1 07	1.2	1.1	0.0 - -	1.2 330	0.0 - -	1.6 135
4501	Fisherman Island, 1.4 miles WSW of...		37 04.78	76 00.25	-1 47	-0 57	-0 41	-1 33	1.8	0.7	0.0 - -	1.8 330	0.0 - -	1.1 140
4506	Fisherman I., 1.8 miles south of.....		37 03.58	75 58.77	-1 04	-1 00	-0 27	-1 24	1.6	0.9	0.0 - -	1.6 320	0.0 - -	1.4 120
4511	Fisherman I., 0.4 mile west of.......		37 05.57	75 59.33	-0 59	-1 03	-0 35	-1 13	2.0	1.3	0.0 - -	2.0 005	0.0 - -	2.0 175
4516	Fisherman I., 1.1 miles northwest of.		37 06.50	76 00.00	-1 17	-0 35	-0 06	-0 50	1.8	1.1	0.0 - -	1.8 355	0.0 - -	1.6 165
4521	Cape Charles, off Wise Point.........	5	37 06.88	75 58.30	-0 29	-0 18	+0 27	+0 49	0.7	0.1	0.0 - -	0.7 305	0.0 - -	0.2 075
	Little Creek													
4526	North of east jetty..................	10	36 56.05	76 10.60	-2 00	-2 02	-1 42	-1 59	0.9	0.7	0.0 - -	0.9 280	0.0 - -	1.0 076
4531	0.5 mile north of west jetty.........	10	36 56.32	76 10.81	-1 37	-1 03	-0 42	-1 31	0.9	0.6	0.0 - -	0.9 274	0.0 - -	0.9 108
4536	Old Plantation Flats Light, west of.....		37 14.0	76 04.1	+0 53	+1 06	+1 26	+0 35	1.2	0.9	0.0 - -	1.2 005	0.0 - -	1.3 175
4541	York Spit Channel.......................	7	37 12.9	76 08.5	+0 55	+0 55	+0 55	+0 55	0.8	0.7	0.0 - -	0.8 010	0.0 - -	1.1 195
4546	Wolf Trap Light, 0.5 mile west of.......		37 23.4	76 11.9	+1 05	+1 05	+1 05	+1 05	1.0	0.8	0.0 - -	1.0 015	0.0 - -	1.2 190
4551	Wolf Trap Light, 5.8 miles east of......		37 23.1	76 04.3	+1 45	+1 45	+1 45	+1 45	0.9	0.9	0.0 - -	0.9 015	0.0 - -	1.3 175
4556	Stingray Point, 5.5 miles east of.......		37 35.0	76 10.4	+1 50	+2 41	+2 52	+2 01	1.0	0.6	0.0 - -	1.0 343	0.0 - -	0.9 179
4561	Stingray Point, 12.5 miles east of......		37 33.8	76 02.3	+1 40	+2 05	+1 40	+2 05	1.0	0.5	0.0 - -	1.0 030	0.0 - -	0.8 175
4566	Smith Point, 4.5 miles east of..........		37 52.9	76 08.6	+3 11	+3 14	+3 14	+3 15	0.7	0.5	0.0 - -	0.7 352	0.0 - -	0.8 163
4571	Smith Point Light, 6 miles north of.....		37 58.9	76 11.4	+3 50	+3 35	+3 50	+3 35	0.4	0.7	0.0 - -	0.4 350	0.0 - -	1.0 135
4576	Point Lookin............................		38 06.6	76 13.1	+4 35	+4 15	+4 35	+4 15	0.4	0.3	0.0 - -	0.4 010	0.0 - -	0.5 160
4581	Point No Point..........................		38 09.1	76 14.0	+5 15	+5 10	+5 15	+5 10	0.4	0.4	0.0 - -	0.4 355	0.0 - -	0.6 150
					on BALTIMORE HARBOR APPROACH, p.70									
4586	Cedar Point, 3.2 miles east of..........		38 18.3	76 18.35	- - -	-2 49	- - -	-3 32	0.2	0.8	0.0 - -	0.2 030	0.0 - -	0.6 175
4591	Cedar Point, 1.1 miles ENE of...........		38 18.27	76 21.10	-3 23	-2 50	-2 36	-3 42	0.5	0.8	0.0 - -	0.4 010	0.0 - -	0.6 185
4596	Drum Point, 2.8 miles northeast of......		38 20.18	76 21.95	- - -	-3 12	- - -	-2 42	0.2	0.5	0.0 - -	0.2 335	0.0 - -	0.4 185

Endnotes can be found at the end of Table 2.

TABLE 2. - CURRENT DIFFERENCES AND OTHER CONSTANTS, 1983

NO.	PLACE	METER DEPTH	POSITION Lat.	POSITION Long.	TIME DIFFERENCES Min. before Flood	TIME DIFFERENCES Flood	TIME DIFFERENCES Min. before Ebb	TIME DIFFERENCES Ebb	SPEED RATIOS Flood	SPEED RATIOS Ebb	Minimum before Flood		Maximum Flood		Minimum before Ebb		Maximum Ebb	
		ft	° ' N	° ' W	h. m.	h. m.	h. m.	h. m.			knots	deg.	knots	deg.	knots	deg.	knots	deg.
	CHESAPEAKE BAY Time meridian, 75°W				on BALTIMORE HARBOR APPROACH, p.70													
4601	Cove Point, 0.6 mile northeast of.......		38 23.45	76 22.19	-2 55	-3 04	-3 04	-2 51	0.9	1.0	0.0	- -	0.7	330	0.0	- -	0.8	155
4606	Cove Point, 2.5 miles east of..........		38 23.2	76 19.8	-2 39	-2 48	-2 44	-2 45	0.6	0.8	0.0	- -	0.5	310	0.0	- -	0.6	155
4611	Cove Point, 3.3 miles east of..........		38 23.65	76 18.95	-3 18	-3 41	-3 48	-3 20	0.5	0.6	0.0	- -	0.4	320	0.0	- -	0.5	160
4616	Kenwood Beach, 1.5 miles northeast of...		38 31.1	76 28.9	-1 56	-2 41	-2 46	-2 37	0.2	0.4	0.0	- -	0.2	340	0.0	- -	0.3	160
4621	James Island, 3.4 miles west of........		38 31.5	76 25.2	-2 16	-2 39	-3 01	-2 02	0.5	0.4	0.0	- -	0.4	005	0.0	- -	0.3	175
4626	James Island, 2.5 miles WNW of.........		38 32.0	76 23.6	-2 31	-2 42	-2 18	-2 36	0.5	0.6	0.0	- -	0.4	000	0.0	- -	0.5	175
4631	Plum Point, 1.4 miles ESE of...........		38 36.75	76 28.65	-1 31	-1 37	-2 20	-2 04	0.2	0.7	0.0	- -	0.2	000	0.0	- -	0.6	155
4636	Sharps Island, 3.3 miles WNW of........		38 38.13	76 26.00	- - -	-1 30	- - -	-1 57	0.5	0.4	0.0	- -	0.4	345	0.0	- -	0.3	185
4641	Holland Point, 1.6 miles east of........		38 43.47	76 29.58	-1 05	-0 52	-1 20	-1 20	0.2	0.8	0.0	- -	0.2	010	0.0	- -	0.6	180
4646	Holland Point, 6.2 miles east of........		38 43.9	76 23.8	-2 02	-2 07	-1 31	-1 44	0.4	0.3	0.0	- -	0.3	355	0.0	- -	0.2	135
4651	Holland Point, 4.7 miles ENE of........		38 44.7	76 26.0	-0 50	-0 38	-1 05	-0 45	0.2	0.8	0.0	- -	0.2	340	0.0	- -	0.6	180
4656	Kent Point, 4 miles southwest of........		38 47.50	76 26.00	-1 03	-1 04	-1 11	-1 05	0.6	0.6	0.0	- -	0.5	025	0.C	- -	0.5	210
4661	Kent Point, 1.3 miles south of.........		38 49.00	76 21.85	-3 27	-3 38	-3 53	-3 47	0.6	0.5	0.0	- -	0.4	055	0.0	- -	0.4	235
4666	Horseshoe Point, 1.7 miles east of......		38 50.30	76 27.20	-0 52	-0 39	-0 49	-1 10	0.6	0.6	0.0	- -	0.5	005	0.0	- -	0.5	200
4671	Bloody Point Bar Light, 0.6 mi. NW of...	19	38 50.37	76 24.17	-0 08	-0 23	+0 02	-0 05	0.9	0.6	0.0	- -	0.7	035	0.0	- -	0.5	190
4676	Thomas Pt. Shoal Lt., 1.8 mi. SW of.....		38 52.50	76 27.70	-2 24	-2 27	-1 43	-2 17	0.5	0.4	0.0	- -	0.4	340	0.0	- -	0.3	190
4681	Thomas Pt. Shoal Lt., 0.4 mi. SE of.....		38 53.85	76 25.77	-0 14	-0 40	-1 06	-0 53	0.9	1.1	0.0	- -	0.7	010	0.0	- -	0.9	185
4686	Tolly Point, 1.6 miles east of..........		38 56.07	76 25.02	-0 03	-0 19	-0 32	-0 24	0.6	0.9	0.0	- -	0.5	355	0.0	- -	0.7	190
4691	Chesapeake Bay Bridge, main channel.....		38 59.50	76 23.10	+0 16	+0 08	-0 17	+0 13	0.9	1.1	0.0	- -	0.7	025	0.0	- -	0.9	230
4696	BALTIMORE HBR. APP. (off Sandy Point)...		39 00.78	76 22.10	Daily predictions						0.0	- -	0.8	025	0.0	- -	0.8	189
4701	Love Point, 1.3 miles ESE of...........		39 02.12	76 16.45	- - -	-0 39	-1 17	-0 57	0.3	0.4	0.0	- -	0.3	170	0.0	- -	0.3	345
4706	Love Point, 2.8 miles NNE of...........		39 04.7	76 16.3	Current weak and variable													
4711	Love Point, 2.5 miles north of..........		39 04.78	76 18.73	-0 48	+0 19	+0 27	-0 07	0.8	0.5	0.0	- -	0.6	055	0.0	- -	0.4	240
4716	Craighill Channel, NE of Mountain Pt....		39 04.88	76 23.67	+0 28	+0 40	+0 25	+0 34	0.8	0.9	0.0	- -	0.6	350	0.0	- -	0.7	175
4721	Craighill Angle, right outside quarter..		39 07.70	76 23.27	+0 12	+0 27	+0 34	+0 23	0.6	0.6	0.0	- -	0.5	345	0.0	- -	0.5	170
4726	Sevenfoot Knoll Light, 0.8 mi. NE of....		39 09.83	76 23.67	-0 07	+0 44	+0 44	+0 27	0.5	0.2	0.0	- -	0.4	345	0.0	- -	0.2	160
4731	Swan Point, 2.1 miles west of..........		39 08.75	76 19.67	+1 16	+1 01	+1 05	+0 55	0.6	0.8	0.0	- -	0.5	355	0.0	- -	0.6	220
4736	Swan Point, 1.6 miles northwest of......		39 09.75	76 18.28	+0 53	+0 44	+0 38	+0 57	0.8	0.9	0.0	- -	0.6	020	0.0	- -	0.7	215
4741	North Point, 2.5 miles northeast of.....	7	39 12.87	76 23.72	+1 25	+1 00	+0 53	+1 06	0.4	0.5	0.0	- -	0.3	035	0.0	- -	0.4	225
4746	Pooles Island, 4 miles southwest of.....		39 13.60	76 19.88	+0 59	+0 48	+0 56	+1 12	0.6	0.8	0.0	- -	0.5	025	0.0	- -	0.6	210
4751	Tolchester Beach, 0.4 mile WNW of.......		39 13.13	76 15.08	+1 52	+1 37	+1 28	+1 35	0.9	1.1	0.0	- -	0.7	015	0.0	- -	0.9	225
4756	Pooles Island, 0.8 mile south of........		39 15.7	76 16.4	+1 29	+1 24	+1 12	+1 20	0.9	1.2	0.0	- -	0.7	060	0.0	- -	1.0	255
4761	Miller Island, 1.5 miles ENE of.........	7	39 16.5	76 19.9	+0 11	+0 15	+0 37	+0 25	0.6	0.3	0.0	- -	0.5	000	0.0	- -	0.2	185
4766	Pooles Island, 1.4 miles east of........		39 17.2	76 13.9	+1 48	+1 31	+1 26	+1 26	1.0	1.5	0.0	- -	0.8	030	0.0	- -	1.2	215
4771	Robins Point, 0.7 mile ESE of..........	5	39 17.75	76 16.10	-0 03	-0 14	+0 37	-0 13	1.4	1.0	0.0	- -	1.1	025	0.0	- -	0.8	210
4776	Worton Point, 1.1 miles northwest of....		39 19.9	76 12.0	+1 43	+1 43	+1 38	+1 32	1.4	1.5	0.0	- -	1.1	040	0.0	- -	1.2	245
4781	Howell Point, 0.4 mile NNW of..........		39 22.6	76 06.9	+1 28	+1 24	+1 20	+1 18	1.1	1.1	0.0	- -	0.9	080	0.0	- -	0.9	245
4786	Grove Point, 0.8 mile northwest of......		39 24.0	76 03.1	+1 54	+1 58	+1 41	+1 39	1.0	1.0	0.0	- -	0.8	060	0.0	- -	0.8	235
4791	Turkey Point, 1.4 miles WSW of..........		39 26.25	76 02.08	+1 27	+1 19	+1 24	+1 22	0.8	0.9	0.0	- -	0.6	030	0.0	- -	0.7	220
4796	Spesutie Island, channel north of.......	7	39 28.83	76 04.90	+1 42	+1 20	+1 49	+1 40	0.8	0.6	0.0	- -	0.6	285	0.0	- -	0.5	100
4801	Rocky Point, 0.5 mile west of..........		39 29.2	76 00.2	+2 15	+2 15	+2 15	+2 15	0.6	0.8	0.0	- -	0.5	030	0.0	- -	0.6	190
4806	Red Point, 0.2 mile W of, Northeast R...	7	39 31.75	75 59.08	+1 42	+1 28	+1 57	+1 47	0.9	0.6	0.0	- -	0.7	- -	0.0	- -	0.5	- -
4811	Havre de Grace, Susquehanna River.......		39 33.13	76 05.08	Current weak and variable													

Endnotes can be found at the end of Table 2.

TABLE 2. - CURRENT DIFFERENCES AND OTHER CONSTANTS, 1983

NO.	PLACE	METER DEPTH	POSITION Lat.	POSITION Long.	TIME DIFFERENCES Min. before Flood	TIME DIFFERENCES Flood	TIME DIFFERENCES Min. before Ebb	TIME DIFFERENCES Ebb	SPEED RATIOS Flood	SPEED RATIOS Ebb	Minimum before Flood knots	Minimum before Flood deg.	Maximum Flood knots	Maximum Flood deg.	Minimum before Ebb knots	Minimum before Ebb deg.	Maximum Ebb knots	Maximum Ebb deg.
		ft	° ′ N	° ′ W	h. m.	h. m.	h. m.	h. m.			knots	deg.	knots	deg.	knots	deg.	knots	deg.
	MOBJACK BAY and PIANKATANK RIVER Time meridian, 75°W				on CHESAPEAKE BAY ENTRANCE, p.64													
5176	New Point Comfort, 1.5 miles west of....		37 17.7	76 18.4	-2 59	-1 58	-2 03	-2 48	0.6	0.3	0.0	- -	0.6	320	0.0	- -	0.5	130
5181	Bland Point, Piankatank River...........		37 31.8	76 21.9	-0 30	-0 30	-0 30	-0 30	0.4	0.1	0.0	- -	0.4	300	0.0	- -	0.2	125
5186	Doctor Point, 0.4 mile west of..........		37 31.1	76 27.0	-0 28	-0 58	-1 17	-0 37	0.4	0.3	0.0	- -	0.4	311	0.0	- -	0.4	142
	RAPPAHANNOCK RIVER																	
5191	Mosquito Point, 0.9 mile SSE of.........		37 35.72	76 21.08	+0 56	+1 31	+1 38	+0 41	0.7	0.6	0.0	- -	0.7	265	0.0	- -	0.8	090
5196	Mosquito Point..........................		37 35.8	76 21.5	+0 45	+0 45	+0 45	+0 45	0.6	0.4	0.0	- -	0.6	290	0.0	- -	0.6	115
5201	Orchard Point, 1.0 mile south of........		37 37.97	76 27.45	+0 49	+1 35	+1 50	+0 52	0.5	0.4	0.0	- -	0.5	270	0.0	- -	0.6	085
5206	Millenbeck Wharf, Corrotoman River......		37 39.9	76 29.0	- - -	- - -	- - -	- - -	- -	- -	0.0	- -	0.3	000	0.0	- -	0.3	186
5211	Towles Point............................		37 37.8	76 30.4	+1 06	+1 07	+2 10	+1 25	0.6	0.3	0.0	- -	0.6	274	0.0	- -	0.5	103
5216	Rogue Point, 0.8 mile WNW of............		37 40.28	76 33.20	- - -	+1 44	- - -	+1 27	0.6	0.4	0.0	- -	0.6	000	0.0	- -	0.6	195
5221	Waterview, 1.3 miles NNE of.............		37 44.95	76 35.92	+1 41	+1 59	+2 46	+2 10	0.7	0.4	0.0	- -	0.7	340	0.0	- -	0.6	155
5226	Tarpley Point, 1.5 miles south of.......		37 46.15	76 39.12	+2 16	+2 37	+3 20	+2 39	0.7	0.5	0.0	- -	0.7	300	0.0	- -	0.7	105
5231	Jones Point, 1.4 miles NNW of...........		37 48.03	76 41.58	+2 04	+2 23	+3 19	+2 27	1.1	0.6	0.0	- -	1.1	315	0.0	- -	0.9	105
5236	Sharps, 1.2 miles south of..............		37 48.18	76 41.92	+2 19	+2 46	+3 52	+3 01	0.9	0.5	0.0	- -	0.9	290	0.0	- -	0.8	095
5241	Bowlers Rock, 0.2 mile north of.........		37 49.58	76 44.00	+2 27	+2 41	+3 37	+2 50	1.0	0.7	0.0	- -	1.0	315	0.0	- -	1.1	135
5246	Accaceek Point, 0.3 mile southwest of...		37 52.52	76 46.40	+2 40	+2 48	+3 27	+3 13	1.2	0.7	0.0	- -	1.2	335	0.0	- -	1.0	150
5251	Tappahannock Bridge, 1.8 miles SE of....		37 55.10	76 49.27	+3 08	+3 07	+3 56	+3 28	1.4	0.9	0.0	- -	1.4	315	0.0	- -	1.3	105
5256	Tappahannock Bridge.....................		37 56.0	76 51.2	+3 40	+3 40	+3 40	+3 40	1.3	0.8	0.0	- -	1.3	315	0.0	- -	1.2	135
5261	Port Royal..............................		38 10.5	77 11.4	+6 10	+6 10	+6 10	+6 10	0.7	0.5	0.0	- -	0.7	310	0.0	- -	0.7	130
	POCOMOKE SOUND																	
5266	Pocomoke Sound Approach.................		37 38.00	75 57.90	- - -	+1 12	- - -	+1 31	0.7	0.5	0.0	- -	0.7	009	0.0	- -	0.7	196
5271	Pungoteague Creek entrance..............	6	37 40.48	75 51.90	- - -	- - -	- - -	- - -	- -	- -	0.0	- -	0.3	094	0.0	- -	0.2	254
5276	Watts Island, 4 miles south of..........	7	37 43.2	75 54.0	+0 17	+0 01	+0 27	-0 04	0.6	0.4	0.0	- -	0.6	027	0.0	- -	0.6	247
5281	Watts Island, 2.2 miles east of.........		37 47.9	75 50.6	+0 44	+1 10	+1 40	+1 03	1.3	0.9	0.0	- -	1.3	027	0.0	- -	1.3	209
5286	Pocomoke R., 0.5 mile below Shelltown...		37 58.3	75 38.7	+3 30	+3 00	+3 30	+3 00	1.1	0.6	0.0	- -	1.1	045	0.0	- -	0.9	170
	TANGIER SOUND																	
5291	Tangier Sound Light, 1.5 miles NE of....		37 48.5	75 57.4	+1 30	+2 02	+2 15	+1 39	1.2	0.7	0.0	- -	1.2	014	0.0	- -	1.1	220
5296	Jane's Island...........................		38 00.0	75 54.5	+3 40	+3 25	+3 40	+3 25	0.9	0.6	0.0	- -	0.9	000	0.0	- -	0.9	210
5301	Kedges Straits, off Solomons Lump.......		38 03.1	76 00.8	+0 20	+0 32	+0 50	+0 09	0.9	0.8	0.0	- -	0.9	104	0.0	- -	1.2	280
5306	Manokin River entrance..................		38 05.5	75 53.6	- - -	+2 04	- - -	+2 32	0.6	0.4	0.0	- -	0.6	019	0.0	- -	0.6	182
5311	Deal Island, 0.9 mile west of...........		38 08.2	75 58.7	+3 08	+3 26	+3 33	+3 15	0.9	0.7	0.0	- -	0.9	354	0.0	- -	1.0	179
5316	Frog Point, 1.6 miles south of..........		38 12.6	75 57.3	+3 19	+3 00	+3 41	+3 31	1.0	0.7	0.0	- -	1.0	048	0.0	- -	1.1	240
	Wicomico River																	
5321	Victor Point, 0.8 mile southwest of..		38 14.3	75 51.8	+3 10	+2 54	+3 49	+3 34	0.6	0.6	0.0	- -	0.6	034	0.0	- -	0.9	242
5326	Whitehaven..........................		38 15.9	75 47.5	+2 56	+3 45	+4 02	+3 01	1.1	0.7	0.0	- -	1.1	089	0.0	- -	1.1	284
5331	Whitehaven, 2.5 miles above.........	4	38 17.8	75 45.5	+3 00	+3 13	+3 45	+2 55	1.0	0.7	0.0	- -	1.0	006	0.0	- -	1.1	188
5336	Salisbury, 2 miles below............	4	38 20.4	75 38.3	+3 23	+3 31	+4 03	+3 28	0.6	0.5	0.0	- -	0.6	085	0.0	- -	0.8	258
5341	Sandy Point, Nanticoke River............		38 14.8	75 55.7	+3 14	+3 36	+4 21	+3 39	1.2	0.7	0.0	- -	1.2	000	0.0	- -	1.1	182

Endnotes can be found at the end of Table 2.

TABLE 2. - CURRENT DIFFERENCES AND OTHER CONSTANTS, 1983

NO.	PLACE	METER DEPTH	POSITION Lat.	Long.	TIME DIFFERENCES Min. before Flood	Flood	Min. before Ebb	Ebb	SPEED RATIOS Flood	Ebb	AVERAGE SPEEDS AND DIRECTIONS Minimum before Flood		Maximum Flood		Minimum before Ebb		Maximum Ebb	
		ft	° ' N	° ' W	h. m.	h. m.	h. m.	h. m.			knots	deg.	knots	deg.	knots	deg.	knots	deg.
	PORT ROYAL SOUND Time meridian, 75°W				on CHARLESTON HARBOR, p.82													
6726	Beaufort River..........................	15	32 24.2	80 40.3	+0 31	+0 45	+1 04	+0 21	0.4	0.4	0.1	286	0.9	012	0.0	- -	1.0	200
6731	Beaufort, Beaufort River................	12	32 25.8	80 40.6	+0 22	+0 44	+1 11	+0 05	0.6	0.5	0.0	- -	1.1	073	0.0	- -	1.1	257
6736	Beaufort Airport, Beaufort River........	15	32 27.0	80 39.8	+0 52	+1 05	+1 24	+0 56	0.5	0.4	0.0	- -	0.9	333	0.0	- -	0.9	152
6741	Brickyard Creek.........................	10	32 28.4	80 41.5	+1 15	-0 04	+2 53	+2 46	0.4	0.4	0.0	- -	0.8	351	0.0	- -	0.8	171
6746	Skull Creek, north entrance.............		32 15.8	80 44.5	-2 23	-1 54	-1 55	-2 26	0.4	0.5	0.0	- -	0.7	222	0.0	- -	1.2	035
6751	Daws Island, SE of, Broad River.........	15	32 18.1	80 43.5	+0 13	-0 29	+0 42	+0 19	0.7	0.7	0.0	- -	1.4	330	0.1	048	1.5	150
6756	Parris Island Lookout Tower, Broad River	15	32 18.7	80 42.4	+0 06	-0 41	+0 32	+0 04	0.6	0.6	0.0	- -	1.1	339	0.0	- -	1.4	152
6761	Daws Island, south of, Chechessee River.	15	32 17.2	80 44.6	-0 02	-0 56	+0 37	+0 19	0.5	0.6	0.1	232	1.0	317	0.1	048	1.3	142
6766	Lemon Island South, Chechessee River....	10	32 21.0	80 48.4	0 00	+0 45	+0 41	-0 14	0.5	0.6	0.0	- -	0.9	359	0.0	- -	1.3	175
6771	Broad River Bridge, S of, Broad River...	15	32 22.9	80 46.6	+0 19	-0 49	+0 52	-0 05	0.6	0.6	0.0	- -	1.1	341	0.0	- -	1.5	156
6776	Byrd Creek Entrance, SE of, Broad River.	12	32 27.4	80 49.1	+0 54	+0 17	+1 35	+0 40	0.5	0.4	0.0	- -	0.9	354	0.0	- -	1.0	174
6781	Little Barnwell I., E of, Whale Branch R	6	32 30.1	80 47.2	+1 08	+2 29	+1 57	+0 28	0.5	0.4	0.0	- -	1.0	354	0.0	- -	0.8	175
	CALIBOGUE SOUND				on SAVANNAH RIVER ENTRANCE, p.88													
6786	Braddock Point, SW of, Calibogue Sound..	10	32 06.3	80 50.2	-0 55	+0 04	+0 11	-1 17	1.0	0.8	0.0	- -	1.6	006	0.1	095	2.0	183
6791	Haig Point Light, NW of, Cooper River...	10	32 08.9	80 50.5	-1 31	-0 17	-0 25	-1 25	0.5	0.5	0.0	- -	0.8	278	0.0	- -	1.4	094
6796	Ramshorn Creek Light, E of, Cooper River	6	32 07.8	80 52.9	-0 34	-1 05	+0 30	-1 30	0.6	0.5	0.0	- -	1.0	280	0.0	- -	1.3	098
6801	Spanish Wells, Calibogue Sound..........	30	32 11.2	80 47.1	-0 54	+0 39	+0 27	-1 23	0.8	0.6	0.0	- -	1.4	028	0.0	- -	1.5	204
6806	Skull Creek, south entrance.............	10	32 13.4	80 47.1	-0 02	+2 45	+1 38	+0 42	0.5	0.4	0.0	- -	0.7	053	0.1	309	0.9	231
6811	MacKay Creek, south entrance............	10	32 13.2	80 47.4	-0 34	-0 09	+0 27	-0 39	0.4	0.4	0.0	- -	0.7	033	0.0	- -	1.2	212
	NEW and WRIGHT RIVERS																	
6816	Bloody Pt., 0.5 mile north of, New R....		32 05.3	80 52.8	-1 43	-0 12	-0 38	-2 26	0.8	0.5	0.0	- -	1.2	332	0.0	- -	1.3	147
6821	Bloody Pt., 0.5 mile west of, New R.....		32 04.9	80 53.0	-1 27	-0 33	-0 21	-1 39	1.1	0.7	0.0	- -	1.7	267	0.0	- -	1.8	092
6826	Wright R., 0.2 mile above Walls Cut.....		32 05.1	80 55.3	-1 18	-0 28	-0 23	-1 29	0.7	0.6	0.0	- -	1.2	332	0.0	- -	1.6	142
6831	Fields Cut <39>.........................		32 05	80 57			-1 45	-2 04		0.7					0.0	- -	1.9	042
6836	Walls Cut, Turtle Island................	6	32 04.9	80 55.0	-3 09	-1 09	-0 57	-3 18	0.6	0.4	0.2	087	1.0	294	0.1	060	0.9	100
6841	Daufuskie Landing Light, south of.......	10	32 06.1	80 53.9	-0 33	+0 52	+0 17	-1 58	0.9	0.7	0.0	- -	1.5	043	0.0	- -	1.7	226
	SAVANNAH RIVER																	
6851	Savannah Light, 1.2 miles southeast of..		31 57	80 40	See table 5.													
6861	SAVANNAH RIVER ENT. (between jetties)...		32 02.2	80 51.5	Daily predictions						0.0	- -	1.6	260	0.0	- -	2.6	082
6871	Fort Pulaski............................		32 02.2	80 54.1	+0 02	+0 39	+0 30	-0 04	1.1	1.2	0.0	- -	1.8	283	0.0	- -	3.1	098
6881	Fort Pulaski, 1.8 miles above...........		32 02.7	80 55.9	-0 15	+0 06	+0 14	-0 01	1.4	1.1	0.0	- -	2.2	316	0.0	- -	2.8	140
6891	Fort Pulaski, 4.8 miles above...........		32 04.5	80 58.6	-0 04	+0 19	+0 21	-0 29	1.3	1.2	0.0	- -	2.1	296	0.0	- -	3.0	116
6896	McQueen Island Cut......................	10	32 03.9	80 59.2	-3 19	-2 57	-0 49	-2 57	0.4	0.5	0.0	- -	0.7	251	0.0	- -	1.2	069
						-0 25			0.2				0.4	252				
						+0 55			0.5				0.8	249				
6901	Elba Island Cut, NE of, Savannah River..	10	32 04.4	80 57.9	-0 14	+0 03	-0 22	-0 27	0.9	1.0	0.1	202	1.4	288	0.1	183	2.6	104
6906	Elba Island, NE of, Savannah River......	10	32 05.4	80 59.6	+0 21	+0 28	-0 20	-0 40	0.7	1.0	0.0	- -	1.1	329	0.0	- -	2.5	149
6911	Elba Island, west of, Savannah River....	10	32 05.7	81 01.2	-0 03	+0 04	-0 15	-1 06	0.6	0.6	0.0	- -	0.9	219	0.0	- -	1.6	040
6921	Fig Island, north of, Back River........		32 05.1	81 03.0	-0 26	+0 54	-0 10	-1 13	0.6	0.6	0.0	- -	1.0	280	0.0	- -	1.5	094
6931	South Channel, western end..............		32 05.3	81 01.0	+0 02	+0 06	-0 18	-0 48	0.6	0.6	0.0	- -	1.0	300	0.0	- -	1.5	122

Endnotes can be found at the end of Table 2.

TABLE 2. - CURRENT DIFFERENCES AND OTHER CONSTANTS, 1983

NO.	PLACE	METER DEPTH	POSITION Lat.	POSITION Long.	TIME DIFFERENCES Min. before Flood	Flood	Min. before Ebb	Ebb	SPEED RATIOS Flood	Ebb	AVERAGE SPEEDS AND DIRECTIONS Minimum before Flood		Maximum Flood		Minimum before Ebb		Maximum Ebb	
		ft	° ' N	° ' W	h. m.	h. m.	h. m.	h. m.			knots	deg.	knots	deg.	knots	deg.	knots	deg.
	BOCA CIEGA BAY and ST. JOSEPH SOUND Time meridian, 90°W				on TAMPA BAY ENTRANCE, p.112													
8731	The Narrows (Indian Rocks Beach Br.)....		27 52.6	82 51.0	-0 55	-0 38	-0 55	-1 16	0.5	0.2	0.0	- -	0.6	180	0.0	- -	0.2	000
8741	Clearwater Pass, 0.2 mi. NE of Sand Key.		27 57.4	82 49.4	-2 56	-3 02	-1 56	-2 12	1.3	0.8	0.0	- -	1.3	179	0.0	- -	1.1	348
8751	Clearwater Harbor......................		27 57.9	82 48.4	- - -	- - -	- - -	- - -	- -	- -	0.0	- -	0.4	021	0.0	- -	0.3	214
8761	St. Joseph Sound, off..................		28 05.0	82 55.0	- - -	- - -	- - -	- - -	- -	- -	0.0	- -	0.4	018	0.0	- -	0.6	195
					on MIAMI HARBOR ENTRANCE, p.100													
8771	Anclote Anchorage......................		28 10.0	82 49.8	+2 42	+2 24	+2 28	+2 18	0.3	0.4	0.0	- -	0.6	006	0.0	- -	0.8	195
	APALACHEE BAY				on TAMPA BAY ENTRANCE, p.112													
8781	St. Marks River approach...............		30 02.8	84 10.8	-1 29	-0 59	+0 12	-0 30	0.6	0.4	0.0	- -	0.6	339	0.0	- -	0.5	170
8791	Four Mile Point, St. Marks River........		30 06.7	84 12.2	-0 45	-0 27	+0 46	-0 48	0.4	0.3	0.0	- -	0.4	358	0.0	- -	0.4	187
8801	St. Marks, St. Marks River..............		30 09.3	84 12.1	+1 06	+0 51	-0 01	+0 01	0.3	0.3	0.0	- -	0.3	067	0.0	- -	0.4	247
	PENSACOLA BAY Time meridian, 90°W				on MOBILE BAY ENTRANCE, p.118													
8811	Pensacola Bay entrance, midchannel......		30 20.1	87 18.0	-0 48	-0 31	+0 18	-1 15	1.1	1.2	0.0	- -	1.6	074	0.0	- -	1.8	256
	MOBILE BAY																	
8821	Main Ship Channel entrance..............		30 09.2	88 03.2	- - -	+0 50	- - -	+0 50	0.5	0.7	0.2	235	0.7	344	0.0	175	1.0	182
8831	MOBILE BAY ENTRANCE (off Mobile Point)..		30 13.6	88 02.1	Daily predictions						0.0	- -	1.4	027	0.0	- -	1.5	190
8841	Channel, 6 miles N of Mobile Point......		30 19.8	88 01.7	+0 15	+1 16	+1 26	+0 43	0.4	0.3	0.0	- -	0.6	032	0.0	- -	0.5	208
8851	Great Point Clear, channel west of......		30 29.4	88 01.1	Current weak and variable													
8861	Mobile River entrance...................		30 40.2	88 02.0	+5 36	+4 54	+2 44	+2 45	0.2	0.5	0.0	- -	0.3	333	0.0	- -	0.7	151
8871	Tensaw River entrance (bridge)..........		30 40.9	88 00.7	+2 04	+1 35	-1 00	-0 21	0.3	0.7	0.0	- -	0.4	029	0.0	- -	1.0	222
8881	Pass Aux Herons Entrance to Mississippi Sound <48>...		30 17.3	88 07.8	+0 09	+0 15	+0 22	+0 02	0.9	0.9	0.0	- -	1.3	068	0.0	- -	1.3	245
	MISSISSIPPI SOUND																	
8891	Pascagoula River highway bridge <27>....		30 22.3	88 33.8	- - -	+0 48	- - -	-1 02	0.9	0.8	0.0	- -	1.2	016	0.0	- -	1.2	201
	LOUISIANA COAST																	
8901	Quatre Bayoux Pass, Barataria Bay.......		29 18.6	89 51.1	+1 37	+1 04	+0 43	+0 06	0.9	0.9	0.0	- -	1.2	288	0.0	- -	1.3	103
8911	Pass Abel, Barataria Bay................		29 17.7	89 54.2	+0 53	+1 00	+0 13	-0 03	0.6	1.1	0.0	- -	0.9	317	0.0	- -	1.6	143
8921	Barataria Pass, Barataria Bay...........		29 16.3	89 56.9	+2 29	+1 23	+1 01	+0 19	1.1	0.9	0.0	- -	1.5	315	0.0	- -	1.3	120
8931	Barataria Bay, 1.1 mi. NE of Manilla....		29 26.2	89 57.6	+4 41	+3 35	+3 10	+4 12	0.3	0.3	0.0	- -	0.4	356	0.0	- -	0.5	160
8941	Caminada Pass, Barataria Bay............		29 11.9	90 02.8	+1 44	+0 03	+0 56	+0 38	1.1	1.0	0.0	- -	1.5	297	0.0	- -	1.5	118
8951	Seabrook Bridge, New Orleans <1>........		30 01.9	90 02.1	- - -	+7 37	- - -	+7 57	0.9	0.6	0.0	- -	1.2	350	0.0	- -	0.9	170

Endnotes can be found at the end of Table 2.

TABLE 2. - CURRENT DIFFERENCES AND OTHER CONSTANTS, 1983

NO.	PLACE	METER DEPTH	POSITION Lat.	POSITION Long.	TIME DIFFERENCES Min. before Flood	TIME DIFFERENCES Flood	TIME DIFFERENCES Min. before Ebb	TIME DIFFERENCES Ebb	SPEED RATIOS Flood	SPEED RATIOS Ebb	Minimum before Flood knots	Minimum before Flood deg.	Maximum Flood knots	Maximum Flood deg.	Minimum before Ebb knots	Minimum before Ebb deg.	Maximum Ebb knots	Maximum Ebb deg.
		ft	° ' N	° ' W	h. m.	h. m.	h. m.	h. m.			knots	deg.	knots	deg.	knots	deg.	knots	deg.
	LOUISIANA COAST Time meridian, 90°W				on GALVESTON BAY ENTRANCE, p.124													
8961	Cat Island Pass, Terrebonne Bay........		29 04.8	90 34.4	-2 45	-1 25	-2 40	-3 40	0.6	0.6	0.0	- -	1.1	013	0.0	- -	1.5	195
8971	Wine Island Pass........................		29 04.2	90 38.0	-4 46	-4 31	-5 13	-4 58	1.0	0.8	0.0	- -	1.7	325	0.0	- -	1.9	160
8981	Caillou Boca, Caillou Bay..............		29 03.5	90 48.5	-0 46	-0 09	+1 24	-0 46	0.8	0.3	0.0	- -	1.3	095	0.0	- -	0.7	264
8991	Calcasieu Pass..........................		29 46.4	93 20.7	-0 18	-0 43	+2 12	-0 44	1.0	1.0	0.0	- -	1.7	020	0.0	- -	2.3	205
9001	Calcasieu Pass, 35 miles south of.......		29 10.15	93 19.23	Current weak and variable													
9011	Calcasieu Pass, 67 miles south of <49>..		28 39.80	93 19.95	- - -	- - -	- - -	- - -	- -	- -	- -	- -	- -	- -	- -	- -	- -	- -
	TEXAS																	
	Sabine Pass																	
9021	Texas Point, 1.7 miles SSE of........		29 39.0	93 49.6	-0 14	-0 34	-0 15	-0 21	0.6	0.7	0.0	- -	1.1	335	0.0	- -	1.6	145
9031	Sabine, channel east of.............		29 43.3	93 51.7	-0 15	-0 02	-0 15	+0 04	0.9	0.7	0.0	- -	1.6	335	0.0	- -	1.7	140
9041	Port Arthur Canal entrance..........		29 45.6	93 54.1	+0 53	+1 34	+0 55	+1 12	0.5	0.6	0.0	- -	0.9	310	0.0	- -	1.3	110
9051	Mesquite Pt., La. Causeway bridge....		29 45.95	93 53.70	-0 21	-0 22	-0 20	-0 35	0.9	1.0	0.0	- -	1.6	330	0.0	- -	2.2	150
	GALVESTON BAY																	
9061	GALVESTON BAY ENT. (between jetties)....		29 20.8	94 42.3	Daily predictions						0.0	- -	1.7	299	0.0	- -	2.3	102
9071	Bolivar Roads, 0.5 mi. N of Ft. Point...		29 20.8	94 46.1	+0 25	+0 26	+1 15	+0 14	1.0	0.8	0.0	- -	1.7	287	0.0	- -	1.8	111
9081	Quarantine Station, 0.3 mile S of <27>..		29 19.8	94 46.7	- - -	-1 21	- - -	-0 59	0.6	0.4	0.0	- -	1.1	196	0.0	- -	0.8	009
9091	Galveston Channel, west end <27>.......		29 18.6	94 49.2	- - -	+0 01	- - -	-0 17	1.0	0.6	0.0	- -	1.7	272	0.0	- -	1.5	103
9101	Galveston Causeway RR. bridge..........		29 17.80	94 53.13	-0 24	-0 32	- - -	+0 05	0.4	0.4	0.0	- -	0.7	210	0.0	- -	0.8	025
9111	Houston Channel, W of Port Bolivar......		29 21.8	94 47.8	+0 18	+0 35	+1 18	+0 24	0.8	0.6	0.0	- -	1.3	330	0.0	- -	1.4	166
9121	Houston Ship Channel (Red Fish Bar).....		29 30.2	94 52.5	+3 11	+1 51	+0 12	+1 29	0.8	0.8	0.0	- -	1.3	321	0.0	- -	1.8	146
	TEXAS COAST																	
9131	Matagorda Channel (entrance jetty)......		28 25.3	96 19.4	-0 56	-0 28	-0 18	-1 14	1.2	0.8	0.0	- -	2.0	317	0.0	- -	1.9	142
9141	Aransas Pass............................		27 50.1	97 02.65	+0 34	+1 03	+0 50	-0 08	0.5	0.5	0.0	- -	0.9	312	0.0	- -	1.2	116
9151	Sabine Bank <54>......................		29 18.20	94 00.20	- - -	- - -	- - -	- - -	- -	- -	- -	- -	- -	- -	- -	- -	- -	- -
9161	Heald Bank, 28 miles SSE of <54>........		28 40.17	93 59.60	- - -	- - -	- - -	- - -	- -	- -	- -	- -	- -	- -	- -	- -	- -	- -
	PUERTO RICO Time meridian, 60°W				on VIEQUES PASSAGE, p.130													
9171	Punta Ostiones, 1.5 miles west of.......		18 05.2	67 13.6	-0 26	-0 52	-0 04	-0 35	1.7	1.3	0.0	- -	1.0	187	0.0	- -	0.9	001
9181	VIEQUES PASSAGE.........................		18 11.3	65 37.1	Daily predictions						0.0	- -	0.6	250	0.0	- -	0.7	057
9191	Vieques Sound...........................		18 15.87	65 34.20	-0 44	-1 16	-1 28	-1 05	0.7	0.9	0.0	- -	0.4	180	0.0	- -	0.6	355
9201	Largo Shoals, west of...................		18 19	65 35	-0 52	-1 28	-1 33	-1 08	0.7	1.0	0.0	- -	0.4	186	0.0	- -	0.7	330
9211	Ramos Cay, 0.3 mile SE of <1>..........		18 18.6	65 36.4	- - -	-0 42	- - -	-0 44	0.3	0.1	0.0	- -	0.2	120	0.0	- -	0.1	284
9221	Palominos Island, 0.9 mile SW of <13>...		18 20.1	65 34.8	- - -	- - -	- - -	-0 48	- -	0.7	- -	- -	- -	- -	- -	- -	0.5	307
9231	Fajardo Harbor (channel)................		18 20	65 37	-1 13	-1 52	-2 27	-1 45	0.5	1.6	0.0	- -	0.3	162	0.0	- -	1.1	339
9241	Isla Marina, 0.2 mile west of <1> <13>..		18 20.50	65 37.38	- - -	- - -	- - -	-2 06	- -	1.0	- -	- -	- -	- -	- -	- -	0.7	335
9251	Coronala Laja, 0.4 mile NW of <1> <13>..		18 21.6	65 37.3	- - -	- - -	- - -	-1 33	- -	0.4	- -	- -	- -	- -	- -	- -	0.3	000
9261	Pasaje de San Juan <1> <13>............		18 23.9	65 36.9	- - -	- - -	- - -	-1 15	- -	1.7	- -	- -	- -	- -	- -	- -	1.2	310
9271	Bahia de San Juan......................		18 27.23	66 06.6	Current weak and variable													
9281	Bahia de San Juan entrance <50>.........		18 28.3	66 07.6	- - -	- - -	- - -	- - -	- -	- -	- -	- -	- -	- -	- -	- -	- -	- -

Endnotes can be found at the end of Table 2.

ENDNOTES

< 1> The times of minimum before flood and ebb are indefinite.

< 2> Current speeds up to 9.0 knots have been observed in the vicinity of the Boilers.

< 3> Current turns westward just before the end of the flood.

< 4> Current tends to rotate counterclockwise, flood direction swinging from westward to southward.

< 5> Observations indicate that current floods about 11 hours and ebbs about 1 1/2 hours. Minimum before flood occurs about 4 1/2 hours earlier, maximum flood about 1 hour later, minimum before ebb about 1/2 hour later, and maximum ebb about 1 1/2 hours earlier than corresponding predictions at Portsmouth Harbor Entrance. Average ebb speed is less than 0.5 knot.

< 6> Current is variable; current speeds are usually less than 1 knot. Currents are strong in the entrance to Menemsha Pond.

< 7> In the open waters of Buzzards Bay, except in the entrance and off Penikese Island and West Island (see table-2, no. 1080-1190), the current is too weak and variable to be predicted.

< 8> The currents in Narragansett Bay have a pronounced irregularity which is evidenced at times during the month by a long period of approximate slack water preceding the flood, and at other times by a double flood of two distinct maximums of speed seperated by a period of lesser speed. These peculiarities appear to be somewhat unstable, consequently, flood currents differing from those predicted should be expected. The ebb current is fairly regular and the predictions for maximum ebb will usually agree closely with the current encountered.

< 9> At minimum flood, current sometimes ebbs for a short period.

<10> At minimum flood, current frequently ebbs for a short period.

<11> Flood is too weak to be predicted. Time difference gives mid-point of 4 hour stand of weak and variable current and time of maximum ebb.

<12> Inside breakwaters, in channel, the current is only 0.4 knot.

<13> Current seldom floods.

<14> Near Tongue Point, Bridgeport Harbor, the current is weak and irregular.

<15> The current on the Manhattan side of the channel is about 0.5 knot stronger, and on the Brooklyn side about 0.5 knot weaker, than at this station.

<16> The ebb or northerly current is weak and variable. East of the channel the current flows southward practically all the time, but with changing speed, the maximum speed being about the same as in mid-channel and occuring about the same time. On the Manhattan side, just off the piers, the flood or southerly current is weak and variable but the ebb or northerly current has an average maximum speed of about 2 knots which occurs about the time of maximum ebb at Hell Gate.

<17> Tidal current is weak, averaging about 0.1 knot at maximum.

<18> For maximum southward current only, the gates of the lock being closed to prevent northward flow. Apply difference and ratio to maximum ebb at The Narrows.

<19> Current is rotary, turning clockwise. Minimum current of 0.9 knot sets southwest about time of "Minimum before flood" at The Narrows. Minimum current of 0.5 knot sets northeast about 1 hour before "Minimum before ebb" at The Narrows.

<20> The values for the Hudson River are for the summer months, when the freshwater discharge is a minimum.

<21> In Roundout Creek entrance between lights, eddies on the flood make navigation difficult. Litle difficulty will be experienced on the ebb.

<22> Current does not flood.

<23> Current is rotary, turning clockwise. It flows northwest at times of "Minimum before flood" at The Narrows; northeast 1 hour after maximum flood; southeast 1 1/2 hours after "Minimum before ebb"; and southwest 2 hours after maximum ebb.

<24> Current is rotary, turning clockwise. Minimum current of 0.2 knot sets west about the time of "Minimum before flood" at The Narrows. Minimum current of 0.2 knot sets ENE about the time of "Minimum before ebb" at The Narrows.

<25> In Sandy Hook Bay (except in southern extremity) the current is weak.

<26> Tidal current is weak and rotary, averaging about 0.1 knot at maximum.

<27> The times of minimum before flood and ebb are variable.

<28> Current usually ebbs during period 3 hours before to 3 hours after maximum ebb. Flood is weak and variable.

<29> To obtain speeds in midchannel use speed ratio 0.8.

<30> Flood is usually weak and of short duration. A weak ebb or flood current occurs about 6 hours after maximum flood at Delaware Bay Entrance.

<31> Tidal current is weak and rotary, averaging less than 0.1 knot.

<32> Current tends to rotate clockwise. At times for "Minimum before flood" there may be a weak current flowing southward while at times for "Minimum before ebb" there may be a weak current flowing northward.

<33> Just off southernmost point, current turns about 1 hour earlier than in midchannel.

<34> Current tends to rotate clockwise. At times for "Minimum before flood" there may be a weak current flowing WSW while at times for "Minimum before ebb" there may be a weak current flowing ENE.

<35> Do not use difference or ratio for lesser maximum ebb current as it is weak and variable.

<36> Current tends to rotate clockwise. At times for "Minimum before flood" there may be a weak current flowing southwest, while at times for "Minimum before ebb" there may be a weak current flowing north.

<37> Flood usually flows northward, however, direction is variable.

<38> The combination of currents from Stono River and North Edisto River in the vicinity of the Southern S.A.L. Ry. bridge produces eight changes a day in direction of flow instead of the usual four. Approximate times of the minimums are as follows: current turns south about 2h 50m before flood begins and 3h 00m before ebb begins at Charleston Harbor; current north about 1h 10m after flood begins and 20 minutes before ebb begins at Charleston Harbor. Caution is advised when running north with a fair current as a cross current from the old channel of the Stono River is encountered at the south approach to the bridge.

<39> Flood is variable, current sometimes changing to ebb for a short time during the flood period.

<40> Due to changes in the waterway average speed values given are probably too large.

<41> Flood usually occurs in a southerly direction and the ebb in a northeastwardly direction.

<42> Flood is weak and variable.

<43> Current tends to rotate clockwise. At times for "Minimum before flood" there may be a weak current flowing northward while at times for "Minimum before ebb" there may be a weak current flowing southeastward.

<44> For greater ebb only.

<45> Tidal current is rotary, turning clockwise, with an average speed of about 0.3 knot.

<46> The strength of flood is usually about 2 knots. The speed ratio for strength of ebb is 0.8, except for an ebb speed at Tampa Bay entrance less than 1 knot or marked with an asterisk. In this case take the ebb speed at Johns Pass to be about 1 knot.

<47> For greater ebb. Lesser ebb is almost equal to greater ebb.

<48> Currents are materially affected by winds.

<49> Current is weak and variable. Current is somewhat rotary turning clockwise.

<50> Current is normally weak and variable, but winds may cause heavy swells.

<51> Minimum ebb is extremely weak, possibly flooding for a short period.

<52> Every other ebb phase exhibits a double ebb pattern. For single ebb phases use time differences and speed ratios of the first ebb.

<53> Ebb is weak and variable.

<54> Current is somewhat rotary, speed seldom exceeds 0.3 knot.

<55> Flood is weak and variable with speeds less than or equal to 0.2 knot. Minimums are indefinite.

<56> Turbulence with hazardous current speeds of 6 to 7 knots have been reported near the bridges in the canal. Extreme caution should be exercised.

CAUTION--During the first 2 hours of flood in channel north of Governers Island the current in Hudson River is still ebbing while during the first 1 1/2 hours of ebb in this channel the current in Hudson River is still flooding. (See Tidal Current Charts, New York Harbor.) At such times special care must be taken by large ships in navigating this channel.

ROTARY TIDAL CURRENTS

Station No.	Depth (ft.)	0.0	0.5	1.0	1.5	2.0	2.5	3.0	3.5	4.0	4.5	5.0	5.5	6.0	6.5	7.0	7.5	8.0	8.5	9.0	9.5	10.0	10.5	11.0	11.5	12.0	
		(Time: Hours after Minimum before Flood at Boston Harbor)																									
393	10	0.03	0.22	0.23	0.24	0.23	0.26	0.25	0.27	0.32	0.33	0.33	0.32	0.31	0.28	0.29	0.28	0.27	0.27	0.28	0.27	0.26	0.27	0.23	0.21	0.21	knots
		265	266	265	268	270	268	282	303	319	327	333	340	357	025	067	068	070	074	073	080	076	079	073	073	051	degrees
395	10	0.30	0.40	0.45	0.43	0.46	0.48	0.50	0.53	0.51	0.52	0.50	0.51	0.51	0.52	0.49	0.50	0.48	0.52	0.49	0.46	0.46	0.43	0.40	0.40	0.36	knots
		210	261	258	247	248	247	262	280	280	304	340	345	009	044	049	061	068	070	074	079	082	081	090	081	123	degrees
397	10	0.29	0.30	0.30	0.31	0.32	0.34	0.34	0.35	0.37	0.36	0.35	0.35	0.34	0.34	0.34	0.35	0.34	0.36	0.35	0.34	0.36	0.35	0.34	0.32	0.18	knots
		200	209	212	222	229	243	247	259	265	268	284	331	002	018	042	056	058	064	065	075	080	085	086	095	132	degrees
399	10	0.50	0.49	0.52	0.55	0.56	0.57	0.54	0.53	0.55	0.54	0.55	0.55	0.52	0.50	0.52	0.50	0.49	0.51	0.51	0.51	0.50	0.51	0.49	0.50	0.49	knots
		138	140	220	243	284	260	252	241	250	244	240	228	211	160	078	062	081	093	085	093	091	087	095	116	130	degrees
401	10	0.20	0.20	0.21	0.22	0.24	0.23	0.25	0.25	0.26	0.24	0.26	0.25	0.24	0.24	0.23	0.24	0.23	0.22	0.21	0.21	0.21	0.20	0.20	0.20	0.20	knots
		306	342	340	244	228	232	223	232	200	210	216	271	290	351	357	051	059	048	045	028	037	052	028	035	011	degrees
403	10	0.42	0.44	0.43	0.45	0.46	0.46	0.46	0.47	0.48	0.48	0.49	0.46	0.48	0.30	0.50	0.50	0.49	0.48	0.47	0.47	0.47	0.47	0.45	0.42	0.41	knots
		221	223	214	221	213	211	215	219	219	227	235	230	221	254	019	015	009	357	052	053	055	070	135	193	206	degrees
405	10	0.42	0.44	0.45	0.45	0.47	0.50	0.46	0.47	0.45	0.44	0.44	0.40	0.45	0.47	0.44	0.44	0.47	0.44	0.42	0.42	0.43	0.47	0.40	0.43	0.45	knots
		213	197	193	182	175	135	178	183	222	247	267	306	330	346	328	344	335	327	334	341	337	338	306	274	240	degrees
417	15	0.11	0.26	0.51	0.53	0.55	0.52	0.50	0.54	0.47	0.50	0.46	0.45	0.46	0.45	0.48	0.51	0.57	0.62	0.66	0.67	0.64	0.62	0.51	0.40	0.25	knots
		191	292	295	304	303	312	308	319	313	331	354	358	010	030	046	059	089	108	109	122	121	119	132	129	134	degrees
419	10	0.30	0.30	0.38	0.39	0.38	0.36	0.37	0.37	0.36	0.36	0.35	0.34	0.30	0.20	0.19	0.25	0.30	0.33	0.35	0.36	0.38	0.38	0.36	0.36	0.32	knots
		251	307	331	342	332	336	343	341	343	350	347	006	029	081	114	138	146	160	165	172	173	173	190	203	233	degrees
461	10	0.34	0.39	0.41	0.42	0.35	0.35	0.34	0.37	0.39	0.38	0.35	0.35	0.32	0.32	0.36	0.40	0.41	0.35	0.31	0.32	0.31	0.27	0.07	0.20	0.25	knots
		267	264	261	261	259	251	235	230	220	209	199	197	146	087	069	070	071	046	030	018	024	046	024	269	272	degrees
489	10	0.33	0.35	0.36	0.35	0.36	0.34	0.40	0.39	0.40	0.42	0.45	0.37	0.35	0.32	0.35	0.37	0.34	0.33	0.35	0.35	0.34	0.03	0.29	0.31	0.24	knots
		007	010	024	034	060	343	348	007	063	025	095	064	081	103	102	103	104	117	135	139	158	215	339	353	355	degrees
*513	10	0.17	0.16	0.18	0.16	0.13	0.17	0.19	0.21	0.22	0.18	0.19	0.21	0.18	0.22	0.25	0.24	0.26	0.27	0.28	0.28	0.29	0.28	0.25	0.23	0.18	knots
		086	095	090	088	090	095	090	093	083	083	081	077	082	072	072	070	069	067	070	070	073	077	085	082	085	degrees
565	10	0.22	0.27	0.29	0.09	0.37	0.40	0.44	0.45	0.44	0.44	0.44	0.48	0.50	0.51	0.47	0.42	0.39	0.37	0.37	0.37	0.36	0.32	0.30	0.23	0.10	knots
		217	199	209	199	052	061	074	077	066	047	032	025	029	041	061	077	082	076	071	070	070	064	069	070	085	degrees
565	20	0.15	0.22	0.24	0.05	0.28	0.30	0.31	0.36	0.34	0.33	0.35	0.36	0.40	0.43	0.39	0.30	0.28	0.34	0.35	0.34	0.32	0.29	0.23	0.16	0.09	knots
		271	238	231	251	030	031	076	073	064	040	029	021	021	030	049	067	067	058	056	050	050	047	044	032	005	degrees
617	10	0.20	0.23	0.27	0.45	0.41	0.40	0.35	0.30	0.28	0.32	0.34	0.35	0.33	0.29	0.29	0.32	0.33	0.33	0.33	0.32	0.32	0.30	0.26	0.24	0.24	knots
		246	232	282	351	019	025	024	009	355	343	338	339	345	007	013	008	002	356	345	336	333	331	331	320	305	degrees
617	20	0.15	0.19	0.20	0.33	0.34	0.30	0.24	0.21	0.22	0.28	0.31	0.33	0.32	0.29	0.26	0.27	0.28	0.29	0.31	0.29	0.26	0.21	0.17	0.14	0.10	knots
		220	214	232	001	020	027	024	003	345	340	333	332	331	351	009	008	003	350	339	334	329	322	322	315	254	degrees

* In Reserved Channel, the tidal current is weak, averaging less than 0.1 knot. During a 7-day observation period, the total current set was consistently eastward.

TABLE 3.—VELOCITY OF CURRENT AT ANY TIME

EXPLANATION

Though the predictions in this publication give only the slacks and maximum currents, the velocity of the current at any intermediate time can be obtained approximately by the use of this table. Directions for its use are given below the table.

Before using the table for a place listed in table 2, the predictions for the day in question should first be obtained by means of the differences and ratios given in table 2.

The examples below follow the numbered steps in the directions.

Example 1.—Find the velocity of the current in The Race at 6:00 on a day when the predictions which immediately precede and follow 6:00 are as follows:

(1)	Slack Water	Maximum (Flood)	
	Time	*Time*	*Velocity*
	4:18	7:36	3.2 knots

Directions under the table indicate table A is to be used for this station.

(2) Interval between slack and maximum flood is 7:36−4:18=3^h18^m. Column heading nearest to 3^h18^m is 3^h20^m.

(3) Interval between slack and time desired is 6:00−4:18=1^h42^m. Line labeled 1^h40^m is nearest to 1^h42^m.

(4) Factor in column 3^h20^m and on line 1^h40^m is 0.7. The above flood velocity of 3.2 knots multiplied by 0.7 gives a flood velocity of 2.24 knots (or 2.2 knots, since one decimal is sufficient) for the time desired.

Example 2.—Find the velocity of the current in the Harlem River at Broadway Bridge at 16:30 on a day when the predictions (obtained using the difference and ratio in table 2) which immediately precede and follow 16:30 are as follows:

(1)	Maximum (Ebb)		Slack Water
	Time	*Velocity*	*Time*
	13:49	2.5 knots	17:25

Directions under the table indicate table B is to be used, since this station in table 2 is referred to Hell Gate.

(2) Interval between slack and maximum ebb is 17:25−13:49=3^h36^m. Hence, use column headed 3^h40^m.

(3) Interval between slack and time desired is 17:25−16:30=0^h55^m. Hence, use line labeled 1^h00^m.

(4) Factor in column 3^h40^m and on line 1^h00^m is 0.5. The above ebb velocity of 2.5 knots multiplied by 0.5 gives an ebb velocity of 1.2 knots for the desired time.

When the interval between slack and maximum current is greater than 5^h40^m, enter the table with one-half the interval between slack and maximum current and one-half the interval between slack and the desired time and use the factor thus found.

Table A

Interval between slack and desired time	Interval between slack and maximum current													
	h. m. 1 20	*h. m.* 1 40	*h. m.* 2 00	*h. m.* 2 20	*h. m.* 2 40	*h. m.* 3 00	*h. m.* 3 20	*h. m.* 3 40	*h. m.* 4 00	*h. m.* 4 20	*h. m.* 4 40	*h. m.* 5 00	*h. m.* 5 20	*h. m.* 5 40
h. m.	*f.*	*f.*	*f.*	*f.*	*f.*	*f.*	*f.*	*f.*	*f.*	*f.*	*f.*	*f.*	*f.*	*f.*
0 20	0.4	0.3	0.3	0.2	0.2	0.2	0.2	0.1	0.1	0.1	0.1	0.1	0.1	0.1
0 40	0.7	0.6	0.5	0.4	0.4	0.3	0.3	0.3	0.3	0.2	0.2	0.2	0.2	0.2
1 00	0.9	0.8	0.7	0.6	0.6	0.5	0.5	0.4	0.4	0.4	0.3	0.3	0.3	0.3
1 20	1.0	1.0	0.9	0.8	0.7	0.6	0.6	0.5	0.5	0.5	0.4	0.4	0.4	0.4
1 40	......	1.0	1.0	0.9	0.8	0.8	0.7	0.7	0.6	0.6	0.5	0.5	0.5	0.4
2 00	......	......	1.0	1.0	0.9	0.9	0.8	0.8	0.7	0.7	0.6	0.6	0.6	0.5
2 20	......	......	......	1.0	1.0	0.9	0.9	0.8	0.8	0.7	0.7	0.7	0.6	0.6
2 40	......	......	......	......	1.0	1.0	1.0	0.9	0.9	0.8	0.8	0.7	0.7	0.7
3 00	......	......	......	......	......	1.0	1.0	1.0	0.9	0.9	0.8	0.8	0.8	0.7
3 20	......	......	......	......	......	......	1.0	1.0	1.0	0.9	0.9	0.9	0.8	0.8
3 40	......	......	......	......	......	......	......	1.0	1.0	1.0	0.9	0.9	0.9	0.9
4 00	......	......	......	......	......	......	......	......	1.0	1.0	1.0	1.0	0.9	0.9
4 20	......	......	......	......	......	......	......	......	......	1.0	1.0	1.0	1.0	0.9
4 40	......	......	......	......	......	......	......	......	......	......	1.0	1.0	1.0	1.0
5 00	......	......	......	......	......	......	......	......	......	......	......	1.0	1.0	1.0
5 20	......	......	......	......	......	......	......	......	......	......	......	......	1.0	1.0
5 40	......	......	......	......	......	......	......	......	......	......	......	......	......	1.0

Table B

Interval between slack and desired time	Interval between slack and maximum current													
	h. m. 1 20	*h. m.* 1 40	*h. m.* 2 00	*h. m.* 2 20	*h. m.* 2 40	*h. m.* 3 00	*h. m.* 3 20	*h. m.* 3 40	*h. m.* 4 00	*h. m.* 4 20	*h. m.* 4 40	*h. m.* 5 00	*h. m.* 5 20	*h. m.* 5 40
h. m.	*f.*	*f.*	*f.*	*f.*	*f.*	*f.*	*f.*	*f.*	*f.*	*f.*	*f.*	*f.*	*f.*	*f.*
0 20	0.5	0.4	0.4	0.3	0.3	0.3	0.3	0.3	0.2	0.2	0.2	0.2	0.2	0.2
0 40	0.8	0.7	0.6	0.5	0.5	0.5	0.4	0.4	0.4	0.4	0.3	0.3	0.3	0.3
1 00	0.9	0.8	0.8	0.7	0.7	0.6	0.6	0.5	0.5	0.5	0.4	0.4	0.4	0.4
1 20	1.0	1.0	0.9	0.8	0.8	0.7	0.7	0.6	0.6	0.6	0.5	0.5	0.5	0.5
1 40	......	1.0	1.0	0.9	0.9	0.8	0.8	0.7	0.7	0.7	0.6	0.6	0.6	0.6
2 00	......	......	1.0	1.0	0.9	0.9	0.9	0.8	0.8	0.7	0.7	0.7	0.7	0.6
2 20	......	......	......	1.0	1.0	1.0	0.9	0.9	0.8	0.8	0.8	0.7	0.7	0.7
2 40	......	......	......	......	1.0	1.0	1.0	0.9	0.9	0.9	0.8	0.8	0.8	0.7
3 00	......	......	......	......	......	1.0	1.0	1.0	0.9	0.9	0.9	0.9	0.8	0.8
3 20	......	......	......	......	......	......	1.0	1.0	1.0	1.0	0.9	0.9	0.9	0.8
3 40	......	......	......	......	......	......	......	1.0	1.0	1.0	1.0	0.9	0.9	0.9
4 00	......	......	......	......	......	......	......	......	1.0	1.0	1.0	1.0	0.9	0.9
4 20	......	......	......	......	......	......	......	......	......	1.0	1.0	1.0	1.0	0.9
4 40	......	......	......	......	......	......	......	......	......	......	1.0	1.0	1.0	1.0
5 00	......	......	......	......	......	......	......	......	......	......	......	1.0	1.0	1.0
5 20	......	......	......	......	......	......	......	......	......	......	......	......	1.0	1.0
5 40	......	......	......	......	......	......	......	......	......	......	......	......	......	1.0

Use table A for all places except those listed below for table B.
Use table B for Cape Cod Canal, Hell Gate, Chesapeake and Delaware Canal and all stations in table 2 which are referred to them.

1. From predictions find the time of slack water and the time and velocity of maximum current (flood or ebb), one of which is immediately before and the other after the time for which the velocity is desired.
2. Find the interval of time between the above slack and maximum current, and enter the top of table A or B with the interval which most nearly agrees with this value.
3. Find the interval of time between the above slack and the time desired, and enter the side of table A or B with the interval which most nearly agrees with this value.
4. Find, in the table, the factor corresponding to the above two intervals, and multiply the maximum velocity by this factor. The result will be the approximate velocity at the time desired.

TABLE 4.—DURATION OF SLACK

The predicted times of slack water given in this publication indicate the instant of zero velocity, which is only momentary. There is a period each side of slack water, however, during which the current is so weak that for practical purposes it may be considered as negligible.

The following tables give, for various maximum currents, the approximate period of time during which weak currents not exceeding 0.1 to 0.5 knot will be encountered. This duration includes the last of the flood or ebb and the beginning of the following ebb or flood, that is, half of the duration will be before and half after the time of slack water.

Table A should be used for all places *except* those listed below for table B.

Table B should be used for **Cape Cod Canal, Hell Gate, Chesapeake and Delaware Canal,** and all stations in table 2 which are referred to them.

Duration of weak current near time of slack water

TABLE A

Maximum current	Period with a velocity not more than—				
	0.1 knot	0.2 knot	0.3 knot	0.4 knot	0.5 knot
Knots	*Minutes*	*Minutes*	*Minutes*	*Minutes*	*Minutes*
1.0	23	46	70	94	120
1.5	15	31	46	62	78
2.0	11	23	35	46	58
3.0	8	15	23	31	38
4.0	6	11	17	23	29
5.0	5	9	14	18	23
6.0	4	8	11	15	19
7.0	3	7	10	13	16
8.0	3	6	9	11	14
9.0	3	5	8	10	13
10.0	2	5	7	9	11

TABLE B

Maximum current	Period with a velocity not more than—				
	0.1 knot	0.2 knot	0.3 knot	0.4 knot	0.5 knot
Knots	*Minutes*	*Minutes*	*Minutes*	*Minutes*	*Minutes*
1.0	13	28	46	66	89
1.5	8	18	28	39	52
2.0	6	13	20	28	36
3.0	4	8	13	18	22
4.0	3	6	9	13	17
5.0	3	5	8	10	13

When there is a difference between the velocities of the maximum flood and ebb preceding and following the slack for which the duration is desired, it will be sufficiently accurate for practical purposes to find a separate duration for each maximum velocity and take the average of the two as the duration of the weak current.

TABLE 5.—ROTARY TIDAL CURRENTS

EXPLANATION

Offshore and in some of the wider indentations of the coast, the tidal current is quite different from that found in the more protected bays and rivers. In these inside waters the tidal current is of the reversing type. It sets in one direction for a period of about 6 hours after which it ceases to flow momentarily and then sets in the opposite direction during the following 6 hours. Offshore the current, not being confined to a definite channel, changes its direction continually and never comes to a slack, so that in a tidal cycle of about 12½ hours it will have set in all directions of the compass. This type of current is therefore called a *rotary current.*

A characteristic feature of the rotary current is the absence of slack water. Although the current generally varies from hour to hour, this variation from greatest current to least current and back again to greatest current does not give rise to a period of slack water. When the velocity of the rotary tidal current is least, it is known as the minimum current, and when it is greatest it is known as the maximum current. The minimum and maximum velocities of the rotary current are thus related to each other in the same way as slack and strength of current, a minimum velocity of the current following a maximum velocity by an interval of about 3 hours and being followed in turn by another maximum after a further interval of 3 hours.

In the following table there are given for a number of offshore stations the direction and average velocity of the rotary tidal current for each hour of the tidal cycle referred to predictions for a station in table 1. All times are eastern standard for the 75th meridian.

The velocities given in the table are average. The Moon at new, full, or perigee tends to increase the velocities 15 to 20 percent above average. When perigee occurs at or near the time of new or full Moon the velocities will be 30 to 40 percent above average. Quadrature and apogee tend to decrease the velocities below average by 15 to 20 percent. When apogee occurs at or near quadrature they will be 30 to 40 percent below average. The velocities will be about average when apogee occurs at or near the time of new or full Moon and also when perigee occurs at or near quadrature. (See table of astronomical data.)

The direction of the current is given in degrees, *true*, reading clockwise from 0° at north, and is the direction *toward* which the water is flowing.

The velocities and directions are for the tidal current only and do not include the effect of winds. When a wind is blowing, a wind-driven current will be set up which will be in addition to the tidal current, and the actual current encountered will be a combination of the wind-driven current and tidal current. See the chapters on "Wind-Driven Currents" and "The Combination of Currents."

As an example, in the following table the current at Nantucket Shoals is given for each hour after maximum flood at Pollock Rip Channel. Suppose it is desired to find the direction and velocity of the current at Nantucket Shoals at 3:15 p.m. (15:15) eastern standard time on a day when maximum flood at Pollock Rip Channel is predicted in table 1 to occur at 13:20 eastern standard time. The desired time is therefore about 2 hours after maximum flood at Pollock Rip Channel, and from the following table the tidal current at Nantucket Shoals at this time is setting 15° *true* with an average velocity of 0.8 knot. If this day is near the time of new Moon and about halfway between apogee and perigee, then the distance effect of the Moon will be nil and the phase effect alone will operate to increase the velocity by about 15 percent, to 0.9 knot. If a wind has been blowing, determine the direction and velocity of the wind-driven current from the chapter on "Wind-Driven Currents" and combine it with the above tidal current as explained in the chapter on "The Combination of Currents."

Caution.—Velocities from 1½ to 3 knots have been observed at most of the stations in this table. Near Diamond Shoal Light a velocity of 4 knots has been recorded.

At some offshore stations, such as near the entrance to Chesapeake Bay, the tidal current is directed alternately toward and away from the bay entrance with intervening periods of slack water, so that it is essentially a reversing current. For such places, differences for predicting are given in table 2.

Georges Bank
Lat. 41°50′ N., long. 66°37′ W.

Time		Direction (true)	Velocity
		Degrees	*Knots*
Hours after maximum flood at Pollock Rip Channel, see page 28	0	285	0.9
	1	304	1.1
	2	324	1.2
	3	341	1.1
	4	10	1.0
	5	43	0.9
	6	89	1.0
	7	127	1.3
	8	147	1.6
	9	172	1.4
	10	197	0.9
	11	232	0.8

Georges Bank
Lat. 41°54′ N., long. 67°08′ W.

Time		Direction (true)	Velocity
		Degrees	*Knots*
Hours after maximum flood at Pollock Rip Channel, see page 28	0	298	1.1
	1	325	1.4
	2	344	1.5
	3	0	1.2
	4	33	0.7
	5	82	0.8
	6	118	1.1
	7	138	1.5
	8	153	1.2
	9	178	1.1
	10	208	0.9
	11	236	0.8

Georges Bank
Lat. 41°48′ N., long. 67°34′ W.

Time		Direction (true)	Velocity
		Degrees	*Knots*
Hours after maximum flood at Pollock Rip Channel, see page 28	0	325	1.5
	1	332	2.1
	2	342	2.0
	3	358	1.3
	4	35	0.7
	5	99	0.8
	6	126	1.3
	7	150	2.0
	8	159	1.9
	9	169	1.7
	10	197	1.2
	11	275	0.9

Georges Bank
Lat. 41°42′ N., long. 67°37′ W.

Time		Direction (true)	Velocity
		Degrees	*Knots*
Hours after maximum flood at Pollock Rip Channel, see page 28	0	316	1.1
	1	341	1.3
	2	356	1.0
	3	16	0.8
	4	43	0.6
	5	92	0.8
	6	122	1.0
	7	146	1.1
	8	170	1.1
	9	195	1.0
	10	215	1.0
	11	272	0.9

Georges Bank
Lat. 41°41′ N., long. 67°49′ W.

Time		Direction (true)	Velocity
		Degrees	*Knots*
Hours after maximum flood at Pollock Rip Channel, see page 28	0	318	1.6
	1	320	1.8
	2	325	1.4
	3	330	0.8
	4	67	0.3
	5	111	0.9
	6	117	1.5
	7	126	1.7
	8	144	1.7
	9	160	1.1
	10	242	0.8
	11	202	1.2

Georges Bank
Lat. 41°30′ N., long. 68°07′ W.

Time		Direction (true)	Velocity
		Degrees	*Knots*
Hours after maximum flood at Pollock Rip Channel, see page 28	0	312	1.5
	1	338	1.7
	2	346	1.5
	3	14	1.1
	4	59	0.9
	5	99	0.9
	6	123	1.3
	7	144	1.7
	8	160	1.6
	9	187	1.3
	10	244	1.0
	11	274	1.1

Georges Bank
Lat. 41°29′ N., long. 67°04′ W.

Time		Direction (true)	Velocity
		Degrees	*Knots*
Hours after maximum flood at Pollock Rip Channel, see page 28	0	277	1.0
	1	302	1.2
	2	329	1.4
	3	348	1.3
	4	15	1.2
	5	48	1.1
	6	85	1.2
	7	122	1.4
	8	145	1.5
	9	166	1.3
	10	194	1.2
	11	223	1.1

Georges Bank
Lat. 41°14′ N., long. 67°38′ W.

Time		Direction (true)	Velocity
		Degrees	*Knots*
Hours after maximum flood at Pollock Rip Channel, see page 28	0	305	1.4
	1	332	1.6
	2	355	1.6
	3	15	1.4
	4	38	1.1
	5	77	0.9
	6	112	1.2
	7	141	1.6
	8	162	1.6
	9	187	1.5
	10	214	1.4
	11	252	1.2

Georges Bank
Lat. 41°13′ N., long. 68°20′ W.

Time		Direction (true)	Velocity
		Degrees	*Knots*
Hours after maximum flood at Pollock Rip Channel, see page 28	0	319	1.5
	1	332	2.0
	2	345	1.4
	3	9	0.8
	4	42	0.6
	5	80	0.7
	6	118	1.0
	7	138	1.3
	8	154	1.4
	9	169	1.5
	10	188	1.3
	11	236	0.9

Georges Bank
Lat. 40°48′ N., long. 67°40′ W.

Time		Direction (true)	Velocity
		Degrees	*Knots*
Hours after maximum flood at Pollock Rip Channel, see page 28	0	304	0.9
	1	340	0.9
	2	353	0.8
	3	29	0.6
	4	56	0.6
	5	83	0.6
	6	107	0.9
	7	140	1.0
	8	156	1.0
	9	175	0.9
	10	202	0.8
	11	245	0.8

Georges Bank
Lat. 40°49′ N., long. 68°34′ W.

Time		Direction (true)	Velocity
		Degrees	*Knots*
Hours after maximum flood at Pollock Rip Channel, see page 28	0	301	1.2
	1	326	1.5
	2	345	1.4
	3	8	1.1
	4	36	0.8
	5	69	0.8
	6	106	1.0
	7	139	1.4
	8	153	1.5
	9	175	1.4
	10	201	1.1
	11	237	0.9

Great South Channel, Georges Bank
Lat. 40°31′ N., long. 68°47′ W.

Time		Direction (true)	Velocity
		Degrees	*Knots*
Hours after maximum flood at Pollock Rip Channel, see page 28	0	320	0.7
	1	331	0.9
	2	342	1.1
	3	3	1.0
	4	23	0.8
	5	63	0.4
	6	129	0.7
	7	140	0.9
	8	164	1.0
	9	179	1.0
	10	190	0.8
	11	221	0.6

Nantucket Shoals
Lat. 40°37′ N., long. 69°37′ W.

Time: Hours after maximum flood at Pollock Rip Channel, see page 28	Direction (true)	Velocity
	Degrees	*Knots*
0	323	0.6
1	355	0.7
2	15	0.8
3	38	0.8
4	55	0.8
5	85	0.7
6	125	0.6
7	162	0.7
8	192	0.8
9	212	0.8
10	232	0.8
11	257	0.7

Great South Channel, Georges Bank
Lat. 41°10′ N., long. 68°56′ W.

Time: Hours after maximum flood at Pollock Rip Channel, see page 28	Direction (true)	Velocity
	Degrees	*Knots*
0	318	0.5
1	349	0.7
2	352	1.1
3	356	1.0
4	359	0.7
5	18	0.4
6	108	0.4
7	157	0.7
8	165	1.0
9	173	1.0
10	180	0.8
11	204	0.6

Davis Bank, Nantucket Shoals, 15 miles SE. of Nantucket I.
Lat. 41°07′ N., long. 69°41′ W.

Time: Hours after maximum flood at Pollock Rip Channel, see page 28	Direction (true)	Velocity
	Degrees	*Knots*
0	15	1.5
1	28	2.1
2	32	2.4
3	35	2.1
4	37	1.1
5	128	0.4
6	197	1.2
7	204	1.9
8	205	2.2
9	206	2.2
10	213	1.6
11	307	0.7

Davis Bank, Nantucket Shoals (west), 15 miles SE. of Nantucket I.
Lat. 41°03′ N., long. 69°47′ W.

Time: Hours after maximum flood at Pollock Rip Channel, see page 28	Direction (true)	Velocity
	Degrees	*Knots*
0	346	0.9
1	28	1.2
2	47	1.3
3	73	1.1
4	103	0.8
5	132	0.9
6	182	0.8
7	215	1.2
8	240	1.1
9	251	0.9
10	267	0.7
11	302	0.7

Davis Bank, Nantucket Shoals (middle), 17.5 miles SE. of Nantucket I.
Lat. 41°02′ N., long. 69°43′ W.

Time: Hours after maximum flood at Pollock Rip Channel, see page 28	Direction (true)	Velocity
	Degrees	*Knots*
0	23	0.8
1	27	1.5
2	28	1.9
3	29	1.8
4	46	1.1
5	115	0.4
6	191	1.2
7	202	1.9
8	215	1.7
9	225	1.5
10	233	0.9
11	270	0.2

Davis Bank, Nantucket Shoals (east), 18.5 miles SE. of Nantucket I.
Lat. 41°02′ N., long. 69°41′ W.

Time: Hours after maximum flood at Pollock Rip Channel, see page 28	Direction (true)	Velocity
	Degrees	*Knots*
0	30	0.6
1	36	1.3
2	38	1.5
3	50	1.4
4	80	1.1
5	105	0.8
6	178	0.6
7	230	1.3
8	235	1.7
9	238	1.4
10	241	1.0
11	265	0.3

Nantucket Island, 28 miles east of
Lat. 41°20′ N., long. 69°21′ W.

Time: Hours after maximum flood at Pollock Rip Channel, see page 28	Direction (true)	Velocity
	Degrees	*Knots*
0	19	0.9
1	7	1.3
2	359	1.4
3	351	1.1
4	334	0.5
5	221	0.3
6	198	0.8
7	185	1.1
8	184	1.1
9	184	0.9
10	183	0.7
11	60	0.1

Monomoy Point, 23 miles east of
Lat. 41°35′ N., long. 69°30′ W.

Time: Hours after maximum flood at Pollock Rip Channel, see page 28	Direction (true)	Velocity
	Degrees	*Knots*
0	320	0.7
1	324	1.0
2	326	0.9
3	330	0.7
4	334	0.3
5	144	0.1
6	145	0.5
7	146	0.8
8	147	0.9
9	148	0.8
10	150	0.4
11	230	0.1

Nauset Beach Light, 5 miles NE. of
Lat. 41°56′ N., long. 69°54′ W.

Time: Hours after maximum flood at Pollock Rip Channel, see page 28	Direction (true)	Velocity
	Degrees	*Knots*
0	315	0.5
1	327	0.6
2	340	0.5
3	357	0.2
4	16	0.1
5	124	0.2
6	132	0.4
7	135	0.6
8	139	0.6
9	145	0.4
10	269	0.2
11	297	0.2

Great Round Shoal Channel entrance Nantucket Sound entrance.
Lat. 41°26′ N., long. 69°44′ W.

Time: Hours after maximum flood at Pollock Rip Channel, see page 28	Direction (true)	Velocity
	Degrees	*Knots*
0	32	1.6
1	45	1.4
2	68	1.3
3	95	1.1
4	140	0.8
5	192	1.2
6	210	1.5
7	220	1.5
8	235	1.2
9	264	0.9
10	303	0.8
11	350	1.2

Great Round Shoal Channel Buoy 9, 0.3 mile NE. of
Lat. 41°24′ N., long. 69°55′ W.

Time: Hours after maximum flood at Pollock Rip Channel, see page 28	Direction (true)	Velocity
	Degrees	*Knots*
0	47	1.0
1	60	1.3
2	70	1.3
3	91	0.8
4	153	0.5
5	211	0.7
6	234	0.9
7	247	1.3
8	252	1.1
9	260	0.9
10	305	0.3
11	35	0.4

Great Round Shoal Channel, 4 miles NE. of Great Pt., Nantucket Sound.
Lat. 41°26′ N., long. 69°59′ W.

Time: Hours after maximum flood at Pollock Rip Channel, see page 28	Direction (true)	Velocity
	Degrees	*Knots*
0	80	0.8
1	88	1.1
2	96	1.3
3	104	1.0
4	129	0.5
5	213	0.5
6	267	1.1
7	275	1.4
8	280	1.2
9	284	0.7
10	328	0.2
11	42	0.4

Cuttyhunk I., 3¼ miles SW. of
Lat. 41°23′ N., long. 71°00′ W.

Time	Direction (true)	Velocity
Hours after maximum flood at Pollock Rip Channel, see page 28	*Degrees*	*Knots*
0	356	0.4
1	15	0.3
2	80	0.2
3	123	0.3
4	146	0.5
5	158	0.5
6	173	0.4
7	208	0.3
8	267	0.2
9	306	0.3
10	322	0.3
11	335	0.4

Gooseberry Neck, 2 miles SSE. of Buzzards Bay entrance.
Lat. 41°27′ N., long. 71°01′ W.

Time	Direction (true)	Velocity
Hours after maximum flood at Pollock Rip Channel, see page 28	*Degrees*	*Knots*
0	52	0.6
1	65	0.4
2	108	0.2
3	168	0.3
4	210	0.4
5	223	0.5
6	232	0.5
7	249	0.3
8	274	0.2
9	321	0.2
10	16	0.3
11	38	0.5

Browns Ledge, Massachusetts.
Lat. 41°20′ N., long. 71°06′ W.

Time	Direction (true)	Velocity
Hours after maximum flood at Pollock Rip Channel, see page 28	*Degrees*	*Knots*
0	330	0.3
1	12	0.3
2	28	0.3
3	104	0.4
4	118	0.4
5	123	0.4
6	168	0.3
7	205	0.2
8	201	0.3
9	270	0.3
10	282	0.4
11	318	0.5

Point Judith, Harbor of Refuge, Block Island Sound (west entrance).
Lat. 41°22′ N., long. 71°31′ W.

Time	Direction (true)	Velocity
Hours after maximum flood at The Race, see page 34	*Degrees*	*Knots*
0	197	0.2
1	160	0.2
2	151	0.4
3	159	0.5
4	146	0.5
5	124	0.5
6	109	0.4
7	104	0.2
8	90	0.1
9	30	0.1
10	336	0.1
11	209	0.1

Point Judith, 4.5 miles SW. of, Block Island Sound.
Lat. 41°18′N., long. 71°33′ W.

Time	Direction (true)	Velocity
Hours after maximum flood at The Race, see page 34	*Degrees*	*Knots*
0	264	0.6
1	270	0.6
2	270	0.5
3	280	0.2
4	62	0.2
5	70	0.6
6	78	0.7
7	95	0.5
8	105	0.3
9	120	0.1
10	286	0.1
11	277	0.3

Grace Point, 2 miles NW. of, Block Island Sound.
Lat. 41°12′ N., long. 71°38′ W.

Time	Direction (true)	Velocity
Hours after maximum flood at The Race, see page 34	*Degrees*	*Knots*
0	304	0.2
1	2	0.2
2	28	0.4
3	28	0.6
4	37	0.7
5	71	0.6
6	86	0.6
7	126	0.4
8	137	0.2
9	213	0.1
10	256	0.1
11	267	0.1

Little Gull I., 3.7 miles ESE. of, Block Island Sound.
Lat. 41°11′ N., long. 72°02′ W.

Time	Direction (true)	Velocity
Hours after maximum flood at The Race, see page 34	*Degrees*	*Knots*
0	271	0.8
1	284	0.5
2	320	0.2
3	68	0.2
4	77	0.7
5	95	1.1
6	118	1.6
7	128	1.2
8	150	0.6
9	171	0.2
10	221	0.4
11	228	0.7

Sandy Hook Approach Lighted Horn Buoy 2A, 0.2 mile W. of
Lat. 40°27′ N., long. 73°55′ W.

Time	Direction (true)	Velocity
Hours after maximum flood at The Narrows, N.Y. Hbr., see page 46	*Degrees*	*Knots*
0	313	0.4
1	325	0.3
2	356	0.2
3	55	0.2
4	94	0.3
5	118	0.4
6	136	0.6
7	147	0.5
8	177	0.2
9	256	0.2
10	290	0.3
11	298	0.4

Fenwick Shoal Lighted Whistle Buoy 2 off Delaware coast.
Lat. 38°25′ N., long. 74°46′ W.

Time	Direction (true)	Velocity
Hours after maximum flood at Delaware Bay Entrance, see page 52	*Degrees*	*Knots*
0	342	0.2
1	349	0.2
2	357	0.1
3	43	0.1
4	110	0.1
5	135	0.2
6	150	0.3
7	165	0.3
8	185	0.2
9	226	0.1
10	282	0.1
11	318	0.2

*Frying Pan Shoals, off Cape Fear,
Lat. 33°34′ N., long. 77°49′ W.

Time	Direction (true)	Velocity
Hours after maximum flood at Charleston Harbor, see page 76	*Degrees*	*Knots*
0	335	0.3
1	10	0.2
2	50	0.2
3	90	0.3
4	110	0.3
5	128	0.3
6	150	0.3
7	188	0.2
8	235	0.2
9	268	0.3
10	290	0.3
11	305	0.3

Cape Romain, 5 miles SE. of
Lat. 32°57′ N., long. 79°17′ W.

Time	Direction (true)	Velocity
Hours after maximum flood at Charleston Harbor, see page 76	*Degrees*	*Knots*
0	6	0.2
1	38	0.2
2	55	0.3
3	67	0.3
4	93	0.3
5	114	0.3
6	167	0.2
7	212	0.2
8	242	0.3
9	244	0.4
10	262	0.3
11	292	0.3

Cape Romain, 6.9 miles SW. of
Lat. 32°54′ N., long. 79°26′ W.

Time	Direction (true)	Velocity
Hours after maximum flood at Charleston Harbor, see page 76	*Degrees*	*Knots*
0	317	0.3
1	350	0.2
2	19	0.2
3	71	0.3
4	115	0.3
5	111	0.3
6	132	0.2
7	160	0.2
8	216	0.2
9	251	0.2
10	266	0.3
11	303	0.3

*Current during June–August usually sets eastward, average velocity ½ knot.

Capers Inlet, 1.9 miles east of
Lat. 32°50′ N., long. 79°40′ W.

Time		Direction (true)	Velocity
		Degrees	*Knots*
Hours after maximum flood at Charleston Harbor, see page 76	0	12	0.1
	1	58	0.1
	2	52	0.2
	3	53	0.2
	4	67	0.1
	5	98	0.1
	6	129	0.1
	7	214	0.1
	8	222	0.2
	9	254	0.2
	10	246	0.1
	11	247	0.1

Capers Inlet, 3.6 miles SE. of
Lat. 32°49′ N., long. 79°38′ W.

Time		Direction (true)	Velocity
		Degrees	*Knots*
Hours after maximum flood at Charleston Harbor, see page 76	0	302	0.2
	1	357	0.1
	2	34	0.1
	3	17	0.2
	4	89	0.2
	5	94	0.2
	6	112	0.2
	7	116	0.2
	8	189	0.1
	9	249	0.2
	10	268	0.2
	11	282	0.2

Charleston Entrance, 37 miles east of
Lat. 32°42′ N., long. 70°06′ W.

Time		Direction (true)	Velocity
		Degrees	*Knots*
Hours after maximum flood at Charleston Harbor, see page 76	0	328	0.3
	1	350	0.3
	2	20	0.2
	3	65	0.2
	4	95	0.3
	5	118	0.3
	6	140	0.3
	7	163	0.3
	8	195	0.2
	9	235	0.2
	10	268	0.2
	11	295	0.3

Charleston Lighted Whistle Buoy 2C,
off Charleston Harbor entrance.
Lat. 32°41′ N., long. 79°43′ W.

Time		Direction (true)	Velocity
		Degrees	*Knots*
Hours after maximum flood at Charleston Harbor, see page 76	0	300	0.2
	1	332	0.2
	2	17	0.1
	3	55	0.2
	4	77	0.3
	5	93	0.3
	6	117	0.3
	7	153	0.2
	8	207	0.2
	9	242	0.2
	10	260	0.3
	11	275	0.3

Folly Island, 2 miles east of
Lat. 32°39′ N., long. 79°52′ W.

Time		Direction (true)	Velocity
		Degrees	*Knots*
Hours after maximum flood at Charleston Harbor, see page 76	0	346	0.1
	1	24	0.2
	2	58	0.3
	3	76	0.3
	4	102	0.3
	5	121	0.2
	6	164	0.1
	7	222	0.2
	8	256	0.2
	9	256	0.3
	10	271	0.3
	11	290	0.2

Folly Island, 3.5 miles east of
Lat. 32°38′ N., long. 79°50′ W.

Time		Direction (true)	Velocity
		Degrees	*Knots*
Hours after maximum flood at Charleston Harbor, see page 76	0	322	0.1
	1	47	0.2
	2	69	0.2
	3	86	0.2
	4	96	0.2
	5	115	0.2
	6	148	0.1
	7	215	0.1
	8	256	0.2
	9	260	0.2
	10	265	0.2
	11	285	0.1

Martins Industry, 5 miles east of, off
Port Royal Sound.
Lat. 32°06′ N., long. 80°28′ W.

Time		Direction (true)	Velocity
		Degrees	*Knots*
Hours after maximum flood at Charleston Harbor, see page 76	0	282	0.4
	1	293	0.3
	2	330	0.1
	3	30	0.1
	4	75	0.3
	5	92	0.4
	6	102	0.5
	7	110	0.4
	8	140	0.2
	9	200	0.2
	10	250	0.3
	11	271	0.4

Savannah Light, 1.2 miles SE. of
Lat. 31°57′ N., long. 80°40′ W.

Time		Direction (true)	Velocity
		Degrees	*Knots*
Hours after maximum flood at Savannah River Entrance, see page 82	0	296	0.3
	1	308	0.2
	2	326	0.1
	3	45	0.1
	4	90	0.2
	5	107	0.3
	6	114	0.3
	7	123	0.3
	8	145	0.2
	9	213	0.1
	10	267	0.2
	11	283	0.3

Brunswick Lighted Whistle Buoy 2B,
off St. Simons Sound.
Lat. 31°00′ N., long. 81°10′ W.

Time		Direction (true)	Velocity
		Degrees	*Knots*
Hours after maximum flood at Miami Harbor Entrance, see page 94	0	308	0.3
	1	340	0.2
	2	42	0.1
	3	90	0.3
	4	111	0.4
	5	122	0.4
	6	130	0.3
	7	141	0.2
	8	220	0.1
	9	260	0.2
	10	289	0.4
	11	297	0.4

Miami Outer Bay Cut Entrance
Lat. 25°46′ N., long. 80°06′ W.

Time		Direction (true)	Velocity
		Degrees	*Knots*
Hours after maximum flood at Miami Harbor Entrance, see page 94	0	338	0.1
	1	319	0.1
	2	352	0.1
	3	18	0.1
	4	36	0.1
	5	30	0.2
	6	25	0.1
	7	32	0.1
	8	25	0.1
	9	26	0.1
	10	6	0.2
	11	355	0.1

Fire Island Inlet, N.Y., 22 miles south of:
Tidal current is weak, averaging about 0.1 knot at strength.

Fire Island Lighted Whistle Buoy 2 FI:
Tidal current is weak, averaging about 0.2 knot at strength.

Ambrose Light, New York Harbor entrance:
Tidal current is weak, averaging about 0.2 knot at strength.

Cape May, N.J., 72 miles east of:
Tidal current is weak, averaging about 0.1 knot at strength.

Five-Fathom Bank Northeast Lighted Whistle Buoy 2 FB:
Tidal current is weak, averaging about 0.2 knot at strength.

Winter-Quarter Shoal Lighted Whistle Buoy 6WQS, 9.2 miles SE. of, off Assateague I.:
Tidal current is weak, averaging less than 0.1 knot.

Cape Charles, 70 miles east of:
Tidal current is weak, averaging about 0.2 knot at strength.

Chesapeake Light, 4.4 miles NE. of, off Chesapeake Bay entrance, Va.:
Tidal current is weak and variable.

Cape Lookout Shoals Lighted Whistle Buoy 14:
Tidal current is weak, averaging about 0.2 knot at strength. Current during June-August usually sets eastward, average velocity ½ knot.

Ocracoke Inlet, 3¼ miles SSE. of:
Tidal current is weak, averaging about 0.1 knot at strength.

Diamond Shoal Light, 3.9 miles SSW. of:
Tidal current is weak, averaging less than 0.1 knot at strength. Current during June-August usually sets northeastward, average velocity ¾ knot.

Frying Pan Shoals Light, 14.3 miles NW. of:
Tidal current is weak, averaging about 0.2 knot at strength. Current during June-August usually sets eastward, average velocity ½ knot.

St. Johns Point, 5 miles east of, Fla.:
Tidal current is weak, averaging about 0.2 knot at strength.

Fowey Rocks Light, 1.5 miles SW. of:
Tidal current is weak and variable.

THE GULF STREAM

The region where the Gulf of Mexico narrows to form the channel between Florida Keys and Cuba may be regarded as the head of the Gulf Stream. From this region the stream sets eastward and northward through the Straits of Florida, and after passing Little Bahama Bank it continues northward and then northeastward, following the general direction of the 100-fathom curve as far as Cape Hatteras. The flow in the Straits is frequently referred to as the Florida Current.

Shortly after emerging from the Straits of Florida, the stream is joined by the Antilles Current, which flows northwesterly along the open ocean side of the West Indies before uniting with the water which has passed through the straits. Beyond Cape Hatteras the combined current turns more and more eastward under the combined effects of the deflecting force of the Earth's rotation and the eastwardly trending coastline, until the region of the Grand Banks of Newfoundland is reached.

Eastward of the Grand Banks the whole surface is slowly driven eastward and northeastward by the prevailing westerly winds to the coastal waters of northwestern Europe. For distinction, this broad and variable wind-driven surface movement is sometimes referred to as the North Atlantic Drift or Gulf Stream Drift.

In general, the Gulf Stream as it issues into the sea through the Straits of Florida may be characterized as a swift, highly saline current of blue water whose upper stratum is composed of warm water.

On its western or inner side, the Gulf Stream is separated from the coastal waters by a zone of rapidly falling temperature, to which the term "cold wall" has been applied. It is most clearly marked north of Cape Hatteras but extends, more or less well defined, from the Straits to the Grand Banks.

Throughout the whole stretch of 400 miles in the Straits of Florida, the stream flows with considerable velocity. Abreast of Havana, the average surface velocity in the axis of the stream is about 2½ knots. As the cross-sectional area of the stream decreases, the velocity increases gradually, until abreast of Cape Florida it becomes about 3½ knots. From this point within the narrows of the straits, the velocity along the axis gradually decreases to about 2½ knots off Cape Hatteras, N.C. These values are for the axis of the stream where the current is a maximum, the velocity of the stream decreasing gradually from the axis as the edges of the stream are approached. The velocity of the stream, furthermore, is subject to fluctuations brought about by variations in winds and barometric pressure.

The following tables give the mean surface velocity of the Gulf Stream in two cross sections in the Straits of Florida:

Between Rebecca Shoal and Cuba

Distance south of Rebecca Shoal	Mean surface velocity observed
Nautical miles	*Knots*
20	0.3
35	0.7
50	2.2
68	2.2
86	0.8

Between Fowey Rocks and Gun Cay

Distance east of Fowey Rocks	Mean surface velocity observed
Nautical miles	*Knots*
8	2.7
11½	3.5
15	3.2
22	2.7
29	2.1
36	1.7

Crossing the Gulf Stream at Jupiter or Fowey Rocks, an average allowance of 2½ knots in a northerly direction should be made for the current.

Crossing the stream from Havana, a fair allowance for the average current between 100-fathom curves is 1.1 knots in an east-north-easterly direction.

From within the straits, the axis of the Gulf Stream runs appromixately parallel with the 100-fathom curve as far as Cape Hatteras. Since this stretch of coast line sweeps northward in a sharper curve than does the 100-fathom line, the stream lies at varying distances from the shore. The lateral boundaries of the current within the straits are fairly well fixed, but when the stream flows into the sea the eastern boundary becomes somewhat vague. On the western side, the limits can be defined approximately since the waters of the stream differ in color, temperature, salinity, and flow from the inshore coastal waters. On the east, however, the Antilles Current combines with the Gulf Stream, so that its waters here merge gradually with the waters of the open Atlantic. Observations of the National Ocean Survey indicate that, in general, the average position of the inner edge of the Gulf Stream as far as Cape Hatteras lies inside the 50-fathom curve. The Gulf Stream, however, shifts somewhat with the seasons, and is considerably influenced by the winds which cause fluctuations in its position, direction, and velocity; consequently, any limits which are assigned refer to mean or average positions.

The approximate mean positions of the inner edge and axis (point where greatest velocity may be found) are indicated in the following table:

Approximate mean position of the Gulf Stream

Locality	Inner edge	Axis
	Nautical miles	*Nautical miles*
North of Havana, Cuba		25
Southeast of Key West, Fla.	....	45
East of Fowey Rocks, Fla.	....	10
East of Miami Beach, Fla.	....	15
East of Palm Beach, Fla.	....	15
East of Jupiter Inlet, Fla.	....	20
East of Cape Canaveral, Fla.	10	45
East of Daytona Beach, Fla.	25	75
East of Ormond Beach, Fla.	25	75
East of St. Augustine, Fla. (coast line)	40	85
East of Jacksonville, Fla. (coast line)	55	90
Southeast of Savannah, Ga. (coast line)	65	95
Southeast of Charleston, S.C. (coast line)	55	90
Southeast of Myrtle Beach, S.C.	60	100
Southeast of Cape Fear, N.C. (light)	35	75
Southeast of Cape Lookout, N.C. (light)	20	50
Southeast of Cape Hatteras, N.C.	10	35
Southeast of Virginia Beach, Va.	85	115
Southeast of Atlantic City, N.J.	120	....
Southeast of Sandy Hook, N.J.	150	....

At the western end of the Straits of Florida the limits of the Gulf Stream are not well defined, and for this reason the location of the inner edge has been omitted for Havana, Cuba, and Key West, Fla., in the above table. Between Fowey Rocks and Jupiter Inlet the inner edge is deflected westward and lies very close to the shore line.

Along the Florida Reefs between Alligator Reef and Dry Tortugas the distance of the northerly edge of the Gulf Stream from the edge of the reefs gradually increases toward the west. Off Alligator Reef it is quite close inshore, while off Rebecca Shoal and Dry Tortugas it is possibly 15 to 20 miles south of the 100-fathom curve. Between the reefs and the northern edge of the Gulf Stream the currents are ordinarily tidal and are subject at all times to considerable modification by local winds and barometric conditions. This neutral zone varies in both length and breadth; it may extend along the reefs a greater or less distance than stated, and its width varies as the northern edge of the Gulf Stream approaches or recedes from the reefs.

The approximate position of the axis of the Gulf Stream for various regions is shown on the following National Ocean Survey Charts: No. 1002, Straits of Florida; No. 1007, South Carolina to Cuba; No. 1112, Cape Canaveral to Key West; No. 1113, Alligator Reef to Havana. Chart No. 1001 shows the axis and the position of the inner edge of the Gulf Stream from Cape Hatteras to Straits of Florida.

WIND-DRIVEN CURRENTS

A wind continuing for some time will produce a current the velocity of which depends on the velocity of the wind, and unless the current is deflected by some other cause, the deflective force of the earth's rotation will cause it to set to the right of the direction of the wind in the northern hemisphere and to the left in the southern hemisphere.

The current produced at off-shore locations by local winds of various strengths and directions has been investigated from observations made at 20 lightships (some of which have since been moved) from Portland, Maine, to St. Johns River, Fla. The observations were made hourly and varied in length from 1 to 2 years at most of the locations to 5½ years at Nantucket Shoals and 9 years at Diamond Shoal. The averages obtained are given below and may prove helpful in estimating the probable current that may result from various winds at the several locations.

Caution.—There were of course many departures from these averages of velocity and direction, for the wind-driven current often depends not only on the length of time the wind blows but also on factors other than the local wind at the time and place of the current. The mariner must not, therefore, assume that the given wind will always produce the indicated current.

It should be remembered, too, that the current which a vessel experiences at any time is the resultant of the combined actions of the tidal current, the wind-driven current, and any other currents such as the Gulf Stream or currents due to river discharge.

Velocity.—The table below shows the average velocity of the current due to winds of various strengths.

Wind velocity (miles per hour)	10	20	30	40	50
Average current velocity (knots) due to wind at following lightship stations:					
Boston and Barnegat	0.1	0.1	0.2	0.3	0.3
Diamond Shoal and Cape Lookout Shoals	0.5	0.6	0.7	0.8	1.0
All other locations	0.2	0.3	0.4	0.5	0.6

Direction.—The position of the shore line with respect to the station influences considerably the direction of the currents due to certain winds. The following table shows for each station the average number of degrees by which the wind-driven current is deflected to the right or left (—) of the wind. Thus at Cape Lookout Shoals the table indicates that with a north wind the wind-driven current flows on the average 030° west of south, and with an east wind it flows 029° south of west.

Average deviation of current to right of wind direction

[A minus sign (−) indicates that the current sets to the left of the wind]

Wind from	Lat.	Long.	N.	NNE.	NE.	ENE.	E.	ESE.	SE.	SSE.	S.	SSW.	SW.	WSW.	W.	WNW.	NW.	NNW.
Old Lightship Stations	° ′	° ′	°	°	°	°	°	°	°	°	°	°	°	°	°	°	°	°
Portland	43 32	70 06	24	14	9	8	−2	−14	0	26	15	18	18	24	15	34	13	18
Boston	42 20	70 45		−1		21		32		29		20		2		19		15
Pollock Rip Slue	41 37	69 54	6	5	48	−38	30	−53	−24	−75	−25	167	70	59	36	53	20	19
Nantucket Shoals	40 37	69 37	44	46	28	24	9	16	12	3	25	0	6	18	30	39	41	48
Hen and Chickens	41 27	71 01	16	14	−7	−1	−14	3	−39	−36	25	55	35	30	20	16	16	8
Brenton Reef	41 26	71 23	34	25	22	19	25	1	−7	8	27	48	23	41	41	31	21	24
Fire Island	40 29	73 11	35	23	15	8	2	−17	31	55	40	41	31	14	−2	0	25	37
Ambrose Channel	40 27	73 49	30	40	21	11	18	72	27	112	82	70	63	46	37	22	23	21
Scotland	40 27	73 55	16	−12	−26	−36	−61	−36	−92	−150	90	33	77	44	15	30	27	13
Barnegat	39 46	73 56	6	5	−13	−9	−16	−7	33	54	55	30	14	8	0	−5	21	29
Northeast End	38 58	74 30	30	14	−3	−11	−20	−31	−42	−28	37	44	25	18	7	16	25	18
Overfalls	38 48	75 01	28	−6	−1	2	−40	−56	−78	−22	68	28	56	54	32	31	32	45
Winter-Quarter Shoal	37 55	74 56	18	−1	−5	−21	−27	−35	−19	31	23	20	4	14	9	8	28	27
Chesapeake	36 59	75 42	18	−2	−4	5	−6	23	73	71	57	38	27	26	22	18	15	22
Diamond Shoal	35 05	75 20	11	3	−3	30	65	88	74	52	40	22	7	−10	−13	−17	−25	−4
Cape Lookout Shoals	34 18	76 24	30	24	2	2	−29		21	80	54	31	32	21	2	18	5	−5
Frying Pan Shoals	33 34	77 49	34	34	18	6	2	9	48	55	48	38	26	14	−7	−12	−27	−6
Savannah	31 57	80 40	12	12	−9	−18	−23	−46	17	50	43	17	7	−8	−10	7	15	33
Brunswick	31 00	81 10	17	−2	−10	−28	−18	−21	37	29	23	2	6	−21	−21	−26	16	18
St. Johns	30 23	81 18	3	−12	−27	−47	−84	30	35	26	26	27	1	16	−8	−17	6	8

THE COMBINATION OF CURRENTS

In determining from the current tables the velocity and direction of the current at any time, it is frequently necessary to combine the tidal current with the wind-driven current. The following methods indicate how the resultant of two or more currents may be easily determined.

Currents in the same direction.—When two or more currents set in the same direction it is a simple matter to combine them. The resultant current will have a velocity which is equal to the sum of all the currents and it will set in the same direction.

For example, a vessel is near the Nantucket Shoals station at a time when the tidal current is setting 120° with a velocity of 0.6 knot, and at the same time a wind of 40 miles per hour is blowing from west; what current will the vessel be subject to at that time? Since a wind of 40 miles from west will give rise to a current setting 120° with a velocity of 0.5 knot, the combined tidal and wind-driven currents will set in the same direction (120°) with a velocity of 0.6+0.5=1.1 knots.

Currents in opposite directions.—The combination of currents setting in opposite directions is likewise a simple matter. The velocity of the resultant current is the difference between the opposite setting currents, and the direction of the resultant current is the same as that of the greater current.

As an example, let it be required to determine the velocity of the current at the Nantucket Shoals station when the tidal current is setting 205° with a velocity of 0.8 knot, and when a wind of 40 miles per hour is blowing from south. The current produced by a wind of 40 miles per hour from south would set 025° with a velocity of 0.5 knot. The tidal and wind-driven currents therefore set in opposite directions, the tidal current being the stronger. Hence the resultant current will set in the direction of the tidal current (205°) with a velocity of 0.8—0.5=0.3 knot.

Currents in different directions.—The combination of two or more currents setting neither in the same nor in opposite direction, while not as simple as in the previous cases, is nevertheless not difficult, the best method being a graphic method. Taking the combination of two currents as the simplest case, we draw from a given point as origin, a line the direction of which is the direction of one of the currents to be combined and whose length represents the velocity of that current to some suitable scale; from the end of this line we draw another line the direction and length of which, to the same scale, represents the other of the currents to be combined; then a line joining the origin with the end of our second line gives the direction and velocity of the resultant current.

As an example, let us take Nantucket Shoals station at a time when the tidal current is 0.7 knot setting 355° and a wind of 50 miles per hour is blowing from west-southwest; the wind-driven current according to the preceding chapter would therefore be about 0.6 knot setting 085°.

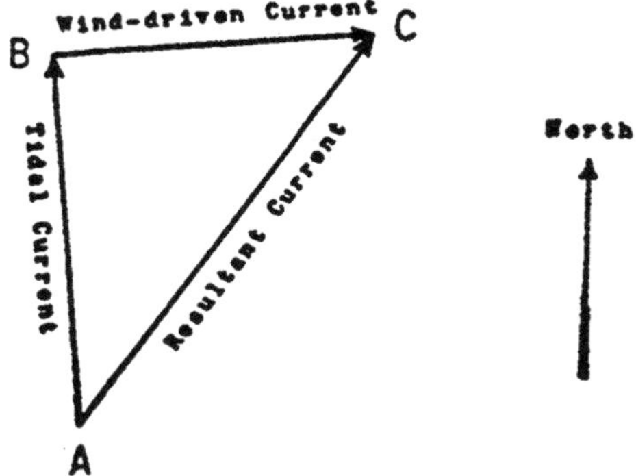

Combination of tidal current and wind-driven current

Using a scale of 2 inches to the knot we draw from the point A in the diagram above, the line AB 1.4 inches in length directed 355° to represent the tidal current. From B we then draw the line BC 1.2 inches in length directed 085° to represent the wind current. The line AC represents the resultant current and on being measured is found to be about 1.8 inches in length directed 035°. Hence the resultant current sets 035° with a velocity of 0.9 knot.

The combination of three or more currents is made in the same way as above, the third current to be combined being drawn from the point C, the resultant current being given by joining the origin A with the end of the last line. For drawing the lines, a parallel rule and compass rose will be found convenient, or a protractor or polar coordinate paper may be used.

CURRENT DIAGRAMS

EXPLANATION

"Current diagram" is a graphic table that shows the velocities of the flood and ebb currents and the times of slack and strength over a considerable stretch of the channel of a tidal waterway. At definite intervals along the channel the velocities of the current are shown with reference to the times of turning of the current at some reference station. This makes it a simple matter to determine the approximate velocity of the current along the channel for any desired time.

In using the diagrams, the desired time should be converted to hours before or after the time of the *nearest* predicted slack water at the reference station.

Besides showing in compact form the velocities of the current and their changes through the flood and ebb cycles, the current diagram serves two other useful purposes. By its use the mariner can determine the most advantageous time to pass through the waterway in order to carry the most favorable current and also the velocity and direction of the current that will be encountered in the channel at any time.

Each diagram represents average durations and average velocities of flood and ebb. The durations and velocities of flood and ebb vary from day to day. Therefore predictions for the reference station at times will differ from average conditions and when precise results are desired the diagrams should be modified to represent conditions at such particular times. This can be done by changing the width of the shaded and unshaded portions of the diagram to agree in hours with the durations of flood and ebb, respectively, as given by the predictions for that time. The velocities in the shaded area should then be multiplied by the ratio of the predicted flood velocity to the average flood velocity (maximum flood velocity given opposite the name of the reference station on the diagram) and the velocities in the unshaded area by the ratio of the predicted ebb velocity to the average ebb velocity.

In a number of cases approximate results can be obtained by using the diagram as drawn and modifying the final result by the ratio of velocities as mentioned above. Thus if the diagram in a particular case gives a favorable flood velocity averaging about 1.0 knot and the ratio of the predicted flood velocity to the average flood velocity is 0.5 the approximate favorable current for the particular time would be $1.0 \times 0.5 = 0.5$ knot.

VINEYARD AND NANTUCKET SOUNDS

EXPLANATION OF CURRENT DIAGRAM

The current diagram on the opposite page represents average conditions of the surface currents along the middle of the channel from Gay Head to the east end of Pollock Rip Channel, the scale being too small to show details.

Easterly streams are designated "Flood" and westerly streams "Ebb." The small figures in the diagram denote the velocity of the current in knots and tenths. The times are referred to slack waters at Pollock Rip Channel (Butler Hole), daily predictions for which are given in Table 1 of these current tables.

The speed lines are directly related to the diagram. By transferring to the diagram the direction of the speed line which corresponds to the ship's speed, the diagram will show the general direction and velocity of the current encountered by the vessel in passing through the sounds or the most favorable time, with respect to currents, for leaving any place shown on the left margin.

To determine velocity and direction of current.—With parallel rulers transfer to the diagram the direction of the speed line corresponding to normal speed of vessel, moving edge of ruler to the point where the horizontal line representing place of departure intersects the vertical line representing the time of day in question. If the ruler's edge lies within the shaded portion of the diagram, a flood current will be encountered; if within the unshaded, an ebb current; and if along the boundary of both, slack water. The figures on the diagram along the edge of the rule will show the velocity of the current encountered at any place indicated on the left margin of the diagram.

Example.—A 12-knot vessel bound westward enters Pollock Rip Channel at 0700 of a given day, and it is desired to ascertain the velocity and direction of the current which will be encountered on its passage through the sounds. Assuming that on the given day ebb begins at Pollock Rip Channel at 0508 and flood begins at 1120, the time 0700 will be about 2 hours after ebb begins. With parallel rulers transfer to the diagram the 12-knot speed line "Westbound", placing edge of rule on the point where the vertical line "2 hours after ebb begins at Pollock Rip Channel" intersects the horizontal 47-mile line which is the starting point. It will be found that the edge of the ruler passes through the unshaded portion of the diagram, the velocities along the edge averaging about 1.4 knots. The vessel will therefore have a favorable ebb current averaging about 1.4 knots all the way to Gay Head. It will also be seen that the edge of the ruler crosses the horizontal 16-mile line (at East Chop) about halfway between the figures 1.6 and 2.2. Therefore, when passing the vicinity of East Chop she will have a favorable current of almost 2 knots.

To determine the time of a favorable current for passing through the sounds.—With parallel rulers transfer to the diagram the direction of the speed line corresponding to normal speed of vessel, moving the rule over the diagram until its edge runs as nearly as possible through the general line of largest velocities of shaded portion if eastbound and unshaded portion if westbound, giving consideration only to that part of the diagram which lies between place of departure and destination. An average of the figures along the edge of the ruler will give the average strength of current. The time (before or after flood begins or ebb begins at Pollock Rip Channel) for leaving any place shown on the left margin will be indicated vertically above the point where the ruler cuts a line drawn horizontally through the name of the place in question.

Example.—A 12-knot vessel will leave Gay Head for Pollock Rip Channel on a day when flood begins at Pollock Rip Channel at 0454 and ebb begins at 1104. At what time should she get under way so as to carry the most favorable current all the way through the sounds?

Place parallel rulers along the 12-knot speed line "Eastbound." Transfer the direction to the shaded portion of the diagram and as near as possible to the axis so as to include the greatest possible number of larger current velocities. It will be found that the edge of the rule cuts the horizontal line at Gay Head at the point representing "3 hours after flood begins at Pollock Rip Channel", and that the average of the currents along the edge of rulers is about 0.8 knot in a favorable direction. For the given day flood begins at Pollock Rip Channel at 0454; hence, if the vessel leaves Gay Head 3 hours later, or about 0754, whe will average a favorable current of almost 1 knot all the way.

ASTRONOMICAL DATA, 1983

January

	d.	h	m
E	5	22	..
◑	6	04	00
S	13	06	..
A	14	05	..
●	14	05	08
E	20	17	..
◐	22	05	33
N	27	05	..
P	28	11	..
O	28	22	26

February

	d.	h	m
E	2	06	..
◑	4	19	17
S	9	12	..
A	10	08	..
●	13	00	32
E	16	22	..
◐	20	17	32
N	23	14	..
P	25	22	..
O	27	08	58

March

	d.	h	m
E	1	16	..
◑	6	13	16
S	8	18	..
A	9	23	..
●	14	17	43
E	16	04	..
$\odot_1$	21	04	39
◐	22	02	25
N	22	20	..
P	25	22	..
O	28	19	27
E	29	02	..

April

	d.	h	m
S	5	01	..
◑	5	08	38
A	6	18	..
E	12	11	..
●	13	07	58
N	19	02	..
◐	20	08	58
P	21	08	..
E	25	11	..
O	27	06	31

May

	d.	h	m
S	2	10	..
A	4	13	..
◑	5	03	43
E	9	20	..
●	12	19	25
N	16	08	..
P	16	16	..
◐	19	14	17
E	22	18	..
O	26	18	48
S	29	18	..

June

	d.	h	m
A	1	08	..
◑	3	21	07
E	6	05	..
●	11	04	37
N	12	17	..
P	13	06	..
◐	17	19	46
E	18	23	..
$\odot_2$	21	23	09
O	25	08	32
S	26	01	..
A	28	23	..

July

	d.	h	m
◑	3	12	12
E	3	14	..
N	10	03	..
●	10	12	18
P	11	10	..
E	16	05	..
◐	17	02	50
S	23	07	..
O	24	23	27
A	26	07	..
E	30	20	..

August

	d.	h	m
◑	2	00	52
N	6	13	..
P	8	19	..
●	8	19	18
E	12	13	..
◐	15	12	47
S	19	12	..
A	22	09	..
O	23	14	59
E	27	01	..
◑	31	11	22

September

	d.	h	m
N	2	21	..
P	6	05	..
●	7	02	35
E	8	22	..
◐	14	02	24
S	15	18	..
A	18	17	..
O	22	06	36
E	23	06	..
$\odot_3$	23	14	42
◑	29	20	05
N	30	04	..

October

	d.	h	m
P	4	11	..
E	6	08	..
●	6	11	16
S	13	02	..
◐	13	19	42
A	16	08	..
E	20	13	..
O	21	21	53
N	27	10	..
◑	29	03	37

November

	d.	h	m
P	1	03	..
E	2	18	..
●	4	22	21
S	9	10	..
◐	12	15	49
A	13	03	..
E	16	22	..
O	20	12	29
N	23	16	..
P	26	02	..
◑	27	10	50
E	30	01	..

December

	d.	h	m
●	4	12	26
S	6	19	..
A	11	01	..
◐	12	13	09
E	14	07	..
O	20	02	00
N	21	00	..
$\odot_4$	22	10	30
P	22	18	..
◑	26	18	52
E	27	06	..

LUNAR DATA:

● – new Moon
◐ – first quarter
O – full Moon
◑ – last quarter
A – Moon in apogee
P – Moon in perigee
N – Moon farthest north of Equator
E – Moon on Equator
S – Moon farthest south of Equator

SOLAR DATA:

$\odot_1$ – March equinox
$\odot_2$ – June solstice
$\odot_3$ – September equinox
$\odot_4$ – December solstice

Greenwich mean time (GMT) or universal time (UT) is the mean solar time on the Greenwich meridian reckoned in days of 24 mean solar hours written as 00^h at midnight and 12^h at noon. To convert the above times to those of other standard time meridians, add 1 hour for each 15° of east longitude of the desired meridian and subtract 1 hour for each 15° of west longitude.

This table was compiled from data taken from the American Ephemeris and Nautical Almanac.

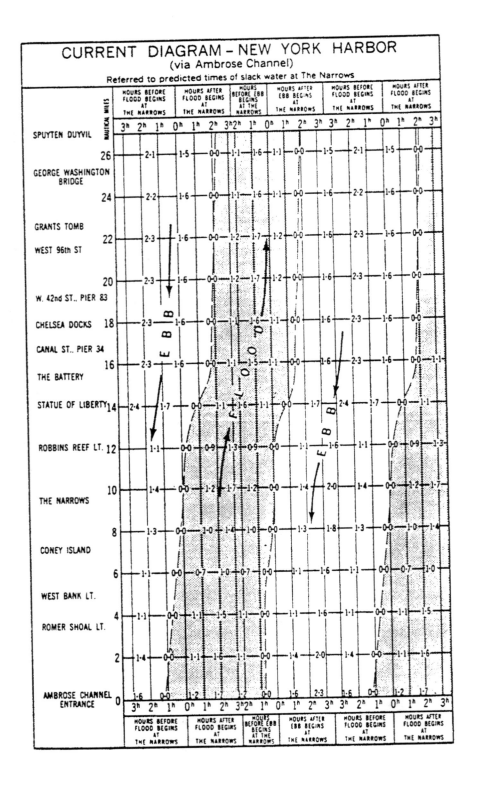

CURRENT DIAGRAM – NEW YORK HARBOR
(via Ambrose Channel)

Referred to predicted times of slack water at The Narrows

Location	Nautical miles	Hours before flood begins at The Narrows (3ʰ 2ʰ 1ʰ 0ʰ)		Hours after flood begins at The Narrows (1ʰ 2ʰ 3ʰ)		Hours before ebb begins at The Narrows (2ʰ 1ʰ 0ʰ)		Hours after ebb begins at The Narrows (1ʰ 2ʰ 3ʰ)		Hours before flood begins at The Narrows (3ʰ 2ʰ 1ʰ 0ʰ)		Hours after flood begins at The Narrows (1ʰ 2ʰ 3ʰ)	
SPUYTEN DUYVIL													
	26	2·1	1·5	0·0	1·1	1·6	1·1	0·0	1·5	2·1	1·5	0·0	
GEORGE WASHINGTON BRIDGE													
	24	2·2	1·6	0·0	1·1	1·6	1·1	0·0	1·6	2·2	1·6	0·0	
GRANTS TOMB													
	22	2·3	1·6	0·0	1·2	1·7	1·2	0·0	1·6	2·3	1·6	0·0	
WEST 96th ST													
	20	2·3	1·6	0·0	1·2	1·7	1·2	0·0	1·6	2·3	1·6	0·0	
W. 42nd ST., PIER 83													
CHELSEA DOCKS	18	2·3	1·6	0·0	1·1	1·6	1·1	0·0	1·6	2·3	1·6	0·0	
CANAL ST., PIER 34													
	16	2·3	1·6	0·0	1·1	1·5	1·1	0·0	1·6	2·3	1·6	0·0	1·1
THE BATTERY													
STATUE OF LIBERTY	14	2·4	1·7	0·0	1·1	1·6	1·1	0·0	1·7	2·4	1·7	0·0	1·1
ROBBINS REEF LT.	12	1·1	0·0	0·9	1·3	0·9	0·0	1·1	1·6	1·1	0·0	0·9	1·3
	10	1·4	0·0	1·2	1·7	1·2	0·0	1·4	2·0	1·4	0·0	1·2	1·7
THE NARROWS													
	8	1·3	0·0	1·0	1·4	1·0	0·0	1·3	1·8	1·3	0·0	1·0	1·4
CONEY ISLAND													
	6	1·1	0·0	0·7	1·0	0·7	0·0	1·1	1·6	1·1	0·0	0·7	1·0
WEST BANK LT.													
	4	1·1	0·0	1·1	1·5	1·1	0·0	1·1	1·6	1·1	0·0	1·1	1·5
ROMER SHOAL LT.													
	2	1·4	0·0	1·1	1·6	1·1	0·0	1·4	2·0	1·4	0·0	1·1	1·6
AMBROSE CHANNEL ENTRANCE	0	1·6	0·0	1·2	1·7	1·2	0·0	1·6	2·3	1·6	0·0	1·2	1·7

EBB — FLOOD — EBB

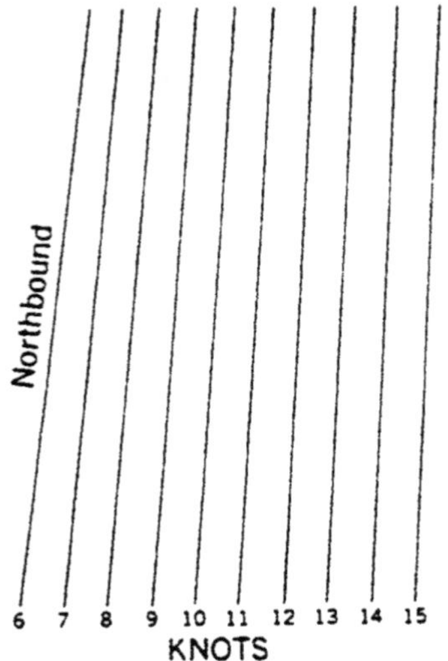

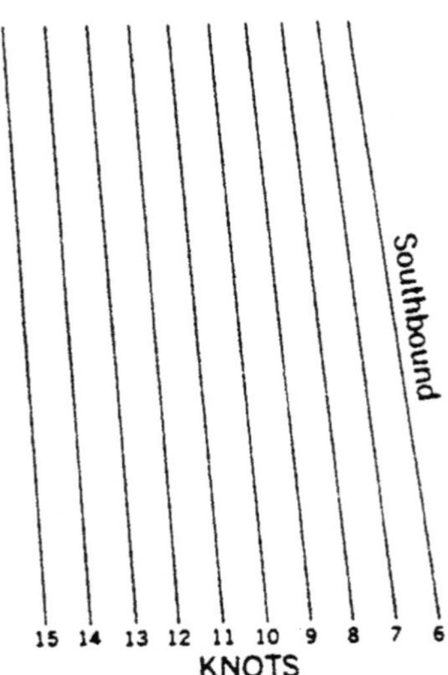

DELAWARE BAY AND RIVER

EXPLANATION OF CURRENT DIAGRAM

This current diagram represents only average conditions of the surface currents along the middle of the channel between Bristol and Delaware Bay Entrance, the scale being too small to show details.

Northerly streams are designated "Flood" and southerly streams "Ebb." The small figures in the diagram denote the velocity of the current in knots and tenths. The times are referred to slack waters at Delaware Bay Entrance, daily predictions for which are given in Table 1 of these current tables.

The speed lines are directly related to the diagram. By transferring to the diagram the direction of the speed line which corresponds to the ship's speed, the diagram will show the general direction and velocity of the current encountered by the vessel in passing up or down the bay and river or the most favorable time, with respect to currents, for leaving any place shown in the left margin.

To determine velocity and direction of current.—With parallel rulers transfer to the diagram the direction of the speed line corresponding to the normal speed of vessel, moving edge of ruler to the point where the horizontal line representing place of departure intersects the vertical line representing the time in question. If the ruler's edge lies within the shaded portion of the diagram, a flood current will be encountered; if within the unshaded, an ebb current, and if along the boundary of both, slack water. The figures in the diagram along the edge of the ruler will show the velocity of the current encountered at any place indicated in the left margin of the diagram.

Example.—A 15-knot vessel bound southward leaves Philadelphia (Chestnut Street) at 0330 of a given day and it is desired to ascertain the velocity and direction of the current which will be encountered between Philadelphia and Delaware Bay Entrance. Assuming that on the given day flood begins at Delaware Bay Entrance at 0436 and ebb begins at 1038, the time 0330 will be about 1 hour before flood begins. With parallel rulers transfer to the diagram the 15-knot speed line "Southbound" placing the edge of ruler on the intersection of the vertical line "1 hour before flood begins at Delaware Bay Entrance" and a horizontal line through Philadelphia (Chestnut Street) which is the starting point. It will be found that the edge of the ruler passes through an unshaded (ebb) portion with an average velocity of about 1.3 knots from Philadelphia to the vicinity of Arnold Point, and the rest of the way through a shaded (flood) portion with an average velocity of about 0.8 knot. The vessel will therefore have a favorable current averaging about 1.3 knots to the vicinity of Arnold Point and an unfavorable current averaging about 0.8 knot the rest of the way to Delaware Bay Entrance.

To determine the time of a favorable current for passing up or down the bay and river.—With parallel rulers transfer to the diagram the direction of the speed line corresponding to normal speed of vessel, moving the ruler over the diagram until its edge runs as nearly as possible through the general line of largest velocities of shaded portion if northbound or unshaded portion if southbound giving consideration only to that part of diagram which lies between places of departure and destination. An average of the figures along edge of ruler will give the average velocity of current. The time (before or after flood begins or ebb begins at Delaware Bay Entrance) for leaving any place shown in the left margin will be indicated vertically above or below the point where the ruler cuts a line drawn horizontally through the place in question.

Example.—A 12-knot vessel will leave Delaware Bay Entrance on a day when flood begins at 0505 and ebb begins at 1112. At what time should she get under way so as to carry the most favorable current all the way to Philadelphia? With parallel rulers transfer the direction of 12-knot speed line "Northbound" to the shaded portion of diagram and as near as possible to the axis so as to include the greatest number of larger velocities. The edge of the ruler will cut the horizontal line at Delaware Bay Entrance near the vertical line "2 hours after flood begins at Delaware Bay Entrance" and the velocities along the ruler's edge will average about 1.7 knots. On the given day flood begins at Delaware Bay Entrance at 0505, hence, if the vessel leaves about 2 hours later, i.e., about 0700, she will have a favorable current averaging about 1.7 knots all the way.

Note.—It is readily seen by transferring southbound speed lines to this diagram that southbound vessels can carry a favorable current for about 50 miles only.

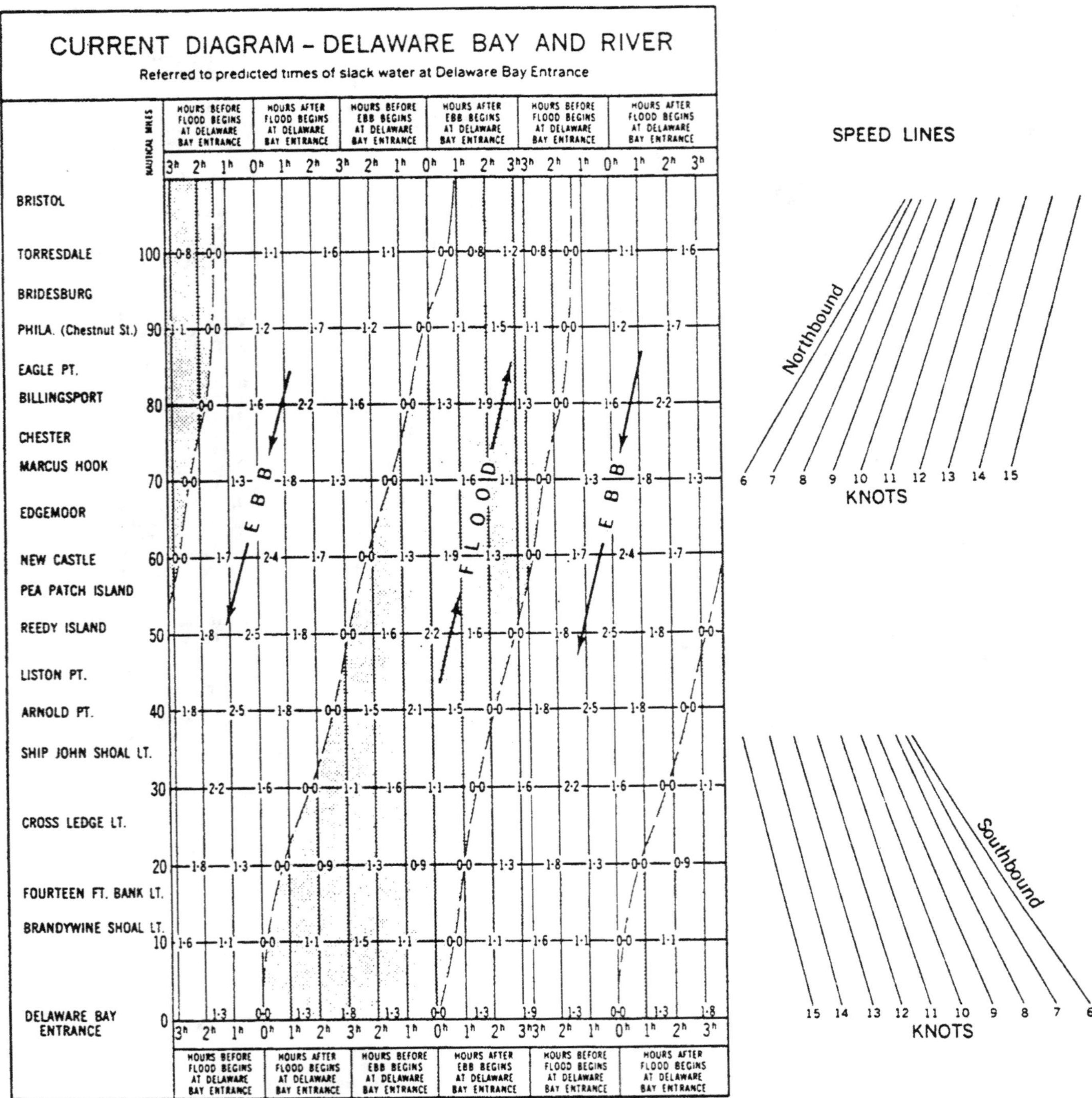
CURRENT DIAGRAM – DELAWARE BAY AND RIVER
Referred to predicted times of slack water at Delaware Bay Entrance
HOURS BEFORE FLOOD BEGINS AT DELAWARE BAY ENTRANCE
HOURS AFTER FLOOD BEGINS AT DELAWARE BAY ENTRANCE
HOURS BEFORE EBB BEGINS AT DELAWARE BAY ENTRANCE
HOURS AFTER EBB BEGINS AT DELAWARE BAY ENTRANCE
HOURS BEFORE FLOOD BEGINS AT DELAWARE BAY ENTRANCE
HOURS AFTER FLOOD BEGINS AT DELAWARE BAY ENTRANCE
NAUTICAL MILES
BRISTOL
TORRESDALE
BRIDESBURG
PHILA. (Chestnut St.)
EAGLE PT.
BILLINGSPORT
CHESTER
MARCUS HOOK
EDGEMOOR
NEW CASTLE
PEA PATCH ISLAND
REEDY ISLAND
LISTON PT.
ARNOLD PT.
SHIP JOHN SHOAL LT.
CROSS LEDGE LT.
FOURTEEN FT. BANK LT.
BRANDYWINE SHOAL LT.
DELAWARE BAY ENTRANCE
EBB
FLOOD
EBB
SPEED LINES
Northbound
KNOTS
Southbound
KNOTS

CHESAPEAKE BAY

EXPLANATION OF CURRENT DIAGRAM

This current diagram represents only average conditions of the surface currents along the middle of the channel from Cape Henry Light to Baltimore, the scale being too small to show details.

Northerly streams are designated "Flood" and southerly streams "Ebb." The small figures in the diagram denote the velocity of the current in knots and tenths. The times are referred to slack waters at Chesapeake Bay entrance, daily predictions for which are given in Table 1 of these current tables.

The speed lines are directly related to the diagram. By transferring to the diagram the direction of the speed line which corresponds to the ship's speed, the diagram will show the general direction and velocity of the current encountered by the vessel in passing up or down the bay or the most favorable time, with respect to currents, for leaving any place shown in the left margin.

To determine velocity and direction of current.—With parallel rulers transfer to the diagram the direction of the speed line corresponding to the normal speed of vessel, moving edge of ruler to the point where the horizontal line representing place of departure intersects the vertical line representing the time in question. If the ruler's edge lies within the shaded portion of the diagram, a flood current will be encountered; if within the unshaded, an ebb current, and if along the boundary of both, slack water. The figures in the diagram along the edge of the ruler will show the velocity of the current encountered at any place indicated in the left margin of the diagram.

Example.—A 12-knot vessel bound for Baltimore passes Cape Henry Light at 1430 of a given day, and it is desired to ascertain the velocity and direction of the current which will be encountered. Assuming that on the given day flood begins at Chesapeake Bay entrance at 1256 and ebb begins at 1803, the time 1430 will be about 1½ hours after flood begins. With parallel rulers transfer to diagram the 12-knot speed line "Northbound," placing edge of ruler so that it will cross the horizontal line opposite Cape Henry at a point "1½ hours after flood begins at the entrance." It will be found that the edge of the ruler passes through strength of current in the shaded portion of diagram averaging about 0.7 knot. The vessel will, therefore, have a favorable current averaging about 0.7 knot all the way to Baltimore.

To determine the time of a favorable current for passing through the bay.—With parallel rulers transfer to the diagram the direction of the speed line corresponding to normal speed of vessel, moving the ruler over the diagram until its edge runs approximately through the general line of greatest current of unshaded portion if southbound and shaded portion if northbound. An average of the figures along edge of ruler will give average strength of current. The time (before or after ebb or flood begins at the entrance) for leaving any place in the left margin of diagram will be found vertically above the point where the parallel ruler cuts the horizontal line opposite the place in question.

Example.—A 12-knot vessel in Baltimore Harbor desires to leave for Cape Henry Light on the afternoon of a day when flood begins at Chesapeake Bay entrance at 1148 and ebb begins at 1718. At what time should she get under way so as to carry the most favorable current?

Place parallel rulers along the 12-knot speed line "Southbound." Transfer this direction to the diagram and move it along so as to include the greatest possible number of larger current velocities in the unshaded portion of the diagram. The most favorable time for leaving Baltimore thus found is about 1 hour after flood begins at the entrance, or about 1248. There will be an unfavorable current of about 0.2 knot as far as Seven Foot Knoll Light; after passing this light there will be an average favorable current of about 0.3 knot as far as Cove Point Light; from Cove Point Light to Bluff Point a contrary current averaging about 0.3 knot will be encountered; from Bluff Point to Tail of the Horseshoe there will be an average favorable current of about 0.9 knot; and from Tail of the Horseshoe to Cape Henry an average contrary current of about 0.2 knot will again be encountered.

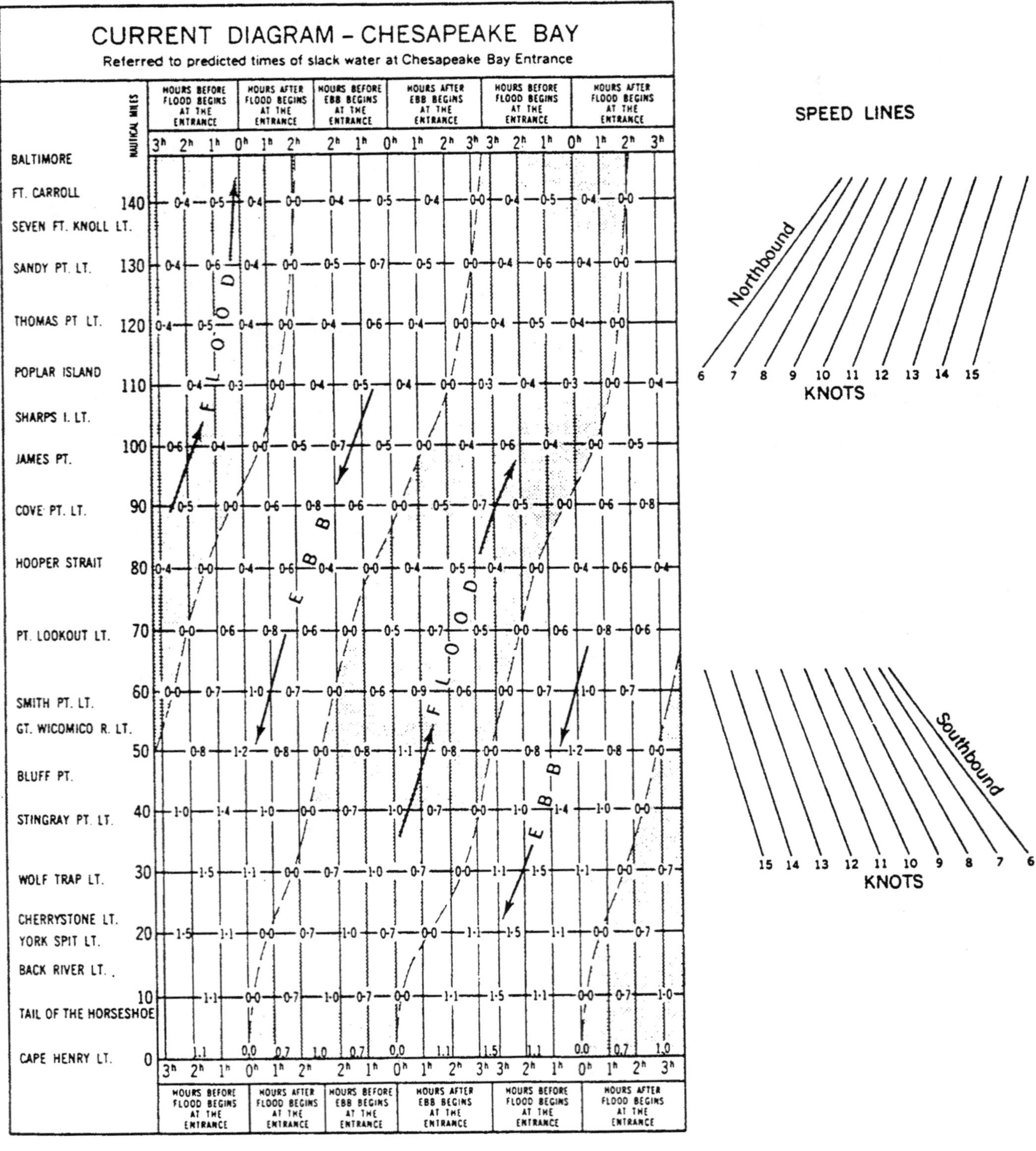

CURRENT DIAGRAM - CHESAPEAKE BAY
Referred to predicted times of slack water at Chesapeake Bay Entrance
NAUTICAL MILES
HOURS BEFORE FLOOD BEGINS AT THE ENTRANCE
HOURS AFTER FLOOD BEGINS AT THE ENTRANCE
HOURS BEFORE EBB BEGINS AT THE ENTRANCE
HOURS AFTER EBB BEGINS AT THE ENTRANCE
BALTIMORE
FT. CARROLL
SEVEN FT. KNOLL LT.
SANDY PT. LT.
THOMAS PT LT.
POPLAR ISLAND
SHARPS I. LT.
JAMES PT.
COVE PT. LT.
HOOPER STRAIT
PT. LOOKOUT LT.
SMITH PT. LT.
GT. WICOMICO R. LT.
BLUFF PT.
STINGRAY PT. LT.
WOLF TRAP LT.
CHERRYSTONE LT.
YORK SPIT LT.
BACK RIVER LT.
TAIL OF THE HORSESHOE
CAPE HENRY LT.
FLOOD
EBB
SPEED LINES
Northbound
6 7 8 9 10 11 12 13 14 15
KNOTS
Southbound
15 14 13 12 11 10 9 8 7 6
KNOTS

TIDE TABLES

Advance information relative to the rise and fall of the tide is given in annual tide tables. These tables include the predicted times and heights of high and low waters for every day in the year for a number of reference stations and differences for obtaining similar predictions for numerous other places.

Tide Tables, Central and Western Pacific Ocean and Indian Ocean.
Tide Tables, East Coast of North and South America (Including Greenland).
Tide Tables, Europe and West Coast of Africa (Including the Mediterranean Sea).
Tide Tables, West Coast of North and South America (Including the Hawaiian Islands).

TIDAL BENCH MARKS

To provide permanent points for the observed heights of the tide and the tidal datum planes determined therefrom, a system of bench marks is established at each tide station. The descriptions and elevations of these bench marks along our coast are compiled, published, and available for distribution. Requests for such bench mark data should specify the coastal locality for which the information is desired.

TIDAL CURRENT TABLES

Accompanying the rise and fall of the tide is a periodic horizontal flow of the water known as the tidal current. Advance information relative to these currents is made available in annual tidal current tables which include daily predictions of the times of slack water and the times and velocities of strength of flood and ebb currents for a number of waterways together with differences for obtaining predictions for numerous other places.

Tidal Current Tables, Atlantic Coast of North America.
Tidal Current Tables, Pacific Coast of North America and Asia.

TIDAL CURRENT CHARTS

Each publication consists of a set of 12 charts which depict, by means of arrows and figures, the direction and speed of the tidal current for each hour of the tidal cycle. The charts, which may be used for any year, present a comprehensive view of the tidal current movement in the respective waterways as a whole and also supply a means for readily determining for any time the direction and speed of the current at various localities throughout the water areas covered. The Narragansett Bay tidal current chart is to be used with the annual tide tables. The other charts require the annual tidal current tables.

Tidal Current Charts, Boston Harbor.
Tidal Current Charts, Charleston Harbor, S.C.
Tidal Current Charts, Delaware Bay and River.
Tidal Current Charts, Long Island Sound and Block Island Sound.
Tidal Current Charts, Narragansett Bay.
Tidal Current Charts, Narragansett Bay to Nantucket Sound.
Tidal Current Charts, New York Harbor.
Tidal Current Charts, Puget Sound, Northern Part.
Tidal Current Charts, Puget Sound, Southern Part.
Tidal Current Charts, San Francisco Bay.
Tidal Current Charts, Upper Chesapeake Bay.
Tidal Current Charts, Tampa Bay.

TIDAL CURRENT DIAGRAMS

The tidal current diagrams are a series of 12 monthly diagrams to be used with the tidal current charts to give the user a convenient method to determine the current flow on a particular day.

Tidal Current Diagrams for Long Island Sound and Block Island Sound.
Tidal Current Diagrams for Boston Harbor.
Tidal Current Diagrams for New York Harbor.
Tidal Current Diagrams for Upper Chesapeake Bay.

ANNUAL INEQUALITY—Seasonal variation in the water level or current, more or less periodic, due chiefly to meteorological causes.

APOGEAN TIDES OR TIDAL CURRENTS—Tides of decreased range or currents of decreased speed occurring monthly as the result of the Moon being in apogee (farthest from the Earth).

AUTOMATIC TIDE GAGE—An instrument that automatically registers the rise and fall of the tide. In some instruments, the registration is accomplished by recording the heights at regular intervals in digital format, in others by a continuous graph in which the height, versus corresponding time of the tide, is recorded.

BENCH MARK (BM)—A fixed physical object or marks used as reference for a vertical datum. A *tidal bench mark* is one near a tide station to which the tide staff and tidal datums are referred. A *geodetic bench mark* identifies a surveyed point in the National Geodetic Vertical Network.

CHART DATUM—The tidal datum to which soundings on a chart are referred. It is usually taken to correspond to a low water elevation of the tide, and its depression below mean sea level is represented by the symbol Zo.

CURRENT—Generally, a horizontal movement of water. Currents may be classified as *tidal* and *nontidal*. Tidal currents are caused by gravitational interactions between the Sun, Moon, and Earth and are a part of the same general movement of the sea that is manifested in the vertical rise and fall, called *tide*. Nontidal currents include the permanent currents in the general circulatory systems of the sea as well as temporary currents arising from more pronounced meteorological variability.

CURRENT DIFFERENCE—Difference between the time of slack water (or minimum current) or strength of current in any locality and the time of the corresponding phase of the tidal current at a reference station, for which predictions are given in the *Tidal Current Tables*.

CURRENT ELLIPSE—A graphic representation of a rotary current in which the velocity of the current at different hours of the tidal cycle is represented by radius vectors and vectorial angles. A line joining the extremities of the radius vectors will form a curve roughly approximating an ellipse. The cycle is completed in one-half tidal day or in a whole tidal day according to whether the tidal current is of the semidiurnal or the diurnal type. A current of the mixed type will give a curve of two unequal loops each tidal day.

CURRENT METER—An instrument for measuring the speed and direction or just the speed of a current. The measurements are usually Eulerian since the meter is most often fixed or moored at a specific location.

DATUM (vertical)—For marine applications, a base elevation used as a reference from which to reckon heights or depths. It is called a *tidal datum* when defined by a certain phase of the tide. Tidal datums are local datums and should not be extended into areas which have differing topographic features without substantiating measurements. In order that they may be recovered when needed, such datums are referenced to fixed points known as *bench marks*.

DAYLIGHT SAVING TIME—A time used during the summer in some localities in which clocks are advanced 1 hour from the usual standard time.

DIURNAL—Having a period or cycle of approximately 1 tidal day. Thus, the tide is said to be diurnal when only one high water and one low water occur during a tidal day, and the tidal current is said to be diurnal when there is a single flood and single ebb period in the tidal day. A rotary current is diurnal if it changes its direction through all points of the compass once each tidal day.

DIURNAL INEQUALITY—The difference in height of the two high waters or of the two low waters of each day; also the difference in speed between the two flood tidal currents or the two ebb tidal currents of each day. The difference changes with the declination of the Moon and to a lesser extent with the declination of the Sun. In general, the inequality tends to increase with an increasing declination, either north or south, and to diminish as the Moon approaches the Equator. *Mean diurnal high water inequality* (DHQ) is one-half the average difference between the two high waters of each day observed over a specific 19-year Metonic cycle (the National Tidal Datum Epoch). It is obtained by subtracting the mean of all high waters from the mean of the higher high waters. *Mean diurnal low water inequality* (DLQ) is one-half the average difference between the two low waters of each day observed over a specific 19-year Metonic cycle (the National Tidal Datum Epoch). It is obtained by subtracting the mean of the lower low waters from the mean of all low waters. *Tropic high water inequality* (HWQ) is the average difference between the two high waters of the day at the times of the tropic tides. *Tropic low water inequality* (LWQ) is the average difference between the two low waters of the day at the times of the tropic tides. Mean and tropic inequalities as defined above are applicable only when the type of tide is either semidiurnal or mixed. Diurnal inequality is sometimes called *declinational inequality*.

DOUBLE EBB—An ebb tidal current where, after ebb begins, the speed increases to a maximum called *first ebb;* it then decreases, reaching a *minimum ebb* near the middle of the ebb period (and at some places it may actually run in a flood direction for a short period): it then again ebbs to a maximum speed called *second ebb* after which it decreases to slack water.

DOUBLE FLOOD—A flood tidal current where, after flood begins, the speed increases to a maximum called *first flood*; it then decreases, reaching a *minimum flood* near the middle of the flood period (and at some places it may actually run in an ebb direction for a short period): it then again floods to a maximum speed called *second flood* after which it decreases to slack water.

DOUBLE TIDE—A double-headed tide, that is, a high water consisting of two maxima of nearly the same height separated by a relatively small depression, or a low water consisting of two minima separated by a relatively small elevation. Sometimes, it is called an *agger*.

DURATION OF FLOOD AND DURATION OF EBB—*Duration of flood* is the interval of time in which a tidal current is flooding, and the *duration of ebb* is the interval in which it is ebbing. Together they cover, on an average, a period of 12.42 hours for a semidiurnal tidal current or a period of 24.84 hours for a diurnal current. In a normal semidiurnal tidal current, the duration of flood and duration of ebb will each be approximately equal to 6.21 hours, but the times may be modified greatly by the presence of a nontidal flow. In a river the duration of ebb is usually longer than the duration of flood because of the freshwater discharge, especially during the spring when snow and ice melt are the predominant influences.

DURATION OF RISE AND DURATION OF FALL—*Duration of rise* is the interval from low water to high water, and *duration of fall* is the interval from high water to low water. Together they cover, on an average, a period of 12.42 hours for a semidiurnal tide or a period of 24.84 hours for a diurnal tide. In a normal semidiurnal tide, the duration of rise and duration of fall will each be approximately equal to 6.21 hours, but in shallow waters and in rivers there is a tendency for a decrease in the duration of rise and a corresponding increase in the duration of fall.

EBB CURRENT—The movement of a tidal current away from shore or down a tidal river or estuary. In the mixed type of reversing tidal current, the terms *greater ebb* and *lesser ebb* are applied respectively to the ebb tidal currents of greater and lesser speed of each day. The terms *maximum ebb* and *minimum ebb* are applied to the maximum and minimum speeds of a current running continuously ebb, the speed alternately increasing and decreasing without coming to a slack or reversing. The expression *maximum ebb* is also applicable to any ebb current at the time of greatest speed.

EQUATORIAL TIDAL CURRENTS—Tidal currents occurring semimonthly as a result of the Moon being over the Equator. At these times the tendency of the Moon to produce a diurnal inequality in the tidal current is at a minimum.

EQUATORIAL TIDES—Tides occurring semimonthly as the result of the Moon being over the Equator. At these times the tendency of the Moon to produce a diurnal inequality in the tide is at a minimum.

FLOOD CURRENT—The movement of a tidal current toward the shore or up a tidal river or estuary. In the mixed type of reversing current, the terms *greater flood* and *lesser flood* are applied respectively to the flood currents of greater and lesser speed of each day. The terms *maximum flood* and *minimum flood* are applied to the maximum and minimum speeds of a flood current, the speed of which alternately increases and decreases without coming to a slack or reversing. The expression *maximum flood* is also applicable to any flood current at the time of greatest speed.

GREAT DIURNAL RANGE (*Gt*)—The difference in height between mean higher high water and mean lower low water. The expression may also be used in its contracted form, *diurnal range*.

GULF COAST LOW WATER DATUM—A chart datum. Specifically, the tidal datum designated for the coastal waters of the Gulf Coast of the United States. It is defined as *mean lower low water* when the type of tide is mixed and *mean low water* when the type of tide is diurnal.

HALF-TIDE LEVEL—*See mean tide level.*

HIGH WATER (HW)—The maximum height reached by a rising tide. The height may be due solely to the periodic tidal forces or it may have superimposed upon it the effects of prevailing meteorological conditions. Use of the synonymous term, *high tide*, is discouraged.

HIGHER HIGH WATER (HHW)—The higher of the two high waters of any tidal day.

HIGHER LOW WATER (HLW)—The higher of the two low waters of any tidal day.

HYDRAULIC CURRENT—A current in a channel caused by a difference in the surface level at the two ends. Such a current may be expected in a strait connecting two bodies of water in which the tides differ in time or range. The current in the East River, N.Y., connecting Long Island Sound and New York Harbor, is an example.

KNOT—A speed unit of 1 international nautical mile (1,852.0 meters or 6,076.11549 international feet) per hour.

LOW WATER (LW)—The minimum height reached by a falling tide. The height may be due solely to the periodic tidal forces or it may have superimposed upon it the effects of meteorological conditions. Use of the synonymous term, *low tide*, is discouraged.

LOWER HIGH WATER (LHW)—The lower of the two high waters of any tidal day.

LOWER LOW WATER (LLW)—The lower of the two low waters of any tidal day.

LUNAR DAY—The time of the rotation of the Earth with respect to the Moon, or the interval between two successive upper transits of the Moon over the meridian of a place. The mean lunar day is approximately 24.84 solar hours long, or 1.035 times as long as the mean solar day.

LUNAR INTERVAL—The difference in time between the transit of the Moon over the meridian of Greenwich and over a local meridian. The average value of this interval expressed in hours is 0.069 L, in which L is the local longitude in degrees, positive for west longitude and negative for east longitude. The lunar interval equals the difference between the local and Greenwich interval of a tide or current phase.

LUNICURRENT INTERVAL—The interval between the Moon's transit (upper or lower) over the local or Greenwich meridian and a specified phase of the tidal current following the transit. Examples: *strength of flood interval* and *strength of ebb interval*, which may be abbreviated to *flood interval* and *ebb interval*, respectively. The interval is described as local or Greenwich according to whether the reference is to the Moon's transit over the local or Greenwich meridian. When not otherwise specified, the reference is assumed to be local.

LUNITIDAL INTERVAL—The interval between the Moon's transit (upper or lower) over the local or Greenwich meridian and the following high or low water. The average of all high water intervals for all phases of the Moon is known as *mean high water lunitidal interval* and is abbreviated to *high water interval* (HWI). Similarly the *mean low water lunitidal interval* is abbreviated to *low water interval* (LWI). The interval is described as local or Greenwich according to whether the reference is to the transit over the local or Greenwich meridian. When not otherwise specified, the reference is assumed to be local.

MEAN HIGH WATER (MHW)—A tidal datum. The average of all the high water heights observed over the National Tidal Datum Epoch. (See High Water.) For stations with shorter series, simultaneous observational comparisons are made with a control tide station in order to derive the equivalent of a 19-year datum.

MEAN HIGHER HIGH WATER (MHHW)—A tidal datum. The average of the highest high water height of each tidal day observed over the National Tidal Datum Epoch. For stations with shorter series, simultaneous observational comparisons are made with a control tide station in order to derive the equivalent of a 19-year datum.

MEAN HIGHER HIGH WATER LINE (MHHWL)—The intersection of the land with the water surface at the elevation of mean higher high water.

MEAN LOW WATER (MLW)—A tidal datum. The average of all the low water heights observed over the National Tidal Datum Epoch. (See Low Water.) For stations with shorter series, simultaneous observational comparisons are made with a control tide station in order to derive the equivalent of a 19-year datum.

MEAN LOW WATER SPRINGS (MLWS)—A tidal datum. Frequently abbreviated *spring low water*. The arithmetic mean of the low water heights occurring at the time of the spring tides observed over a specific 19-year Metronic cycle (the National Tidal Datum Epoch).

MEAN LOWER LOW WATER (MLLW)—A tidal datum. The average of the lowest low water height of each tidal day observed over the National Tidal Datum Epoch. For stations with shorter series, simultaneous observational comparisons are made with a control tide station in order to derive the equivalent of a 19-year datum.

MEAN RANGE OF TIDE (Mn)—The difference in height between mean high water and mean low water.

MEAN RIVER LEVEL—A tidal datum. The average height of the surface of a tidal river at any point for all stages of the tide observed over a 19-year Metonic cycle (the National Tidal Datum Epoch), usually determined from hourly height readings. In rivers subject to occasional freshets the river level may undergo wide variations, and for practical purposes certain months of the year may be excluded in the determination of tidal datums. For charting purposes, tidal datums for rivers are usually based on observations during selected periods when the river is at or near low water stage.

MEAN SEA LEVEL (MSL)—A tidal datum. The arithmetic mean of hourly water elevations observed over a specific 19-year Metonic cycle (the National Tidal Datum Epoch). Shorter series are specified in the name; e.g., monthly mean sea level and yearly mean sea level.

MEAN TIDE LEVEL (MTL)—Also called half-tide level. A tidal datum midway between mean high water and mean low water.

MIXED TIDE—Type of tide with a large inequality in the high and/or low water heights, with two high waters and two low waters usually occurring each tidal day. In strictness, all tides are mixed but the name is usually applied to the tides intermediate to those predominantly semidiurnal and those predominantly diurnal.

NEAP TIDES OR TIDAL CURRENTS—Tides of decreased range or tidal currents of decreased speed occurring semimonthly as the result of the Moon being in quadrature. The *neap range* (Np) of the tide is the average semidiurnal range occurring at the time of neap tides and is most conveniently computed from the harmonic constants. It is smaller than the mean range where the type of tide is either semidiurnal or mixed and is of no practical significance where the type of tide is diurnal. The average height of the high waters of the neap tides is called *neap high water* or *high water neaps* (MHWN) and the average height of the corresponding low waters is called *neap low water* or *low water neaps* (MLWN).

PERIGEAN TIDES OR TIDAL CURRENTS—Tides of increased range or tidal currents of increased speed occurring monthly as the result of the Moon being in perigee or nearest the Earth. The *perigean range* (Pn) of tide is the average semidiurnal range occurring at the time of perigean tides and is most conveniently computed from the harmonic constants. It is larger than the mean range where the type of tide is either semidiurnal or mixed, and is of no practical significance where the type of tide is diurnal.

RANGE OF TIDE—The difference in height between consecutive high and low waters. The *mean range* is the difference in height between mean high water and mean low water. Where the type of tide is diurnal the mean range is the same as the diurnal range. For other ranges, see great diurnal, spring, neap, perigean, apogean, and tropic tides.

REFERENCE STATION—A tide or current station for which independent daily predictions are given in the *Tide Tables* and *Tidal Current Tables,* and from which corresponding predictions are obtained for subordinate stations by means of differences and ratios.

REVERSING CURRENT—A tidal current which flows alternately in approximately opposite directions with a slack water at each reversal of direction. Currents of this type usually occur in rivers and straits where the direction of flow is more or less restricted to certain channels. When the movement is towards the shore or up a stream, the current is said to be flooding, and when in the opposite direction it is said to be ebbing. The combined flood and ebb movement including the slack water covers, on an average, 12.42 hours for the semidiurnal current. If unaffected by a nontidal flow, the flood and ebb movements will each last about 6 hours, but when combined with such a flow, the durations of flood and ebb may be quite unequal. During the flow in each direction the speed of the current will vary from zero at the time of slack water to a maximum about midway between the slacks.

ROTARY CURRENT—A tidal current that flows continually with the direction of flow changing through all points of the compass during the tidal period. Rotary currents are usually found offshore where the direction of flow is not restricted by any barriers. The tendency for the rotation in direction has its origin in the Coriolis force and, unless modified by local conditions, the change is clockwise in the Northern Hemisphere and counterclockwise in the Southern. The speed of the current usually varies throughout the tidal cycle, passing through the two maxima in approximately opposite directions and the two minima with the direction of the current at approximately 90° from the direction at time of maximum speed.

SEMIDIURNAL—Having a period or cycle of approximately one-half of a tidal day. The predominating type of tide throughout the world is semidiurnal, with two high waters and two low waters each tidal day. The tidal current is said to be semidiurnal when there are two flood and two ebb periods each day.

SET (OF CURRENT)—The direction *towards* which the current flows.

SLACK WATER—The state of a tidal current when its speed is near zero, especially the moment when a reversing current changes direction and its speed is zero. The term is also applied to the entire period of low speed near the time of turning of the current when it is too weak to be of any practical importance in navigation. The relation of the time of slack water to the tidal phases varies in different localities. For standing tidal waves, slack water occurs near the times of high and low water, while for progressive tidal waves, slack water occurs midway between high and low water.

SPRING TIDES OR TIDAL CURRENTS—Tides of increased range or tidal currents of increased speed occurring semimonthy as the result of the Moon being new or full. The *spring range* (Sg) of tide is the average semidiurnal range occurring at the time of spring tides and is most conveniently computed from the harmonic constants. It is larger than the mean range where the type of tide is either semidiurnal or mixed, and is of no practical signficance where the type of tide is diurnal. The mean of the high waters of the spring tide is called *spring high water* or *mean high water springs* (MHWS), and the average height of the corresponding low waters is called *spring low water* or *mean low water springs* (MLWS).

STAND OF TIDE—Sometimes called a platform tide. An interval at high or low water when there is no sensible change in the height of the tide. The water level is stationary at high and low water for only an instant, but the change in level near these times is so slow that it is not usually perceptible. In general, the duration of the apparent stand will depend upon the range of tide, being longer for a small range than for a large range, but where there is a tendency for a double tide the stand may last for several hours even with a large range of tide.

GLOSSARY OF TERMS

STANDARD TIME—A kind of time based upon the transit of the Sun over a certain specified meridian, called the *time meridian*, and adopted for use over a considerable area. With a few exceptions, standard time is based upon some meridian which differs by a multiple of 15° from the meridian of Greenwich.

STRENGTH OF CURRENT—Phase of tidal current in which the speed is a maximum; also the speed at this time. Beginning with slack before flood in the period of a reversing tidal current (or minimum before flood in a rotary current), the speed gradually increases to flood strength and then diminishes to slack before ebb (or minimum before ebb in a rotary current), after which the current turns in direction, the speed increases to ebb strength and then diminishes to slack before flood completing the cycle. If it is assumed that the speed throughout the cycle varies as the ordinates of a cosine curve, it can be shown that the average speed for an entire flood or ebb period is equal to $2/\pi$ or 0.6366 of the speed of the corresponding strength of current.

SUBORDINATE CURRENT STATION—(1) A current station from which a relatively short series of observations is reduced by comparison with simultaneous observations from a control current station.

(2) A station listed in the *Tidal Current Tables* for which predictions are to be obtained by means of differences and ratios applied to the full predictions at a reference station.

SUBORDINATE TIDE STATION—(1) A tide station from which a relatively short series of observations is reduced by comparison with simultaneous observations from a tide station with a relatively long series of observations. (2) A station listed in the *Tide Tables* for which predictions are to be obtained by means of differences and ratios applied to the full predictions at a reference station.

TIDAL CURRENT TABLES—Tables which give daily predictions of the times and speeds of the tidal currents. These predictions are usually supplemented by current differences and constants through which additional predictions can be obtained for numerous other places.

TIDAL DIFFERENCE—Difference in time or height of a high or low water at a subordinate station and at a reference station for which predictions are given in the *Tide Tables*. The difference, when applied according to sign to the prediction at the reference station, gives the corresponding time or height for the subordinate station.

TIDE—The periodic rise and fall of the water resulting from gravitational interactions between the Sun, Moon, and Earth. The vertical component of the particulate motion of a tidal wave. Although the accompanying horizontal movement of the water is part of the same phenomenon, it is preferable to designate the motion as tidal current.

TIDE TABLES—Tables which give daily predictions of the times and heights of high and low waters. These predictions are usually supplemented by tidal differences and constants through which additional predictions can be obtained for numerous other places.

TIME MERIDIAN—A meridian used as a reference for time.

TROPIC CURRENTS—Tidal currents occurring semimonthly when the effect of the Moon's maximum declination is greatest. At these times the tendency of the Moon to produce a diurnal inequality in the current is at a maximum.

TROPIC RANGES—The *great tropic range* (Gc), or *tropic range*, is the difference in height between tropic higher high water and tropic lower low water. The *small tropic range* (Sc) is the difference in height between tropic lower high water and tropic higher low water. The *mean tropic range* (Mc) is the mean between the great tropic range and the small tropic range. The small tropic range and the mean tropic range are applicable only when the type of tide is semidiurnal or mixed. Tropic ranges are most conveniently computed from the harmonic constants.

TROPIC TIDES—Tides occurring semimonthly when the effect of the Moon's maximum declination is greatest. At these times there is a tendency for an increase in the diurnal range. The tidal datums pertaining to the tropic tides are designated as *tropic higher high water* (TcHHW), *tropic lower high water* (TcLHW), *tropic higher low water* (TcHLW), and *tropic lower low water* (TcLLW).

TYPE OF TIDE—A classification based on characteristic forms of a tide curve. Qualitatively, when the two high waters and two low waters of each tidal day are approximately equal in height, the tide is said to be *semidiurnal;* when there is a relatively large diurnal inequality in the high or low waters or both, it is said to be *mixed*; and when there is only one high water and one low water in each tidal day, it is said to be *diurnal*.

VANISHING TIDE—In a mixed tide with very large diurnal inequality, the lower high water (or higher low water) frequently becomes indistinct (or vanishes) at time of extreme declinations. During these periods the diurnal tide has such overriding dominance that the semidiurnal tide, although still present, cannot be readily seen on the tide curve.

INDEX TO STATIONS, 1983
(Numbers refer to table 2)

[Stations marked with an asterisk (*) are reference stations for which daily predictions are given in table 1. Page numbers of reference stations are given in parentheses.]

D

NO.

E

F

☆U.S. GOVERNMENT PRINTING OFFICE: 1982-360-997/2198

ISBN 0-16-042688-X
9 780160 426889 90000

Printed in the USA
CPSIA information can be obtained
at www.ICGtesting.com
LVHW080329270324
775528LV00011B/233